A SHORT HISTORY OF THE MIDDLE EAST

I. THE MIDDLE EAST

A SHORT HISTORY OF THE MIDDLE EAST

From the Rise of Islam to Modern Times

by

GEORGE E. KIRK

Sixth Revised Edition

*"Universal history . . . is not a burden on the memory,
but an illumination of the soul."*   (LORD ACTON)

FREDERICK A. PRAEGER, *Publisher*
NEW YORK

BOOKS THAT MATTER

Sixth Edition published in the United States of America in 1960
by Frederick A. Praeger, Inc., Publisher
64 University Place, New York 3, N. Y.

Third printing, 1963.

The Third, Fourth, and Fifth Editions of this book
were published in 1955, 1957, and 1959 respectively
by Frederick A. Praeger, Inc., New York.
The present edition has been revised, expanded,
and brought up to date.

Printed in the United States of America

TO MARGARET

'for the Resurrection of the dead,
and the life of the world to come.'

Contents

Maps

From drawings by S. O. Pritchard and N. S. Hyslop

Introduction to Sixth Edition

THE PRESENT volume has grown out of a course of lectures
delivered in 1945-7 at the Middle East Centre for Arab
Studies (then located in Jerusalem) to British students who
required a general grounding in Middle East history and current
affairs to assist in fitting them for active careers in that region,
but not to make them historical specialists. The views expressed
throughout were not required to conform to any official programme or doctrine; there was no access to unpublished official
information; and *a fortiori* the Centre bears no responsibility for
the new material introduced into the later editions, which has
been coloured by the author's subsequent experience at Beirut
and now at Harvard.

Chapter VIII was entirely re-written for the Fourth Edition by
a colleague in the American University of Beirut, Mr. Arthur
Mills, and has not been retouched except for bringing the oil
figures up to date. The final chapter has been updated to the
beginning of 1960; included are portions from the author's
article 'The Middle Eastern Scene', which appeared in *The Year
Book of World Affairs, 1960* (reprinted here by permission of
The London Institute of World Affairs). There are three ap-
pendices on topics which have called for recent reconsideration
of views expressed in the body of the work; and a number of
important additions have been made to the List of Authorities,
especially with regard to the final chapter.

2. THE MIDDLE EAST IN THE SEVENTH CENTURY

A.D. 600—The Middle East in Disintegration

THE POSITION that the Middle East occupies in history is a unique one. It was there in all probability that Man, having lived for perhaps one million years in complete dependence on the wild vegetable and animal foods that he could acquire by gathering and hunting, learnt by laborious trial and error some 8,000 or so years ago to cultivate food-plants and to domesticate certain useful animals, and so for the first time became capable of advancing to a higher civilization. From between three and two thousand years ago, as that higher civilization in the Middle East attained its peak, almost simultaneously in Hellas and Judaea a few men became aware of the moral problem of history, of the gulf that separates human aspiration from human attainment. The Hebrew prophets warned of God's judgement on a disobedient People; Plato taught that we are citizens of two worlds at once, and our only real progress that of the spirit, *ex umbris et imaginibus in veritatem*. In Christianity these two strains were fused, in that doctrine of the Word made flesh that flesh might be redeemed. In so far as our civilization still recognizes its spiritual roots, therefore, it cannot ignore the Middle Eastern soil in which they grew.

Man's great step forward from food-gathering to agriculture, his Response to a great Challenge[1] presented by fundamental changes in his natural environment, has been well set forth by archaeologists in the last thirty years. So many learned and brilliant books have been written about the Greek genius, and about the origins and growth of our Christian Faith, that one would be perplexed where to advise the enquiring reader to turn first for enlightenment on these subjects. On the Silver Age of the Middle East also, the age of the Islamic or so-called Arab Civilization, there are numerous scholarly works.

---

[1] cf. A. J. Toynbee, *A Study of History*, one vol. abridgement, part II, especially 68 ff.

There are also first-class studies of various aspects of the contemporary or nearly-contemporary Middle East; but there is a dearth of general works that attempt to connect the contemporary and the medieval scenes,[1] although their interrelation is stimulating to the historical imagination. Here is manifest the irony of history—as when the varied fecundity of the medieval Islamic civilization petrified after *c.* A.D. 1300, just when Western civilization was entering on a new phase of experimentation that has persisted to the present day; or when the reawakening of the Middle East by nineteenth-century Western modes of thought and techniques has led to new estrangement and explosion in our own day—so that we are vividly made aware that history is no orderly progress, no end in itself, but rather the vehicle through which the Judgement that is beyond history manifests itself.

*   *   *

Climatic changes covering thousands of years, which may be summarized in popular language as the recession of the last Ice Age, had by about 6000 B.C. reduced large tracts of the Middle East to the virtually rainless and desert conditions which still obtain in the Sahara, lying athwart Africa with a depth of 1000 miles from north to south, and its extension, the Arabian Desert. To the north of this sterile belt, the mountain-ranges of Syria, Anatolia, and Persia receive an adequate winter rainfall from the Mediterranean; and this relatively well-watered region is flanked to west and east by the basins of two great river-systems, the Nile and the Euphrates-Tigris, to form a Fertile Crescent which was in all probability the home of the original Agricultural Civilization to which reference has been made above.[2]

The state of society in the Middle East in A.D. 600 was still the direct outcome of the expansion and development of this Agricultural Civilization. Agriculture had naturally not been possible in the vast desert regions, except in small oases isolated from one another, where subterranean water could be tapped by wells; but in the marginal steppe-lands one of the arts of this civilization, the

[1] Since the first printing of this book, the English translation of Carl Brockelmann's *History of the Islamic Peoples* has appeared (New York, 1947; London, 1949).
[2] For a study of the historical process, see Henri Frankfort, *The Birth of Civilization in the Near East*, pp. 34–40.

taming of useful animals, had enabled man to gain a precarious footing and win a hard livelihood as nomad Bedouin with their herds of sheep and goats and camels. The more favoured lands produced abundant grain and fruits for consumption and export, while in the towns secondary manufactures were worked up, and there was eventually a lively commerce in luxury goods between India and the Mediterranean, and in objects of less value over shorter distances. The distribution of the products of labour was, however, so far from equitable that it had become a brake on material inventiveness and economic enterprise. While the precarious little communities of men in a 'food-gathering' state, before the discovery of agriculture, had probably practised a primitive communism of goods as the only way of ensuring their group-survival, the growth of the Agricultural Civilization with its rapid development of new techniques had (like the Industrial Revolution of the nineteenth century) temporarily caused the supply and variety of goods to outstrip the increase of population; and it was probably with general approval that those sections of the population deemed most instrumental in bringing about or maintaining this new abundance had acquired an unequal share of the goods. These privileged sections were the priesthoods, originally the repositories and guardians of the traditional science and other learning of each community, and the military leaders who protected the community's goods against the depredations of uncivilized raiders from the wastes or struggled with jealous neighbours over some debatable right. On successively lower levels came the small class of public servants, the merchants, the artisans, and, on the lowest level of all, the cultivators, close to the soil and scarcely reached by the higher material and intellectual gifts of successive periods of civilization. Such is the force of tradition that the individual's place in one of these social and occupational classes was generally determined by his parenthood and upbringing, though the Middle East never knew the rigidity of the Hindu caste-system and it was always possible for an exceptional man to improve his station.

Since a large section of the population, the artisans and peasants, received so small a share of manufactured goods, there was little incentive to expand their production, beyond the limit of what was consumed by the small privileged classes or exported, by the harnessing of power other than that supplied by human or animal effort. Consequently, although the motive power of steam had become known as a scientific curiosity, it was not applied to industry or transport, and both were restricted to the tempo furnished by muscular power. Thus circumscribed, technical inventiveness, which had been lively in the earlier stages of the Agricultural Civilization, had slackened, and the rate of material progress had tended to slow down.

In the realm of ideas, however, there was still plenty of activity on various planes. Politics had grown out of economic needs, a community's quest for materials not present in its own area, or the defence of its goods against a predatory neighbour. From this beginning war-leaders-become-kings had sought to bring ever larger areas under their domination in the will-o'-the-wisp pursuit of economic self-sufficiency or complete security. Successive empires had crossed the stage of history—Egyptians,. Hittites, Assyrians, Babylonians, Persians, Alexander the Great and his generals, the Roman Empire—each uniting an ever larger area under their domination, but finding it continuously difficult to maintain that unity in view of local separatisms and the slowness of communications. While the earlier of these warlike peoples had done little more than impose their tax-collectors and impart some elements of their civilization to the conquered peoples, the unification that ensued under the later ones had gone deeper. The Persian Empire had a common coinage and a common everyday language of commerce: in the Hellenistic kingdoms that followed Alexander the Great's conquests in Egypt and Western Asia the Greek language and the elements of Greek intellectual civilization had spread over the urban middle-classes, and commerce extended almost to the limits of the Old World; and this process had been confirmed and intensified by the Roman Empire, which was the lineal heir of the Hellenistic civilization.

Nevertheless, in spite of the fact that the peoples of the Roman Empire enjoyed greater security and a higher general level of material, social, and intellectual civilization than had ever been known before, there were millions of peoples who were unhappy and dissatisfied and saw no prospect of improving their lot in existing circumstances, or who felt more profoundly that contentment did not lie in the acquisition of material goods. Many of these had, through captivity in war or through commerce, been displaced from their homes and flung together to form a proletariat of the great cities—Rome, Alexandria, Antioch—where their various traditions of thought and belief were fused in a cosmopolitan crucible, with the added flux of Greek philosophical speculation. Displacement from one's home meant losing contact with that normal type of religious cult that had fixed local associations, and had caused lonely men to turn for comfort and hope to the unlocalized mystery-religions that had found favour throughout the Mediterranean, offering in this world communion with the divine and the hope of a blessed hereafter.

One originally localized cult, that of the Hebrew god Yahweh, had itself suffered displacement when the Jewish people were taken away into exile. It had already acquired moral and spiritual overtones of exceptional richness through the teaching of prophets in protest against religious laxity or social injustice; and in the humiliation of the Exile it had survived only by its enlargement from being the national cult of a small people into a religion with a universal message in the teaching of the Second Isaiah. But the Return from the exile, giving the Yahweh-cult once more a local habitation in Jerusalem, had reversed this spiritual expansion, and the Jewish religion had become bound in those fetters of national exclusiveness and legalistic minutiæ from which it has never escaped. Individuals had however broken loose from time to time; and in His human aspect the Founder of Christianity had met the fate of such a rebel against Jewish authority. St. Paul, a Jew of Greek education, and others had propagated their Master's Gospel of Love among the cities of the Levant; and when the Graeco-Roman classicism had begun to stagnate, much of the intellectual vigour of the age had been transferred into the evolving, painfully and (to human eye) empirically, of the catholic Trinitarian theology. When in A.D. 313, after two generations of military anarchy had brought the Roman Empire near to economic and political ruin, the emperor Constantine had sought some institution to take into partnership for the restoration of order and the preservation of civilization, he had found it in the Christian Church which, though still a minority in the Empire as a whole, had withstood the shock of the 'Time of Troubles' and gained adherents despite intermittent persecution, and now had no rival. Constantine's recognition of Christianity as the official religion of the Roman Empire, and the close association of Church and State in the highly institutional type of government that followed, had caused Christianity to spread rapidly throughout the settled lands of the Empire until only scattered pockets of paganism were left there, and it also spread beyond the Roman frontiers along the routes of commerce.

Nevertheless, the temporal triumph of Christianity had not brought the majority of men spiritual freedom or fundamentally altered the springs of their conduct. The Church had become bound to the state-machine which, faced with the task of salvaging as much as possible from the third-century anarchy which had destroyed the middle-class liberalism of the self-governing cities of the earlier Roman Empire, had been forced to truss up the shattered body-politic in a harness of compulsory enactments that, while it averted total collapse, hindered free economic and social development and imposed a constant burden of heavy taxation. The unity conferred by the Greek language and culture and by the Christian religion was moreover only partial, since the former did not effectively descend beyond the urban middle-classes and barely reached the artisans or the large rural population who maintained their local languages and customs ; and Christianity had come to these multitudes in translations from its original Greek, and through the mouths of men of their own stock, so that the masses without Greek culture were not brought by Christianity very much closer to one another. National particularism and the general resentment for the heavy-handed, exacting, and corrupt bureaucracy through which they were ruled from Constantinople, having no outlet in politics, found expression in the dogmatic disputes to which the Christian Church had become a prey when men had brought the keen edge of Greek philosophical reasoning to bear upon the difficult concept of the Triune Godhead. In the Levant early in the fifth century a dispute between the theologians, concerning the relative degrees to which our Lord's Nature during His life on earth had been divine or human, was taken up by the fanatical Egyptian monks and the ignorant populace of Alexandria, who made of the Monophysite doctrine of the One Divine Nature a rallying-cry against Greek reasoning and thought. A Council of the entire Church, held at Chalcedon in A.D. 451, adopted a compromise formula which neither emphasized the Humanity of Christ on earth to the extent favoured by the followers of the patriarch Nestorius, nor subordinated it to His Divinity as totally as did the extreme Monophysites. The result was a violent Monophysite reaction: the Patriarch of Alexandria was murdered on Good Friday in his own cathedral and his body dragged through the streets by the mob. Despite harsh attempts by the imperial government to repress the secession, the movement spread through that majority of the population of Egypt and Syria that had never effectively been reached by Greek civilization, and they broke away to form two national churches, the Coptic Church of Egypt and the Syrian or Jacobite Church, using in their respective liturgies, in place of the Greek which was the cultivated language of the Eastern Mediterranean and the language of the Church throughout that region, their native Coptic (the contemporary form of Ancient Egyptian) and Syriac.[1]

Thus in the civilization of the Middle East at the beginning of the seventh century A.D. it was difficult to find a single unifying factor. Two great military empires, the Later Roman or Byzantine and the Persian, had contended for centuries for mastery over the region, the Byzantines holding the Levant lands but failing to make a lasting conquest of Mesopotamia, while during the sixth century the Persians had made several serious inroads into Syria, once destroying its capital of Antioch and in 614 capturing Jerusalem and burning its churches. Despite these wars, commerce and industry were far from inactive. There was a sufficient surplus of wealth to make possible the founding of many new churches, especially in the reign of Justinian (527–65), to whom we owe the rebuilding of Constantine's Church of the Nativity at Bethlehem, as well as Hagia Sophia at Constantinople. The towns, of which Jerash in Transjordan and Palmyra are the best extant examples, together with many lesser sites in Syria, presented a picture of busy life, though the archaeologist, looking below the surface, finds much of the apparent opulence to have been Ersatz.[2] While landed

---

[1] These churches, together with the followers of Nestorius, have survived to the present day among those Oriental churches which are little known in Western Europe: the Copts, despite thirteen centuries of Muslim rule, still number over a million adherents in Egypt, and the national Church of Ethiopia also derives from them; the Syrian Church has 150-200,000 followers in North Mesopotamia, Syria, and Southern India; the Nestorians, after evangelizing a large part of Central Asia during the Middle Ages, have shrunk to the few score thousands of homeless 'Assyrians'.

[2] Lankester Harding, *Official Guide to Jerash* (Transjordan Dept. of Antiquities, 1944), 8.

proprietors, the wealthy religious houses, and merchants prospered, the urban and rural masses were oppressed by heavy taxation and corrupt officials, and had no sense of loyalty to the régime. The Christian Church, in becoming an established institution, had itself become as stratified as official society; and while the monasteries did a valuable service for posterity in keeping alive some part of the tradition of Greek science and scholarship that would otherwise have been irreparably lost, there was no longer that sense of brotherhood in the Church which had characterized primitive Christianity as it was to characterize primitive Islam. Moreover the Church had ceased to be universal and undivided; but the nationalism betokened by the breaking away of the Monophysite churches was manifested only in opposition to the centralizing and Hellenizing tendency of the bureaucracy and the œcumenical church, it did not make a positive patriotic appeal to their adherents: there was nothing that could be called an Egyptian or Syrian nation, only a congeries of individuals at the mercy of any determined external force. Successive emperors after the Council of Chalcedon were fully aware of the political danger to the Empire of the estrangement of the Levant provinces, and sought to reclaim them by doctrinal concessions to the Monophysites: but the latter were hard bargainers, and the emperors' freedom of negotiation was restricted by the watchfulness of the Popes who, while less concerned in Rome than the emperors in Constantinople with the political exigencies of the Levant, were insistent that orthodoxy should not be imperilled by excessive indulgence of the Monophysite heresy; and for thirty years they broke off relations with an over-accommodating emperor. The Monophysites for their part were not disposed to compromise with the hated Greeks, and periodically imperial conciliation was replaced by savage persecution. Thus the breach with the Levant provinces was never bridged, and they were ripe to fall to any invader who would offer them greater freedom from imperial interference.[1]

[1] cf. Steven Runciman: *History of the Crusades*, Vol. I, ch. i.

CHAPTER II

The Rise and Decline of the Muslim Civilization
(610–1517)

THE ARID climate of the Arabian Peninsula had caused its
level of civilization to remain well below that reached in the
Fertile Crescent, except for the Yemen with its monsoon
rains, where the legend of the Queen of Sheba and archaeological
evidence combine to indicate a more advanced culture founded on
the profits of seafaring in the Red Sea and the Indian Ocean. The
greater part of the Peninsula, however, was suitable only for the
nomad tribes whose livelihood depended on the rearing of camels
and small cattle, and whose characteristic social trait was the raiding
of other tribes for plunder, for prestige, and in the pursuit of
traditional feuds, and the celebration of these raids in heroic lays
handed down from generation to generation. Such nomads,
speaking a family of languages that has been termed Semitic, had
from the beginnings of the Agricultural Civilization pressed upon
the inner margins of the Fertile Crescent and at intervals broken
in to pillage the cultivated lands and sometimes settled there. It was
one such wave of invaders that brought the Hebrews into Palestine
soon after 1400 B.C. Later, Arabic-speaking peoples had begun to
appear in North Arabia, among the first of them the Naba-
taeans who from about 300 B.C. were settled in Southern Transjordan round their stronghold of Petra, and lived by agriculture
based on highly-developed water-conservation and by the tolls
they exacted from the profitable trade in incense and other luxuries
that came up by caravan through their territories on their way from
Southern Arabia to the Mediterranean coast and Syria. Early in the
Christian era other Arab tribes had succeeded them, and in the
sixth century the Bani Ghassan were enlisted by the Byzantine
Emperors to protect the desert borders of Syria and Transjordan
against the Persians and their Arab allies.

The land-route from Southern Arabia up through Western

Arabia to the Mediterranean remained commercially important after the decline of Petra; and among the goods which the Fertile Crescent exported in return were the elements of its higher civilizations, Christianity and Judaism: colonies of adherents of these faiths lived in the towns along this route, side-by-side with the Arabs who worshipped the manifold forces of nature through the medium of idols. The principal town in the sixth century A.D. was Mecca, where the road to the Mediterranean branched from another leading to Mesopotamia and the Persian Gulf; it had an important pagan cult centring round a meteoric Black Stone built into a sanctuary called the Ka'ba; and it was in this environment, culturally outlandish but impregnated by its commercial contacts with the higher civilization of the Fertile Crescent, that the Prophet Mohammed was born in 570.

When he began to undergo his religious experience about A.D. 610, he could have had no adequate first-hand knowledge of the Jewish or Christian scriptures, which had not been translated into Arabic while he knew no other language; but he had opportunities for conversations with Jews and Christians both on his caravan-journeys and in Mecca itself; and his religious experience, which took the form of an uncompromising monotheism in opposition to the polytheistic idol-worship of Mecca, was affected to a considerable degree by indirectly-acquired and imperfect notions of these two developed religions. At the time a dissatisfaction with the traditional polytheism was evidently stirring in the minds of other Arab thinkers, whose personalities have been obscured for posterity by the triumphant Muslim tradition.[1]

At the early stage of his ministry Mohammed evidently did not regard himself as the founder of a new religion, but merely as one whose mission it was to warn his fellow-townsmen of the impending Judgement Day revealed to Christians and Jews in their scriptures. Though his preaching made no great headway, it aroused the opposition of the leading merchant-tribe of Mecca, the Quraish (to a somewhat unimportant family of which Mohammed himself belonged): not only had he attacked their traditional beliefs, but he threatened the commercial profits which the town derived from the annual pilgrimage (hajj) which the inhabitants of the surrounding country paid to the Ka'ba. The menaces of the Quraish eventually constrained Mohammed to

---

[1] cf. *Encyclopaedia of Islam*, arts. Hanif and Musailima.

seek another home; and after receiving overtures from merchants of Madina (then called Yathrib), some 200 miles to the north of Mecca, where the presence of a substantial minority of the Jewish faith offered a more sympathetic milieu than conservative Mecca, he followed his three hundred adherents thither in A.D. 622. From this Flight (Hijra) the Muslim world dates the beginning of its era.

It was now that Mohammed first found it necessary to act as lawgiver for his little community of refugees from Mecca (Muhajirun), and for the converts that he made among the people of Madina (Ansar). He had hoped to receive cordial support from the Jewish community in Madina, since he regarded himself as the successor of the major Hebrew prophets, notably Abraham, and he adopted some Jewish forms of worship, including especially that of facing Jerusalem when at prayer. But it soon became obvious that the Jews of Madina had no use for this new revelation, and they ridiculed his misunderstanding of various Old Testament narratives and Jewish rituals. He retaliated by denouncing them as concealing or falsifying parts of the divine revelation given to them; and since he had already begun to regard current Christian doctrine as a perversion of the original teaching of Jesus, in so far as he had any clear idea of either of these two things, he underwent a sharp revulsion from the two religions which had hitherto inspired him, and instead proclaimed the true and uncorrupted revelation of God to himself as the 'seal of the prophets'; this revelation he termed Islam, resignation to the will of God. Reverting to his Meccan traditions, he transferred the direction of prayer to the Ka'ba and proclaimed the Hajj one of the obligations of the Muslim faith. He revived or invented a tradition that the Ka'ba and the rites connected with it, though since corrupted by polytheism and idol-worship, had been founded by none other than Abraham and his son Ishmael, the ancestor of the Arabs. It was his mission to restore this cult in its original purity.

From this time onwards it appears that Mohammed experienced little in the way of spiritual exaltation, and that the rest of his career was devoted to the more mundane tasks of regulating the public and private conduct of his devoted Muslim followers at Madina, and of asserting his supreme authority over the townsmen of Mecca who had rejected him. Faced by this striking change in the motivation of the Prophet's teaching, some European writers[1]

[1] Summarized by Tor Andrae: *Mohammed, the Man and his Faith*, ch. VII.

have in the past declared that he was never anything more than an ambitious politician who insincerely professed a new religion as a vehicle for attaining political power. But this cynical interpretation will not bear analysis: there are too many hazards in the preaching of a new religion to commend it to the politically ambitious. Mohammed himself had to endure twelve years of neglect, derision, and growing hostility before he attained political authority over the small band who followed him into exile. It is far more reasonable to suppose that his original religious experience was entirely genuine, but that when the call came to undertake the governance of the Muslim community at Madina, it opened up or confirmed in him a rich vein of practical authority which from now on superseded his spiritual powers. 'Had not God laid upon him the duty of conveying the revelation of God's truth to his fellow-men, and would he not be executing this duty if he embraced this heaven-sent opportunity of providing the new religion, whose path had been obstructed for ten years by human *force-majeure*, with a human political vehicle without which, as personal experience showed, Islam could make no further practical progress?'[1]

He now proclaimed a holy war (jihad) against the people of Mecca who had rejected his teaching and driven him out, and induced some of his followers to attack a Meccan caravan during the truce of a holy month. This was the prelude to a series of minor skirmishes with the Meccans (622–28), in most of which the Muslims gained the upper hand. During this period he expelled two of the Jewish tribes from Madina, and had the third tribe massacred on suspicion of treasonable correspondence with his enemies in Mecca. By this time an increasing number in Mecca had grown tired of the desultory warfare which interfered with the caravan-trade and was prepared to compromise with Mohammed, especially now that he had incorporated the Pilgrimage into the Muslim ritual. In 628 they agreed by the Pact of Hudaibiya to allow him to make the Pilgrimage in the following year, on which occasion some of the leading personalities of Mecca embraced the new faith. In 630 he advanced upon Mecca at the head of his armed forces and, meeting with resistance only from a few irreconcilables, received

[1] A. J. Toynbee: *A Study of History*, iii. 466 ff., and cf. Gibb: *Mohammedanism*, p. 129. For a comparable defence of the institutionalizing of the Christian Church after Constantine the Great, see Dr. J. W. Wand, Bishop of London: *The Spirit of Church History* (1947), pp. 53–54.

the submission to Islam of almost all the townspeople, and destroyed all the idols in and around Mecca. His triumph was complete, and the small Jewish and Christian communities of the Hijaz, and Arabs from as far away as Bahrein, Oman, and Southern Arabia recognized him as their overlord.[1]

His sudden death in 632 left the Muslim community in confusion, since he left no son and had not designated a successor. The very real danger of a breach between the diverse sections of the community was averted by the selection of the venerable and respected Abu Bakr as Khalifa (successor, hence our 'caliph') of Mohammed in his secular capacity as ruler and lawgiver only, but not in his spiritual role as prophet. In Abu Bakr's short reign of two years the whole of Arabia was brought under the dominion of Islam. Already in the lifetime of the Prophet the Muslim bands had essayed a raid across the borders of the Byzantine Empire into Southern Transjordan, but had met with a serious reverse. Now however, under the second elected caliph 'Umar able commanders led large raiding-parties into Palestine, Syria, Iraq, and Egypt, and met with astonishingly little effective resistance. What began as raids for booty after the customary Arab fashion thus developed imperceptibly into campaigns of permanent conquest. Muslim historians attribute the great successes of their ancestors to the inspiration of Islam but though it cannot be denied that the new religion played an important part in providing a social bond which held together for the time the fickle loyalties of the tribes, the main factor in the Arab conquests was the feebleness of the forces that opposed them. The Byzantine and Persian Empires were both exhausted by a generation of warfare; the Semitic majority of the inhabitants of Syria, Palestine, and Mesopotamia were more nearly akin to the Arabs, in race and sympathies, than to their Byzantine and Persian rulers, from whom they were further estranged by generations of excessive taxation and bureaucratic misrule; the Bani Ghassan, who should have taken the first shock of the invasion of the Byzantine Empire, had been alienated because the Emperor Heraclius, his treasury emptied by his victorious Persian expedition, had in 629 stopped his annual subsidy to them;

[1] The Muslim tradition that the whole of Arabia was converted in the Prophet's lifetime, and that he addressed to the rulers of the great Empires to the North demands that they also should accept Islam, is probably fabulous. Effectively, his political control did not extend beyond the Hijaz. (Fr. Buhl, in *Encyclopaedia of Islam*, Art. Muhammad, 653 ff.)

in Egypt the Patriarch of Alexandria had attempted to impose a doctrinal compromise on the Monophysite Copts by force, and in his complementary role of civil governor had been ruthless in the collection of taxes, with the result that the Coptic Bishop of Alexandria ordered his coreligionaries not to resist the Arabs. The only effective resistance to them came therefore from such centres of Greek civilization as Alexandria, Caesarea, and Jerusalem; and by 660, one generation after Mohammed's death, his green banner was flying over an empire which extended from Persia in the east, through the Fertile Crescent, Egypt, and Libya, to Tunisia in the west. Of these the only country to offer a determined resistance was Persia, which had been the seat of an empire with a thousand-year-old tradition of proud domination. It is this period of conquering puritanism, of the very essence of Islam, and not the great age of cosmopolitan culture that was to follow, which Muslims themselves have always regarded as their Golden Age, the age of the rightly-guided (Rashidun) caliphs.[1]

The task of improvising an administrative system for the vast Arab empire was taken up in the main by the second caliph 'Umar. Authority in the provinces was placed in the hands of the Arab military commanders who had conquered them. Arab garrisons were established in newly-created cantonments in each of the conquered countries, of which Fustat, by Old Cairo, and Basra in Lower Iraq, are examples. In order to maintain their separate identity from the conquered peoples the Arabs were not at first allowed to acquire land outside Arabia. Civil administration was left in the hands in which the Arab conquerors found it—Christians of Greek education in the lands of the Roman Empire, and non-Muslims of Persian education in the lands of the former Persian Empire. It is doubtful whether Arabs, in the stricter racial sense, have ever acquired any taste, or much aptitude, for such prosaic occupations.

For the Muslim conquerors themselves the Qur'an, the compilation of the divine revelations received by Mohammed throughout his ministry, provided the rudiments of a civil and criminal code of laws, as enunciated by him in the ten years in which he governed the Muslim community at Madina. This was supplemented where necessary by reference to what his Companions could remember of his day-to-day habits, his Sunna or custom;

[1] Christopher Dawson, op. cit., 143.

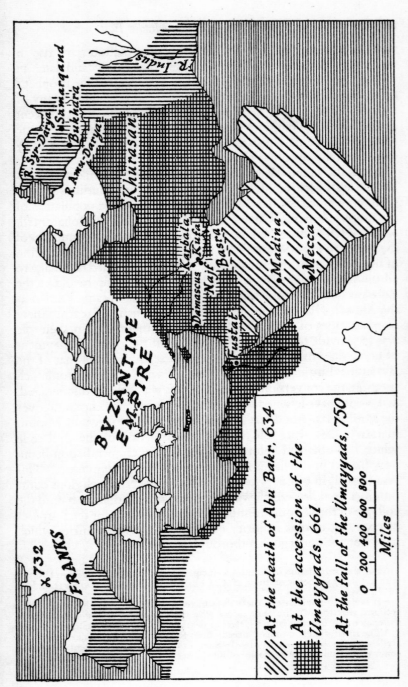

FRANKS

×732

BYZANTINE
EMPIRE

R. Syr-Darya
Samarqand
Bukhāra
R. Amu-Darya

Khurāsān

R. Indus

Karbala
Kufa
Najaf
Basra
Damascus
Fusṭāṭ

Madīna
Mecca

///// At the death of Abu Bakr, 634

At the accession of the
Umayyads, 661

At the fall of the Umayyads, 750

0   200 400 600 800
Miles

3. THE EXPANSION OF THE ARAB EMPIRE

and the constant necessity for such supplementation gave rise in succeeding decades to the production, first orally and later in writing, of many scores of thousands of Traditions of the Prophet's conduct, each enshrining some legal or ritual principle. Many of these Traditions were fictitious, but the fiction was an innocent device whereby religious sanction could be obtained for some necessary piece of legislation, generally borrowed at this early stage from the customary law of Madina.[1]

It was also necessary, however, for the new Arab rulers to regulate the legal position of the millions of their non-Muslim subjects, who represented the overwhelming majority of the population of the Empire.[2] In this 'Umar followed the example of Mohammed, who had left undisturbed the Christian and Jewish communities of the northern Hijaz whom he brought under his sway, on condition of the payment of an annual tribute. 'Umar extended this usage to all the Christian and Jewish inhabitants of the Empire and to the Zoroastrians of Persia; and these subjects thus became known as the Ahl adh-Dhimma or 'people of the covenant'. Far from there being any idea of compulsorily converting them to Islam, their role was to provide revenues for the Arab ruling-race by the payment of taxation, which apparently was at first lighter than that of the Byzantine Empire; and since Muslims were exempt from such taxation, the conversion of non-Muslims was actually discouraged, as it would have lessened the number of taxpayers. Since moreover the Muslim law (the Shari'a) was not applicable to the non-Muslim majority, they were left under the jurisdiction of the civil code which had obtained before the Conquest, such jurisdiction being now placed in the hands of their own religious dignitaries. This was the origin of the system of self-administering religious communities or *millets* which was to prevail throughout Islam until the collapse of the Ottoman Empire, and still survives for the purposes of civil law in that majority of Middle Eastern countries which have not yet undergone a thorough secularization.[3]

---

[1] For the compilation of fictitious documents by the early Christian Church with similarly innocent motives, cf. C. De lisle Burns, *The First Europe* (London, 1947), 354f.

[2] It is hardly necessary in these days to remark that the traditional Christian account, that the Muslim conquerors gave the conquered Christians and Jews the choice only of conversion to Islam or death by the sword, is totally erroneous.

[3] The institution had indeed already been foreshadowed in the dealings of the Hellenistic monarchies and the Roman Empire with the Oriental temple-communities under the authority of local priesthoods. In Alexandria under the

In spite of these statesmanlike foundations laid for the Empire by 'Umar, it was not destined to enjoy a long period of peaceful consolidation. After the murder of 'Umar by a discontented slave after a reign of ten years, the caliphate passed by election among the Muslims to the elderly and ineffectual 'Uthman, a member of the aristocratic House of Umayya, a section of the Quraish tribe of Mecca which had been one of the last to accept conversion to Islam. Under 'Uthman his Umayyad kinsmen acquired most of the leading positions in the Empire, and aroused the active jealousy of the earlier converts, the Muhajirun and the Ansar. 'Uthman was murdered in 655, and the caliphate passed by election to Ali, who as cousin and son-in-law of the Prophet was his male next-of-kin, but had been passed over in the previous three elections. Nor did he now show that the doubts of the Muslims concerning his fitness to govern had been misplaced. 'Ali had almost every virtue except those of the ruler: energy, decision, and foresight. He was a gallant warrior, a wise counsellor, a true friend, and a generous foe . . . but he had no talent for the stern realities of statecraft, and was outmatched by unscrupulous rivals who knew that "war is a game of deceit" '.[1] When his attempt to remove the Umayyad governors appointed by 'Uthman was resisted by a show of force by Mu'awiya, the able Umayyad governor of Syria, Ali weakly agreed to submit the matter to arbitration. This brought upon him in Iraq, a strategic centre of the Empire to which he had removed his seat of government from too-remote Madina, the revolt of a group of Arab conservatives, who insisted that he had no right to submit the caliphate to arbitration, as it had been conferred upon him by the God-guided judgement of the whole body of the Faithful. One of this group, the Khawarij or Seceders,[2] murdered Ali in 661, after the arbitrators had awarded the caliphate to Mu'awiya, no doubt on the grounds of his greater fitness to govern.

Mu'awiya ruled for some twenty years, and for seventy years more the caliphate remained hereditary in the House of Umayya, thus bringing to an end the original elective caliphate and replacing it by a hereditary monarchy of the traditional oriental kind. Syria,

Ptolemies the Greek civil law applied only to the Greek community and to Hellenized Egyptians; the large Jewish community and the non-Hellenized Egyptians remained subject to their traditional civil law administered by their own priesthoods.

[1] Nicholson, op. cit., 191.

[2] In the singular, Kharij. The movement survives to this day as the Ibadi sect of Oman and Zanzibar, and some scattered communities in North Africa.

the seat of Mu'awiya's power before his elevation to the caliphate, now became the centre of gravity of the Empire, and Damascus its capital.

Under the Umayyads the military extension of the Arab Empire continued, until by 732, the centenary of the Prophet's death, it had reached its geographical limits, Transoxiana and Northern India in the east, Spain in the west. The Muslims had indeed invaded France, but in the centenary year itself were decisively checked half-way to the English Channel, at a battle fought between Tours and Poitiers, by the Frank Charles Martel. Though the Muslims had conquered Crete, they had twice failed to take Constantinople, which remained the capital of a substantial Byzantine Empire comprising the Balkans and Asia Minor.[1] In the south the Sahara remained a barrier, and it was some centuries before Islam effectively penetrated up the Nile beyond Aswan.

The Umayyads maintained the broad lines of internal administration laid down by 'Umar, those of an Arab military aristocracy. The Arab military governors of the provinces throughout the vast Empire enjoyed a freedom from central control amounting almost to independence. Civil administration remained in the same non-Arab and mainly non-Muslim hands as before. For a whole century, from the Arab conquest in 636 down to 743, the financial administration of the city of Damascus itself remained in the hands of a Syrian Christian family, one of whose members has been canonized by the Church as St. John of Damascus.

Already at this stage however, the great social defect of the Arab character, its unreadiness to subordinate its overmastering self-will and self-interest, whether of individual, of family, or of tribe, to the good of a larger group, was manifesting itself in incidents that boded ill for the future of the Arab Empire. 'The Arabs are incapable of founding an empire', wrote the fourteenth-century Muslim historian Ibn Khaldun, 'unless they are imbued with religious enthusiasm by a prophet or a saint'; and the social cohesive force of Mohammed's teaching was already largely spent on the generation which personally knew him. The most im-

---

[1] Their recognition of the de facto independence of the Byzantine Empire conflicted with their theoretical duty to bring about the conversion of the whole world to Islam. The orthodox explanation was that a respite had been granted to the Byzantine Empire because Heraclius, unlike the Persian King who had torn to pieces the Prophet's fictitious letter bidding him adopt Islam, had preserved his letter in musk! (D. S. Margoliouth, *The Early Development of Mohammedanism*, 103.)

portant dissident group, the Shi'at 'Ali (party of Ali), upheld the rights of the dead Ali and maintained that the caliphate should pass hereditarily to his sons Hasan and Husain. The elder son Hasan was a colourless figure who did not press his claim; but Husain raised his banner in Iraq and was killed by the Umayyad troops at Karbala in 680. Round his tomb, and that of Ali in the neighbouring city of Najf, there rapidly grew an emotional Shi'i martyrology among the large numbers of poor Arabs who had not benefited materially from the spoils of conquest and the Persian converts to Islam who were denied equality of status by the race-proud Arabs. They evolved the doctrine that Ali and his descendants had inherited with the caliphate, not merely Mohammed's temporal authority over all Islam, but also his spiritual inspiration. Some Shi'is indeed went so far as to maintain that Ali was greater than Mohammed; that while the mission of the latter was merely to transmit to mankind the text of the Qur'an, its inner spiritual significance was contained in Ali; while the Muslim profession of faith declared Mohammed the apostle of God, the Shi'is proclaimed Ali the *saint* of God. His death and that of Husain were conceived as a martyrdom for the salvation of mankind, a notion probably inspired by the Christian doctrine of the Atonement. The spiritual inspiration of Ali and his sons was held to be passed on to their descendants, the Saiyids descended from Husain and the Sharifs descended from Hasan, who are to this day objects of Shi'i veneration. In particular, both temporal and spiritual power was believed to pass from Husain to his legal heir in each generation, to whom as the infallible Imam (leader) the implicit obedience of the Shi'a was due in all matters, religious or secular. Had any of the descendants of Ali possessed something of the political talent of the best Umayyads, he would certainly have been able to supplant them, such was the superstitious reverence of the Shi'is for their imams;[1] but in fact the Umayyads, whose power rested on the mass of moderate people, Muslim and non-Muslim alike, who wanted above all things law and order, were able with some difficulty to maintain their ascendancy.

In addition to the rising of the Shi'a the early Umayyads had to contend with a revolt of Madina, the city of the Prophet, which resented the passing of authority from it to Damascus; there were feuds between great Arab tribal groups drawn originally from

[1] Snouck Hurgronje, *Mohammedanism*, 91.

Northern and Southern Arabia respectively; and the Khawarij overran Iraq, Southern Persia, and the greater part of Arabia. As a contemporary poet sang:

> 'They are split in sects: each province hath its own Commander of the Faithful, each its throne. . . .'

Thus the Arab nation was torn asunder by the old tribal pretensions which Mohammed sought to abolish. That they ultimately proved fatal to the Umayyads is no matter for surprise; the sorely-pressed dynasty was already tottering, its enemies were at its gates. But by good fortune it produced in this crisis an exceptionally able and vigorous ruler, Abd ul-Malik (685–705), who not only saved his house from destruction, but re-established its supremacy and gave the Muslim civilization an opportunity to enrich itself culturally. His iron-handed governor of Iraq ruthlessly put down the rebellion in the eastern provinces, and for twenty years provided peace and security by his despotic rule. In order to knit together the far-flung empire and curb the separatist tendencies of the provinces Abd ul-Malik borrowed from earlier empires the institution of an official postal system by means of relays of horses; he substituted for the Byzantine and Persian coins, which had hitherto been in general use, new gold and silver pieces on which he caused sentences from the Qur'an to be engraved; and he made Arabic, instead of Greek or Persian, the official language of financial administration.[1]

This reform does not mean that the non-Arab personnel of the administration, largely Christian by religion in the Levantine provinces, were replaced. But by this time the social barrier which 'Umar had attempted to impose between the Arab garrisons and the non-Arab and non-Muslim majority of the population was beginning to break down. The Arab cantonments had soon grown into towns and cities; Arabs had acquired land; and, as formerly between Alexander's Greeks and Orientals, social contact and intermarriage (for Muslims were permitted to take non-Muslim wives) were doing their levelling work. Moreover, non-Muslims

---

[1] Nicholson, op. cit., 199 ff. It is of interest that, because these coins bore quotations from the Qur'an, the eighth-century founder of one of the four schools of Muslim jurisprudence objected to their being given in payment to non-Muslims. (D. S. Margoliouth, *The Early Development of Mohammedanism*, 119.)

were being attracted to Islam by reason of the social prestige and freedom from taxation that it conferred, to such an extent that under the later Umayyads of the early eighth century new legislation compelled Muslims acquiring land, and non-Arab converts to Islam, to continue to pay the appropriate tax.

Nevertheless, the majority of the inhabitants of Syria and Lower Egypt were still Christian in the ninth century, and Baghdad itself is stated to have had as late as A.D. 900 à Christian population of 40–50,000. Except for the brief reigns of two bigoted Umayyad caliphs the still influential Christian Church was tolerated. The adoption of the Arabic language and of Islam seems to have been most rapid in Iraq, where the Semitic mass of the population had been comparatively little affected by Greek influences. In Syria and Palestine the process was slower, and Aramaic remained the principal language there till the ninth century. In Persia with its strong national culture Arabization was very superficial, and the Arabic language was adopted only temporarily and by a small proportion of the population for official purposes. Islam had made considerable headway in Persia by 750, and a reliable class of Muslim Persian officials had come into being; but Persia did not become completely Muslim till the tenth or eleventh century. In conservative Egypt the official adoption of the Arabic language under Abd ul-Malik affected only the smallest fraction of the population; but the language of their Arab rulers was gradually adopted, and by the tenth century a Coptic ecclesiastic had to write in Arabic to be understood by his coreligionaries. 'The chief factor in the spread of Arab culture in Egypt, which gave it so much greater effect than the preceding Hellenism, was the gradual settlement of the country districts by Arab nomads. . . . Sections, or even whole tribes, gradually succumbed to the advantages of settled life, and thus a strong strain of Arab blood was constantly being added to that of the Copts. It was apparently a considerable migration, which even sent offshoots as far as the Sudan. . . . The ancient civilization of the Nile Valley assimilated these nomad Arabs, and only their Arabic language remained. The Arabs became Nilotized, but also the Copts were Arabicized, and it is inexplicable that the essentially conservative Copts should have adopted another language without a great deal of mixing.'[1]

The Umayyad caliphs were descendants and representatives of

[1] C. H. Becker, *Encyclopaedia of Islam*, art. Egypt.

the pagan aristocracy of Arabia who, fully exposed in their new Syrian environment to the influences of the old blend of Greek and Oriental civilization, were ready to assimilate it and adapt it to both their secular and religious purposes. The almost total deficiency of Arab culture in the sciences and liberal and useful arts, and the supremacy in these matters of the Christians, Jews, and Persians, were freely acknowledged. The conquered peoples were regularly employed in commerce and industry, banking, the arts, as architects, engineers, and irrigation-specialists, as schoolmasters and secretaries, even as court-physicians and political advisers. The caliphs at Baghdad in the ninth and tenth centuries had some Christian wazirs (viziers), and most of the court-physicians in the early centuries of Muslim rule were Nestorians. The employment of Christian advisers in Egypt as late as the fourteenth century was a cause of annoyance to fanatical Muslims.[1] The only function absolutely reserved to Muslims was service in the army and navy. Not only were the Umayyad caliphs' country-palaces decorated in a mixture of Graeco-Syrian and Mesopotamian-Persian styles which completely disregarded the orthodox Muslim ban on the human figure,[2] but also Graeco-Syrian influences strongly affected the development of the mosque, whose architecture was still rudimentary at the beginning of the Umayyad period. Though the Dome of the Rock at Jerusalem (often miscalled the Mosque of Omar), which was founded in 691 by Abd ul-Malik, was a shrine built for Muslim worship, it must nevertheless be regarded as a product of Christian art. Its plan, a circle within an octagon, existed in the Church of the Ascension then standing on the Mount of Olives, and elsewhere in Palestine and Syria. The geometric setting-out of the plan and elevation of the Dome of the Rock appears to be derived from Syrian-Christian architectural practice. Before its exterior was re-covered with Persian tiles in the sixteenth century it was covered with marble and mosaic, and its external appearance must then have been as Byzantine as its internal appearance still largely is.[3] The Great Mosque at Damascus, founded in 708, was likewise the work of architects and builders supplied from the Byzantine Empire.

[1] A. S. Tritton, *The Caliphs and their Non-Muslim Subjects*. J. H. Kraemer, *Encyclopaedia of Islam*, art. Egypt, 7.
[2] e.g. the recently-discovered palace at Khirbat Mafjar near Jericho: *Quarterly of the Dept. of Antiquities of Palestine*, XII (1945), 17 ff.
[3] E. T. Richmond, *Moslem Architecture* (623–1516), ch. II.

The increased penetration of the Muslim culture by Christian and Persian civilization even affected Muslim law and theology. The greater complexity of the civilization of which the Muslims now found themselves a part made necessary new elaborations of their legal code, mainly by the assimilation of the Roman Law existing in the conquered provinces of the Levant. By the end of the Umayyad period a new critical approach to the mass of Traditions had begun to appear, and the science of Muslim jurisprudence was beginning to take shape. Contact with the older and more subtle Christian religion, which had retained some of the questioning Greek spirit, was causing some Muslims to look more deeply into the foundations of their own faith, where they found numerous ambiguities and inconsistencies amid the obscure and uncoordinated phraseology of the Qur'an. This new spirit of inquiry in Islam was stimulated, as it had been among the Christians, by the disputes of rival sects: in this case the Shi'a and the Sunnis, as the mass of moderate believers called themselves, claiming to be following the custom (Sunna) of the Prophet. In particular, some were brought to question the Prophet's doctrine of the eternal and uncreated Qur'an, which seemed to them to place a second eternal existence in conflict with the essential unity (*tawhid*) of God. Secondly, they were exercised by the alternative of free-will or predestination, which the Qur'an characteristically left ambiguous. Thus a sect, known to Muslim historians as the Mu'tazila or secession, which came into being towards the end of the Umayyad period, adopted a rationalist attitude towards both of these questions, and was to exert an important influence on the history of the following century.

In spite of the readiness with which they had assimilated what survived of Greek civilization, the Umayyad period was marked by a certain economic decline when compared with the later Roman Empire. Mediterranean commerce, already shaken in the West by the Germanic invasions, was even more seriously affected by the partition of the Mediterranean coastlands between two conflicting civilizations, the Christian on the northern shores and the Muslim on the south. Moreover the Muslims in the West had conquered Spain and were energetically raiding into Italy and Provence, while in the East they were making every attempt, though vainly, to conquer the remainder of the Byzantine Empire. Though in spite of frequent Muslim raids the trading cities of Southern Italy maintained some commerce with the Southern Mediterranean and the Levant, the effect of the Muslim conquests was gradually to check the flow of Oriental goods to Christian Western Europe.[1]

The fertility of Egypt was maintained on about the same level as before the Muslim conquest by a policy of non-interference with the Coptic administration and irrigation-specialists. Historians no longer hold, as formerly, that the Muslim conquest abruptly ended the prosperity of Syria and Palestine; instead they ascribe the beginnings of their economic decline to the shifting of the centre of gravity from the Levant to Iraq and Persia which followed the transfer of the capital from Damascus to Baghdad with the accession of the Abbasid dynasty in the middle of the eighth century.

The Umayyads never succeeded in securing the loyalty of the whole of even the Arab inhabitants of their vast Empire; and their non-Arab subjects became increasingly estranged by the oppressive rule of their deputies. The Arabs 'lived as soldiers at the expense of the native population whom they inevitably regarded as an inferior race. If the latter thought to win respect by embracing the religion of their conquerors, they found themselves sadly mistaken. The new converts were attached as clients (mawali) to an Arab tribe: they could not become Muslims on any other footing. Far from obtaining the equal rights which they coveted, and which, according to the principles of Islam, they should have enjoyed, the Mawali were treated by their aristocratic patrons with contempt, and had to submit to every kind of social degradation.... And these Clients, be it remembered, were not ignorant serfs, but men whose culture was acknowledged by the Arabs themselves—men who formed the backbone of the influential learned class and ardently prosecuted those studies, divinity and jurisprudence, which were then held in highest esteem. Here was a situation full of danger. Against Shi'is and Khawarij the Umayyads might claim with some show of reason to represent the cause of law and order, if not of Islam; against the bitter cry of the oppressed Mawali they had no argument save the sword. . . .'

Active propaganda against the Umayyads was made, not only by the Shi'is, but also by a branch of the Prophet's family descended from his uncle Abbas. These Abbasids 'had genius enough to see that the best soil for their efforts was distant Khurasan, the extensive north-eastern provinces of the old Persian Empire,

[1] H. Pirenne, *Mahomet et Charlemagne*, 148 ff.

These countries were inhabited by a brave and high-spirited people who in consequence of their intolerable sufferings under the Umayyad tyranny, the devastation of their homes and the almost servile condition to which they had been reduced, were eager to join in any desperate enterprise that gave them hope of relief.'[1] While the Abbasids succeeded in persuading the Shi'is into allying themselves with them, the Umayyad rulers had become soft and negligent in the civilized luxury of sophisticated Syria. Quarrels broke out within the royal house over the succession to the caliphate, which changed hands no fewer than four times in the Muslim year 743/4. In these circumstances the warnings of the loyal governor of Khurasan were disregarded. In 747 the Abbasids openly raised the standard of revolt. By 750 they had supplanted and virtually exterminated the Umayyads, and the victor transferred the seat of the new dynasty to Iraq, where in 762 a new capital was founded at Baghdad.

* * *

This shifting of the political centre of gravity brought with it a decline in the Arab influence which had formerly been predominant, and an increase in that of the Persians who had done so much to place the Abbasids in power; for the first fifty years of their rule, for example, the Abbasid caliphs drew their prime ministers (wazirs) from the Persian Barmaki family, the 'Barmecides' of the Arabian Nights. With this relative decline of Arab supremacy, the many races of the Empire became fused into a common Muslim culture, the non-religious aspects of which were shared by the many Christians and Jews who had not embraced Islam. In the Empire as a whole, the relative decline in the importance of Syria was far more than compensated by the economic advance of its eastern provinces. The Abbasids, completing the work of the Sassanian Persians, restored to Lower Iraq a rudimentary but sound system of irrigation and land-drainage which checked the formation of stagnant water and the salination of the land. Baghdad, the new capital, rapidly became a rival of Constantinople in its material prosperity. A second centre of agricultural development and urban civilization was promoted in Transoxiana, with its great cities of Bukhara and Samarqand, and in Khurasan. This

[1] Nicholson, op. cit., 248 ff.

agricultural progress was of special benefit to the landowning class, but wider circles of the population must also have profited from it. Sea-borne trade through the Persian Gulf, already of great antiquity owing to the eminence of Mesopotamia as one of the earliest centres of urban civilization and commerce, underwent a great revival, with Basra assuming great importance as the port of Baghdad. By about 850 Muslim ships had reached China to trade for silk, and there was a considerable Muslim colony at Canton; some Muslim traders pushed further north, and probably reached Japan and Korea. Trade with East Africa was less important, but was carried as far south as Madagascar. There was even some revival of trade between the Levant ports and those of Christian Europe, especially Venice and the ports of southern Italy, with Jews playing an important part as middle-men, since they enjoyed a comparative toleration from both sides which neither Christian nor Muslim was yet prepared to extend to each other. More important than the Mediterranean trade at this period, however, was that with the Swedish masters of Russia and the Baltic, evidence for which is furnished by the enormous numbers of Muslim coins found in that region; they were struck in the mints of Tashkent and Samarqand and extend over a period from A.D. 700 to 1500. Muslim indirect influence even reached the British Isles: a gold coin struck by King Offa of Mercia in the eighth century closely imitates an Arabic dinar, even to the Arabic inscription; and a gilt-bronze cross found in an Irish bog bears the inscription *b'ismi'llah* (in the name of God) in Arabic characters.[1]

This material prosperity has become legendary through the popularity of the Arabian Nights, with their stories of Baghdad under the Abbasid caliph Harun ar-Rashid (786–809), the contemporary of Charlemagne with whom he was on friendly relations. Of the immense cultural superiority of the Muslim East to Western Europe at this time there can be absolutely no question. With its material wealth there went also an increasing interest in matters of the intellect. The rising Muslim civilization felt the growing need of certain branches of practical knowledge which could be supplied by the higher civilizations on which it had impinged: medicine; mathematics for land-survey, architecture, and navigation; geography for the promotion of commerce; and

[1] J. H. Kramers, in *The Legacy of Islam*, 94 ff. Christopher Dawson, op. cit. 243 f.

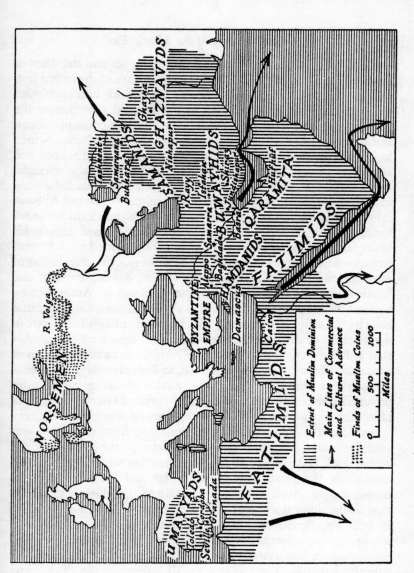

4. MUSLIM DOMINION IN THE TENTH CENTURY

astronomy, to determine the direction of Mecca and the dates of the beginning and end of Ramadhan, the month of the sacred fast, and also for astrology. Already the Umayyads had employed architects and craftsmen trained in the Byzantine-Syrian or the Persian tradition. They had also attracted to their court physicians and other scholars from Jundishapur in south-west Persia, which had had since Sassanian times an important medical school and academy where Greek, Syrian, Persian, and Indian scientific knowledge was pooled; but the Umayyads had done little consciously to promote and encourage learning. The second Abbasid caliph al-Mansur (754–75), the founder of Baghdad, on the other hand, had astronomers, engineers, and other learned men at his court, and the plans of his new city were prepared by a Persian astronomer and a Jew. From this time began the translation of scientific works into Arabic from Greek, Syriac, Persian, and Sanskrit, the work being done in the main not by Arabs, but by Syrian Christians and Persians. This work was put on an organized basis by the caliph al-Ma'mun, who founded at Baghdad in 830, in the interests of the rationalist Mu'tazila sect which he favoured, a Bait al-Hikma or 'house of learning', which was a combination of academy, library, translation-bureau, and observatory. By means of such translation-enterprises the Arabic-speaking world soon became possessed of the outstanding works of Greek science and philosophy at a time when Western Europe was almost entirely ignorant of the Greek learning. Translation from the Greek was sometimes direct, but more frequently through the Syriac versions which had been made some centuries before by the Syrian Christians; the Nestorians in particular had been assiduous in translating the Greek philosophers in order to use them as ammunition in theological controversy with their orthodox opponents. In addition, Persian and Indian mathematical and astronomical works were translated into Arabic; and early in the ninth century the simple Indian system of numerals with its arrangement in columns by powers of ten and the all-important use of the zero (our so-called 'Arabic' numerals) was introduced into the Middle East, which had previously known only the clumsy Semitic, Greek, and Roman numerals.[1]

[1] It was not until the twelfth century that Christian arithmeticians in Europe began to adopt the 'Arabic' system. (Carra de Vaux, in *The Legacy of Islam*, 384 ff.)

Following this work of translation it was not long before original research, observation, and speculation began to be practised within the Muslim Empire. But before this the *political* unity of that Empire had been shattered for ever. Ibn Khaldun, looking back over Muslim history from the end of the fourteenth century, came to the conclusion that kingdoms are born, attain maturity, and die within a period which rarely exceeds three generations, or 120 years.[1] The Umayyad Empire had been precariously maintained by the awe with which his Sunni subjects regarded the caliph as temporal successor of the Prophet. But dynastic struggles were bound to diminish that awe: in the West the success of one of the few Umayyad survivors of the collapse of their dynasty in making himself independent ruler of Spain in 756 was followed in the next half-century by the breaking-away from the Abbasids of North-West Africa under two separate dynasties. In the heart of the empire, moreover, the Abbasid caliphs, realizing from the fall of the Umayyads that the fickle and inconstant Arab individualism intolerant of discipline provided a most unstable military basis for their authority, had begun to recruit from the north-eastern confines of the Empire mercenaries from among the Turks, a people less gifted intellectually than the Arabs and Persians, but with those more solid and stable qualities of obedience and endurance that have made them such excellent soldiers through the centuries. Already in 808 we find Turks serving in Egypt; but they soon realized the military and moral weakness of their Arab masters, and were not content to remain subordinates. The Turkish body-guard with which the caliph al-Mu'tasim had provided himself clashed so frequently and violently with the populace of Baghdad that the caliph was obliged in 836 to quit the city and found a new capital at Samarra, three days journey up-river, where he and his successors rapidly came under the political domination of the commanders of their own mercenaries. In 868 the Turkish soldier Ahmed ibn Tulun made himself the independent ruler of Egypt, Palestine, and Syria, and introduced a short period of sound government in place of the reckless exhaustion of the economic resources of Egypt which she had suffered under the tax-farming governors of the Abbasids, and which had provoked a great rising of the oppressed Copts in 831.[2] In 874 Transoxiana and the

[1] Nicholson, op. cit., 440.
[2] C. H. Becker in *Encyclopaedia of Islam*, art. Egypt.

greater part of Persia, which had already been in revolt against the Abbasids, became finally independent under the Persian Samanid dynasty. In Iraq itself, which was practically all that now remained under the direct rule of Samarra, the authority of the caliph was challenged by the ferocious revolt in Lower Iraq of the Zanj or negro slaves (870–83). And worse was to follow. Though the Shi'is had helped the first Abbasid to overthrow the Umayyads, the new dynasty proved itself no less oppressive of the Shi'a than its predecessor had been, no doubt because the sect with its tendency to fanatical extravagances was regarded as potentially subversive of all ordered government. Driven underground by oppression, the Shi'is remained numerous especially in Lower Iraq, and both there and in the cities of Persia they perhaps found especial support from the artisan class, as an expression of class-consciousness against the ruling aristocracy, whether composed of Arabs, Persians, or Turks.[1]

In this atmosphere of suppressed ferment it was natural that schisms over doctrine should occur within the Shi'a. In particular there was a difference of opinion which of the two sons of the sixth Imam, who died in 760, should succeed him. The minority who supported the claim of the elder son Isma'il held that the succession of imams ended with him. They thus regarded Isma'il as the Hidden or Expected Imam, who according to Shi'i doctrine was shortly to return among men as the Mahdi (the divinely-guided) to restore true Islam, conquer the whole world, and introduce a short millenium before the end of all things. In the ninth century a Persian, Abdullah ibn Maymun, began to organize a secret esoteric cult of Isma'il in nine degrees in which all religious belief was progressively allegorized away until only an atheistic philosophy was left.[2] This cult was extensively propagated by enthusiastic missionaries and made many converts among the unhappy and discontented who always constitute the majority of mankind. At the end of the century an Isma'ili sect, called the Qaramita or Carmathians, organized itself as an independent political state on the Arabian coast of the Persian Gulf and in the Yemen. Declaring total war on all non-Isma'ilis its armies menaced Baghdad, interfered with the pilgrim-traffic, and in 930 actually sacked Mecca and carried off

[1] H. A. R. Gibb, *Mohammedanism*, pp. 122–5.
[2] The most recent study of this intricate subject is Bernard Lewis's *The Origin of Isma'ilism*.

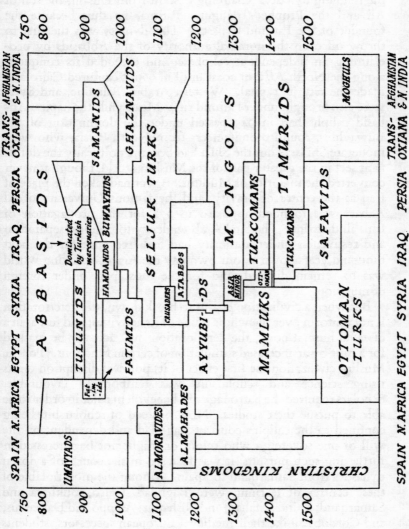

5. PRINCIPAL MUSLIM DYNASTIES

(after S. Lane-Poole, *The Mohammedan Dynasties*)

the Black Stone. Meanwhile the grandson of Abdullah ibn May-mun, in danger in Syria, escaped to Tunisia, where he won sup-port, was proclaimed Imam in 909, and succeeded in overthrowing the reigning dynasty. Claiming descent from Husain, the son of Ali and the Prophet's daughter Fatima, he thus became the founder of the Fatimid dynasty. This dynasty was the first to throw off even the nominal authority of the Abbasids by pro-claiming an independent caliphate, and extended its conquests along the North African coast until in 969 it captured Cairo and made the city its capital. Western Arabia, Palestine, and Syria were also brought under Fatimid rule. Meanwhile the hapless Ab-basid caliphs had in 945 passed under the domination of the Buwayhids, rough mountaineers from North Persia, who were moderate Shi'is. Thus the Shi'a had become politically the domi-nant sect in the greater part of the Muslim world, though it never converted the majority of Muslims. Egypt had taken the place of Iraq as the centre of gravity, and the famous University of Al Azhar[1] was founded at Cairo in 972 for the propagation of Isma'ili doctrine. The fatal Arab tendency to political separatism and restiveness under authority had had free rein: for the next thousand years down to our own day the Arabic-speaking world was to remain divided, and for the most part under foreign domination.

But when a civilization begins to break down, the deterioration is not uniform over the whole range of its activities; and just as in a diseased human body, the deterioration may actually be masked for a time by an increased stimulation of certain functions.[2] For the Muslim civilization the first effect of its political disruption on its rising science and scholarship was temporarily favourable. Scholars required the patronage of a benevolent ruler in order to be able to pursue their studies. Now, instead of scholarship being confined to the caliph's court at Baghdad and dependent on the will of one sovereign who might or might not be interested in furthering such pursuits, it was fostered in the courts of a dozen dynasties from Samarqand to Spain. Among the most notable of these centres of learning were Baghdad, Cairo, Bukhara and Samarqand; Shiraz, Isfahan, and Nishapur; Aleppo and Damascus; and Cordoba. Like their medieval European successors, students

---

[1] Pronounced, Áz-har.
[2] cf. Lewis Mumford, *The Condition of Man*, 153.

made long and laborious journeys to sit at the feet of some famous master. For example, al-Ghazzali, born at Tus in north-east Persia, studied at Nishapur, Baghdad, and Damascus, a total journey of some 1,400 miles.

Though Arabic was the principal language of scholars, with Persian steadily increasing in importance, only a small minority of the scientists and scholars of the Muslim world were Arabs by race. An analysis of the origins of the leading scholars and scientists of the Muslim East indicates that over the whole chronological range of Muslim culture from its rise to its decline Persia and Transoxiana furnished consistently some 40 per cent. of the distinguished names. Christians were predominant in the initial period of the translators, but fell away later, and Jews in the East were relatively unimportant in contrast to their great contribution to the culture of Muslim Spain.[1]

The assessment of the contribution of the Muslim world to science and scholarship has tended to run to two extremes. On the one hand, some protagonists of Greek civilization have been willing to see little originality in the Muslim achievement, and to concede them only the credit for preserving and handing on what survived of Greek learning to Western Europe in the later Middle Ages. On the other hand, modern Arab writers, and also some European historians of science, reacting too far against the excessive exaltation of Greek civilization by students of the classics, have claimed too much for the medieval Muslim scientists, exaggerating their original achievement out of all proportion to what they had received from the Greeks or from their oriental forerunners. The true assessment lies between these two extremes, and has been well embodied in a vivid word-picture: 'Islamic medicine and science reflected the light of the Hellenic sun, when its day had fled; and shone like a moon, illuminating the darkest night of the

---

[1] This is based on data given by A. Mieli, op. cit., for three successive periods: (I) the period of translators and first beginnings, eighth-ninth centuries; (II) the 'Golden Age', tenth-eleventh centuries; (III) the age of decline, twelfth-thirteenth centuries:

	I	II	III
Christians	12	8	5
Jews	0	3	4
Persians (including Transoxiana)	10	23	18
Iraqis	2	9	3
Syrians	3	7	9
Egyptians	1	4	5
Arabians	0	0	0

In Spain one-quarter of seventy-three names cited by Mieli are those of Jews.

European Middle Ages; some bright stars lent their own light; but moon and stars alike faded at the dawn of a new day—the Renaissance.'[1] The Muslim contribution to mathematics and astronomy is exemplified by the number of Arabic loan-words in the terminology of these sciences: algebra, azimuth, zenith; and the names of many stars, such as Algol, Aldebaran, Betelgeuze. In medicine considerable progress was made, thanks to the numerous hospitals founded in the principal cities by benevolent rulers: there were said to be six thousand medical students in eleventh-century Baghdad. Though Muslim law forbade dissection of the human body, the course of diseases was carefully and systematically observed and recorded. The knowledge of chemistry and other natural sciences was advanced, and Muslim cartography and descriptive geography greatly influenced medieval European map-making in the Mediterranean. When all has been justly claimed for the originality of Muslim science, however, the fact remains that it was essentially the pupil and continuation of Greek science, Though it made some important original contributions to learning, its great service lay in the systematization and preservation of older learning at a time when Western Europe was ignorant of it and incapable of preserving it. The Muslim scholars lacked in general the scientific imagination and originality of thought of the Greeks: they found difficulty in passing from the accumulation of practical data to a theoretical conclusion, and in the unifying of detail into a harmonious system.[2]

Muslim thought at its best has had its gaze turned upwards toward the One God; and, entirely absorbed by contemplation of Him, has not looked about itself at Man. Muslim society has always tended towards aristocracy; and Muslim science and learning, as compared with that of the Greeks, has suffered in the absence of a substantial middle-class, which has given it less vitality to survive great political upheavals. When all the necessary discounting of the 'democratic' character of the ancient Greek city-state has been done, the fact remains that Greek culture was genuinely the property of a considerable urban middle-class, which grew in importance till it reached its peak in the second century A.D. Islam, on the other hand, 'has known periods of intellectual life only under the protection of isolated princes here and there. It has

[1] Max Meyerhof, in *The Legacy of Islam*, 354.
[2] cf. Edward Atiyah's criticism, in *An Arab Tells His Story*, 186.

had Augustan ages; it has never had great popular yearnings after wider knowledge. Its intellectual leaders have lived and studied and lectured at courts; they have not gone down and taught the masses of the people.'[1]   The masses have remained in much the same economic and social conditions and at much the same intellectual level as their ancestors four thousand years ago.

Little Muslim science and scholarship found its way to medieval Europe via the Byzantine Empire, whose cultural contacts with the Muslim world were tenuous, though Arabic medical works were being translated into Byzantine Greek in the eleventh century.[2] The Crusaders, settled during the twelfth and thirteenth centuries in a strip of the Levant lands whose depth from the coast rarely exceeded fifty miles, were for the most part rough, unpolished adventurers, whose contacts with the native population were mainly with the peasantry, not with its scholars. Consequently, though there was an appreciable cultural interchange between the 'Franks' and the people of the Levant, it was mainly of a material kind. In any case, by the time of the First Crusade (1099) the intellectual ossification of the Muslim East was already beginning, and consequently the Crusades played no greater part than the Byzantine Empire in the transmission of Muslim learning to the West.[3]

Of considerably greater importance in this connexion was Sicily, which had been conquered by the Muslims of North Africa in the course of the ninth century, and enjoyed a period of stable and orderly Muslim government from c. 950 until Sicily was reconquered for Christendom towards the end of the eleventh century by the Normans, 'a dynasty of gifted pirates' which had entered the service of the Byzantine Greeks and then wrested Southern Italy from them. At the time of the Muslim conquest Sicily had long been rich with the past civilization of Greece and Rome. Though Eastern cultural currents had streamed in during the period of Muslim domination, the Arab rulers had been too involved in warfare to develop the finer arts of peace. But under the tolerant rule of the Normans the varied culture-strains were able to intermingle and flower. H. A. L. Fisher draws an attractive miniature pen-picture of the civilization of Sicily under Roger II (1130–54), whom his critics called the 'half-heathen king': 'His kingdom was

---

[1] D. B! Macdonald, op. cit., 153 f.
[2] R. Walzer, in *Bulletin of the John Rylands Library*, 1945, 171.
[3] Hitti, op. cit., 662.

half-oriental, half-western, providing a shelter for Greek, Latin, Moor, and Jew, and better organized . . . than any other European government of that age. Among the orange-groves of Palermo Roger, the descendant of the Vikings, sat upon his throne, robed in the dalmatic of the apostolic legate and the imperial costume of Byzantium, his ministers part Greek, part English, his army composed as to half of Moors, his fleet officered by Greeks, himself a Latin Christian but, in that balmy climate of the south, ruling in half-Byzantine, half-oriental state . . . a true representative of his lovely island, shared then as ever between east and west.'[1] Roger's grandson Frederick II (1215–50), Holy Roman Emperor and King of Sicily, still kept a semi-oriental court, and incurred the excommunication of the fierce Pope Innocent III by his reluctance to undertake the Crusade; for he was in friendly political and commercial relations with Muslim rulers, and eventually won back Jerusalem temporarily for Christendom, not by the way of the sword but by a treaty-compromise with the tolerant Sultan of Egypt. In 1224 Frederick founded the University of Naples,[2] and encouraged the translation into Latin of Arabic science and philosophy. Here at Naples studied St. Thomas Aquinas (1226–74), who made a profound study of the Arabic commentators on the Greek philosophers, but had the originality to go beyond them to the original Greek texts, which were now at last becoming available to the Western world.

But the country of outstanding importance for the transmission of Muslim learning to the West was Spain, whose level of civilization at the time of the Muslim conquest had been almost as high as that of Sicily. In particular, her cities contained many thousands of literate and energetic Jews, endowed with that spirit of restless inquiry which characterizes their race. During the ninth century Muslim Spain became one of the wealthiest and most thickly-populated lands of Europe, sending abundant industrial and agricultural exports both to Christian Europe and to the Muslim East. Cordoba, the capital, was the most cultivated city in Europe, the rival of Constantinople, Baghdad and Cairo. With its population of half-a-million, its three hundred public baths, its seventy libraries, and its miles of paved streets lit at night, it was centuries in

[1] *History of Europe*, one-vol. ed., 190 f.
[2] For Muslim influence on the Medical School of Salerno in the eleventh century or even before, see Mieli, op. cit., 219 f.

advance of the barbarous condition of contemporary Paris or London, and was the cultural metropolis for the Christian rulers of the petty states of Northern Spain. Nevertheless, the intellectual tone in Muslim Spain was still one of rigid orthodoxy and strict conservatism. There was scant sympathy with the rationalist innovations of some of the Abbasid caliphs, and little evidence yet of intellectual originality. Both Muslims and Jews wishing to complete their education went to the Eastern Mediterranean and on to Iraq. In the first half of the ninth century, however, the Umayyad Abd ur-Rahman II sent a scholar to Iraq to obtain copies of translations of Greek and Persian scientific works, and surrounded himself with a group of astronomers.[1]   A century later the University of Cordoba was founded by Abd ur-Rahman III, who proclaimed himself Caliph independently of the Abbasids. His successor invited professors to Cordoba from the East, established twenty-nine free schools in the city, and employed agents to buy learned manuscripts in the eastern cities. At the same time the centre of Jewish scholarship began to be transferred from Iraq to Spain. Early in the eleventh century the Umayyad dynasty collapsed, and for eighty years Spain was torn by civil wars, with Muslim military commanders playing the same role as they had done in the East when the Abbasid dynasty fell into decline. But just as in the East, the partitioning of the caliphate among provincial rulers led to the diffusion of the culture of the metropolis over a number of provincial capitals, such as Seville, Toledo, and Granada. And as the Christian kingdoms of Northern Spain seized the opportunity to invade the disunited Muslim state, so they began increasingly to absorb Muslim cultural influences.

The Muslims, finding themselves hard-pressed by the aggressive Christians in the north, appealed for help to the Berbers of North-West Africa, who had been united for the last fifty years in a militant Muslim brotherhood, al-Murabitun (whence their Spanish name of Almoravides). At the end of the eleventh century these defeated the Christians under their legendary leader the Cid, but remained in Spain as the ruling Muslim dynasty, only to succumb to its luxuries. Meanwhile another Puritan movement, al-Muwah-hidun (Almohades in Spanish) had arisen among the Berbers. These overthrew the Almoravides in the middle of the twelfth century and replaced them as rulers of an empire extending from

[1] E. Levi-Provençal, *La Civilisation arabe en Espagne* (Cairo, 1938), 65.

Central Spain to the borders of Egypt. Both Berber dynasties were rigidly orthodox in matters of Muslim thought, and according to a fairly reliable tradition even had the writings of the great Ghazzali, the 'restorer of the faith', publicly burned in the market-place of Cordoba. While, however, they imposed the severest orthodoxy on the mass of the people, they did not interfere with the speculations of the Muslim philosophers, provided that these did not reach the multitude and disturb their faith. Thus twelfth-century Spain, ruled by religious conservatives, was yet the home of two outstanding Arabic philosophers, Ibn Bajja (Avempace) and Ibn Rushd (Averroes), the latter of whom asserted that the Qur'an, being but an imperfect presentation of truths which might be learnt more completely and correctly from Aristotle, was a dis-cipline fit only for the masses whose intelligence neither desired nor was capable of philosophical reasoning. But while the Moorish rulers tolerated such heresy, so long as it did not reach the people, they vigorously persecuted the many thousands of Christians and Jews in their Spanish province, and periodically expelled to the Christian North all who refused conversion to Islam. The twelfth century thus marked the beginning of the decline of scholarship in Muslim Spain. The refugees took north with them their advanced culture, especially to the kingdom of Toledo, which had been cap-tured by the Christians in 1085. Here Archbishop Raymond set up early in the twelfth century a college for the translation of Arabic philosophy and science, which flourished for 150 years and attracted scholars from all parts of Europe, including Britain.[1] The following century, the thirteenth, was the great period of translation from Arabic into Latin. It was encouraged notably by Alfonso the Wise of Castile, who was interested in philosophy and astronomy, and had two Jews translate an Arabic record of planet-ary movements which was still authoritative enough to be con-sulted by Galileo and Kepler in the seventeenth century. It was through such translations that in the following centuries the cream of Arabic scholarship, the legacy of their Greek and oriental fore-runners and the original Muslim contribution, was passed on to the rising universities of the West.

*   *   *

[1] An attractive and imaginative picture of the procedure followed by these scholars, and the linguistic and interpretative difficulties they encountered, is given by Chas. and Dorothy Singer, in *The Legacy of Israel*, 204 ff.

Already by the second half of the tenth century the acute and manifest disunity of the Muslim East had encouraged the Byzantine Empire, which 250 years before had been threatened at its very heart by the Arab armies, to take the offensive against its enemies, raid the Levant coasts, recover Cilicia, Cyprus and Antioch, and push its frontiers into North Syria and east to the Euphrates. In Hitti's words, 'in the first half of the eleventh century . . . political and military confusion prevailed everywhere. Islam seemed crushed to the ground.'[1]

Nor was this confusion confined only to externals. It penetrated to the very core of the Muslim faith. The caliph al-Ma'mun, who had founded the enlightened Bait al-Hikma in his enthusiasm for the rationalist views of the Mu'tazila, had encountered the opposition of the rigorous theologians of Baghdad. Regarding this opposition with considerable justification as obscurantist and pernicious, the Caliph proceeded to impose on theologians and lawyers the rationalist doctrine, that the Qur'an was created and not eternal, by the illiberal mechanism of an inquisition.[2] The death of al-Ma'mun's successor was followed by an officially-supported orthodox reaction, upholding the Qur'an and the Sunna as the only valid sources of knowledge, and again enforced by inquisitorial methods. The more extreme theologians, led by Ibn Hanbal, rejected all the findings of exact science and philosophical speculation, as leading to heresy, unbelief, and atheism. But speculation could not be completely suppressed, and Islam could not exist in a self-created vacuum. To justify its first principles to those Muslims of an enquiring mind, and they were not a few, it had to resort to those very methods of logical argument, derived from the Greek philosophers, which the extreme reactionaries deplored. A compromise was attempted early in the tenth century by al-Ash'ari, using logical argument in the demonstration of theological truth. But while this satisfied a large central block of Muslim thought, it offended on the one hand the philosophers, who were tending increasingly to reject the Qur'an and Sunna where they conflicted with the more subtle and plausible speculations of Aristotle and later Greek philosophy; and on the other hand it outraged the followers of Ibn Hanbal, who rejected any process of thought or argument, including al-Ash'ari's logical defence of Muslim revelation,

---

[1] op. cit., 473.
[2] *Encyclopaedia of Islam*, art. Mihna; cf. Gibb, *Mohammedanism*, pp. 112–18.

which was not expressly authorized by the scriptures. Meanwhile a third strain of Muslim religious thought, the mystical strain of Sufism, which had developed in the eighth and ninth centuries, had gained many adherents.[1] The mystics were impelled by the insistent desire to find a more intimate and personal approach to, and union with God than was provided by Sunni formalism and detachment, which placed Man at an almost infinite distance from his Creator and provided the Prophet as merely an interpreter of God's word, but not as a mediator between God and Man. Though the Sufis sought justification for their ritual practices in some few and exceptional passages of the Qur'an, their main inspiration was in fact drawn from other religions, in particular from Christian mysticism, the Zoroastrians of Persia, and the mystery-religions of the pre-Christian Middle East. So great is man's natural desire, amid the trials of this unsympathetic world, for consolation in grief and hope in adversity from some more-than-human source, that many thousands of Muslims were attracted as disciples of the mystics, who originally practised their devotions individually and without any sort of mutual association. Following only their individual inspirations, some of them were led into doctrinal extravagances, imagining themselves filled with the divine spirit, even declaring 'I am the Truth' and so claiming to be the Godhead, and disparaging orthodox Islam as a 'religion of the limbs' immeasurably inferior to their own 'religion of the heart'.

Thus by the eleventh century Muslim theology was undergoing a real internal crisis, from which it has never completely recovered. 'While the (mystic) saints, with their innumerable followers and worshippers, menaced the Islam of history and tradition, the ortho-dox party, divided against itself, either clinging fanatically to the letter of the Qur'an or disputing over legal and ritual minutiae or analysing theological dogmas in the dry light of the intellect, was fast losing touch with the inward spirit and life which makes religion a reality. Many earnest Muslims must have asked themselves how long such a state of things could last. Was there no means of preserving what was vital to the Faith without rending the community asunder?'[2]

[1] Sufi was originally a nickname, derived from *suf*. wool: the wearer of an ascetic woollen garment, like that of the Christian monks.
[2] R. A. Nicholson, in *The Legacy of Islam*, 220 f.; cf. Gibb, op. cit., pp. 134–9.

In this desperate political, religious, and moral crisis, the salvaging of what could be saved of Muslim civilization was to come through human instruments as unpredictable as the salvaging of what could be saved of the Graeco-Roman civilization at the end of the third century A.D. through the rough Illyrian soldiers Diocletian and Constantine. Like that earlier first-aid process, the permanent loss of lifeblood from the wounded body-politic was considerable, and the lesion was repaired only with coarser, and less sensitive and flexible tissue.

The rise in the tenth century of the Fatimid and the lesser Shi'i dynasties, Arab and Persian, had for the time deprived the Turks of the political ascendancy they had been gaining in the Muslim world; but it did not make them any the less indispensable as garrison-troops and bodyguards. The Arab and Persian dynasts—Fatimid, Buwayhid, Samanid—continued to employ Turks in considerable numbers. Early in the eleventh century the Turkish tribe which later became known as the Seljuks pressed down from north of the Oxus into north-east Persia, becoming converted to Sunni Islam as they did so. To these unlettered, unimaginative soldiery the pedestrian matter-of-factness of orthodox Sunni Islam was more attractive and suitable than the spiritual exaltation or over-elaborated subtleties of the Shi'i sects or the Sufis. By 1055 the Seljuk Turks had entered Baghdad at the invitation of the effete Abbasid caliph to rescue the caliphate from its Shi'i masters who were intriguing with the rival and schismatic Fatimid caliphate. To the Sunni majority of the Muslim world, whom a century of Shi'i political supremacy and systematic religious propaganda had failed to convert, the Turks were the more acceptable masters. In 1071 the Seljuks inflicted a crushing defeat on the Byzantine army, which delivered into their hands the greater part of Asia Minor, never conquered by the Arabs, as a region for Turkish settlement; from this time onwards Asia Minor has continuously been predominantly Turkish in speech and Muslim in faith. The Seljuks now ruled a vast empire extending from the Aegean to India. While its first Sultans remained culturally uncouth, they were fortunate in having as their wazir a gifted and intellectual Persian who bore the title Nizam al-Mulk. This statesman founded at Baghdad in 1066 the first real university of the Muslim world, named after him the Nizamiya, a centre for propagating the Sunni orthodoxy of al-Ash'ari as a counterblast to the Shi'i heresies taught at Al Azhar in Fatimid Cairo, and for training administrators for the Seljuk Empire.[1]

One of the lecturers at the Baghdad Nizamiya at the end of the century was a thirty-four-year-old Persian, al-Ghazzali, who had made a comprehensive study of theology, philosophy, and the sciences, and became a great success as a teacher and interpreter of Muslim law. But, as he tells us in his Confessions, he went through an intellectual and spiritual crisis of scepticism, finding that orthodoxy lacked an adequate logical basis, and that on the other hand philosophy failed to answer the ultimate problems raised in man's quest for understanding, and led only to heresy and unbelief. Accordingly he gave up his lectureship at the age of thirty-eight, and spent the next two years of his life in strict ascetic retreat. After his re-emergence he lived for fourteen years more, mainly in retirement devoted to study and writing, but with short periods of public teaching at Baghdad, Damascus, and Nishapur. His teaching rejected the subtleties of both the professional theologians and the philosophers, and sought to lead men back to living contact with the Qur'an and the Traditions, while admitting the use of logical thinking as an intellectual discipline. His great contribution was to demonstrate the validity and importance of the personal mystical experience which, he taught, enabled the human soul to renew the contact with the changeless world of divine Reality from which it had become separated by its entry into the mortal body: in this way a direct communion with God, bringing enlightenment and revelation, was possible. But he insisted that mystical practice must conform with both the letter and the spirit of the Prophet's teaching, and condemned such extreme forms of mystical belief as pantheism and the individual's identification of himself with God. Thus, while on the one hand al-Ghazzali referred Islam back from theological and philosophical subtleties to its first principles, on the other hand he reconciled the mystical appeal to the spiritual emotions with those same austere first principles, and so gave mysticism a legitimate place in the system of Muslim belief. Called the 'Restorer of the Faith', it has been said that 'Islam has never outgrown him, has never fully understood him.'[2] For nearly eight centuries he found no worthy suc-

---

[1] Nizam al-Mulk also founded in Iraq and Persia five other colleges which bore his name, and was the patron of 'Umar al-Khayyam.
[2] Macdonald, op. cit.

cessor, with the result that, while the transfusion of warm and living blood which he administered to the Muslim religion averted a fatal outcome of its crisis, he could not arrest the creeping paralysis, the choking of the spirit by the letter, which in the following centuries spread progressively over its members. The only vitality that survived was in the mystics, and as the centuries passed they diverged ever further from orthodoxy into extravagance or vulgar chicanery. Meanwhile, original scientific and scholarly speculation tended to be abandoned for less original and intellectually-exacting pursuits, such as the compilation of encyclopaedias and universal histories; and even the Nizamiya was devoted to the amassing of conventional learning rather than the promotion of research.

The Seljuk Turkish unification of the greater part of the Middle East lasted less than forty years. Immediately after 1092 their empire broke up into independent Seljuk principalities, leaving Syria and Palestine a crazy quilt of Turkish and Arab petty states. Christian Europe, which saw in the pilgrimage to the Holy Land a means of absolution from the most grievous sins, and had enjoyed access to the Holy Places with only the minimum of molestation from the Fatimids and their predecessors, had found that a generation of warfare between the Seljuks and the Fatimids had made travel more hazardous for the pilgrims. After the Seljuk conquest of Asia Minor the Byzantine Emperor had appealed to the Pope for a Christian alliance against Islam. The energetic Nordic peoples who dominated Western Europe were seeking new outlets for their warlike instincts, and now that the expulsion of the Muslims from Spain was making progress, they were attracted further afield. The feudal laws of succession produced a numerous class of landless younger sons who, with other adventurers, were eager to carve out for themselves estates in new lands. The Italian and other rising commercial cities of the Mediterranean were anxious to develop a larger trade in the luxury products of the Levant and further Asia. All these martial and material impulses were canalized, directed, and consecrated by the powerful influence of the Church into the First Crusade, which took the Levant by storm in 1099.

The importance of the Crusades in the cultural history of Western Europe can hardly be overestimated for their effect in throwing open the windows of men's minds to the influences of the Middle East, whose level of civilization was still far higher than that of the West; but their influence on the history of the Middle East itself is much more restricted. The cultural contribution which the Crusader settlers in the Levant could make was comparatively slight, except in the field of military architecture and tactics; and their presence in the Levant for two centuries was detrimental to it, in that their final expulsion was accompanied by the destruction of such important cities as Antioch, Tripoli, and Akka. The psychological impact of their invasion on the Muslim world was much smaller than might be supposed. While the Christian minorities in the Levant welcomed the Franks and gave them valuable help, the petty Muslim princes of Syria, impressed by their warlike prowess, preferred to pay them tribute rather than to resist. Appeals for help to the feeble Abbasid caliph in Baghdad were ignored. The centre of Seljuk authority was now in Isfahan, six weeks' journey from the Levant coast in those days; and the Seljuk sultan paid no heed to such distant alarms. The Crusaders were unable to consolidate their position more deeply than some fifty miles inland from the coast, and never occupied such strategic Muslim cities as Aleppo or Damascus. They were not, therefore, regarded for some time as a dangerous enemy to Islam, and no general jihad was declared against them. Instead they became a factor in the internecine intrigues and petty wars of the Muslim principalities, the parties to which had no aversion from making alliances with the Crusaders against their own coreligionaries. Hence for the first thirty years the Crusaders had matters much their own way, and succeeded by their expansion across the Jordan in cutting the communications between Fatimid Egypt and Muslim Syria. Then, however, they found themselves threatened by the Turkish atabeg (prince) of Mosul, whose ambitions for territorial aggrandizement found the exposed Crusader County of Edessa in 1144 an easier victim than his Muslim neighbours. As the Fatimid dynasty was now fast degenerating, the contest between the Crusaders and the Atabegs resolved itself from 1154 onwards, when the Atabegs had occupied Damascus, into a struggle for the possession of Egypt. This was won by the Atabegs, whose Kurdish commander became the master of the Nile Valley in 1169. Two years later his nephew, the famous Saladin (Salah ud-Din al Ayyubi), deposed the last feeble Fatimid and reigned as Sultan in his stead. Asserting his independence of the Atabegs, he made himself by 1183 ruler of a kingdom comprising Egypt and inland Syria,

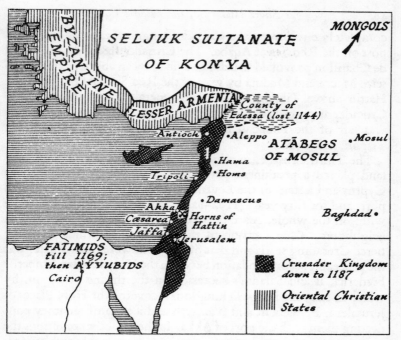

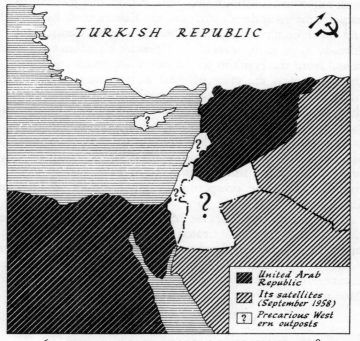

6. WESTERN BEACH-HEADS: A.D. 1150 AND 1958

completely enveloping the Crusader kingdom except for its outpost on the Red Sea at Aqaba. The Crusader freebooter Raynald de Chatillon provoked Saladin to a jihad by an abortive attempt to seize Mecca and Madina by way of the Red Sea. At the Horns of Hattin above Tiberias Saladin outgeneralled and shattered the Crusader army in 1187; Jerusalem fell, and two years later all that was left of the Frankish kingdom were the ports of Antioch, Tripoli, and Tyre.

The Third Crusade, in which Richard Coeur-de-Lion of England played a prominent part, failed to do more than recover Cyprus and a strip of the Levant coast with Akka as its principal port; and for fifty years (1192–1244) the situation was a stalemate with, on the whole, peace between the Franks and their Muslim neighbours. Characteristic of the new age, in which both the fierce Crusading spirit and that of the jihad were out-of-date, was the peaceable accommodation between the Holy Roman Emperor Frederick II and Saladin's successor on the throne of Egypt, by which in 1229 the Frankish kingdom recovered the Holy Places of Jerusalem, Bethlehem and Nazareth and a strip of territory connecting them with the port of Akka. In these pacific conditions the most important contribution of the Crusades was able to take root: namely, the great development of the Eastern trade by the Italian and other commercial cities, notably Venice, Genoa, and Pisa. Already in the early years of the Crusader kingdom they had obtained from the Frankish feudal rulers important concessions for their traders as the price of their participation in the material fitting-out of the Crusades: exemption from taxation and customs-dues, and legal autonomy in their special quarters in the Levant ports under the jurisdiction of their own consuls. Their friendly relations with Egypt at the beginning of the thirteenth century enabled them to extend their commerce to that country, by treaties with the Ayyubid sultans dating from 1208, and so to lay the foundations of the prosperous Levant trade of Mediterranean Europe.

After Saladin's victories the Muslims no longer had any fear of the Crusader power, but treated them as a convenient minor piece on the Middle Eastern chessboard. Early in the thirteenth century, however, the Muslims had to face a far more deadly menace in the invasion of their eastern lands by the heathen and desperately cruel Mongols, who, under their leader Jingiz Khan, came out of the

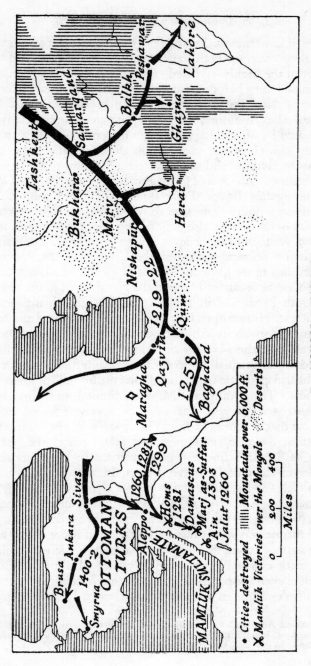

7. MONGOL INVASIONS

Tashkent

Samarqand

Bukhara

Balkh

Peshawat

Lahore

Ghazna

Herat

Mery

Nishapūr

1219-22

Qum

Qazvīn

1258

Baghdad

Maragha

1260 1281

1299

Aleppo

Homs
1281

Sivas

Damascus

Marj as-Suffar 1303

Ain Jalut 1260

Ankara

Brusa

1400-2

Smyrna

OTTOMAN TURKS

MAMLŪK SULTANATE

• Cities destroyed ||||| Mountains over 6,000 ft.
✗ Mamlūk Victories over the Mongols   ∴∴∴ Deserts

0   200   400
Miles

steppes of Eastern Asia that still bear their name. Between 1219 and 1224 they overran Transoxiana and North Persia, and utterly destroyed the highly-civilized cities of those lands and massacred their inhabitants, before passing on across South Russia to establish an empire which extended from the Vistula to the Pacific. Such is the mental tortuousness of political strategists, especially those dominated by an ideology, that the directors of Christian policy actually conceived the idea of an alliance with these savages against the civilized and treaty-keeping Muslims of the Levant. In 1245, following the loss of Jerusalem, largely as a result of Crusader intrigue against Egypt, Pope Innocent IV sent John de Piano Carpini on a political mission to Mongolia, and three years later St. Louis of France was also negotiating with the Mongols and sent the friar William of Rubruquis to their homeland. These missions brought no political success to the Crusader cause; but in 1253 another and more grievous blow fell on the Muslim world in a Mongol invasion under Hulagu, the grandson of Jingiz. He overran South Persia and in 1258 captured Baghdad, massacring its inhabitants. He laid open Iraq to uncouth Turcoman[1] and Mongol herdsmen from the north-east, who by their neglect allowed the elaborate irrigation-system on which the country's fertility depended to fall gradually into decay. Hulagu finally put an end to the Abbasid caliphate in Baghdad, that pitiful relic of former Arab greatness. The triumphant Mongols pressed on to invade Syria and destroyed Aleppo, but were decisively defeated in North Palestine by the armies of Egypt in 1260. In Egypt, meanwhile, an important dynastic revolution had taken place: the last feeble sultan of Saladin's line had been deposed by the Turkish commander-in-chief of his slave armies, himself originally a slave (mamluk); and for the next 250 years a 'dynasty' of these Mamluk commanders—usually Turkish by birth, sometimes Mongol or Circassian—was to rule Egypt, Palestine and Syria. The succession to the throne was sometimes hereditary, but more often the prize of the strongest, and intrigue and assassination were the rule. The millions of native Egyptians and Syrians, Muslim and Christian alike, had even less part in the government of their countries under this turbulent foreign soldateska than they had known in previous

---

[1] Medieval Arab and Persian historians apply this term to all the Turks of Western Asia, including the Seljuks and even sometimes the Ottoman Turks (*Encyclopaedia of Islam*, art. Turcoman).

centuries; but the day-to-day administration of Egypt, inherited from its Byzantine and Fatimid governors and in all probability the most efficient instrument of government which existed in the Middle Ages,[1] remained in the same patient Coptic and Jewish hands as before, sometimes to the unruly indignation of the Muslim city mobs, who vented their anger in pogroms.

Some of the Frankish towns and strong-points of the Levant had assisted the Mongol invasion; and now the Mamluk Sultan Baybars took a merciless revenge. Between 1265 and 1268 he wrested from them Jaffa, Caesarea, Nazareth, and the great city of Antioch. From 1272 to 1282 there was a precarious truce, during which his successor Qalawun inflicted another heavy defeat on the Mongols in Syria. In 1289 the Crusaders lost Tripoli, and two years later Akka, their last stronghold, fell and the seat of the Frankish kingdom was withdrawn to Cyprus. A third Mongol invasion of Syria c. 1300 was again checked by the Mamluk armies.

By thus turning back from the Levant the threat of Mongol invasion, with its insensate lust for destruction of all that was finest and most civilized, the early Mamluk sultans have deserved well of history. Like the Ayyubids they were given overmuch to self-indulgence in military and palace architecture and the pleasures of the flesh. Nevertheless, consciously imitating Saladin and his forerunner the Atabeg Nur ud-Din of Aleppo, the earlier Mamluks did spare an appreciable fraction of their revenues for the development of irrigation-canals, aqueducts and harbours, and for building hospitals, libraries, and schools. The primary purpose of these schools, however, was not so much to promote science and general learning as to propagate Sunni orthodoxy and combat the Shi'a, which was evidently still formidable.[2] The great Jewish physician and philosopher Moses Maimonides had found a welcome at Saladin's court when Moorish intolerance had driven him from his native Spain; and for a century Jewish and other doctors continued his medical tradition in Egypt. By 1300, however, original scientific research was almost at an end in the Muslim East. In Egypt ancient superstition and magic, deeply rooted in the masses of the people as it still is, was reasserting itself; and scientific and scholarly activity was running to seed in unoriginal imitativeness

---

[1] H. A. R. Gibb, *Ibn Battuta: Travels in Asia and Africa*, 20.
[2] Saladin had grimly closed the Fatimid network of Shi'i schools, the Diyar al-'Ilm, and dispersed their libraries. It was now that al-Azhar became a *Sunni* mosque.

and facile compilation. A high level of esoteric scholarship had been maintained in the higher grades of the Isma'ili sect, which was re-propagated c. 1090 in North Persia and North Syria; but both these centres were practically exterminated in the late thirteenth century by the Mongols and the Mamluks respectively.[1] Strangely enough, a temporarily fertile ground for at least some branches of science and scholarship was provided in North Persia and Transoxiana by the courts of the Mongols themselves. Inspired by his unlettered interest in astrology as a means of foretelling the future, Hulagu, the destroyer of Baghdad, founded an astronomical observatory and library at his capital of Maragha near Tabriz. About 1300 one of his descendants, who had been converted to Islam, endowed an observatory, library, and schools at Tabriz. A century later the Turco-Mongol conqueror Timur Leng (Tamberlane) deported to his capital at Samarqand scholars, architects and craftsmen from the cities he had destroyed, such as Aleppo and Damascus; and his successor was patron of a flourishing astronomical observatory at Samarqand in the first half of the fifteenth century.

Instead of the resurgence of uncouth Turk and Mongol ending abruptly the growing commercial penetration of the Middle East from Europe, as might be supposed, it actually fostered it. Although the Mamluks severely punished the native Christians of the Levant for their complicity, real or suspected, with the Mongol invaders,[2] the Christian pilgrim-traffic to the Holy Places was too profitable a source of Mamluk revenue to be stopped; and this material consideration applied still more to the trade in the silks, spices, and other products of the further East, for which the peoples of Europe, now growing in sophistication, had acquired an insatiable appetite. Consequently, the Mamluks encouraged and took a heavy toll of this trade through Alexandria and the Levant

---

[1] On Alamut, the Persian centre, see Freya Stark, *The Valley of the Assassins*. The Isma'ilis continued a ruthless underground struggle against the Sunni rulers of the Muslim world, and gained the sinister title of 'Assassins' (originally Hashshashin) by allegedly furnishing with 'Dutch courage' in the form of hashish members chosen from their lower grades whom they used to murder their political opponents. One of their first and most distinguished victims was the enlightened Seljuk wazir Nizam al-Mulk.

A minority of the Isma'ilis survived the destruction of their centres, and to-day some 200,000, who have long abandoned the aggressive tendencies of their forerunners, venerate as their Imam the Agha Khan, who claims descent from Ali in the forty-seventh generation, through the medieval Grand Masters of Alamut.

[2] V. Minorsky, *Royal Central Asian Journal*, XXVII (1940), 436.

ports, while the Mongols permitted Marco Polo and his kinsmen to make their famous journeys to Mongol-dominated China in the late thirteenth century. In the following century we find merchants of Venice, Genoa, and other European cities trading with the Mongol capital at Tabriz via the Black Sea; and though the reassertion of exclusive Chinese independence under the Ming dynasty once more closed China to Europeans, Timur Leng and his successors in the fifteenth century continued to encourage European trade with their dominions in West-central Asia. Trade with the Mamluk kingdom in the Levant became a virtual monopoly of Venice, who had finally disposed of her rival Genoa in a ruthless commercial war. Both Venice and the Mamluks extracted an exorbitant profit from the trade; but in the fifteenth century Mamluk predatoriness became too much even for the Venetians, and when the exacting Sultan Bars-bay raised his excise-duty on pepper to 160 per cent. they successfully brought pressure on him by threatening to withdraw their merchants from Alexandria.

Meanwhile, the political stability of the Middle East countries had continued to deteriorate, until only an enforced re-unification, however roughly and arbitrarily imposed and with whatever further loss of cultural vitality, could save the whole from ruin. The raids of Timur Leng c. 1400 had ruined Aleppo, Damascus, and other Syrian cities; had erected 120 towers of skulls of the inhabitants of Baghdad alone; and had completed the work begun by Hulagu in converting Iraq from a land of irrigated agriculture to a land given over in the main to the nomadic herds of the Turcoman and the Bedouin. Mamluk rule likewise deteriorated sharply after c. 1340. In the next 128 years there were no fewer than twenty-nine Mamluk sultans, ruling for an average of only four and a half years apiece. In Egypt, Palestine and Syria alike the cultivator was oppressed by the irresponsible Mamluk feudal landlords, whose incomes depended on the amount of land-tax they could extort from their peasantry. Bedouin and Turcoman raiders pillaged the settled lands, and the former actually sacked Jerusalem in 1480. The cities of Syria and Palestine were largely ruined by the continual revolts of local governors, and the public benefactions of better days, such as schools and hospitals, were extensively converted by the trustees to their personal profit. A contemporary Muslim historian estimated that the population of the Mamluk empire was reduced to one-third of its figure at the beginning of their rule;[1] and though his figures cannot be statistically verified, the hundreds of archaeological sites, which are abundantly covered with medieval Arab pottery but are now abandoned, bear material testimony to the extent of the depopulation. An important factor contributing to this depopulation in the later fourteenth century was the Black Death and the famine which accompanied it in two appalling visitations in successive generations. 'In a young and vigorous society the effects of such a disaster soon disappear; but where the social order is already reeling, many decades are required before equilibrium can be regained. This respite was not granted to the Islamic world.'[2]

For already the political forces which were to fill the anarchic vacuum of the Mamluk empire and of equally disorganized Iraq and Persia were taking shape. The Seljuk unity of Asia Minor had been shattered by the Mongol invasions of the mid-thirteenth century, but without basically altering the Turkish character of the dominant section of the population. About 1300 a small Turkish principality founded by one Othman around Brusa in the north-west of the peninsula was beginning to expand at the expense of its Turkish neighbours and the moribund Byzantine Empire to the north. In 1353 Othman's descendants invaded Europe and in 1361 established their European capital at Adrianople (Edirne), blocking the route from Constantinople to the Balkan hinterland and so isolating the capital of Orthodox Christianity from its potential Orthodox allies, the Slavs. A powerful coalition led by the Serbs was shattered by the Ottoman Turks in the battle of the Kossovo Plain in 1389. By 1400 they had extended their northern frontier to the Danube and incorporated the greater part of Asia Minor; Constantinople itself was on the point of falling; but at this moment the irresistible thunderbolt of Timur Leng struck them. Crushingly defeated at Ankara in 1402, the Ottomans lost Asia Minor, but their kingdom survived in the Balkans. From 1420 onwards they began to acquire from Western Europe the use of firearms; in 1453 they gave the coup-de-grace to the Byzantine Empire by taking Constantinople; and by 1468 they had completed the reconquest of Asia Minor, and so became neighbours and rivals of the Mamluk empire on the borders of North Syria. For a generation they were kept in check by Qait Bey (1468–95), a

---

[1] Hitti, op. cit., 696.
[2] H. A. R. Gibb, *Ibn Battuta: Travels in Asia and Africa*, 24 f.

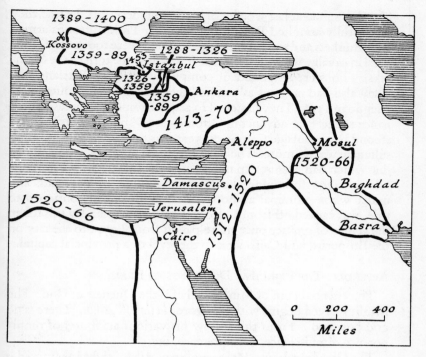

8. THE EXPANSION OF THE OTTOMAN EMPIRE

Mamluk sultan at last worthy of his first predecessors. Instead they successfully assaulted Persia.[1] In 1514 the Turkish troops armed with muskets and supported by 300 cannon were too much for the Persian cavalry without firearms. It was now the turn of the Mamluks, who were suspected of complicity with the Persian shah. They also had no guns as yet, and their cavalry were routed near Aleppo in 1516. They hastened to acquire some few pieces of ordnance to meet the advancing Ottoman army, but the outcome of a second battle outside Cairo next year was the same. The Mamluk sultanate was no more. The pitiful Abbasid puppet-caliph, last of a line which had been set up in Cairo by the first of the great Mamluks in 1260 following the Mongol sacking of Baghdad, and under whose nominal authority the Mamluks had continued to rule, was carried off from Cairo to Constantinople. By this token the centre of gravity once more passed from Egypt to the city on the Bosporus; and Cairo sank to the level of a provincial capital.

APPENDIX: THE PRINCIPAL DOCTRINES OF ISLAM.

The essential core of Muslim belief is the Oneness of God. The Muslim Creed begins with the words *la ilah ill'Allah*, 'There is no god but God'. From this follow his various attributes of omnipotence, omniscience, omnipresence, etc.

The Creeds ends, *wa-Mohammed rasul Allah*, 'and Mohammed is the apostle of God'. No divinity is thereby claimed for the Prophet. He is wholly human, the last and greatest of an ascending series of prophets, borrowed from the Jewish Old Testament. The series comprises the Patriarchs culminating in Moses, and the kings David and Solomon, but not the prophets of the periods immediately before and after the Exile. Higher than all, and next in rank to Mohammed himself comes Jesus, 'from the breath (spirit) of God' as the Qur'an describes him. He and His Mother are honoured by Muslims; but Jesus again is regarded as wholly human, and the Christian doctrines of His Incarnation, Crucifixion, and Resurrection are held to be misguided.

Muslims accordingly hold the Christian doctrine of the Trinity to be an offence against the essential Unity of God, and therefore

[1] A new dynasty, the Safavid, winning the support of the populace of the Persian cities by its adoption of moderate Shi'i doctrines as the religion of dynasty and state, had newly unified Persia c. 1500 after centuries of disunion and anarchy. Their dynasty lasted until 1722.

a flagrant heresy. The orthodox Muslim belief in the eternal, un-created Qur'an, the archetype of that dictated to Muhammad by the Archangel Gabriel, serves to bridge the gulf which divides the Muslim worshipper from his wholly transcendent God. 'The Word was made Book and dwelt among us', a Muslim might paraphrase St. John's Gospel, and such a dilution (in effect) of the Christian doctrine of the Incarnation has perhaps eased the passage to Islam of its occasional Western adherents unable to stomach the richer diet of the Catholic Faith.

Muslims believe in a Resurrection of the body preceding the Last Judgement, with physical rewards in Heaven and punishments in Hell. These Last Things will be preceded by the coming of the Mahdi, the divinely-guided, having the same names as the Prophet himself. This concept of the Mahdi has been left obscurely in the background of orthodox Sunni Islam, but among the poor and underprivileged sections of the Sunni community self-styled Mahdis have appeared from time to time to deliver them from oppression and institute a reign of righteousness; and in the Shi'a the Mahdi has much greater importance, since he is there none other than the Hidden Imam returning to his people.

In its dogmatic essentials Islam is thus closely akin to Judaism, with some superficial borrowings from Christianity, the whole given a distinctively Arabian orientation after its rejection by the Jews of Madina. Modern Muslim apologists emphasize the de-generation of moral behaviour in Christendom from the standards prescribed by the New Testament, and compare this situation unfavourably with the more attainable (because less ideal) system of legal and social regulations prescribed for Muslims by the Qur'an and the Traditions of the Prophet. It was these regula-tions, superimposed on the simple dogmatic foundation, that originally brought together the individualist Arab tribes as a con-quering force, that imposed a social unity upon the national and cultural diversity of the Muslim world in its greatest days, and that maintains a sense of unity even to-day after centuries of decay and neglect. The present machine-age may have under-mined the belief of many 'educated' Muslims in the dogmas of their religion; but though they have become free-thinkers or even atheists, they remain notwithstanding within the social com-munity of Islam.

The Ottoman and Persian Empires and the Growth of European Enterprise (1517–1770)

L IKE THE Byzantine Empire, the Ottoman Turks had to divide their effective power between the Middle East and their even more important interests in the Balkans. Both empires were essentially Levantine; but they wasted their resources in continual wars against a powerful rival in Persia, from which they were estranged by deep religious differences. Just as the inconclusive Byzantine-Persian wars weakened both states and exposed them to the Arab invasion and conquest, so the inconclusive Ottoman-Persian wars of the sixteenth–eighteenth centuries weakened both and exposed them to European commercial penetration, leading eventually to their helpless manipulation by European Powers in the nineteenth century. In both the Byzantine and the Ottoman periods the possession of Iraq was disputed with Persia, and in both periods likewise the sovereign in Constantinople, being also the master of Egypt, was led by force of geographical propinquity to seek to control the opposite Arabian coast of the Red Sea; but with little permanent effect, so that in both periods the greater part of the Arabian peninsula remained practically independent of the Great Power ruling in the Levant, and was only lightly touched by its civilization.

The Ottoman principles of provincial administration were not unlike the Byzantine, though in a cruder form. The Empire was essentially military in its organization, and its object was frankly the power and well-being of the state, personified by the sovereign, with little thought for the well-being of its subjects. It distributed large tracts of land in feudal fiefs to its military commanders, though without disturbing the existing tenant-cultivators. The function of the provinces was to provide the central government with revenue in the form of material wealth and manpower for the armies, and the function of the provincial governor to collect this revenue, with only secondary thought for the social or economic good of the provincials. Provided that these demands were met, there was little deliberate interference with the racial or religious status of the population, except such as might arise locally from the presence of garrisons and officials of the ruling race and creed. The Christians in the Ottoman Empire continued to fare much as they had fared under preceding Muslim rulers, and their lot was distinctly better than that of the Jews in medieval and twentieth-century Central and Eastern Europe. The Turks showed greater toleration to the Christians in the Asiatic provinces, where they were a small and submissive minority, than in the Balkans, where they constituted a rebellious majority constantly intriguing with the neighbouring enemy Powers, Austria and Russia.[1] Catholic missions were admitted, not only to the Levant, but to Baghdad and Basra as early as the seventeenth century, though they were always exposed to the caprice of changing local authority. In the depopulated Palestine of the eighteenth century the pilgrim-dues were the most important item of revenue. The yearly pilgrimage of some 4,000 persons c. 1750 had risen to 10–12,000 when the French traveller Volney visited Palestine in 1784, and the tax collected for their visit to the Jordan alone amounted to three times the tax-assessment of the town of Gaza, then the most populous town in Palestine.[2]

The Turks were a racial minority in their great empire, and made no attempt at the general colonization of the conquered provinces. The empire was conceived on no narrow Turkish-national basis, but was a comprehensive empire like the Abbasid or the Roman. Whatever a man's race or birthplace, he was eligible for government-service and could attain the highest office, provided that he conformed to the general cultural pattern of the empire: the religion and social customs of Sunni Islam; a military background of training and experience; and the Turkish language, which under the Ottomans (while absorbing a multitude of forms of expression and loan-words from Arabic and Persian) had yet triumphantly asserted itself as the language of the ruling-class against those two languages of an older and higher civilization. While the bulk of

[1] The 'slaughter and obliteration of a great part of the Armenian nation' were the 'logical and morbid sequence' of a 'game of plots, incitements and solicitations, of counter-plots and massacres' carried on between the Russian, Ottoman, and Persian Empires for over 300 years; see W. E. D. Allen: *History of the Georgian People* (1932), p. 164.   [2] De Haas, op. cit., 357 f., with references.

senior officials were Turks, Syrian and Palestinian townsmen gained by their innate keenness of intellect an appreciable number of senior posts; the sturdy and vigorous Kurds found openings in the military and administrative career; but Iraqis were mainly confined to the lower grades; and before 1850 the native Egyptian was treated, like the fellahin everywhere in the empire, as a beast of burden. The Turks left considerable local authority to non-Turkish ruling-groups, especially in the less accessible districts: examples are the Kurds in their mountain-valleys; the Shi'i Arab tribal chiefs of Lower Iraq; the Druze[1] amirs who then dominated the Lebanese mountains. Even the defeated Mamluks remained more numerous than the Turkish officials and soldiery in Egypt. They were indispensable for the administration of that country; their amirs remained governors of the sanjaqs (sub-provinces); and they continued through the centuries to maintain their numbers by importing fresh slaves, especially from the Caucasus. By 1600 no distinction could be made between the Mamluks and the Ottoman Turks in Egypt. Both were called 'Turks' to differentiate them from the native Egyptians; Turkish blood and speech had preponderated among the Mamluks from the beginning. A new and authoritative study of this period has concluded that, despite all its defects, Ottoman rule provided the Arab provinces (at least down to the beginning of the eighteenth century) with a period of relative tranquillity after the disasters of the 150 years that had preceded the Ottoman conquest.[2]

The absence of a constructive long-term policy of administration was greatly aggravated by the shortness of tenure of the pashas, or provincial governors. They were often changed annually; in 280 years of direct Ottoman rule Egypt had 100 pashas, while Damascus had 133 in the first 180 years of Ottoman dominion. High office was purchased by bribery, and retained only by the prompt

---

[1] The Druze sect, numbering to-day some 150,000 persons in the Jebel Druze (Southern Syria), Lebanon and North Palestine, originated in the eccentric Fatimid caliph al-Hakim, the fanatical destroyer of the Church of the Holy Sepulchre in Jerusalem, who in 1017 declared himself the incarnation of God on earth, and shortly afterwards mysteriously disappeared. His followers declared that he was not dead, but merely in hiding till his return as Mahdi. Persecuted by his successors on the Fatimid throne, they found a refuge in Syria under the leadership of one Darazi, after whom the Druze are named. Practising their cult in secret to avoid persecution through the centuries, they have always been considered by Muslims of all sects to be so extreme in heresy as to constitute a distinct religion.

[2] Gibb and Bowen, p. 209, and ch. IV, *passim*.

forwarding of tribute to Istanbul and repeated bakhshish to powerful courtiers. The pasha compensated himself out of the provincial revenues, and by farming out the collection of taxes to the highest bidder. Such impermanent and irresponsible administration could not be better than indifferent. The far-seeing Sultan Sulaiman I (surnamed by Turks the Lawgiver, and by contemporary Europeans the Magnificent, 1520–66) carried out useful public works, such as the improvement of the water-supply of Jerusalem and Mecca, and work on canals and flood-prevention in stricken Iraq. There were pashas who founded new mosques under the impulse of piety or the prickings of overburdened consciences; but on the whole the Ottoman administration built very few roads, or hospitals, or schools; as late as 1838 a traveller could not find a single bookshop in either Damascus or Aleppo. The Turks paid little attention to the improvement or maintenance of agriculture and irrigation, or to the settlement and control of the Bedouin, who had greatly encroached on the settled lands in the Time of Troubles of the preceding centuries. Many villages were abandoned and towns dwindled in size, except such ports as were temporarily favoured with European trade. Great Alexandria, by-passed by the opening of the Cape Route and left with only a meagre trade in the products of Egypt, the Sudan, and Southern Arabia, shrank from a populous city to a town of 10,000 people or less. The peasant sowed only sufficient land to produce a crop he could harvest quickly and hide away from the tax-collector. In Syria cultivators abandoned their fields and sought a living in the towns or took refuge in the less accessible mountain-valleys. In Egypt irrigation was allowed to decay, and the orderly distribution of water lapsed. 'Village fought village for the right to a water-channel; farmers came in the night, cut the dykes, and emptied their neighbours' water on to their own land. Deprived of water, beaten and oppressed by their overlords, many of the fellahin deserted their land and turned to a life of brigandage and crime on the waste lands between the villages.'[1] By the eighteenth century, Egypt, once the granary of the Roman Empire with seven to ten million inhabitants, had become barely self-supporting in food, even though her estimated population had fallen to two and a half millions. Famine was frequent, and so was pestilence, by which half-a-million died in Egypt in 1619, and 230

[1] Crouchley, op. cit., 14.

villages were desolated in 1643. In the mid-seventeenth century the country between Aleppo and that part of the Euphrates nearest to the city was fertile and efficiently irrigated, but a century later the land had become a desert;[1] and at the end of the eighteenth century it is stated that only one-eighth of the villages formerly on the tax-register of the Aleppo pashaliq were still inhabited. The population of Syria and Palestine combined was then estimated at only one and a half millions, with that of Palestine shrunken to perhaps under 200,000.

Already by 1600 the authority of the provincial governors was weakening as the brief noontide of the Ottoman Empire passed. Sometimes the provinces relapsed into anarchy; but sometimes the power of the pashas was superseded by that of local rulers who afforded greater internal stability, the possibility of sounder economic life, and freer commercial enterprise to European merchants, than did the transient and rapacious Turkish administrators. The Druze amirs of the Lebanon became virtually independent of the Porte, and the relative security of life under their rule attracted a considerable immigration from other parts of Syria. Outstanding among them was Fakhr ud-Din, who carved out a kingdom for himself in Lebanon and North Palestine between 1585 and 1635. He made his own diplomatic agreements with European Powers; encouraged the production and export of silk and cotton through his ports of Sidon and Beirut in exchange for European goods; and introduced Christian missions and European engineers. From 1600 to 1669 the pashaliq of Basra enjoyed firm government and prosperity under the local family of Afrasyab. Later it was the turn of the Baghdad pashaliq to find stability and tolerant rule under Hasan Pasha and his son Ahmed Pasha, 1704–47. After the death of the latter, effective control remained till 1832 in the hands of a corps of Georgian Mamluks, the majority Christian by birth, which the two pashas had built up. The Georgian Sulaiman Pasha the Great united the three pashaliqs of Baghdad, Basra, and Mosul from 1780 to 1802, paying only formal recognition to the Ottoman Sultan in the form of 'constant reports, rarer presents, and yet less frequent tribute.'[2] Until about 1750 Egypt was less fortunate. The Ottoman pashas had long ceased to exercise any real authority, and the unhappy country was torn by the struggles

[1] C. P. Grant, *The Syrian Desert*, 161, n. 1.
[2] Longrigg, op. cit., 199.

for supremacy of the Mamluk beys. Their tyranny and oppression of the weak went uncontrolled. 'In no province did Muslim fervour burn so bright against the infidel; nowhere was the power of the Sultan more relaxed; and the Franks who dwelt there were subjected to a régime of extortion and ill-treatment at the hands of the beys, which in its insolence and regularity far exceeded that experienced elsewhere in the Levant. . . . The natives seem to have had an innate antipathy to all Europeans, and lost no opportunity of molesting or reviling them with ferocity and fanaticism.'[1] The situation was temporarily improved by Ali Bey, who tried to reform the financial system and the administration of justice and suppress the brigandage of the Bedouin. In 1770 he declared his complete independence of the Sultan, and allied himself with adh-Dhahir, the governor of Galilee, who had expelled the Turkish officials from his province, revived the derelict port of Akka for the export of cotton and silk, and was in the habit of distributing free seed to the fellahin and remitting their taxes in bad years. Before the two rebels could achieve much in their respective provinces, however, they met their deaths in 1773 at the hands of jealous rivals.

★   ★   ★

In antiquity the Mediterranean had been the main focus of European civilization and commerce; and though the importance of that sea as a channel of cultural contacts had been diminished when the Muslims overran and conquered its southern shores, the Crusades had done much to restore its former commerce. Even after the expulsion of the Franks from the Levant, the Mediterranean trading-cities, especially Venice and Genoa, had continued to enjoy a lively commerce with the Muslim East. In the meantime, however, the small Atlantic kingdom of Portugal had succeeded in the fourteenth century in freeing itself from the Muslims, and under the inspiration of Prince Henry the Navigator (1394–1460) her seamen began to explore the Atlantic coast of Africa southwards. Henry's general motive was evidently to carry on the Crusades by an attempt to outflank the Dar ul-Islam both strategically and commercially; to divert the trade in the gold and other

[1] Wood, op, cit., 124, 234.

products of West Africa from Muslim hands; to make contact south of the Sahara with the Negus of Ethiopia ('Prester John') and jointly assail the Muslims from the south; and he may also have planned in his later life to win control for Portugal of the Indian trade, which was now the main source of wealth of the Muslim world.[1] The progress of Portuguese exploration was naturally slow at first, and by the time of Henry's death had gone no further south than Sierra Leone; but in the following generation their seamen pushed onwards, until in 1488 Bartholomew Diaz at last rounded the Cape of Good Hope. Ten years later Vasco da Gama went on to reach the Muslim coastal towns of East Africa, where he secured an Indian pilot who conducted him on to Southern India. The King of Portugal now adopted the grandiose title of 'Lord of the Conquest, Navigation, and Commerce of Ethiopia, Arabia, Persia, and India', and in spite of Muslim resistance further trading expeditions were sent to their station at Calicut, bringing home cargoes of spices.

The Mamluks of Egypt and the Republic of Venice were equally alarmed at this by-passing of their extremely profitable joint monopoly of the Indian trade with Europe. The Mamluk Sultan threatened to destroy the Christian Holy Places if the Portuguese did not abandon their Indian voyages, and the Prior of St. Catherine's Monastery on Sinai actually journeyed to Rome and tried to persuade the Pope to forbid them. The Venetians, who had instigated the so-called Fourth Crusade against Constantinople in order to destroy a trade-rival and had looked with complacency on the fall of the same city to the Ottoman Turks, even went so far as to supply timber to the Mamluks to build warships in an attempt to sweep the Portuguese from the Indian Ocean. But the Portuguese ocean-going ships and mariners were more than a match for the Muslim vessels and sailors, accustomed in the main to the more sheltered seas of the Levant and the Middle East. They occupied the strategically-placed islands of Socotra and Hormuz in an attempt to blockade the Muslim fleets within the Red Sea and the Persian Gulf respectively, and repelled a Mamluk naval attack on their Indian ports. Lisbon rapidly took the place of Venice as the European clearing-house for Indian goods, and the Cape Route began to supersede the old sea and land-routes to the Mediterranean. Admiral de Albuquerque is even said to have formed a

[1] Prestage, op. cit., 29 ff., 165 ff.

plan to divert the Upper Nile into the Red Sea and so deprive Egypt of her vital water-supply.

In the Persian Gulf the Portuguese had occupied by 1515 the strategic and trading posts of Muscat, Hormuz, and Bahrain; but they were never able to seize permanent bases in the Red Sea, since the opposition of the Mamluk and subsequently the Ottoman navies held them in check. Though they enjoyed for the moment a monopoly of the Cape Route, they had by no means diverted all the traffic from the Overland Route. Throughout the sixteenth century Arab traders were still bringing the silks, spices, dyes and drugs of the East and the coffee of the Yemen up the Red Sea and across the desert to Cairo and Alexandria, and trade also continued to follow the route from the Persian Gulf via the Syrian steppe to the Levant ports. Caravans of four to six hundred camels were common, and Aleppo became the leading trading-centre of Syria; there are several references to the city in Shakespeare. In 1521 Venice obtained from the Sultan a commercial concession of the form which was to become common, granting her traders freedom from customs-duties or other taxation beyond a stated limit, and judicial extraterritoriality under the authority of their own consuls. These were the so-called Capitulations (i.e. the 'chapters' of the concession) modelled on precedents of the Crusader and Mamluk periods.[1] Commercial pre-eminence in the Mediterranean was now, however, passing from Venice to France, to whom capitulations were granted in 1536. By the time Elizabethan England entered upon the Levantine commercial scene, founding in 1581 the Levant Company of Merchants to trade her good woollen cloth and tin for eastern products, the French were already well established; and though they could not prevent the English from opening a consulate in Aleppo, they did successfully obstruct the opening of an English consulate at Alexandria. In any case, the stout English woollens found little sale in torrid Egypt.

Already before the accession of Queen Elizabeth the English had begun to chafe at the Portuguese monopoly of the Far Eastern trade. The population was increasing. The manufacture of woollen cloth was outstripping the demands of the home market; but not yet feeling strong enough to challenge the Portuguese by attempt-

---

[1] They were destined to survive down to the twentieth century and make difficulties for diplomats and administrators in the altered conditions of the Middle East.

ing the Cape Route, the English tried to by-pass it by seeking a North-East Passage round northern Europe to the Far East, and in 1553 founded the Muscovy Company for this purpose. 'The advocates of the scheme asserted with confidence that in Cathay with its cool climate, its teeming and (it was believed) wealthy population, a lucrative market for English woollens would certainly be found; while, once the dangers of the northern ice had been passed, it would be a comparatively easy matter to proceed from Cathay to the Moluccas, and there lade for the return voyage the spices so much in demand in the European markets.'[1] The climatic difficulties of the North-East Passage frustrated these hopes; but Antony Jenkinson, commander of the Company's fleet, travelled from Moscow down the Volga and crossed the Caspian to establish trade-relations with the Persian capital at Qazvin in 1561. This roundabout route was, however, abandoned twenty years later owing to the founding of the Levant Company and to the anarchy which was already threatening Persia.

In 1583 four English travellers set out on an exploratory journey from Aleppo to Malacca via Baghdad and the Persian Gulf. In 1591, the year in which the sole survivor of this expedition arrived in England, three English ships were sent via the Cape to the Far East on a voyage of reconnaissance, the Portuguese power being now in decline. Meanwhile the Dutch had in 1581 wrested their independence from Spain, and were now ready to embark on the commercial enterprises which the dense population of their small country, totalling about half that of contemporary England, forced upon them. By 1599 the Dutch had sent successful expeditions to the East Indies; and in that year the English East India Co. was founded, largely by merchants of the Levant Co., 'to set forth a voyage to the East Indies and the other isles and countries thereabouts.' In its infancy the Company undertook a voyage only once every two or three years, each being separately financed by subscriptions and levies from its members. The Dutch companies, on the other hand, were federated in 1602 into the 'United East India Company', practically a department of state with a permanently subscribed capital of the then immense sum of over half-a-million pounds.[2] Soon it was 'covering the Indian Ocean with its fleets, threatening to displace the loose Portuguese monopoly in favour

[1] Foster, op. cit., 5 f.
[2] J. A. Williamson, *Short History of British Expansion*, I, 219.

of one far more complete and aggressive, and making the effort of the English company seem puny.'[1] The English company was indeed for the first fifty years of its existence chaotically financed and administered, and it was obstructed rather than helped by the early Stuart governments.[2]

Meanwhile the English brothers Sir Antony and Sir Robert Sherley had in 1598 received a warm welcome from the illustrious and enterprising Shah Abbas the Great of Persia (1587-1629), who was seeking the most favourable market for Persia's raw silk, her main commodity for export and largely a royal monopoly. The Persian Gulf was still dominated from Hormuz by the Portuguese, who 'were everywhere hated by the native populations on account of the savage cruelty which they had constantly used to mask their deficiency in real force';[3] the route to the Levant coast was controlled by the Shah's enemy, the Ottoman Sultan, for his own profit; and the Caspian route was impossibly roundabout. The Shah accordingly sent first Antony and then Robert as his ambassador to the capitals of Europe to seek alliance against the Ottoman Empire and trade-relations. The East India Co., which had already opened a factory (trading-station) at Surat north of Bombay in 1612, accepted the Shah's proposals, and sent ships in 1616 to the Persian Gulf to trade with his capital at Isfahan. The Portuguese at Hormuz made a determined attempt to intercept the Company's merchant-ships, in return for which a joint Anglo-Persian expedition in 1622 expelled them from Hormuz and the Persians drove them out of Bahrain also. Their decline was accelerated by their loss of Muscat in 1650 and the closing of their factory at Basra.

The East India Co. now had factories at the Shah's new port of Bandar Abbas, with branches at Isfahan and Shiraz; at Mokha for the Yemen coffee-trade; and soon afterwards at Basra for trade by river-boat with Baghdad. However, the reorganization of the Company in 1661 was followed by a change of policy and the abandoning of all these factories. Experience had shown that it was not profitable for the Company to operate the local coastal trade, which was the natural business of the highly efficient Asiatic shipping. The Company accordingly concentrated its staffs at a few

---

[1] Foster, op. cit., 183.
[2] J. A. Williamson, *The Ocean in English History*, 104 ff.
[3] Williamson, *Short History*, I. 223.

central factories, but without losing the local trade, since its regular liners making the Cape passage continued to be fed by the 'country ships' not under its command.[1]

The successful development of the Cape Route had largely diverted the trade in East Indian products from the Overland Route. The transport costs of the long desert crossing and the profits exacted by the several middlemen through whose hands the goods passed raised the cost of pepper from $2\frac{1}{2}d.$ per lb. in India to 2s. at Aleppo, and that of cloves from 9d. per lb. to 4s. The spices which reached Western Europe via the Cape cost only one-third of what they cost via Aleppo, and thus it was actually profitable for the Levant Co. in 1614 to re-export Indian goods from England to the Levant, since they could still undersell the same commodities brought there by the Overland Route. By the second half of the seventeenth century the Levant Co., three-quarters of whose imports into England had consisted of Persian silk, was feeling severely the competition of the East India Co., which was importing Persian raw silk and Indian manufactured silks and calicos via the Cape Route. But the Privy Council had the foresight to support the East India Co.; and the silk trade through Aleppo continued to decline to one-half of its former figure.

The strain of the wars of the later seventeenth century, first against England and then against Louis XIV of France, was too much for the vitality of the Dutch state, and her commercial activities in the Indian Ocean and the Persian Gulf began to flag. Meanwhile France, under Louis XIV's far-seeing minister Colbert, had begun to plan the creation of a maritime commercial empire. He opened factories in India, sent an embassy to Persia in 1664 and obtained trading-rights at Bandar Abbas and Isfahan. French competition in the Levant also was stimulated by Colbert, and during the eighteenth century her commercial interests in these lands were always greater than the English. In Egypt France secured a virtual monopoly, with fifty merchants in Cairo in 1702 and other establishments at Alexandria and Rosetta, compared with only two English merchants at Cairo and Alexandria. The policy of the Levant Co., which was content to secure a high rate of profit on a comparatively small volume of sales, was partly responsible for the

---

[1] Williamson, *The Ocean in English History*, 101 ff., and especially 109 ff., correcting the older hypothesis that the withdrawal of the East India Co. from local trading was primarily due to successful Dutch competition.

sharp decline in English trade in favour of France. While the English cloth had the highest reputation, the French was lighter and better suited to the climate, It was, moreover, 10 per cent. cheaper; and when English clothiers did produce a thinner and cheaper cloth its quality was so inferior that the Levant merchants would not touch it. It was said that the Turks of Istanbul 'could neither be clothed, at the price and in the manner they wished, nor have coffee to drink' without buying from the French.[1] French trade with the Levant increased with extraordinary rapidity, and on the eve of the French Revolution was three times as great as the volume of English trade to those countries. Between 1778 and 1791 the English Levant Co. was compelled to close down its four factories in Syria, leaving the French in full possession of the trade. Politically also France was acknowledged by the Sultan as protector of all the Catholics within his Empire.

In Persia and Iraq however, the commercial situation in the eighteenth century was far different. The French East India Co. was ill-organized and ill-supported from Paris; and consequently the decline of the Dutch left the English to enjoy the bulk of the Persian Gulf trade through the prosperous factories which it reopened at Bandar Abbas and Basta. As a result of the internal anarchy in Persia which followed on the Afghan invasion of 1722, however, most of the European factories in that country had eventually to be closed, and in 1761 the main seat of British trade was shifted to Basra, where the East India Co.'s resident was raised to the rank of consul. In 1766 the Company lent the Pasha of Baghdad six ships to deal with unruly tribesmen in Lower Iraq, and in 1780 it helped Sulaiman Pasha the Great to secure his succession to the pashaliq and so won his friendship. Britain's commercial position in the Gulf was now pre-eminent, and she was acquiring through it a growing political influence also. In 1798 the Company's Resident at Bushire, which had become the principal station on the Persian coast after the closing of Bandar Abbas, was asked to arbitrate in a dispute between the Pasha of Baghdad and the Sultan of Oman.

Like the Chinese, the rulers and inhabitants of the Ottoman Empire continued, long after their civilization and power had passed its peak, to regard the European strangers in their midst as

[1] They had made a trade treaty with the Governor of Mokha in 1709, and in 1738 temporarily occupied the port in a dispute over debts to French traders.

immeasurably their inferiors. Till about 1830 a foreign ambassador was kept waiting on a bench in the courtyard of the Serai to await the Grand Vezir's pleasure, and was finally introduced to the Sultan as 'the naked and hungry barbarian who has ventured to rub his brow upon the Sublime Porte'. The Grand Vezir informed the English Ambassador c. 1680: 'You and all other ambassadors are sent here by your respective princes to answer for the lives and estates of all Muslims all over the world that are endangered or suffer by their respective subjects, and you are a hostage here to answer for all damage done by Englishmen all over the world.' As late as 1798, when the Ottoman Empire went to war with a European state its ambassador was flung into the Prison of the Seven Towers, 'a pile of noisome dungeons'. If this was the prevailing tone of diplomatic courtesies, it is not surprising that European merchants in the Levant were obliged to wear Oriental dress to minimize the risk of insult by the populace. The merchants were beginning to revert to European dress c. 1700 in Istanbul and Smyrna, and about 1750 in Aleppo; but in the more distant parts of the Levant, and especially in Egypt, they were still obliged to wear full Turkish dress till nearly 1800. It is entertaining to speculate whether the English merchants in Aleppo continued to wear the enormous Turkish turbans and voluminous pantaloons for the games of cricket which they played on the 'Green Platte' outside the city.

CHAPTER IV

The Growth of Western Imperialism
(1770—1914)

'Power-politics is the only kind of politics there is.'
(James Burnham, *The Struggle for the World*).

IN THE EARLY eighteenth century European political influence in the Middle East and India was still slight. The Ottoman, Persian and Mogul Empires were still relatively strong; and though Western Europe was now well in advance of the stagnating East in technical skill and in the quality of its manufactures, its traders still lived in these lands as clients, dependent on the good-will of the Oriental rulers and officials. Their insecurity led them to make common cause among themselves, and even the outbreak of a general war in Europe did not greatly affect their mutual relations. In 1696, for example, the English chaplain at Aleppo and his companions travelling to Jerusalem met with hospitable treatment from French merchants on their journey and at their destination, even though their countries were at war; and during the same war British and Dutch merchants in the Persian Gulf made an agreement with the French merchants for their mutual protection against the nuisance of piracy.

However, with conditions in the Oriental empires becoming more anarchic, local Oriental rulers increasingly courted the assistance of the European traders with their gold, their garrisons and naval units, and it was not long before the Europeans began to enter into the complexities of Oriental political intrigue and turn it to their own advantage. In this way the strategic rivalries of the European Powers at home were at length reproduced in the East. Since the Mogul Empire was the most advanced in decay, it was there that the English and French trading companies first came into conflict. As late as the outbreak in Europe of the War of Jenkins' Ear in 1739, indeed, the French company was still anxious that it and the English company should continue to observe a strict neutrality. Hostilities however broke out between them in 1745, and there followed sixteen years of fierce Anglo-French struggle with each company using Indian rulers as allies. By 1761 the French hopes of empire had been shattered and the English East India Co. was on the way to becoming the supreme authority over large parts of India.

The next country to become the scene of these Anglo-French rivalries was Egypt. On the initiative of Ali Bey, for a few years the independent ruler of Egypt, and of Warren Hastings, the vigorous and unconventional governor of Bengal, the East India Co. sent more than one expedition in the 1770's from India to Suez,[1] whence the freight was transported under Egyptian guarantee to the Mediterranean for shipment to England. By opening up this route, which foreshadowed the speeding-up of communications in the following century, Calcutta was brought within two months of London, as compared with five months by the Cape Route. Although a variety of jealous influences interrupted this traffic after a few years, it had been enough to alarm the French for the future of their virtual monopoly of the Egyptian trade; and English and French interests competed for the favour of the Mamluk rulers of Egypt, with control of the Red Sea-Mediterranean route as the prize, until the attention of both countries was diverted by the French Revolution and the European war which grew out of it.

By 1797 Napoleon, commanding the French armies at the age of twenty-eight, had knocked Austria out of the coalition of counter-revolutionary Powers, leaving France free to turn on her next most formidable enemy, Britain. Since a direct invasion across the Channel was considered too difficult, the French government decided on an expedition to conquer Egypt. This project, which had been mooted by French political thinkers at various times since the beginning of the century, had been considered impolitic as long as Egypt was an integral part of the Ottoman Empire, with which France had continually been on good terms in opposition to their common enemy Austria. But now that the Ottoman authority over Egypt had ceased to be more than nominal and that Britain had shown signs of establishing commercial interests there, the

---

[1] The Ottoman government, jealous for its customs-revenues, did not allow European trading-ships to sail north of Jidda.

French case for annexation was strengthened, especially now that her victories in Italy and her alliance with Spain had caused the British fleet to withdraw from the Mediterranean to the shelter of Gibraltar. The instructions which the French government gave Napoleon for the Egyptian expedition included the expulsion of British interests from the Red Sea in favour of France and the cutting of a canal through the Isthmus of Suez. If the expedition were successful, there were reasonable hopes of ousting the British from India, since their hold on that country was still far from complete, and French military adventurers and mercenary troops exerted a powerful influence on several important Indian princes.

Napoleon's force landed near Alexandria in July 1798, and proclaimed its ostensible purpose of overthrowing the Mamluks and restoring the authority of the Ottoman Sultan. But though the French met with little resistance from the decadent Mamluk army, their hopes of consolidating their position were shattered by Nelson's destruction of the French fleet at the battle of Abuqir on 1 August. Napoleon was now cut off by superior British sea-power from supplies, from reinforcements, and even from news from France; and he could do little more than mark time in Egypt. In January 1799 Britain, Russia, and the Ottoman Empire reached an agreement to expel him. Learning that an Ottoman army was being assembled in Syria for the invasion of Egypt, he advanced through Palestine to meet it, but was checked before the fortress of Akka, which was held by its Bosnian tyrant Ahmed al-Jazzar ('the Butcher') supported by a British naval squadron. After two months Napoleon was forced to raise the siege and retire with his plague-stricken army to Egypt. Meanwhile the situation in Europe had deteriorated for the French, and Napoleon himself slipped away ignominiously to France in August 1799. The French army stayed on ineffectually, and was eventually withdrawn by agreement with Britain in 1801. Its only direct achievement was the great 'Description of Egypt' compiled by the staff of scholars which had accompanied it. Nevertheless, it had the enormously important indirect effect of 'bringing to the attention of a few men in Egypt a keen sense of the advantage of an orderly government, and a warm appreciation of the advance that science and learning had made in Europe', with results that were to galvanize into new life the torpid economic and social system of Egypt and the Levant.

The romantic interest of the Egyptian expedition has over-shadowed other, and not less significant, proceedings in other parts of the Middle East. Until about 1770 Britain had been content to be represented in the Middle East by trader-consuls 'humbly asking for nothing but capitulations and to be left alone'. From 1770 on-wards, in their dealings with an Ali Bey or a Sulaiman Pasha of Iraq, her representatives were attaining the status of equals in power and authority. But, just as it had been the bid to create a French empire in India which turned the East India Co. from trade to the tasks of empire, so it was Napoleon's threat to that growing empire in India which first constrained Britain to increase her political influence in the Middle East; and in both instances, once committed, she followed the course thus imposed on her with greater tenacity than the more opportunist French, and so achieved success and empire almost in spite of herself.

In the Southern Red Sea Britain immediately countered Napoleon's thrust towards India by occupying Perim, in the nar-rowest part of the Straits of Bab al Mandab. But soon, when living conditions on this torrid rock had proved intolerable, the occupy-ing force was moved to Aden, by agreement with its ruler, the Sultan of Lahaj. A treaty was made with him in 1802, and six years later Lord Valentia commented prophetically, 'Aden is the Gibraltar of the East'. In 1799 Napoleon had made overtures from Egypt to the Sultan of Oman, who by his possession of harbours on either side of the Straits of Hormuz (he held Bandar Abbas at this time) could control the entrance to the Persian Gulf. The Sul-tan was however persuaded to conclude with the East India Co. a treaty excluding from his territories French and Dutch subjects (Holland was now under French domination) for the duration of the war; and in 1800 the Company established a permanent Resident at Muscat.

Both at Basra and Baghdad French consuls had been established earlier than those of the East India Co.; but since they were ill-paid, ill-provided, often ill-chosen, and no great volume of French trade passed through their hands, they failed to impress the ruling Pashas. In 1798 the French consuls were arrested, their papers confiscated, and their premises occupied. It is not clear whether this was done entirely on the initiative of Sulaiman Pasha on ac-count of the Ottoman declaration of war on France following the invasion of Egypt, or whether perhaps it may have been suggested to him by the East India Co.'s Resident, now permanently established in Baghdad and on friendly terms with him. The French consuls were eventually released, but the Pasha rejected with little ceremony their claim to formal precedence over the British representatives. In 1802 the Resident at Baghdad was promoted to the rank of Consul with a guard of Sepoys, and Britain's position in Iraq grew in prestige and prosperity to the jealous indignation of the French.

For nearly ten years, from 1800 to 1809, the French were engaged in tortuous intrigues with Fath Ali Shah of Persia, with a view to an overland invasion of India in which they hoped to have the Russians as allies; and after the crushing French victories in Europe in 1805-6 a French military mission was sent to Persia following a treaty between the two countries. But this entente was broken when Napoleon went on in 1807 to make the Treaty of Tilsit with Russia, who had been steadily encroaching on Persian territory in Transcaucasia for the past eighty years and against whom the Persians looked for French assistance. In these new circumstances the British authorities in India had little difficulty in reasserting their own influence with the Shah and squeezing out the French military mission.

Meanwhile in 1806 Britain had regarded an ephemeral alliance between the Sultan of Turkey and Napoleon as likely once more to open Egypt to the French. A small British force accordingly occupied Alexandria, but twice failed to take Rosetta and suffered considerable losses. The Albanian Mohammed Ali, who had made himself Pasha of Egypt in 1805, now offered, provided that the British force was withdrawn, to oppose any European force that might attempt either to occupy Egypt or pass through it en route for India. He had rightly concluded that the French army was a much more remote instrument of power than the British navy, which in the later years of the war practically drove the French merchant fleet from the Levant. There was a flourishing British trade with Egypt in grain for the Mediterranean naval squadrons and for the army in the Iberian Peninsula.[1]

In 1810 the British capture of Mauritius, which had been the base for French privateers in the Indian Ocean, was a severe blow to

[1] Nevertheless, Mohammed Ali was already so intent on consolidating his position as master of Egypt that in 1810 he offered the French an alliance if they would recognize him as independent; but in view of the French desire to remain on good terms with the Ottoman Empire, they rejected his proposal.

what remained of French prestige in the Persian Gulf area. In the following years France's increasing difficulties in the Russian and Peninsular campaigns gave her no opportunity for further adventures in the Middle East; and the fall of Napoleon left Britain as the dominant and unquestioned authority in that region.

*   *   *

Mohammed Ali combined ambition with perspicacity to a greater degree than any other Oriental ruler of the nineteenth century. Conscious of the declining powers of the Ottoman Empire, he was anxious to confirm himself and his heirs in hereditary possession of Egypt. He was content to recognize the nominal suzerainty of the Sultan provided that he enjoyed autonomy in practical matters. But the impact of the Napoleonic wars had taught him that, if he was to attain and maintain such a position, he must have an army and navy equipped and trained on Western lines; and to Western Europe he consequently turned for armaments and technical experts. He would have preferred to obtain these from Britain, for whose dominant position as a sea-power he always had the greatest respect, and of whose friendship he was always genuinely desirous. He told the Swiss traveller Burckhardt in 1815, 'The great fish swallow the small . . . England must someday take Egypt as her share of the spoil of the Turkish Empire.' But the main imperial principle of British governments was already the maintenance of the British position in India, and to this the preservation of the status quo in the Middle East, i.e. the support of the Ottoman Empire which had assisted in checking Napoleon's ambitions in this direction, was a corollary. As Palmerston put it in 1833, with reference to the pan-Arab policy of Mohammed Ali's son Ibrahim Pasha in Syria: 'Turkey is as good an occupier of the road to India as an active Arabian sovereign would be.' When therefore his overtures to Britain were declined, Mohammed Ali turned for material help and guidance to France, who, in spite of the fall of Napoleon, survived through Talleyrand's diplomacy as a leading European Power. French officers, doctors, and savants accompanied Mohammed Ali's armies in the successful campaigns which subdued the wild Wahhabis of Central Arabia (1811–18).[1]

---

[1] The religious teacher Mohammed ibn Abdul Wahhab, a follower of the school of the ninth-century Ibn Hanbal in his desire to return to the simplicity of the Qur'an and the Sunna and cleanse Islam of all later excrescences, had

A French colonel, who became a Muslim and is commemorated as Sulaiman Pasha by one of Cairo's principal streets, was engaged to reorganize and train the Egyptian army on French lines. Another Frenchman planned and organized the naval dockyard, and others came as doctors, engineers, surveyors, and as managers of the numerous factories founded by Mohammed Ali in his attempt to modernize and develop the whole productive economy of Egypt. Anxious to build up a cadre of young Egyptians with a modern technical training, it was natural that he should send them to France, whose educational system had been entirely modernized since the Revolution and now provided the finest scientific and technical instruction in the world. In contrast, all that contemporary England could offer was the unreformed medieval structure of Oxford and Cambridge, the few great collegiate schools, and the country grammar schools, all greatly mouldered by the neglect of two centuries—a crumbling monumental ruin not unlike the Great Pyramid, and of about as much utility to the ambitious Pasha. It was therefore to Paris that his young men were sent to study.

French educational influence was predominant in the fifty elementary and secondary schools which were opened in Egypt from 1836 onwards, and French scientific and technical works were translated into Arabic as text-books. A French military mission and ten naval officers were lent to Mohammed Ali in 1824 to accompany the forces with which he undertook to suppress the revolt of the Greeks against the Ottoman Sultan; and when the Great Powers had finally agreed on a joint intervention to end the Revolt, lest it should provoke a general European war, the French naval officers were withdrawn only two days before Ibrahim Pasha's fleet was destroyed by a joint Anglo-French fleet at Navarino. The French continued to intrigue with Mohammed Ali for their own ends and, having set their minds on annexing Algeria but not wishing to disturb the concert of Europe by a direct attack on what was still nominally Ottoman territory, they suggested to the Pasha in 1829 that he should conquer and annex the whole of North Africa with French help. But the British government

---

won the ear of the Najdi noble Mohammed ibn Sa'ud about the middle of the eighteenth century. The Wahhabi tribesmen, influenced by this puritan creed, extended the domain of the Sa'udi rulers, and at the beginning of the nineteenth century occupied and 'purified' Mecca and Madina and sacked the Shi'i shrine of Husain at Karbala. These acts brought down upon them the vengeance of the Ottoman Empire, with Mohammed Ali as its instrument.

warned him off such a scheme, and he then turned in 1831 to the conquest of Syria and Palestine, which he had been previously promised by the Sultan for his part in opposing the Greek Revolt; moreover, he wished to use the forests of the Lebanon to rebuild the fleet he had lost at Navarino. By 1833 Ibrahim Pasha had conquered Syria and his army, for which the feeble Ottoman army was absolutely no match, was less than 150 miles from Istanbul. 'We rejoice,' commented the French Foreign Office, 'that we have facilitated the birth and development of a Power worthy of our collaboration and as interested as we are in the prosperity of the Mediterranean. We shall always be ready to give to the Pasha in the future the same evidence of our friendship and goodwill as he has received in the past from the French government.'

The Ottoman Sultan appealed to Britain for support; but Britain, preoccupied with a delicate situation in Western Europe, could spare no naval detachments for the Eastern Mediterranean at this moment. In his helplessness the Sultan was compelled to accept an offer of aid from Russia, who had emerged a Great Power from the Napoleonic Wars.[1] She had encouraged the Greek Revolt, in the hope of eventually dominating that country through the medium of the Orthodox Church; and now a Russian force was promptly sent to the Asiatic side of the Bosporus to 'protect' the Sultan. Alarmed at the prospect of Russian domination of the Ottoman Empire, Britain and France were at length impelled to concerted action. Mohammed Ali was pressed to recall his army from Anatolia; the Sultan ceded him Palestine, Syria, and Cilicia, which were henceforth administered by Ibrahim Pasha; and the Russian force was withdrawn from Turkey. The crisis of the First Syrian War was over; but it had had the effect of stimulating in the mind of Palmerston, who was to dominate British foreign policy for the next thirty years and whose constant concern was the possibility of a Franco-Russian combination against Britain, a lasting, deep, and possibly exaggerated mistrust of Mohammed Ali as a pawn in the hands of these Powers.

[1] Her bid to replace the Ottoman Empire as the dominant power in the Black Sea had begun with Peter the Great's invasion of the Ukraine a hundred years before, and had advanced her frontiers by 1815 to the Lower Danube. By the treaties of Edirne (1829) and Hunkiar Iskelesi (1833) she forced the Ottoman Empire to concede her the control of the Straits. Meanwhile, in 1813 she had forced Persia to acknowledge the cession to her of Transcaucasia; and when Persia attempted to set aside this treaty by an ill-advised act of aggression, Russia forced on her in 1828 the Treaty of Turkmanchai, which made serious inroads on Persian sovereignty to the economic advantage of Russia.

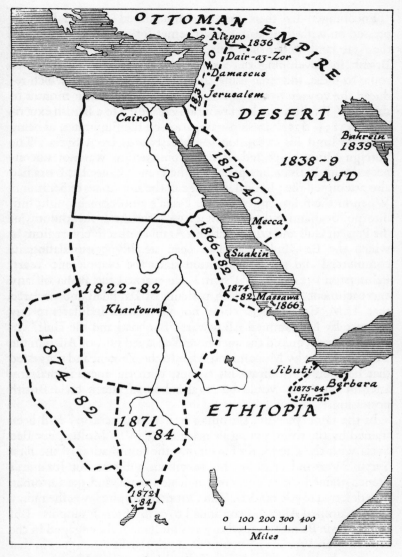

9. THE EGYPTIAN 'EMPIRE' IN THE NINETEENTH CENTURY

Encouraged by their success, Mohammed Ali and Ibrahim pressed on with their ambitious schemes for uniting the whole of the Arab lands under their rule. While the Pasha encouraged the British in developing once more the Mediterranean-Red Sea route to India, this time using the first paddle-steamers which reduced the voyage from London to Bombay from four months to six weeks, Ibrahim was less favourably disposed to a British experiment in 1835-6 at steamship-navigation on the Euphrates, as being liable to limit his expansion south-eastwards from Syria. The Foreign Office suspected that this obstruction was not unconnected with Russian intrigues, and the French Consul at Basra had also attempted the physical sabotage of the Euphrates expedition.[1] When in the following years the Pasha's ambitions brought him into political and military contact with the Arab sheikhdoms of the Persian Gulf and with Southern Arabia respectively, regions in which the East India Co. had been steadily consolidating its commercial and strategic position since the Napoleonic Wars, Palmerston's response was swift. He warned the Pasha off any encroachment on the Turkish pashaliq of Baghdad and declared that 'H.M. Government could not view with indifference any advance by Mohammed Ali towards Baghdad and the Gulf.' In 1839 Britain acquired the ancient and decayed port of Aden in the teeth of a drive by Mohammed Ali into the Yemen, and suggested that he should withdraw his troops, with the menace that any attempt on Aden would be regarded as an attack on a British possession.[2]

In the same year the Ottoman Sultan, whose army had been trained by the rising young Prussian officer Von Moltke, invaded Syria with the intention of avenging the humiliation of the First Syrian War and crushing his rebellious subject; but Ibrahim's French-trained forces decisively defeated them, and the Ottoman fleet deserted to Alexandria. The Ottoman Empire lay at the mercy of Mohammed Ali, who continued to enjoy French support. But by this time Palmerston, who was simultaneously engaged in the First Afghan War in an attempt to check Russian intrigues in that country, had become convinced that Mohammed Ali was acting in the interests of Russia; and he decided that the only way to

[1] Longrigg, op. cit., 293.
[2] H. L. Hoskins, 'The Background of the British Position in Arabia,' in *Middle East Journal*, I (Washington, 1947), 137 ff.

prevent the collapse of the Ottoman Empire was to oust Ibrahim from Syria. He accordingly succeeded in July 1840 in bringing about an agreement between Britain, Russia, Austria, and Prussia, by which Mohammed Ali was presented with an ultimatum to evacuate Syria, with the threat of losing all his possessions if he procrastinated unduly. This threat to their protégé caused great indignation in Paris and the French government threatened war; but Palmerston knew that it was unprepared for such extremes and kept up the pressure of the Powers on Mohammed Ali. While the French government vacillated and eventually fell, British and Ottoman forces blockaded and occupied Beirut and Akka, and forced Ibrahim to evacuate Syria and Palestine. His father had to give back the Ottoman fleet, but was confirmed in the hereditary pashaliq of Egypt. The Second Syrian War was over. As the French historian Driault ruefully comments, 'All the advantages had fallen to Britain. She had pushed back Mohammed Ali and France in the south, Russia in the north, and kept open for the future the overland route to India via Iraq. She had made safe the development of her influence along this route. She was pre-eminent in the lands of the Levant.'

In the previous twenty years, while numbers of French officials were being introduced into Mohammed Ali's service, Britain was less obviously, and certainly less consciously, establishing her commercial predominance in Egypt. The key to this was the Egyptian production of high-grade cotton, which had been fostered by Mohammed Ali and was first introduced to the spinners of Lancashire in 1821. The export of cotton from Egypt actually increased 200 times in the next three years and became from now on her principal export. It was absorbed in the main by Britain, whose factory-made cottons now displaced the more expensive hand-woven French fabrics. Soon after 1830 British trade with Egypt was greater than that of any other country. By 1849, the year of Mohammed Ali's death, she provided 41 per cent. of Egypt's imports and took 49 per cent. of her exports.

But since the defence of her position in India remained a cardinal feature of her overseas policy, she was not anxious to see communications through the Middle East modernized or made more speedy to give an opportunity to any jealous and aggressive Power to assail her. She had refused in 1834 to give any financial guarantees for a proposed railway to connect Alexandria, Cairo, and

Suez; and when the French government showed itself ready to sponsor the cutting of the Isthmus of Suez, Palmerston commented that however great the commercial advantages might be, this 'second Bosporus' might be a source of grave political embarrassment to Britain. In the declining years of the aged Mohammed Ali the project was not pressed, and nothing could be done under his reactionary and anti-European successor Abbas I.[1] But the murder of Abbas brought to the throne in 1854 the fat, indolent, and easygoing Sa'id, who had as a boy been friendly with Ferdinand de Lesseps, the young son of the French Political Agent. On his friend's accession de Lesseps, who had subsequently been French Consul at Alexandria for seven years, sent him a letter of congratulation and was invited to revisit Egypt. These were the go-getting days of Napoleon III: within ten days of his arrival de Lesseps had presented the Pasha with a detailed scheme for the cutting of a Suez Canal which Sa'id accepted; and a fortnight later the Pasha signed the concession for the 'Compagnie Universelle', subject to the approval of his Ottoman suzerain. It was alleged that he had not even read the agreement, and it had certainly not been examined by his judicial and financial advisers. But de Lesseps was his friend, and he was promised 15 per cent. of the profits. What more was needed?

De Lesseps took the opportunity of the Franco-Ottoman friendship during the Crimean War to go to Istanbul to obtain the Sultan's approval for the concession. He found himself however vigorously opposed by the British Ambassador, who represented to the Ottoman government that such a concession would eventually lead to a French protectorate over Egypt. That British opposition to the scheme was not without justification is shown by the fact that the anti-British section of the French press had been exulting that 'in piercing the Isthmus of Suez, we are piercing the weak point in the British armour'. While British commercial interests, such as the East India Co. and the P. & O. Steamship Co., favoured the scheme, Palmerston strongly opposed it as 'profitable to France, but hostile to British interests'. In 1858 the British government warned the Turks that if the Sultan gave his consent he could no longer count on Britain to maintain the integrity of his Empire. When work on the alignment of the Canal began in 1859, Sa'id replied blandly to British protests that under the

[1] Ibrahim had died before his father.

Capitulations he had no control over what French subjects did in Egypt. The French won the support of Russia and Austria for the scheme. Britain, thus isolated in her opposition, was reduced to creating prejudice against it by attacking the use of forced Egyptian labour, though she had urged its use on the British-built Cairo-Suez railway a few years before. Nevertheless the work went on; Palmerston, its arch-opponent, died in 1865 and the British opposition died with him. The Sultan finally approved the undertaking in 1866, and the Canal was opened to the shipping of the world by the Empress Eugenie in 1869.

Britain's statesmen had not however been content merely with obstructing the Canal project. They had also taken active steps to strengthen her defences along the short sea-route to India in case the Canal became an accomplished fact. In 1863 the harbours and docks of Malta were extended, and its fortifications strengthened. In 1854 Britain had acquired from the Sultan of Oman for use as a cable-station the Kuria Muria Islands, which the French also had made several attempts to acquire. In 1857 Britain re-occupied Perim. In 1862 she reached a mutual agreement with France to respect the independence of Oman, which was in fact already under strong influence from the Government of India. By 1870 British influence was being extended from Aden along the southern coast of Arabia to the ports of Mukalla and Shihr, whose trade with East Africa passed largely through Aden and whose ruling sultan usually resided in India. Britain thus established here a protectorate in fact, if not yet in name; and in 1876 she took Socotra under her formal protection.

★   ★   ★

During the nine years of his occupation of Syria (1831–40), Ibrahim Pasha had encouraged European and American missionaries to settle there. In particular the French Jesuits were eager to resume their work, which had stagnated since the temporary suppression of their order by the Pope in 1773; and by 1840 they had re-established a powerful influence over the Maronites[1] of the Lebanon, which was exercised not only in ecclesiastical matters

---

[1] This Christian sect, which forms the majority of the inhabitants of the Mountain Lebanon, entered into communion with the Church of Rome at the time of the Crusades, but is distinguished by its retention of Syriac as its liturgical language.

but also for the furtherance of French policy in the Levant. During the intrigues of the Second Syrian War Britain, on the other hand, had made use of the friendship of some of the Druze chiefs of Southern Lebanon. Ibrahim Pasha's government, and the steady increase of population in the mountain-valleys of the Lebanon, had had the effect of unsettling the peasantry and making them less tolerant of their subservience to their landlords. Social relationships were complicated by the fact that, while in North Lebanon landlords and peasantry were both mainly Maronite, in the South there were both Maronite and Druze peasantry in the service of Druze lords. The proclamation in 1839 of the equality before the law of all religions within the Ottoman Empire had encouraged the Christian communities; and the Maronite priesthood, which was drawn largely from the peasantry and was anxious to extend its influence over the people, stimulated the social unrest. It finally came to a head in 1857, when the peasants of North Lebanon, incited by their clergy, rose against their Maronite lords and divided up the large estates, while those in South Lebanon were forbidden by their priests to pay rents to their Druze landlords. This show of Maronite truculence had the effect of uniting the Druze peasantry with the Druze lords, since they saw that the Maronites already outnumbered them in fighting-men and were increasing at a faster rate. The antagonism of the two unruly communities was fanned by the Turkish Pasha in Beirut, who hoped to see them weaken one another; while the rival intrigues of French and British agents, the one taking seriously France's rôle as protector of the Maronites, the other giving some encouragement to the Druze, added to the tension. In 1860 the Druze made a general attack on the Maronites, in which some 14,000 of the latter were massacred.[1] In Damascus the Druze, helped by Kurdish and Syrian Muslims, attacked the Christian population and killed some 5,000. The news of the Damascus massacres caused horror in Western Europe, coming as it did soon after the attacks on Christians in Jidda in 1858 as a second example of anti-Christian fanaticism in the Ottoman Empire. In France it was welcomed as providing an opportunity for a military adventure in the Lebanon, for which immediate

---

[1] It is stated that the smaller Protestant communities, evangelized in the main by the American missionaries, were left for the most part in peace, except where they sided with the Maronites to resist the Druze (J. Richter, *History of Protestant Missions in the Near East*, 199). See in general the objective summing-up by Pierre Rondot, *Les Institutions Politiques du Liban* (Paris, 1947), 44 ff.

preparations were made. The other Powers gave their consent to the French expedition. When it landed at Beirut there was little for it to do, as the Turks had already practically completed the task of restoring order. The French wished to keep the force there indefinitely as a guarantee against a recurrence of the disorders, but the British government insisted that, calm having been restored, the French should withdraw after nine months. This they reluctantly did: 'the undertaking had failed to realize the hopes of the Protecting Power'.[1] In place of the protectorate envisaged in Paris, an international commission created in 1864 the autonomous sanjaq of the Lebanon, no longer subject to the Pasha of Beirut, but to a Christian governor appointed by the Ottoman Government. Under this satisfactory compromise, which kept the peace in the Lebanon down to the First World War, French educational missions were free to continue their cultural work, and it was claimed that in 1914 more than half of the school-going children in Syria and Palestine attended French schools.[2]

Immediately after the Damascus massacres Napoleon III had summoned to Paris from Syria the Jesuit priest William Gifford Palgrave, who had been an Indian Army officer before he took Holy Orders. He presented himself to the Emperor as a likely envoy to Arab societies, on account of his facility in Semitic languages (his grandfather was a Jew), and was sent on a mission to the Amir of the Shammar in Northern Arabia, 'the one effective power in the lands east of the Red Sea'. The nature of his mission has never been disclosed, but it was regarded by the British government sufficiently seriously for the Resident at Bushire to counter it by a visit in 1864 to the rival North Arabian Power, the Sa'udi Amir.

At the same time France also took an active interest in the efforts of the Ottoman government to reform and modernize itself. 'The Turks were the only bond capable of preventing all the races of the Empire—Slav, Greek, Arab—from disintegrating into Russian, Austrian, or British dust. It was necessary to change Muslim habits, to destroy the age-old fanaticism which was an obstacle to the fusion of races, and to create a modern secular state. It was necessary to transform even the education of both conquerors and subjects, and inculcate in both the unknown spirit of

[1] Lammens, op. cit., II, 186 f.
[2] id., II, 201.

7

tolerance—a noble task, worthy of the great renown of France.' In 1863 the Ottoman Bank was founded with the controlling interest in French hands, British interests being secondary; it had the monopoly of the banknote-issue and branches in every important town in the Empire. In 1867 the French government invited the Sultan to visit Paris, and recommended to him a system of secular public education and the undertaking of great public works and communications. As a contribution to the first, there was opened in 1868 under the joint direction of the Turkish Ministry of Foreign Affairs and the French Ambassador the Lycée of Galata-Serai, a great secondary school open to Ottoman subjects of every race and creed, where more than six hundred boys were taught by Europeans in the French language—'a symbol of the action of France, exerting herself to teach the peoples of the Orient in her own language the elements of Western civilization'. In the same year a company consisting mainly of French capitalists received a concession for railways to connect Istanbul and Salonica with the existing railways on the Middle Danube.[1]

But all these schemes for establishing a French cultural and financial dominion in the Middle East were 'brutally interrupted' by the disaster of the Franco-German War of 1870. France emerged from the War permanently weakened, and her imperial energies were now focused in the main on her expanding colonies in N.W. Africa. Not that she has ever renounced her aspirations in the Middle East; but after 1870 her relation to Britain in this region was that of an envious, and sometimes spiteful, loser in a race, rather than that of a serious rival. She could for twenty years obstruct the efforts of Lord Cromer to restore the financial stability and promote the economic progress of Egypt;[2] in the 'nineties she could intrigue against Britain at Muscat, or seek to forestall her in establishing a position on the Upper Nile,[3] but whereas from 1815 to 1870 British imperial interests in the Middle East had been thought to be challenged by France and Russia to a roughly equal degree, from 1870 to 1900 there is no doubt that the Russian challenge, real or imagined, easily assumed the first place.

*   *   *

Palmerston's fears of a Franco-Russian coalition against Britain

[1] Driault, op. cit., 187 ff.
[2] Lord Milner. *England in Egypt*. ch. XIII.
[3] A. L. Kennedy, 'Fashoda', *Quarterly Review*, April 1948, pp. 145–61.

had been allayed by the development of a dispute between those two Powers over the respective claims of the Catholic and the Orthodox Churches to the Holy Places in Palestine. In the first half of the nineteenth century the Russians had established numerous claims which the Ottoman Empire had accorded in previous centuries to the Catholic Church and its French protector, but which had been allowed to lapse during the Revolution and the Napoleonic Wars. Napoleon III, however, wishing to win for his régime the support of French Catholics, revived in 1852 all the Latin claims to the Holy Places which had been conferred by the Capitulations of 1740, and demanded that any subsequent concession to the Orthodox Church which conflicted with them should be set aside. The Russian government responded with counter-claims, and went so far as to demand the right to protect all Orthodox Christians of whatever nationality throughout the Ottoman Empire. Such a claim was deemed by the Powers to disturb the European Balance of Power by encroaching on the authority of the Sultan over his millions of Orthodox subjects in the Balkans. Negotiations produced agreement on the question of the Holy Places, but on the larger issue Russia remained obdurate. She allowed herself to be diplomatically outmanoeuvred by the British Ambassador in Turkey, and had to fight the Crimean War against an alliance of Britain, France, and the Ottoman Empire. The Treaty of Paris which ended the war in 1856 forbade the Russians to launch warships on the Black Sea, and thus removed one potential danger from Britain's Mediterranean route to the East.

While the other Powers were preoccupied with the Franco-German War, however, Russia resumed her freedom of action in the Black Sea. She had for forty years been progressively bringing under her direct rule what is now Russian Turkestan, for her important trade-route across Siberia, the forerunner of the Trans-Siberian Railway, had been continually harassed by the lawless Turcomans to the south. Her southward expansion seemed to have been completed with the ratification of the Anglo-Russian Convention of 1873, in which the Amu-Darya was recognized as the definitive Russian frontier, and the Russian government acknowledged that Afghanistan was 'completely outside the sphere within which Russia might be compelled to exercise her influence'. Within four years Russia was engaged in a war against the Ottoman Empire which would certainly have left her predominant in the Balkans, had it not been for the intervention of the other European Powers. Simultaneously, British opinion was alarmed 'almost to the point of panic'[1] by the Amir of Afghanistan's leanings towards the dynamic Russians rather than the seemingly irresolute British. While Britain embarked upon the Second Afghan War to reassert her authority in this vital quarter, her apprehensions extended also to the Persian Gulf, and Lord Salisbury, the Foreign Secretary, proclaimed that 'The people of this country will never allow Russian influence to be supreme in the valleys of the Euphrates and Tigris'. Britain had for sixty years been steadily establishing her authority over the Arab sheikhdoms of the Persian Gulf: first using her good offices to put down piracy and the slave-trade; then arranging for the submission of disputes between the sheikhs to the British Resident at Bushire, who thus became virtually ruler of the Gulf; and finally in 1869 persuading the sheikhs of the Trucial Coast to undertake not to make any territorial concessions or enter into agreements with any government other than Britain. Following the Russian scare of 1878, this 'exclusive agreement' was extended to the sheikhs of Bahrain and Qatar when treaties with them were renewed in 1880, with the additional proviso that they should not accept any diplomatic or consular representatives, except with the approval of Britain. In 1885, after a further Russian annexation to the very borders of Afghanistan, war between the two Great Powers was narrowly averted, and British apprehensions once more inflamed. Curzon, at thirty years of age a budding British authority on the Middle East, could in 1889 express the moderate view that Russian movements in the direction of India were designed, not for conquest, but to draw British attention from her real objectives in the Balkans;[2] but three years later, having been appointed Under-Secretary for India, he wrote: 'I should regard the concession by any Power of a port upon the Persian Gulf to Russia (that dear dream of so many a patriot from the Neva or the Volga) as a deliberate insult to Britain, as a wanton rupture of the status quo,

---

[1] K. W. B. Middleton observes that 'As a maritime Power, with comparatively weak land-forces, Britain has always been particularly nervous about the frontier of her Indian possessions, by far the most valuable and important part of her subject empire. She has therefore tended to magnify out of proportion to reality any development which could conceivably constitute a threat to Indian security.' (*Britain and Russia* (1947), 11).

[2] cf. W. E. Wheeler, in *Journal of the Royal Central Asian Society*, XXI (1934), 596 f.

and as an international provocation to war; and I should impeach the British minister who was guilty of acquiescing in such a surrender as a traitor to his country.' At the same time he applauded Britain's imposing on the Sultan of Oman the customary prohibition from ceding or leasing any concessions, and commented, 'We subsidize its ruler; we dictate its policy; we should tolerate no rival influence'. While the two Powers were locked in tense rivalry for obtaining preponderance in Persia through loans and commercial concessions, several countries were canvassing plans for a railway connecting the Levant with the Persian Gulf. The Russian Consul at Baghdad was scheming to obtain a Russian port and naval base on the Gulf; and it was learnt in 1898 that an Austro-Russian syndicate had applied to the Ottoman government for a concession for a railway from Syrian Tripoli to Kuwait, the finest natural harbour on the Persian Gulf. Britain had recently declined a request for protection from Sheikh Mubarak of Kuwait, who had come to the throne by murdering his pro-Turkish brother; but in these new circumstances Lord Curzon, now Viceroy of India, sent the Resident in the Persian Gulf to negotiate a secret agreement with the Sheikh, in which he too undertook to grant no leases or concessions without Britain's agreement. Curzon now summed up British policy in this region in a series of Olympian rhetorical questions. 'Are we prepared to surrender control of the Persian Gulf and divide that of the Indian Ocean? Are we prepared to make the construction of the Euphrates Valley Railroad or some kindred scheme an impossibility for England and an ultimate certainty for Russia? Is Baghdad to become a new Russian capital in the south? Lastly, are we content to see a naval station within a few day's sail of Karachi, and to contemplate a naval squadron battering Bombay?'

At this stage no one could have foreseen that within seven years of the beginning of the new century these longstanding and bitter conflicts of interest between Britain on the one hand, and Russia and France on the other, were destined to be temporarily liquidated in the powerful flux of a still more formidable challenge to all three Powers from the recently-born German Empire.

★　　　★　　　★

Until 1870 German interests in the Middle East had been confined to missionary activities in Syria and Palestine and to a small volume of trade, and her political influence had been negligible. But the War of 1870 naturally increased her prestige greatly with the Turks, ever respectful of military power and success. The influence of France in the Ottoman Empire was correspondingly reduced. The steps Britain had recently taken to render her influence in the Persian Gulf exclusive were resented by the Turks as an encroachment on their nebulous territorial sovereignty over the coasts of Arabia, which they were at this time attempting to make more real; and Britain's occupation of Cyprus in 1878 and Egypt in 1882 prejudiced her further in the eyes of the Turks. Consequently, when in 1872 the Ottoman government was seeking an adviser for the construction of the Balkan railway-system, it was a German engineer whom they called in; and in 1883 the German Ambassador had little difficulty in persuading Sultan Abdul Hamid II to invite the Kaiser to send a German military mission to Turkey.

By 1886 the Balkan railways were approaching completion, and the forward-looking Sultan was already contemplating their extension to his Asiatic provinces in order to strengthen his administrative control and assist their economic development. After overtures to British and American financiers had met with no response, a German syndicate undertook in 1888 the extension of the railway to Ankara, under the name of the Anatolian Railway Co. The new company was not exclusively German: more than a quarter of its first loan was subscribed in Britain, and the British chairman of the Ottoman Public Debt Administration became one of its directors. In 1889 Kaiser Wilhelm II, who had succeeded his father in the previous year at the age of twenty-nine, visited Istanbul, and the Deutsche Levant Linie was formed for steamship services between the North Sea and the Levant. This was followed by a German-Turkish trade agreement in 1890, and from this time onwards German consuls in the Ottoman Empire were assiduous in the help they gave to German commercial interests. The Kaiser's visit to Istanbul and this forward commercial policy were not favoured by the veteran Bismarck, who was primarily concerned in keeping France weak and isolated, and in avoiding any other foreign disagreements: he thus disliked the idea of commercial expansion in Asia Minor as likely to arouse the hostility of Russia, whom he had continually sought to draw into friendly association with Germany and Austria. But in 1890 the young Kaiser dismissed the old Chancellor and became himself the pilot of foreign

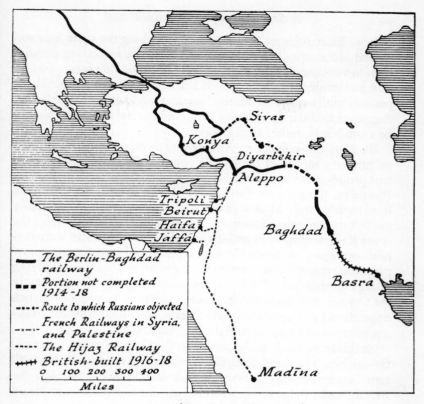

10. THE 'DRANG NACH OSTEN'

policy. Bismarck's intentness on not disturbing the status quo was indeed becoming obsolete: Germany's rapidly increasing population, in a country where the possibility of expanding food-production had evident limits, impelled her to a policy of industrial expansion with a quest for foreign markets; and her naval inferiority suggested that the direction of such commercial expansion should be continental, rather than oceanic.

By 1893 the railway to Ankara had been completed, and the preliminary survey of the further route to Baghdad begun. The first proposal, for a route via Sivas and Diyarbekir, was opposed by Russia on the grounds that it would lie too near her Caucasian frontier and might be used strategically against her; and eventually in 1898 the Anatolian Railway Co. applied for a concession for the route Konya-Aleppo-Mosul-Baghdad. Although there were certain competing interests, German commercial influence was now preponderant in Turkey beyond any doubt, and she was supplying a large proportion of Turkey's armament needs. Consequently the German company obtained the concession, buying out French opposition by an agreement which gave French railway and banking interests an equal share in the undertaking.

At this stage the British attitude to the German project was still favourable. The threat to Britain's position in the Middle East still came overwhelmingly from Russia and France. In 1892 the British Ambassador in Berlin had urged the Germans to develop a commercial interest in the Persian Gulf as a counterpoise to Russia in that region, and in 1898 the British reaction to the German railway-concession was favourable. Lord Salisbury was reported to have said, 'We welcome these concessions, for in this way Germany comes into line with our interests in the Persian Gulf'. *The Times* commented that if the development of the Turkish railways was not to be in British hands, the Germans were to be preferred to any other. The *Morning Post* remarked that the concession gave Germany a reason for resisting aggression in Asia Minor from the North. Imperialists of the standing of Cecil Rhodes and Joseph Chamberlain also gave the scheme their blessing. The Under-Secretary for Foreign Affairs alone sounded a warning note by stating that the government had every intention of maintaining the status quo in the Persian Gulf.

In 1900 the German technical mission which was planning the route the railway was to follow visited Kuwait and made a tempting offer to the Sheikh for a concession for a terminus and port. When he resisted their offer in accordance with his secret agreement with the Government of India a year before, the Germans induced the Ottoman Government, which the Sheikh nominally regarded as his suzerain, to send an expedition to assert its authority over him; but the presence of a British gunboat at the head of the Gulf caused them to desist. In other parts of the Gulf German traders were beginning to find the British 'exclusive agreements' an obstacle to their enterprises.

In 1903 the Anatolian Railway Co. had carried its plans for the Baghdad Railway to the stage at which it required to raise additional capital for their execution, and invited British capitalists to participate on equal terms with the existing German and French interests. The Balfour government favoured the acceptance of the offer, but the Cabinet was not unanimous, remembering perhaps Curzon's dictum of 1892 that 'Baghdad must be included in the sphere of indisputable British supremacy'. The proposal was hotly attacked by the imperialist and big-business section of the press, which was concerned by the progress made by German commercial competition in capturing overseas markets from Britain, and resented the German support for the Boers in the South African War; moreover, German publicists had been tactless and provocative in discussing the opportunities which a war in the Middle East involving Britain would present for German expansion. Consequently the government declined the German offer, and the Foreign Secretary, Lord Lansdowne, redefined Britain's policy in the Persian Gulf: her aim was to promote and protect British trade without excluding the legitimate trade of other powers; the establishment of a naval base or fortified port in the Gulf by any other power would be a very grave menace, 'and we should certainly resist it with all the means at our disposal. I say that in no minatory spirit because, as far as I am aware, there are no proposals on foot for the establishment of a foreign naval base in the Gulf.'

The following year, 1904, saw the culmination in the Entente Cordiale of the negotiations into which the British and French governments had been impelled by their growing fear of the expansionist policy of their 'vigorous and talented competitor' Germany. In this emergency all the outstanding points at issue between Britain and France were settled. In particular, France at last acknowledged Britain's de facto position in Egypt, though she insisted to the end on her stating a time-limit for her occupation, and only yielded on Britain's undertaking not to alter the legal status quo.[1] In 1907 the Entente Cordiale was extended to include Russia, whose prestige and sense of security had been abased by her defeat in the Japanese War of 1904–5, and who was consequently more ready to compromise with her long-standing British rival. An Anglo-Russian Agreement was reached 'to obviate any cause of misunderstanding in Persian affairs' and to delimit the Russian and British spheres-of-interest in North and South Persia respectively, leaving a no-man's-land between them. The Russian government acknowledged that Afghanistan lay within the British sphere of influence, while Britain undertook not to encourage the Amir to take any action threatening Russia. The Russian government 'explicitly stated that it did not deny Britain's special interest' in the Persian Gulf. The Agreement has subsequently been severely criticized by political moralists as a cynical partitioning of Persia, 'absolute respect for whose independence and integrity' was declared to be the fundamental principle of the two Powers; but the fact is that Persia had ceased to be a Great Power since the time of Shah Abbas the Great, three hundred years before; she had become a minor piece in the game of Great-Power chess at the time of Napoleon; and had ceased to be effectively independent since Russia imposed on her the Treaty of Turkmanchai in 1828. In her weakness Persian politicians had been reduced to playing off Britain and Russia against one another. The Agreement did at least have the effect of temporarily reducing the tension of Anglo-Russian rivalry in Persia; and it consolidated Britain's position in South Persia, where British concessionaires at last struck oil at Masjid-i-Sulaiman in 1908, actually after the directors in London, disappointed by several years' efforts without results, had cabled orders for the work to be abandoned. In 1909 the Anglo-Iranian Oil Co. was formed with a capital of £2,000,000.

The 'Committee of Union and Progress' which made the Young Turk Revolution of 1908 aimed at substituting a liberal and constitutional government for the autocracy of Abdul Hamid, and so looked initially for support to liberal and constitutional Britain and France rather than to autocratic Germany. However, the enthusiasm for liberalism and modernization was short-lived,

[1] *Round Table*, December 1936, 111.

and was soon followed by a nationalist reaction of which the Armenian massacres of 1909 were a feature. While the British and French press denounced these atrocities, the Germans were silent. In the next year, after the Turks had applied to France and Britain for a loan without success, they eventually obtained it from Germany on conditions which, unlike those proposed by France, were 'consistent with the dignity of Turkey'.

Meanwhile, in 1907 the new Liberal government in Britain had announced that its objection to a railway to the Persian Gulf would be removed if the construction and operation of the section south of Baghdad were left to British capitalists. Negotiations were protracted over a period of six years, and eventually resulted in an agreement between Britain, Germany, and Turkey in 1913–14. Britain finally consented to the construction of the Baghdad Railway on terms which may be summarized as follows:

(1) Basra was to be the terminus. The existing status of Kuwait was confirmed. No harbour or railway-station was to be built on the Persian Gulf, and Germany was not to support the effort of any other Power to this end.

(2) Britain was to have two directors on the board of the Baghdad Railway Co.

(3) An Ottoman River Navigation Co. with exclusive rights on the rivers of Iraq, and an Ottoman Ports Co. to build and administer ports and termini at Baghdad and Basra, were to be formed on British initiative, generous shares being allotted to the Turkish government and the Baghdad Railway Co.

(4) The Germans recognized the exclusive right of the Anglo-Iranian Oil Co. to prospect for and extract oil in South Persia and the vilayet of Basra. The oil-exploitation of the vilayets of Baghdad and Mosul was to be entrusted exclusively to a Turkish Petroleum Co., in which British interests were to hold three-quarters, and German interests one-quarter, of the shares.

It seemed, therefore, as if a compromise over this tangled question had at last been reached, and Britain's jealously-guarded control over the Persian Gulf preserved in its essentials. But it has been rightly said that Germany's interest in the Railway, like Britain's interest in the Persian Gulf, was now as much imperial as economic. The 'Drang nach Osten' had become a principal aspiration of German imperialists, while on the other hand their Social-Democrats warned against the Railway as the 'first great triumph of

German capitalist-imperialism' and likely to embitter relations with Britain. A Turkish liberal Minister of Finance had said, 'When you entered the board-room of the Baghdad Railway Co., you breathed the atmosphere of the Minister's office in the Wilhelmstrasse'. Germany had made great efforts to gain influence in Persia also, exploiting the extreme Persian dislike of the Anglo-Russian Agreement of 1907. Her Ministers 'fished assiduously in the troubled waters of Tehran'; there was a steady increase in German imports; and a new college at Tehran received a handsome subsidy from the German government and was staffed with German teachers. The energetic and resourceful German Consul at Bushire, Wassmuss, recruited a strong pro-German faction among the tribesmen of Fars province. The officers of the Persian gendarmerie, and the Swedish officers who had been training them, became in effect German agents. So successful was this German penetration of the British and neutral zones of Persia that, following the outbreak of the First World War, by the end of 1915 German influence was predominant there, except for the Gulf ports. The Allied colonies had to be withdrawn, and seven branches of the British-controlled Imperial Bank of Persia fell into enemy hands. The German Meissner Pasha had undertaken for Abdul Hamid the building of the Hijaz Railway which, besides its ostensible purpose of taking Muslim pilgrims to the Holy Cities, had the strategic advantage of affording the rapid movement of Turkish troops to Western Arabia without passing through the Suez Canal. In Egypt the Germans were at some pains to establish friendly relations with the growing Nationalist party.[1]

Britain likewise had not been slow to strengthen her position in the Middle East. Already in January 1912 a special committee set up by the Government of India had proposed the occupation of Basra in the event of war. In 1913 the Admiralty, having decided to convert the Navy to the use of oil-fuel, bought a controlling interest in the Anglo-Iranian Oil Co., which had by now sunk two hundred wells and completed the pipeline from its fields to the Abadan refinery. The Sheikh of Muhammara, Arab by race but a Persian subject, who ruled the Abadan district, was assured of British support in maintaining his local authority against the Sultan and the Shah alike. In anticipation that oil might be found in Bahrain, its Sheikh had been induced in 1911 to undertake to

[1] Sir Ronald Storrs, *Orientations*, definitive ed. (1943), 120 ff.

grant no concessions without the agreement of the Government of India.

Meanwhile in Europe the naval and military armament-race had gone on inexorably gathering momentum, like a huge fly-wheel which those who had set it in motion were apparently powerless to stop. Turkey was drawn irretrievably into the German orbit by her nationalist leaders. After all, the privileged positions of Britain and France in Lower Iraq and Syria respectively were encroachments on full Turkish sovereignty; Russia, ever anxious to expand at the expense of Turkey, was constantly encouraging the Balkan, Armenian, and Kurdish nationalists; whereas Germany was the one Power whose interest it was to favour a stronger Turkey. In October 1913, two months after the French General Joffre had gone to Petersburg to re-organize the Russian army, the German General Liman von Sanders was chosen to re-organize the Turkish army, and introduced hundreds of German staff and regimental officers. When the Triple Entente Powers protested, the Turks pointed out that their navy was trained by British officers, their gendarmerie by French, and that the military connexion with Germany went back thirty years. In March 1914 plans were concerted between Germany and Turkey for the co-ordination of their railway-systems in the event of war; and following the murder of the Austrian Archduke Ferdinand, which precipitated the First World War, Turkey was formally admitted as a member of the Triple Alliance.

CHAPTER V

The Growth of Nationalism
(1800—1917)

AT THE BEGINNING of the nineteenth century Muslim civilization in the Middle East, once far in advance of anything that the Europe of the 'Dark Ages' could show, was but a ruin, picturesque when viewed superficially by the romantic traveller, but displaying all the marks of squalor and decay when approached more closely. Such innovations as had been effected by missionaries in the Levant, under the Amir Fakhr ud-Din in the early seventeenth century for example, were limited in their geographical scope and did not penetrate deeply into the lives of the people; the Muslim majority was practically untouched by them. Agriculture, the mainstay of the economy of the region, languished under a régime which taxed unmercifully and could not provide security against administrative extortion or the raids of the Bedouin. In the cities little public building had been done for three hundred years, and the imposing remains of the Mamluks or earlier dynasties were crumbling unheeded and unrepaired amid the encroaching congestion of ramshackle dwellings. Outside the decaying city-walls vast mounds of rubble and garbage accumulated for centuries, the haunt of lawless beggars and scavenging dogs, extended like veritable ranges of hills towering fifty feet or more above the natural ground-level, or invaded waste plots within the city itself. Water-supply, sanitation, the care of the sick, depended on such benefactions as had survived the slow ruin of the centuries or were left for the individual to arrange for himself. Periodic famine and epidemic were regarded as a normal visitation of the wrath of Allah, not as inconveniences which might be prevented by human action. Government was rapacious, arbitrary, venal, slipshod; the life of the subject depended on the whim of the ruler, and might be lightly taken for the slightest fault.[1] Higher

[1] e.g. Lord Zetland, *Lord Cromer*, 161 f.; Clara Boyle, *A Servant of Empire*, 45 ff.

education was confined to the study of the theology and jurisprudence of Islam; elementary education, to the learning of the
Qur'an by heart; and only the exceptional individual could read a
book or write more than his own name. The establishment of
Islam had inhibited the development of political ideas. Travel was
slow and beyond the means of the majority: Damascus was three
weeks' journey by caravan from either Baghdad or Cairo; such
rare travel-books as existed were accessible only to a few; and the
average man's experience and imagination were therefore confined to his immediate environment. Consequently the idea of
nationality was unknown; all were subjects of the Padishah, but no
one thought of himself as belonging to a Syrian or an Iraqi, still less
an Arab nation. Instead men were distinguished by their *millet*, or
by the town of their origin: as Sunni Muslim, Orthodox, Jew,
Druze, Armenian, or Shi'i; as Baghdadi, Halabi (Aleppine),
Shami (Damascene), or Misri (Cairene).

The dominating purpose of Mohammed Ali was to secure his
personal position in Egypt, by making the country a formidable
military and naval power, and to this end he consistently devoted
one-half of the revenues of the state. The well-being of the people,
to whom he was foreign, did not interest him in the slightest; but
to provide the necessary finances for his military schemes, he had to
raise the agricultural productivity of Egypt from the miserable
state to which nearly five hundred years of misrule had reduced it,
and to create industries which did not yet exist. By 1814 he had
bought out or expropriated almost all the landowners of the
Mamluk period, vesting the ownership in his own government,
i.e. in himself, but leaving the use and cultivation of the lands in the
hands of the existing tenants. From about 1820 he began the construction of numerous canals in the Delta for the purpose of cultivating that district by perennial irrigation in place of the artificial
basins into which the annual Nile flood was admitted to fertilize
the ground for the main winter crop. By superseding the age-old
basin-irrigation by this new system, incomplete and imperfect
though it was in its beginnings, two or three crops could be grown
from a plot in one year, producing profitable yields of cotton,
indigo, flax, or rice as well as the basic winter grain-crop. Thus it
is estimated that between 1824 and 1840 the area under cultivation
was increased by about a quarter, in spite of the heavy demand on
man-power for military and industrial conscription. Agricultural

policy was closely centralized, as it had been under the Greek rulers of Egypt after the conquest of Alexander the Great. Mohammed Ali directed what crops should be grown, giving preference to those which were exportable at a good profit, especially cotton. Seeds were lent to the cultivators, and funds advanced to cover the cost of cultivation. A large staff of inspectors was employed to ensure that the Pasha's orders were faithfully carried out. Most classes of crops were declared government monopolies, compulsorily purchased by the government at a fixed price which was sometimes a half or less of their market-value. The goods were then either consumed for state needs, as supplies for the army or raw materials for the state factories, or they were sold abroad at a handsome profit. In 1836 it was estimated that 95 per cent. of Egypt's exports, and 40 per cent. of her imports, were for the government's account. In 1816 the existing manufactures had similarly been declared government monopolies. The government, at a considerable profit to itself, supplied the artisans with the raw materials it had purchased from the fellahin, bought back the finished articles at an imposed low price, and resold them at the highest prices possible. The Pasha established a number of new industries, mainly to supply goods for the public service or for export. They were conducted on the whole at a loss, on account of the high cost of imported machines and spare parts, the lack of suitable overseers and engineers, the apathy and discontent of the workers, dragged from their field and workshops to labour in 'dark satanic mills', the waste of raw material, the breakage of machinery, delays, confusion, even deliberate sabotage and obstruction in the working of the factories. A British observer found in 1838 that cotton cloth produced in Egypt cost 16 per cent. more than imported English cloth of the same quality. By 1840 the strain of the accumulated losses on these undertakings had become unbearable, and the ultimate failure of the industrial enterprise had become evident even to the Pasha. During the Second Syrian War many factories were closed to save expense, and thousands of the workpeople were conscripted into the army. Orders were given that all factories that could not show a profit on their operations were·to be closed down. Many of them were closed immediately, others dragged on for a few years. Their ruin was completed in 1842 when, as part of the settlement of the Syrian War, the British Government compelled the Pasha to accept the application to

Egypt of the Anglo-Ottoman Commercial Treaty of 1838, by which British merchants were given the right to enter any part of the Ottoman dominion and buy from the natives the products of the soil and of the industry of the country. A few years later all that remained of the vast industrial structure, which had cost millions to create, was a quantity of rusting machinery in old, deserted buildings, scattered throughout the country. The attempt to make Egypt an industrial country had failed.

'Its failure was perhaps inevitable. The attempt to impose upon a primitive agricultural and guild economy a totally new system of industrial production was bound to meet with very great obstacles.... The managers of the factories were for the most part salaried government officials, ignorant and unenthusiastic about the work they were called upon to do. The machines imported were still novelties and enormously expensive, while very few in Egypt had mastered the new machine technique.... The attempt to stimulate agricultural production was no more successful. The low prices which were paid to the farmers for their crops took away their incentive to work.... They had to be literally driven to the fields and obliged to work by threats and punishments. Thousands of them deserted their farms. From time to time the fugitives were rounded up, in the towns and marshes in which they had taken refuge, and were sent back to the villages.... The monopoly system did not help in the production of new wealth. Its only effect was to keep down the standard of living of the farmers, and to divert into the hands of the government the additional wealth created by higher prices and increased production.'[1]

The experience of our own day has shown how difficult it is to bring about the rapid modernization and industrialization of an undeveloped agricultural economy by imposing a bureaucratic collectivized régime. The resistance which the Soviet government has encountered in this respect is well-known; and Mohammed Ali, despite his great energy and iron determination, lacked a popular ideological appeal which could evoke the co-operation of thousands of assistants. He was dealing, not merely with a backward peasantry, but with one exceptionally apathetic by reason of

---

[1] Crouchley, op. cit., 74 f., 103 f. The similarity to the labour-situation created by the bureaucratic control attempted by the Greek and Roman rulers of Egypt is very striking.

its isolation in the closed environment of the Nile Valley[1] and its debilitation by endemic disease; and he had no instrument for the execution of his plans comparable for energy, devotion, training, powers of leadership, and ruthlessness towards opposition or incompetence, with the Communist party in the U.S.S.R.[2] Another instructive comparison is with the Westernization of the Japanese economy in the second half of the nineteenth century. Here again the initial advantages were all with the Japanese since, although their economic and social system was already being undermined by degenerative processes, Japan even in her isolation was a far more healthy organism than decayed and depopulated Egypt. The Emperor was an institution with divine attributes that could be used as a focus for the absolute loyalty and fanatical devotion of a people who had learnt by tradition to regard these as the supreme virtues of their race. The ruling-class, while enjoying prestige and self-confidence, was not rigidly separated from the rest of the population, but provided opportunities for men of talent to rise into its ranks. 'In every class there was a capacity for co-operation and organized effort which was in part the product of a long experience of group action in the family, the clan, and the guild.'[3]

In the light of these comparisons, so unfavourable to the exhausted condition of Egypt at the accession of Mohammed Ali, the cause for surprise is not that he failed to achieve his plans for material re-organization, but that he was able to effect what must have seemed impossible fifty years before, the lifting of Egypt out of the morass in which centuries of misrule were smothering her. He permanently increased the agricultural productivity of the country by the introduction of perennial irrigation, though at the cost of thereby lowering the natural fertility of the soil, formerly enriched annually by the Nile mud but now requiring the addition of fertilizers. It is some index of the improved agricultural productivity that, after centuries in which the population of Egypt had declined to perhaps only one-third or one-quarter of its ancient maximum, it should, according to estimates, have increased by some 75 per cent. in one generation between 1821 and 1847, not-

---

[1] This factor is well brought out by D. G. Hogarth, *A Wandering Scholar in the Levant* (1896), 156 ff.

[2] This comparison has been independently developed by Dr. A. Bonné, in *Journal of the Middle East Society*, I, No. 3–4 (Jerusalem, 1947), 40 ff.

[3] G. C. Allen, *A Short Economic History of Modern Japan*, 156.

withstanding the drain of war and conscription. Mohammed Ali moreover introduced to some thousands of young Egyptians the elements of Western education and culture.[1] And, not least, he left his country free from debt.

★   ★   ★

During his nine years government of Syria and Lebanon (1831–40), Ibrahim Pasha followed his father's example in encouraging education with a military and technical intention. While government elementary and secondary schools were opened for Muslims in the principal towns, he provided for the Christian majority in the Lebanon, a community outstanding in the Middle East for its combination of intelligence with application and adaptability, by encouraging the establishment of foreign missions. The French Jesuits were allowed to return in 1831 and rapidly opened schools, finally founding their Université de St. Joseph at Beirut in 1875. The American Presbyterian Mission which had first arrived at Beirut in 1820 established a printing-press in that town in 1834.[2] By 1860 they had thirty-three schools with a thousand children, and in 1866 they founded the Syrian Protestant College, subsequently renamed the American University of Beirut. While the Jesuits' printing-press produced from 1853 onwards a series of scholarly works in French or Latin, the Americans devoted themselves to the production of school-texts *in Arabic*. Thus, while the French Catholics made a valuable contribution to the progress of Syrian education in general, the Americans played the greater part in the revival of Arabic as a literary language, after three centuries of neglect in favour of the official Turkish, and so unconsciously inspired the first Arab nationalist aspirations, in the propagation of which some of their students and locally-recruited teachers played a leading part. What began as cultural societies came to assume an air of political conspiracy in the sacred name of liberty from Ottoman oppression. About 1880 a secret society of twenty-two members, including Muslims and Druze but founded by young Christians educated at the Syrian Protestant College, displayed a

---

[1] The number of students who passed through the government schools has been estimated at 10–12,000 (J. Lugol, *Le Panarabisme* (Cairo, 1946), 166 f., quoting A. Sammarco).

[2] Two Christian monasteries in Lebanon had printing-presses from the early 18th century, contemporary with the establishment of the first press at Istanbul; but they had negligible effect on the general culture of the region.

series of placards in the cities of Syria, demanding in increasingly
violent language the adoption of Arabic as the official language,
the freedom of the press from censorship, self-government for
Syria in union with Lebanon, etc. About 1883, however, the young
conspirators became so nervous of the ubiquitous Ottoman secret
police that they closed down the society and destroyed their records, while several of the most active members found it prudent to
retire to the tolerance of Egypt under its new British rulers. George
Antonius, who alone records this first incident in the history of
Syrian nationalism, has been at some pains to demonstrate, by
eliciting after some fifty years the testimony of surviving partici-
pants or contemporary Arab observers, that the appeal of this
'enlightened elite' to Arab national sentiment had a widespread
effect;[1] but in spite of his argument that their secret activities could
not, in the nature of things, have been fully appraised by the British
consular agents then resident in Beirut, his patriotism seems to have
led him to exaggerate the influence of these pioneers, and the consuls' assessment of the movement as 'a damp squib which excited an
apathetic population only to a faint show of curiosity' is borne out
by the sequel. For the next twenty-five years Arab nationalist
activity was conducted in the main from the safe remoteness of
Cairo and Paris. In Syria, except for the temporary excitement
provoked by an agitator who was imprisoned in the 'nineties for
his outspoken denunciations of Ottoman tyranny, the movement
'lay prone as though in sleep, held down by Abdul Hamid's
tyranny, and drugged by the opiates of his pan-Islamic policy'.
The resourceful Sultan,[2] indeed, besides encouraging the revival
of Muslim sentiment by such measures as the construction of the
Hijaz Railway to Madina, had systematically bestowed benefactions on Arab learned institutions, had spent large sums on the
Muslim Holy Cities, had employed large numbers of Arabs in his
personal service, and had had an Arab battalion in his royal Guards.
In these ways, and through his far-reaching spy-system, the incipient growth of political thought among his Arab subjects was
diverted from a nationalist direction into the safer channel of
pan-Islam. A number of Christian Arabs, on the other hand, and a
few Muslim modernists, were seduced from their cultural tradition

---

[1] op. cit., 79 ff.
[2] He was still regarded by the townsmen of Iraq with 'very remarkable
veneration' as late as 1925 (Longrigg, op. cit., 312, n. 1).

by the European education provided by the French mission-schools and became 'Levantines', 'living in two worlds or more at once, without belonging to either; . . . no longer having a standard of values of their own, unable to create but able only to imitate; and so not even to imitate correctly, since that also needs a certain originality', in the penetrating diagnosis of Albert Hourani.[1]

✶   ✶   ✶

In Persia and Iraq the impact of Europe was much more lightly felt. While the coasts of the Levant and Egypt were directly exposed to the influences of Europe, they reached Tehran and Baghdad only after they had passed through the filters of Moscow, Bombay, or Istanbul, which greatly lessened their vitality and penetrating power. The influence of Christian missions was confined in the main to the small Christian minorities. More important was the impact of European commerce and techniques, the influence of European traders and mechanics, of travellers and archaeologists. In Persia the printing-press had reached Tabriz in 1812 and Tehran in 1823. Persian medical and other students were sent to England as early as 1810–15. In 1852 the Persian government granted a large subsidy to found and maintain the Dar al-Funun or House of Sciences, intended to educate a hundred boys, primarily as army-officers. The subjects taught included some sciences and French, English, and Russian; and there were European as well as Persian teachers. In 1855 the Persian Ministry of Education was set up, and three years later forty-two students were sent to Europe. However, during his long reign the policy of Nasir ud-Din Shah (1848–96) was to discourage his subjects from visiting Europe, and he did not as a rule allow the sons of notables to be educated abroad. Modernism had thus to come in trickles through the indirect and uncertain channels of mission-schools and hospitals, European military missions, consuls, bank and telegraph-company officials, and traders. In Baghdad schools and the first printing-press were established under Da'ud Pasha (1817–32), and by the middle of the century the efforts that were being made in Istanbul to modernize the Ottoman administration were beginning slowly to take effect even in this remote and neglected province. 'If government be judged by the freedom and

[1] *Syria and Lebanon*, 70 f.

happiness of its subjects, the new era showed no great advance on
the old: security was as low, justice as rare, exaction as cruel, policy
as foolish. In certain aspects indeed there was progress. . . .In-
creasingly officials appointed to high office had something of
modern education. There was greater specialization of function.
There were, in fact, the bones of reasonable government into
which the rare ability and goodwill of a governor might yet infuse
life.'[1] For example, the 'honest, vigorous, and liberal' Mohammed
Rashid Pasha, who governed for five years from 1853, re-opened a
score of disused irrigation-canals and founded a company for river-
navigation; and he was only the precursor of Midhat Pasha who
in three short years 1869–72 began to organize for the first time a
system of land-registration, in an attempt to put an end to tribal
lawlessness. He made plans for river-reclamation, river-naviga-
tion, industrialization, town improvements. He founded muni-
cipalities and administrative councils, enforced conscription, tried
but failed to suppress corruption, and in Baghdad started a newspaper, military factories, a hospital, an alms-house, an orphanage,
and numerous schools whereby the literacy-rate among townspeople rose from perhaps $\frac{1}{2}$ per cent. in 1850 to some 5 to 10 per
cent. by 1900. In this mass of projects completed or attempted 'it
is not difficult to find traces of hastiness, of economic considerations mistaken or ignored, of excessive confidence in the catchwords of progress, of a preference for the spectacular to the
judicious. . . . Yet his vision, his patriotic energy, his absolute
integrity performed greater works than his imperfect education
could mar', and as recently as twenty years ago his name was still
'constantly on the lips of townsmen and tribesmen, and always as
an enlightened innovator'.[2] Midhat applied in its entirety the
modernized Ottoman administrative system. 'A numerous class
of regular officials, the Effendis, stepped into the place of the old
arbitrary Pashas. Literate but not otherwise educated, backward
but decorous in social habit, uniform in a travesty of European
dress, exact and over-refined in the letter of officialdom, completely remote from a spirit of public service, identifying the body-
public with their own class, contemptuous of tribe and cultivator,
persistent speakers of Turkish among Arabs and, finally, almost
universally corrupt and venal—such were the public servants in

[1] Longrigg, op. cit., 281.
[2] Longrigg, op. cit., 298 ff.

whose sole hands lay the functions of government.'[1] The period is marked by 'the change of turban to fez, of flowing beard to the stubble of the half-shaven, of careless medieval rule to corrupt sophistication'.[2] In spite of the coming of steamship and telegraph and a rudimentary postal-system, the historian of modern Iraq concludes: 'The country passed from the nineteenth century little less wild and ignorant, as unfitted for self-government, and not less corrupt, than it had entered the sixteenth; nor had its standards of material life outstripped its standards of mind and character. Its resources lay untouched, however clearly indicated by the famous ages of the past and by the very face of the country. Government's essential duty of leading tribe and town together in the way of progress had scarcely been recognized, barely begun . . . ; in the yet clearer task of securing liberty and rights to the governed, however backward, it had failed more signally perhaps than any government of the time called civilized.'[3]

★   ★   ★

The discretion, the judgment, the basic financial soundness which, in spite of many errors and miscalculations in detail, characterized the work of Mohammed Ali, were lacking in his successors in Egypt. When Sa'id Pasha died in 1863 he left debts of about £12,000,000, composed of his obligations to the Suez Canal Co. for his 44 per cent. share of the capital issue, of public works of various kinds, personal loans, etc. But whereas the keynote of Sa'id's character had been easygoing indolence and complacency, his thirty-three-years-old successor Isma'il was a man of large and ambitious ideas which had been stimulated by his education in Paris. Moreover, he came to the throne at the height of the American Civil War, when the interruption of the supply of American cotton to Lancashire led to a tremendous boom in Egyptian cotton. Between 1861 and 1864 the export of cotton increased threefold and its value more than fourfold. Consequently Isma'il was led by prosperity into extravagant dreams of expanding and modernizing his country's economy. He began by taking exception to some of the more audacious terms of the Suez Canal Co.'s concession which De Lesseps had foisted upon his complacent pre-

[1] Longrigg, op. cit., 281 f.
[2] Longrigg, op. cit., 277.
[3] Longrigg, op. cit., 321 f.

decessor, and to indemnify the Company and meet other liabilities Isma'il raised in 1864 his first foreign loan, a matter of £5,700,000 from the 'British' banking-house of Frühling and Goschen.[1] In the years 1863–5 an outbreak of cattle-disease swept Egypt; in order to restore the herds and carry out a plan for extending the railways, Isma'il went to Frühling and Goschen again in 1866 for another loan of £3,000,000. Heavy expenditure on the army and public works—railways, telegraphs, canals, etc.—caused his budget for 1867 to be in deficit by some £4,000,000. He accordingly contracted with the 'British' bank of Oppenheim & Co. a new loan of £11,900,000, which was so discounted by the bank that he actually received only £7,200,000. The end of the American Civil War having been followed by a fall in the sale of Egyptian cotton, Isma'il had attempted to redress the economic situation by encouraging the planting and processing of sugar on a large scale. To finance this he went in 1870 to the firm of Bischoffsheim for a new loan of £7,000,000, which discounting reduced to about £5,000,000 in ready cash. He conceived an ambitious scheme for opening up the Sudan to modern influences and suppressing the slave-trade 'throughout Central Africa', an enterprise in which he was enthusiastically abetted by the British soldier Sir Samuel Baker, who promised him that he would place the Egyptian flag 'at least one degree south of the Equator'. The total cost of this, and other expeditions to extend Egyptian dominion along the Somali coast to Cape Guardafui and as far south as Kisimayu (from where he was warned off by the British government, on behalf of its protégé the Sultan of Zanzibar) is not known; but Baker's four-year expedition to the Equatorial Sudan cost about half-a-million. Baker himself received £10,000 a year and all expenses; he was accompanied by his wife and nephew; and his successor Gordon was amazed to discover the superb china, the Bohemian glass, fine cutlery, damask linen, and the best French wines which had alleviated the rigours of the expedition. With the lavish expense on such enterprises, on railways and irrigation-canals, the Suez Canal, on European-style schools, harbours, bridges, shipping, urban development, telegraphs, water-works, and lighthouses, on the Army, on presents to the Sultan and bakhshish to his ministers and courtiers, on personal display, pageantry, and self-indulgence, on

---

[1] Sa'id had already three times taken the insidiously tempting bait of foreign loans, but for smaller sums.

interest and sinking-fund payments on the loans which never amounted to less than 12 per cent. per annum on the principal, it is not surprising that, despite a great increase in the taxes levied on the fellahin, expenditure during Isma'il's reign amounted to nearly double the total revenue for the period. In 1873 the floating debt had risen to £23,000,000; and in order to gain temporary relief from this burden the Khedive[1] contracted with Oppenheim & Co. a new loan of £32,000,000, but at a disastrous discount: after discount, interest and commission had been deducted, he received less than £20,000,000 in hard cash. In order to execute his ambitious programme of public works, moreover, Isma'il had had recourse to large numbers of European contractors (by 1871 the foreign population had increased to about five and a half times its size in 1836), and many of these were unscrupulous adventurers who undertook concessions only in order to find some alleged breach-of-contract on the part of the Egyptian government and extract an exorbitant indemnity in the appropriate consular court to which the Capitulations gave them access. When the Mixed Courts were set up in 1873 to regulate foreign litigation, there was £40,000,000 in foreign claims outstanding against the government: one case is on record in which the courts awarded £1,000 to a claimant who had sued for £1,200,000. So accustomed was the Khedive to victimization by these sharks from Europe that he is reported to have remarked sarcastically in the presence of one of them, 'Shut that window; if this gentleman catches cold, it will cost me £10,000'. Lord Milner, a far from sympathetic critic of the extravagance of Isma'il, summed up the situation: 'The European concession-hunter and loan-monger, the Greek publican and pawnbroker, the Jewish and Syrian moneylender and land-grabber, who could always with ease obtain the protection of some European Power, battened on the Egyptian Treasury and the poor Egyptian cultivator to an almost incredible extent.'[2]

By the end of 1875 Ism'ail, whose debts now amounted to £91,000,000, was four millions short on his next payment of interest. In this plight he decided to dispose of his 44 per cent. share in the capital of the Suez Canal Co.; and, as is well known, Disraeli bought these shares for Britain for just under £4,000,000. Isma'il's

---

[1] He had purchased this impressive but empty Persian title from the Sultan in 1866.

[2] *England in Egypt*, thirteenth ed., 15; cf. also 176 ff.

rueful comment was, 'This is the best financial and political trans-action ever made even by a British government; but a very bad one for us'.[1] The end could not now be long delayed. By April 1876 the state was bankrupt; and an international Caisse de la Dette Publique was set up, with British and French commissioners to receive the Egyptian revenues, supervise the railways and the port of Alexandria, and maintain the payments due to the creditors. 'In short, the bailiffs were in', and the Dual Control, British and French, had begun to regulate the public life of Egypt.

Egyptian nationalists in our own day have claimed that Isma'il was an enlightened ruler actuated primarily by the desire to develop his country, and that it was his misfortune, due to inex-perience of the pitfalls in international finance, that submerged him and Egypt under the burden of debt.[2] Closer examination of his character, however, fails to exonerate him to this extent. He was the first of his dynasty to be superficially Europeanized in education and tastes. To instal in Egypt all the external evidences of European material civilization, regardless of the cost, was for him to be in the forefront of progress, to be hailed by the world as a truly illustrious prince. He was actuated by personal ambition and an inordinate love of display, rather than by prudent regard for the lasting improvement of his country's economy. Vast and costly development-schemes were embarked on after entirely inadequate study of their practicability. Intoxicated by the showers of gold which descended on him so frequently in the first ten glorious years of his reign, it was all one to the Khedive whether they were expended on public works or an agricultural scheme, the annexa-tion of some remote Equatorial province, or on a new palace and lavish entertainments; Milner doubted whether the portion of Isma'il's loans devoted to works of permanent utility, excluding the Suez Canal, equalled 10 per cent. of the amount of debt which he contracted; and meanwhile his agents drove and pillaged the peasantry without mercy.[3]

[1] In 1871 Gladstone had refused to discuss an offer to buy a share in the Canal Co., regarding it as purely a matter for private financiers, and unbefitting a government; but Disraeli with Levantine tuition grasped its imperial implica-tions, and immediately on coming to power in 1874 had sent Baron Lionel de Rothschild to Paris to try to re-open negotiations for a purchase.

[2] This is the case put forward by P. Crabites: *Ismail, the Maligned Khedive*, and by M. Rifaat Bey, op. cit., ch viii, 'Ismail the Magnificent'.

[3] Milner, op. cit., 179. For a summary of the impressions of an unofficial and sympathetic British resident in Egypt, cf. Gordon Waterfield, *Lucie Duff Gordon*, ch. XLIII.

The European penetration of Egypt in the previous fifty years and the inauguration of a system of education along formally European lines, had created a small class of young men with a modern outlook, the Effendis. These young men, who through their education had imbibed some of the liberal and nationalist ideas of contemporary Western Europe, were further stimulated by the agitation of the Saiyid Jamal ud-Din al-Afghani, a propagandist for the liberation of all Islam from European influence and exploitation, and its union under a strong Caliphate; expelled from Istanbul in 1871, he lived and taught in Cairo for eight years. Moreover, while Isma'il's public-works schemes had greatly improved Egypt's communications, production, and trade,[1] they had brought little profit to the masses who bore the main burden of the heavy taxation, which had risen by 1875 to five times its figure in 1861. Thus a strong undercurrent of popular discontent was added to the nationalists' criticism of Isma'il for his favouritism for Europeans, his ruinous financial policy, and the preference he showed for the Turco-Circassians, who survived from Mamluk times as the ruling-class over the native Egyptians. The inferior position of the native element in the army especially excited their indignation. The first nationalist newspapers appeared in 1877, and the slogan 'Egypt for the Egyptians' began to be heard.

In 1878 a ministry led by the Armenian Nubar Pasha, and containing a British Minister of Finance and a French Minister of Public Works, ordered, among other measures for reducing expenditure and so furnishing sums to meet Egypt's creditors, the drastic reduction in the size of the army to 11,000 men from a previous maximum of 80,000. Two thousand officers were placed on half-pay without settlement of their year-long arrears of pay. This naturally caused the greatest indignation, and in 1879 a riot of officers forced the resignation of the government. The British and French Controllers suspected that this demonstration had been instigated by Isma'il himself, who resented the Nubar government as an encroachment on his own authority. Accordingly the Powers obtained from the Sultan the deposition of Isma'il in favour of his

[1] The railway-system was increased to nearly five times its size at the beginning of Isma'il's reign, telegraphs to nearly ten times, and postal services were greatly improved. Egyptian exports rose by 50 per cent. The population of Egypt as a whole increased between 1848 and 1882 by 50 per cent., and that of Alexandria, which had already grown about ten-fold between the beginning of the century and its middle, jumped by another 60 per cent. between 1848 and 1882.

more amenable son Tawfiq, and the restoration with greater powers of the Dual Control, whose financial policy was based on the principle, financially orthodox but extremely callous when applied to the poverty-stricken masses of Egypt, that 'no sacrifice should be demanded from the creditors till every reasonable sacrifice had been made by the debtors', i.e. by the fellahin who paid the bulk of the taxes. The nationalist unrest grew, unchecked by the weak-willed new Khedive, until in September 1881 a military demonstration headed by Colonel Arabi, an Egyptian of fellah origin who had played a minor part in the officers' riot of 1879 and was now the accepted leader of the native-Egyptian junior officers against their Turco-Circassian seniors, forced the Khedive to accept a nationalist government with Arabi as Under-Secretary for War. Encouraged by this nationalist success, the Chamber of Notables, a body previously without political authority, had the temerity to claim the right to vote the Budget without heeding the representations of the foreign financial Controllers. Concerned at this intransigence the French government, zealous as always in its protection of the interests of the bond-holders who were mainly French, proposed to the British government a joint armed intervention in Egypt.

The British Liberal government showed itself reluctant to interfere so drastically in the affairs of a nominally sovereign state, but as the situation in Egypt showed no signs of improvement it finally accepted the French suggestion in January 1882. Before any action could be taken however, the French government fell on a domestic issue, and its successor proved singularly irresolute on the subject of Egypt. In February a full-blooded nationalist government came into power in Cairo with Arabi now Minister for War. He made plans to expand the army and place the effective political power in the hands of the native-Egyptian officers. The British and French governments, now thoroughly alarmed at the course of events, joined in despatching naval squadrons to Alexandria, and in sending a note to the Khedive demanding the dismissal of the nationalist government. At the same time the British government invited the Ottoman government to intervene, and was willing to refer the whole Egyptian question to an international conference composed of the ambassadors of the Great Powers at Istanbul; gestures which appear to rule out any idea of a pre-conceived British plan to annex Egypt. The dismissal of the nationalist government was followed by anti-foreign disorders, the worst of which occurred at Alexandria and caused the deaths of 57 Europeans and 140 Egyptians. Arabi began to strengthen the military defences of Alexandria, presumably to meet the threat of a landing from the British and French squadrons. On 5 July, the British government decided to demand the cessation of these military works at Alexandria, with the threat that the fleet would otherwise destroy them. The French government, however, declined to co-operate, and withdrew its ships the day before the British on 11 July, having had no reply to their ultimatum, destroyed Arabi's defences by a heavy bombardment. The commander of the British force disembarked at Alexandria, faced by the Egyptian army in prepared positions twelve miles away, resolved on an outflanking movement from the Suez Canal. The French government now proposed to concert with Britain action limited to safeguarding the neutrality of the Canal; but the Opposition overwhelmingly defeated the motion, arguing the impossibility of separating the Canal from the general Egyptian question. While the French chamber debated, British troops were landed at Port Said. They shattered the Egyptian army at Tell el-Kebir on 13 September and entered Cairo two days later. In the following month Britain informed France of her intention to withdraw from the Dual Control. In the following July a Khedivial decree abolished it altogether, and Evelyn Baring, later Lord Cromer, became for twenty-four years the de facto ruler of Egypt. The French historian Driault claimed that the abstention of France was due to 'her desire not to conflict with Egyptian national sentiment, which she had believed capable of more energetic resistance'. French public opinion had, however, made no objection to the systematic exploitation of the inexperience of Egypt's rulers to the profit largely of French investors in the previous twenty-eight years, nor to the pitiless spoliation of the Egyptian fellahin to meet the payment of usurous interest.[1] The abstention of France was due to her government's indecision, the besetting weakness of her political system under the Third Republic. But French public opinion has never forgiven Britain for taking action when she hung back, and for twenty-two years she bitterly obstructed every constructive British effort to restore and improve the economic condition of the Egyptian people.

[1] Lord Cromer, *Modern Egypt*, 28 ff.

With the trial and exile of Arabi the first Egyptian nationalist movement collapsed utterly.[1] It had originally been the genuine intention of the British government, with the concurrence of Baring, to withdraw from Egypt as soon as the authority of the Khedive had been restored. This is clearly demonstrated by telegrams exchanged between the Foreign Office and Baring as late as January 1884.[2] As late as 1887 the government negotiated with the Ottoman government for a withdrawal at the end of three years, provided that at that time the security of Egypt was not threatened either from within or without. This proposal was however brought to nothing, mainly (ironically enough) by the opposition of France to the conditions imposed. The principal factor behind the continued British occupation was the rising in 1881 of the Sudanese Muslims, under the religious leadership of the self-styled Mahdi Mohammed Ahmed of Dongola, against grievous Egyptian oppression and misrule, and their destruction of Egyptian armies under British command sent to repress them. It was felt that Britain could not allow this fanatic horde to overrun Egypt, as it might well have done in view of the collapse of authority there, and threaten Britain's imperial communications. The killing of General Gordon at Khartoum in 1885 let loose a surge of patriotic sentiment in Britain and finally made it impossible for the government to withdraw from Egypt.

The collapse of the nationalist movement gave Cromer some twenty years to re-organize the finances and promote the economic development of Egypt with the passive co-operation of the Egyptians, except for some opposition from the headstrong young Abbas II, who succeeded as Khedive in 1892, and his advisers, jealous of Cromer's power. The restoration of Egypt's solvency, the extension of the crop-area by nearly one-fifth in the 'nineties as a result of the completion of the Delta Barrage and the extension of perennial irrigation, and the abolition of the age-old institution of compulsory unpaid labour (the corvée), which thus gave the fellahin the first rudimentary rights of free men: these elements of progress, which form one of the finer chapters in the history of British imperialism, were possible only because of Cromer's

---

[1] The judgements of Egyptian writers on Arabi and his associates are apt to vary with the contemporary political climate. Since Egypt's military revolution of 1952, Arabi has been treated more sympathetically than he was during the reigns of the successors of the Khedive whom he had defied.

[2] Lord Zetland, *Lord Cromer*, 88 ff.

creation of an administrative machine which was summed up as consisting of 'British heads and Egyptian hands'. The Egyptian upper and middle classes were not yet capable of the necessary administrative efficiency and integrity to occupy positions of responsibility in so complicated a machine. The Khedive and the Prime Minister had continually to accept the 'advice' of the august and masterful British Agent and Consul-General. Each Egyptian minister had his British adviser, and each provincial governor his British inspector, who through their direct access to Cromer wielded the effective power of government. Hence the Turco-Egyptian upper-class resented the British encroachment on their freedom to manipulate the governance of their country to their own advantage, and the growing literate middle-class (the number of newspapers published in Egypt increased more than four-fold from 1892 to 1899) envied the British their control of the best positions in the administration,[1] and was humiliated by that chilly reserve which afflicts so many Englishmen in the presence of strangers and foreigners. These grievances were to some extent fanned by the French, for it was to France that progressive Egyptian fathers continued to send their sons to finish their education, and the Egyptian secondary-school system, such as it was, was still modelled on the French pattern. The necessity for keeping the capitulatory Powers acquiescent towards Britain's de facto position in Egypt by interfering as little as possible with the international status quo there prevented Cromer from entering into effective competition with the French virtual monopoly of higher education and cultural and political propaganda, even had the *laissez-faire* attitude towards education of successive British governments admitted such an idea. When Cromer did at length come to organize an educational system, it was for the utilitarian purpose of training Egyptian junior officials for the administration, and served no cultural or political end.[2]

Thus it was in anti-British circles in Paris that the apostle of the second phase of Egyptian nationalism, the consumptive young law-student Mustafa Kamil, was encouraged to make his first inflammatory speeches against the British occupation. On his return to Egypt about 1895 he formed the Nationalist Party, al-Hizb al-Watani, founded a newspaper, and set up a school for

[1] cf. the rather naive comments of M. Rifaat Bey, op. cit., 225 f., 234.
[2] cf. Lloyd, op. cit., Vol. I, ch. xi.

propagating his political creed among the young men. The Anglo-French Entente of 1904 was a setback for the Nationalists, since the French could no longer actively support Britain's enemies in Egypt. But the defeat by Asiatic Japan of Russia, the European Great Power that had encroached so extensively and so consistently on the Dar ul-Islam, encouraged them greatly; and they were fanned to fury in 1906 by the 'barbarity dictated by panic' with which the British-controlled administration, during Cromer's absence on leave, punished the villagers of Dinshawai for a murderous attack on British officers who had mistakenly shot their tame pigeons. In the following year Lord Cromer retired from his long proconsulship. He was not a man who sympathized with the pretensions of mediocrities nor, as he grew older, with the head-strongness of youth; and his final Annual Report did not spare the weaknesses of the Nationalist movement: 'It can be no matter for surprise that the educated youth should begin to clamour for a greater share than heretofore in the government and administration of their country. Nothing could be more ungenerous than to withhold a certain amount of sympathy for these very legitimate aspirations. Nothing, on the other hand, could be more unwise than to abstain, at this early period of the National movement, from pointing out to all who are willing to listen to reason the limits which, for the time being, must be assigned to those aspirations. . . . The programme of the National Party is quite incapable of realization at present, and it may well be doubted whether, in the form in which it is now conceived, it can ever be realized. . . . In any case I must wholly decline to take any part in furthering proposals, the adoption of which would in my opinion constitute a flagrant injustice, not only to the very large foreign interests involved, but also to those ten or twelve millions of Egyptians, to the advancement of whose moral and material welfare I have devoted the best years of my life.' While Cromer did not reject the idea of self-government as the ultimate goal of Egypt's political evolution, he had many doubts of Egyptian administrative capacity, and the 'very large foreign interests' he had in mind comprised not only the $2\frac{1}{2}$ per cent. of the population that was foreign, but the fact that 78 per cent. of the Egyptian public debt and joint-stock capital was in foreign hands. Hence his preference, underestimating the emotional forces which national sentiment generates, for 'a constitution which will enable all the dwellers in cosmopolitan Egypt, be they Muslim or Christian, European, Asiatic, or African, to be fused into one self-governing body'. He gave his encouragement to the newly-formed reformist party Hizb al-Umma, inspired by the distinguished theological reformer Sheikh Mohammed Abduh, probably the first great thinker that Eastern Islam had produced since al-Ghazzali; and he had recently approved the appointment of one of the most promising members of that party as Minister of Education: his name was Sa'd Zaghlul.

Cromer's successor Sir Eldon Gorst had served under him with considerable distinction; but he returned to Egypt in 1907 with 'strong, if not very precise instructions' to introduce political reforms. The British general-election landslide of 1906 had brought into power after twenty years in the political wilderness a Liberal government which contained a considerable proportion of humanist Radicals who regarded constitutional representative government as something of a panacea for the ills of the world. The kind of directive which Gorst received has been summarized as to 'relax British control and give the Egyptian government greater freedom of action in matters of policy and administration, even at the cost of less efficiency; to help the Egyptian people to learn for themselves the first lessons of self-government which some measure of responsibility, however slight, alone could teach them'.[1] It was, however, to be no programme of headlong surrender to the Nationalists, though it was represented as such by diehards among the official and unofficial British colony in Egypt. Gorst declared in his first Annual Report that 'until the people have made a great deal more progress in the direction of moral and intellectual development, the creation of representative institutions, as understood in England, would only cause more harm than good, and would give a complete setback to the present policy of administrative reform'. He accordingly sought to win the co-operation of the Khedive Abbas II, now a man of thirty-five, in the hope of moulding him into a constitutional monarch, who would provide stability at the apex for the pyramid of the Egyptian polity; and he planned to strengthen the base of the pyramid by a constructive extension of the very limited powers of the Provincial Councils. Thus, underpinned from below and held in place from

[1] Chirol, op. cit., 108.

9

above, there was a prospect that the central Legislature might grow in responsibility and wisdom.

It was not to be. The Young Turk Revolution of 1908 had forced the Sultan to restore the constitution which he had suspended in 1876; and in an access of emotional liberalism it had declared equal all the races of the Ottoman Empire. The sympathetic enthusiasm generated among the Egyptian Nationalists was great, and found expression in violent and unrestrained agitation. The campaign reached its climax in 1910 in the murder of the Coptic[1] Prime Minister Butros Ghali, who had given the Nationalists some reason on three occasions in his career to regard him as a Quisling of the British. His murderer was characteristic of the type that commits such political crimes: a physically weak, bankrupt young chemist of fair education, moody and introspective.

In 1911 Sir Eldon Gorst retired, fatally stricken with cancer and disappointed by the failure of his experiment in the gradual introduction of representative institutions. He stated in his last Annual Report: 'We have to make the Egyptians understand that the British government do not intend to allow themselves to be hustled into going further or faster in the direction of self-government than they consider to be in the interests of the Egyptian people as a whole. Institutions really representative of the people are obviously impossible in a country in which only 6 per cent. of the population can read and write.' A critic might have asked why Britain persisted in imposing her rule on this people whose vocal elements were so ungrateful. The fact was, of course, that since the German Drang nach Osten had become a serious factor in her Middle East policy, the control of the Suez Canal was more than ever vital to her imperial communications; and in addition, her prestige and a large sum of British capital were now committed in Egypt. But it was not the British way to admit openly these material *arcana imperii*. Instead, the *Spectator* could write, 'It would be an inhuman devolution of our duty in the world to sacrifice the *poor* Egyptians, to allow them to become once more the prey of extortioners and bullies', and *The Times* could declare with less than its customary objectivity,

---

[1] There had never been an Egyptian-Muslim Prime Minister since the British occupation in 1882: one was Armenian, one a Turkish Jew, two Turkish Muslims, and now the Copt Butros Ghali.

'The real object (of the Nationalists) is a return to the old system of class-privilege, oppression, and corruption'.[1]

In choosing a successor to Sir Eldon Gorst the British government made one of those sharp reversals of policy which are not uncommon when a previous policy has proved unsuccessful. After consulting Lord Cromer, whose scepticism of the Egyptian capacity for self-government had hardened in view of the events which had followed his retirement, it appointed that formidable soldier Lord Kitchener, who regarded Western political institutions as an unqualified danger to Oriental peoples. 'Party spirit', he once said, 'is to them like strong drink to uncivilized African natives. . . . The future development of the vast mass of the inhabitants depends upon improved conditions of agriculture which, with educational progress, are the more essential steps towards the material and moral advance of the people.' He declared in his Annual Report for 1912 his strong disapproval of any encouragement of the 'so-called political classes', and in his Organic Law of 1913 he sought to re-organize the existing legislative bodies so as to secure adequate representation for the agricultural population: 'Noisy extremists and outside political influences must be eliminated if the Assembly is really to represent the hardworking, unheard masses of the people.' At the same time the administration provided additional irrigation-water for agriculture by raising the height of the Aswan Dam, and sought to protect the small proprietor from the seizure of his holding for debt through the Five Feddan Law. The prestige attaching to Kitchener's past career, and the strength of his personality did restore a measure of political tranquillity, and his vigorously prosecuted agricultural policy engendered prosperity and confidence. Nevertheless the Legislative Assembly, as elected after the passing of the new Organic Law, continued its factious obstruction. A clash between the administration and Zaghlul who, after losing his ministerial office as a result of his incurring the enmity of the Khedive, had become leader of the Nationalist opposition with a solid group of followers, was averted only by the outbreak of the First World War. Moreover, the administration had deteriorated in quality owing to Kitchener's

[1] J. Alexander, *The Truth About Egypt* (1911), 209, 92; this work is an excellent example of contemporary 'Egyptophobia'. As late as 1934 Lord Lloyd could write, 'From 1889 to 1922 our *foremost concern* had been to secure the humane and stable administration of the affairs of the Egyptian masses.' (*Egypt since Cromer*, II, 354; the italics are mine.)

high-handed methods, unwillingness to accept advice, and personal prejudices. Some valuable British servants of the Egyptian government had resigned in consequence, and had been replaced by men with poorer qualifications. Thus, while the number of British officials had rapidly increased since Cromer's time, their standard had steadily deteriorated. It was said also that Kitchener's choice of Egyptian advisers and assistants was not always of the happiest.[1] A contemporary appreciation clearly saw the dangers which lay below the surface: 'The superficial quiet is that of suppressed discontent—a sullen, hopeless mistrust towards the government of occupation. The government has not yet succeeded in endearing, or even recommending, itself to the Egyptian people, but is on the contrary an object of suspicion, an occasion of enmity. Nationalist feeling is very strong in spite of determined attempts to stamp out all freedom of political opinion. The wholesale muzzling of the press has not only reduced the Muslim majority to a condition of internal ferment, but has seriously alienated the hitherto loyal Copts.'[2] However, the entry of the Ottoman Empire into the War was followed by the declaration of martial law in Egypt, and the whole political question was suspended, and discontent driven still further underground, to fester until the end of the world conflict.

*   *   *

Meanwhile, although Arabs were not strongly represented in the Young Turk Committee of Union and Progress, the nationalists of Syria had been greatly encouraged by the Turkish Revolution, and in September 1908 they formed at Istanbul the Arab-Ottoman Brotherhood, al-Ikha al-'Arabi al-'Uthmani, whose objects were to unite all the races of the Empire in loyalty to the Sultan, to protect the new liberal constitution, to promote the well-being of the Arab provinces on a footing of real equality, etc. However, following an attempted counter-revolution promoted by Abdul Hamid in 1909, the Young Turks introduced new security measures, one of which was the prohibition of all societies founded by non-Turkish groups. The Ikha was shut down, and the Arab Nationalists were driven underground to continue their

[1] Amin Yusuf, *Independent Egypt*, 53.
[2] *Asiatic Review* (April, 1914), quoted by Lothrop Stoddard, *The New World of Islam*, 154 f.

political activities in secret. The first of their secret societies, the Qahtaniya, was dissolved after one year for fear that it had been betrayed to the Turks. In Paris seven Muslim students, who included Jamil Mardam (later Prime Minister of Syria) and Awni 'Abdul Hadi (now a Palestine Arab 'elder statesman'), founded the Young Arab Association, al-Jam'iya al-'Arabiya al-Fatat, with the object of securing Arab independence from Turkish or any other foreign rule. The society grew and in 1913 organized in Paris a six-day congress attended by twenty-four delegates, eleven of them Christians, drawn mainly from Syria and Iraq (the Iraqi delegates included Tawfiq as-Suwaidi, a subsequent Prime Minister of Iraq). The congress expressed a general desire to remain within the Ottoman Empire, provided that home-rule could be secured, and stressed the importance of preventing European Powers from meddling in the question. In the same year al-Fatat moved its headquarters to Syria. By this time its membership had risen to over 2,000, mainly Muslim, and included Shukri al-Quwwatli and Faris al-Khuri (who became respectively the first President of a genuinely independent Syria, and her first representative on the Security Council).

Nor was Iraq without its local nationalist stirrings. A Patriotic Society, founded at Baghdad to expel the Turks and establish an autonomous government, numbered among its members more than a hundred army-officers and many local notables; among those who came to the unfavourable notice of the Turkish authorities were Hamdi al-Pachaji (who was Prime Minister of Iraq early in 1946). In March 1913 a conference of Arab notables of Lower Iraq and neighbouring territories was held at Muhammara, in Persian territory, to work for the independence of Iraq and Turkish Arabia. In November the Iraqi nationalists made overtures to the young Amir Abdul Aziz ibn Sa'ud, who had by now made himself master of Najd with an outlet on the Persian Gulf. He expressed his sympathy for their cause, but could at present do no more, neutralized as he was strategically by his ancestral enemy, the pro-Turkish Amir of the Jebel Shammar to the north. The Turks were partly aware of this growth of nationalist sentiment, and attempted to disrupt both the Syrian and the Iraqi movements by offers of high political positions to some of their leading figures; but though some few were seduced in this way, the Turks were not prepared to offer any such concessions in the direction of local autonomy as would disarm the politically-ambitious Arab notables who were as yet the sole exponents of nationalism.

Meanwhile Aziz Ali al-Misri, a young Arab officer who had distinguished himself in the Ottoman service, but who had resigned his commission feeling that his services had been unworthily rewarded by the Young Turks, founded early in 1914 as a substitute for the defunct Qahtaniya a society called al-'Ahd, the 'Solemn League and Covenant'. It consisted almost entirely of Arab army-officers and consequently contained a preponderance of Iraqis, since they were the most numerous regional group of Arabs in the Ottoman Army. Branches of the society were founded at Baghdad and Mosul, and it is said to have recruited 4,000 members throughout the Empire. It became to the Arab army-officer what al-Fatat was to the civilian upper-class intellectual; but neither society knew as yet of the existence of the other, and contact between them was not established till early in 1915. In January 1914 the Young Turks had Aziz al-Misri arrested in Istanbul on charges of trying to set up an Arab kingdom in North Africa, of receiving bribes from the Italians during the Tripolitanian War of 1911, etc. He received a death-sentence, but was reprieved and finally released only on the intervention of the British Ambassador, as a result of representations from Lord Kitchener in Egypt.

An index of the spread of intellectual, and consequently of political, interest in the Arab world at this time is provided by the great increase in the numbers of newspapers published between 1904 and 1914. They rose in Lebanon from twenty-nine to 168, in Syria from three to eighty-seven, in Palestine from one to thirty-one, in Iraq from two to seventy, in the Hijaz from none to six, a ten-fold expansion over the entire area. In addition, nationalist newspapers published by Arab emigrés abroad were smuggled in through the foreign post-offices which existed under the Capitulations. The nationalist movement was, however, still confined to a very small group of army-officers and upper-class intellectuals, and touched the masses hardly at all; and behind the façade of the secret societies one may without prejudice infer the interplay of 'personal rivalries, religious differences, and sectional animosities, arising out of the essential individuality of the Arab character.'[1] Their disunity was of course aggravated by the lack of liaison occasioned by the slowness of communications. Of the capitals of states and the chief

[1] Ireland, op. cit., 237.

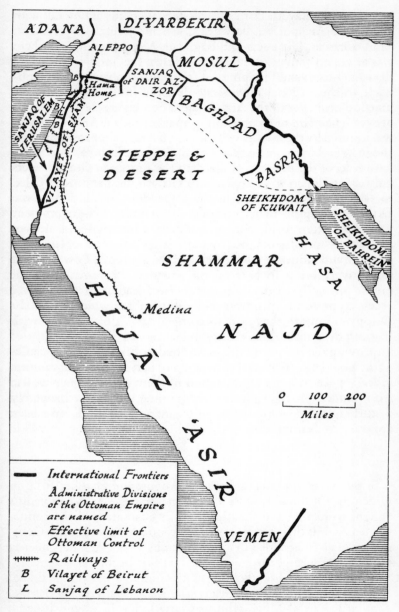

II. ARAB ASIA, 1914

towns of the vilayets, Damascus alone was connected by rail with Beirut and Aleppo; but between Cairo and Jerusalem, Jerusalem and Damascus, Damascus and Baghdad, Aleppo and Mosul, there was as yet no conveyance more rapid than the horse-carriage and the camel-caravan. This physical factor was, however, less an obstacle to the national movement than the immoderate and unpractical character of the Arab imagination was in the long run to prove. Their aim of reconstituting an independent Arab kingdom was inspired by the memory of the far-off Arab caliphate of history, and in its ambitious and unpractical flights bore little relation to the hard facts of the present. Regarding the European Great Powers only as interlopers to be kept at arm's length, the nationalists failed to realize to what extent, in the impending dissolution of the Ottoman Empire, their prospects of attaining self-government would be determined, not by grandiose aspirations and utopian and wordy manifestoes, but by the relative amounts of material pressure and influence which they and the interested Powers could respectively bring to bear on the situation. National freedom meant primarily to them, as members of leading Arab families, access to positions of power and authority for which under the Ottoman Empire they had to compete at a disadvantage with Turkish aspirants. There is no evidence that the desirability of improving the economic and social conditions of the poorer classes of the population played at this stage any part in their programme; indeed, since so large a proportion of them derived their wealth from landed property, such a programme would, by inevitably disturbing the present relation of tenant and landlord, have been contrary to their interests.

★   ★   ★

In the uncertain interval between August and October 1914, in which the Ottoman Empire was still neutral, the Arab nationalists sought to exploit the situation to win guarantees of their independence, but their tactics remained cautious. The Higher Committee of al-Fatat added to a resolution in favour of independence the following reservation, 'In the event of European designs appearing to materialize, the society is bound to work on the side of Turkey in order *to resist foreign penetration of whatever kind or form.*' Similarly Aziz al-Misri, who was now living in Egypt, issued a warning to the leading members of al-'Ahd not to be tempted into hostile action against the Ottoman Empire, as her entry into the war would expose the Arab provinces to European conquest; they were to stand by Turkey until effective guarantees against European designs were obtained. These nationalist suspicions of European intentions are important in the light of the conflict with Britain and France that was to develop after the War.

Meanwhile, Kitchener and his Oriental Secretary Ronald Storrs had been in correspondence since February 1914 with the Sharif Husain of Mecca, who ruled the Muslim Holy Cities on medieval theocratic lines and heartily disliked the efforts of his Ottoman suzerain to centralize provincial administration and thus subordinate him to the Turkish wali appointed from Istanbul. This threat to his hereditary authority had become acute with the advent of the Young Turks, and had been held off only by Husain's skill in tortuous and non-committal diplomacy. He had, however, found it prudent to seek the support of the British in Egypt, though his sons Abdullah and Faisal were anxious not to commit themselves to the 'Franks' and make an open breach with the Turks prematurely. The British negotiators were similarly cautious as long as Turkey remained neutral, but in October 1914 they did commit themselves in general terms to 'the emancipation of the Arabs' and 'an Arab nation' in return for Arab support against Turkey. At the same time Storrs and Gilbert Clayton of the military Intelligence approached Aziz al-Misri and others concerning the possibility of starting an Arab revolt; but these nationalists insisted as an indispensable preliminary on guarantees of Arab independence which the British spokesmen were not empowered to give. In January 1915 a member of the prominent Bakri family of Damascus, travelling to Mecca on Turkish official business, took with him a message from al-Fatat to the Sharif, asking him to concert measures with them for an Arab rising. The Sharif accordingly sent his son Faisal to Istanbul, ostensibly on official business, but really to sound the disposition of both the Ottoman authorities and the Syrian nationalists. On his northward journey he visited the Bakris, met members of both al-Fatat and al-'Ahd, was admitted to both societies, and informed them of the Sharif's parleys with the British. On his return to Damascus in May he found that in the meantime the two secret societies had prepared a joint Protocol requiring, as a condition of an Arab revolt against the Ottoman

Empire, that Britain should recognize an independent Arab kingdom comprising Arabia (except Aden), Palestine, Syria and Iraq.

In July, after Britain had announced her intention of recognizing an independent Arab state in the Arabian Peninsula, the Sharif sent to Sir Henry McMahon, the British High Commissioner in Egypt, a note which repeated the requirements of the Damascus Protocol brought back by Faisal. The British Arab Bureau in Cairo had still only vague knowledge of the existence of the two secret societies, and the notion consequently became established in British minds that the Sharif's demands for a Greater Arab Kingdom were solely the product of his own personal ambition, whereas in fact they faithfully represented the views of the nationalist movement, (except that its Syrian exponents did not necessarily regard Husain as a suitable King of the whole Arab world). Husain's note inaugurated the famous Husain-McMahon Correspondence, the interchange of which continued till January 1916. In the course of it the British negotiators made reservations on behalf of French interests in those parts of the Levant 'west of the districts of Damascus, Homs, Hama, and Aleppo', as not being wholly Arab; another reservation was made for British interests in Lower Iraq. The Sharif, who insisted that he was waiting only for an opportunity to revolt ,suggested that the solution of both these problems should be left till the end of the War. The British agreed, but warned him that 'when victory is attained, the friendship of Britain and France will be stronger and closer than ever'.

Meanwhile the policy of the Turkish governor and commander-in-chief under martial law in Syria, Jamal Pasha, had hardened against the Arabs since the failure of the first Turco-German attack on the Suez Canal in February 1915. Before that he had seized French consular documents incriminating various Syrian and Palestinian personalities with treasonable conspiracy with France before the War: the French Consul-General Picot had failed to destroy these highly secret documents,[1] but had left them in the charge of the American Consul, who innocently supposed that the Turkish police would respect the inviolability of the consular seals. During 1915 and the early part of 1916 Jamal Pasha held a series of treason trials: thirty-four nationalists, of whom twenty-seven were Muslim, were executed and hundreds of prominent

---

[1] Picot's neglect of an elementary responsibility towards those who had confided in him has never been satisfactorily explained.

persons deported to remote parts of Anatolia. In the spring of 1916 the Turkish High Command despatched a picked force of brigade strength with German staff-officers attached to reinforce their troops in the Yemen, which had driven back the small British garrison in the Aden Protectorate almost to the narrow confines of Aden Colony itself. This Turkish force travelling south by the Hijaz Railway arrived at Madina in May 1916. Its arrival greatly alarmed the Sharif, who feared that his correspondence with the British might have become known to the Turks, and that the force had been sent to deal with him. In addition, the recent news from Syria of the last and largest crop of political executions had finally convinced the sceptical Faisal that nothing was to be gained by further procrastination and haggling with both sides. The Arab Revolt was accordingly begun on 5 June 1916. Lord Wavell has commented, 'Its value to the British commander was great, since it diverted considerable Turkish reinforcements and supplies to the Hijaz, and protected the right flank of the British armies in their advance through Palestine. Further, it put an end to German propaganda in south-western Arabia and removed any danger of the establishment of a German submarine base on the Red Sea. These were important services, and worth the subsidies in gold and munitions expended on the Arab forces.'[1]   That the Revolt did not succeed in raising the civil populations of the Arab provinces is partly due in Syria to the effectiveness of the Turkish repression, and in Iraq to the unsympathetic attitude of the Indian Army authorities, who withheld or minimized the news of the progress of the Revolt in order not to encourage ideas of independence in the local Arab population. The Government of India, aiming at an outright British annexation of Lower Iraq, regarded the Cairo Arab Bureau policy of encouraging Arab independence as visionary, and its support of an Arab rising against the Ottoman Sultan-Caliph[2] as liable to cause unrest among the ninety million Muslims of India, whose sentimental attachment to the Caliphate was magnified by their immunity from the realities of Ottoman rule. The Viceroy of India actually described the Arab Revolt as 'a displeasing surprise whose collapse would be far less prejudicial to us

[1] *The Palestine Compaign*, 56.
[2] Later Ottoman sultans, and especially Abdul Hamid II with his pan-Islamic policy, had elaborated a fiction that the medieval Caliphate had passed from the last Abbasid to them in 1517. cf. T. W. Arnold, *The Caliphate*, ch. XIV.

than would our military intervention in support of it'. Sir Ronald Storrs declared that the passive resistance of the civil population of Syria and Palestine to the Turks following the Revolt was worth almost nothing to the British forces; on the other hand, the German commander Liman von Sanders has recorded that after the successful Third Battle of Gaza 'the British advancing towards Jerusalem found themselves fighting in friendly country, while the Turks were faced with a decidedly hostile population'. We may, however, ask how far this was due to their enthusiasm for the Arab Revolt, and how much to a natural desire to be in on the winning side: Allenby now had a superiority in fighting strength over the enemy of more than two to one. But whatever the limitations of the value of the Arab Revolt as a military operation, its importance in stimulating the aspirations of politically-minded Arabs cannot be overstated, with effects that were to be immediately felt after the end of the War.

CHAPTER VI

The Clash of Political Interests (1918—39)

THE WAR OF 1914–18 was the first total war in modern times, in which the peoples of even the 'victorious' countries are left more or less exhausted, and disillusioned about the ideals which, they were given to believe, they went to war to defend. The reaction that followed was consequently all the more acute because it had not been anticipated by most political thinkers. In Britain the strong current of imperialist sentiment that had flowed towards the end of the nineteenth century had already been greatly reduced by the sordid motives and material setbacks of the South African War. The 'Great War' left in the public mind a strong disinclination for any foreign or imperial policy which would call for further efforts from the war-weary people; and there was thus everywhere support for a policy of 'appeasement', which was strong enough to affect the judgments of statesmen. Furthermore, the statesmen themselves had been overworked and over-driven during four years of deadly struggle. They had had to subordinate, even more than is normal, any long-term considerations of policy to the short-term aim of securing immediate tactical advantages over the enemy. They had been driven by force of circumstances into making a number of contradictory commitments—in the Middle East, for example, to the Arabs on the one hand, and to the French, the Zionists, and to British self-interest on the other. In addition, an important section of informed British opinion, which may be labelled 'liberal' in the wider, non-party sense, regarded self-government for all peoples as the ultimate ideal of imperial politics, however remote the attainment of that ideal might be.

The English people had fought for their independence of the Spaniard and the Pope, of royal absolutism, and of the French; they had looked with sympathy on the struggles for independence of the Greeks, the Italians, and the peoples of the Balkans; they had acquiesced in the British Dominions' gradual acquisition of the right to manage their own affairs; and many of them regarded the political aspirations of nationalist Indians or Egyptians as having greater moral force than the interests of Britain in those lands. Such idealists were only a minority; but for the reasons previously stated, the majority of the British people were reluctant to resort to any extreme measures to maintain the imperial status-quo unchanged. The nationalists of the Middle East and elsewhere were consequently able from 1918 onwards to obtain greater concessions by pressure and violence than reasoned argument would probably have achieved; and not being aware of the symptoms in the British public mind which favoured their own violent course, they attributed their success solely to that violence and were encouraged to continue in it.[1]

In the flush of their victorious power in the immediate post-war period Britain and France extended and intensified their interests in the Middle East at the expense of the nationalist movements which were rising there. Britain sought from 1919 to 1921 to make permanent her direct protectorate over Egypt, which had been proclaimed as a temporary expedient at the outbreak of war to replace the undefined proconsulship of Cromer.   British and French pre-war cultural and economic penetration of the Fertile Crescent crystallized into the imposition of their direct rule over the whole region, Palestine and Transjordan, Syria and Lebanon, Iraq. Nor was this imposition mitigated in fact by the invention of the Mandates system as much as might appear on the surface. The Mandates system was little more than a polite fiction created in order to satisfy President Wilson and the idealists who had inaugurated the League of Nations. Britain and France arrogated to themselves their mandates over the Middle East by the Treaty of San Remo in April 1920, and the League dutifully subscribed to their will. In June 1920 Lord Curzon, then Foreign Secretary, could tell the House of Lords, 'It is quite a mistake to suppose that under the Covenant of the League or any other instrument the gift of a mandate rests with the League of Nations. It rests with the Powers who have conquered the territories, which it then falls to them to distribute.' The Permanent Mandates Commission of the League could in theory recommend the withdrawal of a mandate from an offending Power, but this authority was never exercised.   It could, and sometimes did, animadvert critically on the conduct of a Mandatory; but it had no powers to inspect

[1] cf. A. J. Toynbee, *The Islamic World since the Peace Conference*, 11 f.

on the spot the conditions in a mandated territory. It failed to induce the French to make timely concessions to nationalism in Syria. It could not order the adoption, nor the reversal, of a policy unless it could be shown to be contrary to the original mandate; and in the special case of Palestine the Mandate, framed to give legal sanction to a political experiment whose components had received insufficient preliminary study, was found in the next twenty years to be incapable of sufficiently flexible interpretation to meet rapidly changing conditions.[1]

It was not surprising that the reaction of the growing nationalisms of the Middle East to this intensifying of foreign control, this virtual annexation by Britain and France, should be a violent one. Examined from this standpoint, the inter-war period falls into two unequal parts, with the dividing line between them varying by several years from one country to another. In the first period, the post-war settlement, the efforts of the nationalists to throw off the European imperialisms were violent, and they resorted in some countries to armed rebellion. In the second, or inter-war period proper, the agitation was more constitutional in character, though armed action still sometimes occurred. In Palestine, owing to the special local circumstances, the violence was spread over both periods, and was actually more intense in the later one; but even here there was a pause of seven years, from 1922 to 1929, which makes the division into two periods applicable here also. It is convenient in both periods to examine the subject country by country, since it was only toward the end of the second period that the co-ordination of nationalist activity between the various Arab countries, which was to culminate in 1944 in the creation of the Arab League, became of any significance.

A. The Post-War Settlement

In Egypt, while the imposition of martial law had ensured a respite from political agitation during the War, the exigencies of the campaign combined with a considerable measure of British

[1] After the 1929 Riots in Palestine, which were a direct result of the clash of the Zionist and Arab nationalisms, the Permanent Mandates Commission, ignoring the realities of the situation, commented that, had the Mandatory more vigorously carried out a constructive programme in the interest of the peaceful masses of the population, it 'would have enabled them to convince the fellahin more easily of the *undeniable material advantages* that Palestine has derived from the efforts of the Zionists'.

ignorance did much to aggravate the grievances of the Nationalists. The country was flooded with inexperienced British army
officers and civil officials who treated Egypt, now proclaimed a
British protectorate, almost as an occupied territory in which the
rights and wishes of the inhabitants counted for little. The shortage
of man-power and of transport for the Palestine campaign led to
the conscription of thousands of fellahin for the Labour Corps and
the Camel Transport Corps, and the requisitioning of their draught-
animals. Although such measures were theoretically regulated to
cause the minimum hardship—the conscription period, for example, was limited to six months—their execution was largely left,
owing to the heavy demand on British personnel for the Army, to
Egyptian provincial and local officials, who naturally applied
them with a view to their own profit: the fellah who paid the
necessary bakhshish to the village 'umda was exempt from conscription or requisitioning; the fellah who could not or would not
pay found himself included in the conscription-list for one six
months' period after another, and his camel or donkey carried
away by the requisitioning authorities. The fellahin were thus
filled with a strong sense of injury, and blamed the British all the
more because, under their rule, they had acquired some measure of
personal liberty and had lost some of their servile respect for
authority and the patient endurance of oppression. The urban
population was made discontented by the shortage of imported
supplies, especially of cereals in a country whose profitable cotton-
growing had to a great extent supplanted grain; and they were
offended by the tactless collection of subscriptions for the Red
Cross, from a predominantly Muslim population and by methods
which locally sometimes approximated to compulsion. Politically-
minded Egyptians were further irritated by the establishment of
the Protectorate, which seemed to make the prospect of self-
government more remote. The kind of post-war constitution
which senior British officials in Egypt envisaged was exemplified
by a Note on Constitutional Reform drawn up by the Judicial
Adviser, which leaked out to the Cairo press despite the censorship. It 'entirely ignored the existence of the national sentiment
which the War had stimulated . . . and did not spare the deficiencies of the politically-minded classes in an incisive review of their
past activities. It proposed the creation of a new legislature in
whose upper chamber, the Senate, not only British Advisers and

Egyptian Ministers were to have seats, but also representatives of the large foreign communities, chosen by special electorates, to voice their commercial, financial, and professional interests. . . . The opinion of the Senate was to prevail in all matters of essential policy . . . clearly with a view to securing the passage of whatever the British government might consider necessary for the maintenance of their controlling authority.'[1]

In this atmosphere of discontent it is not surprising that, as the war drew to an end, Zaghlul was able to recruit strong support for his campaign to bring about a radical change in the political status of Egypt. Two days after the Armistice he headed a delegation (Wafd) to the High Commissioner, informing him 'on behalf of the whole Egyptian people' of the desire for complete independence, and requesting permission to go to Europe to lay Egypt's case before the Peace Conference. The Egyptian Prime Minister then asked permission for a ministerial delegation to go to London, which the High Commissioner urged the Foreign Office to receive; but Lord Curzon, the acting Foreign Secretary, refused, feeling that it would raise hopes in Egypt which it would be impossible to satisfy, especially as the government was preoccupied with the greater problems of the settlement of Europe and would prefer to postpone consideration of the Egyptian question until the pressure of more urgent business was relieved. To the Egyptian nationalists, however, their case was the most urgent matter in the world. They saw Syrians, Arabs, and even Cypriots sending delegations to the Conference, and interpreted the Foreign Office refusal as proof that Britain intended to impose her own solution by force. Zaghlul began a nation-wide campaign for independence. The Foreign Office then reversed its decision and agreed to receive the ministerial delegation; but Zaghlul's campaign had already gathered so much momentum that the Egyptian Prime Minister now insisted that Zaghlul should be included in the delegation and share its responsibility; otherwise he knew well that whatever the delegation achieved in London would be repudiated by the nationalists at home. But Lord Curzon was not prepared to accept Zaghlul; as late as 24 February 1919 he continued to receive optimistic reports from the Residency in Cairo: 'The agitation which the Nationalist leaders have organized is dying out, or is at any rate quiescent in the country at large. . . . Zaghlul is trusted by

[1] Chirol, op. cit., 145 f.

10

no one. . . . The agitation has from the beginning been entirely pacific in character. . . . The present movement cannot be compared in importance with that of Mustafa Kamil, and there seems to be no reason why it should affect the decisions of H.M. Government on constitutional questions and the proper form to be given to the protectorate.'

The Egyptian Prime Minister, denied permission to plead his country's case at the Peace Conference, resigned on 1 March 1919, and strikes, disturbances and riots followed. The Residency counselled firmness: four nationalist leaders, three of whom—Zaghlul, Isma'il Sidqi, and Mohammed Mahmud—have made their mark in subsequent politics, were deported to Malta. This was followed by a widespread insurrection among the fellahin, inspired by the middle-class nationalists. Railways and telegraph and telephone communications was extensively cut, and Cairo was isolated from the rest of the country, where British authority had ceased to be effective. Provincial 'republican governments' were proclaimed and even villages set up their own independent authorities. Isolated parties of British troops and some European residents were massacred. By 23 March however railway communication between Cairo and the north had been restored, and three weeks later the army had re-imposed order almost everywhere.

The Residency subsequently tried to explain the revolution by allegations that the hand of Bolshevist, Young Turk and even German agents had been 'clearly discernible'; but the Milner Commission placed these hypotheses in their true perspective: 'The Anglo-Egyptian authorities appear to have been so greatly out of touch with native sentiment that such statements must be accepted with reserve. They have shown a complete lack of foreknowledge for which it is almost impossible to account.' The internal organization of the Residency had in fact become far from adequate for its increased responsibilities; the duties of the various senior officials had never been clearly defined, and it had no sound system for obtaining and assessing intelligence.

Meanwhile Lloyd George had recalled the High Commissioner and appointed in his place Lord Allenby, the victor of the Palestine campaign, 'to maintain the Protectorate on a secure and equitable basis'. The new High Commissioner adopted a conciliatory policy towards the nationalists. The four deported deputies were released, and Zaghlul went off to Europe to lay Egypt's case before the Peace Conference; but his intransigence and rigid inability to compromise made a poor impression there, and his case was weakened by the fact that President Wilson had given his recognition to the British Protectorate. The British Government set up, under the chairmanship of the Colonial Secretary Lord Milner, a commission 'to enquire into the form of government which, *under the Protectorate*, will be best calculated to promote peace and prosperity, the progressive development of self-governing institutions, and the protection of foreign interests'. In the same document British policy was defined as seeking 'to defend Egypt against all external danger and the interference of a foreign power, and to establish constitutional government, under British guidance as far as may be necessary, so that the Sultan[1] and his ministers and the elected representatives of the people may in their several spheres and in an increasing degree co-operate in the management of Egyptian affairs'. The Mission was met by a complete boycott; their residence was picketed by the Wafdists (as the followers of Zaghlul now called themselves), and any Egyptian who ventured to call upon them was pursued by menaces. On the return of the Mission to London Milner continued negotiations with the Egyptian Prime Minister and with Zaghlul, and finally in August 1920 produced a memorandum proposing a definite settlement provided that Zaghlul would urge its acceptance upon his followers. It recommended 'a treaty of alliance under which Britain will recognize the independence of Egypt as a constitutional monarchy with representative institutions, and Egypt will confer upon Britain the rights necessary to safeguard her special interests and to enable her to give foreign Powers guarantees which will secure the relinquishment of capitulatory rights. Britain will defend the integrity of Egyptian territory, and Egypt will in case of war render Britain all assistance in her power within her own borders. Egypt will not adopt an attitude inconsistent with the alliance, or enter into any agreement with a foreign power prejudicial to British interests. Egypt will confer on Britain the right to maintain a military force on Egyptian soil for the maintenance of her imperial communications.... Egypt will recognize the right of Britain to intervene, should legislation operate inequitably against foreigners. The British representative

---

[1] This title was substituted for that of Khedive in 1914 when Ottoman suzerainty was renounced upon the Turkish entry into the War.

will enjoy a special position and precedence', etc. This memorandum, which provided the basis for Anglo-Egyptian relations until 1946, was received not unfavourably in Egypt, though Zaghlul had made the significant counter-proposal that British troops should be specifically limited in number and confined to the Canal Zone. The main opposition came from the British cabinet, parliament, and public, 'many of whom had come to regard Egypt as an integral part of the British Empire and were beyond measure astonished that Milner, whose imperialism was unimpeachable, should have proposed what they regarded as the surrender and abandonment of British territory'.[1] Milner, however, showed how untenable historically this unaccommodating attitude was: 'Unless all our past declarations have been insincere and all our professions hypocritical, the establishment of Egypt as an independent state in intimate alliance with Britain is the goal to which all our efforts have been directed. It may indeed be argued that the goal has not yet been reached, that Egypt is not yet strong enough to stand on her own feet. Such arguments are entitled to respectful consideration. But what cannot be maintained, with any regard for historical accuracy, is that these changes in themselves are not absolutely in accordance with the constantly declared policy of Great Britain.'[2]

During 1921 the British government carried on negotiations with moderate Egyptian ministers drawn from the Turkish ruling class; but these broke down on the Egyptian insistence that the British garrison should in peace-time be confined to the Canal Zone, where it could not be used so readily to exert pressure upon Egyptian internal politics. The British Army, on the other hand, apparently insensible of the constant irritant presented to Egyptian susceptibilities by the presence of a British garrison in their capital, stubbornly opposed its withdrawal from Cairo. A familiar theme of those who opposed any concessions was that 'the real fellahin, if their voice could be heard, preferred British rule to that of their own leaders; yet all the evidence conclusively proved that these misguided peasants preferred indifferent government by their own compatriots to the efficient and honest administration of an alien power'.[3] The Cabinet, dependent on an unstable coalition in the

[1] *Round Table*, December, 1936, 110 ff.
[2] Preface to the thirteenth edition of *England in Egypt*, October, 1920.
[3] N. G. D., reviewing Lord Wavell's '*Allenby in Egypt*' in *Royal Central Asian Journal*, XXXI (1944), 213.

House of Commons, and fearful that it would be attacked by the imperialist wing of the press if, after its recent surrender to Sinn Fein in Ireland, it now made concessions to militant nationalism in Egypt, followed the lead of the Colonial Secretary, Winston Churchill, who characteristically was much more alive to the broad bearing of the question on imperial strategy than to the intensity of feeling in Egypt itself. Finally Allenby, realizing the hopelessness of trying to get any agreement in Egypt without some concessions and holding that Britain was pledged by the Milner Report to offer a measure of independence, forced the government's hands by tendering his resignation with that of the four principal British advisers to the Egyptian government. The Cabinet yielded and Allenby was allowed to proceed with his policy of granting conditional independence. On 28 February 1922 the Sultan was informed that the Protectorate was terminated, and Egypt declared to be an independent sovereign state. The following four points were however absolutely reserved to the discretion of H.M. Government pending the reaching of agreement on them: (1) The security of imperial communications; (2) the defence of Egypt against all foreign aggression or interference direct or indirect; (3) the protection of foreign residents and minorities; (4) the Sudan. This unilateral declaration was followed by a Note to the foreign Powers warning them that Britain would not admit any questioning or discussion of her special relations with Egypt, and would regard as an unfriendly act[1] any attempt at intervention in Egyptian affairs. Egypt was not proposed for admission to the League of Nations; and in November 1924 the Conservative government which had newly come to power informed the League that, should Egypt sign the Geneva Protocol for the Pacific Settlement of International Disputes, H.M. Government would not admit that the act entitled her to invoke the intervention of the League in any matter covered by the Four Reserved Points. As Toynbee commented, the granting of independence to Egypt was so limited by these reservations that it amounted in fact to less than Dominion Status. Egyptians received it without gratitude as merely an instalment of independence; as the Iraqi soldier Ja'far al-'Askari had remarked, 'Complete independence is never given; it is always taken.'

* * *

[1] The diplomatic euphemism for an act which would be resisted by force.

As Iraq was progressively occupied during the War, it came under a military administration whose tone, set by the Indian Army and the Government of India, was unsympathetic to the new idea of Arab nationalism as fostered by the British Arab Bureau in Cairo. An interim compromise plan produced by the British government in March 1917 provided for the annexation of the Basra vilayet, while that of Baghdad was to be administered as far as possible by Arabs, but to be in everything but name a British protectorate having no relations with foreign Powers. A new factor was introduced by an Anglo-French Declaration of 7 November 1918 which stated that: 'France and Britain agree to further and assist the setting-up in Syria and Iraq of indigenous governments and administrations, deriving their authority from the free exercise of initiative and choice of the indigenous populations. The only concern of France and Britain is to offer such support and efficacious help as will ensure the smooth working of these governments and administrations.' This Declaration caused great excitement among the young nationalists of Baghdad, but, in the opinion of the distinguished Arabist and traveller Gertrude Bell who was serving on the staff of the Administration, 'the prematurity of the national movement has so clearly been manifest that it has found no support among the stable elements of the population.'

At this stage the Chief Civil Commissioner, Sir Percy Cox, a man of great experience and personal prestige, was transferred as British Minister to Tehran, and was succeeded by his assistant Colonel Arnold Wilson. This thirty-four-year-old Indian Army officer had rapidly come to the fore for his energy and vigour; but his previous acquaintance with Arabs and his knowledge of their character was limited to his experience in the Persian Gulf and on the Lower Tigris. He had no experience of or sympathy with the Ottomanized effendi of Baghdad, whose political aspirations were those of al-'Ahd. More than this, his admirable positive qualities were offset by a strong vein of self-righteousness and self-justification. On taking over from Cox he advised the Foreign Office that 'There is an almost entire absence of political, racial, and other connexion of Iraq with the rest of Arabia. . . . The average Arab, as opposed to the handful of amateur politicians of Baghdad, sees the future as one of fair dealing and material and moral progress under the aegis of Britain. Iraq should not be assimilated politically to the rest of the Arab and the Muslim world, but should remain

insulated as far as may be, as a wedge of British-controlled territory'; and he comments in his apologia *Loyalties*: 'A small
independent state of under three millions seemed a retrograde,
almost anarchic step. . . . My imagination envisaged some form
of protectorate which might develop ere long into a fully-fledged
Arab state with Dominion status under the British crown.'
Having determined in November 1918 to obtain confirmation for
his thesis by holding a plebiscite, he was at some pains to ensure
that it produced the desired result. His instructions to his Divisional
Officers stated, 'When public opinion appears likely to take a
definitely satisfactory line, you are authorized to convene an
assembly of all leading notables and sheikhs . . . informing them
that their answers will be communicated to me for submission to
the Government. Where public opinion appears likely to be sharply
divided, or in the unlikely event of its being unfavourable, you
should defer holding a meeting and report to me for instructions.'
The effect on the British cabinet of the plebiscite so conducted was
less serious than its effect on Wilson himself, since it led him increasingly to find reasons for disregarding the views of those with
whom he disagreed. Thus, characterizing the Iraqi nationalist
officers with the Amir Faisal in Syria as 'such small fry' and regarding the Shi'i mujtahids and other religious dignitaries with
much justification as 'spiritual tyrants whose principal ambition
was to stem the rising tide of emancipation', he 'underestimated
the influence of the Nationalists, and the susceptibility to their propaganda and that of the dissident 'ulama of the mass of the people
on the Middle Euphrates', as he himself later admitted.[1] He was
not, however, averse to cautious constitutional progress; he proposed
to the Interdepartmental Committee on Eastern Affairs in April
1919: 'The legitimate demand for active participation in the
government and administration can best be met, not by creating
central legislative and deliberative councils, but by giving carefully
selected Arabs of good birth and education from the very outset
positions of executive and administrative responsibility. I would
propose to instal selected Arab officials as governors of (the
principal towns) with a specially chosen British official of ability
and character as principal commissioner and adviser to the
governor.' The Allied Powers were, however, still fully occupied
with imposing terms on Germany, and had not yet approached the

[1] *Loyalties*, II, 254.

problem of the disposal of the Ottoman Empire. Consequently the Foreign Office replied to Wilson that it was premature to attempt constitutional experiments pending the decision of the Peace Conference on the Mandatory Power for Iraq and the nature of the Mandate. In these circumstances it is not surprising that Arab notables who were approached as possible governors of Basra declined to accept the responsibility and commit themselves until the future of their country became clearer.

Meanwhile there had existed in Damascus since its liberation in October 1918 an autonomous Arab government under the Amir Faisal, assisted by British officers who had taken part in the Arab Rebellion and were sympathetic to the Sharifian form of Arab nationalism. Among the officers on Faisal's staff were many Iraqis, members of al-'Ahd, who ardently desired to see their country similarly placed under Arab rule. In 1919 one of these visited Baghdad and was offered the post of Assistant Military Governor of the city. He apparently imagined that he had been invited to assist in setting up a national government; but on finding that he was merely to be an Arab unit in the British administration hurriedly resigned. 'This incident evidently confirmed in the minds of the Iraqi officers in Syria the impression that the British military administration in Iraq was intended to be permanent, and that it regarded them as active enemies who were trying to undermine British influence there.'[1] The Iraqis in Syria thereupon organized a rising wave of political feeling in the towns of Iraq, and brought about a rapprochement between Sunnis and Shi'is. In October 1919 Gertrude Bell remarked in an official Note: 'When we set up a civil administration in this country, the fact that a responsible native government has existed for a year in Syria will not be forgotten by the Iraqi nationalists; and if we seek to make use of those Iraqis who have done best in Syria, they will claim great liberty of action, and will expect to be treated as equals. . . . Local conditions, the vast potential wealth of the country, the tribal character of the rural population, the lack of material from which to draw official personnel, will make the problem harder to solve here than elsewhere. I venture to think that the answer to such objections is that any alternative line of action would create problems whose solution we are learning to be harder still.' Wilson, however, still did not fully grasp the strong, intimate, and constant influence exerted

[1] Sir Hubert Young, *The Independent Arab*, 292, 297.

on Iraqi nationalism by the autonomous Arab government in Syria, and sought to nullify Gertrude Bell's conclusions in his covering despatch: 'The fundamental assumption throughout this Note . . . is that an Arab state in Iraq and elsewhere within a short period of years is a possibility, and that the recognition or creation of a logical scheme of government on these lines would be practicable and popular. . . . My observations in this country and elsewhere have forced me to the conclusion that this assumption is erroneous. . . . I believe it to be impossible in these days to create a new sovereign Muslim state . . . out of the remnants of the Turkish Empire. . . . It is my belief that the Arab public at large would after a very few years prefer the return of the Turks to the continuance of an amateur Arab government. . . . For some time to come the appointment of Arab governors or high officials, except in an advisory capacity, would involve the rapid decay of authority, law and order, followed by anarchy and disorder, and the movement once started would not be checked.' Long afterwards he admitted, 'It is easy to see after the lapse of ten years that I was perhaps unduly sceptical.'

In May 1920 the British government at last obtained by the abortive Treaty of Sèvres the mandate for Iraq, and instructed Wilson to consult the recently-created Divisional Councils on proposals for the development of national life. Wilson and his advisers objected, since the Arab government in Damascus, subsidized with gold from the British treasury, had during the long delay carried on a violent nationalist propaganda with considerable success among the middle-class younger generation, who had been greatly encouraged by the proclamation of Faisal's brother Abdullah as King of Iraq by the 'Ahd in Damascus in March. Wilson's advisers produced a draft constitution: there was to be a Council of State, consisting of British and Arabs in equal numbers, and a Legislature. The members of the Council could, however, be removed at will, and its resolutions overruled, by the British High Commissioner. The powers of the so-called Legislature were to be confined to the passing of resolutions without the force of law and the putting of questions to the government. Although Wilson claimed that 'leading Arabs regarded these proposals as revolutionary and as a generation ahead of the times', Lord Curzon critically commented: 'This is not an Arab government inspired and helped by British advice, but a

British government infused with Arab elements. . . .' Meanwhile nationalist activity had passed from agitation to open defiance. Already early in the year Arab irregulars with encouragement from the Arab government in Damascus had forced the British to withdraw from Dair az-Zor, their furthest outpost in the direction of Syria.[1] In June a force under the Iraqi officer Jamil Midfa'i[2] seized the post of Tell Afar, thirty miles west of Mosul and massacred its small British garrison, but was driven back before it could reach Mosul itself. In the months of May and June £7,000 in gold was reported to have reached extremists at Karbala.

The British government announced on 20 June that Sir Percy Cox would return in the autumn as Chief British Representative in anticipation that the Mandate, when finally promulgated, would constitute Iraq an independent state. But this gesture came too late. Owing presumably to the severe climate and the steady drain of demobilization, the Civil Administration was staffed mainly by very young and inexperienced men, who shared the somewhat headstrong views of their Chief.[3] 'It seems probable that had the Civil Administration been less anxious to justify its continued existence' (with generous pay and allowances, be it noted, at a time of rising unemployment and wage-cuts in Britain) 'by proving its superiority over the previous régime and all other possible régimes . . . had it been staffed by men older and more experienced in dealing with the Arab character and temperament, or had it shown itself more sympathetic to the idea of Arab government instead of merely paying it lip service as a possibility in some remote or indefinite future, many of the classes who hardened their hearts against the once-popular British régime would have continued to support it.'[4] The revenue collected in 1920 was three and a half times that received by the Turks in 1911. Taxation, which was enormously heavier than in India, tended to press most heavily on the fellahin, but was vexatious also to the landlords and dignitaries and to the tribes, who had formerly largely escaped paying taxes. The Iraqis had no say in the objects on which these revenues

---

[1] Under the Ottoman Empire this part of the Euphrates valley had not belonged to any of the vilayets of Iraq, but had formed an independent sanjaq.
[2] He has subsequently been Prime Minister of Iraq, and is now (April 1948) Minister of the Interior.
[3] In the autumn of 1919, out of a total of 233 officers only four were over forty-five years of age. On 1st June 1920 two-thirds of the Divisional Political Officers were under thirty, and almost one-quarter were only twenty-five or less.
[4] Ireland, op: cit., 252. cf. Ph. Graves, *Life of Sir Percy Cox*, 262 f.

were expended. In the financial year 1919-20 16 per cent. of all expenditure was devoted to Headquarters and the costs of administration, and this marked a reduction from previous years; another 11 per cent., nominally for public works, was largely applied to improving the amenities of British and Indian officials. Wilson had expressed the view that the interests of the country would be served by having a large proportion of British personnel in all branches of the administration. The Divisional Advisory Councils, composed of Arabs, had no influence on policy. Less than 4 per cent. of the senior-grade officials were Arab, and on the railways there were nearly five times as many Indian as Iraqi personnel. After the Rebellion had already begun Gertrude Bell wrote, 'On the whole, the wonder is that there are so many moderates and reasonable people. I try to count myself among them, but I find it difficult to maintain a dispassionate calm when I reflect on the number of blunders we have made.'

The garrison consisted of 80,000 troops, nearly half the size of the standing army of India with a hundred times the population. The general situation had long been known to be threatening; but Army H.Q. had tended to place little faith in the reports of the Political Officers of the Civil Administration. When the Rebellion broke out at the end of June, the C.-in-C. and the bulk of his staff were at their Persian hill-station; only 4,200 British troops, almost all new to the country and without previous military experience, and 30,000 Indians were available for service in Iraq; and only 500 British and 2,500-3,000 Indians were available as a mobile force. The main centre of the Rebellion was the tribal area of the Middle Euphrates, and though the moderate nationalists held aloof it lasted from July to September, when it was put down by heavy reinforcements. Over 400 British and Indian troops were killed, and the rebels were estimated to have suffered 8,450 casualties. It cost Britain £20,000,000, and in Iraq the damage to railways and loss of revenue amounted to more than £400,000.

Sir Percy Cox arrived on 1 October to take back the supreme authority from Wilson with the new title of High Commissioner. He had the advantage of his great personal prestige, and handled the situation in a more sympathetic spirit than his predecessor. A provisional Council of State was set up, consisting of Arab ministers, who were, however, subject to the advice of their British Advisers and, in the last resort, to the High Commissioner whose

decision was final in all matters. There was no intention of trans-
ferring the administration to the Iraqis any faster than practical
considerations demanded. The situation was very comparable
with that of Cromer's Egypt: British heads and Iraqi hands; and
in fact the country was at about the same stage of development.
But at least a concession had been made to national aspirations by
appointing Iraqi ministers. The Iraqi officers stranded in Syria
after the French suppression of Faisal's government in July 1920
were encouraged to return to Iraq. The garrisoning of Iraq was in
1921 handed over to the R.A.F., and its cost progressively reduced
in three to four years to one-seventh of its former figure. Nevertheless the extreme nationalists were not appeased, and it was
alleged that they were receiving material help from nationalist
Turkey and Bolshevist Russia. Gertrude Bell wrote, 'If we hesitate in appointing a king, the tide of public opinion may turn overwhelmingly to the Turks.' At the Cairo Conference called by the
Colonial Secretary, Winston Churchill, in March 1921 the choice
finally fell on Faisal, for whom Cox's staff and especially Gertrude
Bell began to make active propaganda in Iraq.[1] The popular
reception on his arrival was lukewarm, but the administration
made every effort to secure a favourable vote in the projected
referendum. A printed form containing a resolution in his favour
was sent to the Divisional Officers to obtain the signatures of the
notables. Annexures asking for the continuance of British control
were encouraged, while any addition of a nationalist character was
punished, and the mutasarrif of Baghdad was forced to resign for
permitting them. The majority-vote of a town or district was
regarded for the purpose of enumeration as unanimous.[2] As
Gertrude Bell remarked with her curious mixture of cynicism
and ingenuousness, it was 'politics running on wheels greased
with extremely well-melted grease'. The official return gave
Faisal 96 per cent. of the votes, while independent observers were
disposed to give him two-thirds.[3]

---

[1] St. John Philby, then Adviser to the Ministry of the Interior, who favoured a
republic, was dismissed for obstructing the official policy.

[2] Similarly in the United States, the party in each state which gains a majority,
however small, fills the whole of that state's seats in the electoral college that
elects the President.

[3] The Kirkuk liwa with its Turcoman population voted against him, and the
Kurdish liwa of Sulaimaniya boycotted the referendum. The Shi'is, who constitute a majority in the whole country, demanded the end of foreign control, as
did over 80 per cent. of the poll in Baghdad.

The nationalists hoped that the creation of the monarchy meant the end of the Mandate, and the establishment of full independence sweetened with British financial support. The British, on the other hand, proposed to retain control of Iraq's foreign relations and 'such measure of financial control as might be necessary'. · The King was to agree to be guided by the advice of the High Commissioner, and British officials were to be appointed to specified posts. Negotiation over the terms of the Treaty to define Anglo-Iraqi relations was protracted through most of 1922 owing to Iraqi reluctance to make such large concessions as Britain required. The King was inclined to associate himself with the nationalist attitude. Five nationalist leaders were deported, including Hamdi al-Pachaji, and unrest in the provinces called for the use of R.A.F. bombers on four occasions. In September Cox delivered an ulti-matum to the King: H.M. Government could not further tolerate his connexion with the nationalist agitation nor the delay in ratifying the Treaty. At this moment the King had a very oppor-tune, though entirely genuine, attack of acute appendicitis, and in October the Council of Ministers ratified a twenty years' Treaty, subject to its subsequent ratification by the Naional Assembly. Every royal Act or ministerial order was to receive the previous approval of the High Commissioner or British Adviser respec-tively. If a minister refused to yield to his Adviser's disapproval, the High Commissioner had the power eventually to 'advise' the King that the measure should not receive the Royal Assent.

The National Assembly did not meet to ratify the Treaty till March 1924. The High Commissioner had taken pains to 'make' a pro-Treaty majority. The Opposition objected to the appoint-ment of British advisers; it claimed that the financial stipulations, which required one-quarter of the revenue to be allotted to national defence and imposed on Iraq a heavy share of the Ottoman Public Debt, constituted an excessive burden; and it complained that Britain had given Iraq no guarantee over the question of the vilayet of Mosul, whose ownership was being vigorously con-tested by the nationalist Turkey of Mustafa Kemal. As the Assem-bly proved unexpectedly obstructive, the High Commissioner finally gave the King a fortnight's warning that, if the Treaty were not ratified in time to place it before the next session of the League of Nations Council, H.M. Government would put its own alter-native proposals before the League. With only twenty-four hours to go, the High Commissioner refused to grant an extension of the time-limit. The Treaty was finally ratified with about an hour to spare by thirty-seven votes to twenty-four, with eight abstentions and thirty-one absentees out of a total of 100 members. Britain had with difficulty safeguarded her essential interests, and the nationalists had 'gone down fighting'. The immediate obstacle had been cleared, and the process of historical evolution could go on without bloodshed.

★   ★   ★

The special position of Palestine as the Holy Land of three great religions had been not unsatisfactorily met during the nineteenth century by the Ottoman creation of the Sanjaq of Jerusalem taking its orders direct from Istanbul, and by allowing a large measure of civil autonomy to the multiplicity of foreign religious communities. Though Sir Henry McMahon stated twenty years afterwards that in his mind Palestine was always excluded from the territories promised to the Arabs by the Husain-McMahon Correspondence in 1915, there is no direct reference to Palestine in that Correspondence.[1] In 1916, with a large-scale invasion of the Levant contemplated from Egypt, it was necessary to reconcile the interests of Britain in that region with those of France, who ever since 1860 had regarded Syria as her special preserve, had continued to expand her schools, had built the railways and obtained other commercial concessions. Some French publicists at this time even insisted that the French special interest extended to Palestine; but such a claim was not tenable in view of the variety of religious interests there other than those of the Church of Rome. In the secret Sykes-Picot Agreement of 1916 it was decided that, while French interests should be paramount in Syria, in the eventual

[1] It has been argued that Palestine was implicitly included in the area 'west of the *wilayât* of Damascus, Homs, Hama, and Aleppo', which was excluded from the proposed Arab kingdom, since the *wilaya* (vilayet) of Damascus extended south as far as Aqaba and consequently Palestine lay immediately to the west of it. This interpretation breaks down on the immediately-following reference to Homs and Homa: there were no 'vilayets' in the strict administrative sense of Homs and Hama, since these towns lay within the vilayet of Damascus. It would therefore follow that the word was intended in its alternative general sense of 'district'; and as the four cities mentioned all lie well to the north of Palestine, to argue that an area to the west of them was intended to include Palestine is as unprofitable as to argue that an area 'west of the districts of Warwick, Sheffield, Leeds, and Newcastle' includes the counties of Hereford and Monmouth.

partitioning of the Ottoman Empire Palestine should come under an international administration.

So far, not a word had been officially said about any special rights for the Jews. In all the centuries that had elapsed since the destruction of Jerusalem in A.D. 70, there had probably never been a time when there was not a small Jewish community in Palestine; and pious Jews of the Dispersion had always dreamed of the restoration, by the will of God, of the Temple and the Kingdom. In 1799, when Napoleon invaded Palestine from Egypt, he issued a manifesto to the Jews of the world offering them 'the patrimony of Israel'. Of more practical importance was the sentiment entertained by many British Protestants in the nineteenth century that the fulfilment of the Scriptures entailed the restoration of the Jews to Palestine. This view was held by the philanthropist Lord Shaftesbury, who as a kinsman of the great Palmerston had some indirect influence on British policy. Both Russia and France, whose activities in the Middle East Palmerston regarded with equal suspicion, were using the benevolence of Ibrahim Pasha in the 1830's to expand their respective Orthodox and Catholic missions in Palestine; and Palmerston therefore sought the opportunity of using some other community to offset their influence. In 1838 he appointed the first British Vice-consul in Jerusalem, and instructed him as part of his duties 'to afford protection to the Jews generally; and you will take an early opportunity of reporting . . . upon the present state of the Jewish population in Palestine'. They were found to number some ten thousand souls, nearly all of them from the Mediterranean countries. In 1840, at the height of the crisis of the Second Syrian War, Palmerston wrote to the British Ambassador in Istanbul, 'It would be of manifest importance for the Sultan to encourage the Jews to return to, and settle in Palestine; because the wealth which they would bring with them would increase the resources of the Sultan's dominions; and the Jewish people, if returning under the sanction and protection and at the invitation of the Sultan, would be a check upon any future evil designs of Mohammed Ali or his successor. . . . Bring these considerations confidentially under the notice of the Turkish government, and strongly recommend them to hold out every just encouragement to the Jews of Europe to return to Palestine.'[1]

This project, however, came to nothing, and there was little

[1] cf. A. N. Hyamson, *The British Consulate in Jerusalem*.

change in the numbers or status of the Jews in Palestine till the 'eighties, when the nationalist reaction in Russia, then the home of two-thirds of world-Jewry, to the murder of the Tsar was followed by an outbreak of anti-Jewish outrages, in which hundreds were killed and thousands ruined, while discriminatory anti-Jewish legislation was enforced over a period of three years. There was a large-scale exodus of Jews from Russia, finding ready admission into North America and Britain in those easygoing and liberal days. A small proportion of the emigrants went to Palestine, where some of them settled on the land with the financial help of Baron de Rothschild, and readily employed the Arab fellahin to cultivate the lands for them. By the outbreak of the First World War the Jewish population of Palestine was over 80,000. The growth of their agricultural settlements, despite many material difficulties, to the number of forty-four with a total population of about 12,000 had already provoked some Arab opposition. The American geographer Ellsworth Huntington, who was in Palestine in 1909, wrote: 'The fellahin of the Plain of Sharon and of other fertile parts of Palestine, such as Carmel and parts of the Jordan Valley, see in the Jew their greatest enemy.... Around Jaffa the Jewish colonies are undoubtedly successful, so much so that the native population is sorely jealous. In enmity towards the colonists they steal the fruit and break the branches in the orchards, turn horses into the grain-fields and break down hedges.'[1] In 1912 there was an angry scene in the Ottoman Chamber of Deputies, when Arab deputies protested against the Jewish acquisition of large areas of arable land in the Plain of Esdraelon from absentee landlords and the threatened dispossession of the tenants.[2]

Meanwhile the growing anti-Jewish prejudice in Europe, which reached flash-point in France in the Affaire Dreyfus, had had a profound effect on a Viennese journalist Theodor Herzl, 'one on whom his Jewish origin lay so lightly that it is probable that ... he often completely forgot it.' But stung now by the sense of helplessness and homelessness of the Jews faced by unreasoning persecution, he

---

[1] *Palestine and its Transformation* (1911), 87.

[2] Geo. Antonius, op. cit. 259. In the early years of the British mandate these lands were transferred to the Jews. Twenty-one Arab villages disappeared from the map of Palestine, and it has never been definitely established what happened to their inhabitants. The tenants (but not the landless labourers) are said to have been compensated by the Jewish purchasers to the extent of about 4 per cent. of the purchase-price. The landlords, a wealthy and cosmopolitan Beirut Christian family, gave them no compensation. (Barbour, op. cit., 117 f.)

produced in 1896 a pamphlet *The Jewish State*, in which he proposed the creation of a Jewish national territory. It fell on fertile soil among Jewish student-societies in European universities, and others whose dream of the return to Zion had been given urgency by the persecution of Jewry in Russia. The three motifs: religious Zionism, the need of asylum from persecution and discrimination, and Herzl's political idea, fused. 'Almost overnight he found himself the head of a great party in Jewry: political Zionism had been born.... Jewry was to be divested of its peculiar attributes and made "as other nations", bound together politically and self-conscious.' After seven years of failure of the Zionist Organization to interest any Great Power in their plans 'to establish for the Jewish people a home in Palestine secured by public law', it received in 1903 an offer from the British government to establish an autonomous Jewish settlement in what was then called British East Africa. Herzl himself, who had never been wedded to Palestine as the only land for his prospective state, was attracted by this so-called 'Uganda Scheme'; but before anything could be finally settled he died, and the Zionist Congress of 1905, dominated by Eastern European Jews imbued with the traditional religious Zionism, resolved on the fundamental principle of the colonization of 'Palestine and the adjacent lands' and nowhere else.[1]

The outbreak of the First World War transferred the centre of gravity of the growing Zionist movement from the continent of Europe to Britain and the U.S.A. In these two countries the principal protagonists of Zionism were respectively Dr. Hayyim Weizmann, born in Russia but for some years lecturer in chemistry at Manchester University, where he had 'converted Prime Minister Balfour to Zionism in the middle of the East Manchester election'[2] (!): and the lawyer Louis D. Brandeis, who actively supported Woodrow Wilson for President of the U.S.A. and was rewarded by being made a Judge of the Supreme Court.[3] A 'British Palestine Committee' formed on Weizmann's inspiration, issued a periodical under the slogan 'To reset the ancient glories of the Jewish nation in the freedom of a new British dominion in Palestine'. The only non-Jewish member of this committee, the journalist Herbert Sidebotham of the *Manchester*

---

[1] Hyamson, *Palestine: A Policy*, ch. V.
[2] Herbert Sidebotham, *Great Britain and Palestine*, 54.
[3] Rabbi Stephen Wise, in *The Jewish National Home, 1917–42* (Paul Goodman, ed.), 41.

Guardian, had in 1915 written a leading-article advocating the permanent British occupation of Palestine for the defence of Egypt. This had attracted the interest of Weizmann, who had asked Sidebotham to write a memorandum to the Foreign Office, proposing a Jewish state in Palestine for the defence of Egypt and the Canal. Sidebotham claimed that it was the needs, political and strategic, of British policy that definitely inclined the scales in favour of Zionism.[1]

Balfour had become Foreign Secretary in 1916. The influential and enthusiastic Sir Mark Sykes,[2] who had helped to make the Sykes-Picot Treaty, had become a temporary convert to Zionism. With the gradual exhaustion of both Russia and France as effective military powers in 1917 it had become imperative to ensure the early armed intervention of the U.S.A., and President Wilson had shown himself 'warmly responsive to the Zionist ideal'. In these circumstances, after much interchange of opinion between British and American Zionists, and while Zionists in Germany and Turkey were conducting parallel negotiations with the enemy governments,[3] a proposal was submitted in 1917 to the British government for the 'recognition of Palestine as the National Home of the Jewish people' with internal autonomy, freedom of immigration, and the establishment of a Jewish National Colonizing Corporation for the resettlement of the country. This bold and uncompromising phraseology was not however acceptable either to the Foreign Office or to some influential British Jews who were concerned about its possible effect on their status as British subjects. After some months of redrafting it finally received official approval as the famous Balfour Declaration of 2 November 1917: 'H.M. Government view with favour the establishment in Palestine of a national home for the Jewish people, and will use their best endeavours to facilitate the achievement of this object, it being clearly understood that nothing shall be done which may prejudice the civil and religious rights of other non-Jewish communities in Palestine, or the rights and political status enjoyed by Jews in any other country.' There was thus a fundamental distinction between the original Zionist proposal and the finally approved Declaration, the one all-embracing, the other ambiguous and hedged with

[1] op. cit., chs. IV–V.
[2] T. E. Lawrence described him as 'the imaginative advocate of unconvincing world-movements' (*Seven Pillars of Wisdom*, 58).
[3] Barbour, op. cit., 54 f., 64 f.

reservations. The Zionists always persisted in interpreting the Declaration in the terms of their original proposal: as recently as August 1946 an official Jewish Agency spokesman claimed that 'the promise to the Jews of the whole of Palestine on both sides of the Jordan was implied in the Balfour Declaration'.[1]

The Army authorities in Palestine did their best to keep the news of the Declaration from the 'non-Jewish communities', i.e. the Arabic-speaking Muslims and Christians who then constituted 90 per cent. of the population; but a report of it reached the Sharif Husain, who with some concern asked Britain for an explanation. The government informed him that its support of the Zionist aspirations went only 'so far as is compatible with the freedom of the existing population, both economic and political'. This promise satisfied the Sharif, and early in 1919 his son Faisal reached with Weizmann a provisional agreement over Zionism in Palestine, subject however to the confirmation by the Powers of the Arab kingdom in Syria; 'but if the slightest modification or departure is made', wrote Faisal, 'I shall not then be bound by a single word of the present agreement.' At this stage the Palestine Arabs had never been consulted; they had given no mandate to Faisal to negotiate on their behalf; and his agreement with the Zionist leader could not be considered binding on anyone but himself and his father.

At the end of the War the political aspirations of the Zionists, kindled by the realization at last of their ancient hopes of returning to the Land of Promise, were heightened by the pressure exerted on Jews to emigrate in large numbers from the highly nationalistic Eastern European states which had emerged from the wreckage of the Austrian and Russian empires;[2] and they were still further encouraged by the pronouncements of such responsible statesmen as President Wilson, Lloyd George, Smuts, and Balfour in favour of an eventual Jewish state or commonwealth. The ignorance of these statesmen with regard to the rise of Arab nationalism was profound, and they apparently thought of the Arabs of Palestine (in so far as they were aware of their existence) as mere Bedouin, as little worthy of consideration as the American Indians, the Bantu, or any other politically unorganized and inarticulate race

[1] *Palestine Post*, 2 August, 1946. We are led to 'the cynical conclusion that Zionism allotted to Britain the role of a stalking-horse' (Owen Tweedy, *The Fortnightly*, October 1950, p. 272).

[2] *Round Table*, 1939, 259.

of 'natives', whose destiny it was to give place to the colonization of more 'progressive' peoples. At the Peace Conference, Dr. Weizmann could state his movement's aspirations in the unequivocal words, 'To make Palestine as Jewish as England is English or America American'; and a volume issued by the promoters of the Zionist Foundation Fund (Keren ha-Yesod) declared: 'The object of the modern Jewish pioneer in Palestine is to prepare room and work for the thousands and millions who wait outside.' 'The potency of Zionism swept like a tide over all the types of Jew on whom Britain's original assumption (the reconcilability of Jew and Arab) had been based—the religious Jews who had always lived unobtrusive lives in the holy cities of Palestine; the pre-war agriculturalists who spoke Arabic and employed Arabs; and the farseeing scholarly Jews who thought that the surest way of fulfilling the Messianic promise was to join with the local population in forming a covenant of peace. Zionism brushed aside every consideration that did not contribute to the immediate increase of the National Home.'[1]

The Arab reaction to the exuberance of the Zionist 'invasion' was swift. Mark Sykes, who revisited the country in 1919 was, in spite of his earlier enthusiasm, 'shocked by the intense bitterness provoked there'. The King-Crane Commission, which toured the Fertile Crescent in 1919 on the instructions of President Wilson to test the reactions of the population to the proposed mandatory arrangements, 'began their study of Zionism with minds predisposed in its favour. . . . They found much to approve in its aspirations and plans, they had warm appreciation for its devotion, and its success by modern methods in overcoming great natural obstacles. . . . Nevertheless, actual facts drove them to recommend a serious modification of the extreme Zionist programme of unlimited immigration. . . . The fact came out repeatedly in the Commission's conference with Zionists that they look forward to a practically complete dispossession of the present non-Jewish population of Palestine by various forms of purchase. More than 72 per cent. of the petitions received by the Commission in the whole of Syria were against the Zionist programme. The whole non-Jewish population of Palestine was emphatically

---

[1] Elizabeth Monroe, *The Mediterranean in Politics*, 58. The pre-war Zionists had had a characteristically self-centred and misleading slogan, 'The people without a land for a land without a people' (James Parkes, *The Emergence of the Jewish Problem*, p. vii).

against the entire Zionist programme. No British officer consulted by the Commission believed that the Zionist programme could be carried out except by force of arms. Officers generally thought that a force of not less than 50,000 soldiers would be required even to initiate the programme.' The American government pigeon-holed the Commission's Report, and it was published unofficially only after Wilson had relinquished the Presidency.

In their intense and passionate enthusiasm and zeal to rebuild their National Home the Zionists in Palestine struck out wildly against anyone who made objections to their extreme demands, anyone who imposed a brake on their dynamic career. Sir Ronald Storrs who became Military Governor of Jerusalem in 1918 with a sincere sympathy for Zionism, has written, 'From the beginning we encountered a critical Zionist press, which soon developed into pan-Jewish hostility. We were inefficient, ill-educated; those with official experience strongly pro-Arab, violently anti-Zionist, even anti-Jewish.'[1] Their incomprehension and intolerance for the British officers who were administering the country extended also to its Arabic-speaking inhabitants. The Anglo-American Committee of 1946 impartially summed up their attitude: 'Too often the Jew is content to refer to the indirect benefits accruing to the Arab from his coming, and leaves the matter there. Passionately loving every foot of Eretz Israel, he finds it impossible to look at the issue from the Arab point of view, and to realize the depth of feeling aroused by his "invasion" of Palestine. He compares his own achievements with the slow improvements made by the Arab village always to the disadvantage of the latter; and forgets the enormous financial and educational advantages bestowed upon him by world Zionism. When challenged on his relations with the Arabs, he is too often content to point out the superficial friendliness of everyday life in town and village—a friendliness which indubitably exists. In so doing, he sometimes ignores the deep political antagonism which inspires the whole Arab community; or thinks that he has explained it away by stating that it is the "result of self-seeking propaganda by the rich effendi class". It is not unfair to say that the Jewish community in Palestine has never, as a community, faced the problem of co-operation with the Arabs. It is, for instance, significant that, in the Jewish Agency's

[1] *Orientations*, 359 ff.

proposal for a Jewish State, the problem of handling one and a quarter million Arabs is dealt with in the vaguest of generalities.'[1] As a shrewd observer had concluded earlier, 'Seeing the Jews and hearing their arguments in Palestine, even an admirer of their great gifts is forced to the conclusion that they are politically an obtuse people—that the very characteristics which give them such force as preservers of a race, a religion, or a business are a hindrance in social intercourse, or in the give-and-take of democratic politics.'[2]

From the beginning they had never been prepared to concede any validity to the growing Arab nationalist movement. Though provincial Palestine had played a smaller part in the movement than the cities of Syria, the young Awni 'Abdul Hadi, members of the Nashashibi family of Jerusalem and other Palestinian notables had been prominent in the nationalist secret societies, and some had suffered death under Jemal Pasha. The Muslim community was divided into two great clan-partisanships, the Husainis and the Nashashibis. 'In the face of Zionism Husainis might be said to represent Church and extreme Arab nationalism, Nashashibis State and making the best of a bad job.'[3] Sir Herbert Samuel as High Commissioner sought to moderate the Husainis by appointing the most active of their younger members Mufti of Jerusalem and head of the Supreme Muslim Council; 'and in fact Hajj Amin was for years denounced by extremist Arab politicians as a British agent.'[4] The Nashashibis, in spite of holding for years the Mayoralty of Jerusalem, were conscious that their influence in the country as a whole was less than that of the Husainis, and sought to redress this inferiority by a loose alliance with the Zionists, receiving some encouragement from their middle-class elements. The Zionist leftists, however, sought from the first to drive a wedge between the Arab ruling-class as a whole, stigmatizing them as 'feudal exploiters', and the unorganized and inarticulate fellahin[5] and town-labourers, holding out promises of material benefits to the former and trade-union organization to the latter. The Arab Rebellion of 1936–9 showed the Zionists that their efforts to divide the Arabs had almost completely failed, and they

[1] Ch. VIII, paras. 4–5.
[2] Eliz. Monroe, op. cit., (1938), 59 f.
[3] Storrs, op. cit., 401 f.
[4] Barbour, op. cit., 130.
[5] F. H. Kisch, *Palestine Diary* (1938), Index, s.vv. Nashashibi; Dajani; Peasants' Party.

subsequently tended to speak plainly to the Arabs as a whole. At a May-Day rally in 1946 the labour-leader Mrs. Golda Meyerson, now head of the Jewish Agency's Political Department, 'told the Arab labourers and fellahin that no force would swerve the Jewish people from their goal'. Three months later the Zionist Labour party Mapai, the strongest Jewish party in Palestine, passed a resolution at its annual conference 'appealing to the Arab people and assuring them that the Jewish people were ready to co-operate as equals for the peaceful development of Palestine. At the same time, all measures intended to destroy the Zionist programme would be fought.'[1] The Zionists were probably right in supposing that the only language the Arabs understood was the language of force. They have behaved as colonists have always behaved towards an indigenous population less well equipped with material and intellectual resources. But the fact remains that this was the language of force, not the language of conciliation; and it contrasted curiously with Dr. Weizmann's habitual pretence of 'stretching out his hands to the Arabs in friendship'.[2]

Finding that the Arab masses still preferred to follow their own ruling-class rather than their Zionist mentors, and that their efforts to divide the Arab community met with little success, the more moderate Zionists criticized the Palestine Government for not suppressing the Arab extremists.[3] The extreme Zionists, however, reacted by creating a myth, which they ventilated with assiduity until 1948, that there was at bottom no clash of interests between Arab and Jew, and that the discord between them was entirely a product of British machinations. While Zionist allegations of British hostility to their aims had been levelled originally at the Administration in Palestine, military and civil alike,[4] since 1939 and especially since 1945, when British policy no longer marched with their own totalitarian demands, they assailed Whitehall and Downing Street also. The London correspondent of the *Palestine Post* pilloried the 'official caste, deeply committed to policies which treat the East as an area hitherto unspoilt by the hideousness of the twentieth century, and if possible to be kept in a state of pristine purity for the benefit of all that is most decorative in Arab and most

---

[1] *Palestine Post*, 10 September, 1946.
[2] e.g. *Palestine Post*, 19 June, 1946.
[3] Kisch, op. cit., 19, and Index, s.v. Officials, Attitude of British.
[4] Storrs, op. cit., 362, makes a frank appreciation of anti-Zionist sentiments in the Military Administration.

snobbish in British, society.'[1] A more candid admission came, as
so often, from a Jewish Revisionist:[2] 'It is to be assumed that a
clash between Jews and Arabs in Palestine would have taken place
even without any prompting from the British administration.
The Jews wanted Palestine for a Jewish state. The Arabs would
sooner or later object to that. . . . There had to come a psychological clash between the Jew and the Arab, a clash between the
Jewish immigrant and the British colonial official. . . . A clash
between Jewish dynamics and dormant Arabia was inevitable.'

From the outset, the atmosphere of total lack of understanding
and sympathy, mistrust and suspicion, steadily darkened. Denied
the independence which they believed had been promised to them,
the Arab ruling-class was not slow to retaliate against the Jews
whom they held responsible. The scene was set for the agitator and
the killer; and at Easter 1920 occurred the first of the many com-
munal riots that have disgraced the Holy Land. The Chief Ad-
ministrator reported, 'I can definitely state that when the strain
came the Zionist Commission did not loyally accept the orders of
the Administration, but from the commencement adopted a
hostile, critical, and abusive attitude. It is a regrettable fact that,
with one or two exceptions, it appears impossible to convince a
Zionist of British good faith and ordinary honesty. They seek, not
justice from the military occupant, but that in every question in
which a Jew is interested, discrimination in his favour shall be
shown. . . . In Jerusalem, being in the majority, they are not
satisfied with military protection, but demand to take the law into
their own hands; in other places where they are in a minority they
clamour for military protection. . . . The representative of the
Jewish community threatens me with mob law, and refuses to
accept the constituted forces of law and order. . . . My own
authority and that of every department of my Administration is
claimed or impinged upon by the Zionist Commission. . . . This
Administration . . . has strictly adhered to the laws governing the
conduct of the military occupant of Enemy Territory, but that has
not satisfied the Zionists, who appear bent on committing the
temporary military administration to a partialist policy before the
issue of the Mandate. It is manifestly impossible to please partisans

---

[1] George Lichtheim, 4 June, 1946.
[2] Eliahu Ben-Horin, *The Middle East: Crossroads of History*, 132. For an explanation of the term Revisionist, see below, p. 179f.

who officially claim nothing more than a "National Home", but in reality will be satisfied with nothing less than a "Jewish State".' The Zionists promptly countercharged that, on account of the sympathy of some members of the military administration for the Arabs, there had been dilatoriness in suppressing the outbreak. The Lloyd George government abolished the military administration and replaced it by a civil one, with the Mandate as its charter.

It is illuminating that in the Mandate the only reference to the predominantly Arabic character of the population was still merely indirect, in the article which recognized Arabic as one of the three official languages.[1] The first High Commissioner Sir Herbert Samuel was, if not himself a Zionist, very sympathetically disposed to Zionism as he then understood it.[2] It must be said, however, that during his tenure of office he was conspicuously impartial, to the point of being strongly criticized by extreme Zionists for being pro-Arab. In 1921 he was violently denounced by the Zionist Congress for having recommended immigration 'within the limits fixed by the numbers and interests of the present population' to develop the country 'to the advantage of all its inhabitants'.[3] Another and more serious outbreak of Arab violence in 1921, arising out of a May-Day riot between two Jewish labour factions, was followed by the first of the many Inquiry Commissions which have visited Palestine. This Haycraft Commission declared that the Zionist Organization had 'desired to ignore the Arabs as a factor to be taken into serious consideration, or else has combated their interests to the advantage of the Jews', and that it had 'exercised an exacerbating rather than a conciliatory influence of the Arab population of Palestine, and has thus been a contributory cause of the disturbances'. In reply to Zionist arguments that Arab antagonism was directed more against British rule than against themselves, and had been artificially stimulated among the uneducated mass of the Arab population by the effendis, it declared that 'feeling against the Jews was too genuine, too widespread, and too intense to be accounted for in the above superficial

---

[1] Elsewhere the Arabs were described as 'the existing non-Jewish communities' (in the Preamble, quoting the Balfour Declaration); 'the inhabitants of Palestine, irrespective of race and religion' (Art. 2); 'other sections of the population' (Art. 6).

[2] Hyamson, op. cit., 131.

[3] Storrs comments, 'I cannot conceive that any Gentile High Commissioner could have weathered the storms of Zionist public opinion for five years.' (op. cit., 358, 392).

manner. If it means that had it not been for incitement by the not-ables, the effendis and the sheikhs, there would have been no riots, the allegation cannot be substantiated. .... Any anti-British feeling on the part of the Arabs that may have arisen in the country originates in the association of the Government with the further-ance of the policy of Zionism.'

Concerned at the continued unrest, the Cabinet resolved to make a new definition of its policy, which appeared in the 'Churchill White Paper' of 1922.   While affirming that the place of the Jews in Palestine was 'of right and not on sufferance', it marked a definite recognition of the hard facts of the situation, in that it did for the first time acknowledge the existence of the Arabs as such.   It remarked that 'unauthorized statements have been made to the effect that the purpose in view is to create a wholly Jewish Palestine. .... H.M. Government regard any such expecta-tion as impracticable and have no such aim in view. Nor have they at any time contemplated ... the disappearance or the subordina-tion of the Arabic population, language, or culture in Palestine. They would draw attention to the fact that the terms of the (Balfour) Declaration referred to do not contemplate that Palestine as a whole should be converted into a Jewish National Home, but that such a home should be founded *in Palestine.*'   The White Paper introduced for the first time the principle of 'economic ab-sorptive capacity' as a regulator of immigration.   It proposed to set up a Legislative Council, but this was boycotted by the Arabs, who refused to recognize the validity of the Mandate. The com-position of the proposed Council was indeed distinctly weighted against the Arabs, since, though Muslims and Christians combined still constituted 89 per cent. of the population, their ten elected members could be outvoted by the ten official members and the two elected Jewish representatives. A proposal to set up an Arab Organization with an official status comparable with that of the Zionist Organization was also rejected by the Arabs, 'since its members were to be nominated by the High Commissioner, him-self a Zionist, and the offer was conditional on its being understood that acceptance signified the settlement of all Arab claims, together with Arab recognition of the Balfour Declaration.'[1]

For the next six years a sullen but superficially quiet status quo was maintained.   By 1926 it had been possible to reduce the gar-

[1] Barbour, op. cit., 111.

rison, and entrust internal security to the R.A.F., to disband the British gendarmerie, and cut down the police. By 1928 the Jewish population had risen to 150,000, about two and a half times what it had been at the end of the War, and now amounted to 16 per cent. of the population. Jewish agricultural settlement had made marked progress, thanks to the boundless enthusiasm and devotion of the Pioneers; but funds for development were scarce, the economic situation difficult, unemployment rife, and in 1927 Jewish emigration exceeded immigration by 2,300. The Arab population also had rapidly increased in numbers, thanks to the very high birthrate, the cessation of the Turkish conscription which had taken many young men never to return, the lowering of the high deathrate for which the Public Health Department of the Government may claim at least some credit, and to some illegal immigration from neighbouring Arab countries. Beneath the superficial order and progress, however, 'a conflict had been created between two national ideals, and under the system imposed by the Mandate it could only be solved if one or both of these ideals were abandoned'.[1]

*   *   *

The lands east of the Jordan, which had been little more than nominally administered by the Ottoman government, were administered from 1918 by Faisal's Arab government at Damascus. However, at the San Remo Conference of April 1920 this region was assigned to Britain as part of the mandate for Palestine, with the proviso, however, that 'in the territories between the Jordan and the eastern boundary of Palestine as ultimately determined, the mandatory shall be entitled, with the consent of the Council of the League of Nations, to postpone or withhold application of such provisions of this mandate as he may consider inapplicable to the existing local conditions, and to make such provision for the administration of the territories as he may consider suitable to those conditions'.[2]   Soon after the collapse of the Damascus Arab government before the French in July 1920, therefore, the High Commissioner for Palestine convened the local Arab notables at as-Salt, then the principal town of the region, and informed them

[1] *Royal Commission Report* (1937), 61.
[2] Mandate, Art. 25.

that H.M. Government intended to grant them immediate self-government with the help of a few British advisers. Local councils were accordingly set up in the four principal towns; but before any coherent administrative system could take shape, the Amir Abdullah arrived in February 1921 with an Arab force at Ma'an, which had been provisionally left within the boundaries of his father's kingdom of the Hijaz, and announced his intention of raising a rebellion against the French in Syria. He advanced to Amman, was welcomed by the local councils and unopposed by the British, and took over the effective administration. At the close of the Cairo Conference in April, the Colonial Secretary, Mr. Churchill, agreed to recognize him as *de facto* ruler of Transjordan, provided that he abandoned his aggressive intentions against the French and accepted British protection and financial help in setting up a modern administration. In September 1922 Britain secured the consent of the Council of the League, as provided for in Art. 25 of the Mandate, to the exemption of Transjordan from all the clauses of the Mandate concerned with the establishment of a Jewish National Home, including the Mandatory's obligation to facilitate Jewish immigration and land-settlement. In 1923 Britain recognized the existence of an 'independent government in Transjordan under the rule of the Amir Abdullah, provided that such government is constitutional.'

From that time Abdullah steered a skilful course towards independence and kingship, which he achieved in 1946.[1] The material poverty of this thinly-populated state on the desert-margin caused him to continue to welcome British financial and technical support for his Arab Legion, which laid him open to the extremist charge of being subservient to Britain; and at the same time it stimulated the King's innate expansionist ambitions and so led to his assassination in July 1951.[2] Abdullah was rumoured to have favoured economic collaboration with the Zionists, if he had been freer to disregard Arab opinion; but it might have proved an unequal partnership, since the Zionists had never excluded from their considerations 'those great, desolate,

[1] On achieving independence Abdullah gave his state the title of The Hāshimi Kingdom of the Jordan. Since its incorporation of the remnant of Arab Palestine in April 1950, the former name Transjordan ceased to be geographically appropriate to the enlarged state.

[2] See Esmond Wright: 'Abdullah's Jordan, 1947–1951', *Middle East Journal*, Summer 1951, p. 439.

and uncultivated [sic] stretches of land across the river'.[1] With the disappearance of Abdullah and the decline of British prestige, the future of Jordan is something of an enigma.

*   *   *

During the war Britain had sought to protect her pre-eminent position in the Arabian Peninsula by agreements with France and Italy by which these powers undertook not to acquire, nor to consent to a third power acquiring, territory in Arabia or a naval base in the Red Sea. Britain had also from the beginning been on friendly terms with the young Wahhabi Amir Abdul Aziz ibn Sa'ud. Early in the war she, like the Arab nationalists, had sent emissaries to him to enlist his support for an Arab rising against the Turks; but the pro-Turkish Amir of the Jebel Shammar to the north, his ancestral enemy, was too nearly a match for him to give more than moral support. It was psychologically difficult for him to make common cause with the Sharif Husain, the ruler of Mecca and Madina, those centres of what the strict Wahhabis regarded as idolatrous and corrupt saint-worship unauthorized by the Qur'an and Sunna; and the Sharif made matters worse by his assumption in 1916 of the title of King of the Arabs. With his Ottoman culture and his overweening personal ambition he evidently regarded Ibn Sa'ud as a barbarian upstart, and behaved to him with 'a show of studied condescension and even discourtesy' combined with 'somewhat highhanded methods'.[2]

Turkish support for the Shammar having ceased with the collapse of the Ottoman Empire, Ibn Sa'ud was able to annex their territory in 1921, and was now in a position to settle scores with King Husain. He had already for some years been making Wahhabi propaganda among the tribes on the Hijaz border to win them away from Husain, and when Abdullah had led a force against him in 1919 had severely defeated him. He was at that time deterred from invading the Hijaz by the British government, which was still supporting Husain. But the old King, with greater consistency than worldly wisdom, broke with Britain, mainly over the political disability imposed on the Arabs of Palestine by the Balfour

---

[1] Moshe Shertok, 24 January 1946 (since 1948 Moshe Sharett, Foreign Minister of Israel).
[2] Antonius, op. cit., 329.

Declaration and the Mandate. Refusing to compromise on this point, he forfeited Britain's support and subsidy. At the same time he had been misguided enough to intrigue against Ibn Sa'ud with such enemies or potential rivals of his as the Shammar, tribal chiefs of outer Najd, and the Imam of the Yemen. He became involved in an unnecessary quarrel with Egypt about the medieval sanitary conditions of the Holy Places; and in 1924 he alienated what remaining support he had in Islam by having himself proclaimed Caliph. Ibn Sa'ud invaded the Hijaz. Husain abdicated in favour of his eldest son Ali; but the Wahhabi prince in the following year drove out Ali and annexed the Hijaz. His former 'semi-vassal' relationship to Britain was now clearly out-of-date; and in 1927 by the Treaty of Jidda Britain recognized him as sovereign and independent King of the Hijaz, Najd, and its Dependencies, which were later fused as the Kingdom of Sa'udi Arabia. Ibn Sa'ud in return undertook to maintain friendly relations with the British-protected sheikhdoms of the Persian Gulf. He had already acknowledged the presence of Husain's two sons Faisal and Abdullah on the thrones of Iraq and Transjordan, and allowed Britain to determine his frontiers with these two states; but in respect of his frontier with Transjordan he has always maintained mental reservations which may yet disturb relations between the two kingdoms.

★   ★   ★

The Sykes-Picot Agreement of 1915 had arranged that the Fertile Crescent should be divided into four areas, two to be directly administered by France and Britain respectively, while the other two should be administered by Arab governments under the guidance and protection of France and Britain respectively. France's direct share was to be the Syrian coastlands and Cilicia, while her protectorate was to consist of the hinterland of Syria including the vilayet of Mosul. By 1919 British troops had however occupied the Mosul vilayet after driving out the Turks; and Lloyd George succeeded with great difficulty in persuading Clemenceau to give up the French claim, so that this oil-bearing district could be added to Iraq. The French were compensated by the transfer to them of the German quarter-share in the Turkish Petroleum Co., now renamed the Iraq Petroleum Co., and the promise that France should have a quarter-share of its output.

Britain handed over to her the military occupation of the Syrian coastlands, while the independent Arabs under Faisal still governed the cities of the interior. The situation was very unstable. The Arabs resented and feared the very presence of the French: France's part in the campaign against the Turks had been confined to the presence of a small token-force, and the Arabs could not be expected to agree that her enormous sacrifices on the Western Front entitled her to claims on Syria. The French, on the other hand, had no sympathy for the Arab Revolt or for Arab nationalism in general, having in mind their millions of Arabic-speaking subjects in North Africa; they regarded these phenomena as a British manoeuvre to trick France out of her rightful legacy in Syria. Her claim was carried back to the Crusades, in which France had played a preponderant part, and was reinforced by the educational missions, and railways and other public utilities she had established in the country. Nevertheless, over 60 per cent. of the petitions presented to the King-Crane Commission in 1919 protested directly and strongly against a French mandate.

In April 1920, one month after a 'General Syrian Congress' of nationalists had proclaimed an independent kingdom of Greater Syria, including Lebanon and Palestine, with Faisal as King, the San Remo Conference awarded France the mandate for the whole of Syria. The French now had legal authority to deal with the unfriendly Arab administration in the interior, whose troops had unofficially attacked French military positions near the demarcation-line between the two zones, while the Arab authorities had carried on anti-French propaganda, and obstructed French commerce; the French in their turn were not guiltless of counter-provocation. In July 1920 General Gouraud sent Faisal an ultimatum demanding satisfaction on all these points, and the unqualified acceptance of the French mandate for the whole country. While Faisal was attempting to negotiate, there were armed clashes between his troops and the French. The latter then occupied Damascus and expelled him from the country. Masters of the situation, they could now reshape the prostrate bulk of Syria at their will. Conscious that their main support lay in the Maronites of the Lebanon, that the other Christian communities were only lukewarm, and that they were cordially disliked by the bulk of the Muslims, they decided to ease their task by an unashamed policy of 'divide-and-rule', by exploiting and widening the religious divisions with which Syria, more than any other Middle Eastern country, is vexed. Sunni Muslim Arabs constitute about 53 per cent. only of the population of Syria and Lebanon combined. Some minorities form more-or-less compact geographical blocks: the 340,000 Maronites in the Mountain Lebanon; the 325,000 Alawis or Nusairiya[1] in the Jebel Nusairiya (Ansariya) along the northern half of the coast; the 160,000 Druze, mainly in the Jebel Druze but also in Lebanon; perhaps as many as 200,000 Kurds in the Jazira of the north-east. The separatist tendencies of all these minorities, which had undoubtedly suffered discrimination at the hands of the Sunnis under Ottoman rule, were encouraged. In 1920 the old sanjaq of Lebanon was expanded to three times its size by the inclusion of the predominantly Muslim towns of Beirut, Tripoli, and Saida (Sidon); South Lebanon down to the Palestine frontier, with a predominantly Shi'i population; and the fertile Biq'a, with a mixed population consisting mainly of Muslims and Orthodox Christians. In this enlarged Lebanon the Maronites no longer had an absolute majority as in the old sanjaq, and Christians of all sects constituted only a precarious majority.[2] This weakening of the Christian position was perhaps designed to make them more dependent on French protection and less inclined to follow a nationalist line of their own. In 1921 the Jebel Druze, and in 1922 the Territory of the Alawis, were recognized by the French as independent. The remainder of Syria was divided in 1920 into the two states of Damascus and Aleppo, in an attempt to exploit the traditional rivalry between the two great cities but this experiment did not last, and in 1924 the two states were united.

Having thus dismembered the country, the French set to work to impose their cultural pattern on it in a fashion which was passively accepted by the inarticulate majority, but was bound to estrange further the minority that had political aspirations. The pinning of the Syro-Lebanese currency to the French franc, though logical, had the unfortunate effect of causing it to follow the franc's severe devaluation. The teaching of French was carried to such a pitch that it was reported that in some districts children

[1] Their religion is a curious amalgam of Shi'i Islam, with early Christian and pagan elements; cf. *Encyclopaedia of Islam*, art. Nusairi.

[2] The Christians may now have ceased to be the majority, in consequence of emigration and the higher Muslim birth-rate; but no census has been held for over twenty years.

who could scarcely read Arabic were taught the Marseillaise. Specially-prepared history-books were at pains to demonstrate that the Syrians were not ethnically Arab. The administrative machine was frequently abused to further the interests of French companies and concession-holders. As instruments of their policy the French made great use of two minority communities foreign to Syria and without any defined habitat in the country: the Circassians, who had been introduced by the Turks fifty years before when their homeland was annexed by Russia; and the Armenians who had escaped the Turkish massacres during and after the War. The former made useful if undisciplined soldiers, especially apt for punitive expeditions and for garrisoning restive districts; the latter, with their keen intelligence and sense of superiority to other Levantines, gave good service as informers.

By 1925 the ruling families of the Jebel Druze, who had not originally been averse to French rule in preference to Sunnis from Damascus, had grown restive under their impetuous French local governor, who may be described as a French equivalent of Arnold Wilson: 'sincere, disinterested, energetic; extremely effective in putting his immediate aims into action, especially when they were related to the production of material results; but he was tyrannical in his methods, and psychologically blind in his dealings with human beings, to a degree which made it inevitable that his well-meant efforts should end in disaster. During twenty months he forced upon the outraged but intimidated Druze a host of material benefits which they neither dreamt of nor desired.'[1] Protests to the French High Commissioner met with a discourteous rebuff and the four principal Druze leaders were arrested as conspirators. This was followed by a general rising in the Jebel, landlords and tenants together, which completely overpowered the French garrison. The revolt spread to the cities of Syria, the rebels being well-organized and led by members of the great families and ex-Ottoman officers with military experience.[2] By November 1925 the French began to gain the upper hand by greatly increasing their garrison, but they did not penetrate the Jebel Druze till the early summer of 1926, and peace was not finally restored for another year. The rebellion had been even more costly in lives and

[1] Toynbee, *Islamic World after the Peace Conference*, Part III, sec. vii.
[2] Such as Fawzi al-Qawuqji, who was to lead the Palestine Arab rebels in 1936 and served the Axis during the Second World War.

money than the Iraq Rebellion, and the French had twice found it necessary to bombard the centre of Damascus by artillery and air-craft, killing over a thousand persons. The revolt had, however, taught the French that it was impossible to hold down Syria in-definitely by martial law. The series of military High Com-missioners was ended in November 1925, and in 1926 the first High Commissioner with civil administrative experience was ap-pointed. The Lebanese Republic had been proclaimed in 1926, and an attempt was made to reach an understanding with the more moderate Syrian nationalists, but without success; the first two nominal Presidents of Syria were both aliens, a Turk and a Cir-cassian.

*   *   *

B. *The Inter-War Period*

The unilateral British declaration of Egyptian independence in 1922 did not immediately bring about the end of violent agitation, since the Wafd refused to accept the limitations imposed on Egyptian sovereignty by the Four Reserved Points. Encouraged by the successes of the Turkish nationalists in extorting major con-cessions from Britain and France by armed force, the Wafd con-ducted a murder campaign inspired by well-educated fanatics and executed by weak-minded students and a number of professional killers. In Cairo four British subjects and two Egyptian moderates were murdered, and nine British wounded. The Egyptian public, intimidated by the terrorists, gave no help to the police, and it was left to a special force under British direction to track them down: three students were executed and ten imprisoned.

At the beginning of 1924 general elections had produced the combination of the first Wafdist government in Egypt and the first Labour government in Britain, some of whose members when in Opposition had shown sympathy for Wafdist aspirations. Zaghlul was invited to London to negotiate, but demanded in effect complete independence, with the withdrawal of all British troops, the return of the Sudan to Egypt, etc. This was far too much for the British government which observed that, while British troops would not interfere in the functioning of the Egyptian government nor encroach on its sovereignty, no British govern-ment could divest itself of all interest in the defence of the Canal, nor could the good administration and development of the Sudan be jeopardized. Zaghlul showed himself as inflexible as ever in negotiation, and returned to Egypt without achieving anything. Meanwhile his government had made gestures hostile to the presence of the British garrison and the position of the Sirdar, the British commander-in-chief of the Egyptian Army. On 19 November the Sirdar, Sir Lee Stack, was murdered in the streets of Cairo. On his own initiative Allenby presented to the Egyptian government an ultimatum in which the following were the principal demands:

(1) The withdrawal from the Sudan of all Egyptian officers and purely Egyptian units, which had been inciting the Sudanese troops to mutiny, with some effect.

(2) Egyptian consent to the unlimited irrigation of the Sudanese cotton-growing district of the Gazira, which had previously been limited to ensure adequate water-supplies to Egypt.

(3) Payment of a fine of £500,000.

The British colony in Egypt, prone as ever to 'Egyptophobia', was indignant at the 'weakness' of Allenby's ultimatum; but the Foreign Office instructed him to moderate the second and third of the above demands; and there is no doubt that the threat to divert Nile water from Egypt for unlimited irrigation in the Sudan has, in spite of subsequent agreement on this vital subject, left Egyptians with the uncomfortable realization that the water supplies on which their economy depends are at Britain's mercy as long as she remains in control of the Sudan.

The Lee Stack murder was the culmination of the murder-campaign, in which a number of the younger Wafd leaders[1] were charged with criminal complicity. The Wafd government fell, leaving the ground free for King Fuad to take a more active part in the country's politics. The son of Isma'il and now in the prime of his life, he had inherited enough of the autocratic spirit of his line not to accept tamely the limited authority of a constitutional monarch. As a Europeanized Turk who spoke but indifferent Arabic, he despised the middle-class Egyptian politicians of the Wafd, and their demagogic appeal to the city-rabble and the ignorant rural masses. The greatest landowner in Egypt, he mis-

---

[1] These included Ahmed Mahir and Mahmud Fahmi an-Nuqrashi, both of whom later became Prime Minister and fell to extremist gunmen, in 1945 and 1948 respectively.

trusted the radical and republican tendencies of the younger Wafdists; and he was therefore ready to exploit to the full the considerable powers left to him under the constitution, especially those of nominating a third of the Senate and dissolving at will the Chamber of Deputies. Even before the Wafd came to power in 1924, he had had an unsuccessful struggle with the moderates in an attempt to enlarge his powers; and now he dissolved the Chamber of Deputies with its overwhelming Wafdist majority and ruled without a parliament through a newly-formed group of 'King's friends', the Ittihad party.[1] So unpopular was this régime, however, that the moderate Liberal party joined the Wafd in a coalition against it; and early in 1926 the new British High Commissioner pressed the King to permit the holding of a general election. It returned the Wafd to power with over 70 per cent. of the seats.[2] In view of the murder-campaign under the previous Wafd government, Britain refused to accept Zaghlul as Prime Minister; and a compromise was reached by which the Liberal leader headed a cabinet of six Wafdists, three Liberals and an Independent, with Zaghlul President of the Chamber.

In 1927 Sarwat Pasha, now Prime Minister in this coalition, came to London and the Foreign Office put forward for negotiation a draft treaty closely following the recommendations of the Milner Report. The Foreign Secretary, Sir Austen Chamberlain, described it as 'the high-water mark of British concessions to Egyptian nationalism'. The difference of views between the two sides was narrowed down to two points: (1) the British personnel in the Egyptian Army, whom Britain was prepared to convert into a military mission, and (2) the maintenance of British officials in the Departments of Police and Public Security pending the reform of the Capitulations. On this point Britain undertook to support an Egyptian appeal to the League of Nations if the reform had not been effected within five years.

At this stage, however, Mustafa an-Nahhas, who had just succeeded to the leadership of the Wafd on the death of Zaghlul, took the party into opposition to the draft treaty because it did not

---

[1] Its founder Hasan Nash'at became Egyptian Ambassador to Britain in the earlier years of the Second World War.

[2] During the thirty years of constitutional government the Wafd was the only party-machine covering the whole country: the other parties were little more than small groups centred round certain personalities without any apparent positive principles other than personal hostility to the Wafdist leaders.

amount to a complete British evacuation of Egypt. A majority of Sarwat's coalition cabinet voted against the treaty and he resigned. Nahhas now headed an entirely Wafdist cabinet, and soon came into conflict with both the High Commissioner and the King. In June 1928, three months after the formation of the Wafd government, some Egyptian newspapers published an alleged agreement by which, before they came into office, Nahhas and the new vice-president of the Chamber of Deputies were stated to have undertaken to secure the handing-over of the insane prince Saif ud-Din's estate, now being administered by the King, to the prince's mother in return for the payment to them of £150,000. The King dismissed Nahhas and issued a royal decree dissolving both Houses of Parliament and legalizing the postponement of elections for three years.

The High Commissioner, Lord Lloyd, whose conception of the British position in Egypt was as conservative as his handling of affairs was masterful, had several times come into conflict with successive Egyptian governments. The Foreign Office came to feel that their representative was in danger of over-stressing Britain's position, and in May 1929, therefore, he was sent a redefinition of British policy, which contained the following important passage: 'Because the interests at stake are of supreme importance to the safety and well-being of the Empire, H.M. Government reserved by the Declaration of 1922 certain matters for its own determination, but even in these cases it is the desire of H.M. Government to act with, and where possible through, the Egyptian Government, respecting in the largest possible measure the liberties and independence which by the same Declaration they conceded to Egypt.

'It is not in the interest of H.M. Government to intervene in the internal affairs of Egypt further than is necessary to secure the political objects defined above. The influence which they must ever possess in the councils of Egypt will be best secured by ensuring that the closest harmony shall always govern the relations between the Residency and the Government, and these conditions can only obtain if the interventions of H.M. Government into the purely internal affairs of Egypt are reduced to a minimum. . . .'[1]

[1] On three occasions between 1927 and 1930 British warships were despatched to Alexandria, twice to exert political pressure on the Egyptian government and once to be in readiness in case political disturbances got out of hand. (*Survey of International Affairs*, 1936, 663, n. 1.)

The advent to office of the second Labour government in 1929 brought the Egyptian Liberal Prime Minister Mohammed Mahmud to London to reopen negotiations, hoping for greater consideration than Sarwat had received from the Conservatives. While these were in progress, however, a general election in Egypt produced once again a sweeping victory for the Wafd, and Nahhas came to London in 1930 to take the place of Mohammed Mahmud. The Sudan proved a stumbling-block, since Nahhas insisted that, pending a final agreement, there should be no restriction on Egyptian immigration into the Sudan, while the furthest concession Britain would make was that 'the Governor-General would not exercise unreasonably the right which any government has to control immigration in the interests of its own nationals'. The Wafdist press had created the impression in Egypt that the Labour government was prepared to concede anything, and Nahhas thus had to justify himself in the eyes of the extremists by obtaining terms conspicuously better than those offered to Mohammed Mahmud. When a report did reach Cairo that Nahhas might be disposed to compromise, he was violently attacked as a traitor.

Meanwhile, mindful of his humiliating dismissal from office by the King in 1928, he had drafted two bills which would prevent the King from ruling without parliament in future. The King refused to give the royal assent to these, holding that, inasmuch as the Wafd was the only party with a country-wide organization, the diminution of the powers of the Crown would amount to the creation of a permanent Wafd dictatorship. Nahhas resigned in protest, and the King invited Isma'il Sidqi, now one of the wealthiest men in Egypt and a bitter opponent of the Wafd, to form a government. Thus driven into opposition, Nahhas began a campaign for non-co-operation with the government and refusal to pay taxes. There were serious disorders all over the country, and Sidqi dissolved parliament and prepared to 'make' an election, returning to the pre-1924 system of voting in two stages as a check on demagogy and providing for the nomination by the King of three-fifths of the Senate. He banned Wafdist newspapers and prohibited the holding of the annual Wafdist congress. This was too much for the Liberal-Constitutionals, to which party Sidqi himself belonged, and they joined the Wafd in boycotting the elections. Nothing daunted,

Sidqi formed round himself a new party, which he cynically called the Sha'b or People. At the election in May 1931 the Sha'b and the Ittihad 'King's Friends' won a comfortable majority. The Wafd tried to organize the growing Trades Union movement to make political difficulties for the government, to which Sidqi replied by dissolving the unions. In 1933, however, he had to resign, as his health had been impaired by overwork. There followed what amounted to the virtual dictatorship of the Director of the Royal Estates. Palace rule did not prove to be appreciably better for Egypt than so-called democratic rule, since public money was now poured out on an enormous civil list and other expenditure without much value to the public.[1]

The Italian invasion of Abyssinia in the summer of 1935 brought a new note of urgency to the question of an Anglo-Egyptian settlement. In December a united front composed of Nahhas, Sidqi, and Mohammed Mahmud sent a note to the High Commissioner declaring their readiness to conclude the draft treaty of 1930. The British replied, however, that in the light of the Abyssinian War the military clauses needed revision, and that it was desirable to reach a preliminary agreement on the status of the Sudan. Negotiations began in March 1936 with an all-party delegation consisting of seven Wafdists and six non-Wafdists. There was still a considerable gap to be bridged between the views of the British and the Egyptian negotiators, and the unaccommodating attitude of the British service advisers, unsympathetic as ever towards Egyptian national aspirations, called forth a reproof from *The Times*: 'It is natural enough that the technical advisers of H.M. Government should recommend such a military agreement as would achieve an ideal security for this country's interests for ever . . . but the military ideal of 100 per cent. security takes no account of the political side of the question. . . . An alliance, if it is to have any real value, must be based on respect for national feeling. It must be freely negotiated, not dictated; and one of its primary conditions . . . is that it should be inspired by a spirit of mutual trust. This spirit will hardly be encouraged by efforts to persuade the delegates to make concessions for which their countrymen would never forgive them, in the hopeless quest for the unattainable ideal of a perfect military security for all time and in all circumstances. An alliance based upon common interests and confidence is surely worth

[1] *Round Table*, December 1936, 110 ff.

minor military risks, some of which are likely to prove imaginary on closer examination. . . .'[1]

In the end a Treaty was successfully negotiated, and signed in August 1936. It was for twenty years, but capable of revision any time after ten years. (1) Its principle was that of a close military alliance, which was to be maintained in any revised form of the Treaty until its final expiration. Each country was to aid the other in the event of war, and was to give Britain all facilities, including the imposition of martial law and an effective censorship, in the event of any threatened international emergency. Each country undertook not to conduct its foreign policy in any way inconsistent with the Treaty.

(2) Egypt recognized the vital interest to Britain of ensuring the liberty and entire security of navigation in the Canal, and accordingly granted Britain the right to retain troops in the Canal Zone, to the number of 10,000 land-troops and 400 R.A.F. pilots with the necessary ancillary services, until it should be agreed that the Egyptian forces could themselves assume full responsibility for the Canal. Egypt was to build specified strategic roads, and to improve the railways in the Canal Zone and the Western Desert. As soon as all these works were sufficiently advanced, British troops would be withdrawn from Cairo. The British Navy might continue to use Alexandria for not more than eight years. Britain would provide a military mission to the Egyptian army, which would obtain its equipment from Britain and send its specialists there for training.

(3) Egyptian troops, officials, and immigrants were once again to be admitted to the Sudan, though the Egyptian government recognized that the primary purpose of the Condominium was the welfare of the Sudanese, and that the Sudan government would appoint British or Egyptian officials only if qualified Sudanese were not available (an important recognition, for the first time, of the growing Sudanese claim to manage their own affairs).

(4) The Egyptian government would henceforth be responsible for the protection of the foreign communities, and Britain undertook to support its approaches to the capitulatory Powers to remove the restrictions on the application of Egyptian legislation to foreigners. Egypt undertook not to impose on foreigners legislation inconsistent with modern principles or to discriminate

[1] Quoted by *Survey of International Affairs*, 1936, 687 f.

against them. The abolition of the Capitulations was finally negotiated in the Montreux Convention of 1937.

(5) Britain was to be represented in Egypt by an Ambassador taking precedence over all foreign representatives.

Thus after seventeen years of fruitless negotiation, the gap that separated the Egyptian demand for complete independence and the British conception of what powers it was necessary to retain in Egypt in the interests of imperial security was bridged by concessions from both sides. But these concessions were made only because both parties were acutely aware of the menace to their respective interests from Italy, now an aggressive Mediterranean and Red Sea Power; and there was no reason to suppose that, if this menace were removed, Egyptian nationalist sentiment would not once more compel its leaders to seek to achieve complete independence by obtaining the evacuation of the British forces, freedom to follow a foreign policy untrammelled by the alliance with Britain, and the reassertion in fact of Egypt's sovereignty over the Sudan.

*　　*　　*

In Iraq the final ratification of the Treaty of 1924 was followed by a marked reduction in the number of British and Indian officials, but left in being a Dual Control whose proper working called for patience and tact on both sides. The nice relation between Iraqi officials and British advisers and inspectors was made more delicate by the fact that the British were paid more than their Iraqi nominal superiors, and that they were permanent while the Iraqis were liable to change with every government; and these changed far too frequently for good administration. Thus there was often friction between the Iraqis and British, leading to deadlocks which sometimes lasted for several months, impeding the administration and confirming the Iraqis in their opinion that the British officials were primarily interested in furthering imperial policy rather than in the welfare of Iraq. The Iraqi officials, on their side, were not yet ready to accept a western type of administration and fiscal system, democratic institutions, and the principle of government by the consent of the governed, in so far as these things varied from the methods and institutions time-honoured under the Ottoman Empire. The privileged ruling-class refused to give up the practices which they had found so lucrative under the Ottomans, and both the tax-system and the execution of the law were given a pronounced bias in their favour.

In 1925 the Council of the League of Nations was so doubtful about the fitness of Iraq for self-government that it recommended that the Mandate should continue for twenty-five years, unless she were previously admitted as a member of the League. Two years later the British government announced that it would propose the admission of Iraq in 1932 'provided that all went well in the interval, and the present rate of progress in Iraq was maintained'; it insisted, however, on a government 'friendly and bound by gratitude and obligation' to Britain. In 1928 the Iraqi government asked that it should be allowed to assume immediate responsibility for external and internal defence, and that British control of the army should cease. It rejected counter-proposals, and for three months Iraq was without a government. Sir Gilbert Clayton, the recently-appointed High Commissioner, urged the British government to break the deadlock by a declaration that would at least partially satisfy Iraqi aspirations. He died in 1929, but was the posthumous father of the Treaty of 1930, which was to come into force when Iraq was admitted to the League of Nations, and to last for twenty-five years: (1) Britain was to have air-bases at Habbaniya, in the desert west of Baghdad, and at Shu'aiba near Basra, and to have the right to move troops and supplies across Iraq by any means.

(2) In the event of war or the threat of war Iraq was to furnish Britain with all facilities and assistance, and place all means of communication at her disposal.

(3) Britain's diplomatic representative was to have precedence over those of all foreign Powers.

(4) Britain would continue to give military assistance to Iraq and send her a military mission. Iraqi service personnel sent abroad for training would normally go to Britain, and when engaging foreign experts Iraq would give preference to British subjects.

(5) Britain would sponsor Iraq's admission to the League of Nations.

The Treaty was ratified by a comfortable majority in the Iraqi parliament, and the progressive transfer of the administration to Iraqis was accelerated, though the High Commissioner had frequently to restrain an inclination to disregard British advice and cancel the contracts of British officials. When Iraq's application for admission came before the League of Nations, there was some scepticism about her fitness which was dissipated only by a British guarantee which stated that 'H.M. Government have never re-garded the attainment of an ideal standard of administrative efficiency and stability as a necessary condition either of the termi-nation of the mandate or the admission of Iraq to membership of the League; nor has it been their conception that Iraq should from the first be able to challenge comparison with the most highly-developed and civilized nations in the modern world.' Britain's argument was accepted and Iraq admitted.

In Faisal's reign 1921-33 Iraq had no fewer than fifteen govern-ments, and twenty-one more in the four years 1933-36. All these were merely the reshufflings of a small and narrow group of professional politicians, well-to-do landowners and merchants, outside which there was no adequate class from which to draw responsible and public-spirited officials, and no substantial body of literate and informed citizens. 90 per cent. of the population was still illiterate. The government was not controlled by the Chamber of Deputies; instead it was the government that 'made' the Chamber, often during the mandatory period under pressure from the British High Commissioner. Confidential orders from the government to the provincial mutasarrifs were sufficient, except in Baghdad, to ensure the election of government candidates. In 1925 all but four of the government candidates were returned. In 1928 half of the twenty-two opposition deputies had previously been given the government coupon. Political parties were abolished as a sign of 'national unity' when Iraq became independent in 1932, and were revived only in 1946. Nuri as-Sa'id has described in an interview with an Egyptian newspaper how elections to the Chamber of Deputies have been managed: 'Nominations to the elections are arranged so as to include the names of all former prime-ministers, all ministers who were in office more than twice, the presiding officers of parliament, eminent ex-officials receiving government pensions, distinguished heads of communities and professional men, tribal chiefs, etc. These make up nearly 60 per cent. of the Chamber; the remainder depends for the most part on the will of the government in power, though such Iraqis as wish to put themselves forward may also submit their candidacy.'[1]

With the diminution and ending of direct British influence the only check on this narrow oligarchy, in which personal interest

[1] Quoted in *Middle East Times* (Jerusalem), 28 February, 1946.

prevailed over public spirit, was that of King Faisal. When the constitution was first promulgated, the King announced his withdrawal from direct participation in the affairs of state. But as time passed, acting on the advice of the British authorities, he not only resumed his place as the executive of the state but even exceeded his constitutional powers. Every Prime Minister had to choose ministers not only prepared to deal sensibly with relations between Britain and Iraq, but also with the King's personal wishes, likes and dislikes. As the point of balance between Britain and his people he had every encouragement to concentrate power within himself. The British used him as an instrument of their control and 'encouraged him to go beyond the strict interpretation of the constitution in order that their control might be more complete'. He manipulated his position adroitly to win concessions, sometimes encouraging the anti-British forces, and at others using his influence in the interests of moderation, e.g. to obtain the ratification of the Treaty of 1930. His influence was on the whole good. He initiated a scheme by which the oil-revenues were earmarked for definite development-projects, and favoured the settlement of the tribes, who still constituted about one-sixth of the total population. It is possible that if the King had not assumed the role of benevolent despot, the political system might have faltered and even collapsed entirely. Without his guiding influence it is probable that in their impatience the people would have refused to agree to the obligations imposed by Britain as the price of her assistance, in which case Britain would either have been forced to resume direct control or withdraw, delaying Iraq's achievement of independence.[1]

King Faisal died in 1933, and was succeeded by his twenty-one year-old son Ghazi. Almost immediately on his accession the country was plunged into the emotional crisis of the Assyrian incident. The Assyrians were Nestorian Christian mountaineers from the region of Lake Van, whom in their original habitat the Commission set up by the League of Nations to inquire into the incident described as 'in normal times just as truculent as the Kurdish tribes and no less savage'. In the Ottoman Empire they had been treated rather better than other Christian minorities, enjoying a fairly large measure of local autonomy under the rule of their hereditary Patriarchs. However, when the Russians invaded north-east Anatolia in 1915, the Assyrians rose in sympathy with

[1] Ireland, op. cit., 420 ff.

them as Christians. Abandoned by the Russians on the outbreak
of the Revolution in 1917, some 20,000 fought their way south
through the Turkish lines to join forces with the British in northern
Iraq, losing twice that number en route. Some were now settled
in northern Iraq and took some 'rather drastic steps' to clear the
area of the existing Muslim population. In 1920 an Assyrian band
attempted to establish a buffer-state on the Turco-Persian frontier,
but the venture degenerated into an indiscriminate raid on both
unfriendly and friendly Turks. In 1921 the British began to form
the 'Iraq Levies' from their excellent fighting-men, as being the
one element in the mixed population on whom they could rely for
suppressing sporadic Kurdish risings and expelling Turkish irregulars from northern Iraq. In 1924 two companies of the Assyrian levies mutinied in Kirkuk, killing fifty of the Turkish
townspeople. From this time onward their exploits were less
remarkable, but they continued to be employed and favoured by
the R.A.F. for their qualities as garrison-troops, and the Anglican
Church encouraged them as a Christian minority which had
suffered persecution and was, moreover, because of its ancient
heresy, not protected by any other Christian church. Thus the
patronage of Britain encouraged the young and inexperienced
Assyrian Patriarch Mar Shimun[1] and some of their secular chiefs to
presume too much, and to isolate themselves still further from the
other inhabitants of Iraq. With the ending of the Mandate in 1932
the Iraqi government was ready to settle old scores with this un-
invited and overweening minority. A party of 800 Assyrians
crossed the Tigris into Syria in the hope that the French would allow
them to settle, but recrossed and destroyed an Iraqi post. The
Iraqi main body defeated this party, with wild excitement at
having broken the Assyrian reputation for invincibility. The same
Iraqi troops then attacked another group of 400 Assyrians, who
were not at all in agreement with their leaders' hostile attitude towards the Iraqi government and had taken refuge in an Iraqi
police-post. The Iraqis first disarmed them, and then murdered
them in cold blood, before going on to sack and destroy twenty
Assyrian villages and badly damage twenty more out of a total of
sixty-four. There is little doubt that the massacre was, if not premeditated, at least arranged by the local army-officers and that
some local civil officials must have connived at it. The news was

[1] He is now in the U.S.A.

received in Baghdad with savage rejoicing, as a national triumph over this Quisling minority.[1]

Young King Ghazi openly displayed his approval of the part played by Iraqi troops in this discreditable affair, decorated the colours of the regiments involved, and conferred on their Kurdish commanding-officer Bakir Sidqi the title of pasha. He thereby won immense popularity, which he tried to exploit for the manipulating of cabinets and governments after the manner of his father; but he lacked his father's personality, and government degenerated into the intrigues of political cliques. Between 1932 and 1936 cabinets rose and fell at an average of more than five a year. Then in 1936 Bakr Sidqi, who had in the meantime suppressed a tribal revolt with great ability and ruthlessness, advanced with a military force and air-support on Baghdad, demanding the dismissal of the cabinet 'with which the army had lost patience' and the formation of a cabinet of 'sincere citizens'. The existing government had suppressed newspapers, heavily bribed tribal leaders to keep the peace, curbed the opposition, and dismissed over 300 officials, many of them highly-placed. There was a general feeling that the country was making no progress; but Sidqi's principal grievance was that the army vote had been cut and that its organization was not being carried out according to his ideas. He was supported by many aspiring politicians who were out of office. In order to shake the morale of the cabinet he had Baghdad bombed from the air; and when the Minister of Defence, the honoured Ja'far al-'Askari, a veteran of the Arab Revolt, sought to negotiate, he had him treacherously murdered. There was no further opposition to the formation of a new government with Bakr Sidqi as military dictator. King Ghazi 'possibly connived at, and certainly did not disapprove' of this coup d'etat, but achieved no increase of power from it. The dictatorship showed itself no more effective than previous governments, and after the murder of Bakr Sidqi in 1937 constitutional government was outwardly restored under the same old round of politicians. But the army had tasted power and sought to hold on to it, backed up by

---

[1] This summary of the historical background of the Assyrian incident draws on the following sources:
Toynbee, *The Islamic World after the Peace Conference*, 483 ff.
Sir H. Dobbs, High Commissioner of Iraq, in *Gertrude Bell's Letters*, II, 551.
G. Antonius, op. cit., 365 ff.
J. Van Ess, *Meet the Arabs*, 152 f.

the young men whose imaginations and desires were kept at fever-heat by the Palestine Rebellion and the grievances of Syria against the French.

* * *

In Palestine the comparatively peaceful years that followed the 1922 White Paper were used by the two contending communities, not to seek an understanding with one another, but to improve their respective organization for further efforts, the one to establish their conception of the National Home, the other to destroy it. In 1921 the government had created the Supreme Muslim Council as an autonomous body for the administration of Muslim religious properties and the direction of the Shari'a courts; but on to this innocuous trunk there was grafted a multitude of political activities by its head, that indefatigable schemer Hajj Mohammed Amin al Husaini, a youngish man proscribed for his part in the 1920 Riots but pardoned and appointed Mufti of Jerusalem (an office hereditary in his family) by Sir Herbert Samuel. The Zionist Organization, which had been recognized by Article Four of the Mandate as the 'appropriate Jewish public body for the purpose of advising and co-operating with the Administration of Palestine, so long as its organization and constitution are in the opinion of the Mandatory appropriate', had passed through some difficult years in the middle 'twenties owing to the inadequacy of its finances; but in 1928 Weizmann finally succeeded in putting through a plan for enlisting the large-scale financial support of American Jewry, non-Zionist and Zionist alike, by broadening the Zionist Organization into a Jewish Agency for Palestine. The constitutional change was more apparent than real, since executive powers were vested in the Zionist Executive with the addition of three non-Zionist members; the last of whom resigned in 1945; but it did have the important practical effect, once the American financial crisis of the early 'thirties was passed, of placing much larger sums at the disposal of the Zionist movement.

Meanwhile, there were some enthusiastic Zionists who were not satisfied with the pace set by their official leaders. These extremists, who later crystallized as the Revisionist Party, so-called because they demanded a revision of the Mandate in favour of the

Zionists, had drawn up after the 1921 Riots comprehensive plans
for an exclusively Jewish defence force to form part of the British
forces in Palestine. The minds of these zealots were formed on a
diet of ancient revolt—the Maccabees (whose name has been given
to a widespread sport organization), the revolt of 66 A.D., and the
desperate revolt in A.D. 132 of Bar Kokhba (whose memory was
enshrined as a Zionist hero at least as early as 1899).[1] While these
young extremists kept up their aggressive attitude, the desire of the
Arab political leaders for independence was stimulated by the
constitutional concessions which were obtained or foreshadowed
in Egypt, Iraq, Transjordan, and Syria. The opposition of the two
rival nationalisms came to a head in 1928 in the dispute over the
Wailing Wall, that shrine of Orthodox Jewry which is yet Muslim
property and the outer face of part of the wall of the chief Muslim
sanctuary of Jerusalem, the Haram ash-Sharif, the third most
holy spot in the Sunni world. While official Zionist bodies had
given no offence, less responsible individuals among them had
expressed their hope of ultimately winning back the Haram, the
site of their historic Temple. The Muslims were therefore made
even more than usually suspicious; and when some Jews began to
encroach slightly on the status quo at the Wailing Wall they interpreted it as the thin end of the wedge, and the Mufti riposted with
vigorous and provocative counter-measures. An attempt by the
government to bring about agreement in the matter was baffled as
much by Jewish reluctance to give way as by the Arabs.[2] In August
1929 there were provocative demonstrations by both Jews and
Arabs. Meanwhile the Arabs had been whipping up fanaticism
throughout the country, and at the end of the month there were
massacres of Jews in all the mixed towns of the country. 133 Jews
were killed and six agricultural settlements totally destroyed. The
security forces in the country had been reduced to small proportions in the quiet years, and were now taken by surprise. There was
little Jewish retaliation, though they killed seven Arabs at Jaffa
and desecrated a mosque in Jerusalem. The Shaw Commission, set up to investigate the causes of the riots, emphasized the
basic conflict of the two opposing nationalisms. 'Neither side have
made any sustained attempt to improve racial relationships. The
Jews, prompted by eager desire to see their hopes fulfilled, have

[1] *Zionist Review*, 15 September 1950, p. 20.
[2] *Royal Commission Report* (1937), 67.

pressed on with a policy at least as comprehensive as the White Paper of 1922 can warrant. The Arabs, with unrelenting opposition, have refused to accept that document and have prosecuted a political campaign designed to counter Jewish activities and to realize their own political ambitions.' The Commission made four main recommendations: (1) A clear statement of policy with the least possible delay, including a definition of the meaning of the passages in the Mandate which purported to safeguard the interests of the 'non-Jewish' communities.

(2) A revision of the immigration regulations to prevent a repetition of the excessive immigration of 1925/6 which had resulted in considerable unemployment, and to provide for consultation with non-Jewish representatives with regard to it.

(3) An expert inquiry into the prospects of improving Arab agricultural methods, and the regulation of land-policy accordingly.

(4) A reaffirmation of the 1922 statement that 'the special position assigned to the Zionist Organization by the Mandate does not entitle it to share in any degree in the government of Palestine'.

Sir John Hope-Simpson, who was sent to Palestine to conduct the agricultural inquiry, reported very conservatively on the extent of lands suitable for development. He did agree that 'with thorough development there will be room, not only for all the present agricultural population on a higher standard of life than it at present enjoys, but for not less than 20,000 families from outside'; but pending the completion of this development he was opposed to the admission of any more Jews as settlers on the land, as tending to displace Arab cultivators. The Passfield White Paper of 1930, based on these two reports, restated the words used by Prime Minister Ramsay MacDonald a few months earlier: 'A double undertaking is involved, to the Jewish people on the one hand, and to the non-Jewish population of Palestine on the other', and added that much of the recent agitation had arisen from the failure, both by Arabs and by Jews, to realize the limits imposed on British policy by this double undertaking. A new Department of Development was to be given control of all disposition of land, and land-transfers would be permitted only in so far as they did not interfere with that authority's plans; any state land becoming available should be earmarked for the settlement of landless Arab cultivators.

13

It came just at a time when the reconstitution of the Jewish Agency with substantial financial support from the U.S.A. had raised Zionist hopes high. Dr. Weizmann protested that the White Paper was inconsistent with the terms of the Mandate, and resigned his presidency of the Jewish Agency and the Zionist Organization. In Britain prominent members of the Conservative opposition—Baldwin, Austen Chamberlain, Amery, Churchill—sought to make political capital out of the situation by supporting the Zionist complaints. 'The public ventilation of the controversy was an impressive demonstration of the political power the Zionists could mobilize in England.' Ramsay MacDonald, with the lack of firm resolution characteristic of the later stages of his career, capitulated to the Zionist pressure, invited the Jewish Agency to confer with the government, and eventually restated its policy to Weizmann in what the Arabs have nicknamed the 'Black Letter'. Defining itself as the 'authoritative interpretation' of the White Paper, it declared that H.M.G. did not intend to prohibit the acquisition of additional land by the Jews, since this could be done without prejudice to the rights and position of other sections of the population, nor to stop or prohibit Jewish immigration.[1]

'The first serious attempt to reduce the implications of the Balfour Declaration to terms compatible with our pledges to the Arabs had failed.'[2] The most important feature of the White Paper, the control of land-transfers, was never put into effect; for in January 1933 the Nazis came into power in Germany and a steadily increasing stream of Jewish refugees began to pour out of that country. Meanwhile the situation of the Jews in Poland and Roumania, where government and unofficial pressure to get rid of them had grown stronger since the creation of the National Home had offered an outlet, was growing steadily worse. The need of the Jews was more widespread, and in some respects more acute, than in the pre-war Russian pogroms. They naturally turned to Palestine as the only country they could enter 'as of right and not on sufferance'. Confronted with this demand for asylum the British government promptly pigeon-holed the Shaw Commission Report, with its admonition that the 1929 Riots were but a symptom of the dangerous and fundamental clash of the two rival

[1] *The Political History of Palestine under British Administration* (Jerusalem, 1947), 13.
[2] *Round Table*, 1939, 463.

nationalisms, and tacitly admitted a new principle not provided for in the Mandate, that Jewish refugees from persecution in Europe should be admitted to Palestine in unprecedented numbers. While Jewish immigration from the promulgation of the Mandate down to 1932 inclusive had averaged 9,000 a year, it rose in 1933 to 30,000; in 1934 to 42,000; and in 1935 to nearly 62,000; and these figures do not include clandestine illegal immigrants, who amounted to thousands per year. Immigrants from Poland continued to constitute over 40 per cent. of the total; but those from Germany, who had been negligible before 1929 and under 4 per cent. of the total in 1932, quadrupled themselves. Official estimates showed that by 1935 the Jewish population had more than doubled itself since 1929 and now amounted to one-quarter of the total. Statistical calculation demonstrated that if the rate of immigration of the last three years were allowed to continue, the Jewish population would equal that of the Arabs by 1952.

It was not surprising that in these circumstances the Arab nationalist leaders felt little sympathy for the persecuted Jews of Europe, failed to understand why their small country should be the principal asylum for them, and treated the nullification of the 1930 White Paper as a British breach of faith. As the Mufti later put it, 'We have had so many commissions; so much has been recommended by them in our favour; and what is the result? Over 60,000 Jewish immigrants in one year.'[1] Arab terrorists began to murder Jews, uproot their trees, maim their cattle, and herdsmen squatted on blocks of land to obstruct their sale to the Jews. The rapid increase of Jewish immigration in 1933 was followed by violent Arab attacks on government policy, alleging that its deliberate purpose was 'to drive the Arab nation away from its homeland'. Demonstrations against the government in several towns in October 1933 led to the deaths of twenty-six Arab civilians and one policeman. Meanwhile the Jewish Revisionists, who demanded the opening of Palestine and Transjordan to, not thousands but millions of Jewish immigrants, were becoming more extreme in their opposition both to Government and to the Jewish Agency, and were generally believed to have been responsible for the murder of Dr. Arlosoroff, a leading member of the Agency. In the following year Sir Herbert (now Lord) Samuel wrote, 'Everyone in Palestine agrees that the economic development is astonishing;

[1] Humphrey Bowman, *Middle East Window*, 335.

no one thinks that the political situation shows any appreciable improvement.' In the summer of 1935, with Jewish prospects in Poland worse and in the rest of Central and Eastern Europe no better, the Zionist Congress recorded its resolve 'to focus the energies of the Jewish people on the extension and acceleration of its resettlement in Palestine'. In November the five Arab parties, in an atmosphere of extreme political excitement stimulated by hopes of progress towards independence in neighbouring Arab countries, presented the High Commissioner with three main demands: (1) The establishment of democratic government; (2) the prohibition of land-transfers from Arabs to Jews;[1] (3) the immediate stopping of immigration.

The High Commissioner was authorized to announce that an Ordinance was to be enacted prohibiting the sale of land unless the owner kept a sufficient amount to provide for his family, and to offer the two communities a scheme for the constitution of a Legislative Council, in which the proportion of unofficial members was, as in the 1922 proposal, weighted somewhat against the Muslims and in favour of the Jews and Christians. The Council was not to be competent to question the validity of the Mandate, and the High Commissioner would be able to override the Council in certain circumstances. While the Arab leaders did not reject the proposal outright, the Zionist Congress denounced it as 'contrary to the spirit of the Mandate . . . at the present state of the development of Palestine', i.e. as long as the Jews were in a minority. In Britain both Houses of Parliament showed strong opposition, partly on general considerations of its inadvisability and partly because of the likelihood that it would operate to the disadvantage of the National Home. The Zionist press hailed the attitude of Par-

---

[1] Arab nationalist appeal at no time had sufficient moral force to bring about, in the absence of legal sanctions, an effective voluntary refusal to sell lands to the Jews. 'Those who sold land, almost all at good prices, fell roughly into three classes: the landlord, very often an absentee, the sale of whose land raised the problem of ejected tenant occupiers; the industrious peasant, who sold part of his land and worked up the remainder on his profits; and the type who sold all his land at prices beyond his dreams of avarice, and who failed to use the substance thus acquired in a way that would keep himself and his family' (*Great Britain and Palestine, 1915–45*, 57). The Jewish Agency generally paid compensation to the uprooted tenants, in addition to the purchase-money. Rumour added that the Jewish organizations made it worth the while of Arab money-lenders holding mortgages on land to foreclose and sell to them at a handsome profit, and that Arab lawyers prominent in the nationalist movement were not above acting as brokers in land-transfers. Such venal Arabs were from time to time murdered by extremists.

liament as 'a great Jewish victory', and indeed the debates were a 'striking illustration of the disadvantage which the Arabs suffer whenever the field of controversy shifts from Palestine to the United Kingdom'.[1]   The Arabs interpreted the abandonment of the proposal as proof that they had no constitutional means of resisting their political subordination to the Jews who, at the present peak of immigration, would be in a majority within twelve years. It must have seemed to them, encouraged by the increase of violence in the whole world since the Japanese invasion of Manchuria four years before, that their only salvation lay in armed insurrection. Disturbances in mid-April 1936 began on a scale hardly greater than had been customary in recent months: two Jews were murdered by Arab bandits; on the following night two Arabs were murdered near a Jewish town, as an act of reprisal as the Arabs believed; the funeral of one of the murdered Jews led to angry Jewish demonstrations and a series of assaults on Arabs in Tel Aviv; excited by false rumours that Arabs had been killed there, Arab mobs in Jaffa murdered three Jews. At this moment an Arab National Committee proclaimed a general strike throughout the whole country until their demands of the previous November were met, and set up the Arab Higher Committee composed of all Arab parties. The strike was effective, and was accompanied by assaults on Jews and much destruction of Jewish trees and crops. The British government announced its intention to send out a Royal Commission to 'investigate the causes of unrest and alleged grievances' of both communities.   Meanwhile Arab violence and sabotage increased, and armed bands appeared in the hills; among them were volunteers from Syria and Iraq. Attempts by the Amir Abdullah of Transjordan and Nuri as-Sa'id, then Foreign Minister of Iraq, to mediate between the Arab leaders and the government came to nothing. The activities of the Arab bands increased in scope and magnitude, they were joined by trained guerilla leaders from outside Palestine, and sabotage to communications became frequent and systematic. There were a few acts of reprisal by Jews, but they were quickly checked by their own authorities; and the government acknowledged the self-restraint of the Jewish community in the face of great provocation by enrolling nearly 3,000 as supernumerary constables and authorizing the acquisition of rifles as an addition to the permitted arms held in the Jewish settle-

[1] *Royal Commission Report*, 92.

ments. The British forces were reinforced to a total of about 20,000, and it became clear that the rebels could not long hold out. The civilian strikers were tiring of incurring financial losses, and the prospect of not participating in the profits of the impending orange season was an additional reason for calling a halt. In October, therefore, the strike was ended, the armed bands dispersed, and the Commission began its work. In all, eighty Jews and twenty eight British had been killed; the total Arab death-roll has been estimated at 800.

The Royal Commission's Report, published in July 1937, has been justly described as 'a great State Paper . . . direct, outspoken, incisive, showing remarkably sympathetic understanding both of the Zionism of the Jews and the nationalism of the Arabs'. After a penetrating analysis of the causes of the antagonism between them, it reached the conclusion that the promises made to Jews and Arabs were irreconcilable and the Mandate in its existing form unworkable. It therefore proposed the radical solution of a surgical operation, dividing the country into a Jewish and an Arab state, with a small residuary enclave from Jaffa to Jerusalem left in charge of the Mandatory. The proposed frontiers would have given the Jewish state (in addition to rounding off their existing holdings in the coastal plain, the plain of Esdraelon, and the upper Jordan valley) the whole of Galilee, which contained thirty times as many Arabs as Jews. It would have included initially 225,000 Arabs, or almost a quarter of all the Arabs in Palestine. The Jews would have had a precarious majority of 53.4 per cent.; but it was recommended that a part of the large Arab minority should be resettled, either voluntarily or compulsorily.[1] If, however, the Mandate were to be continued in its existing form, the High Commissioner should be empowered to prohibit the transfer to Jews of land in certain areas, and to subject immigration to a 'political high level' which should be 12,000 per year for the next five years.

The Zionist Congress authorized its Executive to enter into negotiations with the British government 'with a view to ascertaining the precise terms for the proposed Jewish state'. Ben Gurion, chairman of the Executive, explained to the press, 'The debate has not been for or against the indivisibility of Eretz Israel. No Zionist can forego the smallest portion of Eretz Israel. The debate was over which of two routes would lead quicker to the

[1] p. 391, para. 43.

common goal'; and Dr. Weizmann, defending the non-inclusion cf Southern Palestine within the proposed Jewish frontiers, remarked, 'It will not run away.'[1] The Arabs, supported by the neighbouring Arab states, rejected the partition plan entirely, and asserted their right to independence in the whole of Palestine with an immediate stopping of Jewish immigration and land-purchase. The state of security deteriorated, and the Acting District Commissioner for Galilee and his police-escort were murdered by Arab terrorists; he was widely considered to have been one of the principal authors of the partition scheme. The Mufti was dismissed from his presidency of the Supreme Muslim Council; the Arab Higher Committee and all national committees were dissolved; and five prominent Arab leaders were deported. Jamal al-Husaini escaped to Syria, and the Mufti absconded in disguise to Beirut. But Arab terrorism increased, and some Jewish extremists also began to resort to terrorism, in spite of the restraint previously commanded by the Zionist leaders. In 1938 armed Arab gangs found a footing in all the main towns and rebel bands openly dominated the smaller towns. Communications were everywhere sabotaged. While heavy concentrations of British troops alone preserved a semblance of order in the northern and central parts of the country, Jerusalem and the south passed for a time entirely out of control. The active rebels probably amounted to no more than 1,000–1,500, split up in small bodies and mixed among peaceful citizens; but they had the sympathy and protection of a large part of the Arab population. Under the direction of the Mufti and the remnants of the Arab Higher Committee from outside Palestine, the Husaini faction carried on by intimidation and murder their traditional feud against the Nashashibi faction, the so-called moderates. In 1938 5,700 major acts of terrorism were recorded; casualties increased to fifteen times the figure for 1937; those killed included sixty-nine British, ninety-two Jews, 486 Arab civilians, and 1,138 armed Arab rebels. Some 100 Arabs were convicted by the military courts and hanged. Meanwhile the Woodhead Commission, sent out to prepare a detailed scheme of Partition, reported that it was unable to recommend any plan whatever: it was impossible to give the Jews a workable area without leaving an unfairly large Arab minority and the bulk of the Arab-owned citrus areas in the Jewish state, while the residual Arab state would not be economically self-

[1] Barbour, op. cit., 184 f.

supporting. They therefore suggested a scheme of economic federalism, by which the Mandatory would determine the fiscal policy for Arab and Jewish areas which would be otherwise autonomous. The British government then invited representatives of the Jewish and Arab communities and of the neighbouring Arab states, who had shown themselves increasingly concerned in the Palestine question in the past two years, to a Round-Table Conference in London early in 1939. Both parties rejected new British proposals, and the government was eventually left to announce a new policy in May 1939, when Hitler had occupied Czechoslovakia and the war-clouds were visible even to the most complacent eye.

The 1939 White Paper proposed to create an independent Palestinian state in treaty relations with Britain at the end of ten years. 75,000 Jewish immigrants were to be admitted in the first five years, after which further immigration was to be dependent on Arab consent. The High Commissioner would have powers to regulate or prohibit the transfer of land. The Paper 'declared unequivocally that it was not part of Government's policy that Palestine should become a Jewish State, regarding it as contrary to their obligations to the Arabs under the Mandate'.

The Zionists furiously condemned the White Paper as an outrageous breach of faith, claiming that it denied them the right to reconstitute their National Home in Palestine. Since its publication their vituperation of the Paper never lessened,[1] and they studiously refrained from acknowledging how essential it was for Britain at this time to end the conflict with the Arabs of Palestine, and avert one with those of the neighbouring countries, in view of the impending World War.

The British parliament received the White Paper with little enthusiasm. The Labour opposition naturally opposed it wholeheartedly, and it was also strongly attacked by such strong imperialists as Churchill and Amery, presumably because they regarded a strong Jewish community as a better ally than the fickle Arabs.

In June the seven members of the Permanent Mandates Commission reported unanimously to the League Council that the

---

[1] Gershon Agronsky, the so-called moderate editor of the *Palestine Post* expressed the hope that the report of the Anglo-American Committee of Inquiry of 1946 would 'roll away the perfidy of the monstrous White Paper, a creature of funk spawned by a government dominated by a passion for appeasement'. (*Palestine Post*, 2 May, 1946).

White Paper 'was not in accordance with the interpretation which, in agreement with the Mandatory Power and the Council, the Commission had placed upon the Palestine Mandate'. It also considered whether the Mandate 'might not perhaps be open to a new interpretation which . . . would be sufficiently flexible for the policy of the White Paper not to appear at variance with it'; and the majority of four to three declared that 'they did not feel able to state that the policy of the White Paper was in conformity with the Mandate, any contrary conclusion appearing to them to be ruled out by the very terms of the Mandate and by the fundamental intentions of its authors'. The minority, consisting of the representatives of Britain, France, and Portugal, considered that 'existing circumstances would justify the policy of the White Paper, provided the Council did not oppose it'. The outbreak of the Second World War prevented the Council from discussing the White Paper, which thus remained *de facto* in force. Nevertheless the Zionists continued to defend their opposition to it by the pretence that the disapproval of a majority of one of the Mandates Commission automatically rendered the White Paper illegal; this, although the Commission had no veto over the proposals of a Mandatory, but only the power to advise the League Council. The Mandatory could hardly afford to mark time without a policy till the end of the War. Indeed, as Dr. James Parkes, who cannot be accused of lacking sympathy for Zionism, has commented, the White Paper was not, 'as it might appear to be, a violent reaction against the policies of previous British governments. . . . From the moment when the Balfour Declaration stated that the rights of the existing population would be safeguarded, it was evident that no final solution was possible while these rights, as the population itself understood them, were ignored. The Arabs of Palestine stated their objection to the Declaration quite openly on the first occasion on which they were able. They have never wavered from that position. . . . This being so, then the only possible sequence of events was one in which the original encouragement given to the Jews was steadily whittled down in the face of Arab intransigence.'[1]

*   *   *

In Syria, after the suppression of the Rebellion of 1925/26, the French civilian High Commissioner made a genuine attempt to

[1] op. cit., 63.

allow the Syrian 'moderate' politicians to draw up a constitution. A draft was produced in 1928, but the High Commissioner objected to certain articles deemed to infringe the rights of France, and one which insisted on the political unity of Greater Syria. After many attempts to reach a compromise, the High Commissioner dissolved the Assembly in 1930, promulgating a constitution by his own act. Elections under this constitution were held in 1932, and negotiations begun for a Franco-Syrian Treaty modelled on the Anglo-Iraqi Treaty of 1930. But again no compromise could be found between French interests and the nationalist demands for a limitation in time and location on the French garrison and the inclusion in Syria of the governments of the Jebel Druze and Latakia; and again in 1934 the High Commissioner suspended the Chamber of Deputies *sine die*.

In 1936, after nationalist disorders causing sixty deaths had extorted from the French permission to send a deputation to Paris, the Front Populaire government came into power in France and immediately showed a more sympathetic attitude towards the Syrian demands, with the result that agreement was reached on a Draft Treaty closely modelled on the Anglo-Iraqi Treaty. It was to last for twenty-five years. There would be 'a close alliance between France and Syria, and France would support the admission of Syria to the League of Nations. The governments of Jebel Druze and Latakia would be annexed to Syria, but have special administrations. France would have two air-bases, and maintain troops in the districts of Jebel Druze and Latakia for five years. Syria would provide all facilities required by the French forces. France would be represented by an ambassador taking precedence over the representatives of all other powers. The existing monetary parity between the two countries would be maintained, and Syria would normally recruit foreign advisers and officials from France. A similar draft treaty was agreed between France and the more compliant Lebanon, the main difference being that no limitations were placed on the size or locations of the French forces there.

A government of the National Bloc party was elected in Syria, and exiled nationalists returned. 'It seemed as if the country were entering upon a new period of national construction under leaders whose patriotic energy had only been strengthened by disappointment, imprisonment and long years of exile . . . but the next two years saw the collapse of these hopes.' The Turkish government,

which had agreed in 1921 to the inclusion under the French mandate of the sanjaq of Alexandretta with its large Turkish minority
on condition that it had a special régime, now objected to its subjection to an inexperienced Arab nationalist government of Syria.
A League of Nations Commission was set up in 1937 to supervise
the election of a local assembly with seats allotted proportionately
to the different communities. This placed the Turks in a difficult
position since the population estimates showed only about 39 per
cent. of Turkish-speakers; but if every elector should be 'presumed
to be a member of the community to which he declared himself to
belong', and if the Turks could obtain control of the police and the
electoral machinery, a Turkish majority might be obtained. The
Commission finally gave way to the Turkish demand for registra-
tion by declaration, apparently fair, but in reality opening the door
wide to intimidation; the British representative on the Commission
immediately resigned in protest. But since the Turks were still not
assured of their majority, they brought pressure to bear on the
French, who were anxious to preserve Turkey's friendship as an
offset to Fascist Italy's threatening behaviour in the Mediterranean. A Franco-Turkish Treaty of Friendship in June 1938 permitted Turkish troops to enter the Sanjaq 'to assist the French in
maintaining order'. The electoral Commission abandoned its
work, accusing the French of systematic efforts, by means of
arrests and other forms of intimidation, to deprive the non-Turkish
majority of its freedom of voting. The Turkish troops marched in,
and the final electoral lists only showed the Turks as constituting
63 per cent. of the total. A cabinet consisting entirely of Turks was
formed. Finally, in June 1939, with France's need of Turkish support becoming greater as the shadow of impending war grew
larger, she made a Declaration of Mutual Assistance with Turkey,
in which Turkey was allowed to annex the Sanjaq.[1]

Meanwhile there was unrest in the Jebel Druze, the Latakia
district, and the Jazira, where there were strong separatist movements among the minorities. Undoubtedly some of the inexperienced Syrian officials appointed by the Damascus government had
acted hastily and irresponsibly in their efforts to bring about the
political assimilation of these minorities, but on the other hand the
separatists were encouraged by some French officials on the spot,
anxious to create difficulties for the Syrian government.

[1] It was renamed Hatay ('Hittite-land').

But worst of all for the Syrian government, the Draft Treaty of 1936 had to face a formidable and growing weight of opposition in France. Besides those who were genuinely concerned over the future of the Christian minorities under a predominantly Muslim administration, there were others whose opposition to the tendency towards Syrian independence was less disinterested; and their influence on French policy was greater after the fall of the Front Populaire government. Moreover, the growing tenseness of the international situation made the French increasingly reluctant to weaken their strategic position in the Levant. Towards the end of 1938 the French Foreign Minister assured the Syrian Prime Minister, in return for new guarantees of French and minority interests, that the Treaty would be ratified before 31 January 1939; but a month later he yielded to the opposition of the Foreign Affairs Commission, and announced that the government did not intend for the present to ask parliament to ratify. Six months of deadlock between the nationalists and the French followed; and in July 1939 the High Commissioner once more suspended the Syrian constitution and appointed a council of directors to rule under his own orders. Separate administrations were re-established in the Jebel Druze, the territory of Latakia, and the Jazira.

*   *   *

Thus, while the twenty-one years that elapsed between the two Wars raised the Middle East as a whole out of the stagnation in which it had lain under the Ottoman Empire, and appreciably improved its economic and social conditions under European tutelage, the progress made towards political self-determination had by no means come up to the aspirations of the nationalist forces. Egypt and Iraq had achieved national sovereignty, though with important limitations in the field of foreign affairs, and subject to the presence of British garrisons on their soil; the Syrian nationalists had continually been frustrated of their hopes, most sharply in the last year when sovereignty seemed within their grasp; and whatever economic and social progress the Arabs of Palestine had made under the Mandate, their political status had been markedly worsened by the rapid increase in the Jewish immigrant community, for whose sake Palestine was subjected to crown-colony government with no direct authority for Arab politicians and no opportunity for men of talent and ambition to rise higher than very secondary positions in the administration. The states which had achieved full political independence were those on the outer edge of the Middle East: Turkey, Persia, Sa'udi Arabia, Yemen, under their autocratic rulers Mustafa Kemal Atatürk, Riza Shah, Ibn Sa'ud, and the Imam Yahya;[1] and even these, in ascending order, were hampered in their dealings with greater Powers by their economic weakness and the social backwardness of their peoples.

---

[1] Imam Yahya of the Yemen was murdered in a rising of 'progressive' elements in February, 1948; but the Crown Prince Ahmed succeeded in re-asserting his authority in the following month.

CHAPTER VII

The Second World War and After (1939 — 50)[1]

THE DENIAL of independence to the Arab populations of Palestine and Syria had created intense feeling against Britain and France, not only in these countries but among the politically-conscious younger generation in Egypt and Iraq also. In all these countries the rapid extension of a superficial education along Western lines had greatly widened the cleavage of opinion which naturally exists between middle-aged parents and their adolescent offspring. The young men resented the fact that political power in their own countries remained in the hands of the elderly, who were slow to admit the claims of the young to participate. The nationalists of the older generation had organized the young students and secondary-schoolboys for political agitation against the inhibiting Western imperialisms in such movements as the Wafdist Blueshirts in Egypt; and now the young men were themselves forming new extremist organizations which exalted the principle of devotion to a Leader on distinctly Fascist lines. Among such extremist organizations were the Misr al-Fatat or Young Egypt, also known as the Greenshirts, founded by the lawyer-demagogue Ahmed Husain; the Syrian National Party, founded by Antun Sa'ada, which drew its membership mainly from Lebanese who desired reunion with Syria; the Syrian League of National Action; and the Arab Club of Damascus, founded by a young dentist educated in Germany. In Iraq especially the great influence of the Army in public affairs, which reached a peak under the dictatorship of Bakr Sidqi but remained important down to the outbreak of war, stimulated the youth to the formation of extreme nationalist organizations run on militarist lines.

The Axis Powers were not slow to exploit this favourable situation. It appears that they had reached an agreement that the Levant and Egypt fell within the Italian sphere of interest, while

[1] See the writer's study, *The Middle East in the War*, in the series *Survey of International Affairs, 1939–1946.*

Iraq and Persia should come under the influence of Germany. From 1935 Radio Bari devoted itself through its broadcasts to inciting the Arab world against Britain, especially over the raging question of Palestine. The Italians had built up a powerful propaganda organization in Egypt, working under the auspices of the Italian Legation and through the medium of the 60,000 Italian inhabitants of the cities of Lower Egypt, who were brought under the aegis of the Fascist organizations; there can be no doubt that they were also used to spy on British activities. Having completed the conquest of Abyssinia in 1936, Italy proceeded to build up her strategic position against Britain in the Southern Red Sea. She fortified the port of Assab in southern Eritrea and, by playing on the suspicions of British policy in Aden in the mind of the Imam of the Yemen, persuaded that conservative monarch to admit into his country an Italian medical mission which was a convenient cover for anti-British propaganda and espionage. During the Palestine Rebellion both the German Protestant (Templar) colonies and some Italian Catholic orders extended their protection and material help to the Arab rebels, and some arms and money were smuggled in to them from the Axis Powers.[1] In 1938 the German radio took over from the Italians the broadcasting of anti-British propaganda in Arabic. In Iraq the German Minister, Dr. Grobba, was assiduous and open-handed in cultivating the young nationalists. Germans played cleverly on the Persians' hatred of both Britain and Russia and flattered their boundless vanity by emphasizing their Aryan origins. German propaganda films were provided free, and were believed to have amounted to 40 per cent. of all films shown in Persia. The Lufthansa obtained permission to land at Tehran on their Berlin-Tokyo route. Persian students, like those of the Arabic-speaking countries, were tempted by low fees to finish their studies in German universities; and in 1939-40 a number of German university lecturers and directors of technical institutes were imported into Persia. Leading Nazi personalities, such as Goebbels, Schacht, General von Blomberg, and Baldur von Schirach, paid official visits to Middle Eastern capitals.

In spite of this propaganda campaign the immediate reaction of the Middle Eastern countries to the outbreak of war was not unsatisfactory to Britain and France. Egypt and Iraq immediately

[1] Though the extent of this aid has probably been exaggerated by Zionist propaganda. (Barbour, op. cit., 192; *Great Britain and Palestine*, 1915-45, 119).

broke off diplomatic relations with Germany; the Arab Rebellion in Palestine, already in its dying struggles, ceased with the arrival of a cavalry division and other troops in the autumn of 1939; and the Syrian nationalists were firmly repressed. The months of the 'Sitzkrieg', however, confirmed the idea, already prevalent in Middle Eastern political circles, that this war between European powers was none of their business. The German invasion of France, the entry of Italy into the war, and the capitulation of France, leaving the small British forces in the Middle East denuded of the support of the 100,000 French troops in the Levant States, brought the war to the threshold of the Middle East in one bound. By this time the Allied disasters of that dreadful summer and the isolation of Britain had not surprisingly shaken the confidence of the Middle Eastern politicians in her ability to survive. In Iraq the reckless Prime Minister Rashid Ali al-Qilani and four ambitious colonels nicknamed the 'Golden Square' awaited an opportunity, while a shadow-cabinet of Palestinian extremists was directed by the hostile Hajj Amin. Freya Stark vividly describes how she encountered the Mufti in his hotel and saw 'little good, and certainly nothing disinterested in that face. . . . He sat there all in white, spotless and voluminous, wearing his turban like a halo; his eyes light, blue, and shining, with a sort of radiance, like a just-fallen Lucifer'.[1] In these circumstances the Iraqi government refused to break off diplomatic relations with Italy; and as the Battle of Britain raged, 'the highest military authorities were openly broadcasting to the Iraqi people that their army and air-force had the glorious mission of renewing the heroic days of the Arab conquests and the Crusades, and of liberating the oppressed brethren of Syria and Palestine from the servitude imposed on them by Europe and the Jews'.[2]

　In Egypt the British Embassy and military authorities had reason to suspect the Prime Minister Ali Mahir, son of that Mahir Pasha whom Cromer had caused to be removed from office as Under-Secretary for War as 'a bad adviser, a cause of strife, and an obstacle to harmonious co-operation' between Britain and the young Khedive Abbas II.[3] Following in his father's footsteps,

[1] *East is West*, 143.
[2] *Round Table*, 1941, 705.
[3] Lord Cromer, *Abbas II*, 50–59.

Ali Mahir had acquired great influence over the young King Faruq, who since his accession in 1936 had taken growing offence at the authority and the personal attitude to him of the British Ambassador Sir Miles Lampson (now Lord Killearn).[1] It now appeared that the Prime Minister was actively encouraging the King to adopt a policy of reinsurance with the Axis Powers in view of the impending defeat of Britain, and he resisted British requests for the breaking-off of diplomatic relations with Italy. Such conduct in a country so vital for her imperial strategy could not be tolerated in this crisis of British fortunes; and in June 1940 pressure was exerted to obtain the dismissal of Ali Mahir's cabinet and its replacement by one more ready to co-operate. That the British suspicions were not without grounds was demonstrated some months later, when the columns advancing into Cyrenaica in Wavell's push captured on an Italian general a highly secret letter addressed by the G.O.C. British Troops in Egypt to the Egyptian Minister of Defence and discussing the defence of the Siwa Oasis, which had been entrusted to an Egyptian unit. The British authorities concluded that the Italians had obtained the letter before the departure of the Italian Legation staff, and accordingly suspected Ali Mahir and his 'inner cabinet'— Salih Harb, the Minister of Defence, and Aziz Ali al-Misri, the Chief of Staff—of being responsible for the leakage. The Egyptian authorities subsequently held an enquiry which purported to vindicate these persons, claiming that it was not established whether the leakage had occurred on the British or the Egyptian side.

Although Egypt did not declare war against the Axis, her army did assist in the defence of the Western Desert and in the anti-aircraft defence of the Canal Zone and the cities of Egypt; and in April 1941, stimulated by General Wavell's winter success in routing the Italian armies in Cyrenaica with a force only a fraction of their size, the Egyptian government accepted British representa-

[1] The remarks of Lord Lloyd on the relations between Lord Cromer and Abbas II apply with curious exactness to those between Lord Killearn and King Faruq fifty years later: 'There was a considerable school of thought which held, and not without some justification, that the Khedive was what he was largely because of the method which Cromer had used towards him. It was argued that at his accession Abbas's position vis-à-vis the overshadowing position of the great Consul-General had been one of great difficulty for a young and sensitive ruler, and that by no means enough had been done to help and encourage him.' (*Egypt since Cromer*, I, 71 f.)

tions that the consulates of such neutral, but unfriendly Powers as Japan, Hungary, Roumania and Bulgaria in such strategic centres as Alexandria, Port Said, and Suez were nests of espionage, and closed them down.

But the easy optimism engendered by Britain's swift liquidation of the grandiose Italian African empire in 1940/1 was soon to be rudely awakened. In April 1941 Germany struck at the Balkans and in one month overran Jugoslavia and Greece; at the same time Rommel and his Afrika Korps came to the help of the routed Italians in Libya and drove the British forces, depleted for the Greek campaign, back from the Gulf of Sirte to the Egyptian frontier. In Iraq, where the Golden Square and Rashid Ali had suffered a temporary reverse in an attempted coup d'etat in January, the incitement of the Mufti and his followers to a breach with Britain had been supported by the propaganda of the German Armistice Commission sent to the Levant States after the French collapse. Directed by Baron von Hentig, who had been a member of the German mission to Afghanistan in the First World War, it disposed of large sums of money and won the support of some of the Arab extremists in Syria. It apparently sent emissaries to the Mufti, who was in receipt of subsidies from the Axis through the Italian Minister in Baghdad. Early in April the invasion of Greece seemed to the conspirators in Baghdad to be the signal for their rising. How could Britain, represented in Iraq only by a small air-force and by a 'gentle, pleasant, and optimistic' ambassador with no previous experience of the Middle East, resist them? They over-threw the flabby existing government, reinstated Rashid Ali as Prime Minister, and sought to secure the person of the Regent for the boy-King Faisal II; he was however safely smuggled away by the American Minister. After this coup the Golden Square hesi-tated, since German help was not yet forthcoming. The newly-appointed British Ambassador, Sir Kinahan Cornwallis, with twenty years' experience of the Iraqis, seized this opportunity to secure the landing in Basra, under the terms of the Anglo-Iraqi Treaty, of Indian troops to reinforce the Middle East. When a second contingent arrived, the Iraqi government, encouraged by the German successes in Greece and Libya, demanded that the first contingent should leave Iraqi territory before the second dis-embarked. The British authorities refused to comply. On 1 May the Iraqi army invested the British air-base at Habbaniya with some fifty field-guns, while detachments seized the pumping-stations on the oil-pipeline to Haifa. By all normal rules Habbaniya should have fallen; but after four days' fighting the R.A.F. assisted by their Assyrian and Kurdish Levies succeeded in driving back the Iraqis, and were reinforced by a small motorized column, including the Arab Legion of Transjordan, hastily got together in Palestine and rushed across the desert. The Iraqis now appealed to Germany for help; but Hitler had decided that major operations to expel Britain from the Middle East must wait till after the launching of the invasion of Russia, now in an advanced state of preparation. The Germans were held up in Crete, whose conquest took them eighteen days instead of the two on which they had counted; and they could spare their Iraqi allies only one hundred aircraft. This was insufficient, and the Golden Square had failed to win the support of the apathetic Iraqi people. On 29 May, the British forces, still far inferior in numbers to the Iraqis, had reached the outskirts of Baghdad. Rashid Ali and his ministers, the Golden Square, the Mufti and his shadow-cabinet all decamped in haste, some to Persia, and some to Aleppo and eventually through Turkey to Axis Europe. An armistice was concluded on 31 May. Britain, pressed back on Egypt and Palestine by this apparent pincer-movement of the Axis and its sympathizers, had fought back and won in the first great testing-time of the Middle East campaign. Beyond ensuring the establishment of a friendly government, she imposed no punitive terms on Iraq; but proceeded to attack the Vichy French in Syria, who had in their impotence harboured for many months the spies and propagandists of the Axis Armistice Commission, and had recently allowed German aircraft to refuel on Syrian airfields on their way to Northern Iraq, and material supplies to travel to Iraq by the Syrian railways. The Vichy French fought back grimly against the British and Free French, but by mid-July they were forced to capitulate, and under the Lyttleton-De Gaulle Agreement a Free French government was installed in the Levant States, British forces being free to operate there for the duration of the war. Meanwhile Hitler had invaded Russia. One of the only two routes by which contact between Russia and Britain could be established was through Persia, where the Germans had been steadily building up their staffs of technicians and spies during the past six months. A joint Anglo-Russian demand that the Persian government should expel them met with the rash reply that Persia alone would decide what foreigners to expel. The response to this was the joint Anglo-Russian invasion of Persia in August. The greater part of the Persian army was kept back by Riza Shah to overawe the unruly tribes who hated his tyrannical rule, and what was available was no match for the invading forces. Before September was out the avaricious old Shah had been forced to abdicate in favour of his young son. Russian and British troops occupied the northern and southern parts of Persia respectively, and the Trans-Iranian Railway and road-systems were extensively used for the supply of American and British munitions and supplies to Russia. The political situation was regulated by the Anglo-Soviet-Persian Treaty of 1942, whereby Persia gave the Allies full wartime facilities, and they undertook in return to withdraw their troops within six months of the end of hostilities. Nevertheless the sympathies of most politically-minded Persians remained with the Axis, and some officials continued during 1942 to intrigue with the German agent Franz Mayr, who had escaped when the Germans in Persia were rounded up for internment.

The Middle East political barometer continued to fluctuate with the changing strategic situation. By January 1942 the disasters of Pearl Harbour and Singapore, and the second British retreat in Cyrenaica before Rommel's forces, gave new encouragement to her enemies. In Egypt the government of Husain Sirri had since 1940 co-operated loyally; but having no majority backing in parliament its life was precarious and its policy correspondingly irresolute. Faced in the autumn of 1941 with a growing tide of pro-Axis and anti-British propaganda, in which the powerful and extremist Ikhwan al-Muslimin or Muslim Brotherhood organization played a prominent part, it acceded to British representations by arresting its leader Hasan al-Banna, only to release him a few days later, apparently under pressure from the Palace, which was believed to have been generously subsidizing him. A month later the breaking-off of diplomatic relations with Vichy France at Britain's request caused the resignation of the Foreign Minister, again apparently the victim of royal displeasure. In January 1942 the failure of the Egyptian authorities to break the black market and ensure a proper distribution of bread in Cairo coincided with the military disasters referred to above, and promoted a wave of anti-British feeling, with students marching down main streets shouting 'We are Rommel's soldiers'. For some time the British Embassy and military authorities had been coming to the conclusion that a stronger government in Egypt was necessary to secure the military position, and that this could only be secured by bringing back the Wafd, which had recently been growing restive in opposition. King Faruq, however, who had dismissed Nahhas from office in 1937 and was reported to be on the worst of personal terms with the Wafd leader, refused to accept him as Prime Minister and was believed to be intending to call on Ali Mahir, whom the British authorities obviously could not accept as Prime Minister. The young King was obstinate, and eventually on the evening of 4 February the British Ambassador and the G.O.C. British troops in Egypt found it necessary to present the King with an ultimatum: accept Nahhas or leave the country. The King yielded, the Wafd returned to office and easily secured its position in a general election. Though within a month the party's secretary, the capable but difficult Copt Makram Ubaid, and several of his supporters had seceded, apparently as the result of a personal difference with Nahhas, the Wafd government loyally co-operated with Britain in the anxious days of June–July 1942, when the Eighth Army was forced back from beyond Tobruk to the prepared position of al-'Alamain, only seventy miles west of Alexandria. In this second great military crisis of the Middle East campaign, faced clearly with choosing for Britain or the despised Italians, the Egyptian government and people stood firmly behind Britain. There was none of the prophesied sabotage and little anti-British propaganda; the only incidents were that two or three Egyptian Air Force pilots absconded to the enemy lines, and that the veteran Aziz al-Misri[1] was detected in intrigue with two ineffectual German spies who had been introduced into Cairo via the Western Desert, and was interned for his pains. Arab Asia likewise, though apathetic towards the outcome of the war, did not choose or dare to stab Britain in the back in the perilous days of al-'Alamain and Stalingrad; and in Persia the intriguing Franz Mayr could only dream of the day when he would raise Persia against the British, and meanwhile scribble in his diary of 'those three great strategists—Rommel, Von Bock, and myself'.

As the year of trial and danger 1942 drew towards its close the

---

[1] He had attempted to join the Iraqis in the putsch of May, 1941, but his aircraft was forced down ignominiously when only ten miles from Cairo.

picture changed. Montgomery was advancing from al-'Alamain and the Russians from Stalingrad. The movement had begun which did not stop till the remnant of the Africa Korps surrendered at Cape Bon in May 1943. The German spies, saboteurs, and propagandists who continued to operate against the Middle East from their embassy and consulates in Turkey achieved nothing. In Tehran the British security authorities brilliantly captured two parties of German parachutists who had been sent to reinforce Franz Mayr, and eventually secured the surrender of Mayr himself and the remnants of his little band by the tribesmen among whom he had taken refuge. Apart from British plans for invading the Greek islands, the Middle East campaign was at an end; and the region could revert to its normal condition of political inflammation, exacerbated by its suppression during the war.

★   ★   ★

In Palestine the Arab Rebellion was already petering out during 1939, and in October of that year the Mufti and his entourage of extremists, no longer tolerated by the French in the Levant States, took refuge in Baghdad, from where his influence over the rebellion-weary Arabs of Palestine declined. It was hardly to be expected that the Arabs would take an active part in the war against the Axis, since many of them felt that Axis conquest would at least free them from the Zionist incubus, and few had much reason to feel any loyalty to Britain. On the other hand, they gave little trouble, their attitude remaining essentially neutral. The Jewish authorities pressed for permission to raise forces on a Jewish-national basis, but the government resisted this as it was unwilling to concede the principle of Jewish, as opposed to Palestinian nationality. Separate Jewish sub-units were, however, permitted from the start; the urgent need for man-power prompted further concessions; and the process culminated in 1944 in the creation of the Jewish Brigade with its distinctive Zionist colours. But while the Zionists co-operated whole-heartedly in the struggle against the Nazis, they continued to oppose the hated White Paper. In February 1940 the issue of the Land Transfer Regulations, denying Jews the right to acquire land in the greater part of Palestine, came as a severe blow to them, since they had hoped that the White

Paper policy might, owing to the war, never be put into effect.[1] They organized country-wide demonstrations with arson and some bomb incidents, but their co-operation in the war-effort nevertheless continued. Even the Revisionists concurred in this policy, and only a small fanatical dissident group of the latter, led by one Abraham Stern, and alleged to have contacts with the Italian Fascist government, continued their implacable terrorist antagonism to the Mandatory.

What continued to excite the whole Jewish community to still more furious protest, even with Palestine threatened with enemy invasion, was the insoluble question of immigration. The Mandatory had been compelled to limit this severely, having regard to the extreme sensitivity to this vital question of the Arabs, whose neutrality, both in Palestine and the neighbouring countries, it was essential to maintain during the war. All that the Jews saw was that thousands of their kin were thus denied a refuge in Palestine from the appalling Nazi terror in Europe; and in their horror and despair they were blind to the difficulties of the British government. The first strain came in 1940 with a succession of illegal immigrant ships from Europe, well organized on the Zionist side and encouraged by the Nazis, who saw in them a means of embroiling the British with the Arabs. The *Patria*, chartered to remove nearly 2,000 illegal immigrants from Palestine to Mauritius, was actually blown up in Haifa harbour by Jewish terrorists, causing 268 deaths among its helpless Jewish passengers. Another ship, the *Struma*, was held up in 1942 off Istanbul while the British and Turkish governments negotiated over its disposal. Before this was concluded the Turks ordered the vessel to return to a Black Sea port. She blew up and sank with over 750 Jewish refugees; it was suggested that they also had been made the objects of a political gesture of despair or defiance.

These events caused a hardening of Zionist feeling in Palestine and an increased resort to terrorism. Abraham Stern had been shot in a gun-fight with the police, but some of his followers escaped from prison and continued the terror. The Revisionist Irgun Zvai Leumi (National Military Organization), which had actually assisted the British forces during the Iraq campaign of 1941, once

---

[1] Since the publication of the White Paper they had acquired twenty-five square miles of land in the area which the new Regulations closed to them, and the Colonial Secretary stated that he feared further unrest among the Arabs if land-restriction were not enforced.

more resumed its terrorist activities. Moreover, the official Zionist organization, under the leadership of David Ben Gurion and encouraged by the Zionists of the U.S.A., pleasantly remote from the realities of the Middle East problem, became more exacting and unequivocal in its demands, and in 1942 adopted the Biltmore Programme (drawn up, significantly, in New York). It demanded:

(1) The establishment of Palestine as a Jewish commonwealth.

(2) A Jewish army.

(3) Unlimited immigration, placed under the control of the Jewish Agency, which should also have authority for the development of unoccupied and uncultivated lands.[1] The Zionist underground army, called Hagana (self-defence), became more active. This organization traced its beginning to the self-defence organization formed by young Jews in Russia at the time of the pogroms of 1903.[2] It was transplanted to Palestinian soil before the First World War in the form of an organization of armed watchmen to guard the agricultural settlements from Arab attack. The British military authorities gave it tacit recognition and some arms during the Arab Rebellion of 1936-9, when Wingate's 'Night-Fighters' were organized from its ranks. Again in the perilous days of 1941-2 the Army recognized it as a home-guard in case the Germans broke through to Palestine. It now numbered some 60,000 young men and women, drawn principally from the settlements, who clandestinely carried out periodical training and military exercises. Some of the young Jews called up since the outbreak of war by the National Council of Palestinian Jews (Vaad Leumi) for national service were directed into the Hagana, and the thousands of Jews who were directed by the Zionist authorities into service in the British Middle East Forces continued to be under the clandestine orders of the Hagana high command. Information was now received for the first time of the Palmach, a crack force selected from the Hagana, permanently mobilized for shock-troop action, and numbering some 2,000 strong. The exigencies of the war brought the Palmach also into association with British specialist organiza-

---

[1] One of the foremost leaders of the principal Jewish party in Palestine, the Mapai labour party, explained to the Arabs in a book of essays, 'We shall be ready not to be your foes, and even to support your aspirations for independence, provided you cease disturbing us and provided you recognize Palestine as a Jewish State.' (Quoted by J. L. Magnes, *Foreign Affairs*, 1943, 240).

[2] *Palestine Post*, 25 June 1946.

tions, and some of its members were given commando training for action against the Germans. Many of the Palestinian Jewish troops in the Middle East Forces were employed in supply and ordnance companies along lines of communication and in base areas,[1] an admirable situation for the smuggling of arms to Palestine, to which they resorted on a large scale under Hagana direction. The organization of this 'underground railway' was excellent; there was no lack of funds and transport; and corruptible Allied and British soldiers were drawn into the racket. The difficulty of supplying the Middle East Forces by the dangerous and slow long-sea-route round Africa had caused the British military authorities to give contracts to Palestinian Jewish concerns for the manufacture of small-arms, including mortars, which they produced with efficiency; but these arms also found their way to the armouries of the Hagana. These were well-constructed underground caches, mainly in the collective settlements, though the search of Tel Aviv in July 1946 revealed arms-caches in the basements of the Great Synagogue and of a school. Ostensibly the Hagana's purpose behind all this arming and drilling was the self-defence of the Jewish community against Arab attack, such as had occurred before the war; but the Zionist leaders made it clear that the self-defence of the community included resistance to any limitations placed on immigration or land-purchase, i.e. resistance to the obnoxious 1939 White Paper on all points. The reports of the accumulation of illicit arms were so frequent that late in 1943 two settlements were raided by military and police in order to search them. At Ramat ha-Kovesh the police met with furious resistance from both men and women with missiles and boiling water; and the brigadier in charge of the military party, who had had wide experience of civil disturbances in various parts of the world, declared that he had never seen anything to compare with the ferocity of the villagers. It was not for nothing that Ben Gurion had exhorted the Jewish youth to prepare themselves for the fighting which would fall to their lot at the end of the war.

During 1944 Jewish terrorism increased, in spite of the indefinite extension of the now-expired five-year period in which the final

[1] Which did not prevent an American Revisionist from building up a myth that 'At one time 40 per cent. of Alexander's effectives were Jewish boys from Palestine. They formed the intrepid desert scouts on which Alexander relied for much of his intelligence. . . . It was a Jewish contingent which held Tobruk during the siege.' (W. B. Ziff, *The Rape of Palestine* (New York, 1946), 111.)

75,000 Jewish immigrants allowed by the White Paper might come in. Now that the war had receded from the Middle East, the Zionists were free to begin an all-out campaign against the White Paper policy of strictly limited immigration and land-purchase, and their demand was now for a Jewish State into which any Jew who wished might enter freely. The Irgun Zvai Leumi made an unsuccessful attempt to kidnap the High Commissioner; and the Stern Group went one better by murdering in Cairo the British Minister-Resident, Lord Moyne, who, they believed, had as Colonial Secretary obstructed the admission into Palestine of Jewish refugees from the Axis terror. This murder came as a great shock to the Jewish Agency, who evidently feared drastic action against the whole community; and they made an offer to the British military authorities to co-operate in rounding up the terrorists. This co-operation produced some results over a number of months: a number of suspected terrorists were arrested and interned, and as late as June 1945 the Agency gave the authorities information which assisted in the detection of a terrorist plot to bombard with delayed-action mortars the King David Hotel, the headquarters of the British forces and the government secretariat. But this liaison between the Agency and the British was subsequently discontinued, perhaps because it was found that the Agency was exploiting it as a means of furthering its own subversive purposes.

*   *   *

At the outbreak of war the French had suspended the Lebanese constitution and, there and in Syria, dissolved a number of extreme nationalist organizations believed to be in sympathy with the Axis, sentencing some of their members to long terms of imprisonment. The majority of politically-minded Syrians, like their brethren in Palestine, decided that there was nothing to choose between oppression by a democracy and that exercised in the name of Fascism; and consequently the general attitude towards the war was one of apathy and scepticism towards both sides, though some flirted with the Axis Armistice Commissions and a few committed themselves more deeply.

On the first day of the Allied invasion of the Levant States in

1941, the Free French General Catroux proclaimed that he had come to put an end to the mandatory régime and declare Syria and Lebanon free and independent. But the Free French reluctantly allowed nationalist exiles to return; they made no constitutional concessions beyond a formal declaration of independence; and the Syrian and Lebanese governments were filled with French puppets. There was no change in the methods, and little change in the personnel, of the French administration. In the spring of 1943, however, the French permitted the holding of elections, which resulted in Syria in an overwhelming victory for the National Bloc led by Shukri al-Quwwatli, and in Lebanon for a complete defeat of the French-supported Lebanese separatists led by Emile Edde. The elections were thus a signal defeat for the French, and it was to be expected that the new governments would not be slow to attack the French limitations on their independence. The French Committee of National Liberation, the acting French government in Algiers, insisted, however, that no radical changes could be made without the approval of the League of Nations, which had authorized the original mandate, or its successor; and that any concessions by France depended on the conclusion of treaties recognizing her special position and interests. It was indeed difficult for the French Committee, which still had to justify to the forty million Frenchmen under German occupation its claim to speak in the name of France, to sign away at this stage any of the hard-won and jealously-guarded rights of France in the Levant; and it was equally hard for the two nationalist governments of Syria and Lebanon to admit any further limitation of the sovereignty for which they had struggled for a generation. The first challenge came from the Lebanese government led by Riyad as-Sulh, which in November 1943 unanimously voted amendments to the constitution throwing off all French limitations upon its sovereignty. The French Délégué-Général responded by suspending the constitution, arresting the Lebanese president and the majority of the cabinet, and appointing the pro-French Emile Edde as head of the state. The townspeople proclaimed a general strike, there were bloody clashes with French troops in Beirut and elsewhere, and two ministers who had escaped arrest began to organize their retainers in the mountains into armed bands. The British government declared that it regarded the Lebanon as 'of vital importance to the war-effort both as an operational base and from the point of view of communications' and was therefore 'directly concerned in any threat of a breakdown of law and order'. It accordingly brought pressure upon the French to release and reinstate the imprisoned president and ministers. Having reluctantly and sulkily accepted the inevitable, the French did transfer many services to the new governments, and by the end of 1944 the only important attribute still withheld was the control of the locally-recruited Troupes Speciales, which was, however, of particular importance for Syrian and Lebanese prestige. The French made these concessions with an ill grace, and they execrated the British Minister, Sir Edward Spears, and his staff for their unconcealed sympathy with the nationalists.

Sir Terence Shone, who succeeded Sir Edward Spears early in 1945, made every effort to improve relations between the French and the local governments and bring negotiations to a satisfactory conclusion. But the French demanded the right to maintain bases and troops in both countries, apparently imagining that time had stood still since 1936. Immediately upon VE-day French warships began to arrive at Beirut and disembark troops. The Syrian nationalists immediately assumed that military pressure was about to be exerted on them; the French declared that the troops were merely to replace others who were being repatriated; the British made every effort to dissuade the French from disembarking them at this delicate juncture, but De Gaulle, now installed in Paris as head of the provisional government, was characteristically obstinate.[1] The situation deteriorated rapidly, riots and fighting occurred in the principal Syrian cities, and on 29 May the French repeated their exploits of twenty years earlier by bombarding Damascus with aircraft and field-guns. Next day the British military authorities received instructions to intervene and restore order. As long as the war with Japan continued, Britain could not allow the security of her line-of-communications to be threatened by anti-European disorders which might spread to other Middle Eastern countries. The French commander sulkily complied with a British order to cease fire and confine his troops to barracks, and order was restored. Relations between Britain and France were very strained, the French again accusing the

[1] The French were faced at this moment by a local rising in Algeria in which 110 French citizens were massacred, and several thousand Muslims killed in the subsequent reprisals.

British of having deliberately and consistently abetted the nationalists against them in order to oust France from her position in the Levant. In December 1945 the two Powers agreed to consult on the regrouping and evacuation of French and British troops. Since, however, it was envisaged that they should remain in Lebanon until U.N.O. had decided on the organization of collective security in this region, and since the agreement entailed British recognition of French 'interests and responsibilities' in the Levant, the Syrian and Lebanese governments appealed in February 1946 to the Security Council for the immediate withdrawal of the foreign troops from both countries. Britain and France accepted an American compromise-resolution expressing confidence that the troops would be withdrawn as soon as practicable and that negotiations to that end should be undertaken without delay. The evacuation of Syria was completed in April, and that of Lebanon by the end of the year. French and other journalists did not cease to insinuate that the Franco-British rivalry in the Levant continued, and the mischief-making innuendos reached a climax during the series of military *coups d'état* in Syria in 1949.

*   *   *

Throughout the war the Jewish Agency had kept up an intense and effective propaganda-drive among the British and Allied forces in Palestine, sparing neither effort nor expense in providing them with organized hospitality of every kind, encouraging them to spend their leave in the collective settlements, and demonstrating the high idealism and devotion and the material progress and efficiency of the National Home, to say nothing of its ability to get on with the ordinary Arabs 'if they were not incited against us by the effendis and British officials'. When visitors were in a settlement, its few 'tame' Arabs were paraded for inspection, of course with a Jew to interpret.[1] While this propaganda was variously directed to all interests, imperial, commercial, liberal, and socialist, the demonstration of the collective settlements and of the large part played in the life of the community by the Histadruth trades-union organization appealed particularly to Socialists,

[1] The stage-management of the fellahin sometimes broke down, with revealing results; cf. R. H. S. Crossman, *Palestine Mission*, 157 f.

especially the serious-minded, rather naive young men with a secondary-school education who were numerous among the junior officers and N.C.O.s of the British wartime army.

Consequently, the Zionists were greatly encouraged by the coming to power in July 1945 of the Labour party, whose executive had only six months before declared its support for unlimited Jewish immigration, the Arabs being 'encouraged to move out as the Jews move in'. But the new government, shocked by the plunge into the responsibilities of office, was not stampeded into a precipitate change of official policy. While three months passed without any statement from London, Dr. Moshe Sneh, the 'security member' of the Agency Executive, proposed in September to its London office 'that we cause one serious incident. We would then publish a declaration to the effect that it is only a warning and an indication of much more serious incidents that would threaten the safety of all British residents in the country, should the government decide against us. . . . The Stern Group have expressed their willingness to join us completely on the basis of our programme of activity. This time the intention seems serious. If there is such a union, we may assume that we can prevent independent action by the Irgun Zvai Leumi.'[1] This revealing document demonstrated collusion on a high level between the Agency Executive and the terrorist organizations whose activities they always officially deplored and declared themselves powerless to prevent. How long this collusion had been going on, it is at present impossible to say, but the phrase 'this time' implies that it was nothing new. The London office gave their approval to the proposed operation, Weizmann himself evidently being a party to what was afoot.[2] On the night of 31 October–1 November, the Palmach blew up the railways in 153 places, completely disrupting the system, and destroyed three police launches used for intercepting illegal immigrants. The Irgun Zvai Leumi attacked the railway-yards at Lydda, and the Stern Group attempted to blow up the Haifa oil-refinery. The Agency signalled to its London

[1] *Palestine, Statement on Information relating to Acts of Violence* (Cmd. 6873, July 1946). On the publication of this White Paper the Jewish Agency made a perfunctory denial of its authenticity; but there can be no doubt of the genuineness of the intercepted Jewish Agency telegrams which it publishes in extenso.

[2] Bernard Joseph, acting head of the Agency Political Dept., to London, 10 October 1945: 'If Hayyim meant us only to avoid a general conflict, not isolated cases, send greetings to Chill for the birth of his daughter.' Shertok, head of the Political Dept., duly replied with this code-phrase two days later.

office: 'The activities have made a great impression. The authorities are bewildered . . . and are waiting for instructions from London.' The British government had meanwhile come to the conclusion that in determining a post-war policy for Palestine the collaboration of the U.S.A. must be sought, since both political parties in that country had courted the Jewish vote in the presidential election of 1944 by pledges of support for the full Biltmore Programme, and President Truman had in October 1945 called upon the British government to open the gates of Palestine immediately to 100,000 displaced Jews in Europe. Britain, with her reduced power and authority in the world, could not afford to continue to have American opinion irresponsibly directed against her over Palestine. Accordingly on 13 November the Foreign Secretary announced that it had been agreed to set up a joint Anglo-American Committee of Enquiry, 'to examine the position of Jews in those countries in Europe where they have been the victims of Nazi persecution . . . and the political, economic and social conditions in Palestine as they bear upon the problem of Jewish immigration and settlement therein, and the well-being of the peoples now living therein'.

The Zionists immediately denounced the Foreign Secretary's statement, which had been accompanied by some blunt comments on their recent conduct. A protest strike throughout Palestine was ordered, and in Tel Aviv Jewish hooligans set fire to government buildings. On 12 December the Inner Zionist Council announced, 'The policy to which the British government pledged itself in the Balfour Declaration and the Mandate sprang from the recognition that the Jewish problem can be effectively solved only by the greatest possible concentration of Jews in Palestine and by the restoration of Jewish nationhood. . . . The Jewish Agency . . . upholds the right of every Jew impelled by material or spiritual urge to settle in Palestine. . . . The Jewish people . . . will spare no effort or sacrifice until the restoration of the Jewish Commonwealth of Palestine has been achieved.' As if to add point to this challenge, the Irgun Zvai Leumi a fortnight later blew up the C.I.D. H.Q. in Jerusalem, killing seven police and soldiers, while two more were killed in simultaneous attacks in Jaffa and Tel Aviv. Summoned to Government House, Ben Gurion and Shertok declared that the Agency completely dissociated itself from these murderous attacks and expressed their profound sorrow at the loss of life.

'But,' they stated, 'any effort by the Agency to assist in preventing such acts would be rendered futile by the policy pursued in Palestine by H.M. Government, on which the primary responsibility rests for the tragic situation created in the country. It was difficult to appeal to the Yishuv (the Jewish community) to observe the law at a time when the mandatory government itself was consistently violating the fundamental law of the country embodied in the Mandate.'

The Anglo-American Committee of Enquiry began its hearings in Washington in January, proceeded to London and Europe, and held its hearings in Jerusalem in March. During this period there was a slackening of terrorism, though there was another combined operation in February, the Palmach blowing up the R.A.F. radar-station at Haifa and attacking camps of the Police Mobile Force, while the Irgun and the Stern Group attacked airfields and damaged aircraft to the value of a million pounds. The illicit periodical of the Hagana, now exalted to the title of 'Jewish Resistance Movement', boasted, 'The first warning of 1 November by the Jewish Resistance was disregarded, and the whole Yishuv has been compelled to carry out a second warning.'

With some difficulty in reconciling the British and American points of view, the Committee of Enquiry produced a unanimous report on 1 May. Its effect on British readers was one of disappointment at a series of platitudes and palliatives and evasions of a clear-cut decision.

It turned down proposals for partition in favour of a continuation of the mandate 'until the hostility between Jews and Arabs disappears' (Arts. 3 and 4). 100,000 immigration certificates were to be immediately granted for Jews who had been the victims of persecution, and their admission to Palestine pushed forward as rapidly as conditions permitted; Palestine alone could not meet the immigration needs of the Jewish victims; but immigration was to be promoted under suitable conditions, 'while ensuring that the rights and position of other sections of the population were not prejudiced'. (Arts. 2, 1, 6.) While the Land Transfer Regulations were to be replaced by the free purchase and lease of land, the Jewish National Fund ban on the employment of non-Jewish labour was to be prohibited. (Art. 7.) Art. 8 indirectly criticized the Zionist proposals for a 'Jordan Valley Authority' which would dispose of the waters of the Jordan and its tributaries without reference to the governments of Transjordan and Syria from whose territories an important part of this water is derived.[1] Finally Art. 10 recommended that it should be made clear to both sides that any attempts at violence would be resolutely suppressed: 'furthermore, we express the view that the Jewish Agency should at once resume active co-operation with the Mandatory in the suppression of terrorism and illegal immigration, and in the maintenance of law and order'.

The Arab reaction to the Report was a protest against the modification in favour of the Zionists of the 1939 White Paper which, though they had received it with coldness at the time, they had now come to regard as the palladium of their national aspirations. They demanded the abrogation of the Mandate, the withdrawal of British troops, and the establishment of an Arab democratic state, and threatened to appeal to Russia for support. The Zionists characteristically selected from the Report and publicized, as being the whole Report, those Recommendations which suited them, and were completely silent about those that they found inconvenient. They were in fact prepared to accept the Report as a first instalment, but no more, of progress towards their Jewish State.

The British Prime Minister told the House of Commons that the Report would be considered as a whole in all its implications. It was clear from the facts presented regarding the illegal armies maintained in Palestine that it would not be possible to admit 100,000 immigrants unless and until these formations had been disarmed and their arms surrendered. It was essential that the Agency should take an active part in the suppression of terrorism. The Government wished to ascertain to what extent the Government of the U.S.A. would be prepared to share the additional military and financial responsibilities.

The Zionist leaders were furious at the suggestion that they should agree to the 'liquidation of the Community's defences', and in spite of their recent collusion with the terrorists reverted to their constant pretension that terrorism was but 'the acts of an irresponsible few'.[2] The American President and people, who had clearly imagined that their responsibility for Palestine was

---

[1] cf. M. G. Ionides, 'Irrigation in Palestine', *The World To-day*, III (1947), 188 ff.

[2] *Palestine Post* leading article, 2 May 1946.

ended with the publication of the Committee's report, were embarrassed by the challenge that they should share the burden of imposing the proposed new policy on the country. In June the President was advised by his cabinet to accept an invitation from London to send representatives to discuss the new problems it raised.

On the night of 16–17 June the Palmach attacked the frontier communications of Palestine, destroying five road- and four rail-bridges, and doing damage estimated at £250,000. The illicit Zionist broadcasting-station accepted full responsibility on behalf of the 'Resistance Movement' for the renewal of its activity 'as a result of the delaying policy of the British government'.[1] It was clearly time to put an end to the campaign of 'vilification, incitement, and violence' pursued by the Zionist leaders. On 29 June the military occupied the Jewish Agency building and arrested prominent Zionist leaders, including Shertok and the Canadian-Jewish lawyer Bernard Joseph who was his political second-in-command; Ben Gurion was away in Europe. Many Palmach commanders were interned, and a whole series of well-furnished arms-caches discovered in the settlement of Yagur, a Palmach headquarters.

While conversations between the American cabinet mission and the British experts were in progress, shortly after mid-day on 22 July the Irgun blew up a corner of the King David Hotel, killing ninety-one persons, mainly Arab and Jewish civil-servants.[2] The horror of this outrage had not passed away when the British government announced on 31 July that the Anglo-American Experts had produced a Federal Plan for dividing Palestine into two main autonomous provinces, Arab and Jewish, broadly managing their own affairs, including the control of immigration 'so long as the economic absorptive capacity of a province was not exceeded'.

While the Arab States accepted the British government's

---

[1] Action had already been threatened a month previously in a broadcast 'delivered at the request of Shertok'. (The July 1946 White Paper, quoting a Jewish Agency telegram.)
[2] The high command of the Hagana were accessories before the fact to this outrage and continued their liaison with the I.Z.L. high command after it, according to Menachem Begin: *The Revolt*, pp. 213–26.

invitation to a conference to discuss the details of this plan, the Palestine Arabs, encouraged by the well-timed escape of the Mufti from France to Egypt,[1] refused to attend the conference unless they were given a free choice of their representatives, including the Mufti. The Jewish Agency Executive decided that 'it could not participate in any discussions based on the Federal Plan, since it would deprive the Jewish people of its right under the Mandate in 85 per cent. of Western Palestine;[2] it did not provide genuine self-government; and it did not secure freedom of Jewish immigration and settlement'. It would, however, be prepared to participate 'if the establishment of a viable Jewish State in an adequate area of Palestine were the purpose of the discussion'. This 'viable Jewish State' was later defined as consisting of the whole of Galilee and the coastal plain (as proposed by the Royal Commission's Partition Plan of 1937), plus the Southern District with, if possible, a continuous boundary connecting them, the whole to comprise 65 per cent. of the total area of Palestine. Describing this as a 'supreme sacrifice', the Zionist official spokesman obligingly added that 'the Arabs would be allotted the central plateau', and suggested that the Christian Holy Places should be handed over to an international régime of the Churches.[3]

While these parleys with Zionists and Arabs were going on, the British authorities in Palestine had to deal with the rising flood of unauthorized Jewish immigration by sea from Central and Eastern Europe, where the desperate Jewish survivors of the Hitler terror had, since the collapse of Germany, been encouraged by a concerted barrage of Zionist propaganda to expect and demand immediate admission to Palestine, and were further impelled by pogroms in Poland and Hungary. Jewish troops in the Allied armies and other Zionist agents acting under the direction of the Jewish Agency had skilfully organized escape-routes to the Mediterranean coast, and purchased or chartered ships for their onward voyage to Palestine. Most of the liberal funds for these operations came from Zionist organizations in the U.S.A., which

---

[1] No doubt with the connivance of some French officials.

[2] The proposed extent of the Jewish province approximated to that of Plan B of the Palestine Partition Commission (1938), roughly restricting the Jewish area to the status quo but taking in some small Arab enclaves.

[3] *Palestine Post*, 25 October 1946.

conducted their appeals for subscriptions quite openly in the press.[1] The British government stated that 'food, clothing, medical supplies, and transport provided by U.N.R.R.A. and other agencies for the relief of suffering in Europe were diverted to this "underground railway to Palestine"'. The majority of the immigrants selected by the Zionist authorities were young men and women, to swell the population of the agricultural settlements and the ranks of the Hagana. By mid-August there were sufficient unauthorized immigrants in camps in Palestine awaiting legalization to fill the monthly quota of 1,500 for three months ahead, and thousands more were reported to be on the way. The government therefore resolved to transfer all unauthorized immigrants arriving after 11 August to Cyprus. This policy was received with angry demonstrations and invective by the Zionists. Within a fortnight two attempts were made to sabotage the ships used for the transportation to Cyprus. The Zionists decided to raise £100,000 for the furtherance of immigration 'regardless of the illegal White Paper restrictions which would doom the National Home to stagnation'; they had previously always pretended that the exodus from Europe was entirely a spontaneous, unorganized affair.[2]

The London Conference opened in the presence of representatives of the Arab States, but without either the Arabs or the Jews of Palestine. The Foreign Secretary was reported to have stated that the government was not prepared to consider any solution which disregarded the presence of an organized community of 600,000 Jews who insisted upon their political rights as a group or the necessity for Palestine to contribute to a solution of the refugee-problem. The Arabs, on the other hand, would propose only the creation of an independent state offering equal rights for all citizens permanently resident since 1939 and those acquiring citizenship after that date; freedom of education for the Jews and the use of Hebrew as an official language; but complete stoppage of Jewish immigration and the retention of the existing Land Transfer Regulations, with no modification of these two provisions except with the

[1] Even subscriptions for the terrorist organizations were exempt from American income-tax as 'charitable' donations.

[2] The claim that the National Home would stagnate without a high level of immigration went to confirm the Arab fear that under the government's Federal Plan or under Partition the Zionists would pack their territory with settlers who, at a suitable occasion, would spontaneously invade the Arab territory. By the end of May 1947 the number of Jews in the Cyprus camps was nearly 15,000 or ten months' quota.

consent of the majority of the Arabs in the legislature. Meanwhile, the government carried on parallel negotiations with the Agency with a view to resolving the deadlock, and after the Inner Zionist Council had issued an appeal to the Yishuv to isolate the terrorists and deny them all support, the government on 5 November released the detained Jewish leaders. The effect of this clemency was only to increase the wave of terrorism; and during the entire year more British personnel, military and civil, were killed by the terrorists than in any single year of the Arab Rebellion, the total being seventy-three against the 1938 peak-figure of sixty-nine. The total casualties of all nationalities from political unrest were 212 killed and 428 injured.

The terrorist campaign ceased, however, as if by magic with the opening in December of the twenty-second World Zionist Congress, in the elections for which in Palestine the Revisionists had scored a remarkable success, being second only to the Mapai (Labour) party. However, the Yishuv had only 21 per cent. of all the seats at the Congress, while the American Zionists held first place with 32 per cent. The prevailing mood of the delegates was an extreme one, the great majority of the American Zionists being united with the Revisionists in demanding a Jewish State in the whole of Palestine. Weizmann appealed to the Congress to work for an understanding with Britain for a Jewish state in 'an adequate part' of Palestine. He warned them that they were faced with the alternatives of slow progress or the destruction through terrorism and counter-measures of all they had gained in twenty-nine years, and that he could not continue to remain their president if the Congress saddled the Executive with an unworkable policy. However, the Congress resolved by 171 votes to 154 that the Movement should not participate in the resumed London Conference unless they received immediate concessions in the all-important matter of immigration; and on 7 January 1947 Shertok told a press-conference that since the Agency's compromise-offer of the previous autumn had met with no response from the British, it now stood for an independent Jewish state in the whole of Palestine, guaranteeing equal rights to the Arabs, but aiming at attaining a numerical majority as soon as possible by the introduction of 700,000 immigrants.

Terrorist activity was resumed in the New Year. On 12 January the Stern Group attempted a bomb-outrage comparable with the

King David disaster against the Haifa police compound, killing five persons and injuring thirty-four. The Vaad Leumi passed a resolution repudiating murder as a means of political resistance. It condemned the intimidation of the Jewish community by the terrorists, their impairing of 'national discipline' and their claim 'to decide when or where the struggle of the Jewish people should be waged'. Asked, however, at a press-conference whether the community was called on to intervene if the terrorists attacked the British, an Agency spokesman admitted that 'from the text of the resolution that would not appear to be the case',[1] and subsequently Mrs. Meyerson, head of the Agency Political Dept., and others explained that the Yishuv could not be expected to act as 'informers' against their kin.[2]   On 26 and 27 January the terrorists kidnapped two British civilians, one a judge actually taken from his court, as hostages for a terrorist under sentence of death for his part in an outrage in which five persons were killed. They were set free after the High Commissioner had given an ultimatum to the Agency; but on 31 January, in consequence of a terrorist threat to 'turn Palestine into a bloodbath' if the death-sentence were carried out, the government issued an order for the evacuation of all British women and children and other non-essential civilians, and the concentration in guarded cantonments of those who remained. On 3 February the Government called on the Agency and the Vaad Leumi, in view of their 'open and continued refusals' to co-operate against terrorism, 'to state categorically and at once whether they were prepared publicly to call upon the Jewish community to lend their aid to the Government by co-operating with the police and armed forces in locating and bringing to justice the members of the terrorist groups'.   They replied that 'the Yishuv cannot be called upon to place itself at the disposal of the Government for fighting the evil consequences of a policy which is of that government's own making, and which the Yishuv regards as a menace to its existence. . . .'

On 14 February the British Foreign Secretary announced that the government would submit the question to U.N.O., as both parties had rejected a new federal plan which would have admitted 96,000 Jewish immigrants in the next two years, subsequent immigration being controlled by the High Commissioner after

[1] *Palestine Post*, 22 January 1947.
[2] ibid. 3 February 1947.

consulting both Jews and Arabs. The Arabs had rejected any further immigration, and the Zionists refused to admit the principle that the Arabs should have any say in determining Jewish immigration.

On 1 March, after the detention of an illegal immigrant ship, terrorist outrages caused the deaths of twenty persons and the injury of twenty-five others. The government then imposed statutory martial law on Tel Aviv and neighbouring Jewish towns and on part of Jerusalem, affecting more than 40 per cent. of the whole Jewish population. After eleven days it was officially announced that 'in spite of the refusal of the Jewish official bodies to assist the security forces in combating and rooting out the gangsters, help has been received from members of the Jewish community. . . . The total number of arrests effected during the past fortnight is seventy-eight, of which fifteen are members of the Stern Group, twelve I.Z.L., and fifty-one others connected with terrorism.' Martial law was subsequently withdrawn, it not being desired to extend indefinitely the loss, unemployment, and dislocation of the economic situation, which was reported to have cost the Jewish community £500,000.

At the end of April a special session of the General Assembly of U.N.O. met to consider the Palestine problem, to the accompaniment in Palestine itself of a continuous terrorist campaign. After a fortnight's debate which reflected the many international cross-currents affecting the issue, the Assembly set up a special committee of representatives of small and medium Powers with no direct interests or commitments in Palestine 'to investigate all questions and issues relevant to the problem' and make a report for the next session of the Assembly in September, with proposals for a solution. The Committee conducted its inquiries in the Middle East from 16 June to 24 July, being boycotted throughout by the Arabs of Palestine, but hearing statements from representatives of the Arab states. Jewish terrorist activity, which had ceased while the Anglo-American Committee of 1946 was in the Middle East, went on during the presence of the U.N. Committee, doubtless because three terrorists were under sentence of death for their part in a raid on Akka Prison. Nor did the Hagana allow the Committee to leave without witnessing the arrival of the largest single contingent of illegal immigrants ever to reach Palestine, numbering 4,500 in all; when intercepted, the American-Jewish crew and the passengers fiercely resisted and broadcast a commentary for the benefit of the Committee. On 31 August, while a minority of three made proposals approximating to the Anglo-American Federal Plan of July 1946, a majority of seven of the eleven members recommended to the General Assembly a sharper partition on the lines of the Royal Commission Report of 1937, though the two states so formed would remain in economic union. They proposed to award to the Jewish state, in addition to rounding off its present holdings, the whole of the Beersheba sub-district of Southern Palestine and Eastern Galilee, though the Arabs were to keep Western Galilee. In the transitional period of two years 150,000 Jews were to be admitted, as against the 100,000 proposed for the same period by Britain in January, and the Land Transfer Regulations were to cease in the area of the Jewish state. The scheme contemplated that Britain would continue to administer the country during the transitional period under the auspices of the U.N., and if so desired with the assistance of members of the U.N. The difficulties inherent in the scheme were obvious: while the Zionists' immediate aims were largely met, half-a-million Arabs were to be included in the area of the Jewish state, and by the loss of Jaffa the Arabs were to be left without a port of their own; they were to accept in the interim period an even higher rate of immigration than in the peak years 1934–35 before the Arab Rebellion, with no guarantee that the subsequently unrestricted population of the Jewish state might not at some suitable opportunity erupt in their direction; all this without any compensation except their independence, recognition of which was to be conditional on their guaranteeing fundamental liberties, non-discrimination, and signing the treaty of economic union with the Jewish state; this treaty of economic union would presumably take precedence over any desires the Arabs might have for closer union with other Arab states. Finally, although the six weeks before the publishing of the Report had been marked by the worst riots between the two communities in the Tel Aviv-Jaffa area since the Arab Rebellion the two states were to be presented with an immense problem of policing, since their modest areas would each consist of three separate sectors, touching only by means of two specially-created 'points of intersection'.

On 26 September the Colonial Secretary made it clear that Britain would not feel able to implement a policy not acceptable

International Frontiers

Armistice Lines, 1949

LEBANON

SYRIA

Akka

Haifa

Nazareth

Irbid

Jenin

Mafraq

Tulkarm

Nablus

Qalqiliya

Tel Aviv
Jaffa

J O R D A N

Lydda

As-Salt   Amman

Jericho

Ramla

Latrun

Jerusalem

Beit
Jibrin

Bethlehem

Gaza

Hebron

Beersheba

Kerak

Auja
Hafir
(Demilitarized)

EGYPT

(Province

of

Sinai)

Ma'an

R. Jordan

I S R A E L

D E S E R T

D E S E R T

0   25   50
Miles

Elath   Aqaba

SA'UDI
ARABIA

12.   ISRAEL AND JORDAN, 1950

to Jews and Arabs, and in the absence of a settlement must plan for the early withdrawal of the British forces and administration from Palestine. On 2 October the chairman of the American section of the Jewish Agency told the U.N. General Assembly, 'Should British forces not be available, the Jewish people of Palestine would provide without delay the necessary effectives to maintain public security'. On 29 November the Assembly approved the partition plan with minor amendments, though the necessary two-thirds majority was obtained only by some remarkable lobbying, which at the last moment swung eight doubtful votes into the partition lobby. *The Times* correspondent commented: 'The general feeling among the delegates was that, regardless of its merits and demerits and the joint support given by the U.S.S.R. and the U.S.A., the partition scheme would have been carried in no other city than New York. . . . The strength of the Jewish influence in Washington has been a revelation.'[1] Immediately guerilla warfare broke out in Palestine: 'The Arabs were determined to show that they would not submit tamely to the U.N. plan of partition, while the Jews tried to consolidate the advantages gained at the General Assembly by a succession of drastic operations designed to intimidate and cure the Arabs of any desire for further conflict.'[2] In January 1948 the British Government resisted Zionist claims for recognition of their armed forces and the right to import arms before the ending of the Mandate on 15 May. After the problem of executing the partition scheme had been referred to the Security Council, the United States on 19 March admitted that it could not be carried out peacefully, and proposed instead that Palestine should be placed under temporary United Nations trusteeship. The Security Council's appeal for a truce between Arabs and Jews served once again to protract the discussion without reaching any decision. Meanwhile, as the British troops were withdrawn the Zionists, by a vigorous counter-offensive, had by the end of April achieved complete military superiority over the Palestine Arab 'Liberation Army' in the plains. On the afternoon of 14 May the Jewish state of Israel was proclaimed,[3] and was immediately recognized by the United

---

[1] See Walter J. Lilienthal: *What Price Israel* (1953).
[2] Sir Alexander Cadogan to the U.N. Palestine Commission, 21 January 1948.
[3] The termination of the mandate at midnight was anticipated because the Sabbath began at sunset on 14 May.

States, where an outspoken Zionist supporter had on 28 April been appointed special assistant for Palestine affairs to the Secretary of State. Recognition by Russia and her satellites followed, and the armies of the neighbouring Arab states crossed the frontiers into Palestine.

*   *   *

An Egyptian force crossed the Sinai Desert and advanced north through mainly Arab territory to within 20 miles of Tel Aviv, where it halted before the first Israeli defence-line. The Jordan Arab Legion, which had been ordered to occupy the Arab central highlands, was diverted by an Israeli attempt, immediately upon the termination of the Mandate, to seize the Old City of Jerusalem. In the struggle that followed there the Jewish quarter of the Old City was destroyed and the Jewish inhabitants of the New City brought near to capitulation by the cutting of their water- and food-supplies from the coastal plain, until they were relieved by a four-week truce ordered by the U.N. (9 June). While the Israelis were fighting with resource and the valour of desperation, the Arab effort was being sapped by their poor administration and lack of unity and co-ordination. In particular, Arab reserves of arms and ammunition were running low, and Britain acceded to the United Nations request that she should discontinue the supplies she had made under her treaties with Egypt, Iraq, and Jordan; Israel, on the other hand, received during the truce considerable clandestine reinforcements in aircraft, heavy and small arms, and volunteers from abroad. The armaments came especially from communist Czechoslovakia, against payment in the dollars which Israel received 'charitably' from the United States. When the Arab States, driven on by a press and public opinion that they had been feeding with extravagant propaganda, resumed hostilities on the expiration of the truce, Israel was more than a match for them. Her advantage was increased by the growing faction on the Arab side: King Abdullah had failed to obtain Egyptian and Sa'udi acceptance of his thesis that Arab Palestine should be incorporated into his Jordan Kingdom, and instead they proclaimed a phantom 'Government of All-Palestine' under the discredited Mufti. The Israel Government and public opinion were indignant when the United Nations mediator, Count Bernadotte, made recommendations that would limit Israel's territory to less than was now attainable by military action.

Emboldened by their scot-free escape from the consequences of Bernadotte's murder by terrorists on 17 September, they made Egyptian interference with supplies to isolated Jewish settlements in South Palestine the justification for an attack in October on the Egyptian positions that won Israel a tract of territory extending as far as Beersheba; they had already secured the whole of Galilee. In another offensive begun just before Christmas they drove across the Egyptian frontier, and a tense situation was created when they shot down five R.A.F. aircraft reconnoitring the battle. During this period the Jordan Arab Legion, so far from creating a diversion for their Egyptian 'allies', had negotiated a local truce with the Israelis on the Jerusalem front. The Egyptians, ignoring the extent to which their own intrigues against King Abdullah had aggravated Arab disunity, now complained that they had been 'deserted' and were the first of the Arab States to sign an armistice with Israel (24 February 1949). They were followed by Lebanon, Jordan (after an Israeli column had occupied the Palestinian outlet on the Red Sea, and a small British force had been despatched to the adjacent Jordan harbour of Aqaba to forestall any Israeli designs on that locality), and Syria.[1] In April 1950 Britain gave her *de jure* recognition to Israel, and also extended her treaty obligations to Jordan over the remnant of Arab Palestine that had just been formally incorporated with Jordan. In May the British, French, and United States Governments jointly declared 'their unalterable opposition to the use of force or threat of force' in this region, an act calculated to preclude not only the resumption of hostilities between the Arab States and Israel, but also the possibility of hostilities among the Arab States themselves.

Israel had thus acquired the whole of that 'viable State' that she had postulated in 1946,[2] and was already proceeding to fill it with immigrants as fast as they could be moved from abroad. Only the central highlands, from Jenin to a little south of Hebron, plus a narrow strip about Gaza, remained in Arab hands; despite a United Nations resolution to internationalize Jerusalem, the city remained divided between Israel and Jordan. About 750,000 Arabs had become refugees from Israel. Some with greater

---

[1] Iraq had withdrawn her contingent from Palestine, and so avoided the necessity of an armistice.

[2] Cf. p. 215. It comprised practically the whole of the irrigable lowlands of mandatory Palestine, apart from the southern Jordan valley.

prudence than patriotism had moved to safety betimes; some had allegedly been promised a speedy return in the wake of the 'victorious' Arab armies; some had been quickened by Israeli 'psychological warfare' or panicked by direct terrorism; no doubt many joined in the flight without knowing why. During 1949 United Nations Relief rations were being stretched to cover one million destitute and needy Arabs, or 80 per cent. of the Arab population of mandatory Palestine. When a liberal allowance had been made for fraud and malversation, it was clear that the 'ingathering of the exiles' into Israel had been achieved by the almost total disruption of those 'non-Jewish communities' whose rights had been guaranteed in the Balfour Declaration and the Mandate. They had paid a heavy price for the intransigence and incompetence of their 'leaders'; and in addition the inter-relations of the Arab States had been poisoned by the exacerbation of their jealousies and feuds in this disastrous campaign.

The British administrators had 'had the bitterness of seeing all that we had aimed at building crash round us ... It was a decision of the times, taken in accordance with the spirit of the times; but it was the rejection of a mission';[1] and Britain's reputation emerged from the debacle not a little tarnished. Hated by the Israelis for having obstructed their divine destiny and promoted to the latest place on the long roll of their oppressors,[2] she was reviled by the Arabs, with equal venom but perhaps less excuse, for having 'encouraged' them to count on her support by her coldness towards Israel. Until the diplomatic archives are opened we shall not know whether, or how far, British policy had *over*-estimated Arab strength and determination. In his last year of office Winston Churchill had evidently hoped to deal with the problem by a generous, but still limited, territorial concession to Israel which he would seek American co-operation in imposing on both parties. If successful, such a policy would have avoided the bloodshed, hatred, misery, and humiliation which in fact ensued; but with his justified disparagement of the Arabs as a military force, he may (as in 1940–41) have *under*-estimated their nuisance-potential to the extended zone of British interests; and had he remained Prime Minister, the Soviet 'cold

[1] Sir William Fitzgerald, the last Chief Justice of Palestine, *International Affairs*, January 1950, p. 9.
[2] Though economic necessity was constraining Israeli spokesmen to profess magnanimity by the autumn of 1950.

war' against Persia and Turkey might have compelled him to continue to propitiate the Arab world despite his personal inclinations. The difficulties before the inexperienced Labour Government were very great. They were dealing with two groups of irreconcilable and uncompromising politicians in Palestine, and could not isolate the adjudication of their conflicting claims from formidable external factors. They had to weigh Britain's regional interests in the Arab world against her new financial dependence upon the United States, and that Government's uncritical sympathy with Israeli aspirations. The fact remains that British policy was lacking in coherence; it oscillated between military action against militant Zionism and attempts to conciliate its unrepentant leaders; and it thus alienated both parties to little purpose.

Perhaps, after all, a conflict was necessary to teach the British and United States Governments that all nations are not equally reasonable, and to demonstrate to both Arabs and Israel the physical limitations of their self-will. The Arab discomfiture has already been described. For Israel, independence and victory were only the beginning of the effort to attain her ancient hope. During the years of preparation and struggle elaborate schemes had been prepared for the intensive development of the country's resources, most of which were limited and not a few probably below the margin of economical exploitation. Half a million Jewish immigrants were admitted in the first two and a half years of independence, both to fulfil the promise of the return of the exiles and to provide the emotional basis for an appeal for charity and investment on an ample scale from Jews and sympathizers abroad (since internal finances were totally inadequate for the planned development, and the National Home's balance of trade had never been other than seriously adverse). By the summer of 1950, however, the government planners had to admit that not only had the inflow of capital, though of the order of hundreds of millions of dollars, fallen seriously short of their assessments, but that they had also grossly under-estimated the costs of settlement and development; for since independence wages and prices had risen to one of the highest levels in the world. Markets for Israel's limited range of over-priced non-essential goods were hard to find, except on barter terms; the new immigrants (from Hitler's Europe, the Yemen, North Africa, &c.) lacked the insistent zeal, the devotion and adaptability of the earlier settlers; and an appreciable fraction of the population, accustomed for centuries to the outwitting of alien authority, did not now take easily to imposed 'austerity' in their own State, but resorted instinctively to a widespread black market that attracted even some of the 'zealot' collective settlements. The worsening situation made necessary a radical currency-devaluation in February 1952; but a possible source of relief presented itself when the West German Government undertook late that year to furnish Israel with goods to the value of $822 millions in fourteen years, as reparation for the Nazi atrocities against European Jewry.

*   *   *

Apart from the Soviet Union's 'cold war' against Turkey and Persia which will be examined in a later chapter, the chief post-war international issue was the demand of the politically-conscious minority in Egypt for the evacuation of British troops and for the 'unity of the Nile Valley', with somewhat imprecise assurances of Sudanese self-government. Isma'il Sidqi, an outstanding statesman, who became Premier in February 1946, had King Faruq's support in recognizing that in 'cold war' conditions the United Nations were not a sufficient guarantee of security of a strategically important region like lower Egypt, and that the Anglo-Egyptian alliance, suitably modified, was in Egypt's interest. This view was repugnant to most politicians and the irresponsible press, while the Wafd Party, dismissed from office by the King in October 1944, was engaged in fomenting mob violence, with its left wing apparently in collusion with Soviet agents. When negotiations began in May 1946 the British Government publicly offered complete evacuation on condition of satisfactory arrangements for mutual assistance. After months of fruitless negotiations Sidqi flew to London in October and drafted an agreement with Foreign Secretary Bevin, which compromised on joint action or consultation to meet threats to Middle East security and recognized 'unity between the Sudan and Egypt under the Egyptian crown'. Mindful of the 1936 Treaty pledges to the Sudanese, however, and of the steady 'Sudanization' of administration that had followed, the British Government accompanied this nominal concession with provisions that the Sudanese might freely choose their future status, and that until they and their Egyptian and British 'co-domini' had agreed on this the present regime in the

Sudan should continue. Egyptian public opinion had been taught that the entire Sudan favoured union with Egypt, except for a few British-inspired dissidents. In fact, while most of the 'white-collar' class and groups with traditional connexions with Egypt were unionist, those to whom the Condominium had given authority, and the considerable religious following of Egypt's enemy the Mahdi, were for independence; the illiterate majority were below the level of political consciousness. On returning to Egypt Sidqi announced the unity clause of the agreement without the British reservations. The Sudanese Independence Front boy-cotted the Advisory Council and organized violent demonstra-tions, to which the Unionists replied. The Egyptian Parliament, the press, and probably the King, were so hostile to the British saving clause that Sidqi could only equivocate, until on 7 Decem-ber the Governor-General of the Sudan was authorized from London to calm the Independence Front by assurances of the Sudanese people's free choice of their future status. Sidqi resigned, and was succeeded by Nuqrashi who, having succumbed to Wafdist mob violence in February, now reiterated that self-government 'in permanent union with Egypt' was the 'unani-mous' wish of the Sudanese. Diplomatic exchanges failed to move him from this point, and on 26 January 1947 he announced his intention of referring the whole question of Britain's position in Egypt and the Sudan to the United Nations. The British Government, who were already proceeding with the evacuation of troops and military stores—some to Palestine, some to East Africa, some provisionally to the Canal Zone—replied that they would consequently revert to the 1936 Treaty, i.e. would remain in the Canal Zone until that treaty legally expired in 1956, unless the United Nations ruled otherwise. The Egyptian Government now spent five months in trying to obtain all-party backing for their appeal to the United Nations, which was not presented until 11 July. Their wish to shake off the vestiges of the sixty-five years of British occupation, especially the presence of British troops on their soil, commanded sympathy; but Nuqrashi exposed the weak-ness of his case when he invited the Security Council to declare the unexpired 1936 Treaty void because it was not adapted to Egypt's post-war status; and his insistence on prejudging the wishes of the Sudanese (on the grounds of their pretended racial and religious identity with the Egyptians) failed to win the support even of the U.S.S.R. and Poland, who were eager to secure the immediate evacuation of the British troops. A Brazilian resolution calling for the resumption of direct negotiations secured one vote short of the necessary two-thirds majority, and there the matter was left. Meanwhile, in the Sudan a conference, supported by the Independence Front but boycotted by the Unionists, had recommended the enlargement of the Northern Sudan Advisory Council (established in 1944) into a Legislative Assembly for the entire country, its members to be directly or indirectly elected or nominated according to the political maturity of the different provinces. An enlarged Governor-General's Executive Council would consist as to half its numbers of Sudanese with departmental responsibilities, while the Governor-General would retain considerable reserve powers against a constitutional emergency. After many months of manœuvring, ostensibly to secure a greater measure of popular government, the Egyptian Government joined in negotiations on these proposals in May 1948. A draft agreement making some concessions to the Egyptian views was initialled, but the Egyptian Parliament would accept nothing less than that complete parity implicit in the Condominium, which had never existed in fact owing to Egypt's political immaturity and her resort to violence in 1924. The Sudan's first legislature was thus inaugurated in December 1948 without Egypt's blessing. Her intransigence was promoting the very separatism which she feared (not least because of her total dependence on the Nile waters). The sweeping victory of the Wafd in the Egyptian elections of January 1950 offered new hopes of an Anglo-Egyptian understanding, but after several months of conversations it was evident that Egypt's position had not altered, despite the dangers to world security revealed by the war in Korea.

Meanwhile, Egypt's frustration had found expression in agitation against King Abdullah, whose immoderate propaganda for a Kingdom of 'Greater Syria' was commonly believed, despite denials, to have British encouragement. When the Palestine War of 1948 laid the Syrian nationalist Government open to charges of incompetence and corruption, Nuri as-Sa'id, who was Premier of Iraq, sought this opportunity to pursue his scheme (set out in 1943) for a closer union between Iraq and Syria as a step to wider Arab unity. These efforts were opposed, not only by the Syrian

16

army which dominated the political scene there after the first of three *coups d'état* in March 1949, but by those Arab states hostile to the aggrandizement of the Hashimi dynasty of Iraq and Jordan, namely Sa'udi Arabia, Egypt, and Lebanon. The extreme nationalists in Iraq, who had combined with the left wing to reject the revised Anglo-Iraqi treaty initialled at Portsmouth in January 1948, received greater Egyptian favour than the moderates who sought understanding with Britain.

Thus the Palestine War left the Arab world and Israel at sixes and sevens, a situation which was aggravated by the misery of nearly a million Arab refugees, their constant encroachments across the armistice lines, and punitive (not to say, vindictive) Israeli reprisals. Five years after the armistice of 1949 the situation was still so bad that some observers feared a reopening of active hostilities. British hopes of consolidating the region into a Middle East defence organization, as an obstacle to Soviet expansion, had been constantly frustrated since 1950; and by 1954 the United States Government had turned instead to the fostering of a military alliance, with American material aid, between Turkey and Pakistan—an alliance into which they hoped that a realistic Iraqi Government might eventually lead other Arab states.

CHAPTER VIII

Present-Day Economic and Social Conditions

By ARTHUR MILLS, B.A., B.Com.

(*Department of Commerce, American University of Beirut*)

POVERTY IS the outstanding feature of the Middle East. The annual income per head in Turkey and Lebanon is less than one quarter that in Great Britain; in Egypt and Syria it approaches one fifth, while in Sa'udi Arabia it is less than one tenth. There are local idealists who foresee an economic development on the scale of that in Western Europe or North America; but, though it is true that little surveying and prospecting have been done, and that more mineral resources may exist than are now known, there is a significant paucity of natural resources. There is a lack of coal, offset by an abundance of oil and a potentially great production of hydro-electric power where water can be spared for the purpose. There is nothing to offset the lack of iron; the Egyptian and Turkish deposits can produce only a fraction of the area requirements. Timber is deficient, except in Iran; forests cover only about one fifth of one per cent. of the total area.[1] The oil reserves are estimated to amount to some two-thirds of the world reserves; and production in 1957 amounted to 20 per cent. of the total world output.[2] Only the countries

[1] Sai'd B. Himadeh, 'The Economic Set-Up in the Arab Middle East' *United Asia*, 1953, v. 287.

[2]
Crude oil production in millions of metric tons:

	Bahrain	Iran	Iraq	Kuwait	Neutral Zone	Qatar	Sa'udi Arabia
1938	1·1	10·4	4·4	—	—	—	0·1
1946	1·1	19·5	4·7	0·8	—	—	8·1
1950	1·5	32·2	6·4	17·2	—	1·6	26·1
1953	1·5	1·2	27·6	43·0	—	4·0	40·5
1955	1·5	16·2	33·6	54·8	1·4	5·4	47·5
1957 (provisional)	1·5	36·3	22·0	55·5	3·3	6·8	49·5

The rapid decline in Iranian production from 1951 to 1953, and the consequent rapid increase in other countries, were due to the political dispute between the Iranian Government and the Anglo-Iranian Oil Company, for which see below, pp. 273 ff. The decline in Iraqi production in 1957 was due to the Syrian army's blowing up the pumping-stations on the pipeline to the Mediterranean, at the time of the Suez crisis in Autumn 1956: below, p. 286.

around the Persian Gulf, however, receive royalties from oil, and their populations cover only 30 per cent. of the total population of the Middle East. Though the region is more or less self-sufficient in cereals, edible oil and fats, vegetables, fruit, and meat, there are food-deficit areas of which the most serious is now Egypt. The only agricultural exports of importance to countries outside the Middle East are cotton, dates, wool, tobacco, and citrus. Locally significant exports include Dead Sea chemicals and Turkish chromium. Though the Middle East has about 4 per cent. of the world's population, its share of total world trade amounts to only about 3 per cent.[1]

Poverty is not likely to be eliminated unless supreme efforts are made to improve the principal asset which is the land. Most of it is desert or semi-desert, and the cultivable area is only a small fraction of the total, but 'although somewhat deficient in organic matter, most of the land of the Middle East is quite fertile; some of it is very fertile'.[2] Water supply sets the limit to cultivation and human settlement. It limits the number of crops grown during the year and determines the proportion of land that must lie fallow. The scanty rainfall restricts the volume of water from rivers, and this in turn limits the area that can be irrigated. Climate also gives rise to soil erosion. 'In the dry season the soil bakes and cracks. In the wet season there are often torrential rains and floods which carve gullies and deposit at lower levels the great quantities of silt carried in suspension. Here it may cover fertile land and block natural drainage flows.'[3] Forest denudation and over-grazing have also added to soil erosion. It follows that, in order to take full advantage of the fertile soil of the Middle East, there must be irrigation on a large scale as in ancient times. Irrigation itself is limited by water supply, but there is still enough water in all Middle Eastern countries, except perhaps Egypt, for a large extension of irrigation. The total irrigated area amounts probably to only half of the cultivated area and a little over a quarter of the cultivable area. The Turkish Government has estimated that in Turkey alone nearly $10\frac{1}{2}$ million acres of uncultivated land could be tilled if machinery were available and a further $6\frac{3}{4}$ millions through irrigation. Projects for the pro-

[1] Issawi, Charles P., in *Near East and the Great Powers*, ed. Richard N. Frye, Harvard Univ. Press (1951), pp. 57–8.
[2] United Nations: *Review of Economic Conditions in the Middle East* (supplement to *World Economic Report*, 1949–50), p. 7.　[3] Keen, B. A., op. cit., p. 55.

vision of irrigation are usually planned to provide hydro-electric power. In Turkey there are the Seyhan Valley, Porsuk, Sakarya, Gediz and Mendere River Schemes. The Seyhan and Gediz plans alone will generate 436 million kwh, and are expected to be completed by 1957. In Iraq plans for expansion of irrigation on a very wide scale are under way; but here the major problem has been flood control which is a prerequisite of all other types of development. Work on the Habbaniya Lake Scheme has averted destruction from the Euphrates floods since 1953, but progress on the channelling of the Tigris floods into a dam at Wadi Tharthar had not advanced sufficiently to prevent the 1954 floods from doing about £45 millions worth of damage. This scheme is scheduled for completion in 1956. The Habbaniya reservoir is expected eventually to irrigate over one million hectares. In Lebanon, work on the Litani River Scheme is awaiting completion of the technical study made by the Point Four Administration. In Syria the Ghab Project will irrigate a large area of fertile land from the Orontes River and improve the supply of electric power for Homs and Hama. The Khabbur River Scheme will irrigate 125,000 hectares of desert between Dair az-Zor and the Jazira, and will provide pure drinking water for local inhabitants. Egypt is sharing in the Owen Falls Scheme on the Upper Nile which will increase the storage capacity of Lake Victoria and enable Egypt and the Sudan to extend the area of irrigated land, while the Aswan Dam Scheme is planned to provide, besides irrigation, electric power for the steel industry based on the Aswan deposits of iron ore, and for other local industries, public utilities, and transportation. Political disagreements are delaying work on the Yarmuq Scheme to irrigate 37,000 hectares in Jordan and provide hydro-electric power for both Syria and Jordan, and on the plan to irrigate the Negeb in Israel from the Jordan, Kishon, and Yarkon Rivers.

* * *

Irrigation is rightly being given priority by governments. There are, however, serious social obstacles to any rapid extension of productivity in agriculture. The social structure, health, and educational condition of a community are important determinants of productivity, in industry as well as agriculture. In a modern economy where specialization has made the unskilled and illiterate less and less able to find employment, the supply of manpower depends far less on the size of the population than on its health and skills. The state of ill-health of peoples in under-developed regions allows them a life expectancy of only about one half on the average of that in Britain and U.S.A., and the individual's period of productive work is correspondingly short. Disease saps the energy of available manpower. Malaria is a major scourge in many rural areas, especially in Iraq, Egypt, and Syria. In Egypt three-quarters of the rural population are chronically infected with endemic worm-diseases, and perhaps four-fifths of it suffers from the eye-disease of trachoma, with consequences ranging from impaired vision to total blindness. The incidence of worm-disease has been considerably increased by the great extension of perennial irrigation with its thousands of channels, from which the fellah, working bare-foot, is reinfected as often as he is cured. Since World War II considerable progress has been made, but the measures taken to improve health and life expectancy intensify the rate of increase of the population, and so aggravate the problem of finding the food to keep it alive. This poses for planning authorities the need to achieve a balance between programmes of social betterment and schemes for improving agricultural output.

Over-population exists in Egypt, Israel and Lebanon. It exists, too, in Jordan; the very large number of Arab refugees who have migrated to Jordan has considerably increased the density of population. Iraq and Iran are under-populated, while in Syria and the Arabian Peninsula there is room for expansion of population in line with further development of resources. The population of Egypt, cramped into only $3\frac{1}{2}$ per cent. of the total area of the country, has more than doubled since 1900, and, as it seems likely that there are now diminishing returns from agriculture, the pressure on resources is reaching grave proportions. There is little cultivable land that is not already cultivated, and since rapid industrialization is unlikely on the requisite scale, the only solution to the problem seems to be emigration to under-populated areas such as the Sudan or Iraq. Syria and Iraq have only 3·7 and 5 million inhabitants respectively, considerably fewer than they supported in antiquity; and the extension of irrigation will undoubtedly permit a corresponding increase in their population.

Birth rates in the Middle East range from 25 to 60 per 1,000 according to districts (cf. U.K. 15, U.S.A. 17), while death rates range from 15 to 40 per 1,000 owing to malnutrition and disease. In certain regions, as many as 50 per cent. of babies do not live beyond the age of five.[1] The annual rate of natural increase of population (urban and rural together) averages about 20 per 1,000, a rate which doubles the population in 35 years.[2] While the area is vast in size, only about 5 per cent. is cultivable, and density of population varies sharply according to rainfall and irrigation. With the high rate of increase in population the problems of the densest areas will grow acute. Economically, the Middle East can avoid tragedy only by facilitating the mobility of manpower.

The pressure of population on resources is aggravated by the low productivity of the farmer. The adverse effects of a limited and seasonal rainfall are reinforced by the persistence of antiquated farming methods and systems of land-tenure, comparable with those of Western Europe in the Middle Ages. As a result, production falls far below the standard of more advanced agricultural countries. It is estimated that the average male agricultural worker produces only about one-fifth of the goods produced by his counterpart in Britain, and that the individual's share in the national income is only about one-fifth that of Britain, though still in excess of over-populated India and China. 'The whole area, with the exception of the Jews in Palestine, is included in the groups of population which derive at least 70 per cent. of the energy of their diet from cereals and roots. A considerable part of the population probably belongs to the groups deriving 80 per cent. of its calories. That is to say, the area is included among the worst-nourished parts of the world.[3]

An important cause of the poverty of the rural masses is the inequitable distribution of land.[4] A small number of wealthy landowners own a large proportion of the land, and there are thousands or millions of dwarf-holders, tenants, and landless labourers. Minute holdings are economically wasteful, and yet they are the prevailing mode, because even on the large estates the landlord is an absentee who lets on a share-tenancy basis. In

[1] W. B. Fisher, *The Middle East*, p. 249.
[2] Sa'id B. Himadeh, 'Economic Factors underlying Social Problems in the Arab Middle East', *Middle East Journal*, 1951, v. 272.
[3] Worthington, op. cit., 159.
[4] See Sa'id B. Himadeh in *The Middle East Journal*, loc. cit.

the great majority of cases the absentee owner does nothing to improve the land or the efficiency of the tenancy, and yet takes between one-third and one-half of the crop. The social structure has tended therefore to be one of two tiers, a small group of large landowners and a dependent peasantry for the most part poverty-stricken. The system has produced no sense of responsibility for the well-being either of the land or the workers and, in view of the rapid increase in population, endangers the community. Moreover, the partial conversion of the Fertile Crescent and Egypt from a pre-capitalist to a capitalist economy, which has gathered impetus in the past 30 years, has, together with the inflation of the War and post-War years, tended to increase the disparity of wealth between the very rich and the very poor and to segregate classes. Land distribution is recognized more and more widely as fundamental to progress, but the vested interests which oppose reform are still politically powerful, except in Egypt. In the latter, since 1952, ownerships exceeding 200 acres are being expropriated with compensation and redistributed to small farmers in plots of not less than two acres or more than five, according to the quality of the land. The reform cannot be hurried without dislocating production, and will take many years to complete. Limitation of ownership is provided for in the recent Syrian constitution, but for future land acquisitions and inheritances only, and not retrospectively. Vested interests are strong in Syria, though some improvement will result if the recent law is implemented distributing the public domain to landless tenants and small landowning farmers within the limits of 125 acres of unirrigable land and $12\frac{1}{2}$ acres of irrigable. In Iraq, reform is limited to the distribution of newly irrigated public land, though here some of the political parties are demanding limitation of ownership. In Lebanon there will be no redistribution until there is a radical change of government; the relatively weak Progressive Socialist Party alone demands limitation of ownership. On the whole the likelihood of widespread land reform remains remote, except in Egypt; and rapid and significant progress in production and standards of living cannot accordingly be expected. The problem of rural poverty waits on political evolution.

Industry, though still backward, has since 1930 developed faster than agriculture. Many old industries, such as cotton spinning and weaving, previously using primitive methods and tools, have adopted modern machinery and methods. A variety of new industries have appeared which are protected from foreign competition through the use either of heavy local raw materials or of imported raw materials which are less bulky than the manufactured articles. Examples are building industries such as cement, tiles, bricks, glass, beer and soft drinks, canned fruit or vegetables, pottery, and furniture. Other industries which do not require much fuel and use light raw materials include the textile and clothing industries, tobacco, soap, boots and shoes. Industries requiring large quantities of fuel are at a disadvantage in the Middle East, except in parts of Egypt and Turkey.

Practically all industrial development, apart from large electric plants, has been financed by local capital, except in Turkey and Iran. It has been encouraged by protection: either tariffs on imported manufactures, or duty exemptions on machinery and raw materials.

Earnest efforts are being made in Egypt to utilize surplus population and prevent the fall in living standards by rapid industrialization. Unfortunately it seems at present beyond the means of Egyptian resources to expand industry sufficiently to absorb the surplus labour from the rural areas, estimated at five or six millions; for some time to come the most that can be expected is to absorb the equivalent of the annual increase in the population to avoid intensifying under-employment in the countryside. Indeed, it will require management of a high order to absorb about 750,000 in a single year into industry. In Turkey there is no problem of over-population; resources are plentiful for the development of mining, food processing, and light engineering industries as well as some heavy industry based on domestic iron and coal supplies; and, owing to the strategic importance of Turkey, financial and technical aid from U.S.A. has been and will continue to be readily available to give maximum impetus to industrialization. In Israel a problem similar in some ways to that of Egypt exists, though the supply of technical and managerial skills and of capital is far greater than in Egypt. Jordan is developing the production and export through Aqaba of phosphates at al-Hansa in the south, and also of manganese which exists in considerable quantity just over 100 miles north of Aqaba. Dead Sea potash will also pass through Aqaba. Elsewhere in the Middle

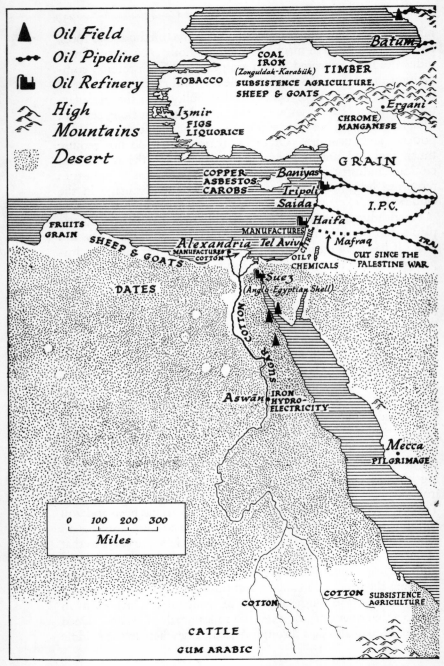

Oil Field ▲
Oil Pipeline ●—●—●
Oil Refinery 🏭
High Mountains ⌃
Desert

COAL
IRON
(*Zonguldak-Karabük*) TIMBER
SUBSISTENCE AGRICULTURE,
SHEEP & GOATS

TOBACCO

Batum

Ergani

CHROME
MANGANESE

Izmir
FIGS
LIQUORICE

GRAIN

COPPER
ASBESTOS,
CAROBS

Baniyas
Tripoli
Saïda

I.P.C.

Haifa

FRUITS
GRAIN

MANUFACTURES
Alexandria *Tel Aviv*
MANUFACTURES
COTTON

SHEEP & GOATS

Mafraq
CUT SINCE THE
PALESTINE WAR

OIL?
CHEMICALS

DATES

Suez
(*Anglo-Egyptian Shell*)

C
O
T
T
O
N

S
U
G
A
R

R. NILE

Aswân IRON
HYDRO-
ELECTRICITY

Mecca
PILGRIMAGE

0   100 200 300
Miles

COTTON

COTTON   SUBSISTENCE
AGRICULTURE

CATTLE
GUM ARABIC

13. **MIDDLE EAST**

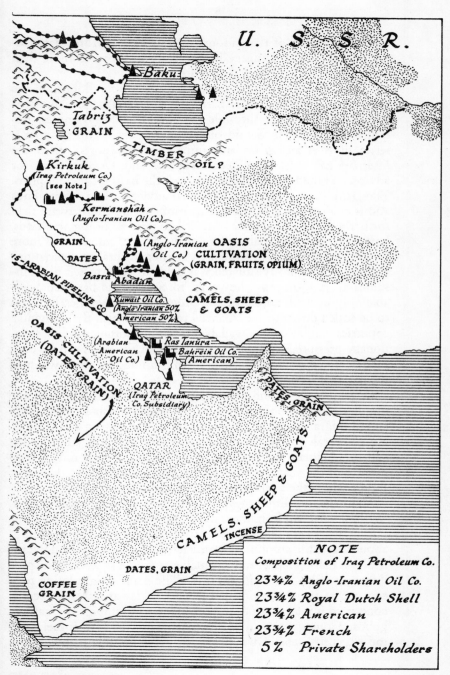

U. S. S. R.

Baku

Tabriz
GRAIN

TIMBER

OIL ?

Kirkuk
(Iraq Petroleum Co)
[see Note]

Kermanshah
(Anglo-Iranian Oil Co.)

GRAIN

DATES

(Anglo-Iranian OASIS
Oil Co.) CULTIVATION
(GRAIN, FRUITS, OPIUM)

TRANS-ARABIAN PIPELINE CO

Basra

Abadan

Kuwait Oil Co.
(Anglo-Iranian 50%
American 50%)

CAMELS, SHEEP
& GOATS

OASIS
CULTIVATION
(DATES, GRAIN)

(Arabian
American
Oil Co.)

Ras Tanura
Bahrein Oil Co.
(American)

DATES, GRAIN

QATAR
(Iraq Petroleum
Co. Subsidiary)

CAMELS, SHEEP & GOATS
INCENSE

DATES, GRAIN

COFFEE
GRAIN

NOTE
Composition of Iraq Petroleum Co.
23¾% Anglo-Iranian Oil Co.
23¾% Royal Dutch Shell
23¾% American
23¾% French
5% Private Shareholders

ECONOMIC RESOURCES

East, the portion of the national income earned from manufacturing and mining industry is not likely to grow to more than 20 per cent. in the next few decades.

Within the severe limits imposed by social conditions, all the governments of the Middle East have endeavoured to make progress since the War through Development Programmes, designed usually with the aid of foreign experts. Turkey, after a series of over-ambitious and impracticable reports, asked the International Bank for Reconstruction and Development for advice, and the Report issued in 1950 is the basis for present plans. The Bank has given similar technical advice to Iraq. Point Four Aid is evidence that Western Governments are more aware than formerly of the importance of trying to raise economic standards, both as a piece of social welfare in the general interest and more specifically because a discontented urban and rural proletariat in a region so strategically situated was liable to be attracted to Communism. In most cases, however, foreign capital has been available only in small amounts, and programmes have therefore had to be scaled down to the financial resources which the individual countries could make available without causing undue inflationary pressure. The short-term effect of the plans can be only modest, since saving to finance them is limited by the lowness of the national incomes.

Development of industries is helping to absorb some of the supplies of idle labour due to under-employment in agriculture and to migration from village to town. The sowing and harvesting of cereals in the dry-farming regions of Syria, Iraq, Jordan and the Arabian Peninsula keep the fellah busy for only 4 to 6 months of the year, and the same is true in the congested areas of Egypt where the average holding is minute.

Many factors limit the potential degree of industrialization. Without coal and iron, there can be no basic heavy industry. Imported machinery tends to be costly. 'The absence of iron ores . . . about halves the amount of manufacturing that could be done for the local market if ores were available. Of course, some metal production can be done without ores. The main weight losing process occurs when the ore is smelted. As far as transport cost is concerned it is as cheap to import ingots as to import the finished goods. Consequently, if productivity is not too low, if fuel is not too expensive, and if wages are low, it is possible to build up a range of foundry products based on imported ingots—such products as agricultural implements, bath tubs, bedsteads, nails, nuts and bolts, locks, and small metal goods.'[1] Unfortunately, indigenous labour is often costly, in spite of low wages and salaries and of unemployment, owing to legally imposed minimum wages, extremely low productivity, and to the acute scarcity of skilled workpeople and administrators. Marketing methods likewise are costly because of their primitiveness. Managerial enterprise suffers from a lack of administrative training facilities, of private and governmental information services on which to base its policies and plans, and a lack of experience and knowledge of costing and control methods which could prevent the enormous waste that prevails of all-too-scarce resources. In most countries there is still too little planning and executive skill in governmental administration to counterbalance the deficiencies of private enterprise. The development of industry is limited, too, by the small size of the home markets: the purchasing power of the rural population is low due to the poverty, and there are tariff barriers between the various countries of the region, to protect their industries which tend to be similar and competitive. Finally, there is, in all but the Persian Gulf countries, the scarcity of finance capital inevitable in countries where the bulk of the population is poverty-stricken and where institutions do not exist to mobilize savings.

The developing economy has in this century called into being a middle-class following various skilled or semi-skilled professions and occupations, and enjoying varying levels of wealth and comfort, but, in common with its prototype in India and Africa, it often tends to consider all forms of business as degrading. Economically it makes little contribution in the field of initiative and enterprise, qualities so conspicuously weak in the management of existing commercial and industrial institutions and none the less vital for future development. This explains to some extent why some governments and professions still fail to give urgent attention to the economic and social factors which can produce disaster through falling standards of living. But there are signs of change. The influence of new social forces is reflected in the concern showed by many governments (half-hearted in some cases, but

[1] W. Arthur Lewis, *Aspects of Industrialisation* (National Bank of Egypt, Cairo, 1953), p. 6.

still conspicuous) for social welfare and justice in their development programmes.[1]

There has been an unfortunate emphasis in the evolution of the educational systems of these countries on training for the civil services and professions rather than for business which, as mentioned above, is felt to be degrading. This now weakens the ability of the governments to find skilled workers to man the projects of development. There is an acute shortage of persons in the intermediate grades of skilled services, clerical workers, etc., which is to some extent being met by technical assistance from U.S.A. and United Nations sources, but which remains acute. Here, too, we see the heavy economic cost of high birth and death rates. In order to secure a given total of work-hours from adults, it is necessary to educate a far larger number of children, owing to the high percentage of deaths before the age of twenty. Under-developed areas can ill afford this enormous waste, for it consumes a considerable portion of their limited budgets and is partly responsible for the low standard of life. Nevertheless, trained manpower is essential for development, and though few realize the fact in these countries, investment in well-directed education brings the highest returns in the long run, from ten to perhaps a hundred times the cost. There may be insufficient allocation of funds to health and education in some budgets, owing to the more obvious attraction of the costly irrigation, power, and transportation schemes. There could be a far greater follow-up of the external assistance in the field of demonstration and extension work, experimental stations, research laboratories and agricultural schools. In the same way as there has been too much concentration on professional and university education (as in Egypt), so the public-health services, especially in those countries least subject to European direction or advice, reflect the wide social gap that separates the professional class from the masses, and the small extent to which the former have as yet acquired a sense of service to the community as a whole. One is left with the impression that the health-services of the independent countries are designed for the benefit of the medical profession rather than for the healing of the sick. In the capital cities there are government hospitals with imposing buildings and well-equipped

[1] See Sa'id B. Himadeh, 'Social Awakening and Economic Development in the Middle East', *International Social Science Bulletin*, Vol. V, 1953.

laboratories. The provincial capitals are equipped on a more modest but similar scale; but even in the largest hospitals the standard of nursing tends to be unsatisfactory, sometimes even deplorable, because the sense of service and duty is wanting; and the great majority of medical men and women produced by the training-schools, 'including nearly all the best, are inevitably attracted to careers in the towns, so that the towns tend to be over-doctored and the rural areas left with few or no medical men. . . . The spirit of service and public responsibility, which is usually associated with the medical profession, is wanted in the Middle East even more than technical advance.'[1]

* * *

In most of the development programmes much attention is paid to means of transportation and communication, without which marketing of all types of commodities is inefficient. Good roads and railways are vital in the disposal of agricultural surpluses from villages to collecting centres and from these to the towns for local consumption or to the ports for export. In Turkey, a network of roads is being constructed to link all the major regions with a system of first-class roads. The Arabian capital of Riyadh has been linked up with Dammam by railway, and improvements are planned in most other countries. The development of adequate means of transport, through widening his market, will give the farmer an incentive, often absent hitherto, to produce a surplus above his needs, for sale in the larger market. His money income will increase and he will be in a better position to purchase some of the manufactured products of the growing local industries. Moreover the removal of transport bottlenecks will reduce delays and spoilage, especially in the movement of perishables. Included in transportation improvements is the construction or extension of ports. New harbours are appearing at Dammam, Latakia in Syria, and Eregli in Turkey. Latakia is becoming the focal point of exit and entry for Syrian trade and is competing with Beirut and Tripoli. The Lebanese Government is planning improvements in Tripoli including handling equipment, pier cranes, cold storage, coal depots and grain bins to be implemented in 1955. The competition of Latakia has already brought cheaper port

[1] Worthington, op. cit., 174 ff.

fees and greater efficiency in Beirut, and there is competition, too, from Aqaba in Jordan, where it has been calculated that it is cheaper to import goods to Amman from Britain through Aqaba, even after payment of Suez Canal dues, than through Beirut at the levels of freight and port costs ruling in January, 1954. Turkey has projects for making ports at Samsun and Izmir among the most modern in the world in order to remove the bottleneck caused by port handling facilities; and improvements are scheduled for Alexandria, Haifa, Jidda and Istanbul.

In the field of marketing, apart from transport and communication, governments have been slow. They could greatly assist not only the internal distribution of goods, but exportation of agricultural surpluses and so relieve the balance of trade deficits. They could improve the laws and inspection of grading and packing procedure, and publish industrial and commercial information to facilitate local businessmen. In this field little investment is required, only action; foreign marketing experts are available with schemes of modernization, but their services are only halfheartedly utilized. Instances have occurred, for instance, in Lebanon when, after signature of trade agreements, foreign buyers have been forced reluctantly to refuse contracts for fruit because of inferior packing and grading which would have made the goods unsaleable.

Not the least important limiting factor of development plans is the capital to finance them. The foreign private investor is no longer willing to risk his money in countries of uncertain political stability, without guarantees from his own government. Western governments, including the U.S.A., are too absorbed with defence requirements to be able to lend more than technical assistance. The loans forthcoming from the International Bank are a mere drop in the stream. With the huge increase in oil royalties in the Persian Gulf countries, however, since 1951, the problem for them has become less one of shortage of capital than one of channelling local money into productive investment. The owners of wealth, besides their traditional fear of investments in industry, often distrust the application of Western modernization schemes in the Middle East, and moreover are unwilling to sacrifice their liquid resources for a rate of interest of about 5 per cent. when they can secure rates of from 30 per cent. to 200 per cent. from loans to peasants or 10 per cent. from real estate and town apartment building. The banking systems are unable to mobilize savings through the public suspicion of banks due to ignorance and conservatism and to occasional bank failures. There are insufficient savings institutions, industrial banks, agencies for agricultural credit, and central banking. There are signs of a change of attitude only in Turkey where the demands for government bonds have shown some increase, though hoarding remains popular among the farming population.

Work in 1954 is proceeding on a suggestion to overcome the inadequacy of finance by means of an Arab Development Bank whose object would be to channel a large part of the oil revenues and private savings in Arab States into development projects, and prevent their being wasted on immediate luxury consumption. The existence of machinery for investment might since 1952 have saved several millions of dollars of oil royalties from consumption and directed them into productive channels. In Iraq which received in 1952 oil royalties amounting to $110 millions,[1] a jump from the 1951 figure of $38·5 millions, it has not been found practicable to spend as fast as revenues have been received. Excess funds could have been invested in a Development Bank for the benefit of projects in other countries in the Middle East. Oil revenue in Kuwait in 1952 was $139 millions (1951 $30 millions) and might have been a further source of funds. The oil companies might also find it strategically wise to invest some of their profits in such a bank, since they have an obvious interest in the economic strength of the region in which they operate.

The scarcity of finance in some countries has led their governments to overhaul their taxation systems and collecting procedures, and a small advance in the establishment of progressive systems of direct taxation has been made. 'In most Arab countries about 80 per cent. of the tax revenue comes from indirect taxes; and the expenditures of the Governments go largely to pay for an inefficient top-heavy administration, and a relatively small proportion goes to development of productive power.'[2] Landowner governments are slow, for obvious reasons, to introduce radical tax reform.

Government administration tends to be weak in the task of co-ordinating plans as well as in collecting revenue. Foreign experts

[1] *The Economist*, 27 February 1954, p. 591.
[2] Himadeh in *United Asia*, 1953, v. 291.

have frequently attributed the slowness of achievement to the lack of suitable integrating machinery and personnel. In Turkey, as a result of advice from T.C.A. and International Bank officials, a Minister of State and Inter-Ministerial Committee were appointed in 1949 to co-ordinate all economic planning. This example is being followed in Egypt, Iraq, Lebanon and Jordan.

Progress is slow, too, owing to the political unrest from which most countries suffer periodically. Changes of government and internal crises such as those in Syria and Egypt in 1954 can retard, if they do not even reverse, economic progress. Their effect is particularly harmful on local and foreign investment, without which development projects come to a standstill.

The precarious nature of development in Middle Eastern countries is emphasized owing to the dependence of each for foreign exchange earnings on one or two principal items of export. Cotton, for instance, accounts for at least 75 per cent. of the total value of Egyptian exports, and dates for an even greater proportion in Iraq. These earnings are subject to fluctuations in world prices. If prices slump, the earnings which help to finance materials for development projects are slashed, while the farmers face ruin.

There would be some relief if substantial intra-regional trade existed to promote larger-scale production through a widening of the market. Such trade is small because the economies of the various countries are not complementary, but competitive, while government policy tends to aim at self-sufficiency. What intra-regional trade exists is based on bilateral agreements; there is little attempt to effect a more balanced economic development through a multilateral approach. The Arab League has quite failed to remove trade barriers, which was originally one of its principal objectives. The Economic Committee of the League, which met in 1945, did not meet again for six years. The League, it may be said, has been far more concerned with weakening Israel's economy than with strengthening its own. This is evidence of the failure of governmental leadership in economic affairs—a failure which is thwarting the little private managerial enterprise that exists. It is significant that pressure for a unified regional economic policy is now appearing in private business circles, organized in the Union of Arab Chambers of Commerce, Industry and Agriculture which had its first conference in Alexandria in 1951. This union is pressing for an Arab Economic Council, provided for in the Arab security pact accepted by all the Arab countries. There has been pressure likewise in United Nations circles for a Regional Economic Commission for the Middle East on the lines of those for Europe, for Asia and the Far East, and for Latin America. The example of the wartime Middle East Supply Centre exists to show what economic progress can be achieved by co-operation to eliminate the import of unnecessary luxuries and to substitute for it the import of essential raw materials and equipment for local production. Political disunity, however, is still dominant.

*   *   *

It is little realized in all sections of the Middle East how much social inefficiency is due to the ignorance of women. If mothers were taught the elementary facts of nutrition and sanitation and the way diseases are caught and spread, the high infant mortality and death rates would be substantially lowered, the health and efficiency of both men and women would be improved, and enormous economic and human waste would be avoided. Most women in under-developed areas, moreover, are not occupied solely in bringing up families; they often care for livestock and milk. Training and education are necessary to do this work efficiently. Then, too, the social seclusion of women tends to restrict the demand for feminine products, the manufacture of which in advanced countries gives work to millions of men and women. In the search for light industries to diversify Middle Eastern economies, it is seldom realized what potentialities exist if women of all classes are given the freedom to develop the taste for modernity. Many of the articles required by women call for skills which can be acquired in the Middle East; the manufacturing process does not require large supplies of bulky and expensive raw materials and is therefore highly suitable to local conditions.

*   *   *

To sum up, the obstacles to raising the depressed standard of living are formidable, but a realistic appraisal of the economic outlook is not necessarily pessimistic. The world problem of the second half of the twentieth century is primarily one of agricultural production. Whereas total world agricultural output increased annually by 1·1 per cent. between 1913 and 1929 and by 1·3 per cent. between 1929 and 1937, between 1937 and 1950 the rate of increase fell to only 0·3 per cent., when rate of growth of world population was over 1 per cent. and is at present possibly 1·25 per cent. It has taken the world 8 years to recover the 1939 level of production per head of foodstuffs, and the pre-war 'per capita' consumption level has still not been overtaken because of the extensive surpluses held in North America which are unavailable for the hungry millions. This food shortage makes the economic outlook for the primary-producing regions bright, for the potential demand for foodstuffs will be enormous. The terms of trade are definitely showing a long-run turn in favour of countries with agricultural surpluses for the world market. Poverty is not inevitably the permanent lot of the population of the Middle East. The problem is so to raise productivity that the agricultural surpluses will be achieved—and maintained in the face of a rapidly increasing home demand for food. Further industrialization of a limited type is likely, consisting of light industries such as food processing, light engineering, and the manufacture of petroleum derivatives such as chemicals and synthetics, in addition to the textile industries which already exist.

CHAPTER IX

Russia and the Middle East

THE SUBJECT falls into six clearly-distinguished chronological phases:

(1) The Tsarist Régime, down to 1917.
(2) The Revolutionary Wars, 1917–21.
(3) The Inter-War Period, 1921–39.
(4) The period of 'Friendship' with Germany, 1939–41.
(5) The War, 1941–45.
(6) The Post-War Period.

*   *   *

(1) The Tsarist Period

With the signing of the Anglo-Russian Agreement over Persia in 1907 the Russian government set to work to absorb completely the northern zone of Persia. Its policy was made easier by the fact that the British government was anxious to avoid friction with Russia, in view of the overriding need to maintain the Triple Entente as a bulwark against Germany, and had instructed its Minister in Tehran in this sense. The Persian constitutional revolution, which had begun in 1905, was now in mid-career, and had inevitably upset what little stability there was in the internal régime of Persia. In 1909 the Russians sent a military force to support the reactionary Mohammed Ali Shah. The Persian constitutionalists succeeded, however, in deposing him, and power passed into the hands of the extremist so-called 'Democrats', whose attitude was exasperatingly hostile to the Russians. In 1911 the ex-Shah, with the connivance of minor Russian officials if not of the government, passed through Russia in disguise with a consignment of arms and ammunition and made a landing on the Caspian coast of Persia, but was defeated and forced to withdraw. The Russians frustrated attempts by the Persian government to meet its great financial difficulties and made impossible the efforts of the American financial adviser. They constantly found or created pretexts for further intervention, protecting rich landowners and merchants in Khurasan, collecting Persian revenues in Azerbaijan, importing Russian subjects into Asterabad to till lands they had bought at a nominal price as a result of pressure. In 1911 Russia went behind her allies' backs to conclude the Potsdam Agreement with Germany, recognizing the German interest in the Baghdad Railway in return for German recognition of her own interest in North Persia, arranging to link the projected Persian railway-system with the Baghdad Railway via Khaniqin, and promising Germany an open door for her trade with Persia.

During the First World War the operation of pro-German armed bands in Central and South Persia, and of the Turks in Western Persia, gave the Russians good reasons for occupying a broad belt of North Persia, including the towns of Kermanshah, Isfahan, and Meshed. By a secret agreement of March 1915 the Allies promised Russia Istanbul and the Straits and full liberty of action in the northern zone of Persia, in return for which Britain was to be free to annex both the southern and the neutral zones laid down by the Agreement of 1907.

$$\star \qquad \star \qquad \star$$

(2) *The Revolutionary Wars*, 1917–21.

The outbreak of the Revolution in March 1917 was followed by the headlong demoralization of the Russian army and its withdrawal from Persia, which gave the Turks an opportunity to invade Western Persia again. In March 1918 the Bolsheviks, who had seized power four months before, were compelled to conclude with Germany the Treaty of Brest-Litovsk, which allowed the Germans to conduct military operations on Russian territory and obtain essential supplies, such as the Caucasian oil. It was this treaty, made at a time when the Allies were fighting for life against Germany, at least as much as any dislike for the Bolshevik régime as such, that caused the Allies to support the local anti-Bolshevik forces and to undertake military operations against the Reds.[1] A small British force operating in North-West Persia temporarily occupied Baku in support of an anti-Bolshevik 'Central Caspian Force' consisting mainly of Armenians, but had to withdraw before a Turkish attack. An Indian force occupied Meshed, and a British naval flotilla operated on the Caspian from the summer of 1918 to that of 1919, re-occupying Baku from the retreating Turks and defeating a Red flotilla.

The great German spring offensive of 1918 on the Western Front had convinced most politically-minded Persians of the certainty of a German victory, and as late as September 1918, when Sir Percy Cox went to Tehran as Minister to bring the Persian government round to a more pro-British way of thinking, he found that it was on the point of throwing in its lot with Germany.[2] When Germany collapsed the extreme 'Democrats', who in their hatred of Russia had backed the Germans and Turks during the war, now turned to support the Turkish nationalists and the Bolsheviks. Cox felt that the country was ripe for Bolshevik revolution on account of the hopeless misgovernment by the Persian ruling-class, and recommended to the Foreign Office that Britain should guarantee the integrity of Persia in return for a new Anglo-Persian agreement. This fell in with the views of Lord Curzon, who had said, 'The integrity of Persia must be registered as a cardinal precept of our imperial creed.' By August 1919 accordingly[3] Cox had negotiated a draft Agreement: the hated Anglo-Russian Agreement of 1907 was considered cancelled; Britain offered to supply advisers, officers, and equipment for the establishment of internal order; there was to be joint Anglo-Persian enterprise in building railways and improving communications generally; and Persia was to receive a loan of £2,000,000. The draft was generally well received in Persia except by the extreme 'Democrats', the most conservative mujtahids (Shi'i divines), and the Russian-officered Cossack Brigade. The Persian Prime Minister could probably have got the draft Agreement ratified by the Majlis (parliament) had he presented it immediately, but he procrasti-

[1] Sir Bernard Pares pertinently compared Britain's reaction to the French armistice in 1940 (*Russia* (1941), 109).
[2] Cox, in *Gertrude Bell's Letters*, II, 521.
[3] The Persian delegation to the Peace Conference had unsuccessfully demanded the cession to Persia of Transcaucasia including the Baku oil-region, Turkish Kurdistan, part of Iraq, and Turkestan as far as the Oxus, in spite of the fact that she had no army capable of defending even her existing territories.

nated and allowed the opposition, which now regarded victorious Britain as a greater menace than defeated Russia, to gather strength.

By the end of 1919 Trotsky had organized the Red armies and broken the threat of the counter-revolutionary Whites. Under trades-union pressure Britain had ceased her active intervention against the Bolsheviks, and in the spring of 1920 the British forces were withdrawn from Transcaucasia. In April the anti-Bolshevik republic of Azerbaijan collapsed, and Soviet troops entered Persian territory. With their support a group of Persian communists set up a Soviet government in the Caspian province of Gilan. Persian politicians, impressed by the proximity and the strength of the Russians, became more and more non-committal about the draft agreement with Britain. There was an inspired press-campaign in favour of Bolshevism, the semi-official *Iran* declaring that its doctrines closely resembled the pure gospel of Islam. The Cossack Brigade, the only organized troops in North Persia, was defeated by the Reds, and the whole country seemed at their mercy; but at this stage an outstanding and determined officer Riza Khan, assumed command of the Cossack Brigade. In February 1921 he marched on Tehran and arrested the cabinet. The new government promptly denounced the draft agreement with Britain, and instead accepted the generous terms offered by the Russians. In the Soviet-Persian Agreement signed in Moscow the Russian government renounced all concessions made to the Tsarist government, on condition that they should not be transferred to any other Power. All debts to the Tsarist government or to Russian capitalists were cancelled, and Russian capitulatory rights abolished. Each party undertook to prohibit organizations conspiring against the other party. Russia undertook to observe Persian sovereignty and territorial integrity, and in return Russian troops were to be allowed to enter Persian territory, if Persia were unable to prevent a third party from preparing an invasion of Russia on Persian soil. The Russians followed up this success by making treaties of mutual assistance against 'an imperialist state which follows a policy of invading and exploiting the East' with the nationalist Turkey of Mustafa Kemal and the nationalist Afghanistan of King Amanullah, both of whom had recently been in conflict with Britain. As a token of goodwill the Russians handed back to Turkey the frontier-provinces of Kars and Ardahan which the Tsars had annexed.

(3) *The Inter-War Period,* 1921–39

In the Treaty of Lausanne of 1923 which established the independence of nationalist Turkey and regulated her relations with
the Western Powers, she had to concede the demilitarization of
the Zone of the Straits: the warships of all nations, with slight
restrictions, were free to enter the Black Sea. This was obnoxious
not only to Turkey, as limiting her sovereignty, but also to Russia,
as exposing her Black Sea coast to the threat of an enemy navy; and
in 1925, while Turkey was involved in the acute dispute with
Britain and Iraq over the possession of the villayet of Mosul,
Russia concluded with her a new Treaty of Friendship and
Neutrality. Though official relations between Russia and Turkey
remained cordial and the Russians gave some technical help with
the industrialization of Turkey, there was little contact or cultural
interchange between the two peoples. The Turkish dictatorship
permitted the works of Marx and Lenin to be read, but imprisoned
active Communists under laws which forbade associations with
the purpose of propagating ideas of class distinction or of class conflict, or with internationalist intentions.[1]   In 1936, when Italy
had emerged as the aggressive naval power which threatened the
status quo in the Mediterranean, Turkey proposed to the signatories
of the Treaty of Lausanne that the régime of the Straits needed
revision, and obtained important concessions in the Montreux
Convention. She was now allowed to fortify the Straits, and in
time of war to close them to the warships of all Powers, unless
acting under the Covenant of the League of Nations. A compromise was thus reached between the Russian claim for wide
discrimination in favour of Black Sea Powers, and the British argument that the Straits should be equally open or equally closed to
the warships of all Powers.[2]   In the early summer of 1939, when
Turkey entered into pacts with Britain and France directed primarily against Fascist Italy, *Izvestia* welcomed them as 'links in the
chain which is the only sure means of preventing the extension of
aggression to new parts of Europe'.

In Persia Riza Shah, like Ataturk, followed a strongly nationalist
and anti-foreign policy, and his commercial relations with Russia

---

[1] Arts. 66 and 69 of the People's Party Programme.
[2] *Survey of International Affairs*, 1936, Part IV (i).

were darkened from time to time by embargoes and boycotts. However, Russia supported him in his dispute with the Anglo-Iranian Oil Co. in 1932, and by 1936 she was taking 28 per cent. of Persia's exports and supplying 30 per cent. of her imports. 'Russian engineers and technicians began to pour into the country. Russian contracts were obtained for flour-mills and bakeries, granaries and workshops. Russian surveyors were employed on new road-projects, and Russian pilots and tank-experts began to appear in unusually large numbers.'[1]

During this period the Soviet government was not in diplomatic relations with any of the other Middle Eastern countries, and her connexion with them was virtually confined to the encouragement given by the Comintern to the embryonic Communist parties in those countries. The conservative governments of the Middle East, whether mandatory or nominally independent, were strongly opposed to Communism, and Egypt went so far as to deprive of his nationality any Egyptian who visited the U.S.S.R.

* * *

(4) *The period of 'Friendship' with Germany, 1939–41*

In August 1939 the Soviet government, having reached the conclusion that Britain and France could not be brought to an alliance on its somewhat exacting terms, preferred to do a deal with Germany, and Molotov concluded with Ribbentrop the opportunist and cynical Treaty of Friendship and Non-Aggression. In furtherance of its new friendship with Hitler, the Soviet government concluded a new commercial treaty with Persia in March 1940, which allowed Persian goods in transit to Germany to cross Russia duty-free, and so assisted the greatly increased German trade with Persia. The Turkish Foreign Minister had been in Moscow at the time of the signing of the Treaty with Germany, but failed to reach an understanding with Molotov, who required as the price of a Black Sea mutual-assistance pact that the Turks should in all circumstances keep the Straits closed to the warships of any nation hostile to the U.S.S.R.; and this the Turkish government held to be inconsistent with their agreements with Britain and

---

[1] Elwell-Sutton, op. cit., 162. Germany, Persia's second-largest customer, took in 1936 13 per cent. of her exports and supplied 15 per cent. of her imports.

France. The Soviet press thereupon linked together Italy and Turkey as attempting to disturb the peace of the Balkans. Anti-Soviet feeling in Turkey was stimulated by the Soviet invasion of Finland, since Turkish theorists were aware of the distant connexion between the Finnish and Turkish languages. Following the German publication of captured French documents in July 1940, the Soviet accused the Turkish government of conniving at Anglo-French plans, now revealed, for bombing the Caucasian oilfields and the pipeline to Batum, as a potential source of supply to Germany. At the Hitler-Molotov meeting in November 1940 the Russians, according to the captured German minutes, asked for the control of the Straits, as well as for the right to expand 'south of Batum and Baku'.[1] In March 1941, when Hitler was on the point of invading Jugoslavia and Greece, Russia assured the Turks of her neutrality. Her establishment in May of diplomatic relations with Rashid Ali's government in Iraq, when it was already in armed conflict with the British, who for their part had warned the Russians of Hitler's preparations to invade them, is an incident whose significance has not yet been clarified.

∗   ∗   ∗

(5) *The War*, 1941–5

After the Anglo-Russian invasion of Persia in August 1941, the northern zone which came under Russian military occupation was withdrawn behind the now familiar 'iron curtain': the Persian government's authority ceased to be effective there, and British and American officers found great difficulty in entering the Russian zone even on official business. The American Dr. A. C. Millspaugh, then Administrator-General of the Finances of Persia, has accused the Soviet government of seeking a 'thorough-going and exclusive domination over the entire country. . . . They intended that Persia should be a puppet-state, and until that end was attained, the Soviet government would not be interested in stability or good government in Persia. Chaos served their purpose better than order. They wanted the kind of government that could be purchased, hoodwinked, or intimidated.'[2] In Tehran the Tudeh or

---

[1] *Nazi-Soviet Relations*, 1939–1941. (U.S. State Department, 1948), 217 ff.
[2] *Americans in Persia* (Washington, D.C., 1946).

Workers' Party came to life, with an ostensibly moderate socialist programme. It did not originally have obvious connexions with the Russians, but unsuccessfully sought the support of the British Embassy; some of its leaders were, however, men who had taken part in the shortlived Soviet Republic of Gilan twenty years before, and had since lived in exile in the U.S.S.R. It formed trades-unions in the principal industrial cities of Tehran, Tabriz, and Isfahan, and obtained for the workers some concessions from their employers; but from 1943 onwards it became openly the pro-Russian party.[1] In March 1944 the Persian government rejected applications by representatives of British and American oil-companies for concessions in south-east Persia, and on 2 September the cabinet resolved that it would make no concessions to any foreign oil company until the foreign armies had been withdrawn from Persian soil. Only four days afterwards the Persian Ambassador in Moscow informed his government that the Assistant Commissar for Foreign Affairs, Kavtaradze, wished to discuss with the Persian government an old oil-concession in Khurasan, which had been registered in 1925 as a Persian company financed by the Soviet government; the Majlis had, however, never ratified this concession, and no oil had in fact been found. M. Kavtaradze arrived in Tehran a week later and asked for a five-years' exploratory concession for almost the whole of North Persia. When the Persian government demurred, it became the object of a violent propaganda attack from the Tudeh party, and M. Kavtaradze issued thinly-veiled threats at his press-conferences. Weeks passed without the negotiations reaching any conclusion; and on 2 December the Majlis finally screwed up its courage, and rushed through a bill prescribing a penalty of eight years imprisonment for any minister or official who approved an oil-concession to any foreign company before the end of the foreign occupation of Persia. M. Kavtaradze had to return to Moscow without achieving his object. During 1945 the attitude of the Soviet military to the Persian authorities in the northern provinces became increasingly unco-operative.[2]

Following the Anglo-Russian Alliance of June 1941, the two Powers sought to reassure Turkey in August by guaranteeing their loyalty to the Montreux Convention, declaring that they had no

[1] On the combination of 'half-baked' ideologues and genuine would-be reformers in the Tudeh membership, see A. C. Edwards, in *International Affairs*, XXIII (1947), 54 f.

[2] For details, see A. K. S. Lambton, *International Affairs*, XXII (1946). 265 ff.

aggressive designs nor any demands to formulate in regard to the Straits, and pledging themselves to respect the territorial integrity of Turkey. As long as the Russians were on the defensive against the Germans, Russian leaders hinted at rewarding Turkey with territorial acquisitions at the expense of Bulgaria, Greece, and Syria.[1] Public opinion in Turkey, however, had not been sorry to see the Germans invade the U.S.S.R. It had come to regard both the German and, after the invasion of Finland, the Russian armies as potential threats to the integrity of Turkey, and was gratified to see them destroying each other; as a popular slogan put it, 'The Germans in the hospital and the Russians in the grave'. The Pan-Turanian irredentists, who dreamed of forming a confederation under the leadership of the Turkish Republic of all the Turkish peoples of Russian and Chinese Turkestan, 'regarded as inevitable the defeat and disintegration of the U.S.S.R. and were confident that the liberation of Russian Turkestan was at hand. When, however, it was the Germans, and not the Russians, who suffered defeat, the Turkish authorities appear to have decided that it would be politic to suppress the pan-Turanians, thinking no doubt that the denunciation of the movement and the arrest and trial of its leaders would gain them good marks in Moscow. The proceedings in 1944 received the greatest possible publicity. Moscow, however, was far from being impressed. In fact the Russians regarded the whole affair as so much eyewash, and did not hesitate to say so in their press and radio.'[2] They began to assail the Turks for the economic aid they had given to the Germans—concessions which, in fact, the Turkish government had felt constrained to make in order to maintain its precarious neutrality, with the German troops occupying the line of the Maritza only 130 miles from Istanbul. In March 1945 the Soviet government denounced the twenty-year-old Turco-Soviet Treaty of Friendship and Neutrality.

*   *   *

(6) *The Post-War Period.*

It appears that when in June 1945, one month after the close of the war in Europe, the Turks approached the Soviet government

[1] *Times* correspondent in Turkey, 3 April 1947.
[2] A. C. Edwards in *International Affairs*, July 1946, 398.

for a new treaty of alliance, they were informed that this was conditional on the establishment of a new régime for the Straits, and also on the return to Russia of the provinces of Kars and Ardahan, which she had voluntarily restored to Turkey in 1921; apparently she now hoped to find oil there. At his speech at Fulton (Missouri) in March 1946 Mr. Churchill disclosed that at the Potsdam Conference the U.S.A. and Britain offered Russia a joint guarantee of the complete freedom of the Straits in peace and war; 'but we were told that this was not enough. Russia must have a fortress inside the Straits from which she could dominate Istanbul'. In the months that followed, Armenians, both within the Soviet Republic of Armenia and in other parts of the world, were encouraged to make propaganda for the return to Russia of Kars and Ardahan. In December 1945 the Soviet press and radio gave wide publicity to the claim put forward by Georgian professors to a coastal belt of north-eastern Turkey some 180 miles in length, on the grounds that this had been Georgian territory 2,000 years ago. The Soviet propaganda contained sinister hints that she desired to see in Turkey a 'government inspiring greater confidence' than the existing one; and any signs of a rapprochement between Turkey and the Arab League were strongly denounced. In August 1946 the Soviet government made positive proposals for the revision of the Montreux Convention, the essential point being that 'The Soviet Union and Turkey, as the Powers most interested in and capable of ensuring the freedom of merchant shipping in the Straits, should organize by joint means the defence of the Straits in order to prevent their use by other states for purposes hostile to Black Sea Powers.' Next month, to the accompaniment of propaganda charges that the Turks had allowed Britain to establish military bases in the neighbourhood of the Straits, the Russians delivered a second Note, rejecting the Turkish proposal of an international conference of the signatories of the Montreux Convention and the U.S.A., and warning them that any attempt to bring in the U.S.A. or Britain, would, of course, run directly contrary to the security interests of the Black Sea Powers. Towards the end of November the Communist bands which had for some months been harassing Northern Greece, with the connivance of the Russian satellite-states in the Balkans, began to operate close to the Turkish frontier. Turkish garrisons were accordingly strengthened, and a home-guard organized in every village in the frontier district. In mid-

December the Istanbul police arrested over seventy persons belonging to two 'Socialist' parties, suppressing the parties and six newspapers and periodicals published by them. The American offer of financial aid to Greece and Turkey in March 1947 greatly changed the strategic situation on this important sector of the Russian war-of-nerves. While *Pravda* denounced the American action as 'the liquidation of Greek and Turkish sovereignty and the brutal establishment of American hegemony', the Turks were at once relieved of the 'crushing sense of insecurity and isolation'[1] which had subjected them during the past two years to the economic and psychological strain of keeping under arms one million men who had already been kept mobilized throughout the war. When the steady consolidation of Russian power in the Balkans caused a member of the Democratic party on 22 December to inquire about Turkey's attitude to the two great ideological blocs, Foreign Minister Hasan Saka replied that Turkey remained loyal to the United Nations and refused to be drawn into ideological quarrels; her policy was to rely on her own forces, to grasp hands extended in a spirit of friendship, and to resist with all her strength aggression from any quarter. This unexpectedly non-committal statement gave rise to some concern in Ankara;[2] and it produced, as it was perhaps designed to do, an announcement from the U.S. Navy Department on 9 January 1948 that fifteen warships, including four modern submarines, would be handed over to Turkey in April.

In October 1945 a new 'Democratic Party' was formed in Azerbaijan, the richest province of Persia, which produces the bulk of its grain and contains about one-third the total population of the country. The province had been under Soviet occupation since 1941, and it appeared that a considerable number of Communists had been introduced from Soviet Azerbaijan, divided from Persian Azerbaijan only by an arbitrary frontier and not by any linguistic or cultural differences. The new party was led by Ja'far Pishevari, who had taken part in the formation of the Soviet Republic of Gilan in 1920 and had returned to Persia with the Soviet army in 1941. All the local members of the Tudeh joined the new party and there followed an armed revolt of a peculiar kind. 'A few Russians in a town or village would let it be known

---

[1] *Reuter's* Correspondent, Istanbul, 19 March 1947.
[2] *Observer* special correspondent, 4 January 1948.

that the Democrats were taking over the administration, and that they would not tolerate intervention from the government gendarmes or anyone else. Then at night the armed Democrats would enter the few key-buildings and take over. Sometimes there would be a little shooting, and a few gendarmes or other opponents killed. In the morning the mass of Democrats would arrive, singing and with banners, and would take over. Throughout, the Russians remained discreetly in the background.'[1] The active Democrats, who with their supporters numbered only about 10 per cent. of the population, advanced southwards on the provincial capital of Tabriz. Its Persian garrison of 400 men was confined to barracks by the Russian military authorities and capitulated to the Democrats on 15 December. An autonomous State of Azerbaijan was proclaimed under the leadership of Pishevari. According to Moscow radio, it had been 'elected by a free vote'. While it recognized private property as legitimate; it undertook to confiscate and share out among the peasants the estates of 'reactionary landlords who have fled the province'. Credits would be made available to peasants to buy land from landlords 'willing to sell at reasonable prices'. The Persian government, receiving no reply to its proposal to the Soviet government to negotiate over Azerbaijan, appealed to the Security Council. When the case came up on 28 January 1946 M. Vyshinsky stated that the Persian government had broken off previous negotiations early in December, and that Russia was now ready to continue them. The Council accordingly resolved that the two parties should inform it of the results of their negotiations. In the meantime, however, the seventy-two-year-old Persian Prime Minister, who had been subject to increasing left-wing pressure to dismiss a number of cabinet ministers and other officials who were alleged to be under British influence, had resigned. The Majlis elected as his successor, by the narrow margin of fifty-two votes to fifty-one Qavam as-Sultana, a wealthy owner of lands in Azerbaijan. When he was previously Prime Minister early in 1942 there was reason to believe that he took some steps towards 'reinsurance' with the Germans; and now it was generally expected that, while taking a strong line with any internal opposition, the 'ancient equivocator'[2] would seek a reasonable compromise with the Russians. The

[1] Jon Kimche, in *Tribune*, 18 January 1946.
[2] Robert Stephens, *Observer*, 24 November 1946.

14.   PERSIANS, KURDS AND THE U.S.S.R.

Soviet Embassy in Tehran, which had for several weeks avoided contact with the previous Prime Minister, promptly paid courtesy visits to Qavam; and on their invitation he set off for Moscow on 19 February at the head of a carefully-picked mission. While American and British troops were withdrawn before 2 March, the day appointed for the withdrawal of all foreign troops from Persia, the Soviet radio announced on 1 March, while Qavam was still negotiating in Moscow, that Russian troops would be withdrawn 'from those parts of Persia which are undisturbed; those in other areas would remain pending a clarification of the situation'. Qavam returned to Persia without reaching any agreement; but on 3 April the Persian delegate informed the Security Council that ten days previously the Soviet Ambassador had informed the Persian government that the Red Army would begin its evacuation immediately and complete it in five to six weeks; he had also proposed a joint Soviet-Persian oil corporation and an autonomous government for Azerbaijan. On 5 April an agreement was signed setting up a joint oil-company in North Persia for a period of fifty years. For the first twenty-five years Russia was to own 51 per cent. of the shares, to pay the costs of prospecting and provide the machinery, and in return receive half the oil. Persia was to be free to dispose of the other half, but for geographical reasons Russia would be the most likely buyer. Concessions to other Powers in North Persia were barred.[1] The evacuation of British troops duly began, and an Azerbaijani mission led by Pishevari arrived in Tehran for talks with the Persian government. Qavam had meanwhile been suppressing the most actively anti-Russian elements in Persian political life, threatening in a radio speech to 'destroy them like harmful insects'. His negotiations with the Azerbaijanis were none the less difficult, since at the first obstacle that presented itself Tabriz radio announced a treaty of mutual assistance with the 'national government' of Persian Kurdistan, where unruly tribes had with Russian support been in revolt against the central government for some years. When a second deadlock was reached, the Persian spokesman having informed the Security Council that his government was unable to confirm the Russian evacuation of Azerbaijan as it did not exercise effective authority there, pressure was again exerted on it through a Tabriz radio allegation of a Persian armed attack and the proclamation of a military government in Azer-

[1] *Times* Tehran correspondent, 11 July 1947.

baijan. Agreement was, however, finally reached in June: Azerbaijan was to have an autonomous provincial council, with a governor-general appointed by the central government; it was to retain three-quarters of the provincial revenues; its 'national army' was to come under the command of the Persian army, details being worked out by a joint commission. While, therefore, the central government received acknowledgment of its *de jure* authority in Azerbaijan, the 'Democrats' remained in actual control; and for five months the name of the province disappeared from the newspaper-headlines. The Soviet propaganda-machine had, however, been carrying on a campaign against the Anglo-Iranian Oil Co. in South Persia for some time. It was accused of encouraging opium-smoking among its Persian workers in order to render them insensible of their poverty, and *Pravda* righteously remarked that 'the brazen and imperious behaviour of the British oil company is an example of disrespect for the sovereignty of a small country'. In July the local Tudeh party organized a political strike of 100,000 of the oil-company's workers, and seventeen people were killed in a clash between Tudeh adherents and Arab workers. Simultaneously the Iraq Petroleum Co. had to deal with a strike at Kirkuk, in which five people were killed in a clash between strikers and police. Evidently this was the beginning of a typical 'softening-up' process, but the despatch of a brigade group of troops from India to Basra prevented further developments. In September the Persian Propaganda Minister, Prince Muza'far Firuz, who had shown himself outspokenly pro-Russian in recent months, announced that while visiting Isfahan he had unearthed a separatist plot among the chiefs of the powerful Bakhtiari tribe to set up with foreign help a 'reactionary feudal tribal government'. Moscow radio named two British consular officials whom it accused of inciting the Bakhtiari to revolt, and the Persian Ambassador in London asked the Foreign Office to inquire into their conduct; but evidence in support of these allegations was not forthcoming from the Persian government. Later in September the great Qashqai tribe revolted in Fars province, seizing the provincial capital of Shiraz and the port of Bushire; simultaneously the Arab tribal chiefs of Khuzistan province appealed to the Arab League for protection against Persian oppression. The Qashqai chiefs demanded the creation of an autonomous provincial council with the right to retain two thirds of the provincial revenues, and to approve or veto the appointment of officials; they also called for the resignation of the Persian cabinet, except for Qavam himself, and the release of the arrested Bakhtiari chiefs. It was evident that the southern tribal chiefs, seeing the apparent drift of the Persian government towards subservience on Russia, had decided to strike in defence of their own traditional authority against the Tudeh, which had been strong enough in Tehran to muster some 50,000 adherents for the May Day labour demonstration and had been given three seats in the cabinet early in August. Warned by these ominous signs of provincial disintegration, and by appeals from merchants and mujtahids to protect the country from foreign ideologies and end the coalition with the Tudeh and the Azerbaijani Democrats, the Prime Minister decided that it was time to 'hedge'. In mid-October he pacified the Qashqai rebels by dropping from his cabinet the three Tudeh representatives and Prince Firuz, whom he appropriately appointed Ambassador to Moscow. He then turned to the question of general elections for a new Majlis, having dissolved the previous one in March. The Tudeh wanted them at once, in order that the new Majlis might ratify the all-important Soviet-Persian oil agreement. The Prime Minister at length announced that they would begin on 7 December, under the supervision of government forces throughout the country in order to ensure freedom of voting and suppress possible disturbances. The Governor-General of Azerbaijan was informed that government forces would enter his province also for that purpose. Despite the protests of the Azerbaijani provincial council and a call to arms, the government troops crossed the provincial border on 10 December. They met with only slight opposition, since the 'Democrat' forces were found to be ill-equipped and undisciplined, and there were many desertions. Tabriz was occupied, evidently to the hearty satisfaction of the overwhelming majority of the population. Some of the 'Democrat' leaders, including Pishevari himself, fled over the border into Soviet territory. The Soviet propaganda treated the collapse of their puppet with remarkably little concern, waiting evidently for Persian ratification of the proposed oil-concession. Persian elections, are, however, a leisurely process, and the new Majlis was not ready for official duties till 26 August 1947. By that time the United States' attitude towards the Soviet forward policy, which had been hesitant in the last year of the war and overlaid immediately after the war by the popular demand to 'bring the boys home', had taken firm shape in the Truman Doctrine's support of Greek and Turkish independence. Already in March 1946 the Soviet Union's violation of the Anglo-American-Soviet undertaking to evacuate their troops from Persia had brought the United States squarely against her at the Security Council. Thenceforward the United States and British Ambassadors at Tehran had supported Qavam as-Sultana against the Tudeh party and their Soviet mentors, while an American colonel supervised the organization of the Persian gendarmerie and on 20 June 1947 Persia received an American military credit of $25 millions. When the new Majlis met, the Soviet renewed their pressure for the ratification of the draft oil agreement of April 1946. The British Government, mindful of Persian nationalist hostility towards the Anglo-Iranian Oil Company's concession in Southern Persia, suggested that if the Majlis saw fit to reject the Soviet draft 'the Persian Government might be well advised to leave the door open for further discussions', rather than give a blank refusal.[1] The United States Ambassador, on the other hand, publicly offered more uncompromising advice. On 22 October 1947 the Majlis, by 102 votes against 2, declared the draft agreement null and void and drove Qavam from office in December. The Soviet Union had thus been completely 'outsmarted' in the Persian poker-game that she had initiated almost as soon as her armies had begun to gain the upper hand over the Germans in 1943. She was now reduced to launching against the Persian Government a series of minatory Notes, accusing them of allowing the United States to establish military bases in their country and reminding them of the Soviet right, under the 1921 Treaty, to send troops into Persia 'if a third party should desire to use Persian territory as a base for operations against Russia'. The Tudeh party had meanwhile been firmly suppressed by legal process and police action; and its membership, greatly inflated by opportunists during the days of its apparent success, had shrunk to a small nucleus of convinced adherents: in other words, the Communist party in Persia had gone 'underground'. However, economic conditions deteriorated in 1949, largely on account of the shortcomings of the administration and the 'general inefficiency and corruption' of private industry,[2] and a rallying of sup-

---

[1] *The Times* diplomatic correspondent, 15 September 1947.
[2] M. Philips Price, M.P., *Manchester Guardian*, 7, 9, and 16 October 1950.

port to the Tudeh was feared. To remedy the situation, the United States and British Governments reaffirmed on 19 May 1950 their concern for the independence, integrity, and security of Persia (together with Greece and Turkey); the State Department transferred to Tehran its Ambassador to Greece, who had had experience of Communist methods there; and in July the young Shah of Persia, exasperated by the selfish dilatoriness and muddling of the professional politicians, entrusted the formation of a government to the competent Chief of General Staff, General Razmara. The Soviet Union's response to these moves was to propose to the Persian Government the resumption of commercial negotiations, exploiting Persian dissatisfaction with United States financial aid. An agreement was concluded on 4 November, for the exchange of £7 million worth of goods and further negotiation over Persian credits sequestered in Russia since the end of the war.

As a result of her wartime alliance with Britain, Russia was able for the first time to open legations in the Middle Eastern capitals—Cairo, Beirut and Damascus, Baghdad. In this new international relationship it was no longer possible for Middle Eastern governments to repress left-wing movements as indiscriminately as hitherto; the prestige won by the Red Armies in the war caused a considerable increase in the membership of left-wing parties in the Middle East; and in Egypt Nahhas welcomed the establishment of a Russian Legation, which might enable him to drive a harder bargain with Britain in the future. The tone of Soviet propaganda was critical of the Arab League, as a British creation representing in the main conservative interests; but it was always ready to abet the nationalists in their efforts to throw off British influence, and in Egypt, Iraq, Palestine, and Cyprus left-wing parties were quick to adopt such catchwords as 'national', 'liberation', and 'democratic' in their titles. An experienced observer recently said: 'I should say Communism follows three lines in Syria. There is the orthodox ideological appeal of Marxism to the workers and the peasants, and I think the lack of success which they have had is quite remarkable in the circumstances. I think if I were a Syrian factory-worker I should be much more interested in Communism than most of them seem to be. I suppose the basic failure is the fact of conservatism through all that part of the world, reinforced by constant and systematic opposition on the part of the Muslim

authorities. The orthodox appeal is not getting anywhere. There
has been a very definite appeal to the nationalist ambitions of
certain minority groups, specifically by turns the Kurds, the
Armenians, and the Assyrians. They have got very little distance
with the Assyrians, so far as I know. The Armenians and Kurds
have discovered that the promises separately offered them overlap,
and that has rather tended to cancel them out. There is the third
line of approach, which is essentially not Communism at all, but
the building of a fifth column for Russia, using Communist
terminology. There is no doubt in my mind that a considerable
system of cells is being built up in Syria, consisting chiefly of the
disgruntled white-collar workers, teachers, doctors, lawyers, of
the type who have not had what they consider justice at the hands
of the Government or society, and who would welcome the
chance to be somebody, and the Communist appeal knows how
to build up such men to a remarkable degree . . . '

There is little doubt that immediately after the war, in the Arab
countries as in Turkey and Persia, Soviet policy set out to assess
the degree of British post-war weakness by encouraging political
agitation, but did not have the means to back it when it came up
against serious resistance. At the time Isma'il Sidqi incurred considerable abuse from 'liberals' for his 'dictatorial' action against
left-wing agitators in Egypt in July 1946 (and certainly a substantial number of people who could by no stretch of the imagination be called Communists came under his somewhat indiscriminate ban, though most of them were soon released). The fact
remains, however, that for several months beforehand the Wafdist
opposition, extreme nationalists, and left-wing organizations had
combined in an unscrupulous campaign of agitation and terrorism, whose purpose was not only to wreck the negotiations with
Britain but to bring down the Egyptian Government and force
new elections. In this congenial exercise they were probably
assisted by Soviet agents, and certainly cheered on by the Communist world-press. The manifesto issued by the 'Workers' Committee for National Liberation', that had been formed by a group
of left-wing organizers immediately after their return from the
Paris conference of the Communist-directed World Federation
of Trade Unions in September 1945, included among its aims 'To
rescue Egypt from the occupying Power by working for the
complete independence of the Nile Valley and winning her a

place among the democratic States'; and on 13 July 1946, in an article entitled 'Fascism in Egypt; Under Bevin's Flail', *L'Humanité* wrote: 'It is evident that the standard-of-living of the masses can be raised only by redoubling the trade-union and anti-imperialist struggle. . . . The strikes, which have been numerous in recent months . . . are more and more assuming a political character: to their material demands the Egyptian workers join the struggle for the complete evacuation by the British of Egypt and the Sudan, the release of the imprisoned trades-unionist militants, and democratic rights. . . .'

In fact, the Soviet post-war drive in the Middle East was a failure almost everywhere, for it probably overestimated the amount of support it would receive from the local population and certainly underestimated the tenacity with which the British Labour Government would defend imperial interests and the alacrity with which the United States would take over responsibilities which Britain was no longer able to carry.[1] At the beginning of 1946 the Soviet Union had seemed in a fair way to absorb the whole of Persia into her orbit; by the summer she had been forced to reduce her pretensions to an oil-concession in the five northern provinces (which she might well have obtained with the agreement of Britain and the United States if she had chosen the way of co-operation instead of suspicion and hostility); by the end of 1947 the Persian Parliament had slammed the door in her face, and she could do precisely nothing about it. Recognizing that she had nothing to expect in the short term from the Arab world, she reversed her traditional attitude to Zionism ('an instrument of bourgeois imperialism') and supported the Zionist claims before the United Nations. She thus achieved the desired result of securing the ending of the British mandate for Palestine, but only because the Zionists had the more influential support of the United States; and since independence was achieved, Israel's policy of neutrality gradually leaned to the West, partly out of financial

---

[1] While Ephraim A. Speiser could write in 1946, 'It would be unfortunate if our interests and policy in the Near East were to remain in a state of permanent vassalage to Britain. . . . An independent American policy . . . would not necessarily be a pro-Russian policy . . .' (*The United States and the Near East*, pp. 230–1), Dr. H. L. Hoskins had already asked 'whether . . . the United States can afford now, any more than Great Britain could formerly, to contemplate the entrenchment of the Soviet Union in strategic positions along that vital line extending from the Mediterranean to India' (*The New Era of Power Politics* (Foreign Policy Association, May–June 1946)).

necessity, partly because of the Eastern bloc's obstruction of Jewish emigration to Israel, and partly because of the crass self-centredness of Soviet policy. The miscarriage of the draft Anglo-Iraqi Treaty of Portsmouth in January 1948, aborted by a combination of Iraqi right-wing and left-wing extremists, may be counted as a limited success for Soviet policy; but by 1949 Anglo-Iraqi relations had once again assumed a more cordial tenor. By 1950 the Soviet-inspired 'Partisans of Peace' campaign was finding numbers of influential adherents among Middle Eastern intellectuals uncritically opposed to Western 'imperialism'; and the British and American efforts to consolidate the Arab world and Persia into a Middle East defence organization with Turkey was systematically opposed by these 'fellow-travellers'. Their campaign, however, had little more than nuisance-value. While it frustrated the over-sanguine Western hopes, it did not immediately threaten the Western position in the Middle East; and the relatively low temperature of the 'cold war' in this region (when compared with the Berlin Blockade or the Korean War) may be ascribed partly to Soviet preoccupation with East-Central Europe and with the Far East, and partly to the slow decline in Stalin's mental vigour during his last years.

The dramatic return to a more active Middle Eastern policy, effected by Stalin's successors two years after his death, is described in its Middle Eastern context in the next chapter[1]; but it may be remarked here that during these years of relative quiet Soviet propaganda had not only continued to use the traditional Russian connexions with the Orthodox and Armenian Churches in the Eastern Mediterranean countries: it had also made a remarkable conquest of the extremer elements among the Muslim majority in the Arab world, and had thus made nonsense of the facile, though oft-repeated, assertion that Islam was 'a safe stronghold' against that 'prince of ill',[2] Communism! As my colleague, Dr. Nabih Faris (who, I think, might fairly be described as an Arab National-Christian[3]), has recently put it:[4]

---

[1] See p. 281.
[2] Martin Luther: *Ein' feste Burg*, trans. Thos. Carlyle.
[3] Luther being a German National-Christian.
[4] 'Islam and the Appeals of Communism', *Middle East Forum* (Beirut), Summer 1956, vol. xxxi, no. 8, p. 9; being a simplification of a longer essay, 'The Islamic Community and Communism', *The Islamic Review* (Woking, England), June 1956, vol. xliv, no. 6, pp. 28–31.

Communism and Islam are alike in their understanding of the nature of evil. There is no conception of original sin in the Muslim religion. If man is evil, it is because of external factors—not because of anything inherent in man himself. Modern Muslim writers have emphasized that an unbalance in certain forces causes the ills of modern life. One wrote in 1951 that 'the perfect society can be hoped for by the establishment of the external order within which, and apart from inward human change, it can be actualized'. The parallel is obvious here with the Communist ideal of a utopia under the classless society to appear after the withering away of the state. . . .

The legacy of ill-will between East and West which began with the Crusades still remains with many Muslims. Naturally it received a tremendous boost from the colonialism of the West. The average Muslim has come to view the West as his mortal foe. Every action taken in the West is suspected of being an attack on his religion, society, institutions, or homeland. Hence many Muslims are understandably delighted when the West encounters difficulties. This tendency has created, especially among intellectuals, many who might be called 'spite communists'. When intellectuals, alive to the sufferings of their co-religionaries from poverty, ignorance, and tyranny, shift their attention from the spiritual to the temporal,[1] Marxism must seem very attractive to them.

. . . There is no possible reconciliation between true Islam and Communism. But to repeat, once a shift from the spiritual to the temporal takes place, the transition would seem easy and natural. . . .

Original Sin . . . to the eighteenth-century 'enlightenment' a stumbling-block, and to the nineteenth-century optimists foolishness; but to one who—foolish, weak, and base—having passed through academic 'enlightenment' and socialist optimism, has begun to discover himself, neither stumbling-block nor foolishness, neither condemnation nor curse, but O *certe necessarium Adae peccatum . . . O felix culpa!*[2] a humbling indication of what Man is, here and now: and, not least, Western Man, burrowing

---

[1] In an earlier paragraph Dr. Faris writes: 'The first consequence of this shift in emphasis is to undermine the principal reason for the existence of Islam: belief in God as the sovereign ruler of the universe. The second result would seem to follow logically. Muslims may well find that Communism presents a social programme in a more attractive form and supported by an apparently perfect and comprehensive philosophy. The materialist faith would appear then to afford all the earthly blessings of Islam, improved, refined and embellished by technology and freed from metaphysical difficulties.'

[2] From the liturgy of the Easter Vigil: 'O truly necessary sin of Adam, which by the death of Christ was done away! O happy fault, which was counted worthy to have such and so great a Redeemer!'

autonomously in cherished darkness;[1] blinder than a mole, since when he began to do without God he began to forfeit the God-given instincts of the animal creation, strangling in his self-made coils of social-economic and international frustration. To this Bent World of Western man (to quote the title which Dr. Lang-mead Casserley[2] has borrowed from Fr. Gerard Manley Hopkins) we shall briefly revert in the Conclusion; but we may close this chapter with the remark that the adjacent worlds of Communism and of Islam, which intersect the Western world and each other, are no less Bent Worlds, in this world-wide vitiated distortion of the geometry of the Divine Order, this 'long exile on Babylon's strand'.[3]

[1] *S. John's Gospel*, iii. 19.
[2] *The Bent World*, a Christian Examination of East-West Tensions (London, 1955).
[3] Peter Abelard: *O quanta qualia*, trans. J. M. Neale.

CHAPTER X

The Middle East in Revolution

THE FIRST four years after the Second World War had witnessed the successful revolt of the Zionists against British mandatory control, and the refusal of political opinion in Egypt and Iraq to negotiate such a revision of their treaties with Britain as would confirm the British tenure of bases on their soil for the defence of the Middle East region in the 'cold war'. The official attitude of the Wafd Government in Egypt during the renewed negotiations in 1950–51 was that immediately upon an outbreak of war they would permit the British to reoccupy the Canal Zone installations, which would in the meantime be maintained in good order by the Egyptian army. When the British military experts reminded them that fighter aircraft defence against 'Blitz' attack necessitated thorough ground services which could not be hastily transferred in an emergency, the Wafdist Ministers retorted that the British were merely finding pretexts for prolonging the Occupation whose unequivocal termination was unanimously demanded by the Egyptian people. In addition the Egyptian Foreign Minister (Muhammad Salah ud-Din) reflected a belief current in Egypt that Egypt's exposure to involvement in world wars was due, not to her geographical situation at a nodal point of air and sea routes, but solely to her alliance with a Great Power, and that her best chance of avoiding the dangers of a third world war was to follow a policy of complete neutrality. This Egyptian tendency to escapism stiffened the British insistence on the necessity of regional defence for the Middle East; and the precarious parliamentary position of the British Labour Government of 1950–51 left it little room for manœuvre in negotiating with Egypt, since the Conservatives' atavistic tendency to be overbearing with the Egyptians was always accentuated in Opposition. Furthermore, since the Wafd's tenure of office was being endangered by the growing criticism of its leaders' unprecedented self-enrichment in the speculative boom created by the Korean War, it was necessary for the Wafd to stick to its maximum demands from the British if it were to continue to be the popular embodiment of Egyptian nationalism.

In the summer of 1951, moreover, the failure of the British Government to concert a common policy with the United States concerning Persia became acute. The United States Government's assumption of responsibility, in the 'Truman Doctrine' of 1947, for assisting Turkey and Greece to withstand the Soviet 'cold war' offensive had at the very least brought those countries a respite, in which the Turkish administration and people had responded positively to American technical and financial aid for the modernization of Turkish communications, agriculture, and industry. It had seemed logical to extend these remedies to Persia, which had been not less threatened by Soviet pressure, and whose expanding revenue from oil royalties had offered the possibility of financing a $650 million Seven Year Plan without recourse to the United States taxpayer; but Persian politicians, the American consultants of the Seven Year Plan, and the British oil concessionaires (the Anglo-Iranian Oil Company) not merely failed to treat the problem as one to be resolved jointly, but seemed fated to diverge ever further as the years passed. Successive Persian Governments from 1947 onwards set their hopes on obtaining a $250 million 'loan' from the United States, whose State Department advisers were insistent that a radical reform of the incompetent and corrupt administration was a first essential. While Persian political extremists won increasing public support for their demand to expropriate the A.I.O.C., the Government became increasingly reluctant to publicize the less spectacular advantages to be gained from a revised agreement with the Company. The British Labour Government's policy of dividend limitation had had the unforeseen effect in 1948 of actually reducing the Persian Government's immediate oil revenues; and though the Company had taken immediate steps to offer compensatory adjustments, it failed to overtake the general trend (first in Venezuela, and then in Sa'udi Arabia) to effect 50–50 profit-sharing agreements between the concessionary company and the government in whose territory the oil was situated. The Persian negotiators persisted for some time in 1949–50 that their 50 per cent. of the profits should be calculated, not merely on Anglo-Iranian's operations in Persia itself but on its part-share in operations in other Middle Eastern countries and on its world-wide oil-distributing business—the Persian argument being that these immensely profitable developments, of which the British Government was the chief beneficiary as holding 56 per cent. of the share capital and as tax-receiver, had been made possible only because the terms of the basic concessions of 1901 and 1933 had been 'dictated' to Persian Governments not representative of the people or had been interpreted by the Company in manners grossly 'unfair' to Persia;[1] few Persian politicians reflected that their countrymen had borne none of the initial financial risks and had been in a position to furnish virtually none of the technical skill. Some of the American consultants of the Seven Year Plan were, or had been, associated with United States oil companies reputed to be envious of Anglo-Iranian's position, and their attitude undoubtedly encouraged the Persian extremists to believe that they could dispossess Anglo-Iranian and obtain better terms from their rivals; playing off the British against the Americans was no serious challenge to a state that had survived for the previous century by playing Britain and Russia one against the other. After the moderate Prime Minister General Razmara had been murdered by an extremist in March 1951 for publicly rejecting as impracticable the demand to nationalize Anglo-Iranian's concession, the nationalist Dr. Musaddiq—an honourable but emotional septuagenarian who now became Prime Minister—was able to play on the publicly expressed concern of the U.S. Ambassador (Dr. Henry Grady) lest the uncompromising attitude of the British Embassy should cause Persia to follow China into Communism (for the Communist Tudeh Party was all the time taking the maximum advantage of the situation). The British Labour Government, precariously situated at home, equivocated between gestures of force to protect its Persian oil interests and compliance with United States 'representations', and finally capitulated to Musaddiq's eviction of the last British technicians from the great Abadan refinery in October 1951.

This shattering blow to British prestige coincided with the deadlock in the Anglo-Egyptian negotiations, and decided the Wafd Government to reject British proposals to associate Egypt

[1] See 'Iran presents its Case for Nationalization', *Oil Forum*, March 1952, and 'Anglo-Iranian Answers with Facts', ibid., April, 1952; Dr. Laurence Lockhart: 'The Causes of the Anglo-Persian Oil Dispute', *Journal of the Royal Central Asian Society*, April 1953.

with the principal North Atlantic powers, including Turkey, in a Middle East defence pact, and instead to declare the Anglo-Egyptian Treaty and the Sudan Condominium abrogated. It soon became evident, however, that the high command of the Egyptian army, associated much more closely with King Faruq than with the Wafd, were not prepared to risk attacking the reinforced British positions in the Canal Zone. When an enforced boycott by Egyptian civilian labour had failed to dislodge the British, the Wafdist boss Fuad Sirag ud-Din (who combined the portfolios of the Interior and of Finance) assumed the direction of a guerilla force, partly volunteer and partly drafted, for the purpose of harassing the British into surrender. The valour of this lightly-equipped force when confronted by British tanks and field-guns was kept up by the threat of trial by court-martial and by die-hard orders telephoned from the safety of Sirag ud-Din's Cairo office—until British exasperation at the constant sniping combined with Sirag ud-Din's reckless demagogy to produce a pitched battle in Isma'iliya in which over 40 Egyptian so-called auxiliary police were killed. As a reprisal, organized incendiary bands on the following day, 26 January 1952, destroyed a considerable part of Cairo's tourist and shopping quarter, taking about a score of European lives and doing millions of pounds' worth of material damage.

King Faruq had been waiting for some such opportunity to dismiss the Wafd and prorogue Parliament, and for the next six months the country was governed by a series of minority governments which, besides putting a stop to the anti-British guerilla, sought to clear the deadlock in Egyptian relations with the Sudanese politicians that had persisted ever since 1946. The Wafd had been adamant that nothing less than the union of the Sudan with Egypt in respect of defence, finance, and foreign policy would be acceptable, but Prime Minister Nagib al-Hilali did not hesitate to open conversations with members of the Sudanese anti-Egyptian 'Independence Front'. His attempt to investigate Wafdist corruption was, however, frustrated by a sordid intrigue on the part of some of the unworthy men who had for years encouraged Faruq in his career of self-willed profligacy. Faruq realized that a group of army officers of the middle ranks were engaged in a revolutionary conspiracy against him, but rejected all advice to conciliate their chosen figure-head, the respectable

Major-General Muhammad Nagib, and determined to destroy them. However, the conspirators moved first, drove Faruq into abdication and exile on 26 July 1952, and completed the revolutionary process by proclaiming Egypt a republic with General Nagib as its first President on 18 June 1953.

With the exception of General Nagib himself, none of the nine colonels, majors, and squadron-leaders who composed the 'Council of the Revolution' was over forty years of age. They made a sincere attempt to introduce discipline into the civil administration, and hastened to promote legislation to limit agricultural estates to a maximum of 200 acres and to distribute the surplus among the landless peasantry as smallholdings. These were to be managed co-operatively under the guidance of officials of the Ministry of Social Affairs; but even if the five years of transition resulted in an unqualified success, only a ·fraction of the problem of Egypt's rural over-population would have been touched; and hopes were entertained of promoting industry by means of hydro-electric works on the Nile. The progressive aspirations of the young revolutionaries won them sympathy among liberal circles in the United States and socialist circles in Britain. Profiting by the initiative of ex-Premier Nagib al-Hilali, whom they had meanwhile consigned to detention for several months with other political notabilities, they offered to the Sudanese political parties a free choice between independence and union with Egypt. This concession once made, the Sudanese parties which relied on Egypt for support against the Independence Front, as representing the personal ambitions of Mahdi Pasha, banded themselves together as the National Unity Party to contest the general election which the British Government had undertaken to hold under the supervision of an international commission. The unknown quantity was the voters in the non-Muslim south and other areas remote from the relatively sophisticated politics of the main towns; but with active Egyptian financial and propaganda support for the National Unity Party, and the British officials refraining from giving any comparable support to the Independence Front, the former ·won a clear majority of seats in November 1953, and the Sudan was launched on a new phase of its history, in which the British officials were to be withdrawn in time for the Sudanese to vote on their future political status _vis-à-vis_ the Egyptians in three years. Encouraged by this success in the Sudan, the

Egyptian revolutionaries and their press (opposition voices having been overawed by a series of treason trials before the Revolutionary Tribunal which was free with sentences of penal servitude for life) called on the British to evacuate the Canal Zone forthwith. They were prepared to accept a limited number of British plain-clothes technicians for a limited period, and to allow the British forces the right of re-entry in the event of aggression against a member-state of the Arab League; but the British insistence on including Turkey and Persia among the countries, in the event of aggression against whom Britain should have the right to return to the Canal Zone, caused a breakdown of negotiations and threats that the Egyptian Government would adopt a policy of complete neutrality. However, after a clash of personalities within the military junta in February 1954 had reduced President Nagib to impotence and concentrated authority in the hands of the Prime Minister, Colonel Gamal 'Abd un-Nasir, strong measures were taken against Communists and negotiations with Britain were reopened. In July agreement was reached on the withdrawal of the British garrison within two years, with the right to return in the event of aggression against an Arab state *or Turkey*; the installations were to be maintained for seven years by British civilian contractors. It was hoped to settle outstanding technical and financial details and ratify in the early autumn; but meanwhile 'Abd un-Nasir was being harassed by the uncompromising and widespread Muslim Brotherhood.

Meanwhile the uncompromising nationalism of Dr. Musaddiq had resulted in national bankruptcy since, although the Court of International Justice had ruled that the dispute with Anglo-Iranian did not come within the category of subjects which the Persian Government had agreed to submit to the Court's jurisdiction, the expansion of production in Iraq, Kuwait, and Sa'udi Arabia had made up for the stoppage of Persian oil production and the difficulties presented by the closing of the Abadan refinery were rapidly being overcome—though at a serious loss of dollar-earning capacity to Britain. Owing to Anglo-Iranian's large degree of control over the world's oil-tanker fleets, furthermore, the Persian Government had been unable to find alternative customers, except in Italy and Japan for derisory amounts; American oil companies had not, in the event, taken advantage of Anglo-Iranian's discomfiture, and the new Republican administration in the United States declined to increase its financial aid to Persia while the latter persisted in its negative oil policy. In August 1953, after Dr. Musaddiq (who had been systematically extending his own powers at the expense of those of the young Shah) had resisted an attempt by the Shah to dismiss him, General Zahidi intervened at the head of the army and after a battle with Musaddiq's supporters arrested the contumacious old man. In the summer of 1954 the Persian Government and an international consortium of oil companies, including Anglo-Iranian, reached an agreement on the resumption of oil production in Persia, on terms calculated to provide Persia with adequate future royalties but (since alternative sources of crude oil and refining capacity had meanwhile been created) not to compensate her, for the losses occasioned by two years of nationalist folly, on a scale which might tempt other countries to repeat the experiment.

Since the Arab states had steadfastly refused to negotiate a formal peace with Israel, there was plenty of scope for friction along the armistice lines which delimited the *de facto* territory of the straggling Jewish state. In the north its efforts to divert the waters of the upper Jordan for irrigation purposes encountered armed and diplomatic resistance from Syria, who claimed that such action infringed the demilitarization of the area affected, within the terms of the 1949 armistice. The chief friction arose, however, on the 330-mile stretch separating Israel from Jordan, for Israel had dictated the tracing of the line on strategic principles which took no account of the scores of thousands of Arab villagers who were thereby separated, wholly or in part, from the fields by which they lived. In these circumstances the Jordan security authorities were unable, or perhaps not wholly willing, to stamp out the constant infiltration of Arabs, whether genuine refugees or predatory adventurers, across the armistice line in search of loot; and the offences against life or property thus committed were a constant source of alarm to the Israeli border settlements, and of irritation to the Israeli security authorities and to Ben Gurion as Minister of Defence. An Israeli policy of organized, large-scale reprisal against suspect villages, initiated at the beginning of 1953, culminated with the destruction of half the village of Qibya in October 1953 and the killing of 66 of its inhabitants. This brutal reprisal was condemned by the U.N. Security Council; but its recommendation that the two Governments should dis-

cuss the amendment of the armistice was condemned by a meeting of the Arab League in December as a device for inducing the
Jordan Government to accept a United States proposal (the
'Johnston Plan') for the joint development of the waters of the
Jordan and its tributaries, which would furnish 65 per cent. of
the water available for irrigation to the Kingdom of Jordan, but
30 per cent. to Israel. Two years later, in 1955, an amended version of the Johnston Plan which, it was said, met 90 per cent. of
the demands of the Arab states, was this time referred back by the
Arab League for further 'expert study'—doubtless of its political
rather than its technical implications, and intended as a means of
indefinitely delaying a decision. The Israel Government thereupon threatened to complete its project for taking off water from
the upper Jordan by a canal lying wholly in territory allotted to
Israel by the U.N. resolutions of 1947–8, though in part demilitarized by the armistice with Syria of 1949; the Syrian Government replied with a counter-threat that they would prevent any
such action by force. Armed clashes ensuing on the Palestine-
Egyptian border made April 1956 a tense moment until a personal visit by the Secretary-General of the U.N. effected a
relaxation which was, however, terminated by mutual violence
on an alarming scale on the Israel-Jordan border in the autumn
of 1956.

But Palestine was by this time far from being the only, or even
the chief, scene of tension and dispute in the Middle East. Already
in 1953 the new Republican administration in the U.S.A. had
realized that the countries constituting the 'northern tier' of the
region, from Turkey to Pakistan, were the least inhibited by
political considerations from accepting U.S. military and economic assistance, proffered in order to give them a better chance
of maintaining their independence against possible Soviet attempts
at subverting their existing non-Communist regimes. Early in
1954 the Egyptian government-controlled press and radio had
hotly attacked the Iraqi Government for showing signs of willingness to accept these offers. Some Western observers were disposed
to concede that this behaviour merely reflected the Egyptian
Revolutionary Council's annoyance at any Arab departure from
the policy of 'neutralism' which Egypt had adopted as a challenge
to the United States to compel Britain to withdraw her forces
from the Canal Zone. The conclusion of the Anglo-Egyptian

agreement of 1954, described above, would (these observers hoped) lead to a more pro-Western orientation of Egyptian policy, though Colonel 'Abd un-Nasir warned Western interviewers that he would need a year or two to re-align Egyptian public opinion after its many years of anti-British indoctrination. However, the concessions to British considerations of the security of the region (including Turkey), which the Revolutionary Council made in the Agreement, aroused a great deal of extremist criticism in Egypt, and an apparent attempt was made on 'Abd un-Nasir's life. The Revolutionary Council, conscious that it lacked any constitutional basis, now engaged in discarding its only truly popular figure, General Muhammad Nagib, seems to have felt the need of restoring its popularity. In the first flush of the evacuation agreement in the autumn of 1954 the Turkish Prime Minister had been invited to visit Cairo; but when it became plain that the Revolutionary Council was unwilling, or unable, to make any early move towards an alliance outside the limits of the Arab League's hitherto ineffectual collective security pact, the Turkish Prime Minister early in 1955 concluded a five-years mutual security pact with Iraq. The fury of the Egyptian Revolutionary Council was then let loose upon the Turkish, but far more upon the Iraqi Government—'the friends of the friends of Israel'—with all the immoderation of which Egyptian polemic was (and is) capable. For the Iraqi Government of Nuri as-Sa'id thus to take the initiative in concluding a pact with a non-Arab state was a disregarding of Egypt's claim to lead the Arab League which the young military autocrats in Cairo could not countenance. When in April 1955 the British Government adhered to this Baghdad Pact, abrogating in its favour the Anglo-Iraqi Treaty of 1930, the Egyptian propaganda machine denounced the pact as an 'imperialist plot' designed to bring about the Arab recognition of Israel, an accusation which found a ready echo among the extremer nationalists in the other Arab states and prevented the possible adherence of Lebanon to the pact; Pakistan and Iran, however, joined it in the course of 1955. The full weight of Egyptian official influence was now thrown behind the autocratic and 'feudal' governments of Sa'udi Arabia and the Yemen in their attempts to undermine British influence or control along the whole maritime fringe of eastern and southern Arabia from the head of the Persian Gulf at Kuwait round to Aden at the entrance to the Red Sea. They were moved partly by the desire to obtain more wealth from the oil which had been, or might be, found along these coasts, and partly by the conviction that the peninsula was the Arab homeland and that Britain's imperial power was tottering everywhere. The Egyptian radio lent its raucous support to all who challenged that power—in Cyprus to the Byzantine-Fascism of Archbishop Makarios and the EOKA leaders, in Kenya to the barbarities of Mau-Mau.

Thus by the first half of 1955 the Egyptian Revolutionary Council, seeking to restore and enhance its prestige in ultra-nationalist eyes, was pursuing a policy of defiance of the Western powers (including France, impaled upon her North African dilemma) and guerilla provocation of Israel. It was all the more necessary for the Revolutionary Council to consider its prestige at home because its efforts to convince Sudanese opinion, by extensive cajolery and bribery, of the advantages of the 'unity of the Nile Valley' under Egyptian leadership were proving a failure, and the Sudan Government was advancing towards its declaration of sovereign independence in January 1956. In the previous September, however, the Revolutionary Council had gained a tremendous access of prestige throughout the Arab world by securing a considerable quantity of aircraft and other heavy armament (after the U.S. and Britain had proved insufficiently responsive, no doubt in view of the Egypto-Israeli tension during the last half-year) from Communist Czechoslovakia with the blessing of the U.S.S.R. Here, in spite of the U.S. policy of the 'northern tier' was a dramatic re-entry of Soviet interest in the heart of the Arab world, after seven years of relative quiescence which had hardly gone beyond the enrolment of 'Partisans of Peace' and had failed (probably owing to the decline of Stalin's physical and mental powers) even to exploit the opportunities presented in Persia by the excesses of Dr. Musaddiq. But now, having given material support to the Egyptian Revolution, the Soviet bloc made similar offers to Egypt's willing satellites in the campaign against the Baghdad Pact and the West, namely Sa'udi Arabia, Syria, and the Yemen. This group was further encouraged when, in the winter of 1955-6, the Jordan Government first refused a British invitation to join the Baghdad Pact—the British price for a revision in Jordan's favour of the Anglo-Jordan treaty of 1948—and then with the maximum of discourtesy dismissed and expelled General Sir John Glubb, who as commander of the 'Arab Legion' had for nearly twenty years given the Arab cause far more devoted service than most of the self-styled Arab patriots who were delirious with joy at his departure. Another 'pillar' of Britain's former power in the Middle East had been undermined, and it seemed that Cyprus might soon follow, so much encouragement did Britain's enemies receive from faint hearts or frustrated wills in Westminster, doctrinaire or defeatist minds in Fleet Street and Manchester and ironic or malicious pleasure in many quarters in Europe and some in the U.S.A.

The U.S. Ambassador to Cairo from 1950 to 1955, Jefferson Caffery, had, in his public pronouncements at least, seemed to regard the Egyptian Revolution as an oriental counterpart to the American Revolution of 1776, and this interpretation apparently found sympathy in some State Department circles, even after the shock of Egypt's purchase of arms behind the 'Iron Curtain'. The conclusion apparently drawn in Washington from this was that the United States must show that she, and not the Soviet Union, was Egypt's true friend, by making a financial offer towards the cost of executing the grandiose Egyptian plan of harnessing the Nile for irrigation and hydro-electricity on an unprecedented scale by means of a 'High Dam' at Aswan in Upper Egypt. The Revolutionary Council, however, so far from immediately taking up this American offer of December 1955 ($70 million from the U.S. and Britain as a 'first step', coupled with a $200 million loan from the World Bank), continued during the first half of 1956 to flirt with the Soviet bloc in the hope of attracting a still larger financial bid from that quarter, whose world-revolutionary strategy had by this time picked on the slogan of 'competitive co-existence' with the 'capitalist' states. The flirtation culminated in June 1956 in the new Soviet Foreign Minister's visiting Cairo and Egypt's recognition of Communist China—to which the U.S. Government replied by changing its ambassador to Cairo and abruptly announcing on 19 July the withdrawal of the High Dam offer.

Faced with this public rebuff, Colonel 'Abd un-Nasir once again needed to re-assert his prestige in the eyes of Egyptian and Arab public opinion. The expedient he found this time was to proclaim in a defiant speech of 26 July the nationalization of the

Suez Canal Co. The step had, in fact, been premeditated for some time; the Company's premises were immediately occupied by armed Egyptian troops, and penalties of imprisonment were arbitrarily decreed against its employees, whether Egyptian or foreign, who might fail to carry out their duties at the orders of the usurping authority. The British Government, acting in consultation with the French Government as representing jointly the interests most immediately affected, convened a meeting in London of twenty-two Governments representing some 90 per cent. of the shipping interests using the Canal, and considerable British reinforcements were sent as a precautionary measure to the eastern Mediterranean. The Egyptian Revolutionary Council boycotted the conference, their supposed interests being represented by the Soviet Foreign Minister while the Indian Government's envoy tried vainly to persuade the majority that the Egyptian Revolutionary Council's offer to keep the Canal open to shipping without discrimination provided a sufficient guarantee for the users of this great international waterway. Eighteen nations, however, including Iran, Pakistan, and Ethiopia, approved a resolution calling for the effective operation, maintenance, and development of the Canal by an international board including Egypt and having due regard for Egypt's sovereign rights and entitlement to a 'fair and equitable' return for its use. The principle that the Canal should be operated 'without political motivation in favour of, or in prejudice against, any user' gained point from the fact that Egypt was still in clear defiance of the Security Council's injunction of 1951 against her blockade of the Canal to ships carrying cargo for Israel.[1]

When the Egyptian Revolutionary Council rejected this proposal, presented to it by a distinguished delegation led by the Australian Prime Minister, the British and French Governments took their complaint to the Security Council, where it was inevitably subjected to the Soviet veto. By this time, however, the solidarity of the eighteen-nation front had been considerably weakened, and that not merely by the unwillingness of some of its lesser members to bring the matter to an issue. More remarkable

[1] A Greek ship so employed had been detained at Port Said for ten weeks during this summer, and kept short of fresh food and water throughout this time, according to statements made by the captain and crew to the Israeli press (*The Times*, 12 September 1956).

were the equivocations of the U.S. President and Secretary of State, which reflected the small immediate American concern with the Canal, the preoccupation of the American public with the impending presidential election, and the traditional reluctance to be associated with what could be represented (and was implied in a maladroit statement of the Secretary of State himself) as the vestiges of Anglo-French 'colonialism'. Another source of weakness was the attitude of the British Labour party which, after its leaders had been one with the Government on 2 August in condemning the Egyptian action,[1] was diverted by its good-hearted, if soft-headed pacifists and its less ingenuous little-Englanders into a policy of opposing for opposing's sake,[2] until in early October the Cairo propaganda machine could congratulate itself on the moral support received from the Labour party annual conference and the party leader found himself constrained to oppose the consensus of speeches from the floor by denying that 'any nation had unlimited rights, in an international waterway, to destroy or threaten the rights of other nations'.

What was at issue, as Mr. Gaitskell had himself proclaimed on 2 August, was not merely the narrow, though economically and strategically important issue of who was to control the Canal, but the whole question of the position of the Middle East in the world's balance of power. The reputation of the West had already been jeopardized by the (originally) British and (more

---

[1] 'The French Prime Minister . . . the other day quoted a speech of Colonel Nasser's and rightly said that it could remind us only of one thing—of the speeches of Hitler before the war.

'. . . I have no doubt myself that the reason why Colonel Nasser acted in the way that he did, aggressively, brusquely, suddenly, was precisely because he wanted to raise his prestige in the rest of the Middle East. . . . He wanted to assert his strength. He wanted to make a big impression. . . . It is all very familiar. It is exactly the same that we encountered from Mussolini and Hitler in the years before the war' (The Leader of the Opposition, *Parliamentary Debates*, House of Commons, 2 August 1956, cols. 1620–1; in a B.B.C. television programme on 21 September Mr. Gaitskell denied having made this comparison).

[2] A few legal members on the Government side also were concerned at the Prime Minister's refusal to renounce the use of force in this dispute except within the provisions of the U.N. Charter. It might, however, be argued that the intention of the Charter had been perverted since 1945. Any decision by the Security Council was at the mercy of a Soviet veto which had already been used on some seventy-seven occasions of generally lesser import; and the General Assembly was swamped with Asian and Latin American states, many of whom were in the habit of automatically registering their vote against 'imperialism'. The International Court's evasion of responsibility for jurisdiction in the Anglo-Iranian oil dispute of 1952 did not, moreover, augur well for reference of the Canal dispute to that body.

recently) American support of Zionist 'colonialism' in Palestine. The British withdrawals from India, Palestine and the Canal Zone; the Communist successes in China and Indo-China; the outbreaks of terrorism so arduously combated in Kenya, Algeria and Cyprus; and the abandonment of the French protectorates in Morocco and Tunisia: all these events had encouraged the uncompromising nationalist forces in the Arab world to hope for total independence at an early date, not merely of Western political influences but also of their so-called 'exploitation' by the oil companies. And in 1955 the impatient opportunism of the Egyptian Revolutionary Council had given a pronouncedly pro-Soviet tilt to what had been hitherto officially described as 'neutralism'. It seemed as if Egypt and Syria, in particular, had thrown off the 'strings' of Western influences only to offer their necks to the yoke by which the Soviet Union drove its plodding satellites over the heavy furrows of 'socialist planning'. To be sure, the yoke held up before these Arab states was thickly camouflaged with verbal flowers and decked with cornucopias; but 'the Arab's understanding is in his eyes'; and the patient Egyptian ox and opinionated Syrian camel had not yet felt on their shoulders the dead weight which was even now oppressing the 'toiling masses' of Poznan and Hungary to the point of desperate rebellion.

If therefore Western prestige were to accept another defeat over the 'nationalization' of the Canal, it was probably only a matter of months before it would be subjected to a similar expropriation of its oil interests in the Persian Gulf. Already the usually circumspect Lebanese Government had carried its manœuvres to extract more revenue from British and American pipeline companies almost to the point of a complete break. Even if the Iraqi and Sa'udi Governments continued for the present to see some advantage in abiding by the existing concessions, the younger nationalists were everywhere inflamed with the revolutionary fever spread abroad from Egypt[1] and were only awaiting a

[1] The pattern of the Middle Eastern revolution has already been ably sketched by Dr. Majid Khadduri: 'The Role of the Military in Middle East Politics', *American Political Science Review*, xlvii, 1953; but the type of its Leadership is now becoming more clearly established, namely the dynamic but frustrated, well-intentioned but intellectually confused military officer of the 30–35 age-group. Examples so far are Gamal 'Abd un-Nasir and his colleagues in Egypt; Lt.-Col. Ali Abu Nuwār, aged 33, appointed Chief of Staff in Jordan after the expulsion of General Glubb; and most recently Col. Abdul-Hamīd Sarrāj, aged 32, emerging in November 1956 as the head of the Intelligence Branch (so-called) of the Syrian army. Western readers should not be misled by the

favourable opportunity to overthrow their 'reactionary' and 'feudal' rulers[1] and defy the foreign 'exploiters'. Though the development of atomic energy might free the industrial West from its large measure of dependence on Middle Eastern oil in twenty years' time, such a challenge in the meantime might present the West with the grim alternatives of economic paralysis or preventive war; and conversely the readiness of the West to give large-scale material assistance to the building-up of the 'under-developed' East was clearly being shaken by indications that the new eastern states were recklessly prepared to sacrifice international obligations to crude national prestige.

*   *   *

The final touches to the fourth edition of this *Short History* were made on the eve of the Suez Crisis in 1956, on 26 October which is the day appointed by the Anglican Provinces of Canterbury and York for the festival of Alfred, King of the West Saxons. Though I had no foreknowledge of the crisis which was so soon to break on an astonished world, the events of the past three months, since the Egyptian dictator's confiscation of the properties of the Universal Company of the Suez Canal, had built up a sense of tension in all observers: so that as I wrote the name of the great Alfred at the end of my text, I had at the back of my mind the stanzas from G. K. Chesterton's *Ballad of the White Horse*:[2]

> I tell you naught for your comfort,
>   yea, naught for your desire,
> save that the sky grows darker yet
>   and the sea rises higher.

> Night shall be thrice night over you,
>   and heaven an iron cope.
> Do you have joy without a cause,
>   yea, faith without a hope?

false archetype of a German lance-corporal who recently smudged the pages of history. These 'angry young men' are Muslims, and their archetype (allowance being made for the passage of time) is Ahmad al-'Arabi who talked and blustered the first Egyptian nationalist movement into disaster in 1882.

[1] In Arab, as in Western, 'progressive' circles the term 'feudal' (*iqtā'i*) has lost all precise significance to become an indiscriminate term of abuse. A graduate student persisted, despite my protests, in referring in his M.A. thesis to 'feudal industrialists'.

[2] It was my dear friend and wartime colleague Evan John, author of *Time in the East*, &c., who first made me aware of these stanzas of Catholic truth. *Lux perpetua luceat ei.*

I had referred to the risk that the West might be presented 'with the grim alternatives of economic paralysis or preventive war'; but on that 26 October 1956 I had not guessed that the choice would be presented within four days and under such ambiguous colours, so that Britain and France were to be repudiated by their closest and greatest ally, the British Commonwealth was itself to be split by the then Canadian government's disapproval (I say nothing of India, whose support for Egyptian nationalism had been made clear by Krishna Menon), and the Parliament at Westminster and even the Cabinet were to be the scenes of tortured consciences and divided loyalties.

As late as July 1958 Stephen Spender, poet and essayist and sometime Communist, could refer in a book-review to 'the Suez Invasion—that strange phantom flashback out of England's imperialist past';[1] but (alas for this Angry Young Man grown older) by the time the article appeared, United States marines had landed in Beirut and judgements in the English-speaking world about the Suez intervention could never be quite the same again. Professed moralists in the United States and professional critics of the Tories in Britain (the two categories are not quite synonymous) were at pains to draw the distinction between the American intervention at the request of the legitimate Government of Lebanon and the Anglo-French intervention against the military clique who had unconstitutionally usurped the government of Egypt; but the fact remained that English speakers (except for the fellow-travellers and absolute pacifists, and it is not clear that Mr. Spender fell into either of these categories) could no longer condemn the 'Suez Invasion' with quite the same confident certainty of moral rectitude. If the U.S. marines had done nothing else, they had injected a dose of wholesome realism and comparative thinking into minds that badly needed such a corrective.

Before the Iraqi *coup d'état* of July 1958 it had been James Morris who had made one of the most sober and objective comments on the Suez intervention;[2] and now the same ready writer was quick with his epitaph on the latest crisis:

The late government of Iraq was, on the whole, the best in the Middle East—autocratic, to be sure, but relatively honest, wise in its

---

[1] 'When the Angry Men Grow Older', *New York Times Book Review*, 20 July 1958.
[2] See *The Market of Seleukia* (London, 1957), p. 236. *Islam Inflamed* (New York, 1957), p. 222.

expenditures, reasonable in its ambitions, loyal to the West. It was doomed by the fiasco of Suez, which proved Western Europe to be impotent without the support of America.[1]

Back in the Spring of 1956 the main preoccupation in Washington had been the impending presidential election, which was probably the chief reason why Sir Anthony Eden's urgent representations, in the month following Glubb Pasha's expulsion from Jordan and the stoning of the British Foreign Secretary in Bahrain, had gone unheeded there.[2] Joseph Alsop of the *New York Herald-Tribune*, after a long journey of inquiry in the Middle East, had reported on 27 June 1956 (a month before the outbreak of the Suez crisis) that the central problem of American foreign policy lay 'not in the Middle East at all, but in Britain'. There was

a pernicious tendency, not least in the State Department, to take Britain for granted. If the Middle Eastern problem has any meaning at all, it very clearly means that Britain cannot prudently be taken for granted any longer . . . because the real foundations of the British structure are still colonial and imperial; and these foundations are now in grave danger. . . .

The British policy-makers understand the danger of British bankruptcy, which means the end of Britain's career as a major power. As Sir Anthony Eden has said, they are convinced that the loss of Cyprus will be only the preliminary to the loss of the Middle Eastern oil sources. So the British have reacted violently, too violently in this reporter's opinion. But so should we react very violently, if we felt hostile hands groping for our jugular.

In these circumstances, it is amazing and pretty terrifying to come home, and to discover that the State Department's chief parlour game seems to be smug carping at the British policy in such places as Cyprus and Buraimi.

What does it matter if Britain's struggles to defend her own jugular have become pretty convulsive, compared to the hard fact that this same Britain also happens to be the jugular of the United States?

. . . A good deal less carping, and a great deal more creative and comradely approach to Britain's present peril would now seem to be rather urgently indicated.

But Mr. Dulles's decision to withdraw the High Dam offer (however much 'Abd un-Nasir's cavalier treatment of the offer

---

[1] 'Nasserism—A Modern Riddle of the Sphinx', *New York Times Magazine*, 27 July 1948, p. 41.

[2] See Stewart Alsop: *New York Herald-Tribune*, 12 April 1956.

had earned the rebuke) seems to have been reached on mainly domestic considerations,[1] without regard for the possible consequences to the United States' European allies.

As for the British Government's critics at home, *Middle East Crisis*, by Guy Wint and Peter Calvocoressi, was by far the most ably reasoned of the Opposition publications evoked by the crisis, the least infected by party rancour. Of the general display of condemnation a Zionist observer remarked sardonically:

As a demonstration of the continued strength of Protestant-liberal morality among the British middle and professional classes, it was impressive. . . . Possibly the whole furor is evidence that the British are still sound at heart; certainly it disclosed that a good many liberal intellectuals are a little soft in the head. But then that is not exactly a new discovery.[2]

It was indeed no discovery to Zionists, who had been systematically exploiting that same softness for the past forty years.

After two months of agonized travail after Suez Washington brought forth, not exactly perhaps a *ridiculus mus* but the Eisenhower Doctrine. At the time it seemed as if the State Department had been at such pains to dot the i's and cross the t's for Congress that the Doctrine would become operative only in the unlikely event of a Middle Eastern country's being the victim of direct aggression by 'international Communism'; but by April 1957 it had served to give decisive United States support to King Husain of Jordan when he moved to reverse the steady leftward shift of his Government, led by the national-socialist Sulaiman an-Nabulsi, and of his young Chief of Staff, Ali Abu Nuwar. Against all expectation Jordan was saved for the west, at least temporarily, and the conservative politicians and army officers who had been displaced after Sir John Glubb's expulsion returned after little more than a year to high office in government and the *Jaish al-'Arabi*, the former Arab Legion. American policy was, however, less successful in trying to steer a course through the

---

[1] See the Alsop Brothers: *New York Herald-Tribune*, 23 July 1956. John Robinson Beal's biography *John Foster Dulles* (1957) may be regarded as semi-official: see pp. 258–60, and cf. pp. 207–10 for the beginning of the breakdown in communications between Washington and London, over the Dienbienphu crisis in the Spring of 1954.

[2] George Lichtheim, in *Commentary* 22 (December 1956), 511. See also (more soberly) Max Beloff: 'Suez and the British Conscience', ibid., 23 (1957), 309.

Syrian war-scare of the autumn of 1957. So tortuous and artificial a labyrinth was this that Washington was not generally to blame for hesitating; but unfortunately Mr. Dulles gave another exhibition of blowing hot on Friday and cold on Tuesday which must have encouraged all the enemies of the West.

During all these months the spotlight had been off Gamal 'Abd un-Nasir, and he and Egypt basked in the reflected splendour of their diplomatic victory but licked the real wounds that they had suffered at the hands of the Israelis in Sinai. The sending of an Egyptian token force to the Syrian-Turkish border was doubtless a move to reassert Egypt's *présence* after the moral defeat received in Jordan; and the holding in Cairo in December of the Asian-African People's Solidarity Conference was a sequel to the Bandoeng conference of 1955 which had been 'Abd un-Nasir's first appearance on the international stage. This time, however, the Soviet delegates were at pains to incite their Asian-African disciples to further acts of 'nationalization' of foreign property, after the Suez Canal model.

Since the end of the Palestine War, nine years earlier, the Syrian Republic had known only the alternation of parliamentary anarchy and dictatorship. After the overthrow of the dictator Adib Shishakli early in 1954, the Ba'th Party, a group of young national-socialists, had acquired an ascendancy out of all proportion to their actual representation in Parliament, since their faction among the army officers had prevailed over the rival 'Syrian National Party' in a series of conspiracy trials. However, the Ba'th still feared that the older conservative groups of landowners and merchants might stage a counter-coup against them, and to strengthen their position they had accordingly, since 1955, been urging the 'progressive' military rulers of Egypt for a federal union. Meanwhile, a potential rival had been improving his position—Khalid al-'Azm, an 'able and ambitious landowner and business-man of ancient family, whose movement to the left has been an important factor in the past two years'.[1] The Ba'th renewed their representations to Cairo in January 1958 and this time, although Syria represented a political liability and only contingently an economic asset to Egypt, 'Abd un-Nasir accepted

---

[1] Albert Hourani: 'The Pull of Arab Unity', *The Times*, 21 May 1958. See also Paolo Minganti: 'Considerazioni sull'unione fra Siria ed Egitto', *Oriente Moderno*, XXXVIII (February 1958), 101–6.

the offer: no doubt the immediate boost of prestige from the proclamation on 1 February of the 'United Arab Republic' outweighed the more practical considerations. Already in the previous summer a scholar had drawn attention to 'the steady revival of the concept of an Islamic community (*umma*) especially in Egypt. . . . The tendency today is to reject the Western origin of nationalism and to base it on Islam';[1] and this was strikingly demonstrated by 'Abd un-Nasir in proclaiming the new *Anschluss* to the Egyptian national assembly:

The inseparability of unity and strength has always been one of the most marked characteristics of the history of our nation. For not once has unity been realized, but it was followed by strength, and not once have we possessed strength, but unity was its natural result. . . .

The way in which the efforts toward unity were pursued differed with the ages, but the aim remained the same, and the end in view was always the realization of these moments we are living now. The area was unified by the force of arms at the time when arms were the means by which humanity in its infancy made itself understood. Then it was unified by the holy prophecies when divine messages began to descend upon the earth to guide humanity. Again it was unified by the power of faith, when the banners of Islam rose on high, bearing the new message of God, in confirmation of those preceding it, and calling for the establishment of justice, [speaking God's final word to God's servants. The area became united in language, the day when Arabic triumphed over all other tongues]. The whole region was united for reasons of mutual security, to face an imperialism coming from Europe and bearing the Cross in order to disguise its ambitions behind the façade of Christianity.

The meaning of unity was never clearer than when the Christianity of the Arab Orient joined the ranks of Islam [sic] to battle the Crusaders until victory. . . .[2]

Three years earlier, in the first flush of the agreement to withdraw

---

[1] P. J. Vatikiotis, in Philip W. Thayer ed.: *Tensions in the Middle East* (proceedings of a conference held by the Johns Hopkins University, August 1957), pp. 172–3.

[2] Speech by President Gamal Abdel Nasser, 5 February 1958 (Information Administration, Press Bureau of the United Arab Republic, New York). This authorized version has bowdlerized the passage printed in square brackets above which is taken from an unofficial translation printed by the *New York Times*, 6 February: the official text has suppressed the reference to 'God's final word'; and the implied reference in the next sentence to the submergence of the Aramaic and Coptic languages, formerly spoken by the Christians of the Middle East, has been smoothed out into a reference to 'the various elements in a single Arab nation'.

the British troops from the Suez Canal zone, it would seem that 'Abd un-Nasir had been even more explicit in proclaiming a Muslim revival, but at that moment of false optimism few Western observers had taken notice:

We are endowed with a spiritual force and a faith in God and a sense of brotherhood which fit us to open a chapter in the history of humanity like that chapter which our forefathers opened 1,300 years ago. Why should we not once again give the world a message of peace and mercy, of brotherhood and equality, so as to dispel all the darkness from the hearts and souls of those who now believe only in material things? In the past we received the Revelation from heaven, to guide the human race towards its destiny; this was the civilization of Islam, which will deliver the world from the darkness of error, ignorance and discord. Today a new revelation springs from our hearts, to guide the human race towards its destiny again. Today again our message is worthy of reaching hearts and souls which are perishing, and of freeing them once again from the darkness of error, ignorance, and discord. . . .

. . . For our religion is the religion of the whole of humanity, not the religion of a single race. For our nation is the first that has proclaimed peace, brotherhood, and humanity on the earth, and it pays no heed to the appeals of racialism. For our land is the land of the Prophecy, and it is not possible that out of it should come an appeal to evil . . .[1]

It was inevitable that the proclamation of the United Arab Republic should make a tremendous appeal to the younger 'intellectuals' of all the eastern Arab countries and should confirm the ascent to heroic stature which the Soviet arms deal of 1955 had begun for 'Abd un-Nasir: his name was now coupled, in Damascus and Cairo, with that of the great Saladin—Salah ud-Din _al-Malik an-Nāsir_.[2] Besides this exaltation the proclamation of the Federal Union of Iraq and Jordan made little echo among the 'intellectuals', for this was merely a federation of unpopular governments and of two scions of the conservative House of Hashim: there was nothing national-socialist about it, and there was no doubt that if a plebiscite had been freely held in Iraq and Jordan the urban 'intellectuals'[3] (meaning everyone

---

[1] Preface to _Oil and Arab Policy_ (Liberation Movement, Cairo, October 1954), quoted by Jean Vigneau: 'L'Idéologie de la révolution égyptienne', _Politique Etrangère_, 22 (1957), p. 455.   [2] 'Victorious King', the title of Saladin.
[3] See Frank Stoakes: 'Les Tendances nationalistes dans l'Iraq d'après-guerre', _Politique Etrangère_, 23 (1958).

who had attended a secondary school) would have polled overwhelmingly for the Egyptian *bikbashi* whose 99 per cent. poll in
the Egypto-Syrian plebiscite, though it was of course a fake in
the absence of any opponent, did represent a very real, if perhaps
ephemeral, popularity.[1]

Already at the end of 1957 I had referred to 'the 'Syro-Egyptian
campaign to harass Lebanon (the Middle Eastern "Austria") into
Gleichschaltung',[2] for neither the Egyptian military junta nor the
Syrian Ba'th had forgiven President Sham'un of Lebanon the
initiative he had taken, in the aftermath of the Suez crisis, to
establish a pro-Western government in Beirut with the redoubt-
able Dr. Charles Malik, graduate of the American University of
Beirut and Harvard and exponent of neo-Thomism at the United
Nations, as Foreign Minister. The Lebanese Opposition, which
was led by the disgruntled Sunni Muslim ward politicians Sa'ib
Salam and Abdullah al-Yafi but also figured the Druze socialist-
aristocrat Kamal Junbalat ('Jumblat'), looked openly to Damascus
for support in the parliamentary election of June 1957; and though
the extent of the Government victory was due in some measure
to administrative interference and to bribery *more Libanico*, Salam
and Yafi had their own recourse to violence two weeks earlier
to thank for their defeat in the Beirut No. 1 District.[3] But this
parliamentary election was only a preliminary to the presidential
election which was due in the autumn of 1958 on the completion
of Kamil Sham'un's six-year term. Article 49 of the Constitution
prescribed that a President might be re-elected only after an
interval of six years; and after President Bishara al-Khuri (who
had had this article waived in his favour, 'as an exceptional case',
in 1948) had been overthrown by the 'rose-water revolution' of
September 1952, Article 49 had been reaffirmed under Sham'un's
auspices. But now his own term was expiring, and where among
Lebanon's 450,000 Maronites was there a political figure who
could be relied on to continue his pro-Western policy, which
went as far as endorsement of the Eisenhower Doctrine? The

---

[1] cf. the 1921 plebiscite in Iraq for King Faisal I, above, p. 144. If in 1970
'Abd un-Nasir can look back over twelve years of consolidation, as Faisal could,
he will not have done badly; but, as the Turkish Ambassador to Egypt had
warned the junta, 'Regardez Napoléon et ce que fut sa fin quand il eut atteint
le sommet' (*Bourse Egyptienne*, 5 January 1954).

[2] *Annual Register*, 1957, p. 288.

[3] See 'Elections in the Lebanese Republic, the Prospects Surveyed', *The
World Today*, 13 (June 1957).

Parliament returned by the 1957 election could furnish the two-thirds majority needed to remove once more the stumbling-block of Article 49; and in the spring of 1958, therefore, the Opposition was resorting increasingly to urban intimidation and arms-smuggling from Syria, while the United Arab Republic propaganda machine ever more vehemently incited the Lebanese 'patriots' against their Government.

The murder of an extremist newspaper-editor on 8 May was immediately followed by open rebellion in the northern Muslim port of Tripoli and in the Shūf, where the behaviour of Junbalat's Druze henchmen by no means conformed with the non-violence prescribed by his *guru*, Mahatma Gandhi. On 20 May Mr. Dulles startled his press conference with the reminder of an amendment that Senator Mansfield had inserted into the Eisenhower Doctrine during its passage through Congress, that 'the independence and integrity of the countries of the Middle East is vital to world peace and the national interest of the United States', which could authorize the President to intervene even though there had been no impact of 'international communism'. But the more the Lebanese civil war (not very bloody, but still far less *chic* than the brief *coup d'état* of 1952) developed, the less simple an aspect did it present to the sympathetic Western observer. Albert Hourani wrote[1] that 'in the last resort most of the Christian half of the population identifies itself with Western Christendom, while most of the Muslim half is finally identified with the "Arabism" of Damascus and Cairo'; but by the end of May the Maronite Patriarch had come out so openly against the Maronite President (in part for personal reasons, apparently) as to deny that there was any interference coming from the United Arab Republic against all the aural evidence provided by the Damascus and Cairo Radios.[2] The Commander-in-Chief remained so determined to keep his little army out of politics, and to preserve his own virginity as a neutral candidate for the Presidency, that he declined to order his troops into action against the rebels. As the Lebanese Government hesitantly moved to indict the U.A.R. before the Security Council, a diplomat at the U.N. asked, 'If Washington cannot save Chamoun and Charles Malik, who will dare to side

---

[1] 'The Pull of Arab Unity', loc. cit.

[2] For the Patriarch's strong statement of 4 March in favour of Lebanon's independence, sovereignty, and freedom, see Paolo Minganti: 'In margine alla crisi libanese', *Oriente Moderno*, XXXVIII (1958), pp. 220–1.

with the United States?', and Lord Salisbury spoke in the House of Lords of the bankruptcy of Washington's 'policy of the fence'.[1]

On 3 July the Swedish secretary-general of the U.N., after a tour of mediation among the Arab capitals, stated with reference to the Lebanese crisis:

The phrase you sometimes find in the newspapers, 'mass infiltration', has not been and is not warranted at present. I am sorry. I would correct myself on one point. I would delete the words 'has not been' and say just straight that to my knowledge we have no foundation for such a judgment now.[2]

The phrase 'mass infiltration' may well have been a rhetorical exaggeration of Charles Malik's; but the hastily improvised team of U.N. observers in Lebanon were not allowed to move freely in the rebel-held areas, were restricted to motor-roads in the mountain areas, did not venture out at night, and spoke no Arabic. Cairo and Damascus were quick to hail Mr. Hammarskjöld's words as proof of their unsullied innocence: to those old enough to remember the Munich 'appeasement' operation of twenty years earlier, the analogy with the whitewashing technique of the Runciman mission was very close.

The Iraqi *coup d'état* of 14 July knocked the linch-pin out of the Baghdad Pact and Mr. Dulles's 'northern tier' concept. Nuri as-Sa'id had been 'dismembered' by the Baghdad mob, visiting Jordanian conservatives and American business-men likewise turned over to the mob and beaten to death, the British Ambassador shot at and his Embassy burnt and looted. The revolutionary regime was headed by soldiers and civilians who had rallied to the 'Golden Square' and Rashid Ali in 1941 and had counted on the Nazi German support which had proved to be too little and too late.[3] At last it seemed to be obvious to Washington as to London that if they did not move immediately, the much feebler governments of Lebanon and Jordan would be swept away as quickly as Nuri's collapsed Tower of Babel; and Gamal 'Abd un-Nasir would be left straddling the Middle East as the 'Corsican usurper' had straddled Europe 150 years before. The U.S. intervention imposed caution upon the Lebanese civil war, so that the presidential election could be held and authority transferred to the new President at the lawful time and by constitutional

---

[1] *Christian Science Monitor*, 23 May 1958; House of Lords, 14 May.
[2] *New York Times*, 4 July 1958, p. 6.   [3] See above, pp. 198–9.

process, not by the fiat of anonymous gang-leaders armed and directed by the Syrian army intelligence. The British intervention preserved Jordan—admittedly a 'kept state' (in the words of Aneurin Bevan, who had no scruples about being the official guest of the Kremlin autocrats with *their* periphery of 'kept' satellites), but also under King Husain a desirable buffer between pan-Arab bellicose posturing and Israeli quickness to resort to preventive warfare in self-defence. In these respects, the American-British intervention of 1958, much as it contravened the theoretic principles of the United Nations and thus made nonsense of spinsterish Washington's equivocating prudery over the High Dam-Suez crisis,[1] justified itself in terms of international realism.

Outside Iraq, Arab nationalists universally rejoiced that the Baghdad mobs had lynched the 'traitors', as the Cairo and Damascus propaganda machines had so long demanded, and that no obstacle to the further advance towards Arab unity apparently remained. Portraits of 'Abd un-Nasir, formerly banned in Iraq, were immediately posted by the thousands in public places.[2] But it soon became evident that the revolutionary regime was an uneasy coalition between those who wanted to press ahead towards closer union with the United Arab Republic and those who, after campaigning against Nuri under the slogan of Arab unity, were less inclined, once in power, to consider sharing Iraq's oil revenues with Egypt, a nation hungry for investment capital, or subordinating Iraq's army to an Egyptian high command whose ineffectiveness had again been demonstrated in Sinai. During the autumn, Colonel Abd us-Salam Arif—second-in-command of the revolutionary junta and the commander whose troops had actually occupied Baghdad on 14 July—made an ill-organized bid to assert his primacy against his senior, Brigadier Abdul Karim Qasim, who had planned the coup with him but whose troops were at Ba'quba, ready to move if Arif failed. There appears to be little evidence that Arif's autumn bid for power had other than

[1] Full use of Sir Anthony Eden's disclosures in his memoirs, entitled *Full Circle* (1960), must await my forthcoming study, *Contemporary Arab Politics*. In South Africa in January 1960, Prime Minister Harold Macmillan, whose mother was a U.S. citizen, described the United States as a 'reluctant debutante' in international affairs.

[2] See *Christian Science Monitor*, 20 October 1958. They were later replaced by portraits of Brigadier Qasim (*az-za'im al-awhad*, 'the one and only Leader').

personal motives,[1] but as a typical 'nearly-have', he had been associated with adherents of the Syrian Ba'th and other pan-Arab elements, with the result that they now shared his disgrace and Qasim came to rely increasingly on the leftist National Democratic Party and on Communists and fellow-travellers, both those who had been interned during Nuri's regime and those who had found sanctuary in leftist Damascus or behind the 'iron curtain'.

A visit paid by the elderly leader of the National Democrats to 'Abd un-Nasir had not been a success. The latter now had in Iraq a rival for Soviet favours, and the governments of Sudan and Tunisia were showing an unwelcome independence of what President Bourguiba called Gamal 'Abd un-Nasir's 'pharaonic' tendencies. In November, pan-Arab propagandists began systematically to ply Western newspaper reporters with alarmist stories of the inroads of Communism in Iraq. In December, while his Government was concluding negotiations for Soviet financing of the construction of the first stage of the long-delayed Aswan High Dam, 'Abd un-Nasir ordered the arrest of several scores of Communists in his Syrian province, where the carrying into effect of administrative unification and particularly the application of a land-reform law were causing difficulties. Speaking on 23 December at Port Said, in celebration of the anniversary of the 'victory' won there two years earlier, he accused the Communists of 'opportunistic' opposition to Arab nationalism,[2] and coupled their activity with those of imperialism and Zionism.

However, his desire not to forfeit the advantages of Soviet economic aid—notably the construction of the first stage of the High Dam and of a new shipyard at Alexandria—remained evident. Even after Khrushchev, speaking at the Twenty-first

---

[1] See Simon Jargy, 'Une page d'histoire de la révolution irakienne: le procès Abd al-Salam Aref', *Orient*, 12 (1959); A. F., 'A Year of Republican Iraq', *The World Today*, 15 (1959).

[2] The well-known Lebanese business-man and politician Emile Bustani has naively commented: 'Local nationalists echoed his words and rounded up their local Communists, although the day before his speech was made, many people had been of the opinion that Arab nationalism and Communism were synonymous'. (*Middle East Forum* [Beirut] 34, no. 4 [April 1959], 45); cf. Walter Z. Laqueur, 'Nasser and the Iraqi Communists', *Commentary*, 27 (February 1959), especially p. 106.)

Communist Party Congress, had issued a warning to 'Abd un-
Nasir, the latter, during the anniversary celebrations of the
establishment of the U.A.R. in February 1959, spoke of his
people 'maintaining sincere feelings of friendship for the people
of the Soviet Union'.[1] He accused 'imperialists and opportu-
nists' of trying to make trouble between the U.A.R. and the
U.S.S.R. and between the U.A.R. and Iraq, and there were reports of his willingness to meet the Iraqi Premier, doubtless in
a competition for popular favour. However, the failure of a
pro-U.A.R. military coup in northern Iraq[2] inflamed passions
again, and by mid-March the puerile and bloodthirsty game . . .
played with terrible earnestness by depraved children'[3] had been
resumed. 'Abd un-Nasir, who had remained in Syria during the
past month, accused the Iraqi Communists of being allied with
Britain to destroy Arab nationalism;[4] and having received a
sharper rebuke from Khrushchev than that administered in
January, he now retorted that during the Suez crisis Egypt had
received 'no sign of help from any country, including the
Soviet Union'.[5]

The political committee of the Arab League met in Beirut
early in April at the instance of the Sudan Government, which
wished to mediate between the U.A.R. and Iraq. The U.A.R.
spokesmen tried to put the Iraqi revolutionary government in
the dock, as they had tried to put Nuri's government in the dock
four years earlier, after the announcement of the Turko-Iraqi
pact. Once again, however, they failed to carry the other Arab
states with them. Iraq, Tunisia, and Jordan boycotted the
meeting altogether because of their respective grievances with
Egypt; Libya did not send a delegation; Sudan abstained from

[1] *Orient*, no. 9 (1959), 134.

[2] See Michel Montserrat, 'L'affaire de Mossoul'; A. F., 'A Year of Republican
Iraq', *The World Today*, 15 (1959), 296-8.

[3] Joseph Conrad: *Nostromo*, p. 49; Conrad was describing Central American
politics in the late nineteenth century.

[4] *Orient*, no. 9 (1959), 158, trans. from *al-Ahram*, 21 March 1959. As early
as 24 January, the *Christian Science Monitor's* correspondent, Harry B. Ellis,
had reported 'a widespread Egyptian conviction that Britain is working against
President Nasser's interests in Iraq' (sic).

[5] *Orient*, no. 9 (1959), 159, trans. from *al-Ahram*, 23 March; and compare
p. 129, trans. from *al-Ahram*, 29 January, in which the editor (a close associate
of 'Abd un-Nasir) had acknowledged 'the help that the Soviet Union . . . gave
us in our struggle for liberty and life'.

voting on the final resolution because it was not conciliatory enough; and a mere rump, only half the League's membership, adopted a resolution which avoided mentioning Communism but equivocally condemned 'any foreign influence, from whatever direction it comes, creating dissension among the Arabs. . . .'[1] It was a major diplomatic defeat for 'Abd un-Nasir, who was reduced to making the following appeal to an Indian left-wing editor:

In Khrushchev's eyes is the group of Communists who do not respect their country more important than the friendship of a great ocean of Arab peoples stretching from the Persian Gulf to the Atlantic? . . . For every gesture on his part in favour of the Arabs we have been grateful ten times over. But for every blow that he directs against us we are hitting back with ten blows in return. . . . The British are like wounded wolves . . . using every tool that comes to the hand, from Qasim to the Communists, to destroy me.[2]

The device of 'positive neutralism' had boomeranged on its inventor,[3] who now tried to compensate by once more playing off (and not without some success) the United States against Britain.[4]

It was evident that, as Western observers had suspected much earlier, the Soviet blandishments so blithely accepted by Egypt and Syria from 1955 through 1958 had been designed to fan the anti-Western feeling of the 'intelligentsia' throughout the eastern Arab world, and especially to make trouble for the West in the oil-producing countries of the Persian Gulf.[5] The reckless and unheeding Egyptian and Syrian campaign of subversion directed against Nuri as-Sa'id had served to neutralize the constructive aspects of his regime, and had helped to bring on the Iraqi revolution of 1958; but then the 'age-old conflict

[1] *Christian Science Monitor,* 8 April 1959.

[2] Interview du Président de la République arabe unie', *Orient,* no. 10 (1959), 184-5, translated from *al-Ahrām* (Cairo), 18 April 1959.

[3] cf. Emile Delestre, 'La République arabe unie face a l'Irak et au communisme', *Orient,* no. 9 (1959), 21.

[4] See Harry B. Ellis, *Christian Science Monitor,* 23 April 1959.

[5] See Delestre, loc. cit.; and the manifesto of the Syrian Communist General Afif al-Bizri attacking the United Arab Republic: 'Instead of sending our armaments to Mosul, would it not have been better to send them to the fighters in Algeria, Oman, and southern Arabia, and any other country struggling against imperialism?' (*Orient,* no. 10, p. 213, translated from the Beirut *al-Akhbār,* 10 May 1959).

of the Euphrates and Nile valleys'[1] had continued to operate; and 'in Cairo as in Baghdad the Arabs, carried away by their rival ambitions, continued to exhaust their strength in empty, sterile quarrelling. On all sides it was the triumph of the Lie.'[2]

By June, however, the indications that the U.A.R. campaign against Qasim was making him more dependent on the Iraqi Communists had penetrated 'Abd un-Nasir's consciousness. The violent attacks on Qasim (as well as on King Husain of Jordan) abated, even though Damascus and Cairo (especially the former) lost no opportunity to magnify the continuing unrest in Iraq. The Egyptians, seeking a new target for popular fervor, resumed a practice which they had for some time discontinued—confiscating goods made in Israel from ships using the Suez Canal, in defiance of the Security Council resolution of 1951 and of the attempts which the U.N. Secretary-General now made to mediate in the matter. The Israelis, for their part, had been congratulating themselves on their growing trade and friendly relations with such countries as Burma, Ceylon, and Ghana.[3] Accordingly, in his speech commemorating the seventh anniversary of the Egyptian revolution, 'Abd un-Nasir sought to counter this by declaring that Israel was being 'used as a spearhead by imperialists to enable them to gain a foothold in the newly independent countries in Africa,' and by calling on the '200 million sufferers from imperialist injustice in Africa and Asia' to cooperate in an economic boycott of Israel.[4]

Meanwhile, in Iraq, the Communists had reached the apogee of their influence about the end of April:

They had owed their success, it would seem, less to their numerical importance than to the clumsy political errors of their opponents.[5] The unrestrained propaganda of the United Arab Republic, the ill-organized efforts of Colonel Abd us-Salam Arif, finally, and above all, Colonel

[1] Albert Hourani, The Middle East and the Crisis of 1956', in St. Antony's Papers No. 4: *Middle Eastern Affairs,* no. 1 (1958), 37.

[2] Delestre, op. cit., p. 20.

[3] See Arnold Rivkin, 'Israel and the Afro-Asian World', *Foreign Affairs,* April 1959.

[4] *New York Times,* 23 July 1959, from Cairo.

[5] cf. the admission of a pan-Arab propagandist that 'the inexperience, hastiness, and operational clumsiness of the Arab nationalists in Iraq was as evident as the shrewdness shown by Iraqi Communist leadership' (Fayiz Sayigh, interviewed by *Middle East Forum,* 35, no. 6 [Beirut, June 1959], 33).

Shawwaf's wretched business at Mosul certainly did much more to assure their popularity than the fiery editorials in their newspapers.[1]

On the eve of the May Day celebrations, they demanded an appropriate representation in the Government, but were rebuffed by Qasim, who declared that a return to party politics was premature. He found support in the British Government's agreement to meet Iraq's armament needs—an undertaking that encountered some criticism in those United States circles which had swallowed 'Abd un-Nasir's anti-Communist bait whole; and he was supported domestically by the readiness with which the National Democrat leaders agreed to discontinue their party activities. During June, Qasim continued to move away from the Communists. The military governor-general of Iraq, Brigadier Ahmad Salih al-Abdi, became increasingly prominent; he announced that the Communist-dominated Popular Resistance Forces (*al-Muqāwama ash-Sha'bīya*), which had been terrorizing the cities, were no longer required for emergency duties and should hand in their arms. The celebration of the anniversary of the revolution in July was marred by a violent clash at Kirkuk between pro-Communist Kurds, aided by an undisciplined Kurdish army unit, and more conservative Turkomans; it was officially admitted that seventy-nine persons were killed and forty-one others buried alive! From this time, Communist influence in Iraq seemed to falter. The party split into two factions, the weaker of which received Qasim's official sanction early in 1960. The pan-Arabs were persecuted anew for their failure to murder Qasim in October 1959.

*   *   *

What is happening in the Arab world today is a genuine social revolution, in that the products of the recently expanded universities and high schools are seeking to break down the wall of privilege which has hitherto preserved high positions in public life, and their material rewards, for a landed and commercial oligarchy. It is true that the achievement of national independence had already done something to widen the circle of privilege: but not nearly enough to satisfy the thousands leaving their *alma mater*

[1] Marcel Colombe, 'Où va l'Irak?', *Orient*, no. 10 (1959), 12-13.

with a diploma, to find only underpaid and subordinate employment. 'Every time I tried to win advancement, the job went to someone's friend or relative', said a young Iraqi graduate.[1]

The programme which these young men and women now profess is compounded of the social justice which they deduce from the teaching of Islam and the welfare legislation which they have seen or read about in the West. In addition, they passionately profess the ideal of Arab unity, as being both economically advantageous and logically essential. They have been taught that the boundaries which the British and French imposed on the Arab world after the First World War were wholly artificial, and they assume without question that, apart from this Western intervention, a unified Arab state formed at that time would have had no difficulty in holding together; they thus ignore the natural barrier, still formidable until broken down by the aircraft and the desert-worthy motor vehicle, of the Syrian desert, and also the factiousness of the Arab character which sets Aleppo against Damascus, Mosul against Baghdad, Tripoli against Beirut. For the states not blessed with abundant oil revenues the ideal of Arab unity offers a convenient way of redistributing more equitably to themselves the oil wealth of Sa'udi Arabia, Kuwait, and Iraq. And it would seem that the transcendent Unity, which Islam predicates so categorically of its God, has been transferred in this politically obsessed age to his Chosen People, the Arabs. Their unity on earth is essential as confirmation of His unity in the eternal realm. The universality of Islam is degraded to the level of Arab nationalism.[2]

These aspirations of the young 'intellectuals' could be regarded with greater sympathy, were it not that in their impatience to achieve their loosely-defined ends they seem largely indifferent to the means employed. This is no doubt true of all revolutions; but we have to take into account also the Arab character with its intense preoccupation with what is immediate and its relative unconcern for continuity, its spurts of passionate energy and its reluctance to undertake the long steady up-hill haul. The young 'intellectuals' have learnt in school how the Arabs of the seventh

---

[1] Reported by Foster Hailey: *New York Times Magazine*, 10 August 1958, p. 12.

[2] Though an empiricist like 'Abd un-Nasir manages to get the best of both worlds; see above, p. 291.

century A.D. sprang from tribalism to imperial dominion in one generation, and have been given an idealized picture of what that empire was like, until its expansion enabled foreign intellectual trends to infiltrate and dilute the Arab spirit.[1] Again, we must remember that Sin is emphasized far less by Muslim than by Christian theology, and its existence is in any case contemptuously denied by 'intellectuals' in the Arab world no less than in the West. Consequently they are blind to the ubiquity and pervasiveness of the corruption that power brings in its wake. In their eyes, the outgoing oligarchy which the revolution is now displacing was corrupt, by definition; but they cannot conceive that a class or a clique newly coming to power is exposed to temptations far more subtle than the venal (and comparatively venial)[2] corruption of an Establishment; and they blandly assume that the supposed purity of their aims will save them from contamination. Yet power in the hands of inexperienced men with old scores to pay off[3] can give rise to the most terrible abuses and perversions, as the lesson of Nazi Germany shows; and a military oligarchy, wielding the direct means of physical power, is particularly liable to become infected by the *libido* of that power.

We see this already in the incitement to political murder which has become so constant a theme of propaganda broadcasts from Cairo and Damascus in recent years. Political murder is a practice rooted in Arab history since the first caliphs and endemic in their tribal intrigues. Restrained by Ottoman and subsequently British and French authority, it has broken forth again with horrid frequency since the achievement of national independence. The young 'intellectuals' seem to regard it with moral indifference, as a convenient way of removing opponents who cannot immediately be dislodged by constitutional means, and they are heedless of the indiscriminate beastliness of the practice. In fact the fallen politician is literally thrown to the urban rabble[4] as the defeated gladiator was once sacrificed to the bloodlust of the Roman *sentina urbis*.

---

[1] Sa'adun Hammadi of Wisconsin University, as reported by Nissim Rejwan, 'Arab Nationalism in Search of an Ideology', in Walter Z. Laqueur, ed.: *The Middle East in Transition* (1958), p. 148.

[2] 'A man is rarely so innocently employed as when he is making money.'

[3] The conspiracy trial of members of the fallen regime, which opened in Baghdad in mid-August, already gave grounds for concern.

[4] Baghdad, July 1958.

It is natural that the Arab 'intellectual' revolution should accept the army as its spearhead, since the junior army officers are identified with the revolt against privilege and have the same social background as the civilian 'intellectuals'. It is doubtful, however, whether the latter are aware of the dangers that military dictatorship may involve them in; and they probably regard this dictatorship, all too facilely, as a mere transition to the Paradise Garden of 'Arab social democracy'.

*   *   *

It is ironical, but part of the same historical process, that just when western Christendom has become ready to admit that its expansion over other continents in recent centuries was a concomitant of that secular European expansion now dubbed 'imperialism' (and has drawn the corollary that such offshoots as the Church of South India must be left free to work out their own salvation), there should now be a revival of militancy on the part of Arab Islam. But this is not surprising, for we have seen that the early centuries of Islam were an imperial success-story, and it therefore became natural for Muslims to regard the Muslim imperial system as the outward and visible sign of God's favour shown to his Chosen People.[1] Even when political leadership passed from the Arabs to Persians and then to Turks, the fact that the new rulers were Muslims maintained unshaken the assurance that the Dar ul-Islam remained strong because Islam was the true faith. But in the nineteenth century this secular prop was rudely knocked away:

The Muslim has been troubled not by questions of truth so much as by questions of power. . . . In Muslim conviction power comes from God, and yet here were the British empire, the Dutch empire, the French empire growing daily more powerful than Islamic society. . . . Islamic backwardness implies that something has gone wrong not only with the Muslim's own development but with the governance of the universe. . . .

The burning of Cairo, the assassination of Prime Ministers, the intimidating of Christians, the vehemence and hatred in their literature —all this is to be understood in terms of a people who have lost their way, whose heritage has proven unequal to modernity, whose leaders

[1] For the Chosen People concept in Islam, see Hazem Zaki Nuseibeh: *The Ideas of Arab Nationalism* (Cornell, 1956), p. 24.

have been dishonest, whose ideals have failed. In this aspect, the new
Islamic upsurge is a force not to solve problems but to intoxicate
those who cannot longer abide the failure to solve them.[1]

'Abd un-Nasir himself was frank enough in 1954 to admit the
extent of the moral anarchy which he and his colleagues discovered in Egypt after their *coup d'état* two years earlier:

Every man we questioned had nothing to recommend except to kill
someone else. Every idea we listened to was nothing but an attack on
some other idea. If we had gone along with everything we heard,
we would have killed off all the people and torn down every idea. . . .

We were deluged with petitions and complaints by the thousands
. . ., and had these complaints and petitions dealt with cases demanding
justice or grievances calling for redress, this motive would have been
understandable and logical. But most of the cases referred to were no
more or less than demands for revenge, as though the revolution had
taken place in order to become a weapon in the hand of hatred and
vindictiveness.[2]

For over two years, as we have seen, the Revolutionary Council
made a sincere attempt to find solutions that were on the whole
moderate for Egypt's internal and external problems; but when,
as a result, they were confronted in autumn 1954 with a militant
Opposition coalition that probably had adherents inside the army
itself, 'Abd un-Nasir and his colleagues took the easier course of
going with the nationalist tide, capturing the extremist slogans:
and though the tide has carried him to his present peak of popularity, where does he go from here?

The essential thing which Western liberals have ignored about
the recent developments of Arab nationalism is that, while it
expresses its aspirations in terms of abstract Right,[3] it bases its
assessment of a situation in terms of concrete Power. It is doubtful, indeed, whether in the traditional Muslim view there is any
contradiction here: for the belief in Islam as the true faith—
'God's final word to the servants of God', in the words of 'Abd
un-Nasir—carries with it the belief that acceptance of the true
faith has been rewarded by God in history, with the abstract
reward of a superior Right and the concrete reward of Power—

[1] Wilfred Cantwell Smith: *Islam in Modern History* (Princeton, 1957), pp.
111–12, 158–9. The second paragraph refers especially to Egypt since 1945,
but is equally applicable to Syria.
[2] *Egypt's Liberation, the Philosophy of the Revolution*, pp. 34–5.
[3] cf. Sa'adun Hammadi, as reported below, p. 308.

the historic Arab and Muslim Empire. The growing subservience of the Muslim world to Western imperialism in the nineteenth and early twentieth centuries was thus a 'cosmic impiety', as was the Babylonian Exile for conventional Jews of the sixth century B.C.—but so far resurgent Islam has not found the spiritual reassurance which the Second Isaiah provided for Judaism.

Instead there have been the political false prophets with their cult of Power; and while Britain and France have been in retreat and the United States writhes Laocoon-like in the coils of her own democratic and egalitarian platitudes—the ideological ecto-plasm of the revolutionary past which she has left behind but cannot slough off—the crude dynamism of the U.S.S.R. has struck the imagination of the Arab nationalists as the crude dynamism of Nazi Germany did some twenty years earlier. The West, in its horror at the bloody Soviet repression of the Hungarian rising of 1956, has expected Arabs to be similarly shocked; but, quite apart from the fact that in Arab minds the repression of Hungary was overlaid by the Suez expedition,[1] this is just how Middle Eastern regimes have always dealt with dissidents. This is how Ibrahim Pasha tried to crush the Greek insurrection in the 1820's; this is how Atatürk and Riza Shah repressed their rebellious Kurdish tribes between the two World Wars; this is how Bakr Sidqi repressed the Assyrians in Iraq in 1933; this is how Abdul Karim Qasim repressed the Mosul conspiracy in March 1959. And this, for all the hypocrisy of those who condemn the South African Government today, is how the 'paleface' consummated the 250 years of genocide of the American Indian. Nothing has changed, except the for-mulae which nationalism sometimes assumes in order to attract the sympathy of 'liberals' who have conveniently forgotten their own bloody past.[2] Perhaps Arab nationalism did believe for a time in the formulae of liberalism and constitutionalism as a passport to national independence; but disillusion came with the imposed settlement after the First World War; and the

---

[1] The Egyptian censorship suppressed all mention of it until 1959.

[2] 'America in the nineteenth century did expand, but into empty land. It is one thing to conquer a subject people; another to occupy vacant real estate' (Adolf A. Berle, Jr., *New York Times Book Review*, 15 February 1959, p. 3; challenged by Edgar I. Stewart, ibid., 29 March 1959, p. 25).

memory of Adolf Hitler is still respected for having shown Arab nationalists the way to deal with Israel.

In 1959 the opposition which 'Abd un-Nasir had encountered —both from Qasim of Iraq and Bourguiba of Tunisia—to his plans for a Cairo-dominated Arab unity, extending from the Atlantic to the Persian Gulf, forced upon him an opportunistic change of tactics or, at least, of slogans. Characteristically African in his aping of more advanced political methods and phrases, he made a Stalin-like switch from Arab-world revolution to 'socialism in the U.A.R.', with his rallying cry the doubling of the national income in ten years. Posturing now as a convinced anti-Communist, he was able to cozen the United States—intent as ever on 'keeping up with the Kremlin' in soliciting the votes of the neutral (i.e., impartially mendicant) new states crowding into the U.N.—into extending him some $200 million for various purposes, including the deepening of the Suez Canal, where Israeli cargoes were still being seized in defiance of the Security Council, Hammarskjold's 'quiet diplomacy', and President Eisenhower's pious assurances of 1957. 'Abd un-Nasir half-heartedly renewed diplomatic relations with a Britain which might once again buy his cotton and thus relieve him of excessive dependence on tricky iron-curtain buyers; but Cairo Radio continued to broadcast virulently anti-British propaganda to Kenya. He bargained with the anti-Soviet government of Western Germany to finance the flooding of the Qattara depression (near the spot where Rommel had been stopped and beaten in 1942) in order to produce hydro-electricity; but he still relied on the Soviet Union to finance and build the second, major stage of his High Dam. He reached an apparently satisfactory agreement with the Sudan over important questions concerning the Nile waters; but restiveness in his 'northern province' (formerly independent Syria) called for increased Egyptian military control and the eclipse of the Ba'th Party, whose leaders might paraphrase the 110th Psalm:

> The Lord said unto my Lord,
> Sit thou at my right hand, until I make thee my footstool.[1]

---

[1] See Marcel Colombe, 'La mission à Damas du maréchal égyptien Abd al-Hakim Amer', *Orient*, no. 12 (1960).

His rancour for the Arab challengers beyond his reach—Qasim, Bourguiba, and King Husain—continued unabated, and was reciprocated by them. Nor, in his public utterances at least, did his objectivity, his respect for historical truth appear to have matured in the school of experience. Visiting Delhi in March 1960, he was reported to have told the Indian Parliament that 'armed aggression and total war' had been brought upon Egypt in the High Dam-Suez-Sinai crisis by her refusal to join military pacts in the Middle East; and at the very moment that the U.S. Government was concluding new agreements to extend technical and economic assistance to his United Arab Republic, 'Abd un-Nasir in Delhi was speaking of the necessity of facing 'the monopoly of science, imperialism's new style'.[1]

Meanwhile, a passing war scare on the Syrian-Israeli armistice line at the beginning of 1960 (recalling the Syrian war scare of 1957,[2] but more serious) allowed the Soviet Government to pose as the all-highest arbiter between the contending parties. And the United States, once again holidaying from hard international realities during the protracted Saturnalia of a presidential election campaign, looked on as impotently as the U.N. Secretary-General. To bring Churchill's phrase up to date, the locusts on the Eisenhower golf courses had devoured more of the free world's initiative than those of the Baldwin-Chamberlain years; and Moscow, which under Ivan the Terrible had vaunted itself as the third Rome, was under Khrushchev well on the way (through the West's increasing loss of faith, extending now to loss of faith in itself) to becoming the third London, in succession to metropolitan North America—and the nineteen-sixties' 'hub of the universe'.

'There was darkness over all the land until the ninth hour.'

In Passiontide, 1960.

---

[1] *The Times*, 1 April 1960.
[2] See my article, 'The Syrian Crisis of 1957—Fact and Fiction', *International Affairs*, 36 (1960).

The Significance of the Crusades in East and West

TEN YEARS AGO, relying on J. La Monte's thoughtful essay 'Crusade and Jihad', I wrote in Chapter II that the psychological impact of the Crusades on the Muslim world was much less than might be supposed (p. 46). More recently Gamal 'Abd un-Nasir has stated in his *Egypt's Liberation, the Philosophy of the Revolution* (p. 62) that 'if the Crusades were the beginning of the Renaissance in Europe, they were the beginning of the dark ages in our country'. This is a bold, soldierly statement of the sort which arouses misgivings in the professional historian, however imprecise the definition to be attached to such terms as 'Renaissance' and 'dark ages'. Western medievalists have learnt during the present century to pay due tribute to the contribution which the Muslim civilization made to the 'renaissance' of the twelfth and thirteenth centuries in Western Europe; but that contribution came essentially from Muslim Spain and Sicily, it was not brought back from the Levant by the Crusades; and though the Crusades may have contributed a few stray elements to the later Italian Renaissance (the Renaissance *par excellence* of nineteenth-century historians), that was essentially a Hellenic, not an Arabic, flowering. Furthermore, the historian would take leave of the Egyptian President to question if the Crusades were the beginning of the dark ages in *his* country, whether by that term he means Egypt or the wider Arab world. The Crusaders' invasion of the Levant was made possible precisely *because* the Muslim empire had begun to fall apart a good half-century earlier, as my quotation from Philip Hitti (above, p. 41) bears witness; and in the case of Egypt the final triumph of Sultans Baybars and Qala'un over the Crusaders was accompanied by a final *floruit* before the Egyptian 'dark age' set in with the later Mamluks *c.* A.D. 1340 (see above, pp. 51–3).

At a much deeper level of historical perception, however, Albert Hourani has remarked[1] that

[1] 'The Decline of the West in the Middle East', *International Affairs*, 29 (1953), p. 32.

the Crusades . . . left behind them memories which are still not dead.
. . . Bishop Pococke, travelling in Egypt in the eighteenth century,
found the peasants around Damietta still denouncing St. Louis and his
followers; and in our own time the memory of the Crusades has been
revived in the Arab popular mind by what has happened in Palestine.

'Abd un-Nasir again, in his speech of 5 February 1958 proclaiming
the establishment of the United Arab Republic, was clearly
referring to the Crusades when he spoke of 'an imperialism
coming from Europe, and bearing the Cross in order to disguise
its ambitions behind the façade of Christianity'.[1] The Muslim
Arab schoolboy is told in his history classes that the Crusades were
a first example of European 'unprovoked aggression':

> History has shown . . . that there are two kinds of nationalism. One
> is sheer intolerance, a narrow emotionalism, the desire for domination,
> superiority, and exploitation; in this category we find all European
> nationalisms ever since the European nations were formed and until
> this day. The other is 'humanist nationalism', which respects the con-
> cepts of right and of justice, which believes in man and in the good,
> and is charged with a mission to other nations. . . .
> And so it is with the Arab nation, formed by clearly humanist
> ideals. . . .[2]

Leaving aside the initial Arab or Muslim advance across North
Africa and conquest of Spain, what followed that had significance
for the political relations of Muslim and Christian in Western
Europe itself? Philip Hitti's monumental *History of the Arabs* is
uncharacteristically reticent, except for one passing reference;[3] but
we find greater explicitness in the outstanding historian of the
Crusades which our generation has seen:

> The western Christian . . . was uneasily aware that in most respects
> Moslem civilization was higher than his own. Moslem power domin-
> ated the western Mediterranean from Catalonia to Tunis. Moslem
> pirates preyed upon his shipping. Rome had been sacked by the
> Moslems [in A.D. 864]. They had built robber castles in Italy and in
> Provence. From their strongholds in Spain it seemed that they might
> again emerge to cross the frontiers and pour over the Pyrenees into

---

[1] Quoted above, p. 291.
[2] Abdul Latif Sharara, in *al-Adab* (Beirut), October 1955, reported by Nissim
Rejwan, 'Arab Nationalism in Search of an Ideology', in Walter Z. Laqueur ed.:
The Middle East in Transition (1958), pp. 160–1.   [3] 5th ed., pp. 604–5.

France. Western Christendom had no organizations that could have met such an attack.[1]

It was from this historical background that the Normans led the Franks to the counter-attack in the course of the eleventh century A.D.

Exit therefore the myth of 'unprovoked aggression' committed by the Crusaders. It belongs to the same class of contemporary Arab myth-making as the Egyptian assertion to Israel since 1955: 'We are still at war with you, but don't you dare to lay a hand on us or we shall run yowling to the U.N.', or the bland Tunisian assumption that they could give all assistance short of war to the Algerian rebels without risking the French reprisal against Saqiyat Sidi Yusuf in February 1958. The conduct of the Crusaders reflects no great credit on Western civilization, and we must freely admit that the Frankish barons and knights were most of them hairy barbarians with little sanctification either from the Church or from the older civilization of the Mediterranean; but the historical episode falls into place in that cycle of the struggle for power in the Mediterranean which (as old Herodotus saw) went back as far as the Trojan War at least, and of which the Arab 'aggression' of the seventh century A.D. was the preceding episode. It is useless for either Muslims or Christians today to seek a position of moral impregnability in the annals of the past. Men of good will on both sides need to acknowledge the historical facts, and try to do better in the future, and to live more tolerantly in the present.

Earlier in the same essay which I have quoted above, Albert Hourani wrote with his usual felicity:

For the Muslim, Christianity is not wholly other than his own religion. Islam rejects Christianity's own interpretation of itself, but claims to be itself the true and perfected Christianity; it denies the Divinity of Christ but regards the message of Jesus—the 'Word of God' and the 'Spirit of God' as the Koran calls Him—as identical with that of Muhammad. The consciousness of Christianity was an essential element in the mind of Muhammad and therefore of all Islam. But to the Christian Islam has normally seemed something wholly alien, a distortion of the Christian truth if not a denial of it, a decline and not

[1] Sir Steven Runciman: *History of the Crusades*, i. 88; for details see Henri Pirenne: *Mahomet et Charlemagne*, pp. 135-43.

a fulfilment, either an enemy of the faith or at best an imperfect and hazardous evangelical preparation.[1]

Here, for serious Muslims and serious Christians (excluding the secularized epigoni of both faiths), is a much more formidable stumbling-block than any debate about the justification of past military adventures. And it is not merely the question whether Muslims or Christians are better at living up the ethical standards of their respective faiths—'Judge not lest ye be judged' covers that issue. What matters is that trinitarian Christianity (and nothing short of that is properly Christian) is to the Muslim a form of polytheism; and to the Christian (whether Catholic, Orthodox or conservative Protestant makes no difference) the theology of Islam is woefully inadequate. So preoccupied has Islam been with the transcendence of God that it has only superficially examined the nature of man. 'He is, as the Qur'an says, born with a balanced soul, without any inherent weaknesses therein.'[2]

There is in man an inborn, original tendency towards Right, which manifests itself in the civilizing work done by nations in the service of humanity. This tension towards Right has been eminently manifest in the civilizations that the Arab nation has given to the world,[3] and the mission of Arabs today is the creation of a new Arab civilization whose highest principle shall be Right. The practice of this principle is respect for man; and the new Arab civilization, if it is true to its aim, will reverence man as the most precious being in the universe, for whose sake all else is sacrificed and to whose service all nature is enslaved. . . .

The Right, a craving for which is the driving force of the movement [Arab nationalism], is but a part of the abstract and absolute Right which moves the whole universe. In the march of history the dominant tendency is towards Right; the divided nations struggle to become united, subject nations to free themselves, societies to enlarge and consolidate civil liberties, and economic systems also develop in the direction of justice.[4]

In this attempt at an Arab nationalist ideology, the bastard

[1] Loc. cit., p. 31.

[2] Dr. Saiyid Abdul Latif, quoted by Dwight M. Donaldson: *Studies in Muslim Ethics* (1953), p. 255; and see the quotation from Dr. Nabih Faris, above, p. 270.

[3] For the tendency to claim the whole of the ancient civilization of the Middle East for 'the illustrious Arab nation', see Sylvia G. Haim, 'Islam and the Theory of Arab Nationalism', in Walter Z. Laqueur, ed.: *The Middle East in Transition*, p. 281.

[4] Sa'adun Hammadi of Wisconsin University, as reported by Nissim Rejwan, 'Arab Nationalism in Search of an Ideology'; Laqueur, op. cit., pp. 151–3.

offspring of the misalliance of Muslim transcendence with Western 'liberal humanism', all apprehension of the pervasiveness of sin, of the need for an Atonement, for a personal Redeemer, is lost: instead, the Word was made *Book* and dwelt among us. It is not surprising that the over-simplified low-temperature cult of Sunni Islam should have attracted the occasional Western escapist (such as H. St. J. B. Philby) from the Christian confrontation of the duality of his own nature; but to anyone who has apprehended, however imperfectly, the truth of the Catholic Faith, Islam can only be 'a decline and not a fulfilment'—in charity be this said, since there is no doubt that a devout Muslim stands nearer to God than a Christian serving God and Mammon, such as a student of international affairs is too often tempted to be.

There are two reasons why the drive-for-power of this neo-Muslim Arab nationalism has only very recently been identified in the West. First, that it has been partly inspired by Western 'liberal humanism', as the above quotations show, so that its militant character has only just begun to emerge. The second reason is the uncritical attitude towards Islam of many Protestant educators and missionaries from the West. As a penetrating commentator has recently observed, during the past half-century these good people, by a species of subconscious deception, have presented (particularly in the United States) 'a picture of Islam as a strictly unitarian, democratic, and egalitarian form of Protestantism'.[1] They have done so partly because their own Protestantism has become so diluted with 'liberal humanism' as now to constitute no more than a bland, uncritical benevolence and wishful thinking; and also because they have failed to win converts from Islam or, indeed, to make any serious inroads upon the main bodies of Orthodox and Catholic Christians in the Middle East.[2] Yet the educators and missionaries have to justify themselves at home, if contributions are to continue to flow into their benevolent enterprises. So they have fallen back in subconscious self-defence upon this pan-Unitarian fiction, this lowest-common-denominator of 'inspirational' wishful thinking; and the American

[1] Elie Kedourie: 'Western Illusions about the Middle East', *Commentary* (1958), p. 16.
[2] 'Having seen only the Oriental type of Christianity, they [Muslims] despise its immorality and idolatry and protest against the creature worship and image worship of both the Greek and Latin Churches. . . . The nominal Christians of Syria are proud, ignorant and self-sufficient' (Henry Harris Jessup, D.D.: *Fifty-Three Years in Syria* (1910), pp. 85, 133).

University of Beirut, that supreme achievement of Protestant benevolence in the Arab world, has been allowed to become a hotbed, not of Communism (as superficial critics have alleged), but of the militant Arab nationalism now degenerating into neo-Muslim imperialism[1] and encouraged by the U.S.S.R. for its own pan-subversive ends.

[1] The arrest in Amman in August 1958 of two young graduates of the University (both nominally Christian, and one a girl), on charges of planting explosives in a public building with intent to overturn the Jordanian Government, is evidence of what was known to every Westerner connected with the University and not blinded by wishful thinking. I had seen the Muslim in charge of the athletics department progress from giving instruction in archery to instruction in small arms. Among his students in 1956–7 were Cypriot supporters of EOKA.

The 'Broken Promises' of the First World War

THE WRY JOKE that during the First World War Palestine became the 'twice-promised Land' is, or was, familiar to people concerned with the modern Middle East; and at a deeper level the tangle of obligations created between 1915 and 1917 by the Husain-McMahon Correspondence, the Sykes-Picot Agreement, and the Balfour Declaration is a common-place for students of the region.[1] Nevertheless, it came as a shock to me, shortly after arriving in New England in autumn 1957, to find how responsible American writers and public speakers would speak unqualifiedly of the British 'broken promises' and 'betrayals' of the Arabs.[2] Attempts to elucidate revealed that American editors were not interested in a closer examination, regarding the matter either as a *chose jugée*, or as too controversial for some of their readers, or as a mere juggling with semantics—'When is a promise not a promise?' That is the justification for raising the question here.

The historical work from which most English-speaking students get their first introduction to the issue is still George Antonius's *The Arab Awakening*. It is worth reminding ourselves, therefore, that that moderate presentation of the Arab case did not itself assert that the British Government had made a 'promise' to the Arabs in the Husain-McMahon Correspondence of 1915–1916. And with good reason, for Antonius knew that the Correspondence had ended inconclusively, and the Arab Revolt had begun in June 1916, without a signed agreement with the British precisely because the Sharif Husain of Mecca had evaded[3]

---

[1] See briefly above, pp. 124–30.

[2] E.g., *New York Times Book Review*, 8 December 1957, pp. 42 and 43; letter from the President of the American Friends of the Middle East, *New York Times*, 13 February 1958, p. 28.

[3] 'We shall deem it our duty, at the earliest opportunity after the conclusion of the war, to claim from you Beirut and its coastal regions which we will overlook for the moment on account of France. . . . Any concession designed to give

the British Government's *caveat* that they could not disregard their ally France's long-standing interest in the coastal region of Lebanon and Syria. Antonius, in fact, was generally content to use such less emphatic words as 'pledge', 'compact', and 'bargain' when referring to the British negotiations with Husain; and it was only when he described Husain, shortly before his death in exile, as speaking of 'the promises made to him' that that more categorical word was employed.[1]

Similarly, the former Netherlands Consul and explorer in Arabia, D. van der Meulen, in his recent distinguished book *The Wells of Ibn Sa'ud* (1957), describes the exiled Husain as speaking of 'the faithless British whose unfulfilled promises he considered to be the cause of all his ills'; and he uses the word 'promise' pretty freely in more general contexts, but usually when reflecting the views of his own former teacher, the distinguished Dutch Arabist Snouck Hurgronje, who as a convert to Islam could hardly be regarded as an objective commentator on this tangle back in the nineteen-twenties.[2]

'Ah yes,' say my students, wary for imperialist juggling with words, 'we will concede for the sake of argument that the Husain-McMahon Correspondence stopped short of an agreement. But what about the secrecy of the Sykes-Picot Agreement which constituted a "betrayal" of the Arabs, and what about all the assurances that Colonel Lawrence no doubt gave verbally to the Arabs after the Revolt had begun? Surely these amounted to a "promise" in Arab eyes, even though Lawrence was giving them without authorization from his Government.' But here we encounter the remarkable fact that when the Amir Faisal came to London and Paris in 1919, to negotiate with the British and French on behalf of his father Husain, the ample official British documentation[3] of his discussions with the British does not show that he ever founded his argument upon any assurances received from Lawrence. Instead, when meeting Lloyd George, Curzon and others at No. 10 Downing Street on 19 September 1919, he asserted that in 1915 the British Government had made a 'treaty',

France or any other Power possession of a single square foot of territory in those parts is quite out of the question' (1 January 1916). Text in Antonius, op. cit., pp. 413–27, and (official publication) Cmd. 5957 (1939).

[1] Op. cit., ch. xiii, and contrast p. 183.
[2] Van der Meulen: *The Wells of Ibn Sa'ud*, pp. 73–4, 81, 87, and 95.
[3] E. L. Woodward and R. Butler: *Documents on British Foreign Policy, 1919–1939*, series I, vol. 4.

a 'definite agreement' with Husain;[1] and he handed to the Foreign Office a document which he had received from his father, purporting to be the text of this treaty.[2] When he met the British statesmen again on 23 September, however, Curzon remarked that the Foreign Office had shown this document to McMahon, who had commented: 'I have read the alleged treaty with amazement; it bears no resemblance to any original document.' It was, in fact, almost identical with an enclosure in a letter which McMahon had received from Husain in August 1918, *which was Husain's own version* of various exchanges between himself and the British; the document 'represented what the Arabs had been pressing, and not what H.M. Government had accepted'. 'There had never', Curzon continued, 'been any signed agreement between H.M. Government and King Husain';[3] and Faisal's repeated subsequent attempts to obtain an elucidation from his father by telegraph produced nothing better than confused answers coupled with a threat to abdicate 'and the country will be left in anarchy'.[4]

The historical pattern of Husain's behaviour has now been systematically set out by Professor C. Ernest Dawn, of the University of Illinois, in an article entitled 'The Amir of Mecca al-Husayn ibn-'Ali and the Origin of the Arab Revolt',[5] to which the reader should refer for fuller documentation. Professor Dawn sums up the Husain-McMahon Correspondence with the remark that its outcome—Husain's offer to 'overlook' the French territorial claims until 'after the conclusion of the war'—was not entirely satisfactory in achieving acceptance of Arab territorial demands.

Even in January, 1916, apparently, Husayn had not decided definitely upon a course of action. . . . Husayn was not entirely satisfied with the British reply, and the situation in Syria was not favorable to an Arab rising. It was decided, therefore, to have Faysal return to Syria in order to allay Turkish suspicions. . . .

While Husayn was arriving at a definite understanding with the British government [for the supply of money and war materials to make an Arab revolt possible], he was also carrying out negotiations with Turkish authorities. The Ottoman government undertook to send money

---

[1] Ibid., No. 283, pp. 399, 404.
[2] Ibid., No. 293, appendix, pp. 418–19.
[3] Ibid., No. 293, pp. 414–15.
[4] Ibid., Nos. 289, 290, 291, 297, 301, 303, 304, 317, 332.
[5] *Proceedings of the American Philosophical Society*, 104 (1960).

and arms . . . and by the beginning of April [1916] the Turks had sent some fifty or sixty thousand Turkish pounds in gold to Husayn. Faysal, in the meantime . . . had been suggesting that . . . the [Ottoman] government should recall the Vali [governor] of the Hijaz and assign his powers and duties to Husayn. . . .

Husayn rose against his government only when that government refused, in the spring of 1916, to guarantee his Amirate in the Hijaz.[1]

It was at this very time that the British and French Governments, in view of the exchanges in the Husain-McMahon Correspondence,[2] were seeking to harmonize their respective long-standing ambitions in the Levant, in the negotiations that resulted in the 'notorious' Sykes-Picot Agreement. When these negotiations were approaching agreement, the British Foreign Secretary, in correspondence with the French Ambassador to London in May 1916, made the proviso 'that the co-operation of the Arabs is secured and that the Arabs . . . obtain the towns of Homs, Hama, Damascus, and Aleppo';[3] he was thus seeking to keep the Sykes-Picot Agreement as consistent as possible with what his government had pledged in the Husain-McMahon Correspondence. While Britain had her inescapable commitments to her French ally, and Husain and Faisal were still negotiating with the Ottoman Government, it is hard to see how the British part in the Sykes-Picot Agreement (embarrassing as its consequences were to be in the post-war settlement) can be accurately described as 'perfidy'; yet this is the uncompromising word used in a new textbook designed for 'the beginning college student or general reader'.[4]

Though the Sykes-Picot Agreement was naturally a 'secret treaty' in that it was not published for the edification of the German and Ottoman enemy, Professor Dawn seems to accept the evidence adduced by Kedourie that the British and French informed Husain 'of at least the general terms of the Sykes-

---

[1] Ibid., pp. 24-25, 28.

[2] Antonius' assertion (op. cit., p. 244) that 'the Foreign Office chose to withhold from the French the terms, and perhaps even the fact, of the compact [sic] made with the Sharif' has been refuted in the French sources by Elie Kedourie: *England and the Middle East, 1914-1921,* p. 35.

[3] Woodward and Butler, op. cit., no. 6, p. 245.

[4] Sydney Nettleton Fisher: *The Middle East, a History* (New York, 1959), 370, and cf. the Preface, p. v.

Picot Agreement'[1] before its publication by the Bolsheviks. It was probably because of this that Husain felt free, as late as the early summer of 1918, to propose negotiations with the Ottoman authorities, to which the German Ambassador in Constantinople was to be a party.[2] That this tortuousness of the principal Arab negotiator should have its counterpart in the tortuousness of those Anglo-French statements in the latter part of the war that were painstakingly rehearsed by Antonius may offend political moralists; but it should enable the historian to dispense with making one-sided moral judgements in this complicated issue. The collection of *Documents on British Foreign Policy* shows us the British statesmen exerting themselves during 1919 to find some compromise between the provisional Arab government in Damascus and the impatient French.[3] On the one occasion in which they show us Faisal and French and British officials together, it is Faisal who was difficult and the French who were accommodating;[4] and though the French were determined to exact the last ounce of the Sykes-Picot Agreement, their final expulsion of Faisal and his government from Syria was largely provoked by the reckless intransigence of the Arab nationalists who rejected Faisal's counsels of moderation.[5]

Palestine—destined to become the permanent trauma in the Arabs' political psyche—had not been explicitly mentioned by either party in the Husain-McMahon Correspondence, and even the question of an implicit reference to it therein has given rise to diametrically opposed interpretations on the Arab and British sides. While McMahon, or his principals in London, may well be blamed for not having been more explicit in this connexion, it is hard to believe that the British, who were making an exception of the Lebanese-Syrian littoral as not being 'purely Arab', did not intend *a fortiori* to make an exception for the international

---

[1] Dawn, op. cit., p. 31; cf. Kedourie, op. cit., 37-40, 97-98. Kedourie has been at some pains to disguise the fact that the Sykes-Picot delineation of British and French zones of influence over the Syrian hinterland was an innovation in no way foreshadowed in the Husain-McMahon Correspondence.

[2] See Dawn, op. cit., p. 30.

[3] Albert Hourani, with his sober detachment, has commented on the common British 'refusal to believe that the compromise which Great Britain is always willing to suggest should seem to both sides like a betrayal' ('British Policy in the Fertile Crescent, Past and Future', *United Empire*, XLI (1950), 213).

[4] 'But for their tact and good sense tonight's meeting might have been a failure', reported the British official: Woodward and Butler, op. cit., No. 315 (11 October 1919).

[5] See Antonius, op. cit., pp. 303-9.

interests in the Christian Holy Places, as well as for that growing Jewish community which, already before 1914, amounted to nearly 10 per cent. of the country's population. It has even been stated, on the authority of Sir Gilbert Clayton, who was generally considered unsympathetic to Zionism, that 'the excision of Palestine from the area of promised independence [to the Arabs] had been asserted orally to King Husain, who fully understood that this was a part of British policy'.[1] It is arguable that the undertaking to favour the establishment of a Jewish national home in Palestine wilfully ignored or belittled the certain Arab reaction and therefore irreparably damaged Britain's wider interests in the region; but it does not follow that it involved a breach of 'promise' to the Arabs.

It is time, therefore, that this phrase also were relegated to the realm of historical mythology where it properly belongs, together with the more recent assertion that the United States offer to help finance the High Dam, although it had lain on the table for seven months awaiting 'Abd un-Nasir's pleasure, had become a 'promise' which was 'broken' when Mr. Dulles withdrew the offer in July 1956[2]—or with the Iranian Government's assertion in 1950 that the U.S. Government had 'promised' to satisfy their request for $250,000,000.[3] Clearly, there is a semantic double-standard between Middle Eastern nationalists and Western governments. When Western obligations to themselves are concerned, the nationalists insist not merely that *pacta sunt servanda*, but that *offerta sunt servanda*; but when their own obligations to the West, however formally ratified, are in question, then we may expect the opposite, never generally acknowledged principle of *rebus sic stantibus* to be trotted out. Does this double standard arise, as our liberal critics suggest, from the sense of Middle Eastern physical inferiority and its accompanying frustrations?

[1] Christopher Sykes (son of Sir Mark Sykes): *Two Studies in Virtue* (1953), appendix B, p. 247.

[2] It is characteristic that two young American liberals, having spoken correctly of the 'Western offer' to finance the Dam, should comment: 'an American promise about arms or a dam was not necessarily a promise when it was made to an Arab' (Richard H. Nolte and William R. Polk: 'Toward a Policy for the Middle East', *Foreign Affairs*, 36 (July 1958), pp. 655–6).

[3] Ambassador Henry Grady, in *Saturday Evening Post*, 5 January 1952, p. 57.

Or does it have a deeper derivation in the time-honoured concept of a double standard as between the Islamic world (*Dar ul-Islam*) and the outer darkness of the unbelievers (*Dar ul-harb*)?[1]

[3] 'Upon this division' the medieval Muslim world 'set up its view of international relations' (Dr. John S. Badeau: 'The Middle East, Conflict in Priorities', *Foreign Affairs*, 36 (1958), 233.

The Proposals for a Palestine Legislature, 1922-3

THIS APPENDIX had its origins in an intention to examine in some detail the information concerning the proposal which the British Government put forward in 1935 to establish a Legislative Council for Palestine. This proposal, as is well known to students of the modern Middle East, was abandoned after debates in both British Houses of Parliament had reflected the refusal of the Zionist organization to take part in any representative institution in Palestine which accorded them less than 50 per cent. representation[1]—this although the numbers of the Jewish community in Palestine at that time amounted to only 27 per cent. of the total population.

This 'great Jewish victory', as the Zionist press in Palestine proclaimed it, played an important part, along with other contemporary factors,[2] in further exacerbating the politically minded Palestine Arabs and so bringing on the Arab general strike and rebellion of 1936-39 and—on the eve of the Second World War—the sharp change in British policy embodied in the White Paper of May 1939. The abandoning of the Legislature proposal was thus a significant link in the chain of circumstances that led to the Arab 'disaster' of 1948 and the present frustrations that have ensued from it.

However, while the Zionists' success at Westminster in stifling the project of 1935 was remarkable, their opposition to the proposal for establishing a Legislative Council on a proportional basis had been made known to responsible British quarters as early as 1930;[3] and the present inquiry was accordingly directed

[1] See Chaim Weizmann: *Trial and Error* (New York, 1949), p. 381.

[2] For which see Great Britain, Colonial Office: *Palestine Royal Commission Report* (1937), Cmd. 5479, p. 92.

[3] Did Weizmann (as he states, op. cit., p. 380) really treat the High Commissioner to such clichés as that 'a legislative council in Palestine would be merely . . . a continuation in power of the family cliques which had held the country in their thrall for centuries and ground down the faces of the poor'? See also Lt.-Col. F. H. Kisch: *Palestine Diary* (London, 1938), p. 350, and Israel Cohen: *The Zionist Movement* (New York, 1946), p. 212.

back to the Palestine Arabs' opposition to the original project of a Legislative Council for Palestine which was made when Winston Churchill was Colonial Secretary in the Lloyd George coalition cabinet, in 1922. At that time a Palestine Arab delegation had been sent to London by the Palestine Muslim-Christian Association (*al-Jam'īya al-Islamīya al-Masīhīya*) to protest against the embodiment of the Balfour Declaration and other clauses favourable to the Zionists in the Mandate which was about to receive the formal approval of the League of Nations. After the clashes between Arabs and Jews in 1920 and 1921 the British Government was in a mood to seek a compromise between the claims of the two communities, and the Colonial Office accordingly produced both the 'Churchill' White Paper of 1922 (which affirmed that the Arab people, culture, and language were not to disappear from Palestine) and a draft Order in Council providing for a Legislative Council whose elected members should be approximately proportional to the size of the communities (eight Muslims, two Christians, two Jews) but should be counterbalanced by the presence of ten official members and by the official chairman's casting vote. The Zionist representative council (*Vaad Leumi*) was with some difficulty persuaded by the chairman of the Zionist executive, a British Jew, to take part in the elections to the new Council;[1] but meanwhile the president of the Arab delegation to London—Musa Kazim Pasha al-Husaini, head of the powerful Husaini clan of Jerusalem, who had declared that the Muslim-Christian Association represented 'the whole of the Muslim and Christian inhabitants of Palestine'— had repeatedly insisted that they would be satisfied with nothing less than the immediate establishment of a representative and constitutional national government (*hukūma watanīya dustūrīya niyābīya*) with full control over the critical issue of immigration.[2] He told the Cairo newspaper *al-Muqattam* that the presence of official members in the Council and the powers of veto and

---

[1] See Kisch, op. cit., p. 32 (diary entry of 14 February 1923).

[2] Great Britain, Colonial Office: *Palestine: Correspondence with the Palestine Arab Delegation, &c.*, Cmd. 1700 (1922), pp. 22, 25, 27: The representation of the Arab and Jewish communities was to be in proportion to their numbers 'as they existed *before the application of the Zionist policy*', according to the general secretary of the executive committee of the Palestine Arab Congress, Jamal al-Husaini (letter of 6 October 1924 to the League of Nations Permanent Mandates Commission: *Minutes of the 5th Session (Extraordinary)*, 1924, p. 173; italics not in the original).

certification reserved to the High Commissioner were unacceptable; and his last word to the Colonial Office before leaving London was that 'it is not to be expected that the Arabs would bow to such a great injustice' as the policy of favouring a Jewish national home 'or that the Zionists would so easily succeed in realizing their dreams'.[1]

The Palestine Arab Congress accordingly commanded a boycott of the elections for the Legislative Council; and though senior officials of the Palestine Government were at pains to urge the Arab electors not to forgo this opportunity to elect their representatives, the fact that the High Commissioner and the Attorney General (Sir Herbert Samuel and Mr. Norman Bentwich) were both Jews, and the Chief Secretary (Sir Wyndham Deedes) a man of warm and unconcealed Zionist sympathies,[2] was not conducive to breaking the Arab boycott. The election was to be in two stages, a procedure introduced into Palestine by the Ottoman Constitution of 1908; but in spite of the prolonging of the period originally allowed for electing the secondary electors, fewer than one-sixth of the Muslim places in the electoral college were filled; and fewer than one-third of the Christian places. To this extent had the boycott campaign been successful, in spite of the High Commissioner's subsequent assurance to the League of Nations Permanent Mandates Commission that the Arab Congress had lost much of its representative character and authority recently, and that many, perhaps most, of the leading families other than the Husainis had dissociated themselves from its Executive.[3] It had been the British Government's intention, stated the High Commissioner, that, had the Legislative Council worked satisfactorily, the next stage, 'after a lapse of perhaps some years, would have been a constitution on more democratic lines'; but as the Palestine Government had 'exercised no pressure in persuading the people to take part in the elections',[4] the people—accustomed to the more positive Ottoman methods of suasion—naturally assumed that the liberty allowed to the propagandists for the boycott implied that the Government were not opposed

---

[1] Cmd. 1700, p. 28, and *Oriente Moderno*, II (1922–3), pp. 226–7.

[2] These three officials had together appealed in vain to the members of the Arab executive committee in nationalist Nablus, according to *Oriente Moderno*, ii. 597.

[3] League of Nations, Permanent Mandates Commission: *Minutes of the 5th Session (Extraordinary)*, 1924, pp. 67–8.

[4] Ibid., p. 55.

to it and were not sincere in their desire to carry through the elections.[1]

The High Commissioner thereupon fell back on his nominated Advisory Council, which had already existed before the publication of the plan for the Legislative Council, and proposed to reorganize it and make its membership drawn from the various communities conform with the pattern proposed for the Legislative Council. He accordingly invited 'ten of the ablest Arabs in the country, well known to be representatives of Arab opinion', to sit on the Advisory Council. All with the exception of Musa Kazim Pasha accepted and, after an 'excellent' substitute for him had been found, the acceptance in writing of all ten was obtained. When their names were published, however, they were subjected to great pressure by means of telegrams and deputations to their houses, with the result (in spite of a Government statement that their acceptance of nomination did not involve acceptance of the Mandate constitution[2]) that seven of them were intimidated and withdrew their names; and the High Commissioner, unwilling to fill their places with less deserving persons, allowed the plan to lapse.[3]

The British Government then (October 1923) fell back on an offer to set up an Arab Agency with a position 'exactly analogous' to that accorded to the Jewish Agency under Article 4 of the Mandate and with an express right to give its views on the crucial question of Jewish immigration. The High Commissioner, on the instructions of the Colonial Secretary, informed an invited assembly of Arab notables that he would take pains to ensure, by means of consultations, that the proposed Arab Agency should

[1] See Kisch, op. cit., pp. 35 and 46–7, diary entries of 26 February and 3 April 1923.

[2] M. F. Abcarius: *Palestine Through the Fog of Propaganda* (London, [1946], p. 81) advanced, as one of the Arabs' reasons for rejecting the Legislative Council offer, that 'their presence on the Council would have effectively stopped them from criticizing a law in the passing of which they had taken part'. This misconception of the powers and privileges of an Opposition under a liberal constitution was no doubt due to their greater familiarity with despotic Ottoman methods. The difficulties experienced by the Turkish Republic to this day in creating and maintaining a parliamentary two-party system of the Anglo-American type are well-known; and the legislatures in the Arab States since their achievement of independence have, generally speaking, been characterized by irresponsibility in Opposition and intolerance of criticism on the part of the governing groups.

[3] League of Nations, Permanent Mandates Commission, op. cit., p. 56; Great Britain, Colonial No. 15 (1925), p. 46.

be fully representative; but, he continued, the offer should be accepted as a settlement on the points which had been in controversy, at all events until some fully representative council was established. Otherwise, the British Government would not be prepared to proceed with the proposal. He added that 'those who anticipate a further declaration in any different sense are misleading themselves and would mislead any others who accept such assurances'.[1]

This warning was afterwards paraphrased[2] in terms which seem to heighten its restrictive character; but the High Commissioner's probable intention was to deflate some passages in the report of a second Arab delegation led by Musa Kazim Pasha which had returned from London one month earlier. This report had asserted that 'the great majority of the government party in the British Parliament[3] has recognized the necessity of solving the Palestine question by establishing a national, constitutional, and representative government', and concluded with the peroration: 'O young and rightly-guided nation who, since you have risen to defend your existence and claim your freedom and independence, have been the object of the admiration of all nations, persevere in your struggle and seek refuge in patience, constancy, and unity. The hour of victory is near, and God is with us'.[4]

When the assembled Arab notables had had time to consider the High Commissioner's proposal, Musa Kazim Pasha as their spokesman returned a negative answer: the offer of an Arab Agency would not satisfy the aspirations of the Arab people, and they had no desire for such an Agency on the same basis as the Jewish Agency whose status they had never recognized.[5] In a subsequent letter to the High Commissioner[6] the same spokesman wrote that:

the Arab owners of the country cannot see their way to accept a proposal which tends to place them on an equal footing with the alien

[1] Great Britain, Colonial Office: *Palestine, Proposed Formation of an Arab Agency*, Cmd. 1989 (1923), pp. 6, 9, 10.

[2] By Nevill Barbour: *Nisi Dominus* (London, 1944), p. 111.

[3] The Conservatives were now in power as a result of the break-up of the Lloyd George Coalition in November 1922.

[4] *Oriente Moderno*, iii (1923), p. 358, quoting the Palestine Arab newspaper *Filastin* of 9 October 1923.

[5] Cmd. 1989, pp. 10–11.

[6] 29 November 1923; text in League of Nations, Permanent Mandates Commission, op. cit., pp. 173–4.

Jews. In addition, the name of Arab Agency would make them feel that they are strangers in their own country.

He added that the High Commissioner's warning to the notables had

made a very bad impression. . . . The legitimate hopes of a people in securing its rights deserve more respect than that. . . . The hopes [of a change of policy in London] are based upon their strong confidence in their express rights.

So the opportunity of securing a Legislative Council on a proportional basis was lost by the Arabs, and was not to be regained twelve years later on account of the increased strength and international influence of the Zionists, and the access of world sympathy which the incipient Nazi persecution had brought them.

In summing up, it is necessary always for Western students of the Middle East to recall in self-criticism the extent of the shock inflicted upon the Arabs of a generation ago by the carrying forward of the Balfour Declaration into the Palestine mandate and by the overthrow of the Amir Faisal's government in Damascus —this last the work of French arms, but with British connivance. In Iraq, where the shock of these two events was substantially less, it is nevertheless on record that the British High Commissioner had in June 1924 to present an ultimatum in order to overcome the negative opposition to the Anglo-Iraqi Treaty which was in the event to launch that country on the road to its sovereign independence.[1] In Palestine the initial loading of the civil administration with Jews and Zionist sympathizers made it all the harder for Arab 'moderates', such as the Nashashibi family of Jerusalem,[2] to advocate a policy of experimental co-operation with the Government[3] as an alternative to the Husainis' doctrine of negation: it was all too easy for the latter to represent the moderates as collaborators with the Zionists and acceptors of the Balfour Declaration. The intransigents justified their attitude, then and since, by reference to the denial of their 'right' of self-determination. Thus the British Government's policy of favouring a Jewish national home undoubtedly was, as Balfour frankly

[1] See S. H. Longrigg: *Iraq, 1900–1950* (London, 1953), pp. 150–1.
[2] See Sir Ronald Storrs: *Orientations* (definitive ed., London, 1943), pp. 333–4, 401–2.
[3] See *Oriente Moderno*, iii, 358–9, for the programme of the Hizb al-Watani, which however never became an effective opposition to the Husainis.

admitted;[1] but at the same time it is difficult not to see in the attitude adopted by the Palestine Arab leaders something of the frustration of the adolescent who finds that he cannot free his wrists from the galling grip of the school bully. Arab nationalist hopes had been raised, and aspirations heightened, since the beginning of the century; but all that war and revolution had changed was the identity of the bully—from the reactionary regime of Abdul Hamid to the nationalism of the 'Young Turks', and from them to the self-will and supposed self-interest of London, Paris, and Pan-Zionism. Underlying the Arab nationalists' complaint of the denial of their 'natural rights' was the awareness of their lack of power to throw off the alien incubus. They therefore resorted to the negative attitude[2] which is the refuge of the impotent and the frustrated—but it is a refuge which, if over-indulged in, becomes successively a prison, a 'little-ease', and a grave.

That this has been the fate of the Palestine Arab political leadership during the past thirty years is patent—and though the counter-charges of Zionist ruthlessness and Anglo-American complicity and irresolution provide some explanation of the Arab defeat, they cannot excuse the chronic negation on the part of the 'leadership' which was most signally demonstrated in the boycott of the United Nations Committee in 1947. That committee was by no means wholly committed to the Zionist thesis, and a more positive attitude on the part of the Palestine Arabs[3] might well have produced recommendations more favourable to them than those which, when adopted by the United Nations General Assembly, were unanimously rejected by Arab opinion in November 1947. It is ironical that the Arabs have now come round to asserting that the Western Powers should compel the Zionists to withdraw to the frontiers proposed in these very recommendations against which the Arabs took up arms eight years ago—a claim as un-

[1] See Great Britain, Foreign Office: *Documents on British Foreign Policy, 1919–1939*, 1st series, vol. iv, p. 345, memo. of 11 August 1919.

[2] To what extent, if any, this negative attitude was encouraged by that minority of senior British officials of the Palestine Government who did not conceal their disapproval of the policy of establishing a Jewish national home, is an unanswered question. For the attitude of this minority of officials, see Ernest Richmond: 'British Policy in Palestine and the Mandate', *The Near East*, xxvii (1925), and H. St. J. B. Philby: 'Palestine and Lord Balfour', *Nineteenth Century and After*, xcvii (1925).

[3] Which the High Commissioner, General Sir Alan Cunningham, begged them in vain to adopt.

realistic in the context of 1955 as Musa Kazim Pasha's claim in 1923 that the British Government should 'cancel the Balfour Declaration and absolve itself therefrom'.[1] The moving finger writes . . .; and whether what it writes is just or unjust, moral or immoral, it cannot simply be 'cancelled' as the Palestine Arab leaders wished in 1923 to 'cancel the Balfour Declaration' and today would like to 'cancel' their defeat in 1948. If the plight of the Palestine Arab refugees is ever to be relieved, it cannot be through a negative attitude of this kind, but only through a leadership which has the discernment (and the independence of a protesting Press and 'street') to seize the fleeting opportunity. Once you have 'missed the bus', it needs an athlete to overtake it, and politicians (least of all, Arab politicians) rarely have the stamina of athletes.

Summer, 1955

[1] League of Nations, Permanent Mandates Commission, op. cit., p. 174.

List of Authorities

*(Works prefixed with a * are important for succeeding chapters also)*

Ch. I

W. B. Fisher: *The Middle East, a Physical, Social and Regional Geography.* (London, 1950.) N.B., caution with chapters on historical geography.

V. Gordon Childe: *What Happened in History.* (London, 1942.)

W. F. Albright: *From Stone Age to Christianity.* (Johns Hopkins Press, 1940.)

Christopher Dawson: *The Making of Europe.* (London, 1934.)

Ch. II

Bernard Lewis: *The Arabs in History.* (London, 1950.)

Ph. Hitti: *History of the Arabs.* (New York, 1937.)

R. A. Nicholson: *Literary History of the Arabs.* (London, 1923.)

H. A. R. Gibb: *Mohammedanism.* (London, 1949.)

Sir. Thos. Arnold and A. Guillaume (edit.): *The Legacy of Islam.* (London, 1931.)

A. Mieli: *La Science Arabe.* (Leiden, 1938.)

D. B. Macdonald: *Muslim Theology, Jurisprudence, and Constitutional Theory.* (London, 1903.)

Ernest Barker: *The Crusades.* (London, 1923.)

Steven Runciman: *History of the Crusades.* (London, 1951–.)

J. La Monte: *Crusade and Jihad* (in *The Arab Heritage,* ed. Nabih A. Faris; Princeton, 1944.)

S. Lane-Poole: *History of Egypt in the Middle Ages.* (London, 1901.)

J. H. Kramers: *Encyclopaedia of Islam*, art. Turks, B.IV.

Ch. III

H. A. R. Gibb and Harold Bowen: *Islamic Society and the West*, vol. I, 'Islamic Society in the Eighteenth Century'. (London, 1950–....)

*A. E. Crouchley: *Economic Development of Modern Egypt.* (London, 1938.)

James W. Parkes: *A History of Palestine from 135 A.D. to Modern Times.* (London, 1949.)

Sir Reader Bullard: *Britain and the Middle East.* (London, 1951.)

*S. H. Longrigg: *Four Centuries of Modern Iraq.* (London, 1925.)

*Sir. A. Wilson: *The Persian Gulf.* (London, 1928.)

*Sir Percy Sykes: *History of Persia.* (London, 1930.)

*D. G. Hogarth: *History of Arabia.* (London, 1922.)

A. C. Wood: *History of the Levant Company.* (London, 1935.)

Edgar Prestage: *The Portuguese Pioneers.* (London, 1933.)

Sir W. Foster: *England's Quest of Eastern Trade.* (London, 1933.)

Ch. IV

J. A. R. Marriott: *The Eastern Question.* (London, 1918.)

E. Driault: *La Question d'Orient.* (Paris, 1898.)

H. Dodwell: *The Founder of Modern Egypt.* (London, 1931.)

Sir Arnold Wilson: *The Suez Canal.* (London, 1933.)

Ph. Graves: *Life of Sir Percy Cox.* (London, 1941.)

E. M. Earle: *Turkey, the Great Powers, and the Baghdad Railway.* (New York, 1923.)

B. H. Sumner: *Tsardom and Imperialism in the Far East and Middle East, 1880–1914.* (London, 1940.)

Ch. V

*John Marlowe: *Anglo-Egyptian Relations, 1800–1953.* (London, 1954.)

Lord Cromer: *Modern Egypt.* (London, 1908.)
*Lord Lloyd: *Egypt since Cromer.* (London, 1933.)
M. Rifaat Bey: *The Awakening of Modern Egypt.* (London, 1947.)

*George Antonius: *The Arab Awakening.* (London, 1938.)
Zeine N. Zeine: *Anglo-Turkish Relations and the Emergence of Arab Nationalism.* (Beirut, 1958: corrects Antonius in some important respects.)

*S. H. Longrigg: *Iraq, 1900 to 1950.* (London, 1953.)
Christopher Sykes: *Two Studies in Virtue.* (London, 1953; part II deals with the background of the Balfour Declaration.)

*Joseph M. Upton: *The History of Modern Iran, an Interpretation.* (Harvard, 1960.)

Chs. VI, VII

George Lenczowski: *The Middle East in World Affairs,* 2nd ed. (Ithaca, N.Y., 1956.)

Elie Kedourie: *England and the Middle East, 1914-1921.* (London, 1956.)

George Kirk: *The Middle East in the War, 1939–1945.* (London, 1952.)
    The Middle East, 1945–1950. (London, 1954.)

Majid Khadduri: *Independent Iraq,* 2nd ed. (London, 1960.)

S. H. Longrigg and
  Frank Stoakes: *Iraq.* (London & New York, 1959.)

S. H. Longrigg: *Syria and Lebanon under French Mandate.* (London, 1958.)

John Marlowe: *The Seat of Pilate, An Account of the Palestine Mandate.* (London, 1959.)

Neville Barbour: *Nisi Dominus, a Survey of the Palestine Controversy.* (London, 1946.)

J. C. Hurewitz: *The Struggle for Palestine.* (New York, 1950.)

A. M. Hyamson: *Palestine Under the Mandate, 1920–1948.* (London, 1950.)

Elie Kedourie: *England and the Middle East, 1914–21.* (London, 1956.)

Nabih Amin Faris and
  Muhammad Tawfiq
  Husayn: *Crescent in Crisis.* (Lawrence, Kansas, 1955.)

Nicola Ziadeh: *Syria and Lebanon.* (London, 1956.)

Ch. VIII

Alfred Bonne: *State and Economy in the Middle East.* (London, 1948.)

Doreen Warriner: *Land Reform and Development in the Middle East.* (London, 1957.)

Royal Institute of In-
  ternational Affairs: *The Middle East, a Political and Economic Survey,* 3rd ed. (London, 1958.)

A. J. Meyer: *Middle Eastern Capitalism.* (Harvard, 1959.)

S. H. Longrigg: *Oil in the Middle East.* (London 1954).

David H. Finnie: *Desert Enterprise, the Middle East Oil Industry in its Local Environment.* (Harvard, 1958.)

George Lenczowski: *Oil and State in the Middle East.* (Cornell, 1960.)

Ch. IX

George Lenczowski: *Russia and the West in Iran, 1918–1948.* (London, 1951.)

W. Z. Laqueur: *Communism and Nationalism in the Middle East.* (London, 1956.)

The Soviet Union and the Middle East. (New York, 1959.)

Ch. X

W. Cantwell Smith: *Islam in Modern History.* (Princeton, 1957.)

H. Z. Nuseibeh: *The Ideas of Arab Nationalism.* (Cornell, 1956.)

W. Z. Laqueur, ed.:   *The Middle East in Transition.* (New York, 1958.)

J. & S. Lacouture: *Egypt in Transition.* (London & New York, 1958.)

Gamal Abdul Nasser: *Egypt's Liberation, the Philosophy of the Revolution.* (Washington, 1955.)

Anwar el-Sadat: *Revolt on the Nile.* (London, 1957.)

Wilton Wynn: *Nasser of Egypt, the Search for Dignity.* (Cambridge, Mass., 1959.)

Sir Anthony Eden: *Memoirs: Full Circle.* (London & New York, 1960.)

John C. Campbell: *Defense of the Middle East, Problems of American Policy.* (New York, 1960.)

Anthony Nutting: *I Saw for Myself, the Aftermath of Suez.* (London, 1958.)

Alan W. Ford: *The Anglo-Iranian Oil Dispute of 1951–1952.* (Berkeley, Cal., 1952.)

L. P. Elwell-Sutton: *Persian Oil: a Study in Power Politics.* (London, 1955; 'seen through Persian eyes'.)

Kemal H. Karpat: *Turkey's Politics, the Transition to a Multi-Party System.* (Princeton, 1959.)

Index

GREET BOOKS OF THE WESTERN WORLD

GREAT BOOKS
OF THE WESTERN WORLD

ROBERT MAYNARD HUTCHINS, *EDITOR IN CHIEF*

29.

CERVANTES

The History of

Don Quixote de la Mancha

By Miguel de Cervantes

Translated by John Ormsby

WILLIAM BENTON, *Publisher*

ENCYCLOPÆDIA BRITANNICA, INC.

CHICAGO · LONDON · TORONTO · GENEVA · SYDNEY · TOKYO · MANILA

THE UNIVERSITY OF CHICAGO

The Great Books
is published with the editorial advice of the faculties
of The University of Chicago

1952
BY ENCYCLOPÆDIA BRITANNICA, INC.

COPYRIGHT UNDER INTERNATIONAL COPYRIGHT UNION

ALL RIGHTS RESERVED UNDER PAN AMERICAN AND UNIVERSAL COPYRIGHT
CONVENTIONS BY ENCYCLOPÆDIA BRITANNICA, INC.

Library of Congress Catalog Card Number: 55–10336

BIOGRAPHICAL NOTE
MIGUEL DE CERVANTES, 1547–1616

CERVANTES was born in the ancient university town of Alcalá de Henares, where he was baptized, October 9, 1547, in the church of Santa María la Mayor. His father was a travelling physician, and it is doubtful whether the family was ever long enough in one place for Cervantes to receive any formal education. According to his own testimony he enjoyed reading from childhood and took especial delight in the dramatic productions of the famous actor-manager, Lope de Rueda. At the age of twenty he made his first appearance as an author, contributing several poems to a volume commemorating the death of Isabel de Valois, the third wife of Philip II.

Shortly after his debut as a writer, Cervantes was in Rome as a member of the retinue of Cardinal Acquaviva. He soon left the Cardinal to enlist as a private in the army which was being mustered to fight against the Turks. He was assigned to the "Marquesa," part of the armada under Don John of Austria. When the fleet came into action at Lepanto, Cervantes lay below, ill with fever. Despite the remonstrances of his comrades, he insisted that he would "rather die for his God and his King" than stay under cover. He received three gunshot wounds, two in the chest and one which maimed his left hand for life; to Cervantes the wounds were "stars lighting one to heaven and to fame," and the left hand was crippled "for the greater glory of the right." After convalescing at Messina, he returned to the army, served three more years in active service, and then was granted leave to return to Spain. He received letters of recommendation from Don John and the Duke de Sessa, viceroy of Sicily, in which he was described as "a soldier, as deserving as he was unfortunate."

The small galley carrying Cervantes back to Spain was attacked by Barbary corsairs near Les Trois Maries, and he, his brother, and the other Spaniards were taken as prisoners to Algiers. Cervantes became the slave of a Greek renegade named Dali Mami, and, since the letters found on him suggested that he was a man of some importance, his ransom was posted at an unusually high figure. He found the life of a captive "enough to sadden the merriest heart on earth" and made many ingenious attempts to escape. Upon the failure of one of them he was brought before the Dey of Algiers, Hassan Pasha, and "threatened with torture and instant death"; but the Dey, struck "by his peculiar grace in all things," remitted the punishment and bought Cervantes for himself. In 1577 he addressed a versified letter to the Spanish Secretary of State, suggesting an expedition to seize Algiers; the project, although practicable, was not attempted. In 1579, after another thwarted escape, Hassan Pasha again spared his life, declaring: "So long as I have the maimed Spaniard in my keeping, my Christians, my ships—aye, and the whole city—are safe." The Dey, however, was willing to release him for money, and Cervantes finally obtained his freedom by the payment of the ransom; his parents sent 250 ducats through the Trinitarian monks and, when this was insufficient, the Christian traders of Algiers contributed the balance.

After his release Cervantes returned to Spain, where he tried to support himself by writing, particularly for the stage. Of the great volume of plays he wrote, he later singled out only one for praise, La Confusa, "which, with all respect to as many sword-and-cloak plays as have been staged up to the present, may take a prominent place as being good among the best." His most serious effort at this time was the prose-pastoral Galatea (1585), and, although it always remained his favorite work, he later remarked that it "proposes something and concludes nothing." The Galatea won him a small measure of repute but brought him no financial return.

The death of his father and his own marriage made it necessary for him to "put aside the pen." His wife's dowry brought him nothing more valuable than five vines, an orchard, some household furniture, four bee-hives, forty-five hens and chickens, one cock, and a crucible. He went to Seville as commissary to provide oil and wheat for the Armada and, after its defeat, continued to act as commissary to the galleys. Although he showed considerable zeal in the work, he soon became convinced that there was no prospect of advancement. He appealed to the king for a vacant post in the American colonies but was refused and given the advice to "look for something nearer home." In an effort to supplement his income, he turned again to writing, and, in 1592, signed a contract to write six plays at fifty ducats each, on the condition that no payment was to be made unless each was "one of the best ever produced in Spain." No opportunity to test the contract arose, since Cervantes was thrown into jail. Although the reason for this imprisonment is not known, it was probably due to disorderliness in his accounts, for shortly after his release, he was in difficulty again with his superiors. When he proved unable to submit receipts for all official moneys he had collected, though no charge of dishonesty was proved, he was again committed to jail. Subsequently he was released in disgrace and dismissed from public service.

Don Quixote appeared during the years of extreme poverty that succeeded his dismissal. From the remark in the prologue that "you may suppose it engendered in some dismal prison," it has been assumed that its conception, if not some of its actual writing, took place during one of his terms in jail. The license for its publication was obtained in 1604, while Cervantes was living in Valladolid in a tiny apartment with his wife and four or five female relatives. A few months after its publication the following year, Don Quixote and Sancho Panza had become proverbial types in Valladolid; and they were soon known throughout Europe. The appearance in 1614 of a spurious second part, issued under the name of Alonso Fernandez de Avellanada, goaded Cervantes to lay aside his other writing and complete his master work, which he accomplished by the end of 1615. During the decade between the two parts of Quixote, Cervantes wrote his Exemplary Novels, the Journey to Parnassus, and several comedies and intermezzos for the theatre.

Although Cervantes was known and celebrated throughout Europe, his fame never brought him wealth, or even comfort. The members of the special French embassy visiting Madrid in 1615 were amazed to learn that Cervantes was "old, a soldier, a gentleman, and poor." He died in Madrid on the same day as William Shakespeare, April 23, 1616. He was borne from his house with "his face uncovered," according to the rule of the Tertiaries of St. Francis, and buried in the church attached to the convent of the Trinitarian nuns.

CONTENTS

BIOGRAPHICAL NOTE, V

THE FIRST PART

THE SECOND PART

CONTENTS

PREFACE

IDLE READER: thou mayest believe me without any oath that I would this book, as it is the child of my brain, were the fairest, gayest, and cleverest that could be imagined. But I could not counteract Nature's law that everything shall beget its like; and what, then, could this sterile, ill-tilled wit of mine beget but the story of a dry, shrivelled, whimsical offspring, full of thoughts of all sorts and such as never came into any other imagination—just what might be begotten in a prison, where every misery is lodged and every doleful sound makes its dwelling? Tranquillity, a cheerful retreat, pleasant fields, bright skies, murmuring brooks, peace of mind, these are the things that go far to make even the most barren muses fertile, and bring into the world births that fill it with wonder and delight. Sometimes when a father has an ugly, loutish son, the love he bears him so blindfolds his eyes that he does not see his defects, or, rather, takes them for gifts and charms of mind and body, and talks of them to his friends as wit and grace. I, however—for though I pass for the father, I am but the stepfather to "Don Quixote"—have no desire to go with the current of custom, or to implore thee, dearest reader, almost with tears in my eyes, as others do, to pardon or excuse the defects thou wilt perceive in this child of mine. Thou art neither its kinsman nor its friend, thy soul is thine own and thy will as free as any man's, whate'er he be, thou art in thine own house and master of it as much as the king is of his taxes—and thou knowest the common saying, "Under my cloak I kill the king"; all which exempts and frees thee from every consideration and obligation, and thou canst say what thou wilt of the story without fear of being abused for any ill or rewarded for any good thou mayest say of it.

My wish would be simply to present it to thee plain and unadorned, without any embellishment of preface or uncountable muster of customary sonnets, epigrams, and eulogies, such as are commonly put at the beginning of books. For I can tell thee, though composing it cost me some labor, I found none greater than the making of this Preface thou art now reading. Many times did I take up my pen to write it, and many did I lay it down again, not knowing what to write. One of these times, as I was pondering with the paper before me, a pen in my ear, my elbow on the desk, and my cheek in my hand, thinking of what I should say, there came in unexpectedly a certain lively, clever friend of mine, who, seeing me so deep in thought, asked the reason; to which I, making no mystery of it, answered that I was thinking of the preface I had to make for the story of "Don Quixote," which so troubled me that I had a mind not to make any at all, nor even publish the achievements of so noble a knight.

"For, how could you expect me not to feel uneasy about what that ancient lawgiver they call the Public will say when it sees me, after slumbering so many years in the silence of oblivion, coming out now with all my years upon my back, and with a book as dry as a rush, devoid of invention, meagre in style, poor in thoughts, wholly wanting in learning and wisdom, without quotations in the margin or annotations at the end, after the fashion of other books I see, which, though all fables and profanity, are so full of maxims from Aristotle, and Plato, and the whole herd of philosophers, that they fill the readers with amazement and convince them that the authors are men of learning, erudition, and eloquence. And then, when they quote the Holy Scriptures!—any one would say they are St. Thomases or other doctors of the Church, observing as they do a decorum so ingenious that in one sentence they describe a distracted lover and in the next deliver a devout little sermon that it is a pleasure and a treat to hear and read. Of all this there will be nothing in my book, for I have nothing to quote in the margin or to note at the end, and still less do I know what authors I follow in it, to place them at the beginning, as all do, under the letters A, B, C, beginning with Aristotle and ending with Xenophon, or Zoilus, or Zeuxis, though one was a slanderer and the other a painter. Also my book must do without sonnets at the beginning, at least sonnets whose authors are dukes, marquises, counts, bishops, ladies, or famous poets. Though if I were to ask two or three obliging friends, I know they would give me them, and

xi

such as the productions of those that have the highest reputation in our Spain could not equal.

"In short, my friend," I continued, "I am determined that Señor Don Quixote shall remain buried in the archives of his own La Mancha until Heaven provide some one to garnish him with all those things he stands in need of; because I find myself, through my shallowness and want of learning, unequal to supplying them, and because I am by nature shy and careless about hunting for authors to say what I myself can say without them. Hence the cogitation and abstraction you found me in, and reason enough, what you have heard from me."

Hearing this, my friend, giving himself a slap on the forehead and breaking into a hearty laugh, exclaimed, "Before God, Brother, now am I disabused of an error in which I have been living all this long time I have known you, all through which I have taken you to be shrewd and sensible in all you do; but now I see you are as far from that as the heaven is from the earth. How? Is it possible that things of so little moment and so easy to set right can occupy and perplex a ripe wit like yours, fit to break through and crush far greater obstacles? By my faith, this comes, not of any want of ability, but of too much indolence and too little knowledge of life. Do you want to know if I am telling the truth? Well, then, attend to me, and you will see how, in the opening and shutting of an eye, I sweep away all your difficulties, and supply all those deficiencies which you say check and discourage you from bringing before the world the story of your famous Don Quixote, the light and mirror of all knight-errantry."

"Say on," said I, listening to his talk; "how do you propose to make up for my diffidence, and reduce to order this chaos of perplexity I am in?"

To which he made answer, "Your first difficulty about the sonnets, epigrams, or complimentary verses which you want for the beginning, and which ought to be by persons of importance and rank, can be removed if you yourself take a little trouble to make them; you can afterwards baptize them, and put any name you like to them, fathering them on Prester John of the Indies or the Emperor of Trebizond, who, to my knowledge, were said to have been famous poets: and even if they were not, and any pedants or bachelors should attack you and question the fact, never care two maravedis for that, for even if they prove a lie against you they cannot cut off the hand you wrote it with.

"As to references in the margin to the books and authors from whom you take the aphorisms and sayings you put into your story, it is only contriving to fit in nicely any sentences or scraps of Latin you may happen to have by heart, or at any rate that will not give you much trouble to look up; so as, when you speak of freedom and captivity, to insert

Non bene pro toto libertas venditur auro;

and then refer in the margin to Horace, or whoever said it; or, if you allude to the power of death, to come in with—

Pallida mors æquo pulsat pede pauperum tabernas,
Regumque turres.

If it be friendship and the love God bids us bear to our enemy, go at once to the Holy Scriptures, which you can do with a very small amount of research, and quote no less than the words of God himself: *Ego autem dico vobis: diligite inimicos vestros.* If you speak of evil thoughts, turn to the Gospel: *De corde exeunt cogitationes malæ.* If of the fickleness of friends, there is Cato, who will give you his distich:

Donec eris felix multos numerabis amicos,
Tempora si fuerint nubila, solus eris.

With these and such like bits of Latin they will take you for a grammarian at all events, and that nowadays is no small honor and profit.

"With regard to adding annotations at the end of the book, you may safely do it in this way. If you mention any giant in your book contrive that it shall be the giant Goliath, and with this alone, which will cost you almost nothing, you have a grand note, for you can put—*The giant Golias or Goliath was a Philistine whom the shepherd David slew by a mighty stone-cast in the Terebinth valley, as is related in the Book of Kings*—in the chapter where you find it written.

"Next, to prove yourself a man of erudition in polite literature and cosmography, manage that the river Tagus shall be named in your story, and there you are at once with another famous annotation, setting forth—*The river Tagus was so called after a King of Spain: it has its source in such and such a place and falls into the ocean, kissing the walls of the famous city of Lisbon, and it is a common belief that it has golden sands,* etc. If you should have anything to do with robbers, I will give you the story of Cacus, for I have it by heart; if with loose women, there is the Bishop of Mondoñedo, who will give you the loan of Lamia, Laida, and Flora, any reference to whom will bring you great credit; if with hard-hearted ones, Ovid will furnish you with Medea; if with witches or enchantresses, Homer has Calypso, and Virgil Circe; if with valiant captains, Julius Cæsar himself will lend you himself in his own *Commentaries,* and Plutarch will give you a thousand Alexanders. If you should deal with love, with two ounces you may know of Tuscan you can go to Leon the Hebrew, who will supply you to your heart's content; or if you should not care to go to foreign countries you have at home Fonseca's *Of the Love of God,* in which is condensed all that you or the most imaginative mind can want on the subject. In short, all you have to do is to manage to quote these names, or refer to these stories I have mentioned, in your own, and leave it to me to insert the annotations and quotations, and I swear by all that's good to fill your margins and use up four sheets at the end of the book.

"Now let us come to those references to authors which other books have, and you want for yours. The remedy for this is very simple: You have only to look out for some book that quotes them all, from A to Z as you say yourself, and then insert the very same alphabet in your book, and though the imposition may be plain to see, because you have so little need to borrow from them, that is no matter; there will probably be some simple enough to believe that you have made use of them all in this plain, artless story of yours. At any rate, if it answers no other purpose, this long catalogue of authors will serve to give a surprising look of authority to your book. Besides, no one will trouble himself to verify whether you have followed them or whether you have not, being no way concerned in it; especially as, if I mistake not, this book of yours has no need of any one of those things you say it wants, for it is, from beginning to end, an attack upon the books of chivalry, of which Aristotle never dreamt, nor St. Basil said a word, nor Cicero had any knowledge; nor do the niceties of truth nor the observations of astrology come within the range of its fanciful vagaries; nor have geometrical measurements or refutations of the arguments used in rhetoric anything to do with it; nor does it mean to preach to anybody, mixing up things human and divine, a sort of motley in which no Christian understanding should dress itself. It has only to avail itself of truth to nature in its composition, and the more perfect the imitation the better the work will be. And as this piece of yours aims at nothing more than to destroy the authority and influence which books of chivalry have in the world and with the public, there is no need for you to go a-begging for aphorisms from philosophers, precepts from Holy Scripture, fables from poets, speeches from orators, or miracles from saints; but merely to take care that your style and diction run musically, pleasantly, and plainly, with clear, proper, and well-placed words, setting forth your purpose to the best of your power and as well as possible, and putting your ideas intelligibly, without confusion or obscurity. Strive, too, that in reading your story the melancholy may be moved to laughter, and the merry made merrier still; that the simple shall not be wearied, that the judicious shall admire the invention, that the grave shall not despise it, nor the wise fail to praise it. Finally, keep your aim fixed on the destruction of that ill-founded edifice of the books of chivalry, hated by some and praised by many more; for if you succeed in this you will have achieved no small success."

In profound silence I listened to what my friend said, and his observations made such an impression on me that, without attempting to question them, I admitted their soundness, and out of them I determined to make this Preface; wherein, gentle reader, thou wilt perceive my friend's good sense, my good fortune in finding such an adviser in such a time of need, and what thou hast gained in receiving, without addition or alteration, the story of the famous Don Quixote of La Mancha, who is held by all the inhabitants of the district of the Campo de Montiel to have been the chastest lover and the bravest knight that has for many years been seen in that neighborhood. I have no desire to magnify the service I render thee in making thee acquainted with so renowned and honored a knight, but I do desire thy thanks for the acquaintance thou wilt make with the famous Sancho Panza, his squire, in whom, to my thinking, I have given thee condensed all the squirely drolleries that are scattered through the swarm of the vain books of chivalry. And so—may God give thee health, and not forget me. *Vale.*

COMMENDATORY VERSES

TO THE BOOK OF DON QUIXOTE OF LA MANCHA

If to be welcomed by the good,
    O Book! thou make thy steady aim,
No empty chatterer will dare
    To question or dispute thy claim.
But if perchance thou hast a mind
    To win of idiots approbation,
Lost labor will be thy reward,
    Though they'll pretend appreciation.

They say a goodly shade he finds
    Who shelters 'neath a goodly tree;
And such a one thy kindly star
    In Béjar hath provided thee:
A royal tree whose spreading boughs
    A show of princely fruit display;
A tree that bears a noble Duke,
    The Alexander of his day.

Of a Manchegan gentleman
    Thy purpose is to tell the story,
Relating how he lost his wits
    O'er idle tales of love and glory,
Of "ladies, arms, and cavaliers": [2]
    A new Orlando Furioso—
Innamorato, rather—who
    Won Dulcinea del Toboso.

Put no vain emblems on thy shield;
    All figures—that is bragging play.
A modest dedication make,
    And give no scoffer room to say,
"What! Álvaro de Luna here?
    Or is it Hannibal again?
Or does King Francis at Madrid
    Once more of destiny complain?"

Since Heaven it hath not pleased on thee
    Deep erudition to bestow,
Or black Latino's gift of tongues, [3]
    No Latin let thy pages show.
Ape not philosophy or wit,
    Lest one who can not comprehend,
Make a wry face at thee and ask,
    "Why offer flowers to me, my friend?"

Be not a meddler; no affair
    Of thine the life thy neighbors lead:
Be prudent; oft the random jest
    Recoils upon the jester's head.
Thy constant labor let it be
    To earn thyself an honest name,
For fooleries preserved in print
    Are perpetuity of shame.

A further counsel bear in mind:
    If that thy roof be made of glass,
It shows small wit to pick up stones
    To pelt the people as they pass.
Win the attention of the wise,
    And give the thinker food for thought;
Whoso indites frivolities,
    Will but by simpletons be sought.

Amadis of Gaul

TO DON QUIXOTE OF LA MANCHA

Sonnet

Thou that didst imitate that life of mine,
    When I in lonely sadness on the great
    Rock Peña Pobre sat disconsolate,
In self-imposèd penance there to pine;
Thou, whose sole beverage was the bitter
    brine
    Of thine own tears, and who withouten plate
    Of silver, copper, tin, in lowly state
Off the bare earth and on earth's fruits didst
    dine;

---

[1] A personage in *Amadis of Gaul* somewhat akin to Morgan la Fay in the Arthur legend, though the part she plays is more like that of Merlin. She derived her title from the faculty which, like Merlin, she possessed of changing her form and appearance at will.

[2] "Le donne, i cavalieri, l'arme, gli amori"—*Orlando Furioso*, i. 1.

[3] Juan Latino, a self-educated Negro slave in the household of the Duke of Sesa, who gave him his freedom. He was for sixty years professor of rhetoric and Latin at Granada.

Live thou, of thine eternal glory sure.
  So long as on the round of the fourth sphere
  The bright Apollo shall his coursers steer,
In thy renown thou shalt remain secure,
Thy country's name in story shall endure,
  And thy sage author stand without a peer.

Don Belianis of Greece

to don quixote of la mancha

Sonnet

In slashing, hewing, cleaving, word and deed,
  I was the foremost knight of chivalry,
  Stout, bold, expert, as e'er the world did see;
Thousands from the oppressor's wrong I freed;
Great were my feats, eternal fame their meed;
  In love I proved my truth and loyalty;
  The hugest giant was a dwarf for me;
Ever to knighthood's laws gave I good heed.
My mastery the Fickle Goddess owned,
  And even Chance, submitting to control,
    Grasped by the forelock, yielded to my
      will.
Yet—though above yon hornèd moon enthroned
    My fortune seems to sit—great Quixote,
      still
    Envy of thy achievements fills my soul.

The Lady Oriana [1]

to dulcinea del toboso

Sonnet

Oh, fairest Dulcinea, could it be!
  It were a pleasant fancy to suppose so—
  Could Miraflores change to El Toboso,
And London's town to that which shelters
    thee!
Oh, could mine but acquire that livery
  Of countless charms thy mind and body show
    so!
  Or him, now famous grown—thou mad'st
    him grow so—
Thy knight, in some dread combat could I
    see!
Oh, could I be released from Amadis
  By exercise of such coy chastity
As led thee gentle Quixote to dismiss!
    Then would my heavy sorrow turn to joy;
    None would I envy, all would envy me,
    And happiness be mine without alloy.

[1] The heroine of *Amadis of Gaul.*

Gandalin, Squire of Amadis of Gaul

to sancho panza, squire of don quixote

Sonnet

All hail, illustrious man! Fortune, when she
  Bound thee apprentice to the esquire trade,
  Her care and tenderness of thee displayed,
Shaping thy course from misadventure free.
No longer now doth proud knight-errantry
  Regard with scorn the sickle and the
    spade;
  Of towering arrogance less count is made
Than of plain esquire-like simplicity.
I envy thee thy Dapple, and thy name,
  And those *alforjas* thou wast wont to stuff
With comforts that thy providence pro-
    claim,
    Excellent Sancho! hail to thee again!
    To thee alone the Ovid of our Spain
Does homage with the rustic kiss and cuff.

From El Donoso, the Motley Poet

on sancho panza and rocinante

On Sancho

I am the esquire Sancho Pan—
Who served Don Quixote of La Man—;
But from his service I retreat—,
Resolved to pass my life discreet—;
For Villadiego, called the Si—,
Maintained that only in reti—
Was found the secret of well-be—,
According to the *Celesti*—: [2]
A book divine, except for sin—
By speech too plain in my opin—.

On Rocinante

I am that Rocinante fa—,
Great-grandson of great Babie—, [3]
Who, all for being lean and bon—,
Had one Don Quixote for an own—;
But if I matched him well in weak—,
I never took short commons meek—,
But kept myself in corn by steal—,
A trick I learned from Lazaril—,
When with a piece of straw so neat—
The blind man of his wine he cheat—. [4]

[2] *Celestina, or Tragicomedy of Calisto and Meli-bæa* (1499).
[3] Babieca, the charger of the Cid.
[4] An allusion to the novel of Lazarillo de Tormes.

Orlando Furioso

TO DON QUIXOTE OF LA MANCHA

Sonnet

If thou art not a Peer, peer thou hast none;
  Among a thousand Peers thou art a peer;
  Nor is there room for one when thou art
    near,
Unvanquished victor, great unconquered one!
Orlando, by Angelica undone,
  Am I; o'er distant seas condemned to steer,
  And to Fame's altars as an offering bear
Valor respected by oblivion.
I cannot be thy rival, for thy fame
  And prowess rise above all rivalry,
    Albeit both bereft of wits we go.
But, though the Scythian or the Moor to tame
  Was not thy lot, still thou dost rival me:
    Love binds us in a fellowship of woe.

The Knight of Phœbus [1]

TO DON QUIXOTE OF LA MANCHA

My sword was not to be compared with thine,
  Phœbus of Spain, marvel of courtesy,
Nor with thy famous arm this hand of mine
  That smote from east to west as lightnings fly,
I scorned all empire, and that monarchy
The rosy east held out did I resign
  For one glance of Claridiana's eye,
The bright Aurora for whose love I pine.
A miracle of constancy my love;
  And banished by her ruthless cruelty,
    This arm had might the rage of Hell to
    tame.
But, Gothic Quixote, happier thou dost prove,
  For thou dost live in Dulcinea's name,
  And famous, honored, wise, she lives in thee.

From Solisdan

TO DON QUIXOTE OF LA MANCHA

Sonnet

Your fantasies, Sir Quixote, it is true,
  That crazy brain of yours have quite upset,

[1] The *Knights of Phœbus,* a romance by Diego
Ortuñez de Calahorra and Marcos Martinez.

But aught of base or mean hath never
    yet
Been charged by any in reproach to you.
Your deeds are open proof in all men's
    view;
  For you went forth injustice to abate,
  And for your pains sore drubbings did you
    get
From many a rascally and ruffian crew.
If the fair Dulcinea, your heart's queen,
  Be unrelenting in her cruelty,
    If still your woe be powerless to move
    her,
  In such hard case your comfort let it be
That Sancho was a sorry go-between:
  A booby he, hard-hearted she, and you no
    lover.

Dialogue

BETWEEN BABIECA AND ROCINANTE

Sonnet

B. How comes it, Rocinante, you're so lean?
R. I'm underfed, with overwork I'm worn.
B. But what becomes of all the hay and
    corn?
R. My master gives me none; he's much too
    mean.
B. Come, come, you show ill-breeding, sir, I
    ween;
  'Tis like an ass your master thus to scorn.
R. *He* is an ass, will die an ass, an ass was
    born;
  Why, he's in love; what's plainer to be
    seen?
B. To be in love is folly?— R. No great
    sense.
B. You're metaphysical.— R. From want of
    food.
B. Rail at the squire, then.— R. Why, what's
    the good?
  I might indeed complain of him, I grant
    ye,
  But, squire or master, where's the differ-
    ence?
They're both as sorry hacks as Rocinante.

THE FIRST PART

Chapter 1

Which treats of the character and pursuits of the famous gentleman Don Quixote of La Mancha

In a village of La Mancha, the name of which I have no desire to call to mind, there lived not long since one of those gentlemen that keep a lance in the lance-rack, an old buckler, a lean hack, and a greyhound for coursing. An olla of rather more beef than mutton, a salad on most nights, scraps on Saturdays, lentils on Fridays, and a pigeon or so extra on Sundays, made away with three-quarters of his income. The rest of it went in a doublet of fine cloth and velvet breeches and shoes to match for holidays, while on week-days he made a brave figure in his best homespun. He had in his house a housekeeper past forty, a niece under twenty, and a lad for the field and market-place, who used to saddle the hack as well as handle the bill-hook. The age of this gentleman of ours was bordering on fifty, he was of a hardy habit, spare, gaunt-featured, a very early riser and a great sportsman. They will have it his surname was Quixada or Quesada (for here there is some difference of opinion among the authors who write on the subject), although from reasonable conjectures it seems plain that he was called Quixana. This, however, is of but little importance to our tale; it will be enough not to stray a hair's breadth from the truth in the telling of it.

You must know, then, that the above-named gentleman whenever he was at leisure (which was mostly all the year round) gave himself up to reading books of chivalry with such ardor and avidity that he almost entirely neglected the pursuit of his field-sports, and even the management of his property; and to such a pitch did his eagerness and infatuation go that he sold many an acre of tillage-land to buy books of chivalry to read, and brought home as many of them as he could get. But of all there were none he liked so well as those of the famous Feliciano de Silva's composition, for their lucidity of style and complicated conceits were as pearls in his sight, particularly when in his reading he came upon courtships and cartels, where he often found passages like *"the reason of the unreason with which my reason is afflicted so weakens my reason that with reason I murmur at your beauty"*; or again, *"the high heavens, that of your divinity divinely fortify you with the stars, render you deserving of the desert your greatness deserves."* Over conceits of this sort the poor gentleman lost his wits, and used to lie awake striving to understand them and worm the meaning out of them; what Aristotle himself could not have made out or extracted had he come to life again for that special purpose. He was not at all easy about the wounds which Don Belianis gave and took, because it seemed to him that, great as were the surgeons who had cured him, he must have had his face and body covered all over with seams and scars. He commended, however, the author's way of ending his book with the promise of that interminable adventure, and many a time was he tempted to take up his pen and finish it properly as is there proposed, which no doubt he would have done, and made a successful piece of work of it too, had not greater and more absorbing thoughts prevented him.

Many an argument did he have with the curate of his village (a learned man, and a graduate of Siguenza [1]) as to which had been the better knight, Palmerin of England or Amadis of Gaul. Master Nicholas, the village barber, however, used to say that neither of them came up to the Knight of Phœbus, and that if there was any that could compare with *him* it was Don Galaor, the brother of Amadis of Gaul, because he had a spirit that was equal to every occasion, and was no finikin knight, nor lachrymose like his brother, while in the matter of valor he was not a whit behind him. In short,

---

[1] Siguenza was one of the *Universidades menores*, the degrees of which were often laughed at by the Spanish humorists.

1

he became so absorbed in his books that he spent his nights from sunset to sunrise, and his days from dawn to dark, poring over them; and what with little sleep and much reading his brains got so dry that he lost his wits. His fancy grew full of what he used to read about in his books, enchantments, quarrels, battles, challenges, wounds, wooings, loves, agonies, and all sorts of impossible nonsense; and it so possessed his mind that the whole fabric of invention and fancy he read of was true, that to him no history in the world had more reality in it. He used to say the Cid Ruy Diaz was a very good knight, but that he was not to be compared with the Knight of the Burning Sword who with one back-stroke cut in half two fierce and monstrous giants. He thought more of Bernardo del Carpio because at Roncesvalles he slew Roland in spite of enchantments, availing himself of the artifice of Hercules when he strangled Antæus the son of Terra in his arms. He approved highly of the giant Morgante, because, although of the giant breed which is always arrogant and ill-conditioned, he alone was affable and well-bred. But above all he admired Reinaldos of Montalban, especially when he saw him sallying forth from his castle and robbing every one he met, and when beyond the seas he stole that image of Mahomet which, as his history says, was entirely of gold. And to have a bout of kicking at that traitor of a Ganelon he would have given his housekeeper, and his niece into the bargain.

In short, his wits being quite gone, he hit upon the strangest notion that ever madman in this world hit upon, and that was that he fancied it was right and requisite, as well for the support of his own honor as for the service of his country, that he should make a knight-errant of himself, roaming the world over in full armor and on horseback in quest of adventures, and putting in practice himself all that he had read of as being the usual practices of knights-errant; righting every kind of wrong, and exposing himself to peril and danger from which, in the issue, he was to reap eternal renown and fame. Already the poor man saw himself crowned by the might of his arm Emperor of Trebizond at least; and so, led away by the intense enjoyment he found in these pleasant fancies, he set himself forthwith to put his scheme into execution.

The first thing he did was to clean up some armor that had belonged to his great-grandfather, and had been for ages lying forgotten in a corner eaten with rust and covered with mildew. He scoured and polished it as best he could, but he perceived one great defect in it, that it had no closed helmet, nothing but a simple morion. This deficiency, however, his ingenuity supplied, for he contrived a kind of half-helmet of pasteboard which, fitted on to the morion, looked like a whole one. It is true that, in order to see if it was strong and fit to stand a cut, he drew his sword and gave it a couple of slashes, the first of which undid in an instant what had taken him a week to do. The ease with which he had knocked it to pieces disconcerted him somewhat, and to guard against that danger he set to work again, fixing bars of iron on the inside until he was satisfied with its strength; and then, not caring to try any more experiments with it, he passed it and adopted it as a helmet of the most perfect construction.

He next proceeded to inspect his hack, which, with more quartos than a real [1] and more blemishes than the steed of Gonela, that *tantum pellis et ossa fuit,* surpassed in his eyes the Bucephalus of Alexander or the Babieca of the Cid. Four days were spent in thinking what name to give him, because (as he said to himself) it was not right that a horse belonging to a knight so famous, and one with such merits of his own, should be without some distinctive name, and he strove to adapt it so as to indicate what he had been before belonging to a knight-errant, and what he then was; for it was only reasonable that, his master taking a new character, he should take a new name, and that it should be a distinguished and full-sounding one, befitting the new order and calling he was about to follow. And so, after having composed, struck out, rejected, added to, unmade, and remade a multitude of names out of his memory and fancy, he decided upon calling him Rocinante, a name, to his thinking, lofty, sonorous, and significant of his condition as a hack before he became what he now was, the first and foremost of all the hacks in the world.

Having got a name for his horse so much to his taste, he was anxious to get one for himself, and he was eight days more pondering over this point, till at last he made up his mind to call himself Don Quixote, whence, as has been already said, the authors of this veracious history have inferred that his name must have been beyond a doubt Quixada, and not Quesada as others would have it. Recollecting, however, that the valiant Amadis was not content to call himself curtly Amadis and nothing more, but added

---

[1] An untranslatable pun on the word *quarto,* which means a sand crack in a horse's hoof, as well as the coin equal to one-eighth of the real. Gonela was a jester in the service of Borso, Duke of Ferrara.

the name of his kingdom and country to make it famous, and called himself Amadis of Gaul, he, like a good knight, resolved to add on the name of his, and to style himself Don Quixote of La Mancha, whereby, he considered, he described accurately his origin and country, and did honor to it in taking his surname from it.

So then, his armor being furbished, his morion turned into a helmet, his hack christened, and he himself confirmed, he came to the conclusion that nothing more was needed now but to look out for a lady to be in love with; for a knight-errant without love was like a tree without leaves or fruit, or a body without a soul. As he said to himself, "If, for my sins, or by my good fortune, I come across some giant hereabouts, a common occurrence with knights-errant, and overthrow him in one onslaught, or cleave him asunder to the waist, or, in short, vanquish and subdue him, will it not be well to have some one I may send him to as a present, that he may come in and fall on his knees before my sweet lady, and in a humble, submissive voice say, 'I am the giant Caraculiambro, lord of the island of Malindrania, vanquished in single combat by the never sufficiently extolled knight Don Quixote of La Mancha, who has commanded me to present myself before your Grace, that your Highness dispose of me at your pleasure?' " Oh, how our good gentleman enjoyed the delivery of this speech, especially when he had thought of some one to call his Lady! There was, so the story goes, in a village near his own a very good-looking farm girl with whom he had been at one time in love, though, so far as is known, she never knew it nor gave a thought to the matter. Her name was Aldonza Lorenzo, and upon her he thought fit to confer the title of Lady of his Thoughts; and after some search for a name which should not be out of harmony with her own, and should suggest and indicate that of a princess and great lady, he decided upon calling her Dulcinea del Toboso—she being of El Toboso—a name, to his mind, musical, uncommon, and significant, like all those he had already bestowed upon himself and the things belonging to him.

Chapter 2

Which treats of the first sally the ingenious Don Quixote made from home

THESE preliminaries settled, he did not care to put off any longer the execution of his design, urged on to it by the thought of all the world was losing by his delay, seeing what wrongs he intended to right, grievances to redress, injustices to repair, abuses to remove, and duties to discharge. So, without giving notice of his intention to any one, and without anybody seeing him, one morning before the dawning of the day (which was one of the hottest of the month of July) he donned his suit of armor, mounted Rocinante with his patched-up helmet on, braced his buckler, took his lance, and by the back door of the yard sallied forth upon the plain in the highest contentment and satisfaction at seeing with what ease he had made a beginning with his grand purpose. But scarcely did he find himself upon the open plain, when a terrible thought struck him, one all but enough to make him abandon the enterprise at the very outset. It occurred to him that he had not been dubbed a knight, and that according to the law of chivalry he neither could nor ought to bear arms against any knight; and that even if he had been, still he ought, as a novice knight, to wear white armor, without a device upon the shield until by his prowess he had earned one. These reflections made him waver in his purpose, but his craze being stronger than any reasoning he made up his mind to have himself dubbed a knight by the first one he came across, following the example of others in the same case, as he had read in the books that brought him to this pass. As for white armor, he resolved, on the first opportunity, to scour his until it was whiter than an ermine; and so comforting himself he pursued his way, taking that which his horse chose, for in this he believed lay the essence of adventures.

Thus setting out, our new-fledged adventurer paced along, talking to himself and saying, "Who knows but that in time to come, when the veracious history of my famous deeds is made known, the sage who writes it, when he has to set forth my first sally in the early morning, will do it after this fashion? 'Scarce had the rubicund Apollo spread o'er the face of the broad spacious earth the golden threads of his bright hair, scarce had the little birds of painted plumage attuned their notes to hail with dulcet and mellifluous harmony the coming of the rosy Dawn, that, deserting the soft couch of her jealous spouse, was appearing to mortals at the gates and balconies of the Manchegan horizon, when the renowned knight Don Quixote of La Mancha, quitting the lazy down, mounted his celebrated steed Rocinante and began to traverse the ancient and famous Campo de Montiel' "; which in fact he was actually traversing. "Happy the age, happy the time," he continued, "in which shall be made known my deeds of fame, worthy to be moulded in brass, carved in marble, limned in pictures, for a memorial forever. And thou, O sage magician, whoever thou art, to whom it shall fall to be the chronicler of this wondrous history, forget not, I entreat thee, my good Rocinante, the constant companion of my ways and wanderings." Presently he broke out again, as if he were love-stricken in earnest, "O Princess Dulcinea, lady of this captive heart, a grievous wrong hast thou done me to drive me forth with scorn, and with inexorable obduracy banish me from the presence of thy beauty. O lady, deign to hold in remembrance this heart, thy vassal, that thus in anguish pines for love of thee."

So he went on stringing together these and other absurdities, all in the style of those his books had taught him, imitating their language as well as he could; and all the while he rode so slowly and the sun mounted so rapidly and with such fervor that it was enough to melt his brains if he had any. Nearly all day he travelled without anything remarkable happening to him, at which he was in despair, for he was anxious to encounter some one at once upon whom to try the might of his strong arm.

Writers there are who say the first adventure he met with was that of Puerto Lápice; others say it was that of the windmills; but what I have ascertained on this point, and what I have found written in the annals of La Mancha, is that he was on the road all day, and towards nightfall his hack and he found themselves dead tired and hungry, when, looking all around to see if he could discover any castle or shepherd's shanty where he might refresh himself and relieve his sore wants, he perceived not far out of his road an inn, which was welcome as a star guiding him to the portals, if not the palaces, of his redemption; and quickening his pace he reached it just as night was setting in. At the door were standing two young women, girls of the district as they call them, on their way to Seville with some carriers who had chanced to halt that night at the inn; and as, happen what might to our adventurer, everything he saw or imagined seemed to him to be and to happen after the fashion of what he had read of, the moment he saw the inn he pictured it to himself as a castle with its four turrets and pinnacles of shining silver, not forgetting the drawbridge and moat and all the belongings usually ascribed to castles of the sort. To this inn, which to him seemed a castle, he advanced, and at a short distance from it he checked Rocinante, hoping that some dwarf would show himself upon the battlements, and by sound of trumpet give notice that a knight was approaching the castle. But seeing that they were slow about it, and that Rocinante was in a hurry to reach the stable, he made for the inn door, and perceived the two gay damsels who were standing there, and who seemed to him to be two fair maidens or lovely ladies taking their ease at the castle gate.

At this moment it so happened that a swineherd who was going through the stubbles collecting a drove of pigs (for, without any apology, that is what they are called) gave a blast of his horn to bring them together, and forthwith it seemed to Don Quixote to be what he was expecting, the signal of some dwarf announcing his arrival; and so with prodigious satisfaction he rode up to the inn and to the ladies, who, seeing a man of this sort approaching in full armor and with lance and buckler, were turning in dismay into the inn, when Don Quixote, guessing their fear by their flight, raising his pasteboard visor, disclosed his dry, dusty visage, and with courteous bearing and gentle voice addressed them, "Your ladyships need not fly or fear any rudeness, for that it belongs not to the order of knighthood which I profess to offer to any one, much less to high-born maidens as your appearance proclaims you to be." The girls were looking at him and straining their eyes to make out the features which the clumsy visor obscured, but when they heard themselves called maidens, a thing so much out of their line, they could not restrain their laughter, which made Don Quixote wax indignant, and say, "Modesty becomes the fair, and moreover laughter that has little cause is great silliness; this, however, I say not to pain or anger you, for my desire is none other than to serve you."

The incomprehensible language and the unpromising looks of our cavalier only increased the ladies' laughter, and that increased his irritation, and matters might have gone farther if at that moment the landlord had not come out, who, being a very fat man, was a very peaceful one. He, seeing this grotesque figure clad in armor that did not match any more than his saddle, bridle, lance, buckler, or corselet, was not at all indisposed to joint the damsels in their manifestations of amusement; but, in truth, standing in awe of such a complicated armament, he thought it best to speak him fairly, so he said, "Señor Caballero, if your worship wants lodging, bating the bed (for there is not one in the inn) there is plenty of everything else here." Don Quixote, observing the respectful bearing of the Alcaide of the fortress (for so innkeeper and inn seemed in his eyes), made answer, "Sir

Castellan, for me anything will suffice, for

> *My armor is my only wear,*
> *My only rest the fray.*

The host fancied he called him Castellan because he took him for a "worthy of Castile," [1] though he was in fact an Andalusian, and one from the Strand of San Lucar, as crafty a thief as Casus and as full of tricks as a student or a page. "In that case," said he,

> *Your bed is on the flinty rock,*
> *Your sleep to watch alway;*

and if so, you may dismount and safely reckon upon any quantity of sleeplessness under this roof for a twelvemonth, not to say for a single night." So saying, he advanced to hold the stirrup for Don Quixote, who got down with great difficulty and exertion (for he had not broken his fast all day), and then charged the host to take great care of his horse as he was the best bit of flesh that ever ate bread in this world. The landlord eyed him over, but did not find him as good as Don Quixote said, nor even half as good, and putting him up in the stable, returned to see what might be wanted by his guest, whom the damsels, who had by this time made their peace with him, were now relieving of his armor. They had taken off his breastplate and backpiece, but they neither knew nor saw how to open his gorget or remove his make-shift helmet, for he had fastened it with green ribbons, which, as there was no untying the knots, required to be cut. This, however, he would not by any means consent to, so he remained all the evening with his helmet on, the drollest and oddest figure that can be imagined; and while they were removing his armor, taking the baggages who were about it for ladies of high degree belonging to the castle, he said to them with great sprightliness:

> *Oh, never, surely, was there knight*
> *So served by hand of dame,*
> *As served was he, Don Quixote hight,*
> *When from his town he came;*
> *With maidens waiting on himself,*
> *Princesses on his hack—*

—or Rocinante, for that, ladies mine, is my horse's name, and Don Quixote of La Mancha is my own; for though I had no intention of declaring myself until my achievements in your service and honor had made me known, the ne-

[1] *Castellano* and *alcaide* both mean governor of a castle or fortress, but the former means also a Castilian.

cessity of adapting that old ballad of Lancelot to the present occasion has given you the knowledge of my name altogether prematurely. A time, however, will come for your ladyships to command and me to obey, and then the might of my arm will show my desire to serve you."

The girls, who were not used to hearing rhetoric of this sort, had nothing to say in reply: they only asked him if he wanted anything to eat. "I would gladly eat a bit of something," said Don Quixote, "for I feel it would come very seasonably." The day happened to be a Friday, and in the whole inn there was nothing but some pieces of the fish they call in Castile *abadejo,* in Andalusia *bacallao,* and in some places *curadillo,* and in others *troutlet;* so they asked him if he thought he could eat troutlet, for there was no other fish to give him. "If there be troutlets enough," said Don Quixote, "they will be the same thing as a trout; for it is all one to me whether I am given eight reals in small change or a piece of eight; moreover, it may be that these troutlets are like veal, which is better than beef, or kid, which is better than goat. But whatever it be let it come quickly, for the burden and pressure of arms cannot be borne without support to the inside." They laid a table for him at the door of the inn for the sake of the air, and the host brought him a portion of ill-soaked and worse cooked stockfish, and a piece of bread as black and mouldy as his own armor; but a laughable sight it was to see him eating, for having his helmet on and the beaver up, he could not with his own hands put anything into his mouth unless some one else placed it there, and this service one of the ladies rendered him. But to give him anything to drink was impossible, or would have been so had not the landlord bored a reed, and putting one end in his mouth poured the wine into him through the other; all which he bore with patience rather than sever the ribbons of his helmet.

While this was going on there came up to the inn a pig-gelder, who, as he approached, sounded his reed pipe four or five times, and thereby completely convinced Don Quixote that he was in some famous castle, and that they were regaling him with music, and that the stockfish was trout, the bread the whitest, the wenches ladies, and the landlord the castellan of the castle; and consequently he held that his enterprise and sally had been to some purpose. But still it distressed him to think he had not been dubbed a knight, for it was plain to him he could not lawfully engage in any adventure without receiving the order of knighthood.

Chapter 3

Wherein is related the droll way in which Don Quixote had himself dubbed a knight

HARASSED by this reflection, he made haste with his scanty pothouse supper, and having finished it called the landlord, and shutting himself into the stable with him, fell on his knees before him, saying, "From this spot I rise not, valiant knight, until your courtesy grants me the boon I seek, one that will redound to your praise and the benefit of the human race." The landlord, seeing his guest at his feet and hearing a speech of this kind, stood staring at him in bewilderment, not knowing what to do or say, and entreating him to rise, but all to no purpose until he had agreed to grant the boon demanded of him. "I looked for no less, my lord, from your High Magnificence," replied Don Quixote, "and I have to tell you that the boon I have asked and your liberality has granted is that you shall dub me knight to-morrow morning, and that to-night I shall watch my arms in the chapel of this your castle; thus to-morrow, as I have said, will be accomplished what I so much desire, enabling me lawfully to roam through all the four quarters of the world seeking adventures on behalf of those in distress, as is the duty of chivalry and of knights-errant like myself, whose ambition is directed to such deeds."

The landlord, who, as has been mentioned, was something of a wag, and had already some suspicion of his guest's want of wits, was quite convinced of it on hearing talk of this kind from him, and to make sport for the night he determined to fall in with his humor. So he told him he was quite right in pursuing the object he had in view, and that such a motive was natural and becoming in cavaliers as distinguished as he seemed and his gallant bearing showed him to be; and that he himself in his younger days had followed the same honorable calling, roaming in quest of adventures in various parts of the world, among others the Curing-grounds of Malaga, the Isles of Riaran, the Precinct of Seville, the Little Market of Segovia, the Olivera of Valencia, the Rondilla of Granada, the Strand of San Lucar, the Colt of Cordova, the Taverns of Toledo, and divers other quarters, where he had proved the nimbleness of his feet and the lightness of his fingers, doing many wrongs, cheating many widows, ruining maids and swindling minors, and in short, bringing himself under the notice of almost every tribunal and court of justice in Spain; until at last he had retired to this castle of his, where he was living upon his property and upon that of others; and where he received all knights-errant, of whatever rank or condition they might be, all for the great love he bore them and that they might share their substance with him in return for his benevolence. He told him, moreover, that in this castle of his there was no chapel in which he could watch his armor, as it had been pulled down in order to be rebuilt, but that in a case of necessity it might, he knew, be watched anywhere, and he might watch it that night in a courtyard of the castle, and in the morning, God willing, the requisite ceremonies might be performed so as to have him dubbed a knight, and so thoroughly dubbed that nobody could be more so. He asked if he had any money with him, to which Don Quixote replied that he had not a farthing, as in the histories of knights-errant he had never read of any of them carrying any. On this point the landlord told him he was mistaken; for, though not recorded in the histories, because in the author's opinion there was no need to mention anything so obvious and necessary as money and clean shirts, it was not to be supposed therefore that they did not carry them, and he might regard it as certain and established that all knights-errant (about whom there were so many full and impeachable books) carried well-furnished purses in case of emergency, and likewise carried shirts and a little box of ointment to cure the wounds they received. For in those plains and deserts where they engaged in combat and came out wounded, it was not always that there was some one to cure them, unless indeed they had for a friend some sage magician to succor them at once by fetching through the air upon a cloud some damsel or dwarf with a vial of water of such virtue that by tasting one drop of it they were cured of their hurts and wounds in an instant and left as sound as if they had not received any damage whatever. But in case this should not occur, the knights of old took care to see that their squires were provided with money and other requisites, such as lint and ointments for healing purposes; and when it happened that knights had no squires (which was rarely and seldom the case) they themselves carried everything in cunning saddle-bags that were hardly seen on the horse's croup, as if it were something else of more importance, because, unless for some such reason, carrying saddle-bags was not very favorably regarded among knights-errant. He therefore advised him (and, as his godson so soon to be, he might even command him) never from that time forth to travel without money and the usual requirements, and he would find the advantage of them when he least expected it.

Don Quixote promised to follow his advice scrupulously, and it was arranged forthwith that he should watch his armor in a large yard at one side of the inn; so, collecting it all together, Don Quixote placed it on a trough that stood by the side of a well, and bracing his buckler on his arm he grasped his lance and began with a stately air to march up and down in front of the trough, and as he began his march night began to fall.

The landlord told all the people who were in the inn about the craze of his guest, the watching of the armor, and the dubbing ceremony he contemplated. Full of wonder at so strange a form of madness, they flocked to see it from a distance, and observed with what composure he sometimes paced up and down, or sometimes, leaning on his lance, gazed on his armor without taking his eyes off it for ever so long; and as the night closed in with a light from the moon so brilliant that it might vie with his that lent it, everything the novice knight did was plainly seen by all.

Meanwhile one of the carriers who were in the inn thought fit to water his team, and it was necessary to remove Don Quixote's armor as it lay on the trough; but he seeing the other approach hailed him in a loud voice, "O thou, whoever thou art, rash knight that comest to lay hands on the armor of the most valorous errant that ever girt on sword, have a care what thou dost; touch it not unless thou wouldst lay down thy life as the penalty of thy rashness." The carrier gave no heed to these words (and he would have done better to heed them if he had been heedful of his health), but seizing it by the straps flung the armor some distance from him. Seeing this, Don Quixote raised his eyes to heaven, and fixing his thoughts, apparently, upon his lady Dulcinea, exclaimed, "Aid me, lady mine, in this the first encounter that presents itself to this breast which thou holdest in subjection; let not thy favor and protection fail me in this first jeopardy"; and, with these words and others to the same purpose, dropping his buckler he lifted his lance with both hands and with it smote such a blow on the carrier's head that he stretched him on the ground so stunned that had he followed it up with a second there would have been no need of a surgeon to cure him. This done, he picked up his armor and returned to his beat with the same serenity as before.

Shortly after this, another, not knowing what had happened (for the carrier still lay senseless), came with the same object of giving water to his mules, and was proceeding to remove the armor in order to clear the trough, when Don Quixote, without uttering a word or imploring aid from any one, once more dropped his buckler and once more lifted his lance, and without actually breaking the second carrier's head into pieces, made more than three of it, for he laid it open in four. At the noise all the people of the inn ran to the spot, and among them the landlord. Seeing this, Don Quixote braced his buckler on his arm, and with his hand on his sword exclaimed, "O Lady of Beauty, strength and support of my faint heart, it is time for thee to turn the eyes of thy greatness on this thy captive knight on the brink of so mighty an adventure." By this he felt himself so inspirited that he would not have flinched if all the carriers in the world had assailed him. The comrades of the wounded perceiving the plight they were in began from a distance to shower stones on Don Quixote, who screened himself as best he could with his buckler, not daring to quit the trough and leave his armor unprotected. The landlord shouted to them to leave him alone, for he had already told them that he was mad, and as a madman he would not be accountable even if he killed them all. Still louder shouted Don Quixote, calling them knaves and traitors, and the lord of the castle, who allowed knights-errant to be treated in this fashion, a villain and a low-born knight whom, had he received the order of knighthood, he would call to account for his treachery. "But of you," he cried, "base and vile rabble, I make no account; fling, strike, come on, do all ye can against me, ye shall see what the reward of your folly and insolence will be." This he uttered with so much spirit and boldness that he filled his assailants with a terrible fear, and as much for this reason as at the persuasion of the landlord they left off stoning him, and he allowed them to carry off the wounded, and with the same calmness and composure as before resumed the watch over his armor.

But these freaks of his guest were not much to the liking of the landlord, so he determined to cut matters short and confer upon him at once the unlucky order of knighthood before any further misadventure could occur; so, going up to him, he apologized for the rudeness which, without his knowledge, had been offered to him by these low people, who, however, had been well punished for their audacity. As he had already told him, he said, there was no chapel in the castle, nor was it needed for what remained to be done, for, as he understood the ceremonial of the order, the whole point of being dubbed a knight lay in the accolade and in the slap on the shoulder, and that could be administered in the middle of a field; and that he had now done all that was needful as to watching the armor, for all requirements were satisfied by a watch of two hours only, while he had been more than four about it. Don Quixote believed it all, and told him he stood there ready to obey him, and to make an end of it with as much despatch as possible; for, if he were again attacked, and felt himself to be a dubbed knight, he would not, he thought, leave a soul alive in the castle, except such as out of respect he might spare at his bidding.

Thus warned and menaced, the castellan forthwith brought out a book in which he used to enter the straw and barley he served out to the carriers, and, with a lad carrying a candle-end, and the two damsels already mentioned, he returned to where Don Quixote stood, and bade him kneel down. Then, reading from his account-book as if he were repeating some devout prayer, in the middle of his delivery he raised his hand and gave him a sturdy blow on the neck, and then, with his own sword, a smart slap on the shoulder, all the while muttering between his teeth as if he were saying his prayers. Having done this, he directed one of the ladies to gird on his sword, which she did with great self-possession and gravity, and not a little was required to prevent a burst of laughter at each stage of the ceremony; but what they had already seen of the novice knight's prowess kept their laughter within bounds. On girding him with the sword the worthy lady said to him, "May God make your worship a very fortunate knight, and grant you success in battle." Don Quixote asked her name in order that he might from that time forward know to whom he was beholden for the favor he had received, as he meant to confer upon her some portion of the honor he acquired by the might of his arm. She answered with great humility that she was called La Tolosa, and that she was a daughter of a cobbler of Toledo who lived in the stalls of Sanchobienaya, and that wherever she might be she would serve and esteem him as her lord. Don Quixote said in reply that she would do him a favor if thenceforward she assumed the "Don" and called herself Doña Tolosa. She promised she would, and then the other buckled on his spur, and with her followed almost the same conversation as with the lady of the sword. He asked her name, and she said it was La Molinera, and that she was the daughter of a respectable miller of Antequera; and of her likewise Don Quixote requested that she would adopt the "Don" and call herself Doña Molinera, making offers to her of further services and favors.

Having thus, with hot haste and speed, brought to a conclusion these never-till-now-seen ceremonies, Don Quixote was on thorns until he saw himself on horseback sallying forth in quest of adventures; and saddling Rocinante at once he mounted, and embracing his host, as he returned thanks for his kindness in knighting him, he addressed him in language so extraordinary that it is impossible to convey an idea of it or report it. The landlord, to get him out of the inn, replied with no less rhetoric though with shorter words, and without calling upon him to pay the reckoning, let him go with a Godspeed.

Chapter 4

Of what happened to our knight when he left the inn

DAY was dawning when Don Quixote quitted the inn, so happy, so gay, so exhilarated at finding himself dubbed a knight, that his joy was like to burst his horse-girths. However, recalling the advice of his host as to the requisites he ought to carry with him, especially that referring to money and shirts, he determined to go home and provide himself with all, and also with a squire, for he reckoned upon securing a farm-laborer, a neighbor of his, a poor man with a family, but very well qualified for the office of squire to a knight. With this object he turned his horse's head towards his village, and Rocinante, thus reminded of his old quarters, stepped out so briskly that he hardly seemed to tread the earth.

He had not gone far, when out of a thicket on his right there seemed to come feeble cries as of some one in distress, and the instant he heard them he exclaimed, "Thanks be to Heaven for the favor it accords me, that it so soon offers me an opportunity of fulfilling the obligation I have undertaken, and gathering the fruit of my ambition. These cries, no doubt, come from some man or woman in want of help, and needing my aid and protection"; and wheeling, he turned Rocinante in the direction whence the cries seemed to proceed. He had gone but a few paces into the wood, when he saw a mare tied to an oak, and tied to another, and stripped from the waist upwards, a youth of about fifteen years of age, from whom the cries came. Nor were they without cause, for a lusty farmer was flogging him with a belt and following up every blow with scoldings and commands, repeating, "Your mouth shut and your eyes open!" while the youth made answer, "I won't do it again, master mine; by God's passion I won't do it again, and I'll take more care of the flock another time."

Seeing what was going on, Don Quixote said in an angry voice, "Discourteous knight, it ill becomes you to assail one who cannot defend himself; mount your steed and take your lance" (for there was a lance leaning against the oak to which the mare was tied), "and I will make you know that you are behaving as a coward." The farmer, seeing before him this figure in full armor brandishing a lance over his head, gave himself up for dead, and made answer meekly, "Sir Knight, this youth that I am chastising is my servant, employed by me to watch a flock of sheep that I have hard by, and he is so careless that I lose one every day, and when I punish him for his carelessness and knavery he says I do it out of niggardliness, to escape paying him the wages I owe him, and before God, and on my soul, he lies."

"Lies before me, base clown!" said Don Quixote. "By the sun that shines on us I have a mind to run you through with this lance. Pay him at once without another word; if not, by the God that rules us I will make an end of you, and annihilate you on the spot; release him instantly."

The farmer hung his head, and without a word untied his servant, of whom Don Quixote asked how much his master owed him.

He replied, nine months at seven reals a month. Don Quixote added it up, found that it came to sixty-three reals, and told the farmer to pay it down immediately, if he did not want to die for it.

The trembling clown replied that as he lived and by the oath he had sworn (though he had not sworn any) it was not so much; for there were to be taken into account and deducted three pairs of shoes he had given him, and a real for two blood-lettings when he was sick.

"All that is very well," said Don Quixote; "but let the shoes and the blood-lettings stand as a set-off against the blows you have given him without any cause; for if he spoiled the leather of the shoes you paid for, you have damaged that of his body, and if the barber took blood from him when he was sick, you have drawn it when he was sound; so on that score he owes you nothing."

"The difficulty is, Sir Knight, that I have no money here; let Andres come home with me, and I will pay him all, real by real."

"I go with him!" said the youth. "Nay, God forbid! no, Señor, not for the world; for once alone with me, he would flay me like a Saint Bartholomew."

"He will do nothing of the kind," said Don Quixote; "I have only to command, and he will obey me; and as he has sworn to me by the order of knighthood which he has received, I leave him free, and I guarantee the payment."

"Consider what you are saying, señor," said the youth; "this master of mine is not a knight, nor has he received any order of knighthood; for he is Juan Haldudo the Rich, of Quintanar."

"That matters little," replied Don Quixote; "there may be Haldudos knights; moreover, every one is the son of his works."

"That is true," said Andres; "but this master of mine—of what works is he the son, when he refuses me the wages of my sweat and labor?"

"I do not refuse, brother Andres," said the farmer; "be good enough to come along with me, and I swear by all the orders of knighthood there are in the world to pay you as I have agreed, real by real, and perfumed." [1]

"For the perfumery I excuse you," said Don Quixote; "give it to him in reals, and I shall be satisfied; and see that you do as you have sworn; if not, by the same oath I swear to come back and hunt you out and punish you; and I shall find you though you should lie closer than a lizard. And if you desire to know who it is lays this command upon you, that you may be more firmly bound to obey it, know that I am the valorous Don Quixote of La Mancha, the undoer of wrongs and injustices; and so, God be with you, and keep in mind what you have promised and sworn under those penalties that have been already declared to you."

So saying, he gave Rocinante the spur and was soon out of reach. The farmer followed him with his eyes, and when he saw that he had cleared the wood and was no longer in sight, he turned to his boy Andres, and said, "Come here, my son, I want to pay you what I owe you, as that undoer of wrongs has commanded me."

"My oath on it," said Andres, "your worship will be well advised to obey the command of that good knight—may he live a thousand years—for, as he is a valiant and just judge, by Roque, if you do not pay me, he will come back and do as he said."

[1] "Perfumed," that is, completely.

"My oath on it, too," said the farmer; "but as I have a strong affection for you, I want to add to the debt in order to add to the payment"; and seizing him by the arm, he tied him up to the oak again, where he gave him such a flogging that he left him for dead.

"Now, Master Andres," said the farmer, "call on the undoer of wrongs; you will find he won't undo that, though I am not sure that I have quite done with you, for I have a good mind to flay you alive as you feared." But at last he untied him, and gave him leave to go look for his judge in order to put the sentence pronounced into execution.

Andres went off rather down in the mouth, swearing he would go to look for the valiant Don Quixote of La Mancha and tell him exactly what had happened, and that all would have to be repaid him sevenfold; but for all that, he went off weeping, while his master stood laughing.

Thus did the valiant Don Quixote right that wrong, and, thoroughly satisfied with what had taken place, as he considered he had made a very happy and noble beginning with his knighthood, he took the road towards his village in perfect self-content, saying in a low voice, "Well mayest thou this day call thyself fortunate above all on earth, O Dulcinea del Toboso, fairest of the fair! since it has fallen to thy lot to hold subject and submissive to thy full will and pleasure a knight so renowned as is and will be Don Quixote of La Mancha, who, as all the world knows, yesterday received the order of knighthood, and hath to-day righted the greatest wrong and grievance that ever injustice conceived and cruelty perpetrated: who hath to-day plucked the rod from the hand of yonder ruthless oppressor so wantonly lashing that tender child."

He now came to a road branching in four directions, and immediately he was reminded of those cross-roads where knights-errant used to stop to consider which road they should take. In imitation of them he halted for a while, and after having deeply considered it, he gave Rocinante his head, submitting his own will to that of his hack, who followed out his first intention, which was to make straight for his own stable. After he had gone about two miles Don Quixote perceived a large party of people, who, as afterwards appeared, were some Toledo traders, on their way to buy silk at Murcia. There were six of them coming along under their sunshades, with four servants mounted, and three muleteers on foot. Scarcely had Don Quixote descried them when the fancy possessed him that this must be some new adventure; and to help him to imitate as far as he could those passages he had read in his books, here seemed to come one made on purpose, which he resolved to attempt. So with a lofty bearing and determination he fixed himself firmly in his stirrups, got his lance ready, brought his buckler before his breast, and planting himself in the middle of the road, stood waiting the approach of these knights-errant, for such he now considered and held them to be; and when they had come near enough to see and hear, he exclaimed with a haughty gesture, "All the world stand, unless all the world confess that in all the world there is no maiden fairer than the Empress of La Mancha, the peerless Dulcinea del Toboso."

The traders halted at the sound of this language and the sight of the strange figure that uttered it, and from both figure and language at once guessed the craze of their owner; they wished, however, to learn quietly what was the object of this confession that was demanded of them, and one of them, who was rather fond of a joke and was very sharp-witted, said to him, "Sir Knight, we do not know who this good lady is that you speak of; show her to us, for if she be of such beauty as you suggest, with all our hearts and without any pressure we will confess the truth that is on your part required of us."

"If I were to show her to you," replied Don Quixote, "what merit would you have in confessing a truth so manifest? The essential point is that without seeing her you must believe, confess, affirm, swear, and defend it; else ye have to do with me in battle, ill-conditioned, arrogant rabble that ye are; and come ye on, one by one as the order of knighthood requires, or all together as is the custom and vile usage of your breed, here do I bide and await you, relying on the justice of the cause I maintain."

"Sir Knight," replied the trader, "I entreat your worship in the name of this present company of princes, that, to save us from charging our consciences with the confession of a thing we have never seen or heard of, and one moreover so much to the prejudice of the Empresses and Queens of the Alcarria and Estremadura, your worship will be pleased to show us some portrait of this lady, though it be no bigger than a grain of wheat; for by the thread one gets at the ball, and in this way we shall be satisfied and easy, and you will be content and pleased; nay, I believe we are already so far agreed with you that even though her portrait should show her blind of one eye, and distilling vermilion and sulphur from the other, we would nevertheless, to gratify your worship, say all in her favor that you desire."

"She distils nothing of the kind, vile rabble," said Don Quixote, burning with rage, "nothing of the kind, I say, only ambergris and civet in cotton; nor is she one-eyed or hump backed, but straighter than a Guadarrama spindle: but ye must pay for the blasphemy ye have uttered against beauty like that of my lady."

And so saying, he charged with levelled lance against the one who had spoken, with such fury and fierceness that, if luck had not contrived that Rocinante should stumble midway and come down, it would have gone hard with the rash trader. Down went Rocinante, and over went his master, rolling along the ground for some distance; and when he tried to rise he was unable, so encumbered was he with lance, buckler, spurs, helmet, and the weight of his old armor; and all the while he was struggling to get up, he kept saying, "Fly not, cowards and caitiffs! stay, for not by my fault, but my horse's, am I stretched here."

One of the muleteers in attendance, who could not have had much good nature in him, hearing the poor prostrate man blustering in this style, was unable to refrain from giving him an answer on his ribs; and coming up to him he seized his lance, and having broken it in pieces, with one of them he began so to belabor our Don Quixote that, notwithstanding and in spite of his armor, he milled him like a measure of wheat. His masters called out not to lay on so hard and to leave him alone, but the muleteer's blood was up, and he did not care to drop the game until he had vented the rest of his wrath, and, gathering up the remaining fragments of the lance, he finished with a discharge upon the unhappy victim, who all through the storm of sticks that rained on him never ceased threatening heaven, and earth, and the brigands, for such they seemed to him. At last the muleteer was tired, and the traders continued their journey, taking with them matter for talk about the poor fellow who had been cudgelled. He when he found himself alone made another effort to rise; but if he was unable when whole and sound, how was he to rise after having been thrashed and well-nigh knocked to pieces? And yet he esteemed himself fortunate, as it seemed to him that this was a regular knight-errant's mishap, and entirely, he considered, the fault of his horse. However, battered in body as he was, to rise was beyond his power.

Chapter 5

In which the narrative of our knight's mishap is continued

Finding, then, that in fact he could not move, he bethought himself of having recourse to his usual remedy, which was to think of some passage in his books, and his craze brought to his mind that about Baldwin and the Marquis of Mantua, when Carloto left him wounded on the mountain side, a story known by heart by the children, not forgotten by the young men, and lauded and even believed by the old folk; and for all that not a whit truer than the miracles of Mahomet. This seemed to him to fit exactly the case in which he found himself, so, making a show of severe suffering, he began to roll on the ground and with feeble breath repeat the very words which the wounded knight of the wood is said to have uttered:

> *Where art thou, lady mine; that thou*
> *My sorrow dost not rue?*
> *Thou canst not know it, lady mine,*
> *Or else thou art untrue."*

And so he went on with the ballad as far as the lines:

> *O noble Marquis of Mantua,*
> *My Uncle and liege lord!*

As chance would have it, when he had got to this line there happened to come by a peasant from his own village, a neighbor of his, who had been with a load of wheat to the mill, and he, seeing the man stretched there, came up to him and asked him who he was and what was the matter with him that he complained so dolefully.

Don Quixote was firmly persuaded that this was the Marquis of Mantua, his uncle, so the only answer he made was to go on with his ballad, in which he told the tale of his misfortune, and of the loves of the Emperor's son and his wife, all exactly as the ballad sings it.

The peasant stood amazed at hearing such nonsense, and relieving him of the visor, already battered to pieces by blows, he wiped his face, which was covered with dust, and as soon as he had done so he recognized him and said, "Señor Don Quixada" (for so he appears to have been called when he was in his senses and had not yet changed from a quiet country gentleman into a knight-errant), "who has brought your worship to this pass?" But to all questions the other only went on with his ballad.

Seeing this, the good man removed as well as

he could his breastplate and backpiece to see if he had any wound, but he could perceive no blood nor any mark whatever. He then contrived to raise him from the ground, and with no little difficulty hoisted him upon his ass, which seemed to him to be the easiest mount for him; and collecting the arms, even to the splinters of the lance, he tied them on Rocinante, and leading him by the bridle and the ass by the halter he took the road for the village, very sad to hear what absurd stuff Don Quixote was talking. Nor was Don Quixote less so, for what with blows and bruises he could not sit upright on the ass, and from time to time he sent up sighs to heaven, so that once more he drove the peasant to ask what ailed him. And it could have been only the devil himself that put into his head tales to match his own adventures, for now, forgetting Baldwin, he bethought himself of the Moor Abindarraez, when the Alcaide of Antequera, Rodrigo de Narvaez, took him prisoner and carried him away to his castle; so that when the peasant again asked him how he was and what ailed him, he gave him for reply the same words and phrases that the captive Abencerrage gave to Rodrigo de Narvaez, just as he had read the story in the *Diana* of Jorge de Montemayor where it is written, applying it to his own case so aptly that the peasant went along cursing his fate that he had to listen to such a lot of nonsense; from which, however, he came to the conclusion that his neighbor was mad, and so made all haste to reach the village to escape the wearisomeness of this harangue of Don Quixote's; who, at the end of it, said, "Señor Don Rodrigo de Narvaez, your worship must know that this fair Xarifa I have mentioned is now the lovely Dulcinea del Toboso, for whom I have done, am doing, and will do the most famous deeds of chivalry that in this world have been seen, are to be seen, or ever shall be seen."

To this the peasant answered, "Señor—sinner that I am!—can not your worship see that I am not Don Rodrigo de Narvaez nor the Marquis of Mantua, but Pedro Alonso your neighbor, and that your worship is neither Baldwin nor Abindarraez, but the worthy gentleman Señor Quixada?"

"I know who I am," replied Don Quixote, "and I know that I may be not only those I have named, but all the Twelve Peers of France and even all the Nine Worthies, since my achievements surpass all that they have done all together and each of them on his own account."

With this talk and more of the same kind they reached the village just as night was beginning to fall, but the peasant waited until it was a little later that the belabored gentleman might not be seen riding in such a miserable trim. When it was what seemed to him the proper time he entered the village and went to Don Quixote's house, which he found all in confusion, and there were the curate and the village barber, who were great friends of Don Quixote, and his housekeeper was saying to them in a loud voice, "Señor licentiate Pero Perez," for so the curate was called, "what does your worship think can have befallen my master? It is six days now since anything has been seen of him, or the hack, or the buckler, lance, or armor. Miserable me! I am certain of it, and it is as true as that I was born to die, that these accursed books of chivalry he has, and has got into the way of reading so constantly, have upset his reason; for now I remember having often heard him saying to himself that he would turn knight-errant and go all over the world in quest of adventures. To the devil and Barabbas with such books, that have brought to ruin in this way the finest understanding there was in all La Mancha!"

The niece said the same, and, indeed, more: "You must know, Master Nicholas"—for that was the name of the barber—"it was often my uncle's way to stay two days and nights together poring over these unholy books of misventures, after which he would fling the book away and snatch up his sword and fall to slashing the walls; and when he was tired out he would say he had killed four giants like four towers; and the sweat that flowed from him when he was weary he said was the blood of the wounds he had received in battle; and then he would drink a great jug of cold water and become calm and quiet, saying that this water was a most precious potion which the sage Esquife, a great magician and friend of his, had brought him. But I take all the blame upon myself for never having told your worships of my uncle's vagaries, that you might put a stop to them before things had come to this pass, and burn all these accursed books—for he has a great number—that richly deserve to be burned like heretics."

"So say I too," said the curate, "and by my faith to-morrow shall not pass without public judgment upon them, and may they be condemned to the flames lest they lead those that read them to behave as my good friend seems to have behaved."

All this the peasant heard, and from it he understood at last what was the matter with his neighbor, so he began calling aloud, "Open, your worships, to Señor Baldwin and to Señor the Marquis of Mantua, who comes badly wounded, and to Señor Abindarraez, the Moor, whom the valiant Rodrigo de Narvaez, the Alcaide of Antequera, brings captive."

At these words they all hurried out, and when they recognized their friend, master, and uncle, who had not yet dismounted from the ass because he could not, they ran to embrace him.

"Hold!" said he, "for I am badly wounded through my horse's fault; carry me to bed, and if possible send for the wise Urganda to cure and see to my wounds."

"See there! plague on it!" cried the housekeeper at this: "did not my heart tell the truth as to which foot my master went lame of? To bed with your worship at once, and we will contrive to cure you here without fetching that Hurgada. A curse I say once more, and a hundred times more, on those books of chivalry that have brought your worship to such a pass."

They carried him to bed at once, and after searching for his wounds could find none, but he said they were all bruises from having had a severe fall with his horse Rocinante when in combat with ten giants, the biggest and the boldest to be found on earth.

"So, so!" said the curate, "are there giants in the dance? By the sign of the Cross I will burn them to-morrow before the day is over."

They put a host of questions to Don Quixote, but his only answer to all was—give him something to eat, and leave him to sleep, for that was what he needed most. They did so, and the curate questioned the peasant at great length as to how he had found Don Quixote. He told him all, and the nonsense he had talked when found and on the way home, all which made the licentiate the more eager to do what he did the next day, which was to summon his friend the barber, Master Nicholas, and go with him to Don Quixote's house.

Chapter 6

Of the diverting and important scrutiny which the Curate and the Barber made in the library of our ingenious gentleman

HE WAS still sleeping; so the curate asked the niece for the keys of the room where the books, the authors of all the mischief, were, and right willingly she gave them. They all went in, the housekeeper with them, and found more than a hundred volumes of big books very well bound, and some other small ones. The moment the housekeeper saw them she turned about and ran out of the room, and came back immediately with a saucer of holy water and a sprinkler, saying, "Here, your worship, señor licentiate, sprinkle this room; don't leave any magician of the many there are in these books to bewitch us in revenge for our design of banishing them from the world."

The simplicity of the housekeeper made the licentiate laugh, and he directed the barber to give him the books one by one to see what they were about, as there might be some to be found among them that did not deserve the penalty of fire.

"No," said the niece, "there is no reason for showing mercy to any of them; they have every one of them done mischief; better fling them out of the window into the court and make a pile of them and set fire to them; or else carry them into the yard, and there a bonfire can be made without the smoke giving any annoyance." The housekeeper said the same, so eager were they for the slaughter of those innocents, but the curate would not agree to it without first reading at any rate the titles.

The first that Master Nicholas put into his hand was the four books of *Amadis of Gaul.* "This seems a mysterious thing," said the curate, "for, as I have heard said, this was the first book of chivalry printed in Spain, and from this all the others derive their birth and origin; so it seems to me that we ought inexorably to condemn it to the flames as the founder of so vile a sect."

"Nay, sir," said the barber, "I, too, have heard say that this is the best of all the books of this kind that have been written, and so, as something singular in its line, it ought to be pardoned."

"True," said the curate; "and for that reason let its life be spared for the present. Let us see that other which is next to it."

"It is," said the barber, "the *Sergas de Esplandian, the lawful son of Amadis of Gaul.*"

"Then verily," said the curate, "the merit of the father must not be put down to the account of the son. Take it, mistress housekeeper; open the window and fling it into the yard and lay the foundation of the pile for the bonfire we are to make."

The housekeeper obeyed with great satisfaction, and the worthy *Esplandian* went flying into the yard to await with all patience the fire that was in store for him.

"Proceed," said the curate.

"This that comes next," said the barber, "is *Amadis of Greece,* and, indeed, I believe all those on this side are of the same Amadis lineage."

"Then to the yard with the whole of them," said the curate; "for to have the burning of Queen Pintiquiniestra, and the shepherd Darinel and his eclogues, and the bedevilled and involved discourses of his author, I would burn with them the father who begot me if he were going about in the guise of a knight-errant."

"I am of the same mind," said the barber.

"And so am I," added the niece.

"In that case," said the housekeeper, "here, into the yard with them!"

They were handed to her, and as there were many of them, she spared herself the staircase, and flung them down out of the window.

"Who is that tub there?" said the curate.

"This," said the barber, "is *Don Olivante de Laura.*"

"The author of that book," said the curate, "was the same that wrote *The Garden of Flowers,* and truly there is no deciding which of the two books is the more truthful, or, to put it better, the less lying; all I can say is, send this one into the yard for a swaggering fool."

"This that follows is *Florismarte of Hircania,*" said the barber.

"Señor Florismarte here?" said the curate; "then by my faith he must take up his quarters in the yard, in spite of his marvellous birth and visionary adventures, for the stiffness and dryness of his style deserve nothing else; into the yard with him and the other, mistress housekeeper."

"With all my heart, señor," said she, and executed the order with great delight.

"This," said the barber, "is *The Knight Platir.*"

"An old book that," said the curate, "but I find no reason for clemency in it; send it after the others without appeal"; which was done.

Another book was opened, and they saw it was entitled, *The Knight of the Cross.*

"For the sake of the holy name this book has," said the curate, "its ignorance might be excused; but then, they say, 'behind the cross there's the devil'; to the fire with it."

Taking down another book, the barber said, "This is *The Mirror of Chivalry.*"

"I know his worship," said the curate; "that is where Señor Reinaldos of Montalvan figures with his friends and comrades, greater thieves than Cacus, and the Twelve Peers of France with the veracious historian Turpin; however, I am not for condemning them to more than perpetual banishment, because, at any rate, they

have some share in the invention of the famous Matteo Boiardo, whence too the Christian poet Ludovico Ariosto wove his web, to whom, if I find him here, and speaking any language but his own, I shall show no respect whatever; but if he speaks his own tongue I will put him up on my head."

"Well, I have him in Italian," said the barber, "but I do not understand him."

"Nor would it be well that you should understand him," said the curate, "and on that score we might have excused the Captain if he had not brought him into Spain and turned him into Castilian. He robbed him of a great deal of his natural force, and so do all those who try to turn books written in verse into another language, for, with all the pains they take and all the cleverness they show, they never can reach the level of the originals as they were first produced. In short, I say that this book, and all that may be found treating of those French affairs, should be thrown into or deposited in some dry well, until after more consideration it is settled what is to be done with them; excepting always one *Bernardo del Carpio* that is going about, and another called *Roncesvalles;* for these, if they come into my hands, shall pass into those of the housekeeper, and from hers into the fire without any reprieve."

To all this the barber gave his assent, and looked upon it as right and proper, being persuaded that the curate was so stanch to the Faith and loyal to the Truth that he would not for the world say anything opposed to them. Opening another book he saw it was *Palmerin de Oliva,* and beside it was another called *Palmerin of England,* seeing which the licentiate said, "Let the Olive be made firewood of at once and burned until no ashes even are left; and let that Palm of England be kept and preserved as a thing that stands alone, and let such another case be made for it as that which Alexander found among the spoils of Darius and set aside for the safe keeping of the works of the poet Homer. This book, gossip, is of authority for two reasons, first because it is very good, and secondly because it is said to have been written by a wise and witty king of Portugal. All the adventures at the Castle of Miraguarda are excellent and of admirable contrivance, and the language is polished and clear, studying and observing the style befitting the speaker with propriety and judgment. So then, provided it seems good to you, Master Nicholas, I say let this and *Amadis of Gaul* be remitted the penalty of fire, and as for all the rest, let them perish without further question or query."

"Nay, gossip," said the barber, "for this that I have here is the famous *Don Belianis.*"

"Well," said the curate, "that and the second, third, and fourth parts all stand in need of a little rhubarb to purge their excess of bile, and they must be cleared of all that stuff about the Castle of Fame and other greater affectations, to which end let them be allowed the over-seas term,[1] and, according as they mend, so shall mercy or justice be meted out to them; and in the meantime, gossip, do you keep them in your house and let no one read them."

"With all my heart," said the barber; and not caring to tire himself with reading more books of chivalry, he told the housekeeper to take all the big ones and throw them into the yard. It was not said to one dull or deaf, but to one who enjoyed burning them more than weaving the broadest and finest web that could be; and seizing about eight at a time, she flung them out of the window.

In carrying so many together she let one fall at the feet of the barber, who took it up, curious to know whose it was, and found it said, *History of the Famous Knight, Tirante el Blanco.*

"God bless me!" said the curate with a shout, "*Tirante el Blanco* here! Hand it over, gossip, for in it I reckon I have found a treasury of enjoyment and a mine of recreation. Here is Don Kyrieleison of Montalvan, a valiant knight, and his brother Thomas of Montalvan, and the knight Fonseca, with the battle the bold Tirante fought with the mastiff, and the witticisms of the damsel Placerdemivida, and the loves and wiles of the widow Reposada, and the empress in love with the squire Hipólito—in truth, gossip, by right of its style it is the best book in the world. Here knights eat and sleep, and die in their beds, and make their wills before dying, and a great deal more of which there is nothing in all the other books. Nevertheless, I say he who wrote it, for deliberately composing such fooleries, deserves to be sent to the galleys for life. Take it home with you and read it, and you will see that what I have said is true."

"As you will," said the barber; "but what are we to do with these little books that are left?"

"These must be, not chivalry, but poetry," said the curate; and opening one he saw it was the *Diana* of Jorge de Montemayor, and, sup-

posing all the others to be of the same sort, "these," he said, "do not deserve to be burned like the others, for they neither do nor can do the mischief the books of chivalry have done, being books of entertainment that can hurt no one."

"Ah, señor!" said the niece, "your worship had better order these to be burned as well as the others; for it would be no wonder if, after being cured of his chivalry disorder, my uncle, by reading these, took a fancy to turn shepherd and range the woods and fields singing and piping; or, what would be still worse, to turn poet, which they say is an incurable and infectious malady."

"The damsel is right," said the curate, "and it will be well to put this stumbling-block and temptation out of our friend's way. To begin, then, with the *Diana* of Montemayor. I am of opinion it should not be burned, but that it should be cleared of all that about the sage Felicia and the magic water, and of almost all the longer pieces of verse; let it keep, and welcome, its prose and the honor of being the first of books of the kind."

"This that comes next," said the barber, "is the *Diana,* entitled the *Second Part, by the Salamancan,* and this other has the same title, and its author is Gil Polo."

"As for that of the Salamancan," replied the curate, "let it go to swell the number of the condemned in the yard, and let Gil Polo's be preserved as if it came from Apollo himself; but get on, gossip, and make haste, for it is growing late."

"This book," said the barber, opening another, "is the ten books of the *Fortune of Love,* written by Antonio de Lofraso, a Sardinian poet."

"By the orders I have received," said the curate, "since Apollo has been Apollo, and the Muses have been Muses, and poets have been poets, so droll and absurd a book as this has never been written, and in its way it is the best and the most singular of all of this species that have as yet appeared, and he who has not read it may be sure he has never read what is delightful. Give it here, gossip, for I make more account of having found it than if they had given me a cassock of Florence stuff."

He put it aside with extreme satisfaction, and the barber went on, "These that come next are *The Shepherd of Iberia, The Nymphs of Henares,* and *The Enlightenment of Jealousy.*"

"Then all we have to do," said the curate, "is to hand them over to the secular arm of the housekeeper, and ask me not why, or we shall never have done."

---

[1] The "over-seas term" was the allowance of time granted in the case of persons beyond the seas, when sued or indicted, to enable them to appear and show cause why judgment should not be given against them.

"This next is the *Pastor de Fílida*."

"No Pastor that," said the curate, "but a highly polished courtier; let it be preserved as a precious jewel."

"This large one here," said the barber, "is called *The Treasury of Various Poems*."

"If there were not so many of them," said the curate, "they would be more relished: this book must be weeded and cleansed of certain vulgarities which it has with its excellences; let it be preserved because the author is a friend of mine, and out of respect for other more heroic and loftier works that he has written."

"This," continued the barber, "is the *Cancionero* of Lopez de Maldonado."

"The author of that book, too," said the curate, "is a great friend of mine, and his verses from his own mouth are the admiration of all who hear them, for such is the sweetness of his voice that he enchants when he chants them: it gives rather too much of its eclogues, but what is good was never yet plentiful: let it be kept with those that have been set apart. But what book is that next it?"

"The *Galatea* of Miguel de Cervantes," said the barber.

"That Cervantes has been for many years a great friend of mine, and to my knowledge he has had more experience in reverses than in verses. His book has some good invention in it, it presents us with something but brings nothing to a conclusion: we must wait for the Second Part it promises: perhaps with amendment it may succeed in winning the full measure of grace that is now denied it; and in the meantime do you, señor gossip, keep it shut up in your own quarters."

"Very good," said the barber; "and here come three together, the *Araucana* of Don Alonso de Ercilla, the *Austriada* of Juan Rufo, Justice of Cordova, and the *Montserrate* of Christobal de Virués, the Valencian poet."

"These three books," said the curate, "are the best that have been written in Castilian in heroic verse, and they may compare with the most famous in Italy; let them be preserved as the richest treasures of poetry that Spain possesses."

The curate was tired and would not look into any more books, and so he decided that, "contents uncertified," all the rest should be burned; but just then the barber held open one, called *The Tears of Angelica*.

"I should have shed tears myself," said the curate when he heard the title, "had I ordered that book to be burned, for its author was one of the famous poets of the world, not to say of Spain, and was very happy in the translation of some of Ovid's fables."

Chapter 7

Of the second sally of our worthy knight Don Quixote of La Mancha

At this instant Don Quixote began shouting out, "Here, here, valiant knights! here is need for you to put forth the might of your strong arms, for they of the Court are gaining the mastery in the tourney!" Called away by this noise and outcry, they proceeded no farther with the scrutiny of the remaining books, and so it is thought that *The Carolea, The Lion of Spain* and *The Deeds of the Emperor,* written by Don Luis de Ávila, went to the fire unseen and unheard; for no doubt they were among those that remained, and perhaps if the curate had seen them they would not have undergone so severe a sentence.

When they reached Don Quixote he was already out of bed, and was still shouting and raving, and slashing and cutting all round, as wide awake as if he had never slept.

They closed with him and by force got him back to bed, and when he had become a little calm, addressing the curate, he said to him, "Of a truth, Señor Archbishop Turpin,[1] it is a great disgrace for us who call ourselves the Twelve Peers, so carelessly to allow the knights of the Court to gain the victory in this tourney, we the adventurers having carried off the honor on the three former days."

"Hush, gossip," said the curate; "please God the luck may turn, and what is lost to-day may be won to-morrow; for the present let your worship have a care of your health, for it seems to me that you are over-fatigued, if not badly wounded."

"Wounded no," said Don Quixote, "but bruised and battered no doubt, for that bastard Don Roland has cudgelled me with the trunk of an oak tree, and all for envy, because he sees that I alone rival him in his achievements. But I should not call myself Reinaldos of Montalvan did he not pay me for it in spite of all his enchantments as soon as I rise from this bed. For the present let them bring me something to eat, for that, I feel, is what will be more to my purpose, and leave it to me to avenge myself."

They did as he wished; they gave him something to eat, and once more he fell asleep, leaving them marvelling at his madness.

[1] Charlemagne's chaplain.

That night the housekeeper burned to ashes all the books that were in the yard and in the whole house; and some must have been consumed that deserved preservation in everlasting archives, but their fate and the laziness of the examiner did not permit it, and so in them was verified the proverb that sometimes the innocent suffer for the guilty.

One of the remedies which the curate and the barber immediately applied to their friend's disorder was to wall up and plaster the room where the books were, so that when he got up he should not find them (possibly the cause being removed, the effect might cease), and they might say that a magician had carried them off, room and all; and this was done with all despatch. Two days later Don Quixote got up, and the first thing he did was to go and look at his books, and not finding the room where he had left it, he wandered from side to side looking for it. He came to the place where the door used to be, and tried it with his hands, and turned and twisted his eyes in every direction without saying a word; but after a good while he asked his housekeeper whereabouts was the room that held his books.

The housekeeper, who had been already well instructed in what she was to answer, said, 'What room or what nothing is it that your worship is looking for? There are neither room nor books in this house now, for the devil himself has carried all away."

"It was not the devil," said the niece, "but a magician who came on a cloud one night after the day your worship left this, and dismounting from a serpent that he rode he entered the room, and what he did there I know not, but after a little while he made off, flying through the roof, and left the house full of smoke; and when we went to see what he had done we saw neither book nor room: but we remember very well, the housekeeper and I, that on leaving, the old villain said in a loud voice that, for a private grudge he owed the owner of the books and the room, he had done mischief in that house that would be discovered by and by: he said too that his name was the Sage Muñaton."

"He must have said Friston," said Don Quixote.

"I don't know whether he called himself Friston or Friton," said the housekeeper, "I only know that his name ended with 'ton.'"

"So it does," said Don Quixote, "and he is a sage magician, a great enemy of mine, who has a spite against me because he knows by his arts and lore that in process of time I am to engage in single combat with a knight whom he befriends and that I am to conquer, and he will be unable to prevent it; and for this reason he endeavors to do me all the ill turns that he can; but I promise him it will be hard for him to oppose or avoid what is decreed by Heaven."

"Who doubts that?" said the niece; "but, uncle, who mixes you up in these quarrels? Would it not be better to remain at peace in your own house instead of roaming the world looking for better bread than ever came of wheat, never reflecting that many go for wool and come back shorn?"

"Oh, niece of mine," replied Don Quixote, "how much astray art thou in thy reckoning: ere they shear me I shall have plucked away and stripped off the beards of all who would dare to touch only the tip of a hair of mine."

The two were unwilling to make any further answer, as they saw that his anger was kindling.

In short, then, he remained at home fifteen days very quietly without showing any signs of a desire to take up with his former delusions, and during this time he held lively discussions with his two gossips, the curate and the barber, on the point he maintained, that knights-errant were what the world stood most in need of, and that in him was to be accomplished the revival of knight-errantry. The curate sometimes contradicted him, sometimes agreed with him, for if he had not observed this precaution he would have been unable to bring him to reason.

Meanwhile Don Quixote worked upon a farm laborer, a neighbor of his, an honest man (if indeed that title can be given to him who is poor), but with very little wit in his pate. In a word, he so talked him over, and with such persuasions and promises, that the poor clown made up his mind to sally forth with him and serve him as esquire. Don Quixote, among other things, told him he ought to be ready to go with him gladly, because any moment an adventure might occur that might win an island in the twinkling of an eye and leave him governor of it. On these and the like promises Sancho Panza (for so the laborer was called) left wife and children, and engaged himself as esquire to his neighbor. Don Quixote next set about getting some money; and selling one thing and pawning another, and making a bad bargain in every case, he got together a fair sum. He provided himself with a buckler, which he begged as a loan from a friend, and, restoring his battered helmet as best he could, he warned his squire Sancho of the day and hour he meant to set out, that he might provide himself with what he thought most needful. Above all, he charged him to take *alforjas*[1] with him. The other said he would, and that he meant to take also a very good ass he had, as he was not much given to going on foot. About the ass, Don Quixote hesitated a little, trying whether he could call to mind any knight-errant taking with him an esquire mounted on ass-back, but no instance occurred to his memory. For all that, however, he determined to take him, intending to furnish him with a more honorable mount when a chance of it presented itself, by appropriating the horse of the first discourteous knight he encountered. Himself he provided with shirts and such other things as he could, according to the advice the host had given him; all which being settled and done, without taking leave, Sancho Panza of his wife and children, or Don Quixote of his housekeeper and niece, they sallied forth unseen by anybody from the village one night, and made such good way in the course of it that by daylight they held themselves safe from discovery, even should search be made for them.

Sancho rode on his ass like a patriarch with his *alforjas* and *bota*,[2] and longing to see himself soon governor of the island his master had promised him. Don Quixote decided upon taking the same route and road he had taken on his first journey, that over the Campo de Montiel, which he travelled with less discomfort than on the last occasion, for, as it was early morning and the rays of the sun fell on them obliquely, the heat did not distress them.

And now said Sancho Panza to his master, "Your worship will take care, Señor Knight-errant, not to forget about the island you have promised me, for be it ever so big I'll be equal to governing it."

To which Don Quixote replied, "Thou must know, friend Sancho Panza, that it was a practice very much in vogue with the knights-errant of old to make their squires governors of the islands or kingdoms they won, and I am determined that there shall be no failure on my part in so liberal a custom; on the contrary, I mean to improve upon it, for they sometimes, and perhaps most frequently, waited until their squires were old, and then when they had had enough of service and hard days and worse nights, they gave them some title or other, of count, or at the most marquis, of some valley or province more or less; but if thou livest and I live, it may well

be that before six days are over, I may have won some kingdom that has others dependent upon it, which will be just the thing to enable thee to be crowned king of one of them. Nor needst thou count this wonderful, for things and chances fall to the lot of such knights in ways so unexampled and unexpected that I might easily give thee even more than I promise thee."

"In that case," said Sancho Panza, "if I should become a king by one of those miracles your worship speaks of, even Juana Gutierrez, my old woman, would come to be queen and my children infantas."

"Well, who doubts it?" said Don Quixote.

"I doubt it," replied Sancho Panza, "because for my part I am persuaded that though God should shower down kingdoms upon earth, not one of them would fit the head of Mari Gutierrez. Let me tell you, señor, she is not worth two maravedís for a queen; countess will fit her better, and that only with God's help."

"Leave it to God, Sancho," returned Don Quixote, "for he will give her what suits her best; but do not undervalue thyself so much as to come to be content with anything less than being governor of a province."

"I will not, señor," answered Sancho, "especially as I have a man of such quality for a master in your worship, who will be able to give me all that will be suitable for me and that I can bear."

Chapter 8

Of the good fortune which the valiant Don Quixote had in the terrible and undreamt-of adventure of the windmills, with other occurrences worthy to be fitly recorded

AT this point they came in sight of thirty or forty windmills that there are on that plain, and as soon as Don Quixote saw them he said to his squire, "Fortune is arranging matters for us better than we could have shaped our desires ourselves, for look there, friend Sancho Panza, where thirty or more monstrous giants present themselves, all of whom I mean to engage in battle and slay, and with whose spoils we shall begin to make our fortunes; for this is righteous warfare, and it is God's good service to sweep so evil a breed from off the face of the earth."

"What giants?" said Sancho Panza.

"Those thou seest there," answered his master, "with the long arms, and some have them nearly two leagues long."

"Look, your worship," said Sancho; "what we see there are not giants but windmills, and wha

[1] A sort of double wallet serving for saddle-bags, but more frequently carried slung across the shoulder.

[2] The *bota* is a leathern wine-bag.

seem to be their arms are the sails that turned by the wind make the millstone go."

"It is easy to see," replied Don Quixote, "that thou art not used to this business of adventures; those are giants; and if thou art afraid, away with thee out of this and betake thyself to prayer while I engage them in fierce and unequal combat."

So saying, he gave the spur to his steed Rocinante, heedless of the cries his squire Sancho sent after him, warning him that most certainly they were windmills and not giants he was going to attack. He, however, was so positive they were giants that he neither heard the cries of Sancho, nor perceived, near as he was, what they were, but made at them shouting, "Fly not, cowards and vile beings, for it is a single knight that attacks you."

A slight breeze at this moment sprang up, and the great sails began to move, seeing which Don Quixote exclaimed, "Though ye flourish more arms than the giant Briareus, ye have to reckon with me."

So saying, and commending himself with all his heart to his lady Dulcinea, imploring her to support him in such a peril, with lance in rest and covered by his buckler, he charged at Rocinante's fullest gallop and fell upon the first mill that stood in front of him; but as he drove his lance-point into the sail the wind whirled it round with such force that it shivered the lance to pieces, sweeping with it horse and rider, who went rolling over on the plain, in a sorry condition. Sancho hastened to his assistance as fast as his ass could go, and when he came up found him unable to move, with such a shock had Rocinante fallen with him.

"God bless me!" said Sancho, "did I not tell your worship to mind what you were about, for they were only windmills? And no one could have made any mistake about it but one who had something of the same kind in his head."

"Hush, friend Sancho," replied Don Quixote, "the fortunes of war more than any other are liable to frequent fluctuations; and moreover I think, and it is the truth, that that same sage Friston who carried off my study and books, has turned these giants into mills in order to rob me of the glory of vanquishing them, such is the enmity he bears me; but in the end his wicked arts will avail but little against my good sword."

"God order it as he may," said Sancho Panza, and helping him to rise got him up again on Rocinante, whose shoulder was half out; and then, discussing the late adventure, they followed the road to Puerto Lápice, for there, said Don Quixote, they could not fail to find adventures in abundance and variety, as it was a great thoroughfare. For all that, he was much grieved at the loss of his lance, and saying so to his squire, he added, "I remember having read how a Spanish knight, Diego Perez de Vargas by name, having broken his sword in battle, tore from an oak a ponderous bough or branch, and with it did such things that day, and pounded so many Moors, that he got the surname of Machuca, and he and his descendants from that day forth were called Vargas y Machuca. I mention this because from the first oak I see I mean to rend such another branch, large and stout like that, with which I am determined and resolved to do such deeds that thou mayest deem thyself very fortunate in being found worthy to come and see them, and be an eye-witness of things that will with difficulty be believed."

"Be that as God will," said Sancho, "I believe it all as your worship says it; but straighten yourself a little, for you seem all on one side, maybe from the shaking of the fall."

"That is the truth," said Don Quixote, "and if I make no complaint of the pain it is because knights-errant are not permitted to complain of any wound, even though their bowels be coming out through it."

"If so," said Sancho, "I have nothing to say; but God knows I would rather your worship complained when anything ailed you. For my part, I confess I must complain however small the ache may be; unless indeed this rule about not complaining extends to the squires of knights-errant also."

Don Quixote could not help laughing at his squire's simplicity, and he assured him he might complain whenever and however he chose, just as he liked, for, so far, he had never read of anything to the contrary in the order of knighthood.

Sancho bade him remember it was dinnertime, to which his master answered that he wanted nothing himself just then, but that he might eat when he had a mind. With this permission Sancho settled himself as comfortably as he could on his beast, and taking out of the *alforjas* what he had stowed away in them, he jogged along behind his master munching deliberately, and from time to time taking a pull at the *bota* with a relish that the thirstiest tapster in Malaga might have envied; and while he went on in this way, gulping down draught after draught, he never gave a thought to any of the promises his master had made him, nor did he rate it as hardship but rather as recreation going in quest of adventures, however dangerous they might be. Finally they passed the night among some trees, from one of which Don Quixote plucked a dry branch to serve him after a fashion as a lance, and fixed on it the head he had removed from the broken one. All that night Don Quixote lay awake thinking of his lady Dulcinea, in order to conform to what he had read in his books, how many a night in the forests and deserts knights used to lie sleepless supported by the memory of their mistresses. Not so did Sancho Panza spend it, for having his stomach full of something stronger than chiccory water he made but one sleep of it, and, if his master had not called him, neither the rays of the sun beating on his face nor all the cheery notes of the birds welcoming the approach of day would have had power to waken him. On getting up he tried the *bota* and found it somewhat less full than the night before, which grieved his heart because they did not seem to be on the way to remedy the deficiency readily. Don Quixote did not care to break his fast, for, as has been already said, he confined himself to savory recollections for nourishment.

They returned to the road they had set out with, leading to Puerto Lápice, and at three in the afternoon they came in sight of it. "Here, brother Sancho Panza," said Don Quixote when he saw it, "we may plunge our hands up to the elbows in what they call adventures; but observe, even shouldst thou see me in the greatest danger in the world, thou must not put a hand to thy sword in my defence, unless, indeed, thou perceivest that those who assail me are rabble or base folk; for in that case thou mayest very properly aid me; but if they be knights it is on no account permitted or allowed thee by the laws of knighthood to help me until thou has been dubbed a knight."

"Most certainly, señor," replied Sancho, "your worship shall be fully obeyed in this matter; all the more as of myself I am peaceful and no friend to mixing in strife and quarrels: it is true that as regards the defence of my own person I shall not give much heed to those laws, for laws human and divine allow each one to defend himself against any assailant whatever."

"That I grant," said Don Quixote, "but in this matter of aiding me against knights thou must put a restraint upon thy natural impetuosity."

"I will do so, I promise you," answered Sancho, "and I will keep this precept as carefully as Sunday."

While they were thus talking there appeared on the road two friars of the order of St. Benedict, mounted on two dromedaries, for not less tall were the two mules they rode on. They wore travelling spectacles and carried sunshades; and behind them came a coach attended by four or five persons on horseback and two muleteers on foot. In the coach there was, as afterwards appeared, a Biscay lady on her way to Seville, where her husband was about to take passage for the Indies with an appointment of high honor. The friars, though going the same road, were not in her company; but the moment Don Quixote perceived them he said to his squire, "Either I am mistaken, or this is going to be the most famous adventure that has ever been seen, for those black bodies we see there must be, and doubtless are, magicians who are carrying off some stolen princess in that coach, and with all my might I must undo this wrong."

"This will be worse than the windmills," said Sancho. "Look, señor; those are friars of St. Benedict, and the coach plainly belongs to some travellers: mind, I tell you to mind well what you are about and don't let the devil mislead you."

"I have told thee already, Sancho," replied Don Quixote, "that on the subject of adventures thou knowest little. What I say is the truth, as thou shalt see presently."

So saying, he advanced and posted himself in the middle of the road along which the friars were coming, and as soon as he thought they had come near enough to hear what he said, he cried aloud, "Devilish and unnatural beings, release instantly the high-born princesses whom you are carrying off by force in this coach, else prepare to meet a speedy death as the just punishment of your evil deeds."

The friars drew rein and stood wondering at the appearance of Don Quixote as well as at his words, to which they replied, "Señor Caballero, we are not devilish or unnatural, but two brothers of St. Benedict following our road, nor do we know whether or not there are any captive princesses coming in this coach."

"No soft words with me, for I know you, lying rabble," said Don Quixote, and without waiting for a reply he spurred Rocinante and with levelled lance charged the first friar with such fury and determination that, if the friar had not flung himself off the mule, he would have brought him to the ground against his will, and sore wounded, if not killed outright. The second brother, seeing how his comrade was treated, drove his heels into his castle of a mule and made off across the country faster than the wind.

Sancho Panza, when he saw the friar on the ground, dismounting briskly from his ass, rushed towards him and began to strip off his gown. At that instant the friars' muleteers came up and asked what he was stripping him for. Sancho answered them that this fell to him lawfully as spoil of the battle which his lord Don Quixote had won. The muleteers, who had no idea of a joke and did not understand all this about battles and spoils, seeing that Don Quixote was some distance off talking to the travellers in the coach, fell upon Sancho, knocked him down, and leaving hardly a hair in his beard, belabored him with kicks and left him stretched breathless and senseless on the ground; and without any more delay helped the friar to mount, who, trembling, terrified, and pale, as soon as he found himself in the saddle, spurred after his companion, who was standing at a distance looking on, watching the result of the onslaught; then, not caring to wait for the end of the affair just begun, they pursued their journey making more crosses than if they had the devil after them.

Don Quixote was, as has been said, speaking to the lady in the coach: "Your beauty, lady mine," said he, "may now dispose of your person as may be most in accordance with your pleasure, for the pride of your ravishers lies prostrate on the ground through this strong arm of mine; and lest you should be pining to know the name of your deliverer, know that I am called Don Quixote of La Mancha, knight-errant and adventurer, and captive to the peerless and beautiful lady Dulcinea del Toboso; and in return for the service you have received of me I ask no more than that you should return to El Toboso, and on my behalf present yourself before that lady and tell her what I have done to set you free."

One of the squires in attendance upon the coach, a Biscayan, was listening to all Don Quixote was saying, and, perceiving that he would not allow the coach to go on, but was saying it must return at once to El Toboso, he made at him, and seizing his lance addressed him in bad Castilian and worse Biscayan after this fashion, "Begone, caballero, and ill go with thee; by the God that made me, unless thou quittest coach, slayest thee as art here a Biscayan."

Don Quixote understood him quite well, and answered him very quietly, "If thou wert a knight, as thou art none, I should have already chastised thy folly and rashness, miserable creature." To which the Biscayan returned, "I no gentleman!—I swear to God thou liest as I am

Christian: if thou droppest lance and drawest sword, soon shalt thou see thou art carrying water to the cat: Biscayan on land, hidalgo at sea, hidalgo at the devil, and look, if thou sayest otherwise thou liest."

"'You will see presently,' said Agrajes," replied Don Quixote; and throwing his lance on the ground he drew his sword, braced his buckler on his arm, and attacked the Biscayan, bent upon taking his life.

The Biscayan, when he saw him coming on, though he wished to dismount from his mule, in which, being one of those sorry ones let out for hire, he had no confidence, had no choice but to draw his sword; it was lucky for him, however, that he was near the coach, from which he was able to snatch a cushion that served him for a shield; and then they went at one another as if they had been two mortal enemies. The others strove to make peace between them, but could not, for the Biscayan declared in his disjointed phrase that if they did not let him finish his battle he would kill his mistress and every one that strove to prevent him. The lady in the coach, amazed and terrified at what she saw, ordered the coachman to draw aside a little, and set herself to watch this severe struggle, in the course of which the Biscayan smote Don Quixote a mighty stroke on the shoulder over the top of his buckler, which, given to one without armor, would have cleft him to the waist. Don Quixote, feeling the weight of this prodigious blow, cried aloud, saying, "O lady of my soul, Dulcinea, flower of beauty, come to the aid of this your knight, who, in fulfilling his obligations to your beauty, finds himself in this extreme peril." To say this, to lift his sword, to shelter himself well behind his buckler, and to assail the Biscayan was the work of an instant, determined as he was to venture all upon a single blow. The Biscayan, seeing him come on in this way, was convinced of his courage by his spirited bearing, and resolved to follow his example, so he waited for him keeping well under cover of his cushion, being unable to execute any sort of manœuvre with his mule, which, dead tired and never meant for this kind of game, could not stir a step.

On, then, as aforesaid, came Don Quixote against the wary Biscayan, with uplifted sword and a firm intention of splitting him in half, while on his side the Biscayan waited for him sword in hand, and under the protection of his cushion; and all present stood trembling, waiting in suspense the result of blows such as threatened to fall, and the lady in the coach and the rest of her following were making a thousand vows and offerings to all the images and shrines of Spain, that God might deliver her squire and all of them from this great peril in which they found themselves. But it spoils all, that at this point and crisis the author of the history leaves this battle impending, giving as excuse that he could find nothing more written about these achievements of Don Quixote than what has been already set forth. It is true the second author of this work was unwilling to believe that a history so curious could have been allowed to fall under the sentence of oblivion, or that the wits of La Mancha could have been so undiscerning as not to preserve in their archives or registries some documents referring to this famous knight; and this being his persuasion, he did not despair of finding the conclusion of this pleasant history, which, Heaven favoring him, he did find in a way that shall be related in the Second Part.

Chapter 9

In which is concluded and finished the terrific battle between the gallant Biscayan and the valiant Manchegan

In the First Part of this history we left the valiant Biscayan and the renowned Don Quixote with drawn swords uplifted, ready to deliver two such furious slashing blows that if they had fallen full and fair they would at least have split and cleft them asunder from top to toe and laid them open like a pomegranate; and at this so critical point the delightful history came to a stop and stood cut short without any intimation from the author where what was missing was to be found.

This distressed me greatly, because the pleasure derived from having read such a small portion turned to vexation at the thought of the poor chance that presented itself of finding the large part that, so it seemed to me, was missing of such an interesting tale. It appeared to me to be a thing impossible and contrary to all precedent that so good a knight should have been without some sage to undertake the task of writing his marvellous achievements; a thing that was never wanting to any of those knights-errant who, they say, went after adventures; for every one of them had one or two sages as if made on purpose, who not only recorded their deeds but described their most trifling thoughts and follies, however secret they might be; and such a good knight could not have been so unfortunate as not to have what Platir and others like him

had in abundance. And so I could not bring myself to believe that such a gallant tale had been left maimed and mutilated and I laid the blame on Time, the devourer and destroyer of all things, that had either concealed or consumed it.

On the other hand, it struck me that, inasmuch as among his books there had been found such modern ones as *The Enlightenment of Jealousy* and *The Nymphs and Shepherds of Henares,* his story must likewise be modern, and that though it might not be written, it might exist in the memory of the people of his village and of those in the neighborhood. This reflection kept me perplexed and longing to know really and truly the whole life and wondrous deeds of our famous Spaniard, Don Quixote of La Mancha, light and mirror of Manchegan chivalry, and the first that in our age and in these so evil days devoted himself to the labor and exercise of the arms of knight-errantry, righting wrongs, succoring widows, and protecting damsels of that sort that used to ride about, whip in hand, on their palfreys, with all their virginity about them, from mountain to mountain and valley to valley—for, if it were not for some ruffian, or boor with a hood and hatchet, or monstrous giant, that forced them, there were in days of yore damsels that at the end of eighty years, in all which time they had never slept a day under a roof, went to their graves as much maids as the mothers that bore them. I say, then, that in these and other respects our noble Don Quixote is worthy of everlasting and notable praise, nor should it be withheld even from me for the labor and pains spent in searching for the conclusion of this delightful history; though I know well that if Heaven, chance, and good fortune had not helped me, the world would have remained deprived of an entertainment and pleasure that for a couple of hours or so may well occupy him who shall read it attentively. The discovery of it occurred in this way.

One day, as I was in the Alcaná of Toledo, a boy came up to sell some pamphlets and old papers to a silk mercer, and, as I am fond of reading even the very scraps of paper in the streets, led by this natural bent of mine, I took up one of the pamphlets the boy had for sale, and saw that it was in characters which I recognized as Arabic, and, as I was unable to read them, though I could recognize them, I looked about to see if there were any Spanish-speaking Morisco at hand to read them for me; nor was there any great difficulty in finding such an interpreter, for even had I sought one for an older and better language I should have found him. In short, chance provided me with one, who when I told him what I wanted and put the book into his hands, opened it in the middle, and after reading a little in it began to laugh. I asked him what he was laughing at, and he replied that it was at something the book had written in the margin by way of a note. I bade him tell it to me; and he, still laughing, said: "In the margin, as I told you, this is written: '*This Dulcinea del Toboso so often mentioned in this history had, they say, the best hand of any woman in all La Mancha for salting pigs.*'"

When I heard Dulcinea del Toboso named, I was struck with surprise and amazement, for it occurred to me at once that these pamphlets contained the history of Don Quixote. With this idea I pressed him to read the beginning, and doing so, turning the Arabic offhand into Castilian, he told me it meant, *History of Don Quixote of La Mancha, written by Cid Hamet Benengeli, an Arab historian*. It required great caution to hide the joy I felt when the title of the book reached my ears, and snatching it from the silk mercer, I bought all the papers and pamphlets from the boy for half a real; and if he had had his wits about him and had known how eager I was for them, he might have safely calculated on making more than six reals by the bargain. I withdrew at once with the Morisco into the cloister of the cathedral, and begged him to turn all these pamphlets that related to Don Quixote into the Castilian tongue, without omitting or adding anything to them, offering him whatever payment he pleased. He was satisfied with two *arrobas* of raisins and two bushels of wheat, and promised to translate them faithfully and with all despatch; but to make the matter more easy, and not to let such a precious find out of my hands, I took him to my house, where in little more than a month and a half he translated the whole just as it is set down here.

In the first pamphlet the battle between Don Quixote and the Biscayan was drawn to the very life, they planted in the same attitude as the history describes, their swords raised, and the one protected by his buckler, the other by his cushion, and the Biscayan's mule so true to nature that it could be seen to be a hired one a bowshot off. The Biscayan had an inscription under his feet which said, *Don Sancho de Azpeitia*, which no doubt must have been his name; and at the feet of Rocinante was another that

said, *Don Quixote*. Rocinante was marvellously portrayed, so long and thin, so lank and lean, with so much backbone and so far gone in consumption, that he showed plainly with what judgment and propriety the name of Rocinante had been bestowed upon him. Near him was Sancho Panza holding the halter of his ass, at whose feet was another label that said, *Sancho Zancas,* and according to the picture, he must have had a big belly, a short body, and long shanks, for which reason, no doubt, the names of Panza and Zancas were given him, for by these two surnames the history several times calls him.[1] Some other trifling particulars might be mentioned, but they are all of slight importance and have nothing to do with the true relation of the history; and no history can be bad so long as it is true.

If against the present one any objection be raised on the score of its truth, it can only be that its author was an Arab, as lying is a very common propensity with those of that nation; though, as they are such enemies of ours, it is conceivable that there were omissions rather than additions made in the course of it. And this is my own opinion; for, where he could and should give freedom to his pen in praise of so worthy a knight, he seems to me deliberately to pass it over in silence; which is ill done and worse contrived, for it is the business and duty of historians to be exact, truthful, and wholly free from passion, and neither interest nor fear, hatred nor love, should make them swerve from the path of truth, whose mother is history, rival of time, storehouse of deeds, witness for the past, example and counsel for the present, and warning for the future. In this I know will be found all that can be desired in the pleasantest, and if it be wanting in any good quality, I maintain it is the fault of its hound of an author and not the fault of the subject. To be brief, its Second Part, according to the translation, began in this way:

With trenchant swords upraised and poised on high, it seemed as though the two valiant and wrathful combatants stood threatening heaven, and earth, and hell, with such resolution and determination did they bear themselves.

The fiery Biscayan was the first to strike a blow, which was delivered with such force and fury that had not the sword turned in its course, that single stroke would have sufficed to put an end to the bitter struggle and to all the adventures of our knight; but that good

[1] *Panza* means "paunch"; *Zancas* means "shanks."

fortune which reserved him for greater things, turned aside the sword of his adversary, so that, although it smote him upon the left shoulder, it did him no more harm than to strip all that side of its armor, carrying away a great part of his helmet with half of his ear, all which with fearful ruin fell to the ground, leaving him in a sorry plight.

Good God! Who is there that could properly describe the rage that filled the heart of our Manchegan when he saw himself dealt with in this fashion? All that can be said is, it was such that he again raised himself in his stirrups, and, grasping his sword more firmly with both hands, he came down on the Biscayan with such fury, smiting him full over the cushion and over the head, that—even so good a shield proving useless—as if a mountain had fallen on him, he began to bleed from nose, mouth, and ears, reeling as if about to fall backwards from his mule, as no doubt he would have done had he not flung his arms about its neck; at the same time, however, he slipped his feet out of the stirrups and then unclasped his arms, and the mule, taking fright at the terrible blow, made off across the plain, and with a few plunges flung its master to the ground. Don Quixote stood looking on very calmly, and, when he saw him fall, leaped from his horse and with great briskness ran to him, and, presenting the point of his sword to his eyes, bade him surrender, or he would cut his head off. The Biscayan was so bewildered that he was unable to answer a word, and it would have gone hard with him, so blind was Don Quixote, had not the ladies in the coach, who had hitherto been watching the combat in great terror, hastened to where he stood and implored him with earnest entreaties to grant them the great grace and favor of sparing their squire's life; to which Don Quixote replied with much gravity and dignity, "In truth, fair ladies, I am well content to do what ye ask of me; but it must be on one condition and understanding, which is that this knight promise me to go to the village of El Toboso, and on my part present himself before the peerless lady Dulcinea, that she deal with him as shall be most pleasing to her."

The terrified and disconsolate ladies, without discussing Don Quixote's demand or asking who Dulcinea might be, promised that their squire should do all that had been commanded on his part.

"Then, on the faith of that promise," said Don Quixote, "I shall do him no further harm, though he well deserves it of me."

Chapter 10

Of the pleasant discourse that passed between Don Quixote and his squire Sancho Panza

Now by this time Sancho had risen, rather the worse for the handling of the friars' muleteers, and stood watching the battle of his master, Don Quixote, and praying to God in his heart that it might be his will to grant him the victory, and that he might thereby win some island to make him governor of, as he had promised. Seeing, therefore, that the struggle was now over, and that his master was returning to mount Rocinante, he approached to hold the stirrup for him, and, before he could mount, he went on his knees before him, and taking his hand, kissed it saying, "May it please your worship, Señor Don Quixote, to give me the government of that island which has been won in this hard fight, for be it ever so big I feel myself in sufficient force to be able to govern it as much and as well as any one in the world who has ever governed islands."

To which Don Quixote replied, "Thou must take notice, brother Sancho, that this adventure and those like it are not adventures of islands, but of cross-roads, in which nothing is got except a broken head or an ear the less: have patience, for adventures will present themselves from which I may make you not only a governor, but something more."

Sancho gave him many thanks, and again kissing his hand and the skirt of his hauberk, helped him to mount Rocinante, and mounting his ass himself, proceeded to follow his master, who at a brisk pace, without taking leave, or saying anything further to the ladies belonging to the coach, turned into a wood that was hard by. Sancho followed him at his ass's best trot, but Rocinante stepped out so that, seeing himself left behind, he was forced to call to his master to wait for him. Don Quixote did so, reining in Rocinante until his weary squire came up, who on reaching him said, "It seems to me, señor, it would be prudent in us to go and take refuge in some church, for, seeing how mauled he with whom you fought has been left, it will be no wonder if they give information of the affair to the Holy Brotherhood and arrest us, and, faith, if they do, before we come out of gaol we shall have to sweat for it."

"Peace," said Don Quixote; "where hast thou ever seen or heard that a knight-errant has been arraigned before a court of justice, however many homicides he may have committed?"

"I know nothing about omecils," answered

Sancho, "nor in my life have had anything to do with one; I only know that the Holy Brotherhood looks after those who fight in the fields, and in that other matter I do not meddle."

"Then thou needst have no uneasiness, my friend," said Don Quixote, "for I will deliver thee out of the hands of the Chaldeans, much more out of those of the Brotherhood. But tell me, as thou livest, hast thou seen a more valiant knight than I in all the known world; hast thou read in history of any who has or had higher mettle in attack, more spirit in maintaining it, more dexterity in wounding or skill in overthrowing?"

"The truth is," answered Sancho, "that I have never read any history, for I can neither read nor write, but what I will venture to bet is that a more daring master than your worship I have never served in all the days of my life, and God grant that this daring be not paid for where I have said; what I beg of your worship is to dress your wound, for a great deal of blood flows from that ear, and I have here some lint and a little white ointment in the *alforjas*."

"All that might be well dispensed with," said Don Quixote, "if I had remembered to make a vial of the balsam of Fierabras, for time and medicine are saved by one single drop."

"What vial and what balsam is that?" said Sancho Panza.

"It is a balsam," answered Don Quixote, "the receipt of which I have in my memory, with which one need have no fear of death, or dread dying of any wound; and so when I make it and give it to thee thou hast nothing to do when in some battle thou seest they have cut me in half through the middle of the body—as is wont to happen frequently—but neatly and with great nicety, ere the blood congeal, to place that portion of the body which shall have fallen to the ground upon the other half which remains in the saddle, taking care to fit it on evenly and exactly. Then thou shalt give me to drink but two drops of the balsam I have mentioned, and thou shalt see me become sounder than an apple."

"If that be so," said Panza, "I renounce henceforth the government of the promised island, and desire nothing more in payment of my many and faithful services than that your worship give me the receipt of this supreme liquor, for I am persuaded it will be worth more than two reals an ounce anywhere, and I want no more to pass the rest of my life in ease and honor; but it remains to be told if it costs much to make it."

"With less than three reals six quarts of it

may be made," said Don Quixote.

"Sinner that I am!" said Sancho, "then why does your worship put off making it and teaching it to me."

"Peace, friend," answered Don Quixote; "greater secrets I mean to teach thee and greater favors to bestow upon thee; and for the present let us see to the dressing, for my ear pains me more than I could wish."

Sancho took out some lint and ointment from the *alforjas*; but when Don Quixote came to see his helmet shattered, he was like to lose his senses, and, clapping his hand upon his sword and raising his eyes to heaven, he said, "I swear by the Creator of all things and the four Gospels in their fullest extent, to do as the great Marquis of Mantua did when he swore to avenge the death of his nephew Baldwin (and that was not to eat bread from a table-cloth, nor embrace his wife, and other points which, though I cannot now call them to mind, I here grant as expressed), until I take complete vengeance upon him who has committed such an offence against me."

Hearing this, Sancho said to him, "Your worship should bear in mind, Señor Don Quixote, that if the knight has done what was commanded him in going to present himself before my lady Dulcinea del Toboso, he will have done all that he was bound to do, and does not deserve further punishment unless he commits some new offence."

"Thou hast said well and hit the point," answered Don Quixote; "and so I recall the oath in so far as relates to taking fresh vengeance on him, but I make and confirm it anew to lead the life I have said until such time as I take by force from some knight another helmet such as this and as good; and think not, Sancho, that I am raising smoke with straw in doing so, for I have one to imitate in the matter, since the very same thing to a hair happened in the case of Mambrino's helmet, which cost Sacripante so dear."

"Señor," replied Sancho, "let your worship send all such oaths to the devil, for they are very pernicious to salvation and prejudicial to the conscience; just tell me now, if for several days to come we fall in with no man armed with a helmet, what are we to do? Is the oath to be observed in spite of all the inconvenience and discomfort it will be to sleep in your clothes, and not to sleep in a house, and a thousand other mortifications contained in the oath of that old fool, the Marquis of Mantua, which your worship is now wanting to revive? Let your worship observe that there are no men in armor travelling on any of these roads, nothing but carriers and carters, who not only do not wear helmets, but perhaps never heard tell of them all their lives."

"Thou art wrong there," said Don Quixote, "for we shall not have been two hours among these cross-roads before we see more men in armor than came to Albraca to win the fair Angelica."

"Enough," said Sancho; "so be it then, and God grant us success, and that the time for winning that island which is costing me so dear may soon come, and then let me die."

"I have already told thee, Sancho," said Don Quixote, "not to give thyself any uneasiness on that score; for if an island should fail, there is the kingdom of Denmark, or of Sobradisa, which will fit thee as a ring fits the finger, and all the more that being on *terra firma* thou wilt all the better enjoy thyself. But let us leave that to its own time; see if thou hast anything for us to eat in those *alforjas,* because we must presently go in quest of some castle where we may lodge tonight and make the balsam I told thee of, for I swear to thee by God, this ear is giving me great pain."

"I have here an onion and a little cheese and a few scraps of bread," said Sancho, "but they are not victuals fit for a valiant knight like your worship."

"How little thou knowest about it," answered Don Quixote; "I would have thee to know, Sancho, that it is the glory of knights-errant to go without eating for a month, and even when they do eat, that it should be of what comes first to hand; and this would have been clear to thee hadst thou read as many histories as I have, for, though they are very many, among them all I have found no mention made of knights-errant eating, unless by accident or at some sumptuous banquets prepared for them, and the rest of the time they passed in dalliance. And though it is plain they could not do without eating and performing all the other natural functions, because, in fact, they were men like ourselves, it is plain too that, wandering as they did the most part of their lives through woods and wilds and without a cook, their most usual fare would be rustic viands such as those thou dost now offer me; so that, friend Sancho, let not that distress thee which pleases me, and do not seek to make a new world or pervert knight-errantry."

"Pardon me, your worship," said Sancho, "for, as I can not read or write, as I said just now, I neither know nor comprehend the rules of the profession of chivalry: henceforward I will stock the *alforjas* with every kind of dry fruit for your worship, as you are a knight; and for myself, as I am not one, I will furnish them with poultry and other things more substantial."

"I do not say, Sancho," replied Don Quixote, "that it is imperative on knights-errant not to eat anything else but the fruits thou speakest of; only that their more usual diet must be those, and certain herbs they found in the fields which they knew and I know too."

"A good thing it is," answered Sancho, "to know those herbs, for to my thinking it will be needful some day to put that knowledge into practice."

And here taking out what he said he had brought, the pair made their repast peaceably and sociably. But anxious to find quarters for the night, they with all despatch made an end of their poor dry fare, mounted at once, and made haste to reach some habitation before night set in; but daylight and the hope of succeeding in their object failed them close by the huts of some goatherds, so they determined to pass the night there, and it was as much to Sancho's discontent not to have reached a house, as it was to his master's satisfaction to sleep under the open heaven, for he fancied that each time this happened to him he performed an act of ownership that helped to prove his chivalry.

Chapter 11

Of what befell Don Quixote with certain goatherds

HE was cordially welcomed by the goatherds, and Sancho, having as best he could put up Rocinante and the ass, drew towards the fragrance that came from some pieces of salted goat simmering in a pot on the fire; and though he would have liked at once to try if they were ready to be transferred from the pot to the stomach, he refrained from doing so as the goatherds removed them from the fire, and laying sheepskins on the ground, quickly spread their rude table, and with signs of hearty good-will invited them both to share what they had. Round the skins six of the men belonging to the fold seated themselves, having first with rough politeness pressed Don Quixote to take a seat upon a trough which they placed for him upside down. Don Quixote seated himself, and Sancho remained standing to serve the cup, which was made of horn. Seeing him standing, his master said to him, "That thou mayest see, Sancho, the good that knight-errantry contains in itself, and how those who fill any office in it are on the high road to be speedily honored and esteemed by the world, I desire that thou seat thyself here at my side and in the company of these worthy people, and that thou be one with me who am thy master and natural lord, and that thou eat from my plate and drink from whatever I drink from; for the same may be said of knight-errantry as of love, that it levels all."

"Great thanks," said Sancho, "but I may tell your worship that provided I have enough to eat, I can eat it as well, or better, standing, and by myself, than seated alongside of an emperor. And indeed, if the truth is to be told, what I eat in my corner without form or fuss has much more relish for me, even though it be bread and onions, than the turkeys of those other tables where I am forced to chew slowly, drink little, wipe my mouth every minute, and can not sneeze or cough if I want, or do other things that are the privileges of liberty and solitude. So, señor, as for these honors which your worship would put upon me as a servant and follower of knight-errantry (which I am, being your worship's squire), exchange them for other things which may be of more use and advantage to me; for these, though I fully acknowledge them as received, I renounce from this moment to the end of the world."

"For all that," said Don Quixote, "thou must seat thyself, because him who humbleth himself God exalteth"; and seizing him by the arm he forced him to sit down beside himself.

The goatherds did not understand this jargon about squires and knights-errant, and all they did was to eat in silence and stare at their guests, who, with great elegance and appetite, were stowing away pieces as big as one's fist. The course of meat finished, they spread upon the sheepskins a great heap of parched acorns, and with them they put down a half cheese harder than if it had been made of mortar. All this while the horn was not idle, for it went round so constantly, now full, now empty, like the bucket of a water-wheel, that it soon drained one of the two wine-skins that were in sight. When Don Quixote had quite appeased his appetite, he took up a handful of the acorns, and contemplating them attentively delivered himself somewhat in this fashion:

"Happy the age, happy the time, to which the ancients gave the name of golden, not because in that fortunate age the gold so coveted in this our iron one was gained without toil, but because they that lived in it knew not the two words '*mine*' and '*thine*'! In that blessed age all things were in common; to win the daily food, no labor was required of any save to stretch forth his hand and gather it from the sturdy oaks that stood generously inviting him with their sweet ripe fruit. The clear streams and running brooks yielded their savory limpid waters in noble abundance. The busy and sagacious bees fixed their republic in the clefts of the rocks and hollows of the trees, offering without usance the plenteous produce of their fragrant toil to every hand. The mighty cork trees, unenforced save of their own courtesy, shed the broad light bark that served at first to roof the houses supported by rude stakes, a protection against the inclemency of heaven alone. Then all was peace, all friendship, all concord; as yet the dull share of the crooked plough had not dared to rend and pierce the tender bowels of our first mother that without compulsion yielded from every portion of her broad fertile bosom all that could satisfy, sustain, and delight the children that then possessed her. Then was it that the innocent and fair young shepherdesses roamed from vale to vale and hill to hill, with flowing locks, and no more garments than were needful modestly to cover what modesty seeks and ever sought to hide. Nor were their ornaments like those in use to-day, set off by Tyrian purple, and silk tortured in endless fashions, but the wreathed leaves of the green dock and ivy, wherewith they went as bravely and becomingly decked as our Court dames with all the rare and far-fetched artifices that idle curiosity has taught them. Then the love-thoughts of the heart clothed themselves simply and naturally as the heart conceived them, nor sought to commend themselves by forced and rambling verbiage. Fraud, deceit, or malice had then not yet mingled with truth and sincerity. Justice held her ground, undisturbed and unassailed by the efforts of favor and of interest, that now so much impair, pervert, and beset her. Arbitrary law had not yet established itself in the mind of the judge, for then there was no cause to judge, and no one to be judged. Maidens and modesty, as I have said, wandered at will alone and unattended, without fear of insult from lawlessness or libertine assault, and if they were undone it was of their own will and pleasure. But now, in this hateful age of ours, not one is safe, not though some new labyrinth like that of Crete conceal and surround her; even there the pestilence of gallantry will make its way to them through chinks or on the air by the zeal of its accursed importunity, and, despite of all seclusion, lead them to ruin. In defence of these, as time advanced and wickedness increased, the order of knights-errant was instituted, to defend maidens, to protect widows, and to succor the orphans and the needy. To this order I belong, brother goatherds, to whom I return thanks for the hospitality and kindly welcome ye offer me and my squire; for though by natural law all living are bound to show favor to knights-errant, yet, seeing that without knowing this obligation ye have welcomed and feasted me, it is right that with all the good-will in my power I should thank you for yours."

All this long harangue (which might very well have been spared) our knight delivered because the acorns they gave him reminded him of the golden age; and the whim seized him to address all this unnecessary argument to the goatherds, who listened to him gaping in amazement without saying a word in reply. Sancho likewise held his peace and ate acorns, and paid repeated visits to the second wine-skin, which they had hung up on a cork tree to keep the wine cool.

Don Quixote was longer in talking than in finishing his supper, at the end of which one of the goatherds said, "That your worship, señor knight-errant, may say with more truth that we show you hospitality with ready good-will, we will give you amusement and pleasure by making one of our comrades sing: he will be here before long, and he is a very intelligent youth and deep in love, and what is more he can read and write and play on the rebeck to perfection."

The goatherd had hardly done speaking, when the notes of the rebeck reached their ears; and shortly after, the player came up, a very good-looking young man of about two-and-twenty. His comrades asked him if he had supped, and on his replying that he had, he who had already made the offer said to him, "In that case, Antonio, thou mayest as well do us the pleasure of singing a little, that the gentleman, our guest here, may see that even in the mountains and woods there are musicians: we have told him of thy accomplishments, and we want thee to show them and prove that we say true; so, as thou livest, pray sit down and sing that ballad about thy love that thy uncle the prebendary made thee, and that was so much liked in the town."

"With all my heart," said the young man, and without waiting for any more pressing he seated himself on the trunk of a felled oak, and tuning his rebeck, presently began with right good grace to sing to these words.

Antonio's Ballad

Thou dost love me well, Olalla;
  Well I know it, even though
Love's mute tongues, thine eyes, have never
  By their glances told me so.

For I know my love thou knowest,
  Therefore thine to claim I dare:
Once it ceases to be secret,
  Love need never feel despair.

True it is, Olalla, sometimes
  Thou hast all too plainly shown
That thy heart is brass in hardness,
  And thy snowy bosom stone.

Yet for all that, in thy coyness,
  And thy fickle fits between,
Hope is there—at least the border
  Of her garment may be seen.

Lures to faith are they, those glimpses,
  And to faith in thee I hold;
Kindness can not make it stronger,
  Coldness can not make it cold.

If it be that love is gentle,
  In thy gentleness I see
Something holding out assurance
  To the hope of winning thee.

If it be that in devotion
  Lies a power hearts to move,
That which every day I show thee,
  Helpful to my suit should prove.

Many a time thou must have noticed—
  If to notice thou dost care—
How I go about on Monday
  Dressed in all my Sunday wear.

Love's eyes love to look on brightness;
  Love loves what is gayly drest;
Sunday, Monday, all I care is
  Thou shouldst see me in my best.

No account I make of dances,
  Or of strains that pleased thee so,
Keeping thee awake from midnight
  Till the cocks began to crow;

Or of how I roundly swore it
  That there's none so fair as thou;
True it is, but as I said it,
  By the girls I'm hated now.

For Teresa of the hillside
  At my praise of thee was sore;
Said, "You think you love an angel;
  It's a monkey you adore;

"Caught by all her glittering trinkets,
  And her borrowed braids of hair,
And a host of made-up beauties
  That would Love himself ensnare."

'T was a lie, and so I told her,
  And her cousin at the word
Gave me his defiance for it;
  And what followed thou hast heard.

Mine is no high-flown affection,
  Mine no passion par amours—
As they call it—what I offer
  Is an honest love, and pure.

Cunning cords the holy Church has,
  Cords of softest silk they be;
Put thy neck beneath the yoke, dear;
  Mine wilt follow, thou wilt see.

Else—and once for all I swear it
  By the saint of most renown—
If I ever quit the mountains,
  'T will be in a friar's gown.

Here the goatherd brought his song to an end, and though Don Quixote entreated him to sing more, Sancho had no mind that way, being more inclined for sleep than for listening to songs; so said he to his master, "Your worship will do well to settle at once where you mean to pass the night, for the labor these good men are at all day does not allow them to spend the night in singing."

"I understand thee, Sancho," replied Don Quixote; "I perceive clearly that those visits to the wine-skin demand compensation in sleep rather than in music."

"It's sweet to us all, blessed be God," said Sancho.

"I do not deny it," replied Don Quixote; "but settle thyself where thou wilt; those of my calling are more becomingly employed in watching than in sleeping; still it would be as well if thou wert to dress this ear for me again, for it is giving me more pain than it need."

Sancho did as he bade him, but one of the goatherds seeing the wound told him not to be uneasy, as he would apply a remedy with which it would be soon healed; and gathering some leaves of rosemary, of which there was a great quantity there, he chewed them and mixed them with a little salt, and applying them to the ear he secured them firmly with a bandage, assuring him that no other treatment would be required, and so it proved.

Chapter 12

Of what a goatherd related to those with Don Quixote

Just then another young man, one of those who fetched their provisions from the village, came up and said, "Do you know what is going on in the village, comrades?"

"How could we know it?" replied one of them.

"Well, then, you must know," continued the young man, "this morning that famous student-shepherd called Chrysostom died, and it is rumored that he died of love for that devil of a village girl the daughter of Guillermo the Rich, she that wanders about the wolds here in the dress of a shepherdess."

"You mean Marcela?" said one.

"Her I mean," answered the goatherd; "and the best of it is, he has directed in his will that he is to be buried in the fields like a Moor, and at the foot of the rock where the Cork-tree spring is, because, as the story goes (and they say he himself said so), that was the place where he first saw her. And he has also left other directions which the clergy of the village say should not and must not be obeyed because they savor of paganism. To all which his great friend Ambrosio the student, he who, like him, also went dressed as a shepherd, replies that everything must be done without any omission according to the directions left by Chrysostom, and about this the village is all in commotion; however, report says that, after all, what Ambrosio and all the shepherds his friends desire will be done, and to-morrow they are coming to bury him with great ceremony where I said. I am sure it will be something worth seeing; at least I will not fail to go and see it even if I knew I should not return to the village to-morrow."

"We will do the same," answered the goatherds, "and cast lots to see who must stay to mind the goats of all."

"Thou sayest well, Pedro," said one, "though there will be no need of taking that trouble, for I will stay behind for all; and don't suppose it is virtue or want of curiosity in me; it is that the splinter that ran into my foot the other day will not let me walk."

"For all that, we thank thee," answered Pedro.

Don Quixote asked Pedro to tell him who the dead man was and who the shepherdess, to which Pedro replied that all he knew was that the dead man was a wealthy gentleman belonging to a village in those mountains, who had been a student at Salamanca for many years, at the end of which he returned to his village with the reputation of being very learned and deeply read. Above all, they said, he was learned in the science of the stars and of what went on yonder in the heavens and the sun and the moon, for he told us of the cris of the sun and moon to the exact time.

"Eclipse it is called, friend, not cris, the darkening of those two luminaries," said Don Quixote; but Pedro, not troubling himself with trifles, went on with his story, saying, "Also he foretold when the year was going to be one of abundance or estility."

"Sterility, you mean, friend," said Don Quixote.

"Sterility or estility," answered Pedro, "it is all the same in the end. And I can tell you that by this his father and friends who believed him grew very rich because they did as he advised them, bidding them 'sow barley this year, not wheat; this year you may sow pulse [chick-peas] and not barley; the next there will be a full oil crop, and the three following not a drop will be got.'"

"That science is called astrology," said Don Quixote.

"I do not know what it is called," replied Pedro, "but I know that he knew all this and more besides. But, to make an end, not many months had passed after he returned from Salamanca, when one day he appeared dressed as a shepherd with his crook and sheepskin, having put off the long gown he wore as a scholar; and at the same time his great friend, Ambrosio by name, who had been his companion in his studies, took to the shepherd's dress with him. I forgot to say that Chrysostom who is dead was a great man for writing verses, so much so that he made carols for Christmas Eve, and plays for Corpus Christi which the young men of our village acted, and all said they were excellent. When the villagers saw the two scholars so unexpectedly appearing in shepherd's dress they were lost in wonder, and could not guess what had led them to make so extraordinary a change. About this time the father of our Chrysostom died, and he was left heir to a large amount of property in chattels as well as in land, no small number of cattle and sheep, and a large sum of money, of all of which the young man was left dissolute owner, and indeed he was deserving of it all, for he was a very good comrade, and kind-hearted, and a friend of worthy folk, and had a countenance like a benediction. Presently it came to be known that he had changed his dress with no other object than to wander about these wastes after that shepherdess Marcela our lad mentioned a while ago, with whom the deceased Chrysostom had fallen in love. And I must tell you now, for it is well you should know it, who this girl is; perhaps, and even without any perhaps, you will not have heard anything like it all the days of your life, though you should live more years than *sarna*."

"Say Sara," said Don Quixote, unable to endure the goatherd's confusion of words.

"The *sarna* [the itch] lives long enough," answered Pedro; "and if, señor, you must go finding fault with words at every step, we shall not make an end of it this twelvemonth."

"Pardon me, friend," said Don Quixote; "but, as there is such a difference between *sarna* and Sara, I told you of it; however, you have answered very rightly, for *sarna* lives longer than Sara: so continue your story, and I will not object any more to anything."

"I say then, my dear sir," said the goatherd, "that in our village there was a farmer even richer than the father of Chrysostom, who was named Guillermo, and upon whom God bestowed, over and above great wealth, a daughter at whose birth her mother died, the most respected woman there was in this neighborhood; I fancy I can see her now with that countenance which had the sun on one side and the moon on the other; and moreover active, and kind to the poor, for which I trust that at the present moment her soul is in bliss with God in the other world. Her husband Guillermo died of grief at the death of so good a wife, leaving his daughter Marcela, a child and rich, to the care of an uncle of hers, a priest and prebendary in our village. The girl grew up with such beauty that it reminded us of her mother's, which was very great, and yet it was thought that the daughter's would exceed it; and so when she reached the age of fourteen to fifteen years nobody beheld her without blessing God that had made her so beautiful, and the greater number were in love with her beyond redemption. Her uncle kept her in great seclusion and retirement, but for all that the fame of her great beauty spread so that, as well for it as for her great wealth, her uncle was asked, solicited, and importuned, to give her in marriage by those not only of our town but of towns many leagues round, and by the persons of highest quality in them. But he, being a good Christian man, though he desired to give her in marriage at once, seeing her to be old enough, was unwilling to do so without her consent, not that he had any eye to the gain and profit which the custody of the girl's property brought him while he put off her marriage; and, faith, this was said in praise of the good priest in more than one set in the town. For I would have you know, Sir Errant, that in these little villages everything is talked about and everything is carped at; and rest assured, as I am, that the priest must be over and above good who forces his parishioners to speak well of him, especially in villages."

"That is the truth," said Don Quixote; "but go on, for the story is very good, and you, good Pedro, tell it with very good grace."

"May that of the Lord not be wanting to me," said Pedro; "that is the one to have. To proceed: you must know that though the uncle put before his niece and described to her the qualities of each one in particular of the many who had asked her in marriage, begging her to marry and make a choice according to her own taste, she never gave any other answer than that she had no desire to marry just yet, and that being so young she did not think herself fit to bear the burden of matrimony. At these, to all appearance, reasonable excuses that she made, her uncle ceased to urge her, and waited till she was somewhat more advanced in age and could mate herself to her own liking. For, said he—and he said quite right—parents are not to settle children in life against their will. But when one least looked for it, lo and behold! one day the demure Marcela makes her appearance turned shepherdess; and, in spite of her uncle and all those of the town that strove to dissuade her, took to going a-field with the other shepherd-lasses of the village, and tending her own flock. And so, since she appeared in public, and her beauty came to be seen openly, I could not well tell you how many rich youths, gentlemen and peasants, have adopted the costume of Chrysostom, and go about these fields making love to her. One of these, as has been already said, was our deceased friend, of whom they say that he did not love but adore her. But you must not suppose, because Marcela chose a life of such liberty and independence, and of so little or rather no retirement, that she has given any occasion, or even the semblance of one, for disparagement of her purity and modesty; on the contrary, such and so great is the vigilance with which she watches over her honor, that of all those that court and woo her not one has boasted, or can with truth boast, that she has given him any hope however small of obtaining his desire. For although she does not avoid or shun the society and conversation of the shepherds, and treats them courteously and kindly, should any one of them come to declare his intention to her, though it be one as proper and holy as that of matrimony, she flings him from her like a catapult. And with this kind of disposition she does more harm in this country than if the plague had got into it, for her affability and her beauty draw on the hearts of those that associate with her to love her and to court her, but her scorn and her frankness bring them to the brink of despair; and so they know not what to say save to proclaim her aloud cruel and hard-hearted, and other names of the same sort which well describe the nature of her character; and if you should remain here any time, señor, you would hear these hills and valleys resounding with the laments of the rejected ones who pursue her. Not far from this there is a spot where there are a couple of dozen of tall beeches, and there is not one of them but has carved and written on its smooth bark the name of Marcela, and above some a crown carved on the same tree as though her lover would say more plainly that Marcela wore and deserved that of all human beauty. Here one shepherd is sighing, there another is lamenting; there love songs are heard, here despairing elegies. One will pass all the hours of the night seated at the foot of some oak or rock, and there, without having closed his weeping eyes, the sun finds him in the morning bemused and bereft of sense; and another without relief or respite to his sighs, stretched on the burning sand in the full heat of the sultry summer noontide, makes his appeal to the compassionate heavens, and over one and the other, over these and all, the beautiful Marcela triumphs free and careless. And all of us that know her are waiting to see what her pride will come to, and who is to be the happy man that will succeed in taming a nature so formidable and gaining possession of a beauty so supreme. All that I have told you being such well-established truth, I am persuaded that what they say of the cause of Chrysostom's death, as our lad told us, is the same. And so I advise you, señor, fail not to be present to-morrow at his burial, which will be well worth seeing, for Chrysostom had many friends, and it is not half a league from this place to where he directed he should be buried."

"I will make a point of it," said Don Quixote, "and I thank you for the pleasure you have given me by relating so interesting a tale."

"Oh," said the goatherd, "I do not know even the half of what has happened to the lovers of Marcela, but perhaps to-morrow we may fall in with some shepherd on the road who can tell us; and now it will be well for you to go and sleep under cover, for the night air may hurt your wound, though with the remedy I have applied to you there is no fear of an untoward result."

Sancho Panza, who was wishing the goatherd's loquacity at the devil, on his part begged his master to go into Pedro's hut to sleep. He did so, and passed all the rest of the night in thinking of his lady Dulcinea, in imitation of the lovers of Marcela. Sancho Panza settled himself between Rocinante and his ass, and slept, not like a lover who had been discarded, but like a man who had been soundly kicked.

Chapter 13

In which is ended the story of the shepherdess Marcela, with other incidents

But hardly had day begun to show itself through the balconies of the east, when five of the six goatherds come to rouse Don Quixote and tell him that if he was still of a mind to go and see the famous burial of Chrysostom they would bear him company. Don Quixote, who desired nothing better, rose and ordered Sancho to saddle and pannel at once, which he did with all despatch, and with the same they all set out forthwith. They had not gone a quarter of a league when at the meeting of two paths they saw coming towards them some six shepherds dressed in black sheepskins and with their heads crowned with garlands of cypress and bitter oleander. Each of them carried a stout holly staff in his hand, and along with them there came two men of quality on horseback in handsome travelling dress, with three servants on foot accompanying them. Courteous salutations were exchanged on meeting, and inquiring one of the other which way each party was going, they learned that all were bound for the scene of the burial, so they went on all together.

One of those on horseback addressing his companion said to him, "It seems to me, Señor Vivaldo, that we may reckon as well spent the delay we shall incur in seeing this remarkable funeral, for remarkable it cannot but be judging by the strange things these shepherds have told us, of both the dead shepherd and homicide shepherdess."

"So I think too," replied Vivaldo, "and I would delay not to say a day, but four, for the sake of seeing it."

Don Quixote asked them what it was they had heard of Marcela and Chrysostom. The traveller answered that the same morning they had met these shepherds, and seeing them dressed in this mournful fashion they had asked them the reason of their appearing in such a guise; which one of them gave, describing the strange behavior and beauty of a shepherdess called Marcela, and the loves of many who courted her, together with the death of that Chrysostom to whose burial they were going. In short, he repeated all that Pedro had related to Don Quixote.

This conversation dropped, and another was commenced by him who was called Vivaldo asking Don Quixote what was the reason that led him to go armed in that fashion in a country so peaceful. To which Don Quixote replied, "The pursuit of my calling does not allow or permit me to go in any other fashion; easy life, enjoyment, and repose were invented for soft courtiers, but toil, unrest, and arms, were invented and made for those alone whom the world calls knights-errant, of whom I, though unworthy, am the least of all."

The instant they heard this all set him down as mad, and the better to settle the point and discover what kind of madness his was, Vivaldo proceeded to ask him what knights-errant meant.

"Have not your worships," replied Don Quixote, "read the annals and histories of England, in which are recorded the famous deeds of King Arthur, whom we in our popular Castilian invariably call King Artus, with regard to whom it is an ancient tradition, and commonly received all over that kingdom of Great Britain, that this king did not die, but was changed by magic art into a raven, and that in process of time he is to return to reign and recover his kingdom and sceptre; for which reason it cannot be proved that from that time to this any Englishman ever killed a raven? Well, then, in the time of this good king that famous order of chivalry of the Knights of the Round Table was instituted, and the amour of Don Lancelot of the Lake with the Queen Guinevere occurred, precisely as is there related, the go-between and confidante therein being the highly honorable dame Quintañona, whence came that ballad so well known and widely spread in our Spain—

> *O never surely was there knight*
> *So served by hand of dame,*
> *As served was he Sir Lancelot hight*
> *When he from Britain came—*

with all the sweet and delectable course of his achievements in love and war. Handed down from that time, then, this order of chivalry went on extending and spreading itself over many and various parts of the world; and in it, famous and renowned for their deeds, were the mighty Amadis of Gaul with all his sons and descendants to the fifth generation, and the valiant Felixmarte of Hircania, and the never sufficiently praised Tirante el Blanco, and in our own days almost we have seen and heard and talked with the invincible knight Don Belianis of Greece. This, then, sirs, is to be a knight-errant, and what I have spoken of is the order of his chivalry, of which, as I have already said, I, though a sinner, have made profession, and what the aforesaid knights professed that same do I profess, and so I go through these solitudes and wilds seeking adventures, resolved in soul to oppose my arm and person to the most perilous that fortune may offer me in aid of the weak and needy."

By these words of his the travellers were able to satisfy themselves of Don Quixote's being out of his senses and of the form of madness that overmastered him, at which they felt the same astonishment that all felt on first becoming acquainted with it; and Vivaldo, who was a person of great shrewdness and of a lively temperament, in order to beguile the short journey which they said was required to reach the mountain, the scene of the burial, sought to give him an opportunity of going on with his absurdities. So he said to him, "It seems to me, Señor Knight-errant, that your worship has made choice of one of the most austere professions in the world, and I imagine even that of the Carthusian monks is not so austere."

"As austere it may perhaps be," replied our Don Quixote, "but so necessary for the world I am very much inclined to doubt. For, if the truth is to be told, the soldier who executes what his captain orders does no less than the captain himself who gives the order. My meaning is, that churchmen in peace and quiet pray to Heaven for the welfare of the world, but we soldiers and knights carry into effect what they pray for, defending it with the might of our arms and the edge of our swords, not under shelter but in the open air, a target for the intolerable rays of the sun in summer and the piercing frosts of winter. Thus are we God's ministers on earth and the arms in which his justice is done therein. And as the business of war and all that relates and belongs to it cannot be conducted without exceeding great sweat, toil, and exertion, it follows that those who make it their profession have undoubtedly more labor than those who in tranquil peace and quiet are engaged in praying to God to help the weak. I do not mean to say, nor does it enter into my thoughts, that the knight-errant's calling is as good as that of the monk in his cell; I would merely infer from what I endure myself that it is beyond a doubt a more laborious and a more belabored one, a hungrier and thirstier, a wretch-

eder, raggeder, and lousier; for there is no reason to doubt that the knights-errant of yore endured much hardship in the course of their lives. And if some of them by the might of their arms did rise to be emperors, in faith it cost them dear in the matter of blood and sweat; and if those who attained to that rank had not had magicians and sages to help them they would have been completely balked in their ambition and disappointed in their hopes."

"That is my own opinion," replied the traveller; "but one thing among many others seems to me very wrong in knights-errant, and that is that when they find themselves about to engage in some mighty and perilous adventure in which there is manifest danger of losing their lives, they never at the moment of engaging in it think of commending themselves to God, as is the duty of every good Christian in like peril; instead of which they commend themselves to their ladies with as much heartiness and devotion as if these were their gods, a thing which seems to me to savor somewhat of heathenism."

"Sir," answered Don Quixote, "that can not be on any account omitted, and the knight-errant would be disgraced who acted otherwise: for it is usual and customary in knight-errantry that the knight-errant who on engaging in any great feat of arms has his lady before him, should turn his eyes towards her softly and lovingly, as though with them entreating her to favor and protect him in the hazardous venture he is about to undertake, and even though no one hear him, he is bound to say certain words between his teeth, commending himself to her with all his heart, and of this we have innumerable instances in the histories. Nor is it to be supposed from this that they are to omit commending themselves to God, for there will be time and opportunity for doing so while they are engaged in their task."

"For all that," answered the traveller, "I feel some doubt still, because often I have read how words will arise between two knights-errant, and from one thing to another it comes about that their anger kindles and they wheel their horses round and take a good stretch of field, and then without any more ado at the top of their speed they come to the charge, and in mid-career they commend themselves to their ladies; and what commonly comes of the encounter is that one falls over the haunches of his horse pierced through and through by his antagonist's lance, and as for the other, it is only by holding on to the mane of his horse that he can help falling to the ground; but I know not how the dead man had time to commend himself to God in the course of such rapid work as this; it would have been better if those words which he spent in commending himself to his lady in the midst of his career had been devoted to his duty and obligation as a Christian. Moreover, it is my belief that all knights-errant have not ladies to commend themselves to, for they are not all in love."

"That is impossible," said Don Quixote, "I say it is impossible that there could be a knight-errant without a lady, because to such it is as natural and proper to be in love as to the heavens to have stars; most certainly no history has been seen in which there is to be found a knight-errant without an amour, and for the simple reason that without one he would be held no legitimate knight, but a bastard, and one who had gained entrance into the stronghold of the said knighthood, not by the door, but over the wall like a thief and a robber."

"Nevertheless," said the traveller, "if I remember rightly, I think I have read that Don Galaor, the brother of the valiant Amadis of Gaul, never had any special lady to whom he might commend himself, and yet he was not the less esteemed, and was a very stout and famous knight."

To which our Don Quixote made answer, "Sir, one solitary swallow does not make summer; moreover, I know that that knight was in secret very deeply in love; besides which, that way of falling in love with all that took his fancy was a natural propensity which he could not control. But, in short, it is very manifest that he had one alone whom he made mistress of his will, to whom he commended himself frequently and very secretly, for he prided himself on being a reticent knight."

"Then if it be essential that every knight-errant should be in love," said the traveller, "it may be fairly supposed that your worship is so, as you are of the order; and if you do not pride yourself on being as reticent as Don Galaor, I entreat you as earnestly as I can, in the name of all this company and in my own, to inform us of the name, country, rank, and beauty of your lady, for she will esteem herself fortunate if all the world knows that she is loved and served by such a knight as your worship seems to be."

At this Don Quixote heaved a deep sigh, and said, "I can not say positively whether my sweet enemy is pleased or not that the world should know I serve her; I can only say in answer to what has been so courteously asked of me, that her name is Dulcinea, her country El Toboso,

a village of La Mancha, her rank must be at least that of a princess, since she is my queen and lady, and her beauty superhuman, since all the impossible and fanciful attributes of beauty which the poets apply to their ladies are verified in her; for her hairs are gold, her forehead Elysian fields, her eyebrows rainbows, her eyes suns, her cheeks roses, her lips coral, her teeth pearls, her neck alabaster, her bosom marble, her hands ivory, her fairness snow, and what modesty conceals from sight such, I think and imagine, as rational reflection can only extol, not compare."

"We should like to know her lineage, race, and ancestry," said Vivaldo.

To which Don Quixote replied, "She is not of the ancient Roman Curtii, Caii, or Scipios, nor of the modern Colonnas or Orsini, nor of the Moncadas or Requesenes of Catalonia, nor yet of the Rebellas or Villanovas of Valencia; Palafoxes, Nuzas, Rocabertis, Corellas, Lunas, Alagones, Urreas, Foces, or Gurreas of Aragon; Cerdas, Manriques, Mendozas, or Guzmans of Castile; Alencastros, Pallas, or Meneses of Portugal; but she is of those of El Toboso of La Mancha, a lineage that, though modern, may furnish a source of gentle blood for the most illustrious families of the ages that are to come, and this let none dispute with me save on the condition that Zerbino placed at the foot of the trophy of Orlando's arms saying,

> These let none move
> Who dareth not his might with Roland prove."

"Although mine is of the Cachopins of Laredo," said the traveller, "I will not venture to compare it with that of El Toboso of La Mancha, though, to tell the truth, no such surname has until now ever reached my ears."

"What!" said Don Quixote, "has that never reached them?"

The rest of the party went along listening with great attention to the conversation of the pair, and even the very goatherds and shepherds perceived how exceedingly out of his wits our Don Quixote was. Sancho Panza alone thought that what his master said was the truth, knowing who he was and having known him from his birth; and all that he felt any difficulty in believing was that about the fair Dulcinea del Toboso, because neither any such name nor any such princess had ever come to his knowledge though he lived so close to El Toboso. They were going along conversing in this way, when they saw descending a gap between two high mountains some twenty shepherds, all clad in sheepskins of black wool, and crowned with garlands which, as afterwards appeared, were, some of them of yew, some of cypress. Six of the number were carrying a bier covered with a great variety of flowers and branches, on seeing which one of the goatherds said, "Those who come there are the bearers of Chrysostom's body, and the foot of that mountain is the place where he ordered them to bury him." They therefore made haste to reach the spot, and did so by the time those who came had laid the bier upon the ground, and four of them with sharp pickaxes were digging a grave by the side of a hard rock. They greeted each other courteously, and then Don Quixote and those who accompanied him turned to examine the bier, and on it, covered with flowers, they saw a dead body in the dress of a shepherd, to all appearance of one thirty years of age, and showing even in death that in life he had been of comely features and gallant bearing. Around him on the bier itself were laid some books, and several papers open and folded; and those who were looking on as well as those who were opening the grave and all the others who were there preserved a strange silence, until one of those who had borne the body said to another, "Observe carefully, Ambrosio, if this is the place Chrysostom spoke of, since you are anxious that what he directed in his will should be so strictly complied with."

"This is the place," answered Ambrosio, "for in it many a time did my poor friend tell me the story of his hard fortune. Here it was, he told me, that he saw for the first time that mortal enemy of the human race, and here, too, for the first time he declared to her his passion, as honorable as it was devoted, and here it was that at last Marcela ended by scorning and rejecting him so as to bring the tragedy of his wretched life to a close; here, in memory of misfortunes so great, he desired to be laid in the bowels of eternal oblivion." Then turning to Don Quixote and the travellers he went on to say, "That body, sirs, on which you are looking with compassionate eyes, was the abode of a soul on which Heaven bestowed a vast share of its riches. That is the body of Chrysostom, who was unrivalled in wit, unequalled in courtesy, unapproached in gentle bearing, a phœnix in friendship, generous without limit, grave without arrogance, gay without vulgarity, and, in short, first in all that constitutes goodness and second to none in all that makes up misfortune. He loved deeply, he was hated; he adored, he was scorned; he wooed a wild beast, he pleaded with marble, he pursued the wind, he cried to the wilderness, he served ingratitude, and for reward was made the prey of death in the midcourse of life, cut short by a shepherdess whom he sought to immortalize in the memory of mankind, as these papers which you see could fully prove, had he not commanded me to consign them to the fire after having consigned his body to the earth."

"You would deal with them more harshly and cruelly than their owner himself," said Vivaldo, "for it is neither right nor proper to do the will of one who enjoins what is wholly unreasonable; it would not have been reasonable in Augustus Cæsar had he permitted the directions left by the divine Mantuan in his will to be carried into effect. So that, Señor Ambrosio, while you consign your friend's body to the earth, you should not consign his writings to oblivion, for if he gave the order in bitterness of heart, it is not right that you should irrationally obey it. On the contrary, by granting life to those papers, let the cruelty of Marcela live forever, to serve as a warning in ages to come to all men to shun and avoid falling into like danger: for I and all of us who have come here know already the story of this your love-stricken and heart-broken friend, and we know, too, your friendship, and the cause of his death, and the directions he gave at the close of his life; from which sad story may be gathered how great was the cruelty of Marcela, the love of Chrysostom, and the loyalty of your friendship, together with the end awaiting those who pursue rashly the path that insane passion opens to their eyes. Last night we learned the death of Chrysostom and that he was to be buried here, and out of curiosity and pity we left our direct road and resolved to come and see with our eyes that which when heard of had so moved our compassion, and in consideration of that compassion and our desire to prove it if we might by condolence, we beg of you, excellent Ambrosio, or at least I on my own account entreat you, that instead of burning those papers you allow me to carry away some of them."

And without waiting for the shepherd's answer, he stretched out his hand and took up some of those that were nearest to him; seeing which Ambrosio said, "Out of courtesy, señor, I will grant your request as to those you have taken, but it is idle to expect me to abstain from burning the remainder."

Vivaldo, who was eager to see what the papers contained, opened one of them at once, and saw that its title was *Lay of Despair*.

Ambrosio hearing it said, "That is the last paper the unhappy man wrote; and that you may see, señor, to what an end his misfortunes brought him, read it so that you may be heard, for you will have time enough for that while we are waiting for the grave to be dug."

"I will do so very willingly," said Vivaldo; and as all the bystanders were equally eager they gathered round him, and he, reading in a loud voice, found that it ran as follows.

Chapter 14

Wherein are inserted the despairing verses of the dead shepherd, together with other incidents not looked for

The Lay of Chrysostom

Since thou dost in thy cruelty desire
The ruthless rigor of thy tyranny
From tongue to tongue, from land to land
    proclaimed,
The very Hell will I constrain to lend
This stricken breast of mine deep notes of woe
To serve my need of fitting utterance.
And as I strive to body forth the tale
Of all I suffer, all that thou hast done,
Forth shall the dread voice roll, and bear along
Shreds from my vitals torn for greater pain.
Then listen, not to dulcet harmony,
But to a discord wrung by mad despair
Out of this bosom's depths of bitterness,
To ease my heart and plant a sting in thine.

The lion's roar, the fierce wolf's savage howl,
The horrid hissing of the scaly snake,
The awesome cries of monsters yet unnamed,
The crow's ill-boding croak, the hollow moan
Of wild winds wrestling with the restless sea,
The wrathful bellow of the vanquished bull,
The plaintive sobbing of the widowed dove,
The envied owl's sad note, the wail of woe
That rises from the dreary choir of Hell,
Commingled in one sound, confusing sense,
Let all these come to aid my soul's complaint,
For pain like mine demands new modes of song.

No echoes of that discord shall be heard
Where Father Tagus rolls, or on the banks
Of olive-bordered Betis; to the rocks
Or in deep caverns shall my plaint be told,
And by a lifeless tongue in living words;
Or in dark valleys or on lonely shores,
Where neither foot of man nor sunbeam falls;
Or in among the poison-breathing swarms
Of monsters nourished by the sluggish Nile.
For, though it be to solitudes remote
The hoarse vague echoes of my sorrows sound
Thy matchless cruelty, my dismal fate
Shall carry them to all the spacious world.

Disdain hath power to kill, and patience dies
Slain by suspicion, be it false or true;

And deadly is the force of jealousy:
Long absence makes of life a dreary void;
No hope of happiness can give repose
To him that ever fears to be forgot;
And death, inevitable, waits in all.
But I, by some strange miracle, live on
A prey to absence, jealousy, disdain;
Racked by suspicion as by certainty;
Forgotten, left to feed my flame alone.
And while I suffer thus, there comes no ray
Of hope to gladden me athwart the gloom;
Nor do I look for it in my despair;
But rather clinging to a cureless woe,
All hope do I abjure for evermore.

Can there be hope where fear is? Were it
    well,
When far more certain are the grounds of fear?
Ought I to shut mine eyes to jealousy,
If through a thousand heart-wounds it appears?
Who would not give free access to distrust,
Seeing disdain unveiled, and—bitter change!—
All his suspicions turned to certainties,
And the fair truth transformed into a lie?
Oh, thou fierce tyrant of the realms of love
Oh, Jealousy! put chains upon these hands,
And bind me with thy strongest cord, Disdain.
But, woe is me! triumphant over all,
My sufferings drown the memory of you.

And now I die, and since there is no hope
Of happiness for me in life or death,
Still to my fantasy I'll fondly cling.
I'll say that he is wise who loveth well,
And that the soul most free is that most bound
In thraldom to the ancient tyrant Love.
I'll say that she who is mine enemy
In that fair body hath as fair a mind,
And that her coldness is but my desert,
And that by virtue of the pain he sends
Love rules his kingdom with a gentle sway.
Thus, self-deluding, and in bondage sore,
And wearing out the wretched shred of life
To which I am reduced by her disdain,
I'll give this soul and body to the winds,
All hopeless of a crown of bliss in store.

Thou whose injustice hath supplied the
    cause
That makes me quit the weary life I loathe,
As by this wounded bosom thou canst see
How willingly thy victim I become,
Let not my death, if haply worth a tear,
Cloud the clear heaven that dwells in thy
    bright eyes;
I would not have thee expiate in aught
The crime of having made my heart thy prey;
But rather let thy laughter gayly ring
And prove my death to be thy festival.
Fool that I am to bid thee! well I know
Thy glory gains by my untimely end.

And now it is the time; from Hell's abyss
Come thirsting Tantalus, come Sisyphus

Heaving the cruel stone, come Tityus
With vulture, and with wheel Ixion come,
And come the sisters of the ceaseless toil;
And all into this breast transfer their pains,
And (if such tribute to despair be due)
Chant in their deepest tones a doleful dirge
Over a corse unworthy of a shroud.
Let the three-headed guardian of the gate,
And all the monstrous progeny of hell,
The doleful concert join: a lover dead
Methinks can have no fitter obsequies.

    Lay of despair, grieve not when thou are
        gone
Forth from this sorrowing heart: my misery
Brings fortune to the cause that gave thee
        birth;
Then banish sadness even in the tomb.

The Lay of Chrysostom met with the approbation of the listeners, though the reader said it
did not seem to him to agree with what he had
heard of Marcela's reserve and propriety, for
Chrysostom complained in it of jealousy, suspicion, and absence, all to the prejudice of the
good name and fame of Marcela; to which Ambrosio replied as one who knew well his friend's
most secret thoughts, "Señor, to remove that
doubt I should tell you that when the unhappy
man wrote this lay he was away from Marcela,
from whom he had voluntarily separated himself, to try if absence would act with him as it
is wont; and as everything distresses and every
fear haunts the banished lover, so imaginary
jealousies and suspicions, dreaded as if they
were true, tormented Chrysostom; and thus the
truth of what report declares of the virtue of
Marcela remains unshaken, and with her envy
itself should not and can not find any fault save
that of being cruel, somewhat haughty, and
very scornful."

"That is true," said Vivaldo; and as he was
about to read another paper of those he had preserved from the fire, he was stopped by a marvellous vision (for such it seemed) that unexpectedly presented itself to their eyes; for on
the summit of the rock where they were digging the grave there appeared the shepherdess
Marcela, so beautiful that her beauty exceeded
its reputation. Those who had never till then
beheld her gazed upon her in wonder and silence, and those who were accustomed to see
her were not less amazed than those who had
never seen her before. But the instant Ambrosio
saw her he addressed her, with manifest indignation, "Art thou come, cruel basilisk of these
mountains, to see if haply in thy presence blood
will flow from the wounds of this wretched being thy cruelty has robbed of life; or is it to ex-

ult over the cruel work of thy humors that thou
art come; or like another pitless Nero to look
down from that height upon the ruin of thy
Rome in ashes; or in thy arrogance to trample
on this ill-fated corpse, as the ungrateful daughter trampled on her father Tarquin's? Tell us
quickly for what thou art come, or what it is
thou wouldst have, for, as I know the thoughts
of Chrysostom never failed to obey thee in life,
I will make all these who call themselves his
friends obey thee, though he be dead."

"I come not, Ambrosio, for any of the purposes thou hast named," replied Marcela, "but
to defend myself and to prove how unreasonable are all those who blame me for their sorrow and for Chrysostom's death; and therefore
I ask all of you that are here to give me your
attention, for it will not take much time or
many words to bring the truth home to persons
of sense. Heaven has made me, so you say,
beautiful, and so much so that in spite of yourselves my beauty leads you to love me; and for
the love you show me you say, and even urge,
that I am bound to love you. By that natural
understanding which God has given me I know
that everything beautiful attracts love, but I can
not see how, by reason of being loved, that
which is loved for its beauty is bound to love
that which loves it; besides, it may happen that
the lover of that which is beautiful may be ugly, and ugliness being detestable, it is very absurd to say, 'I love thee because thou art beautiful, thou must love me though I be ugly.' But
supposing the beauty equal on both sides, it
does not follow that the inclinations must be
therefore alike, for it is not every beauty that
excites love, some but pleasing the eye without
winning the affection; and if every sort of beauty excited love and won the heart, the will
would wander vaguely to and fro unable to
make choice of any; for as there is an infinity of
beautiful objects there must be an infinity of
inclinations, and true love, I have heard it said,
is indivisible, and must be voluntary and not
compelled. If this be so, as I believe it to be,
why do you desire me to bend my will by force,
for no other reason but that you say you love
me? Nay—tell me—had Heaven made me ugly,
as it has made me beautiful, could I with justice complain of you for not loving me? Moreover, you must remember that the beauty I possess was no choice of mine, for be it what it
may, Heaven of its bounty gave it me without
my asking or choosing it; and as the viper,
though it kills with it, does not deserve to be
blamed for the poison it carries, as it is a gift of

nature, neither do I deserve reproach for being beautiful; for beauty in a modest woman is like fire at a distance or a sharp sword; the one does not burn, the other does not cut those who do not come too near. Honor and virtue are the ornaments of the mind, without which the body, though it be so, has no right to pass for beautiful; but if modesty is one of the virtues that specially lend a grace and charm to mind and body, why should she who is loved for her beauty part with it to gratify one who for his pleasure alone strives with all his might and energy to rob her of it? I was born free, and that I might live in freedom I chose the solitude of the fields; in the trees of the mountains I find society, the clear waters of the brooks are my mirrors, and to the trees and waters I make known my thoughts and charms. I am a fire afar off, a sword laid aside. Those whom I have inspired with love by letting them see me, I have by words undeceived, and if their longings live on hope —and I have given none to Chrysostom or to any other—it cannot justly be said that the death of any is my doing, for it was rather his own obstinacy than my cruelty that killed him; and if it be made a charge against me that his wishes were honorable, and that therefore I was bound to yield to them, I answer that when on this very spot where now his grave is made he declared to me his purity of purpose, I told him that mine was to live in perpetual solitude, and that the earth alone should enjoy the fruits of my retirement and the spoils of my beauty; and if, after this open avowal, he chose to persist against hope and steer against the wind, what wonder is it that he should sink in the depths of his infatuation? If I had encouraged him, I should have been false; if I had gratified him, I should have acted against my own better resolution and purpose. He was persistent in spite of warning, he despaired without being hated. Bethink you now if it be reasonable that his suffering should be laid to my charge. Let him who has been deceived complain, let him whose encouraged hopes have proved vain give way to despair, let him whom I shall entice flatter himself, let him whom I shall receive boast; but let not him to whom I make no promise, upon whom I practise no deception, whom I neither entice nor receive call me cruel or homicide. It has not been so far the will of Heaven that I should love by fate, and to expect me to love by choice is idle. Let this general declaration serve for each of my suitors on his own account, and let it be understood from this time forth that if any one dies for me it is not of jealousy or misery he dies, for she who loves no one can give no cause for jealousy to any, and candor is not to be confounded with scorn. Let him who calls me wild beast and basilisk, leave me alone as something noxious and evil; let him who calls me ungrateful, withhold his service; who calls me wayward, seek not my acquaintance; who calls me cruel, pursue me not; for this wild beast, this basilisk, this ungrateful, cruel, wayward being has no kind of desire to seek, serve, know, or follow them. If Chrysostom's impatience and violent passion killed him, why should my modest behavior and circumspection be blamed? If I preserve my purity in the society of the trees, why should he who would have me preserve it among men, seek to rob me of it? I have, as you know, wealth of my own, and I covet not that of others; my taste is for freedom, and I have no relish for constraint; I neither love nor hate any one; I do not deceive this one or court that, or trifle with one or play with another. The modest converse of the shepherd girls of these hamlets and the care of my goats are my recreations; my desires are bounded by these mountains, and if they ever wander hence it is to contemplate the beauty of the heavens, steps by which the soul travels to its primeval abode."

With these words, and not waiting to hear a reply, she turned and passed into the thickest part of a wood that was hard by, leaving all who were there lost in admiration as much of her good sense as of her beauty. Some—those wounded by the irresistible shafts launched by her bright eyes—made as though they would follow her, heedless of the frank declaration they had heard; seeing which, and deeming this a fitting occasion for the exercise of his chivalry in aid of distressed damsels, Don Quixote, laying his hand on the hilt of his sword, exclaimed in a loud and distinct voice:

"Let no one, whatever his rank or condition, dare to follow the beautiful Marcela, under pain of incurring my fierce indignation. She has shown by clear and satisfactory arguments that little or no fault is to be found with her for the death of Chrysostom, and also how far she is from yielding to the wishes of any of her lovers, for which reason, instead of being followed and persecuted, she should in justice be honored and esteemed by all the good people of the world, for she shows that she is the only woman in it that holds to such a virtuous resolution."

Whether it was because of the threats of Don Quixote, or because Ambrosio told them to fulfil their duty to their good friend, none of the shepherds moved or stirred from the spot until, having finished the grave and burned Chrysostom's papers, they laid his body in it, not without many tears from those who stood by. They closed the grave with a heavy stone until a slab was ready which Antonio said he meant to have prepared, with an epitaph which was to be to this effect:

> *Beneath the stone before your eyes*
> *The body of a lover lies;*
> *In life he was a shepherd swain,*
> *In death a victim to disdain.*
> *Ungrateful, cruel, coy, and fair,*
> *Was she that drove him to despair,*
> *And Love hath made her his ally*
> *For spreading wide his tyranny.*

They then strewed upon the grave a profusion of flowers and branches, and all expressing their condolence with his friend Ambrosio, took their leave. Vivaldo and his companion did the same; and Don Quixote bade farewell to his hosts and to the travellers, who pressed him to come with them to Seville, as being such a convenient place for finding adventures, for they presented themselves in every street and round every corner oftener than anywhere else. Don Quixote thanked them for their advice and for the disposition they showed to do him a favor, and said that for the present he would not, and must not go to Seville until he had cleared all these mountains of highwaymen and robbers, of whom report said they were full. Seeing his good intention, the travellers were unwilling to press him further, and once more bidding him farewell, they left him and pursued their journey, in the course of which they did not fail to discuss the story of Marcela and Chrysostom as well as the madness of Don Quixote. He, on his part, resolved to go in quest of the shepherdess Marcela, and make offer to her of all the service he could render her; but things did not fall out with him as he expected, according to what is related in the course of this veracious history, of which the Second Part ends here.

Chapter 15

In which is related the unfortunate adventure that Don Quixote fell in with when he fell out with certain heartless Yanguesans

THE sage Cid Hamet Benengeli relates that as soon as Don Quixote took leave of his hosts and all who had been present at the burial of Chrysostom, he and his squire passed into the same wood which they had seen the shepherdess Marcela enter, and after having wandered for more than two hours in all directions in search of her without finding her, they came to a halt in a glade covered with tender grass, beside which ran a pleasant cool stream that invited and even compelled them to pass there the hours of the noontide heat, which by this time was beginning to come on oppressively. Don Quixote and Sancho dismounted, and turning Rocinante and the ass loose to feed on the grass that was there in abundance, they ransacked the *alforjas*, and without any ceremony very peaceably and sociably master and man made their repast on what they found in them. Sancho had not thought it worth while to hobble Rocinante, feeling sure, from what he knew of his staidness and freedom from incontinence, that all the mares in the Cordova pastures would not lead him into an impropriety. Chance, however, and the devil, who is not always asleep, so ordained it that feeding in this valley there was a drove of Galician ponies belonging to certain Yanguesan carriers, whose way it is to take their midday rest with their teams in places and spots where grass and water abound; and that where Don Quixote chanced to be suited the Yanguesans' purpose very well. It so happened, then, that Rocinante took a fancy to disport himself with their ladyships the ponies, and abandoning his usual gait and demeanor as he scented them, he, without asking leave of his master, got up a briskish little trot and hastened to make known his wishes to them; they, however, it seemed, preferred their pasture to him, and received him with their heels and teeth to such effect that they soon broke his girths and left him naked without a saddle to cover him; but what must have been worse to him was that the carriers, seeing the violence he was offering to their mares, came running up armed with stakes, and so belabored him that they brought him sorely battered to the ground.

By this time Don Quixote and Sancho, who had witnessed the drubbing of Rocinante, came up panting, and said Don Quixote to Sancho, "So far as I can see, friend Sancho, these are not knights but base folk of low birth: I mention it because thou canst lawfully aid me in taking due vengeance for the insult offered to Rocinante before our eyes."

"What the devil vengeance can we take," answered Sancho, "if they are more than twenty, and we no more than two, or, indeed, perhaps, not more than one and a half?"

"I count for a hundred," replied Don Quixote, and without more words he drew his sword and attacked the Yanguesans, and incited and impelled by the example of his master, Sancho did the same; and to begin with, Don Quixote delivered a slash at one of them that laid open the leather jerkin he wore, together with a great portion of his shoulder. The Yanguesans, seeing themselves assaulted by only two men while they were so many, betook themselves to their stakes, and driving the two into the middle they began to lay on with great zeal and energy; in fact, at the second blow they brought Sancho to the ground, and Don Quixote fared the same way, all his skill and high mettle availing him nothing, and fate willed it that he should fall at the feet of Rocinante, who had not yet risen; whereby it may seem how furiously stakes can pound in angry boorish hands. Then, seeing the mischief they had done, the Yanguesans with all the haste they could loaded their team and pursued their journey, leaving the two adventurers a sorry sight and in sorrier mood.

Sancho was the first to come to, and finding himself close to his master he called to him in a weak and doleful voice, "Señor Don Quixote, ah, Señor Don Quixote!"

"What wouldst thou, brother Sancho?" answered Don Quixote in the same feeble suffering tone as Sancho.

"I would like, if it were possible," answered Sancho Panza, "your worship to give me a couple of sups of that potion of the fiery Blas, if it be that you have any to hand there; perhaps it will serve for broken bones as well as for wounds."

"If I only had it here, wretch that I am, what more should we want?" said Don Quixote; "but I swear to thee, Sancho Panza, on the faith of a knight-errant, ere two days are over, unless fortune orders otherwise, I mean to have it in my possession, or my hand will have lost its cunning."

"But in how many days does your worship think we shall have the use of our feet?" answered Sancho Panza.

"For myself I must say I can not guess how many," said the battered knight Don Quixote; "but I take all the blame upon myself, for I had no business to put hand to sword against men who were not dubbed knights like myself, and so I believe that in punishment for having transgressed the laws of chivalry the God of battles has permitted this chastisement to be administered to me; for which reason, brother Sancho, it is well thou shouldst receive a hint on the matter which I am now about to mention to thee, for it is of much importance to the welfare of both of us. It is that when thou shalt see rabble of this sort offering us insult thou art

not to wait till I draw sword against them, for I shall not do so at all; but do thou draw sword and chastise them to thy heart's content, and if any knights come to their aid and defence I will take care to defend thee and assail them with all my might; and thou hast already seen by a thousand signs and proofs what the might of this strong arm of mine is equal to"—so uplifted had the poor gentleman become through the victory over the stout Biscayan.

But Sancho did not so fully approve of his master's admonition as to let it pass without saying in reply, "Señor, I am a man of peace, meek and quiet, and I can put up with any affront because I have a wife and children to support and bring up; so let it be likewise a hint to your worship, as it can not be a mandate, that on no account will I draw sword either against clown or against knight, and that here before God I forgive all the insults that have been offered me or may be offered me, whether they have been, are, or shall be offered me by high or low, rich or poor, noble or commoner, not excepting any rank or condition whatsoever."

To all which his master said in reply, "I wish I had breath enough to speak somewhat easily, and that the pain I feel on this side would abate so as to let me explain to thee, Panza, the mistake thou makest. Come now, sinner, suppose the wind of fortune, hitherto so adverse, should turn in our favor, filling the sails of our desires so that safely and without impediment we put into port in some one of those islands I have promised thee, how would it be with thee if on winning it I made thee lord of it? Why, thou wilt make it well-nigh impossible through not being a knight nor having any desire to be one, nor possessing the courage nor the will to avenge insults or defend thy lordship; for thou must know that in newly conquered kingdoms and provinces the minds of the inhabitants are never so quiet nor so well disposed to the new lord that there is no fear of their making some move to change matters once more, and try, as they say, what chance may do for them; so it is essential that the new possessor should have good sense to enable him to govern, and valor to attack and defend himself, whatever may befall him."

"In what has now befallen us," answered Sancho, "I'd have been well pleased to have that good sense and that valor your worship speaks of, but swear on the faith of a poor man I am more fit for plasters than for arguments. See if your worship can get up, and let us help Rocinante, though he does not deserve it, for he was the main cause of all this thrashing. I never thought it of Rocinante, for I took him to be a virtuous person and as quiet as myself. After all, they say right that it takes a long time to come to know people, and that there is nothing sure in this life. Who would have said that, after such mighty slashes as your worship gave that unlucky knight-errant, there was coming, travelling post and at the very heels of them, such a great storm of sticks as has fallen upon our shoulders?"

"And yet thine, Sancho," replied Don Quixote, "ought to be used to such squalls; but mine, reared in soft cloth and fine linen, it is plain they must feel more keenly the pain of this mishap, and if it were not that I imagine—why do I say imagine?—know of a certainty that all these annoyances are very necessary accompaniments of the calling of arms, I would lay me down here to die of pure vexation."

To this the squire replied, "Señor, as these mishaps are what one reaps of chivalry, tell me if they happen very often, or if they have their own fixed times for coming to pass; because it seems to me that after two harvests we shall be no good for the third, unless God in his infinite mercy helps us."

"Know, friend Sancho," answered Don Quixote, "that the life of knights-errant is subject to a thousand dangers and reverses, and neither more nor less is it within immediate possibility for knights-errant to become kings and emperors, as experience has shown in the case of many different knights with whose histories I am thoroughly acquainted; and I could tell thee now, if the pain would let me, of some who simply by might of arm have risen to the high stations I have mentioned; and these same, both before and after, experienced divers misfortunes and miseries; for the valiant Amadis of Gaul found himself in the power of his mortal enemy Arcalaus the magician, who, it is positively asserted, holding him captive, gave him more than two hundred lashes with the reins of his horse while tied to one of the pillars of a court; and moreover there is a certain recondite author of no small authority who says that the Knight of Phœbus, being caught in a certain pitfall which opened under his feet in a certain castle, on falling found himself bound hand and foot in a deep pit underground, where they administered to him one of those things they call clysters, of sand and snow-water, that wellnigh finished him; and if he had not been succored in that sore extremity by a sage, a great friend of his, it would have gone very hard with

the poor knight; so I may well suffer in company with such worthy folk, for greater were the indignities which they had to suffer than those which we suffer. For I would have thee know, Sancho, that wounds caused by any instruments which happen by chance to be in hand inflict no indignity, and this is laid down in the law of the duel in express words: if, for instance, the cobbler strikes another with the last which he has in his hand, though it be in fact a piece of wood, it can not be said for that reason that he whom he struck with it has been cudgelled. I say this lest thou shouldst imagine that because we have been drubbed in this affray we have therefore suffered any indignity; for the arms those men carried, with which they pounded us, were nothing more than their stakes, and not one of them, so far as I remember, carried rapier, sword, or dagger."

"They gave me no time to see that much," answered Sancho, "for hardly had I laid hand on my *tizona* [1] when they signed the cross on my shoulders with their sticks in such style that they took the sight out of my eyes and the strength out of my feet, stretching me where I now lie, and where thinking of whether all those stake-strokes were an indignity or not gives me no uneasiness, which the pain of the blows does, for they will remain as deeply impressed on my memory as on my shoulders."

"For all that let me tell thee, brother Panza," said Don Quixote, "that there is no recollection which time does not put an end to, and no pain which death does not remove."

"And what greater misfortune can there be," replied Panza, "than the one that waits for time to put an end to it and death to remove it? If our mishap were one of those that are cured with a couple of plasters, it would not be so bad; but I am beginning to think that all the plasters in a hospital almost won't be enough to put us right."

"No more of that: pluck strength out of weakness, Sancho, as I mean to do," returned Don Quixote, "and let us see how Rocinante is, for it seems to me that not the least share of this mishap has fallen to the lot of the poor beast."

"There is nothing wonderful in that," replied Sancho, "since he is a knight-errant too; what I wonder at is that my beast should have come off scot-free where we come out scotched."

"Fortune always leaves a door open in adversity in order to bring relief to it," said Don

[1] Tizon was the name of one of the Cid's two famous swords. It means simply "brand."

Quixote; "I say so because this little beast may now supply the want of Rocinante, carrying me hence to some castle where I may be cured of my wounds. And moreover I shall not hold it any dishonor to be so mounted, for I remember having read how the good old Silenus, the tutor and instructor of the gay god of laughter, when he entered the city of the hundred gates, went very contentedly mounted on a handsome ass."

"It may be true that he went mounted as your worship says," answered Sancho, "but there is a great difference between going mounted and going slung like a sack of manure."

To which Don Quixote replied, "Wounds received in battle confer honor instead of taking it away; and so, friend Panza, say no more, but, as I told thee before, get up as well as thou canst and put me on top of thy beast in whatever fashion pleases thee best, and let us go hence ere night come on and surprise us in these wilds."

"And yet I have heard your worship say," observed Panza, "that it is very meet for knights-errant to sleep in wastes and deserts the best part of the year, and that they esteem it very good fortune."

"That is," said Don Quixote, "when they can not help it, or when they are in love; and so true is this that there have been knights who have remained two years on rocks, in sunshine and shade and all the inclemencies of heaven, without their ladies knowing anything of it; and one of these was Amadis when, under the name of Beltenebros, he took up his abode on the Peña Pobre for—I know not if it was eight years or eight months, for I am not very sure of the reckoning; at any rate he stayed there doing penance for I know not what pique the Princess Oriana had against him; but no more of this now, Sancho, and make haste before some other mishap like Rocinante's befalls the ass."

"The very devil would be in it in that case," said Sancho; and letting off thirty "ohs," and sixty sighs, and a hundred and twenty maledictions and execrations on whomsoever it was that had brought him there, he raised himself, stopping half-way bent like a Turkish bow without power to bring himself upright, but with all his pains he saddled his ass, who too had gone astray somewhat, yielding to the excessive license of the day; he next raised up Rocinante, and as for him, had he possessed a tongue to complain with, most assuredly neither Sancho nor his master would have been behind him. To be brief, Sancho fixed Don Quixote on the ass and secured Rocinante with a leading rein, and taking the ass by the halter, he proceeded more or less in the direction in which it seemed to him the high road might be; and, as chance was conducting their affairs for them from good to better, he had not gone a short league when the road came in sight, and on it he perceived an inn, which to his annoyance and to the delight of Don Quixote must needs be a castle. Sancho insisted that it was an inn, and his master that it was not one, but a castle, and the dispute lasted so long that before the point was settled they had time to reach it, and into it Sancho entered with all his team, without any further controversy.

Chapter 16

Of what happened to the ingenious gentleman in the inn which he took to be a castle

THE innkeeper, seeing Don Quixote slung across the ass, asked Sancho what was amiss with him. Sancho answered that it was nothing, only that he had fallen down from a rock and had his ribs a little bruised. The innkeeper had a wife whose disposition was not such as those of her calling commonly have, for she was by nature kind-hearted and felt for the sufferings of her neighbors, so she at once set about tending Don Quixote, and made her young daughter, a very comely girl, help her in taking care of her guest. There was besides in the inn, as servant, an Asturian lass with a broad face, flat poll, and snub nose, blind of one eye and not very sound in the other. The elegance of her shape, to be sure, made up for all her defects; she did not measure seven palms from head to foot, and her shoulders, which over-weighted her somewhat, made her contemplate the ground more than she liked. This graceful lass, then, helped the young girl, and the two made up a very bad bed for Don Quixote in a garret that showed evident signs of having formerly served for many years as a straw-loft, in which there was also quartered a carrier whose bed was placed a little beyond our Don Quixote's, and, though only made of the pack-saddles and cloths of his mules, had much the advantage of it, as Don Quixote's consisted simply of four rough boards on two not very even trestles, a mattress, that for thinness might have passed for a quilt, full of pellets, which, were they not seen through the rents to be wool, would to the touch have seemed pebbles in hardness, two sheets made of buckler leather, and a coverlet the threads of which any one that chose might have counted without missing one in the reckoning.

On this accursed bed Don Quixote stretched himself, and the hostess and her daughter soon covered him with plasters from top to toe, while Maritornes—for that was the name of the Asturian—held the light for them, and while plastering him, the hostess, observing how full of wheals Don Quixote was in some places, remarked that this had more the look of blows than of a fall.

It was not blows, Sancho said, but that the rock had many points and projections, and that each of them had left its mark. "Pray, señora," he added, "manage to save some tow, as there will be no want of some one to use it, for my loins too are rather sore."

"Then you must have fallen too," said the hostess.

"I did not fall," said Sancho Panza, "but from the shock I got at seeing my master fall, my body aches so that I feel as if I had had a thousand thwacks."

"That may well be," said the young girl, "for it has many a time happened to me to dream that I was falling down from a tower and never coming to the ground, and when I awoke from the dream to find myself as weak and shaken as if I had really fallen."

"There is the point, señora," replied Sancho Panza, "that I without dreaming at all, but being more awake than I am now, find myself with scarcely less wheals than my master, Don Quixote."

"How is the gentleman called?" asked Maritornes the Asturian.

"Don Quixote of La Mancha," answered Sancho Panza, "and he is a knight-adventurer, and one of the best and stoutest that have been seen in the world this long time past."

"What is a knight-adventurer?" said the lass.

"Are you so new in the world as not to know?" answered Sancho Panza. "Well, then, you must know, sister, that a knight-adventurer is a thing that in two words is seen drubbed and emperor, that is to-day the most miserable and needy being in the world, and to-morrow will have two or three crowns of kingdoms to give his squire."

"Then how is it," said the hostess, "that, belonging to so good a master as this, you have not, to judge by appearances, even so much as a county?"

"It is too soon yet," answered Sancho, "for we have only been a month going in quest of adventures, and so far we have met with nothing that can be called one, for it will happen that when one thing is looked for another thing is found; however, if my master Don Quixote gets well of this wound, or fall, and I am left none the worse of it, I would not change my hopes for the best title in Spain."

To all this conversation Don Quixote was listening very attentively, and sitting up in bed as well as he could, and taking the hostess by the hand he said to her, "Believe me, fair lady, you may call yourself fortunate in having in this castle of yours sheltered my person, which is such that if I do not myself praise it, it is because of what is commonly said, that self-praise debaseth; but my squire will inform you who I am. I only tell you that I shall preserve for ever inscribed on my memory the service you have rendered me in order to tender you my gratitude while life shall last me; and would to Heaven love held me not so enthralled and subject to its laws and to the eyes of that fair ingrate whom I name between my teeth, but that those of this lovely damsel might be the masters of my liberty."

The hostess, her daughter, and the worthy Maritornes listened in bewilderment to the words of the knight-errant, for they understood about as much of them as if he had been talking Greek, though they could perceive they were all meant for expressions of good-will and blandishments; and not being accustomed to this kind of language, they stared at him and wondered to themselves, for he seemed to them a man of a different sort from those they were used to, and thanking him in pot-house phrase for his civility they left him, while the Asturian gave her attention to Sancho, who needed it no less than his master.

The carrier had made an arrangement with her for recreation that night, and she had given him her word that when the guests were quiet and the family asleep she would come in search of him and meet his wishes unreservedly. And it is said of this good lass that she never made promises of the kind without fulfilling them, even though she made them in a forest and without any witness present, for she plumed herself greatly on being a lady, and held it no disgrace to be in such an employment as servant in an inn, because, she said, misfortunes and ill-luck had brought her to that position. The hard, narrow, wretched, rickety bed of Don Quixote stood first in the middle of this star-lit stable, and close beside it Sancho made his, which merely consisted of a rush mat and a blanket that looked as if it was of threadbare canvas, rather than of wool. Next to these two beds was that of the carrier, made up, as has been said, of the pack-saddles and all the trappings of the two best mules he had, though there were twelve of them, sleek, plump, and in prime condition, for he was one of the rich carriers of Arévalo, according to the author of this history, who particularly mentions this carrier because he knew him very well, and they even say was in some degree a relation of his; besides which Cid Hamet Benengeli was a historian of great research and accuracy in all things, as is very evident since he would not pass over in silence those that have been already mentioned, however trifling and insignificant they might be, an example that might be followed by those grave historians who relate transactions so curtly and briefly that we hardly get a taste of them, all the substance of the work being left in the ink-bottle from carelessness, perverseness, or ignorance. A thousand blessings on the author of *Tablante de Ricamonte,* and that of the other book in which the deeds of the Conde Tomillas are recounted; with what minuteness they describe everything!

To proceed, then: after having paid a visit to his team and given them their second feed, the carrier stretched himself on his pack-saddles and lay waiting for his conscientious Maritornes. Sancho was by this time plastered and had lain down, and though he strove to sleep the pain of his ribs would not let him, while Don Quixote with the pain of his, had his eyes as wide open as a hare's. The inn was all in silence, and in the whole of it there was no light except that given by a lantern that hung burning in the middle of the gateway. This strange stillness, and the thoughts, always present to our knight's mind, of the incidents described at every turn in the books that were the cause of his misfortune, conjured up to his imagination as extraordinary a delusion as can well be conceived, which was that he fancied himself to have reached a famous castle (for, as has been said, all the inns he lodged in were castles to his eyes) and that the daughter of the innkeeper was daughter of the lord of the castle, and that she, won by his high-bred bearing, had fallen in love with him, and had promised to come to his bed for awhile that night without the knowledge of her parents; and holding as solid fact all this fantasy that he had constructed, he began to feel uneasy and to consider the perilous risk which his virtue was about to encounter, and he resolved in his heart to commit no treason to his lady Dulcinea del Toboso, even though the queen Guinevere herself and the dame Quintañona should present themselves before him.

While he was taken up with these vagaries, then, the time and the hour—an unlucky one for him—arrived for the Asturian to come, who in her smock, with bare feet and her hair gathered into a fustian coif, with noiseless and cautious steps entered the chamber where the three were quartered, in quest of the carrier; but scarcely had she gained the door when Don Quixote perceived her, and sitting up in his bed in spite of his plasters and the pain of his ribs, he stretched out his arms to receive his beauteous damsel. The Asturian, who went all doubled up and in silence with her hands before her feeling for her lover, encountered the arms of Don Quixote, who grasped her tightly by the wrist, and drawing her towards him, while she dared not utter a word, made her sit down on the bed. He then felt her smock, and although it was of sackcloth it appeared to him to be of the finest and softest silk; on her wrists she wore some glass beads, but to him they had the sheen of precious Orient pearls; her hair, which in some measure resembled a horse's mane, he rated as threads of the brightest gold of Araby, whose refulgence dimmed the sun himself; her breath, which no doubt smelt of yesterday's stale salad, seemed to him to diffuse a sweet aromatic fragrance from her mouth; and, in short, he drew her portrait in his imagination with the same features and in the same style as that which he had seen in his books of the other princess who, smitten by love, came with all the adornments that are here set down, to see the sorely wounded knight; and so great was the poor gentleman's blindness that neither touch, nor smell, nor anything else about the good lass that would have made any but a carrier vomit, were enough to undeceive him; on the contrary, he was persuaded he had the goddess of beauty in his arms, and holding her firmly in his grasp he went on to say in a low, tender voice, "Would that I found myself, lovely and exalted lady, in a position to repay such a favor as that which you, by the sight of your great beauty, have granted me; but fortune, which is never weary of persecuting the good, has chosen to place me upon this bed, where I lie so bruised and broken that though my inclination would gladly comply with yours it is impossible; besides, to this impossibility another yet greater is to be added, which is the faith that I have pledged to the peerless Dulcinea del Toboso, sole lady of my most secret thoughts; and were it not that this stood in the way I should not be so insensible a knight as to miss the happy opportunity which your great goodness has offered me."

Maritornes was fretting and sweating at finding herself held so fast by Don Quixote, and not understanding or heeding the words he addressed to her, she strove without speaking to free herself. The worthy carrier, whose unholy thoughts kept him awake, was aware of his doxy the moment she entered the door, and was listening attentively to all Don Quixote said; and jealous that the Asturian should have broken her word with him for another, drew nearer to Don Quixote's bed and stood still to see what would come of this talk which he could not understand; but when he perceived the wench struggling to get free and Don Quixote striving to hold her, not relishing the joke he raised his arm and delivered such a terrible cuff on the lank jaws of the amorous knight that he bathed all his mouth in blood, and not content with this he mounted on his ribs and with his feet tramped all over them at a pace rather smarter than a trot. The bed, which was somewhat crazy and not very firm on its feet, unable to bear the additional weight of the carrier, came to the ground, and at the mighty crash of this the innkeeper awoke and at once concluded that it must be some brawl of Maritornes', because after calling loudly to her he got no answer. With this suspicion he got up, and lighting a lamp hastened to the quarter where he had heard the disturbance. The wench, seeing that her master was coming and knowing that his temper was terrible, frightened and panic-stricken made for the bed of Sancho Panza, who still slept, and crouching upon it made a ball of herself.

The innkeeper came in exclaiming, "Where art thou, strumpet? Of course this is some of thy work." At this Sancho awoke, and feeling this mass almost on top of him fancied he had the nightmare and began to distribute fisticuffs all round, of which a certain share fell upon Maritornes, who, irritated by the pain and flinging modesty aside, paid back so many in return to Sancho that she woke him up in spite of himself. He then, finding himself so handled, by whom he knew not, raising himself up as well as he could, grappled with Maritornes, and he and she between them began the bitterest and drollest scrimmage in the world. The carrier, however, perceiving by the light of the innkeeper's candle how it fared with his lady-love, quitting Don Quixote, ran to bring her the help she needed; and the innkeeper did the same but with a different intention, for his was to chastise the lass, as he believed that beyond a doubt she alone was the cause of all the harmony. And so,

as the saying is, cat to rat, rat to rope, rope to stick, the carrier pounded Sancho, Sancho the lass, she him, and the innkeeper her, and all worked away so briskly that they did not give themselves a moment's rest; and the best of it was that the innkeeper's lamp went out, and as they were left in the dark they all laid on one upon the other in a mass so unmercifully that there was not a sound spot left where a hand could light.

It so happened that there was lodging that night in the inn an officer of what they call the Old Holy Brotherhood of Toledo, who, also hearing the extraordinary noise of the conflict, seized his staff and the tin case with his warrants, and made his way in the dark into the room crying, "Hold! in the name of this Jurisdiction! Hold! in the name of the Holy Brotherhood!" The first that he came upon was the pummelled Don Quixote, who lay stretched senseless on his back upon his broken-down bed, and, his hand falling on the beard as he felt about, he continued to cry, "Help for the Jurisdiction!" but perceiving that he whom he had laid hold of did not move or stir, he concluded that he was dead and that those in the room were his murderers, and with this suspicion he raised his voice still higher, calling out, "Shut the inn gate; see that no one goes out; they have killed a man here!" This cry startled them all, and each dropped the contest at the point at which the voice reached him. The innkeeper retreated to his room, the carrier to his pack-saddles, the lass to her crib; the unlucky Don Quixote and Sancho alone were unable to move from where they were. The officer on this let go Don Quixote's beard, and went out to look for a light to search for and apprehend the culprits; but not finding one, as the innkeeper had purposely extinguished the lantern on retreating to his room, he was compelled to have recourse to the hearth, where after much time and trouble he lit another lamp.

Chapter 17

In which are contained the innumerable
troubles which the brave Don Quixote
and his good squire Sancho Panza endured
in the inn, which to his misfortune
he took to be a castle

BY this time Don Quixote had recovered from his swoon; and in the same tone of voice in which he had called to his squire the day before when he lay stretched "in the vale of the stakes," he began calling to him now, "Sancho, my friend, art thou asleep? sleepest thou, friend Sancho?"

"How can I sleep, curses on it!" returned Sancho discontentedly and bitterly, "when it is plain that all the devils have been at me this night?"

"Thou mayest well believe that," answered Don Quixote, "because, either I know little, or this castle is enchanted, for thou must know— but this that I am now about to tell thee thou must swear to keep secret until after my death."

"I swear it," answered Sancho.

"I say so," continued Don Quixote, "because I hate taking away any one's good name."

"I say," repeated Sancho, "that I swear to hold my tongue about it till the end of your worship's days, and God grant I may be able to let it out to-morrow."

"Do I do thee such injuries, Sancho," said Don Quixote, "that thou wouldst see me dead so soon?"

"It is not for that," replied Sancho, "but because I hate keeping things long, and I don't want them to grow rotten with me from over-keeping."

"At any rate," said Don Quixote, "I have more confidence in thy affection and good nature; and so I would have thee know that this night there befell me one of the strangest adventures that I could describe, and to relate it to thee briefly thou must know that a little while ago the daughter of the lord of this castle came to me, and that she is the most elegant and beautiful damsel that could be found in the wide world. What I could tell thee of the charms of her person! of her lively wit! of other secret matters which, to preserve the fealty I owe to my lady Dulcinea del Toboso, I shall pass over unnoticed and in silence! I will only tell thee that, either fate being envious of so great a boon placed in my hands by good fortune, or perhaps (and this is more probable) this castle being, as I have already said, enchanted, at the time when I was engaged in the sweetest and most amorous discourse with her, there came, without my seeing or knowing whence it came, a hand attached to some arm of some huge giant, that planted such a cuff on my jaws that I have them all bathed in blood, and then pummelled me in such a way that I am in a worse plight than yesterday when the carriers, on account of Rocinante's misbehavior, inflicted on us the injury thou knowest of; whence I conjecture that there must be some enchanted Moor guarding the treasure of this damsel's beauty, and that it is not for me."

"Nor for me either," said Sancho, "for more than four hundred Moors have so thrashed me that the drubbing of the stakes was cakes and fancy-bread to it. But tell me, señor, what did you call this excellent and rare adventure that has left us as we are left now? Though your worship was not so badly off, having in your arms that incomparable beauty you spoke of; but I, what did I have, except the heaviest whacks I think I had in all my life? Unlucky me and the mother that bore me! for I am not a knight-errant and never expect to be one, and of all the mishaps, the greater part falls to my share."

"Then thou hast been thrashed too?" said Don Quixote.

"Didn't I say so? worse luck to my line!" said Sancho.

"Be not distressed, friend," said Don Quixote, "for I will now make the precious balsam with which we shall cure ourselves in the twinkling of an eye."

By this time the officer had succeeded in lighting the lamp, and came in to see the man that he thought had been killed; and as Sancho caught sight of him at the door, seeing him coming in his shirt, with a cloth on his head, and a lamp in his hand, and a very forbidding countenance, he said to his master, "Señor, can it be that this is the enchanted Moor coming back to give us more castigation if there be anything still left in the ink-bottle?"

"It can not be the Moor," answered Don Quixote, "for those under enchantment do not let themselves be seen by any one."

"If they don't let themselves be seen, they let themselves be felt," said Sancho; "if not, let my shoulders speak to the point."

"Mine could speak too," said Don Quixote, "but that is not a sufficient reason for believing that what we see is the enchanted Moor."

The officer came up, and finding them engaged in such a peaceful conversation, stood amazed; though Don Quixote, to be sure, still lay on his back unable to move from pure pummelling and plasters. The officer turned to him and said, "Well, how goes it, good man?"

"I would speak more politely if I were you," replied Don Quixote; "is it the way of this country to address knights-errant in that style, you booby?"

The officer finding himself so disrespectfully treated by such a sorry-looking individual, lost his temper, and raising the lamp full of oil smote Don Quixote such a blow with it on the head that he gave him a badly broken pate;

then, all being in darkness, he went out, and Sancho Panza said, "That is certainly the enchanted Moor, señor, and he keeps the treasure for others, and for us only the cuffs and lampwhacks."

"That is the truth," answered Don Quixote, "and there is no use in troubling one's self about these matters of enchantment or being angry or vexed at them, for, as they are invisible and visionary we shall find no one on whom to avenge ourselves, do what we may; rise, Sancho, if thou canst, and call the alcaide of this fortress, and get him to give me a little oil, wine, salt, and rosemary to make the salutiferous balsam, for indeed I believe I have great need of it now, because I am losing much blood from the wound that phantom gave me."

Sancho got up with pain enough in his bones, and went after the innkeeper in the dark, and meeting the officer, who was looking to see what had become of his enemy, he said to him, "Señor, whoever you are, do us the favor and kindness to give us a little rosemary, oil, salt, and wine, for it is wanted to cure one of the best knights-errant on earth, who lies on yonder bed sorely wounded by the hands of the enchanted Moor that is in this inn."

When the officer heard him talk in this way, he took him for a man out of his senses, and as day was now beginning to break, he opened the inn gate, and calling the host, he told him what this good man wanted. The host furnished him with what he required, and Sancho brought it to Don Quixote, who, with his hands to his head, was bewailing the pain of the blow of the lamp, which had done him no more harm than raising a couple of rather large lumps, and what he fancied blood was only the sweat that flowed from him in his sufferings during the late storm. To be brief, he took the materials, of which he made a compound, mixing them all and boiling them a good while until it seemed to him they had come to perfection. He then asked for some vial to pour it into, and as there was not one in the inn, he decided on putting it into a tin oil-bottle or flask of which the host made him a free gift; and over the flask he repeated more than eighty *paternosters* and as many more *ave-marias, salves,* and *credos,* accompanying each word with a cross by way of benediction, at all which there were present Sancho, the innkeeper, and the officer; for the carrier was now peacefully engaged in attending to the comfort of his mules.

This being accomplished, he felt anxious to make trial himself, on the spot, of the virtue of this precious balsam, as he considered it, and so he drank near a quart of what could not be put into the flask and remained in the pipkin in which it had been boiled; but scarcely had he done drinking when he began to vomit in such a way that nothing was left in his stomach, and with the pangs and spasms of vomiting he broke into a profuse sweat, on account of which he bade them cover him up and leave him alone. They did so, and he lay sleeping more than three hours, at the end of which he awoke and felt very great bodily relief and so much ease from his bruises that he thought himself quite cured, and verily believed he had hit upon the balsam of Fierabras; and that with this remedy he might thenceforward, without any fear, face any kind of destruction, battle, or combat, however perilous it might be.

Sancho Panza, who also regarded the amendment of his master as miraculous, begged him to give him what was left in the pipkin, which was no small quantity. Don Quixote consented, and he, taking it with two hands, in good faith and with a better will, gulped down and drained off very little less than his master. But the fact is, that the stomach of poor Sancho was of necessity not so delicate as that of his master, and so, before vomiting, he was seized with such gripings, and retchings, and such sweats and faintness, that verily and truly he believed his last hour had come, and finding himself so racked and tormented he cursed the balsam and the thief that had given it to him.

Don Quixote seeing him in this state said, "It is my belief, Sancho, that this mischief comes of thy not being dubbed a knight, for I am persuaded this liquor cannot be good for those who are not so."

"If your worship knew that," returned Sancho, "—woe betide me and all my kindred!—why did you let me taste it?"

At this moment the draught took effect, and the poor squire began to discharge both ways at such a rate that the rush mat on which he had thrown himself and the canvas blanket he had covering him were fit for nothing afterwards. He sweated and perspired with such paroxysms and convulsions that not only he himself but all present thought his end had come. This tempest and tribulation lasted about two hours, at the end of which he was left, not like his master, but so weak and exhausted that he could not stand. Don Quixote, however, who, as has been said, felt himself relieved and well, was eager to take his departure at once in quest of adventures, as it seemed to him that all the time he loitered there was a fraud upon the world and those in it who stood in need of his help and protection, all the more when he had the security and confidence his balsam afforded him; and so, urged by this impulse, he saddled Rocinante himself and put the pack-saddle on his squire's beast, whom likewise he helped to dress and mount the ass; after which he mounted his horse and turning to a corner of the inn he laid hold of a pike that stood there, to serve him by way of a lance. All that were in the inn, who were more than twenty persons, stood watching him; the innkeeper's daughter was likewise observing him, and he too never took his eyes off her, and from time to time fetched a sigh that he seemed to pluck up from the depths of his bowels; but they all thought it must be from the pain he felt in his ribs; at any rate they who had seen him plastered the night before thought so.

As soon as they were both mounted, at the gate of the inn, he called to the host and said in a very grave and measured voice, "Many and great are the favors, Señor Alcaide, that I have received in this castle of yours, and I remain under the deepest obligation to be grateful to you for them all the days of my life; if I can repay them in avenging you of any arrogant foe who may have wronged you, know that my calling is no other than to aid the weak, and to avenge those who suffer wrong, and to chastise perfidy. Search your memory, and if you find anything of this kind you need only tell me of it, and I promise you by the order of knighthood which I have received to procure you satisfaction and reparation to the utmost of your desire."

The innkeeper replied to him with equal calmness, "Sir Knight, I do not want your worship to avenge me of any wrong, because when any is done me I can take what vengeance seems good to me; the only thing I want is that you pay me the score that you have run up in the inn last night, as well for the straw and barley for your two beasts, as for supper and beds."

"Then this is an inn?" said Don Quixote.

"And a very respectable one," said the innkeeper.

"I have been under a mistake all this time," answered Don Quixote, "for in truth I thought it was a castle, and not a bad one; but since it appears that it is not a castle but an inn, all that can be done now is that you should excuse the payment, for I can not contravene the rule of knights-errant, of whom I know as a fact (and up to the present I have read nothing to the contrary) that they never paid for lodging or anything else in the inn where they might be; for any hospitality that might be offered them is their due by law and right in return for the insufferable toil they endure in seeking adventures by night and by day, summer and in winter, on foot and on horseback, in hunger and thirst, cold and heat, exposed to all the inclemencies of heaven and all the hardships of earth."

"I have little to do with that," replied the innkeeper; "pay me what you owe me, and let us have no more talk or chivalry, for all I care about is to get to my money."

"You are a stupid, scurvy innkeeper," said Don Quixote, and putting spurs to Rocinante and bringing his pike to the slope he rode out of the inn before any one could stop him, and pushed on some distance without looking to see if his squire was following him.

The innkeeper when he saw him go without paying him ran to get payment of Sancho, who said that as his master would not pay neither would he, because, being as he was squire to a knight-errant, the same rule and reason held good for him as for his master with regard to not paying anything in inns and hostelries. At this the innkeeper waxed very wroth, and threatened if he did not pay to compel him in a way that he would not like. To which Sancho made answer that by the law of chivalry his master had received he would not pay a rap, though it cost him his life; for the excellent and ancient usage of knights-errant was not going to be violated by him, nor should the squires of such as were yet to come into the world ever complain of him or reproach him with breaking so just a law.

The ill-luck of the unfortunate Sancho so ordered it that among the company in the inn there were four wool-carders from Segovia, three needle-makers from the Colt of Cordova, and two lodgers from the Fair of Seville, lively fellows, tender-hearted, fond of a joke, and playful, who, almost as if instigated and moved by a common impulse, made up to Sancho and dismounted him from his ass, while one of them went in for the blanket of the host's bed; but on flinging him into it they looked up, and seeing that the ceiling was somewhat lower than what they required for their work, they decided upon going out into the yard, which was bounded by the sky, and there, putting Sancho in the middle of the blanket, they began to make sport with him as they would with a dog at Shrovetide. The cries of the poor blanketed wretch were so loud that they reached the ears of his master, who, halting to listen attentively, was persuaded that some new adventure was coming, until he clearly perceived that it was his squire who uttered them. Wheeling about he came up to the inn with a laborious gallop, and finding it shut went round it to see if he could find some way of getting in; but as soon as he came to the wall of the yard, which was not very high, he discovered the game that was being played with his squire. He saw him rising and falling in the air with such grace and nimbleness that, had his rage allowed him, it is my belief he would have laughed. He tried to climb from his horse on to the top of the wall, but he was so bruised and battered that he could not even dismount; and so from the back of his horse he began to utter such maledictions and objurgations against those who were blanketing Sancho as it would be impossible to write down accurately: they, however, did not stay their laughter or their work for this, nor did the flying Sancho cease his lamentations, mingled now with threats, now with entreaties, but all to little purpose, or none at all, until from pure weariness they left off. They then brought him his ass, and mounting him on top of it they put his jacket round him; and the compassionate Maritornes, seeing him so exhausted, thought fit to refresh him with a jug of water, and that it might be all the cooler she fetched it from the well. Sancho took it, and as he was raising it to his mouth he was stopped by the cries of his master exclaiming, 'Sancho, my son, drink not water; drink it not, my son, for it will kill thee; see, here I have the blessed balsam (and he held up the flask of liquor), and with drinking two drops of it thou wilt certainly be restored.'

At these words Sancho turned his eyes asquint, and in a still louder voice said, "Can it be your worship has forgotten that I am not a knight, or do you want me to end by vomiting up what bowels I have left after last night? Keep your liquor in the name of all the devils, and leave me to myself!" and at one and the same instant he left off talking and began drinking; but as at the first sup he perceived it was water he did not care to go on with it, and begged Maritornes to fetch him some wine, which she did with right good will, and paid for it with her own money; for indeed they say of her that, though she was in that line of life, there was some faint and distant resemblance to a Christian about her. When Sancho had done drinking he dug his heels into his ass, and the gate of the inn being thrown open he passed out very well pleased at having paid nothing and carried

his point, though it had been at the expense of his usual sureties, his shoulders. It is true that the innkeeper detained his *alforjas* in payment of what was owing to him, but Sancho took his departure in such a flurry that he never missed them. The innkeeper, as soon as he saw him off, wanted to bar the gate close, but the blanketers would not agree to it, for they were fellows who would not have cared two farthings for Don Quixote, even had he been really one of the knights-errant of the Round Table.

Chapter 18

In which is related the discourse Sancho Panza held with his master, Don Quixote, together with other adventures worth relating

SANCHO reached his master so limp and faint that he could not urge on his beast. When Don Quixote saw the state he was in he said, "I have now come to the conclusion, good Sancho, that this castle or inn is beyond a doubt enchanted, because those who have so atrociously diverted themselves with thee, what can they be but phantoms or beings of another world? And I hold this confirmed by having noticed that when I was by the wall of the yard witnessing the acts of thy sad tragedy, it was out of my power to mount upon it, nor could I even dismount from Rocinante, because they no doubt had me enchanted; for I swear to thee by the faith of what I am that if I had been able to climb up or dismount, I would have avenged thee in such a way that those braggart thieves would have remembered their freak forever, even though in so doing I knew that I contravened the laws of chivalry, which, as I have often told thee, do not permit a knight to lay hands on him who is not one, save in case of urgent and great necessity in defence of his own life and person."

"I would have avenged myself too if I could," said Sancho, "whether I had been dubbed knight or not, but I could not; though for my part I am persuaded those who amused themselves with me were not phantoms or enchanted men, as your worship says, but men of flesh and bone like ourselves; and they all had their names, for I heard them name them when they were tossing me, and one was called Pedro Martinez, and another Tenorio Hernandez, and the innkeeper, I heard, was called Juan Palomeque the Left-handed; so that, señor, your not being able to leap over the wall of the yard or dismount from your horse came of something else besides enchantments; and what I make out clearly from all this is, that these adventures we go seeking will in the end lead us into such misadventures that we shall not know which is our right foot; and that the best and wisest thing, according to my small wits, would be for us to return home, now that it is harvesttime, and attend to our business, and give over wandering from Zeca to Mecca and from pail to bucket, as the saying is."

"How little thou knowest about chivalry, Sancho," replied Don Quixote; "hold thy peace and have patience; the day will come when thou shalt see with thine own eyes what an honorable thing it is to wander in the pursuit of this calling; nay, tell me, what greater pleasure can there be in the world, or what delight can equal that of winning a battle, and triumphing over one's enemy? None, beyond all doubt."

"Very likely," answered Sancho, "though I do not know it; all I know is that since we have been knights-errant, or since your worship has been one (for I have no right to reckon myself one of so honorable a number), we have never won any battle except the one with the Biscayan, and even out of that your worship came with half an ear and half a helmet the less; and from that till now it has been all cudgellings and more cudgellings, cuffs and more cuffs, I getting the blanketing over and above, and falling in with enchanted persons on whom I can not avenge myself so as to know what the delight, as your worship calls it, of conquering an enemy is like."

"That is what vexes me, and what ought to vex thee, Sancho," replied Don Quixote; "but henceforward I will endeavor to have at hand some sword made by such craft that no kind of enchantments can take effect upon him who carries it, and it is even possible that fortune may procure for me that which belonged to Amadis when he was called 'The Knight of the Burning Sword,' which was one of the best swords that ever knight in the world possessed, for, besides having the said virtue, it cut like a razor, and there was no armor, however strong and enchanted it might be, that could resist it."

"Such is my luck," said Sancho, "that even if that happened and your worship found some such sword, it would, like the balsam, turn out serviceable and good for dubbed knights only, and as for the squires, they might sup sorrow."

"Fear not that, Sancho," said Don Quixote: "Heaven will deal better by thee."

Thus talking, Don Quixote and his squire were going along, when, on the road they were following, Don Quixote perceived approaching them a large and thick cloud of dust, on seeing which he turned to Sancho and said, "This is the day, O Sancho, on which will be seen the boon my fortune is reserving for me; this, I say, is the day on which as much as on any other shall be displayed the might of my arm, and on which I shall do deeds that shall remain written in the book of fame for all ages to come. Seest thou that cloud of dust which rises yonder? Well, then, all that is churned up by a vast army composed of various and countless nations that comes marching there."

"According to that there must be two," said Sancho, "for on this opposite side also there rises just such another cloud of dust."

Don Quixote turned to look and found that it was true, and rejoicing exceedingly, he concluded that they were two armies about to engage and encounter in the midst of that broad plain; for at all times and seasons his fancy was full of the battles, enchantments, adventures, crazy feats, loves, and defiances that are recorded in the books of chivalry, and everything he said, thought, or did had reference to such things. Now the cloud of dust he had seen was raised by two great droves of sheep coming along the same road in opposite directions, which, because of the dust, did not become visible until they drew near, but Don Quixote asserted so positively that they were armies that Sancho was led to believe it and say, "Well, and what are we to do, señor?"

"What?" said Don Quixote; "give aid and assistance to the weak and those who need it; and thou must know, Sancho, that this which comes opposite to us is conducted and led by the mighty emperor Alifanfaron, lord of the great isle of Trapobana; this other that marches behind me is that of his enemy the king of the Garamantas, Pentapolin of the Bare Arm, for he always goes into battle with his right arm bare."

"But why are these two lords such enemies?" asked Sancho.

"They are at enmity," replied Don Quixote, "because this Alifanfaron is a furious pagan and is in love with the daughter of Pentapolin, who is a very beautiful and moreover gracious lady, and a Christian, and her father is unwilling to bestow her upon the pagan king unless he first abandons the religion of his false prophet Mahomet, and adopts his own."

"By my beard," said Sancho, "but Pentapolin does quite right, and I will help him as much as I can."

"In that thou wilt do what is thy duty, Sancho," said Don Quixote; "for to engage in bat-tles of this sort it is not requisite to be a dubbed knight."

"That I can well understand," answered San-cho; "but where shall we put this ass where we may be sure to find him after the fray is over? For I believe it has not been the custom so far to go into battle on a beast of this kind."

"That is true," said Don Quixote, "and what you had best do with him is to leave him to take his chance whether he be lost or not, for the horses we shall have when we come out victors will be so many that even Rocinante will run a risk of being changed for another. But attend to me and observe, for I wish to give thee some account of the chief knights who accompany these two armies; and that thou mayest the bet-ter see and mark, let us withdraw to that hillock which rises yonder, whence both armies may be seen."

They did so, and placed themselves on a ris-ng ground from which the two droves that Don Quixote made armies of might have been plain-ly seen if the clouds of dust they raised had not obscured them and blinded the sight; neverthe-ess, seeing in his imagination what he did not see and what did not exist, he began thus in a oud voice: "That knight whom thou seest yon-der in yellow armor, who bears upon his shield a lion crowned crouching at the feet of a damsel, s the valiant Laurcalco, lord of the Silver Bridge; that one in armor with flowers of gold, who bears on his shield three crowns argent on an azure field, is the dreaded Micocolembo, grand duke of Quirocia; that other of gigantic frame, on his right hand, is the ever dauntless Branda-barbaran de Boliche, lord of the three Arabias, who for armor wears that serpent skin, and has for shield a gate which, according to tradition, is one of those of the temple that Samson brought to the ground when by his death he revenged himself upon his enemies; but turn thine eyes o the other side, and thou shalt see in front and in the van of this other army the ever victorious and never vanquished Timonel of Carcajona, prince of New Biscay, who comes in armor with arms quartered azure, vert, argent, and bears on his shield a cat or on a field tawny with a motto which says *Miau*, which is the begin-ning of the name of his lady, who according to report is the peerless Miaulina, daughter of the duke Alfeñiquen of the Algarve; the other, who burdens and presses the loins of that powerful charger and bears arms white as snow and a shield blank and without any device, is a nov-ce knight, a Frenchman by birth, Pierres Papin

by name, lord of the baronies of Utrique; that other, who with iron-shod heels strikes the flanks of that nimble party-colored zebra, and for arms bears azure cups, is the mighty duke of Nervia, Espartafilardo del Bosque, who bears for device on his shield an asparagus plant with a motto in Castilian that says, *Rastrea mi su-erte.*[1] And so he went on naming a number of knights of one squadron or the other out of his imagination, and to all he assigned off-hand their arms, colors, devices, and mottoes, carried away by the illusions of his unheard-of craze; and without a pause, he continued, "People of divers nations compose this squadron in front; here are those that drink of the sweet waters of the famous Xanthus, those that scour the woody Massilian plains, those that sift the pure fine gold of Arabia Felix, those that enjoy the famed cool banks of the crystal Thermodon, those that in many and various ways divert the streams of the golden Pactolus, the Numidians, faithless in their promises, the Persians renowned in archery, the Parthians and the Medes that fight as they fly, the Arabs that ever shift their dwell-ings, the Scythians as cruel as they are fair, the Ethiopians with pierced lips, and an infinity of other nations whose features I recognize and descry, though I can not recall their names. In this other squadron there come those that drink of the crystal streams of the olive-bearing Betis, those that make smooth their countenances with the water of the ever rich and golden Tagus, those that rejoice in the fertilizing flow of the divine Genil, those that roam the Tartesian plains abounding in pasture, those that take their pleasure in the elysian meadows of Jerez, the rich Manchegans crowned with ruddy ears of corn, the wearers of iron, old relics of the Gothic race, those that bathe in the Pisuerga renowned for its gentle current, those that feed their herds along the spreading pastures of the winding Guadiana famed for its hidden course, those that tremble with the cold of the pine-clad Pyrenees or the dazzling snows of the lofty Apennine; in a word, as many as all Europe in-cludes and contains."

Good God! what a number of countries and nations he named! giving to each its proper at-tributes with marvellous readiness; brimful and saturated with what he had read in his lying books! Sancho Panza hung upon his words with-out speaking, and from time to time turned to try if he could see the knights and giants his

[1] The motto has a double meaning: "in Fortune's footsteps" or "my fortune creeps on the ground," in allusion to the asparagus.

master was describing, and as he could not make out one of them he said to him, "Señor, devil take it if there's a sign of any man you talk of, knight or giant, in the whole thing; maybe it's all enchantment, like the phantoms last night."

"How canst thou say that!" answered Don Quixote; "dost thou not hear the neighing of the steeds, the braying of the trumpets, the roll of the drums?"

"I hear nothing but a great bleating of ewes and sheep," said Sancho; which was true, for by this time the two flocks had come close.

"The fear thou art in, Sancho," said Don Quixote, "prevents thee from seeing or hearing correctly, for one of the effects of fear is to derange the senses and make things appear different from what they are; if thou art in such fear, withdraw to one side and leave me to myself, for alone I suffice to bring victory to that side to which I shall give my aid"; and so saying he gave Rocinante the spur, and putting the lance in rest, shot down the slope like a thunderbolt. Sancho shouted after him, crying, "Come back, Señor Don Quixote; I vow to God they are sheep and ewes you are charging! Come back! Unlucky the father that begot me! what madness is this! Look, there is no giant, nor knight, nor cats, nor arms, nor shields quartered or whole, nor cups azure or bedevilled. What are you about? Sinner that I am before God!" But not for all these entreaties did Don Quixote turn back; on the contrary he went on shouting out, "Ho, knights, ye who follow and fight under the banners of the valiant emperor Pentapolin of the Bare Arm, follow me all: ye shall see how easily I shall give him his revenge over his enemy Alifanfaron of Trapobana."

So saying, he dashed into the midst of the squadron of ewes, and began spearing them with as much spirit and intrepidity as if he were transfixing mortal enemies in earnest. The shepherds and drovers accompanying the flock shouted to him to desist; but seeing it was no use, they ungirt their slings and began to salute his ears with stones, as big as one's fist. Don Quixote gave no heed to the stones, but, letting drive right and left, kept saying, "Where art thou, proud Alifanfaron? Come before me; I am a single knight who would fain prove thy prowess hand to hand, and make thee yield thy life a penalty for the wrong thou dost to the valiant Pentapolin Garamanta." Here came a sugar-plum from the brook that struck him on the side and buried a couple of ribs in his body. Feeling himself so smitten, he imagined himself slain or badly

wounded for certain, and recollecting his liquor he drew out his flask, and putting it to his mouth began to pour the contents into his stomach; but ere he had succeeded in swallowing what seemed to him enough, there came another almond which struck him on the hand and on the flask so fairly that it smashed it to pieces, knocking three or four teeth and grinders out of his mouth in its course, and sorely crushing two fingers of his hand. Such was the force of the first blow and of the second, that the poor knight in spite of himself came down backwards off his horse. The shepherds came up, and felt sure they had killed him; so in all haste they collected their flock together, took up the dead beasts, of which there were more than seven, and made off without waiting to ascertain anything further.

All this time Sancho stood on the hill watching the crazy feats his master was performing, and tearing his beard and cursing the hour and the occasion when fortune had made him acquainted with him. Seeing him, then, brought to the ground, and that the shepherds had taken themselves off, he came down the hill and ran to him and found him in very bad case, though not unconscious; and said he, "Did I not tell you to come back, Señor Don Quixote; and that what you were going to attack were not armies but droves of sheep?"

"That's how that thief of a sage, my enemy, can alter and falsify things," answered Don Quixote; "thou must know, Sancho, that it is a very easy matter for those of his sort to make us take what form they choose; and this malignant being who persecutes me, envious of the glory he knew I was to win in this battle, has turned the squadrons of the enemy into droves of sheep. At any rate, do this much, I beg of thee, Sancho, to undeceive thyself, and see that what I say is true; mount thy ass and follow them quietly, and thou shalt see that when they have gone some little distance from this they will return to their original shape and, ceasing to be sheep, become men in all respects as I described them to thee at first. But go not just yet, for I want thy help and assistance; come hither and see how many of my teeth and grinders are missing, for I feel as if there was not one left in my mouth."

Sancho came so close that he almost put his eyes into his mouth; now just at that moment the balsam had acted on the stomach of Don Quixote, so, at the very instant when Sancho came to examine his mouth, he discharged all its contents with more force than a musket, and full into the beard of the compassionate squire.

"Holy Mary!" cried Sancho, "what is this that has happened me? Clearly this sinner is mortally wounded, as he vomits blood from the mouth"; but considering the matter a little more closely he perceived by the color, taste, and smell, that it was not blood but the balsam from the flask which he had seen him drink; and he was taken with such a loathing that his stomach turned, and he vomited up his inside over his very master, and both were left in a precious state. Sancho ran to his ass to get something wherewith to clean himself, and relieve his master, out of his *alforjas*; but not finding them, he well-nigh took leave of his senses, and cursed himself anew, and in his heart resolved to quit his master and return home, even though he forfeited the wages of his service and all hopes of the government of the promised island.

Don Quixote now rose, and putting his left hand to his mouth to keep his teeth from falling out altogether, with the other he laid hold of the bridle of Rocinante, who had never stirred from his master's side—so loyal and well-behaved was he—and betook himself to where the squire stood leaning over his ass with his hand to his cheek, like one in deep dejection. Seeing him in this mood, looking so sad, Don Quixote said to him, "Bear in mind, Sancho, that one man is no more than another, unless he does more than another; all these tempests that fall upon us are signs that fair weather is coming shortly, and that things will go well with us, for it is impossible for good or evil to last forever; and hence it follows that the evil having lasted long, the good must be now nigh at hand; so thou must not distress thyself at the misfortunes which happen to me, since thou hast no share in them."

"How have I not?" replied Sancho; "was he whom they blanketed yesterday perchance any other than my father's son? and the *alforjas* that are missing to-day with all my treasures, did they belong to any other but myself?"

"What! are the *alforjas* missing, Sancho?" said Don Quixote.

"Yes, they are missing," answered Sancho.

"In that case we have nothing to eat to-day," replied Don Quixote.

"It would be so," answered Sancho, "if there were none of the herbs your worship says you know in these meadows, those with which knights-errant as unlucky as your worship are wont to supply such-like shortcomings."

"For all that," answered Don Quixote, "I would rather have just now a quarter of bread, or a loaf and a couple of pilchards' heads, than all the herbs described by Dioscorides, even with Dr. Laguna's notes. Nevertheless, Sancho the Good, mount thy beast and come along with me, for God, who provides for all things, will not fail us (more especially when we are so active in his service as we are), since he fails not the midges of the air, nor the grubs of the earth, nor the tadpoles of the water, and is so merciful that he maketh his sun to rise on the evil and on the good, and sendeth rain on the just and on the unjust."

"Your worship would make a better preacher than knight-errant," said Sancho.

"Knights-errant knew and ought to know everything, Sancho," said Don Quixote; "for there were knights-errant in former times as well qualified to deliver a sermon or discourse in the middle of a highway, as if they had graduated in the University of Paris; whereby we may see that the lance has never blunted the pen, nor the pen the lance."

"Well, be it as your worship says," replied Sancho; "let us be off now and find some place of shelter for the night, and God grant it may be somewhere where there are no blankets, nor blanketeers, nor phantoms, nor enchanted Moors; for if there are, may the devil take the whole concern."

"Ask that of God, my son," said Don Quixote; "and do thou lead on where thou wilt, for this time I leave our lodging to thy choice; but reach me here thy hand, and feel with thy finger, and find out how many of my teeth and grinders are missing from this right side of the upper jaw, for it is there I feel the pain."

Sancho put in his fingers, and feeling about asked him, "How many grinders used your worship have on this side?"

"Four," replied Don Quixote, "besides the back-tooth, all whole and quite sound."

"Mind what you are saying, señor," said Sancho.

"I say four, if not five," answered Don Quixote, "for never in my life have I had tooth or grinder drawn, nor has any fallen out or been destroyed by any decay or rheum."

"Well, then," said Sancho, "in this lower side your worship has no more than two grinders and a half, and in the upper neither a half nor any at all, for it is all as smooth as the palm of my hand."

"Luckless that I am!" said Don Quixote, hearing the sad news his squire gave him; "I had rather they had despoiled me of an arm, so it were not the sword-arm; for I tell thee, Sancho, a mouth without teeth is like a mill without a millstone, and a tooth is much more to be prized than a diamond; but we who profess the austere order of chivalry are liable to all this. Mount, friend, and lead the way, and I will follow thee at whatever pace thou wilt."

Sancho did as he bade him, and proceeded in the direction in which he thought he might find refuge without quitting the high road, which was there very much frequented. As they went along, then, at a slow pace—for the pain in Don Quixote's jaws kept him uneasy and ill-disposed for speed—Sancho thought it well to amuse and divert him by talk of some kind, and among the things he said to him was that which will be told in the following chapter.

Chapter 19

Of the shrewd discourse which Sancho held with his master, and of the adventure that befell him with a dead body, together with other notable occurrences

"It seems to me, señor, that all these mishaps that have befallen us of late have been without any doubt a punishment for the offence committed by your worship against the order of chivalry in not keeping the oath you made not to eat bread off a table-cloth or embrace the queen, and all the rest of it that your worship swore to observe until you had taken that helmet of Malandrino's, or whatever the Moor is called, for I do not very well remember."

"Thou art very right, Sancho," said Don Quixote, "but to tell the truth, it had escaped my memory; and likewise thou mayest rely upon it that the affair of the blanket happened to thee because of thy fault in not reminding me of it in time; but I will make amends, for there are ways of compounding for everything in the order of chivalry."

"Why! have I taken an oath of some sort, then?" said Sancho.

"It makes no matter that thou hast not taken an oath," said Don Quixote; "suffice it that I see thou are not quite clear of complicity; and whether or no, it will not be ill-done to provide ourselves with a remedy."

"In that case," said Sancho, "mind that your worship does not forget this as you did the oath; perhaps the phantoms may take it into their heads to amuse themselves once more with me; or even with your worship if they see you so obstinate."

While engaged in this and other talk, night overtook them on the road before they had reached or discovered any place of shelter; and what made it still worse was that they were dying of hunger, for with the loss of the *alforjas* they had lost their entire larder and commissariat; and to complete the misfortune they met with an adventure which without any invention had really the appearance of one. It so happened that the night closed in somewhat darkly, but for all that they pushed on, Sancho feeling sure that as the road was the king's highway they might reasonably expect to find some inn within a league or two. Going along, then, in this way, the night dark, the squire hungry, the master sharp-set, they saw coming towards them on the road they were travelling a great number of lights which looked exactly like stars in motion. Sancho was taken aback at the sight of them, nor did Don Quixote altogether relish them: the one pulled up his ass by the halter, the other his hack by the bridle, and they stood still, watching anxiously to see what all this would turn out to be, and found that the lights were approaching them, and the nearer they came the greater they seemed, at which spectacle Sancho began to shake like a man dosed with mercury, and Don Quixote's hair stood on end; he, however, plucking up spirit a little, said, "This, no doubt, Sancho, will be a most mighty and perilous adventure, in which it will be needful for me to put forth all my valor and resolution."

"Unlucky me!" answered Sancho; "if this adventure happens to be one of phantoms, as I am beginning to think it is, where shall I find the ribs to bear it?"

"Be they phantoms ever so much," said Don Quixote, "I will not permit them to touch a thread of thy garments; for if they played tricks with thee the time before, it was because I was unable to leap the walls of the yard; but now we are on a wide plain, where I shall be able to wield my sword as I please."

"And if they enchant and cripple you as they did the last time," said Sancho, "what difference will it make being on the open plain or not?"

"For all that," replied Don Quixote, "I entreat thee, Sancho, to keep a good heart, for experience will tell thee what mine is."

"I will, please God," answered Sancho, and the two retiring to one side of the road set themselves to observe closely what all these moving lights might be; and very soon afterwards they made out some twenty *encamisados*,[1] all on

[1] Festival-night maskers.

horseback, with lighted torches in their hands, the awe-inspiring aspect of whom completely extinguished the courage of Sancho, who began to chatter with his teeth like one in the cold fit of an ague; and his heart sank and his teeth chattered still more when they perceived distinctly that behind them there came a litter covered over with black and followed by six more mounted figures in mourning down to the very feet of their mules—for they could perceive plainly they were not horses by the easy pace at which they went. And as the *encamisados* came along they muttered to themselves in a low plaintive tone. This strange spectacle at such an hour and in such a solitary place was quite enough to strike terror into Sancho's heart, and even into his master's; and (save in Don Quixote's case) did so, for all Sancho's resolution had now broken down. It was just the opposite with his master, whose imagination immediately conjured up all this to him vividly as one of the adventures of his books. He took it into his head that the litter was a bier on which was borne some sorely wounded or slain knight, to avenge whom was a task reserved for him alone; and without any further reasoning he laid his lance in rest, fixed himself firmly in his saddle, and with gallant spirit and bearing took up his position in the middle of the road where the *encamisados* must of necessity pass; and as soon as he saw them near at hand he raised his voice and said, "Halt, knights, whosoever ye may be, and render me account of who ye are, whence ye come, what it is ye carry upon that bier, for, to judge by appearances, either ye have done some wrong or some wrong has been done to you, and it is fitting and necessary that I should know, either that I may chastise you for the evil ye have done, or else that I may avenge you for the injury that has been inflicted upon you."

"We are in haste," answered one of the *encamisados,* "and the inn is far off, and we can not stop to render you such an account as you demand"; and spurring his mule he moved on.

Don Quixote was mightily provoked by this answer, and seizing the mule by the bridle he said, "Halt, and be more mannerly, and render an account of what I have asked of you; else, take my defiance to combat, all of you."

The mule was shy, and was so frightened at her bridle being seized that rearing up she flung her rider to the ground over her haunches. An attendant who was on foot, seeing the *encamisado* fall began to abuse Don Quixote, who now moved to anger, without any more ado, laying his lance in rest charged one of the men in

mourning and brought him badly wounded to the ground, and as he wheeled round upon the others the agility with which he attacked and routed them was a sight to see, for it seemed just as if wings had that instant grown upon Rocinante, so lightly and proudly did he bear himself. The *encamisados* were all timid folk and unarmed, so they speedily made their escape from the fray and set off at a run across the plain with their lighted torches, looking exactly like maskers running on some gala or festival night. The mourners, too, enveloped and swathed in their skirts and gowns, were unable to bestir themselves, and so with entire safety to himself Don Quixote belabored them all and drove them off against their will, for they all thought it was no man but a devil from hell come to carry away the dead body they had in the litter.

Sancho beheld all this in astonishment at the intrepidity of his lord, and said to himself, "Clearly this master of mine is as bold and valiant as he says he is."

A burning torch lay on the ground near the first man whom the mule had thrown, by the light of which Don Quixote perceived him, and coming up to him he presented the point of the lance to his face, calling on him to yield himself prisoner, or else he would kill him; to which the prostrate man replied, "I am prisoner enough as it is; I can not stir, for one of my legs is broken: I entreat you, if you be a Christian gentleman, not to kill me, which will be committing grave sacrilege, for I am a licentiate and I hold first orders."

"Then what the devil brought you here, being a churchman?" asked Don Quixote.

"What, señor?" said the other. "My bad luck."

"Then still worse awaits you," said Don Quixote, "if you don't satisfy me as to all I asked you at first."

"You shall be soon satisfied," said the licentiate; "you must know, then, that though just now I said I was a licentiate, I am only a bachelor, and my name is Alonzo Lopez; I am a native of Alcobendas, I come from the city of Baeza with eleven others, priests, the same who fled with the torches, and we are going to the city of Segovia accompanying a dead body which is in that litter and is that of a gentleman who died in Baeza, where he was interred; and now, as I said, we are taking his bones to their burial-place, which is in Segovia, where he was born."

"And who killed him?" asked Don Quixote.

"God, by means of a malignant fever that took him," answered the bachelor.

"In that case," said Don Quixote, "the Lord has relieved me of the task of avenging his death had any other slain him; but, he who slew him having slain him, there is nothing for it but to be silent, and shrug one's shoulders; I should do the same were he to slay myself: and I would have your reverence know that I am a knight of La Mancha, Don Quixote by name, and it is my business and calling to roam the world righting wrongs and redressing injuries."

"I do not know how that about righting wrongs can be," said the bachelor, "for from straight you have made me crooked, leaving me with a broken leg that will never see itself straight again all the days of its life; and the injury you have redressed in my case has been to leave me injured in such a way that I shall remain injured forever; and the height of misadventure it was to fall in with you who go in search of adventures."

"Things do not always happen in the same way," answered Don Quixote; "it all came, Sir Bachelor Alonzo Lopez, of your going, as you did, by night, dressed in those surplices, with lighted torches, praying, covered with mourning, so that naturally you looked like something evil and of the other world; and so I could not avoid doing my duty in attacking you, and I should have attacked you even had I known positively that you were the very devils of hell, for such I certainly believed and took you to be."

"As my fate has so willed it," said the bachelor, "I entreat you, sir knight-errant, whose errand has been such an evil one for me, to help me to get from under this mule that holds one of my legs caught between the stirrup and the saddle."

"I would have talked on till to-morrow," said Don Quixote; "how long were you going to wait before telling me of your distress?"

He at once called to Sancho, who, however, had no mind to come, as he was just then engaged in unloading a sumpter mule, well laden with provender, which these worthy gentlemen had brought with them. Sancho made a bag of his coat, and, getting together as much as he could, and as the mule's sack would hold, he loaded his beast, and then hastened to obey his master's call, and helped him to remove the bachelor from under the mule; then putting him on her back he gave him the torch, and Don Quixote bade him follow the track of his companions, and beg pardon of them on his part for the wrong which he could not help doing them.

And said Sancho, "If by chance these gentlemen should want to know who was the hero that served them so, your worship may tell them that he is the famous Don Quixote of La Mancha, otherwise called the Knight of the Rueful Countenance."

The bachelor then took his departure. I forgot to mention that before he did so he said to Don Quixote, "Remember that you stand excommunicated for having laid violent hands on a holy thing, *juxta illud, si quis, suadente diabolo.*"

"I do not understand that Latin," answered Don Quixote, "but I know well I did not lay hands, only on this pike; besides, I did not think I was committing an assault upon priests or things of the Church, which, like a Catholic and faithful Christian as I am, I respect and revere, but upon phantoms and spectres of the other world; but even so, I remember how it fared with Cid Ruy Diaz when he broke the chair of the ambassador of that king before his Holiness the Pope who excommunicated him for the same; and yet the good Roderick of Bivar bore himself that day like a very noble and valiant knight."

On hearing this the bachelor took his departure, as has been said, without making any reply; and Don Quixote asked Sancho what had induced him to call him the "Knight of the Rueful Countenance" more than at any other time.

"I will tell you," answered Sancho; "it was because I have been looking at you for some time by the light of the torch held by that unfortunate, and verily your worship has got of late the most ill-favored countenance I ever saw: it must be either owing to the fatigue of this combat, or else to the want of teeth and grinders."

"It is not that," replied Don Quixote, "but because the sage whose duty it will be to write the history of my achievements must have thought it proper that I should take some distinctive name as all knights of yore did; one being 'He of the Burning Sword,' another 'He of the Unicorn,' this one 'He of the Damsels,' that 'He of the Phœnix,' another 'The Knight of the Griffin,' and another 'He of the Death,' and by these names and designations they were known all the world round; and so I say that the sage aforesaid must have put it into your mouth and mind just now to call me 'The

Knight of the Rueful Countenance,' as I intend to call myself from this day forward; and that the said name may fit me better, I mean, when the opportunity offers, to have a very rueful countenance painted on my shield."

"There is no occasion, señor, for wasting time or money on making that countenance," said Sancho; "for all that need be done is for your worship to show your own, face to face, to those who look at you, and without anything more, either image or shield, they will call you 'Him of the Rueful Countenance'; and believe me I am telling you the truth, for I assure you, señor (and in good part be it said), hunger and the loss of your grinders have given you such an ill-favored face that, as I say, the rueful picture may be very well spared."

Don Quixote laughed at Sancho's pleasantry; nevertheless he resolved to call himself by that name, and have his shield or buckler painted as he had devised.

Don Quixote would have looked to see whether the body in the litter were bones or not, but Sancho would not have it, saying, "Señor, you have ended this perilous adventure more safely for yourself than any of those I have seen: perhaps these people, though beaten and routed, may bethink themselves that it is a single man that has beaten them, and feeling sore and ashamed of it may take heart and come in search of us and give us trouble enough. The ass is in proper trim, the mountains are near at hand, hunger presses, we have nothing more to do but make good our retreat, and, as the saying is, let the dead go to the grave and the living to the loaf"; and driving his ass before him he begged his master to follow, who, feeling that Sancho was right, did so without replying; and after proceeding some little distance between two hills they found themselves in a wide and retired valley, where they alighted, and Sancho unloaded his beast, and stretched upon the green grass, with hunger for sauce, they breakfasted, dined, lunched, and supped all at once, satisfying their appetites with more than one store of cold meat which the dead man's clerical gentleman (who seldom put themselves on short allowance) had brought with them on their sumpter mule. But another piece of ill-luck befell them, which Sancho held the worst of all, and that was that they had no wine to drink, nor even water to moisten their lips; and as thirst tormented them, Sancho, observing that the meadow where they were was full of green and tender grass, said what will be told in the following chapter.

Chapter 20

Of the unexampled and unheard-of adventure which was achieved by the valiant Don Quixote of La Mancha with less peril than any ever achieved by any famous knight in the world

"It can not be, señor, but that this grass is a proof that there must be hard by some spring or brook to give it moisture, so it would be well to move a little farther on, that we may find some place where we may quench this terrible thirst that plagues us, which beyond a doubt is more distressing than hunger."

The advice seemed good to Don Quixote, and, he leading Rocinante by the bridle and Sancho the ass by the halter, after he had packed away upon him the remains of the supper, they advanced up the meadow feeling their way, for the darkness of the night made it impossible to see anything; but they had not gone two hundred paces when a loud noise of water, as if falling from great high rocks, struck their ears. The sound cheered them greatly; but halting to make out by listening from what quarter it came they heard unseasonably another noise which spoiled the satisfaction the sound of the water gave them, especially for Sancho, who was by nature timid and faint-hearted; they heard, I say, strokes falling with a measured beat, and a certain rattling of iron and chains that, together with the furious din of the water, would have struck terror into any heart but Don Quixote's. The night was, as has been said, dark, and they had happened to reach a spot in among some tall trees, whose leaves stirred by a gentle breeze made a low ominous sound; so that, what with the solitude, the place, the darkness, the noise of the water, and the rustling of the leaves, everything inspired awe and dread; more especially as they perceived that the strokes did not cease, nor the wind lull, nor morning approach; to all which might be added their ignorance as to where they were.

But Don Quixote, supported by his intrepid heart, leaped on Rocinante, and bracing his buckler on his arm, brought his pike to the slope, and said, "Friend Sancho, know that I by Heaven's will have been born in this our iron age to revive in it the age of gold, or the golden as it is called; I am he for whom perils, mighty achievements, and valiant deeds are reserved; I am, I say again, he who is to revive the Knights of the Round Table, the Twelve of France and the Nine Worthies; and he who is to consign to oblivion the Platirs, the Tablantes, the Olivantes and Tirantes, the Phœbuses and Belianises, with the whole herd of famous knights-errant of days gone by, performing in these in which I live such exploits, marvels, and feats of arms as shall obscure their brightest deeds. Thou dost mark well, faithful and trusty squire, the gloom of this night, its strange silence, the dull confused murmur of these trees, the awful sound of that water in quest of which we came, that seems as though it were precipitating and dashing itself down from the lofty mountains of the moon, and that incessant hammering that wounds and pains our ears; which things all together and each of itself are enough to instil fear, dread, and dismay into the breast of Mars himself, much more into one not used to hazards and adventures of the kind. Well, then, all this that I put before thee is but an incentive and stimulant to my spirit, making my heart burst in my bosom through eagerness to engage in this adventure, arduous as it promises to be; therefore tighten Rocinante's girths a little, and God be with thee; wait for me here three days and no more, and if in that time I come not back, thou canst return to our village, and thence, to do me a favor and a service, thou wilt go to El Toboso, where thou shalt say to my incomparable lady Dulcinea that her captive knight hath died in attempting things that might make him worthy of being called hers."

When Sancho heard his master's words he began to weep in the most pathetic way, saying, "Señor, I know not why your worship wants to attempt this so dreadful adventure; it is night now, no one sees us here, we can easily turn about and take ourselves out of danger, even if we don't drink for three days to come; and as there is no one to see us, all the less will there be any one to set us down as cowards; besides, I have many a time heard the curate of our village, whom your worship knows well, preach that he who seeks danger perishes in it; so it is not right to tempt God by trying so tremendous a feat from which there can be no escape save by a miracle, and Heaven has performed enough of them for your worship in delivering you from being blanketed as I was, and bringing you out victorious and safe and sound from among all those enemies that were with the dead man; and if all this does not move or soften that hard heart, let this thought and reflection move it, that you will have hardly quitted this spot when from pure fear I shall yield my soul up to any one that will take it. I left home and wife and children to come and serve your wor-

ship, trusting to do better and not worse; but, as covetousness bursts the bag, it has rent my hopes asunder, for just as I had them highest about getting that wretched unlucky island your worship has so often promised me, I see that instead and in lieu of it you mean to desert me now in a place so far from human reach; for God's sake, master mine, deal not so unjustly by me, and if your worship will not entirely give up attempting this feat, at least put it off till morning, for by what the lore I learned when I was a shepherd tells me it can not want three hours of dawn now, because the mouth of the Horn is overhead and makes midnight in the line of the left arm."

"How canst thou see, Sancho," said Don Quixote, "where it makes that line, or where the mouth or head is that thou talkest of, when the night is so dark that there is not a star to be seen in the whole heaven?"

"That's true," said Sancho, "but fear has sharp eyes, and sees things underground, much more above in the heavens; besides, there is good reason to show that it now wants but little of day."

"Let it want what it may," replied Don Quixote, "it shall not be said of me now or at any time that tears or entreaties turned me aside from doing what was in accordance with knightly usage; and so I beg of thee, Sancho, to hold thy peace, for God, who has put it into my heart to undertake now this so unexampled and terrible adventure, will take care to watch over my safety and console thy sorrow; what thou hast to do is to tighten Rocinante's girths well, and wait here, for I shall come back shortly, alive or dead."

Sancho perceiving it his master's final resolve, and how little his tears, counsels, and entreaties prevailed with him, determined to have recourse to his own ingenuity and compel him if he could to wait till daylight; and so, while tightening the girths of the horse, he quietly and without being felt, tied both Rocinante's fore-legs, so that when Don Quixote strove to go he was unable as the horse could only move by jumps. Seeing the success of his trick, Sancho Panza said, "See there, señor! Heaven, moved by my tears and prayers, has so ordered it that Rocinante can not stir; and if you will be obstinate, and spur and strike him, you will only provoke fortune, and kick, as they say, against the pricks."

Don Quixote at this grew desperate, but the more he drove his heels into the horse, the less he stirred him; and not having any suspicion of the tying, he was fain to resign himself and wait till daybreak or until Rocinante could move, firmly persuaded that all this came of something other than Sancho's ingenuity. So he said to him, "As it is so, Sancho, and as Rocinante can not move, I am content to wait till dawn smiles upon us, even though I weep while it delays its coming."

"There is no need to weep," answered Sancho, "for I will amuse your worship by telling stories from this till daylight, unless, indeed, you like to dismount and lie down to sleep a little on the green grass after the fashion of knights-errant, so as to be fresher when day comes and the moment arrives for attempting this extraordinary adventure you are looking forward to."

"What art thou talking about dismounting or sleeping for?" said Don Quixote. "Am I, thinkest thou, one of those knights that take their rest in the presence of danger? Sleep thou who art born to sleep, or do as thou wilt, for I will act as I think most consistent with my character."

"Be not angry, master mine," replied Sancho, "I did not mean to say that"; and coming close to him he laid one hand on the pommel of the saddle and the other on the cantle, so that he held his master's left thigh in his embrace, not daring to separate a finger's length from him; so much afraid was he of the strokes which still resounded with a regular beat. Don Quixote bade him tell some story to amuse him as he had proposed, to which Sancho replied that he would if his dread of what he heard would let him; "Still," said he, "I will strive to tell a story which, if I can manage to relate it, and it escapes me not, is the best of stories, and let your worship give me your attention, for here I begin. What was, was; and may the good that is to come be for all, and the evil for him who goes to look for it—your worship must know that the beginning the old folk used to put to their tales was not just as each one pleased; it was a maxim of Cato Zonzorino the Roman that says 'the evil for him that goes to look for it,' and it comes as pat to the purpose now as ring to finger, to show that your worship should keep quiet and not go looking for evil in any quarter, and that we should go back by some other road, since nobody forces us to follow this in which so many terrors affright us."

"Go on with thy story, Sancho," said Don Quixote, "and leave the choice of our road to my care."

"I say then," continued Sancho, "that in a village of Estremadura there was a goat-shepherd —that is to say, one who tended goats—which shepherd or goatherd, as my story goes, was called Lope Ruiz, and this Lope Ruiz was in love with a shepherdess called Torralva, which shepherdess called Torralva was the daughter of a rich grazier, and this rich grazier"—

"If that is the way thou tellest thy tale, Sancho," said Don Quixote, "repeating twice all thou hast to say, thou wilt not have done these two days; go straight on with it, and tell it like a reasonable man, or else say nothing."

"Tales are always told in my country in the very way I am telling this," answered Sancho, "and I can not tell it in any other, nor is it right of your worship to ask me to make new customs."

"Tell it as thou wilt," replied Don Quixote; "and as fate will have it that I can not help listening to thee, go on."

"And so, lord of my soul," continued Sancho, "as I have said, this shepherd was in love with Torralva the shepherdess, who was a wild buxom lass with something of the look of a man about her, for she had little mustaches; I fancy I see her now."

"Then you knew her?" said Don Quixote.

"I did not know her," said Sancho, "but he who told me the story said it was so true and certain that when I told it to another I might safely declare and swear I had seen it all myself. And so in course of time, the devil, who never sleeps and puts everything in confusion, contrived that the love the shepherd bore the shepherdess turned into hatred and ill-will, and the reason, according to evil tongues, was some little jealousy she had caused him that crossed the line and trespassed on forbidden ground; and so much did the shepherd hate her from that time forward that, in order to escape from her, he determined to quit the country and go where he should never set eyes on her again. Torralva, when she found herself spurned by Lope, was immediately smitten with love for him, though she had never loved him before."

"That is the natural way of women," said Don Quixote, "to scorn the one that loves them, and love the one that hates them: go on, Sancho."

"It came to pass," said Sancho, "that the shepherd carried out his intention, and driving his goats before him took his way across the plains of Estremadura to pass over into the Kingdom of Portugal. Torralva, who knew of it, went after him, and on foot and barefooted followed him at a distance, with a pilgrim's staff in her hand and a scrip round her neck, in which she carried, it is said, a bit of looking-glass, and a piece of a comb and some little pot or other of paint for her face; but let her carry what she did, I am not going to trouble myself to prove it; all I say is, that the shepherd, they say, came with his flock to cross over the river Guadiana, which was at that time swollen and almost overflowing its banks, and at the spot he came to there was neither ferry nor boat nor any one to carry him or his flock to the other side, at which he was much vexed, for he perceived that Torralva was approaching and would give him great annoyance with her tears and entreaties; however, he went looking about so closely that he discovered a fisherman who had alongside of him a boat so small that it could only hold one person and one goat; but for all that he spoke to him and agreed with him to carry himself and his three hundred goats across. The fisherman got into the boat and carried one goat over; he came back and carried another over; he came back again, and again brought over another—let your worship keep count of the goats the fisherman is taking across, for if one escapes the memory there will be an end of the story, and it will be impossible to tell another word of it. To proceed, I must tell you the landing place on the other side was miry and slippery, and the fisherman lost a great deal of time in going and coming; still he returned for another goat, and another, and another."

"Take it for granted he brought them all across," said Don Quixote, "and don't keep going and coming in this way, or thou wilt not make an end of bringing them over this twelve-month."

"How many have gone across so far?" said Sancho.

"How the devil do I know?" replied Don Quixote.

"There it is," said Sancho, "what I told you, that you must keep a good count; well then, by God, there is an end of the story, for there is no going any farther."

"How can that be?" said Don Quixote; "is it so essential to the story to know to a nicety the goats that have crossed over, that if there be a mistake of one in the reckoning, thou canst not go on with it?"

"No, señor, not a bit," replied Sancho; "for when I asked your worship to tell me how many goats had crossed, and you answered you did not know, at that very instant all I had to say passed away out of my memory, and faith, there was much virtue in it, and entertainment."

"So, then," said Don Quixote, "the story has come to an end?"

"As much as my mother has," said Sancho.

"In truth," said Don Quixote, "thou hast told one of the rarest stories, tales, or histories, that any one in the world could have imagined, and such a way of telling it and ending it was never seen nor will be in a lifetime; though I expected nothing else from thy excellent understanding. But I do not wonder, for perhaps those ceaseless strokes may have confused thy wits."

"All that may be," replied Sancho, "but I know that as to my story, all that can be said is that it ends there where the mistake in the count of the passage of the goats begins."

"Let it end where it will, well and good," said Don Quixote, "and let us see if Rocinante can go"; and again he spurred him, and again Rocinante made jumps and remained where he was, so well tied was he.

Just then, whether it was the cold of the morning that was now approaching, or that he had eaten something laxative at supper, or that it was only natural (as is most likely), Sancho felt a desire to do what no one could do for him; but so great was the fear that had penetrated his heart, he dared not separate himself from his master by so much as the black of his nail; to escape doing what he wanted was, however, also impossible; so what he did for peace' sake was to remove his right hand, which held the back of the saddle, and with it to untie gently and silently the running string which alone held up his breeches, so that on loosening it they at once fell down round his feet like fetters; he then raised his shirt as well as he could and bared his hind quarters, no slim ones. But this accomplished, which he fancied was all he had to do to get out of this terrible strait and embarrassment, another still greater difficulty presented itself, for it seemed to him impossible to relieve himself without making some noise, and he ground his teeth and squeezed his shoulders together, holding his breath as much as he could; but in spite of his precautions he was unlucky enough after all to make a little noise, very different from that which was causing him so much fear.

Don Quixote, hearing it, said, "What noise is that, Sancho?"

"I don't know, señor," said he; "it must be something new, for adventures and misadventures never begin with a trifle." Once more he tried his luck, and succeeded so well, that without any further noise or disturbance he found himself relieved of the burden that had given him so much discomfort. But as Don Quixote's sense of smell was as acute as his hearing, and as Sancho was so closely linked with him that the fumes rose almost in a straight line, it could not be but that some should reach his nose, and as soon as they did he came to its relief by compressing it between his fingers, saying in a rather snuffling tone, "Sancho, it strikes me thou art in great fear."

"I am," answered Sancho; "but how does your worship perceive it now more than ever?"

"Because just now thou smellest stronger than ever, and not of ambergris," answered Don Quixote.

"Very likely," said Sancho, "but that's not my fault, but your worship's, for leading me about at unseasonable hours and at such unwonted paces."

"Then go back three or four, my friend," said Don Quixote, all the time with his fingers to his nose; "and for the future pay more attention to thy person and to what thou owest to mine; for it is my great familiarity with thee that has bred this contempt."

"I'll bet," replied Sancho, "that your worship thinks I have done something I ought not with my person."

"It makes it worse to stir it, friend Sancho," returned Don Quixote.

With this and other talk of the same sort master and man passed the night, till Sancho, perceiving that daybreak was coming on apace, very cautiously untied Rocinante and tied up his breeches. As soon as Rocinante found himself free, though by nature he was not at all mettlesome, he seemed to feel lively and began pawing—for as to capering, begging his pardon, he knew not what it meant. Don Quixote, then, observing that Rocinante could move, took it as a good sign and a signal that he should attempt the dread adventure. By this time day had fully broken and everything showed distinctly, and Don Quixote saw that he was among some tall trees, chestnuts, which cast a very deep shade; he perceived likewise that the sound of the strokes did not cease, but could not discover what caused it, and so without any further delay he let Rocinante feel the spur, and once more taking leave of Sancho, he told him to wait for him there three days at most, as he had said before, and if he should not have returned by that time, he might feel sure it had been God's will that he should end his days in that perilous adventure. He again repeated the message and commission with which he was to go on his behalf to his lady Dulcinea, and said he was not to be uneasy as to the payment of his services, for before leaving home he had made his will, in which he would find himself fully recompensed in the matter of wages in due proportion to the time he had served; but if God delivered him safe, sound, and unhurt out of that danger, he might look upon the promised island as much more than certain. Sancho began weeping afresh on again hearing the affecting words of his good master, and resolved to stay with him until the final issue and end of the business. From these tears and this honorable resolve of Sancho Panza's the author of this history infers that he must have been of good birth and at least an old Christian;[1] and the feeling he displayed touched his master somewhat, but not so much as to make him show any weakness; on the contrary, hiding what he felt as well as he could, he began to move towards that quarter whence the sound of the water and of the strokes seemed to come.

Sancho followed him on foot, leading by the halter, as his custom was, his ass, his constant comrade in prosperity or adversity; and advancing some distance through the shady chestnut trees they came up on a little meadow at the foot of some high rocks, down which a mighty rush of water flung itself. At the foot of the rocks were some rudely constructed houses looking more like ruins than houses, from among which came, they perceived, the din and clatter of blows, which still continued without intermission. Rocinante took fright at the noise of the water and of the blows, but quieting him Don Quixote advanced step by step towards the houses, commending himself with all his heart to his lady, imploring her support in that dread pass and enterprise, and on the way commending himself to God, too, not to forget him. Sancho, who never quitted his side, stretched his neck as far as he could and peered between the legs of Rocinante to see if he could now discover what it was that caused him such fear and apprehension. They went it might be a hundred paces farther, when on turning a corner the true cause, beyond the possibility of any mistake, of that dread-sounding and to them awe-inspiring noise that had kept them all the night in such fear and perplexity, appeared plain and obvious; and it was (if, reader, thou art not disgusted and disappointed) six fulling hammers which by their alternate strokes made all the din.

[1] That is, one who had no trace of Moorish blood in his veins.

When Don Quixote perceived what it was, he was struck dumb and rigid from head to foot. Sancho glanced at him and saw him with his head bent down upon his breast in manifest mortification; and Don Quixote glanced at Sancho and saw him with his cheeks puffed out and his mouth full of laughter, and evidently ready to explode with it, and in spite of his vexation he could not help laughing at the sight of him; and when Sancho saw his master begin he let go so heartily that he had to hold his sides with both hands to keep himself from bursting with laughter. Four times he stopped, and as many times did his laughter break out afresh with the same violence as at first, whereat Don Quixote grew furious, above all when he heard him say mockingly, "Thou must know, friend Sancho, that of Heaven's will I was born in this our iron age to revive in it the golden or age of gold; I am he for whom are reserved perils, mighty achievements, valiant deeds"; and here he went on repeating all or most of the words that Don Quixote uttered the first time they heard the awful strokes.

Don Quixote, then, seeing that Sancho was turning him into ridicule, was so mortified and vexed that he lifted up his pike and smote him two such blows that if, instead of catching them on his shoulders, he had caught them on his head, there would have been no wages to pay, unless indeed to his heirs. Sancho seeing that he was getting an awkward return in earnest for his jest, and fearing his master might carry it still further, said to him very humbly, "Calm yourself, sir, for by God I am only joking."

"Well, then, if you are joking I am not," replied Don Quixote. "Look here, my lively gentleman, if these, instead of being fulling hammers, had been some perilous adventure, have I not, think you, shown the courage required for the attempt and achievement? Am I, perchance, being, as I am, a gentleman, bound to know and distinguish sounds and tell whether they come from fulling mills or not; and that, when perhaps, as is the case, I have never in my life seen any as you have, low boor as you are, that have been born and bred among them? But turn me these six hammers into six giants, and bring them to beard me, one by one or all together, and if I do not knock them head over heels, then make what mockery you like of me."

"No more of that, señor," returned Sancho; "I own I went a little far with the joke. But tell me, your worship, now that peace is made between us (and may God bring you out of all the adventures that may befall you as safe and sound as He has brought you out of this one), was it not a thing to laugh at, and is it not a good story, the great fear we were in?—at least that I was in; for as to your worship I see now that you neither know nor understand what either fear or dismay is."

"I do not deny," said Don Quixote, "that what happened to us may be worth laughing at, but it is not worth making a story about, for it is not every one that is shrewd enough to hit the right point of a thing."

"At any rate," said Sancho, "your worship knew how to hit the right point with your pike, aiming at my head and hitting me on the shoulders, thanks be to God and my own smartness in dodging it. But let that pass; all will come out in the scouring; for I have heard say 'he loves thee well that makes thee weep'; and moreover that it is the way with great lords after any hard words they give a servant to give him a pair of breeches; though I do not know what they give after blows, unless it be that knights-errant after blows give islands, or kingdoms on the mainland."

"It may be on the dice," said Don Quixote, "that all thou sayest will come true; overlook the past, for thou art shrewd enough to know that our first movements are not in our own control; and one thing for the future bear in mind, that thou curb and restrain thy loquacity in my company; for in all the books of chivalry that I have read, and they are innumerable, I never met with a squire who talked so much to his lord as thou dost to thine; and in fact I feel it to be a great fault of thine and of mine: of thine, that thou hast so little respect for me; of mine, that I do not make myself more respected. There was Gandalin, the squire of Amadis of Gaul, that was Count of the Insula Firme, and we read of him that he always addressed his lord with his cap in his hand, his head bowed down and his body bent double, more turquesco. And then, what shall we say of Gasabal, the squire of Galaor, who was so silent that in order to indicate to us the greatness of his marvellous taciturnity his name is only once mentioned in the whole of that history, as long as it is truthful? From all I have said thou wilt gather, Sancho, that there must be a difference between master and man, between lord and lackey, between knight and squire: so that from this day forward in our intercourse we must observe more respect and take less liberties, for in whatever way I may be provoked with you it will be bad for the pitcher. The favors and benefits that I have promised you will come in due time, and if they do not your wages at least will not be lost, as I have already told you."

"All that your worship says is very well," said Sancho, "but I should like to know (in case the time of favors should not come, and it might be necessary to fall back upon wages) how much did the squire of a knight-errant get in those days, and did they agree by the month, or by the day like bricklayers?"

"I do not believe," replied Don Quixote, "that such squires were ever on wages, but were dependent on favor; and if I have now mentioned thine in the sealed will I have left at home, it was with a view to what may happen; for as yet I know not how chivalry will turn out in these wretched times of ours, and I do not wish my soul to suffer for trifles in the other world; for I would have thee know, Sancho, that in this there is no condition more hazardous than that of adventures."

"That is true," said Sancho, "since the mere noise of the hammers of a fulling mill can disturb and disquiet the heart of such a valiant errant adventurer as your worship; but you may be sure I will not open my lips henceforward to make light of anything of your worship's, but only to honor you as my master and natural lord."

"By so doing," replied Don Quixote, "shalt thou live long on the face of the earth; for next to parents, masters are to be respected as though they were parents."

Chapter 21

Which treats of the exalted adventure and rich prize of Mambrino's helmet, together with other things that happened to our invincible knight

It now began to rain a little, and Sancho was for going into the fulling mills, but Don Quixote had taken such a disgust to them on account of the late joke that he would not enter them on any account; so turning aside to the right they came upon another road, different from that which they had taken the night before. Shortly afterwards Don Quixote perceived a man on horseback who wore on his head something that shone like gold, and the moment he saw him he turned to Sancho and said, "I think, Sancho, there is no proverb that is not true, all being maxims drawn from experience itself, the mother of all the sciences, especially that one that says, 'Where one door shuts, another opens.' I say so because if last night fortune shut the door of the adventure we were looking for against us, cheating us with the fulling mills, it now opens wide another one for another better and more certain adventure, and if I do not contrive to enter it, it will be my own fault, and I cannot lay it to my ignorance of fulling mills, or the darkness of the night. I say this because, if I mistake not, there comes toward us one who wears on his head the helmet of Mambrino, concerning which I took the oath thou rememberest."

"Mind what you say, your worship, and still more what you do," said Sancho, "for I don't want any more fulling mills to finish off fulling and knocking our senses out."

"The devil take thee, man," said Don Quixote; "what has a helmet to do with fulling mills?"

"I don't know," replied Sancho, "but, faith, if I might speak as I used, perhaps I could give such reasons that your worship would see you were mistaken in what you say."

"How can I be mistaken in what I say, unbelieving traitor?" returned Don Quixote. "Tell me, seest thou not yonder knight coming towards us on a dappled gray steed, who has upon his head a helmet of gold?"

"What I see and make out," answered Sancho, "is only a man on a gray ass like my own, who has something that shines on his head."

"Well, that is the helmet of Mambrino," said Don Quixote; "stand to one side and leave me alone with him; thou shalt see how, without saying a word, to save time, I shall bring this adventure to an issue and possess myself of the helmet I have so longed for."

"I will take care to stand aside," said Sancho; "but God grant, I say once more, that it may be marjoram and not fulling mills."

"I have told thee, brother, on no account to mention those fulling mills to me again," said Don Quixote, "or I vow—and I say no more—I'll full the soul out of you."

Sancho held his peace in dread lest his master should carry out the vow he had hurled like a bowl at him.

The fact of the matter as regards the helmet, steed, and knight that Don Quixote saw, was this. In that neighborhood there were two villages, one of them so small that it had neither apothecary's shop, nor barber, which the other that was close to it had, so the barber of the large served the smaller, and in it there was a sick man who required to be bled and another man who wanted to be shaved, and on this errand the barber was going, carrying with him a brass basin; but as luck would have it, as he was on the way it began to rain, and not to spoil his hat, which probably was a new one, he put the basin on his head, and being clean it glittered at half a league's distance. He rode upon a gray ass, as Sancho said, and this was what made it seem to Don Quixote to be a dapple-gray steed and a knight and a golden helmet; for everything he saw he made to fall in with his crazy chivalry and ill-errant notions; and when he saw the poor knight draw near, without entering into any parley with him, at Rocinante's top speed he bore down upon him with the pike pointed low, fully determined to run him through and through, and as he reached him, without checking the fury of his charge, he cried to him, "Defend thyself, miserable being, or yield me of thine own accord that which is so reasonably my due."

The barber, who without any expectation or apprehension of it saw this apparition coming down upon him, had no other way of saving himself from the stroke of the lance but to let himself fall off his ass; and no sooner had he touched the ground than he sprang up more nimbly than a deer and sped away across the plain faster than the wind.

He left the basin on the ground, with which Don Quixote contented himself, saying that the pagan had shown his discretion and imitated the beaver, which finding itself pressed by the hunters bites and cuts off with its teeth that for which, by its natural instinct, it knows it is pursued.

He told Sancho to pick up the helmet, and he taking it in his hands said, "By God the basin is a good one, and worth a real of eight if it is worth a maravedí," and handed it to his master, who immediately put it on his head, turning it round, now this way, now that, in search of the visor, and not finding it he said, "Clearly the pagan to whose measure this famous headpiece was first forged must have had a very large head; but the worst of it is half of it is wanting."

When Sancho heard him call the basin a head-piece he was unable to restrain his laughter, but remembering his master's wrath he checked himself in the midst of it.

"What art thou laughing at, Sancho?" said Don Quixote.

"I am laughing," said he, "to think of the great head the pagan must have had who owned this helmet, for it looks exactly like a regular barber's basin."

"Dost thou know what I suspect, Sancho?" said Don Quixote. "That this wonderful piece of this enchanted helmet must by some strange accident have come into the hands of some one who was unable to recognize or realize its value, and who, not knowing what he did, and seeing it to be of the purest gold, must have melted down one half for the sake of what it might be worth, and of the other made this which is like a barber's basin as thou sayest; but be it as it may, to me who recognize it, its transformation makes no difference, for I will set it to rights at the first village where there is a blacksmith, and in such style that that helmet the god of smithies forged for the god of battles shall not surpass it or even come up to it; and in the meantime I will wear it as well as I can, for something is better than nothing; all the more as it will be quite enough to protect me from any chance blow of a stone."

"That is," said Sancho, "if it is not shot with a sling as they were in the battle of the two armies, when they signed the cross on your worship's grinders and smashed the flask with that blessed draught that made me vomit my bowels up."

"It does not grieve me much to have lost it," said Don Quixote, "for thou knowest, Sancho, that I have the receipt in my memory."

"So have I," answered Sancho, "but if ever I make it, or try it again as long as I live, may this be my last hour; moreover, I have no intention of putting myself in the way of wanting it, for I mean, with all my five senses, to keep myself from being wounded or from wounding any one: as to being blanketed again I say nothing, for it is hard to prevent mishaps of that sort, and if they come there is nothing for it but to squeeze our shoulders together, hold our breath, shut our eyes, and let ourselves go where luck and the blanket may send us."

"Thou art a bad Christian, Sancho," said Don Quixote on hearing this, "for once an injury has been done thee thou never forgettest it: but know that it is the part of noble and generous hearts not to attach importance to trifles. What lame leg hast thou got by it, what broken rib, what cracked head, that thou canst not forget that jest? For jest and sport it was, properly regarded, and had I not seen it in that light I would have returned and done more mischief in revenging thee than the Greeks did for the rape of Helen, who, if she were alive now, or if my Dulcinea had lived then, might depend upon it she would not be so famous for her beauty as she is"; and here he heaved a sigh and sent it aloft; and said Sancho, "Let it pass for a jest as it can not be revenged in earnest, but I know what sort of jest and earnest it was, and I know it will never be rubbed out of my memory any more than off my shoulders. But putting that aside, will your worship tell me what are we to do with this dapple-gray steed that looks like a gray ass, which that Martino that your worship overthrew has left deserted here? For, from the way he took to his heels and bolted, he is not likely ever to come back for it; and by my beard but the gray is a good one."

"I have never been in the habit," said Don Quixote, "of taking spoil of those whom I vanquish, nor is it the practice of chivalry to take away their horses and leave them to go on foot, unless indeed it be that the victor have lost his own in the combat, in which case it is lawful to take that of the vanquished as a thing won in lawful war; therefore, Sancho, leave this horse, or ass, or whatever thou wilt have it to be; for when its owner sees us gone hence he will come back for it."

"God knows I should like to take it," returned Sancho, "or at least to change it for my own, which does not seem to me as good a one; verily the laws of chivalry are strict, since they can not be stretched to let one ass be changed for another; I should like to know if I might at least change trappings."

"On that head I am not quite certain," answered Don Quixote, "and the matter being doubtful, pending better information, I say thou mayest change them, if so be thou hast urgent need of them."

"So urgent is it," answered Sancho, "that if they were for my own person I could not want them more"; and forthwith, fortified by this license, he effected the *mutatio capparum*, and rigged out his beast to the ninety-nines, making quite another thing of it. This done, they broke their fast on the remains of the spoils of war plundered from the sumpter mule, and drank of the brook that flowed from the fulling mills, without casting a look in that direction, in such loathing did they hold them for the alarm they had caused them; and, all anger and gloom removed, they mounted and, without taking any fixed road (not to fix upon any being the proper thing for true knights-errant), they set out, guided by Rocinante's will, which carried along with it that of his master, not to say that of the ass, which always followed him wherever he led, lovingly and sociably; nevertheless they returned to the high road, and pursued it at a venture without any other aim.

As they went along, then, in this way San-cho said to his master, "Señor, would your worship give me leave to speak a little to you? For since you laid that hard injunction of silence on me several things have gone to rot in my stomach, and I have now just one on the tip of my tongue that I don't want to be spoiled."

"Say on, Sancho," said Don Quixote, "and be brief in thy discourse, for there is no pleasure in one that is long."

"Well, then, señor," returned Sancho, "I say that for some days past I have been considering how little is got or gained by going in search of these adventures that your worship seeks in these wilds and cross-roads, where, even if the most perilous are victoriously achieved, there is no one to see or know of them, and so they must be left untold forever, to the loss of your worship's object and the credit they deserve; therefore it seems to me it would be better (saving your worship's better judgment) if we were to go and serve some emperor or other great prince who may have some war on hand, in whose service your worship may prove the worth of your person, your great might, and greater understanding, on perceiving which the lord in whose service we may be will perforce have to reward us, each according to his merits; and there you will not be at a loss for some one to set down your achievements in writing so as to preserve their memory forever. Of my own I say nothing, as they will not go beyond squirely limits, though I make bold to say that, if it be the practice in chivalry to write the achievements of squires, I think mine must not be left out."

"Thou speakest not amiss, Sancho," answered Don Quixote, "but before that point is reached it is requisite to roam the world, as it were on probation, seeking adventures, in order that, by achieving some, name and fame may be acquired, such that when he betakes himself to the court of some great monarch the knight may be already known by his deeds, and that the boys, the instant they see him enter the gate of the city, may all follow him and surround him, crying, 'This is the Knight of the Sun'— or the Serpent, or any other title under which he may have achieved great deeds. 'This,' they will say, 'is he who vanquished in single combat the gigantic Brocabruno of mighty strength; he who delivered the great Mameluke of Persia out of the long enchantment under which he had been for almost nine hundred years.' So from one to another they will go proclaiming his achievements; and presently at the tumult of the boys and the others the king of that kingdom will appear at the windows of his royal palace, and as soon as he beholds the knight, recognizing him by his arms and the device on his shield, he will as a matter of course say, 'What ho! Forth all ye, the knights of my court, to receive the flower of chivalry who cometh hither!' At which command all will issue forth, and he himself, advancing half-way down the stairs, will embrace him closely, and salute him, kissing him on the cheek, and will then lead him to the queen's chamber, where the knight will find her with the princess her daughter, who will be one of the most beautiful and accomplished damsels that could with the utmost pains be discovered anywhere in the known world. Straightway it will come to pass that she will fix her eyes upon the knight and he his upon her, and each will seem to the other something more divine than human, and, without knowing how or why, they will be taken and entangled in the inextricable toils of love, and sorely distressed in their hearts not to see any way of making their pains and sufferings known by speech. Thence they will lead him, no doubt, to some richly adorned chamber of the palace, where, having removed his armor, they will bring him a rich mantle of scarlet wherewith to robe himself, and if he looked noble in his armor he will look still more so in a doublet. When night comes he will sup with the king, queen, and princess; and all the time he will never take his eyes off her, stealing stealthy glances, unnoticed by those present, and she will do the same, and with equal cautiousness, being, as I have said, a damsel of great discretion. The tables being removed, suddenly through the door of the hall there will enter a hideous and diminutive dwarf followed by a fair dame, between two giants, who comes with a certain adventure, the work of an ancient sage; and he who shall achieve it shall be deemed the best knight in the world. The king will then command all those present to essay it, and none will bring it to an end and conclusion save the stranger knight, to the great enhancement of his fame, whereat the princess will be overjoyed and will esteem herself happy and fortunate in having fixed and placed her thoughts so high. And the best of it is that this king, or prince, or whatever he is, is engaged in a very bitter war with another as powerful as himself, and the stranger knight, after having been some days at his court, requests leave from him to go and serve him in the said war. The king will grant it very readily, and the knight will courteously kiss his hands for the favor done to him; and that night he will take leave of his lady the princess at the grating of the chamber where she sleeps, which looks upon a garden, and at which he has already many times conversed with her, the go-between and confidante in the matter being a damsel much trusted by the princess. He will sigh, she will swoon, the damsel will fetch water, he will be distressed because morning approaches, and for the honor of his lady he would not that they were discovered; at last the princess will come to herself and will present her white hands through the grating to the knight, who will kiss them a thousand and a thousand times, bathing them with his tears. It will be arranged between them how they are to inform each other of their good or evil fortunes, and the princess will entreat him to make his absence as short as possible, which he will promise to do with many oaths; once more he kisses her hands, and takes his leave in such grief that he is well-nigh ready to die. He betakes him thence to his chamber, flings himself on his bed, can not sleep for sorrow at parting, rises early in the morning, goes to take leave of the king, queen, and princess, and, as he takes his leave of the pair, it is told him that the princess is indisposed and can not receive a visit; the knight thinks it is from grief at his departure, his heart is pierced, and he is hardly able to keep from showing his pain. The confidante is present, observes all, goes to tell her mistress, who listens with tears and says that one of her greatest distresses is not knowing who this knight is, and whether he is of kingly lineage or not; the damsel assures her that so much courtesy, gentleness, and gallantry of bearing as her knight possesses could not exist in any save one who was royal and illustrious; her anxiety is thus relieved, and she strives to be of good cheer lest she should excite suspicion in her parents, and at the end of two days she appears in public. Meanwhile the knight has taken his departure; he fights in the war, conquers the king's enemy, wins many cities, triumphs in many battles, returns to the court, sees his lady where he was wont to see her, and it is agreed that he shall demand her in marriage of her parents as the reward of his services; the king is unwilling to give her, as he knows not who he is, but nevertheless, whether carried off or in whatever other way it may be, the princess comes to be his bride, and her father comes to regard it as very good fortune; for it so happens that this knight is proved to be the son of a valiant king of some kingdom, I know not what, for I fancy it is not likely to be on the map; the father dies, the princess inherits, and in two words the knight becomes king. And here comes in at once the bestowal of rewards upon his squire and all who have aided him in rising to so exalted a rank. He marries his squire to a damsel of the princess's, who will be, no doubt, the one who was confidante in their amour, and is daughter of a very great duke."

"That's what I want, no mistake about it!" said Sancho. "That's what I'm waiting for; for all this, word for word, is in store for your worship under the title of The Knight of the Rueful Countenance."

"Thou needst not doubt it, Sancho," replied Don Quixote, "for in the same manner, and by the same steps as I have described here, knights-errant rise and have risen to be kings and emperors; all we want now is to find out what king, Christian or pagan, is at war and has a beautiful daughter; but there will be time enough to think of that, for, as I have told thee, fame must be won in other quarters before repairing to the court. There is another thing, too, that is wanting; for supposing we find a king who is at war and has a beautiful daughter, and that I have won incredible fame throughout the universe, I know not how it can be made out that I am of royal lineage, or even second cousin to an emperor; for the king will not be willing to give me his daughter in marriage unless he is first thoroughly satisfied on this point, however much my famous deeds may deserve it; so that by this deficiency I fear I shall lose what my arm has fairly earned. True it is I am a gentleman of a known house, of estate and property, and entitled to the five hundred sueldos mulct; and it may be that the sage who shall write my history will so clear up my ancestry and pedigree that I may find myself fifth or sixth in descent from a king; for I would have thee know, Sancho, that there are two kinds of lineages in the world; some there be tracing and deriving their descent from kings and princes, whom time has reduced little by little until they end in a point like a pyramid upside down; and others who spring from the common herd and go on rising step by step until they come to be great lords; so that the difference is that the one were what they no longer are, and the others are what they formerly were not. And I may be of such that after investigation my origin may prove great and famous, with which the king, my father-in-law that is to be, ought to be satisfied; and should he not be, the princess will so love me that even though she well knew me to be the son of a water-carrier, she will take me

for her lord and husband in spite of her father; if not, then it comes to seizing her and carrying her off where I please; for time or death will put an end to the wrath of her parents."

"It comes to this, too," said Sancho, "what some naughty people say, 'Never ask as a favor what thou canst take by force'; though it would fit better to say, 'A clear escape is better than good men's prayers.' I say so because if my lord the king, your worship's father-in-law, will not condescend to give you my lady the princess, there is nothing for it but, as your worship says, to seize her and transport her. But the mischief is that until peace is made and you come into the peaceful enjoyment of your kingdom, the poor squire is famishing as far as rewards go, unless it be that the confidante damsel that is to be his wife comes with the princess, and that with her he tides over his bad luck until Heaven otherwise orders things; for his master, I suppose, may as well give her to him at once for a lawful wife."

"Nobody can object to that," said Don Quixote.

"Then since that may be," said Sancho, "there is nothing for it but to commend ourselves to God, and let fortune take what course it will."

"God guide it according to my wishes and thy wants," said Don Quixote, "and mean be he who makes himself mean."

"In God's name let him be so," said Sancho; "I am an old Christian, and to fit me for a count that's enough."

"And more than enough for thee," said Don Quixote; "and even wert thou not, it would make no difference, because I being the king can easily give thee nobility without purchase or service rendered by thee, for when I make thee a count, then thou art at once a gentleman; and they may say what they will, but by my faith they will have to call thee 'your lordship,' whether they like it or not."

"Not a doubt of it; and I'll know how to support the tittle," said Sancho.

"Title thou shouldst say, not tittle," said his master.

"So be it," answered Sancho, "I say I will know how to behave, for once in my life I was beadle of a brotherhood, and a beadle's gown sat so well on me that all said I looked as if I was fit to be steward of the same brotherhood. What will it be, then, when I put a duke's robe on my back, or dress myself in gold and pearls like a foreign count? I believe they will come a hundred leagues to see me."

"Thou wilt look well," said Don Quixote,

"but thou must shave thy beard often, for thou hast it so thick and rough and unkempt that if thou dost not shave it every second day at least, they will see what thou art at the distance of a musket shot."

"What more will it be," said Sancho, "than having a barber, and keeping him at wages in the house? And even if it be necessary, I will make him go behind me like a nobleman's equerry."

"Why, how dost thou know that noblemen have equerries behind them?" asked Don Quixote.

"I will tell you," answered Sancho. "Years ago I was for a month at the capital, and there I saw taking the air a very small gentleman who they said was a very great man, and a man following him on horseback in every turn he took, just as if he was his tail. I asked why this man did not join the other man, instead of always going behind him; they answered me that he was his equerry, and that it was the custom with nobles to have such persons behind them, and ever since then I know it, for I have never forgotten it."

"Thou art right," said Don Quixote, "and in the same way thou mayest carry thy barber with thee, for customs did not come into use all together nor were they all invented at once, and thou mayest be the first count to have a barber to follow him; and, indeed, shaving one's beard is a greater trust than saddling one's horse."

"Let the barber business be my lookout," said Sancho; "and your worship's be it to strive to become a king, and make me a count."

"So it shall be," answered Don Quixote, and raising his eyes he saw what will be told in the following chapter.

Chapter 22

Of the freedom Don Quixote conferred on several unfortunates who against their will were being carried where they had no wish to go

CID HAMET BENENGELI, the Arab and Manchegan author, relates in this most grave, high-sounding, minute, delightful, and original history that after the discussion between the famous Don Quixote of La Mancha and his squire Sancho Panza which is set down at the end of chapter twenty-one, Don Quixote raised his eyes and saw coming along the road he was following some dozen men on foot strung together by the neck, like beads, on a great iron chain, and all with manacles on their hands. With them there came also two men on horseback and two on foot; those on horseback with wheel-lock muskets, those on foot with javelins and swords, and as soon as Sancho saw them he said, "That is a chain of galley slaves, on the way to the galleys by force of the king's orders."

"How by force?" asked Don Quixote. "Is it possible that the king uses force against any one?"

"I do not say that," answered Sancho, "but that these are people condemned for their crimes to serve by force in the king's galleys."

"In fact," replied Don Quixote, "however it may be, these people are going where they are taking them by force, and not of their own will."

"Just so," said Sancho.

"Then if so," said Don Quixote, "here is a case for the exercise of my office, to put down force and to succor and help the wretched."

"Recollect, your worship," said Sancho, "Justice, which is the king himself, is not using force or doing wrong to such persons, but punishing them for their crimes."

The chain of galley slaves had by this time come up, and Don Quixote in very courteous language asked those who were in custody of it to be good enough to tell him the reason or reasons for which they were conducting these people in this manner. One of the guards on horseback answered that they were galley slaves belonging to his majesty, that they were going to the galleys, and that was all that was to be said and all he had any business to know.

"Nevertheless," replied Don Quixote, "I should like to know from each of them separately the reason of his misfortune"; to this he added more to the same effect to induce them to tell him what he wanted so civilly that the other mounted guard said to him, "Though we have here the register and certificate of the sentence of every one of these wretches, this is no time to take them out or read them; come and ask themselves; they can tell if they choose, and they will, for these fellows take a pleasure in doing and talking about rascalities."

With this permission, which Don Quixote would have taken even had they not granted it, he approached the chain and asked the first for what offences he was now in such a sorry case.

He made answer that it was for being a lover.

"For that only?" replied Don Quixote; "why, if for being lovers they send people to the galleys I might have been rowing in them long ago."

"The love is not the sort your worship is

thinking of," said the galley slave; "mine was that I loved a washerwoman's basket of clean linen so well, and held it so close in my embrace, that if the arm of the law had not forced it from me, I should never have let it go of my own will to this moment; I was caught in the act, there was no occasion for torture, the case was settled, they treated me to a hundred lashes on the back, and three years of *gurapas* besides, and that was the end of it."

"What are *gurapas*?" asked Don Quixote.

"*Gurapas* are galleys," answered the galley slave, who was a young man of about four-and-twenty, and said he was a native of Piedrahita.

Don Quixote asked the same question of the second, who made no reply, so downcast and melancholy was he; but the first answered for him, and said, "He, sir, goes as a canary, I mean as a musician and a singer."

"What!" said Don Quixote, "for being musicians and singers do people go to the galleys too?"

"Yes, sir," answered the galley slave, "for there is nothing worse than singing under suffering."

"On the contrary, I have heard say," said Don Quixote, "that he who sings scares away his woes."

"Here is the reverse," said the galley slave; "for he who sings once weeps all his life."

"I do not understand it," said Don Quixote; but one of the guards said to him, "Sir, to sing under suffering means with the *non sancta* fraternity to confess under torture; they put this sinner to the torture, and he confessed his crime, which was being a *cuatrero*, that is a cattle-stealer, and on his confession they sentenced him to six years in the galleys, besides two hundred lashes that he has already had on the back; and he is always dejected and downcast because the other thieves that were left behind and that march here ill-treat, and snub, and jeer, and despise him for confessing and not having spirit enough to say nay; for, say they, 'nay' has no more letters in it than 'yea,' and a culprit is well off when life or death with him depends on his own tongue and not on that of witnesses or evidence; and to my thinking they are not very far out."

"And I think so too," answered Don Quixote; then passing on to the third he asked him what he had asked the others, and the man answered very readily and unconcernedly, "I am going for five years to their ladyships the *gurapas* for the want of ten ducats."

"I will give twenty with pleasure to get you out of that trouble," said Don Quixote.

"That," said the galley slave, "is like a man having money at sea when he is dying of hunger and has no way of buying what he wants; I say so because if at the right time I had had those twenty ducats that your worship now offers me, I would have greased the notary's pen and freshened up the attorney's wit with them, so that to-day I should be in the middle of the plaza of the Zocodover at Toledo, and not on this road coupled like a greyhound. But God is great; patience—there, that's enough of it."

Don Quixote passed on to the fourth, a man of venerable aspect with a white beard falling below his breast, who on hearing himself asked the reason of his being there began to weep without answering a word, but the fifth acted as his tongue and said, "This worthy man is going to the galleys for four years, after having gone the rounds in the robe of ceremony and on horseback."

"That means," said Sancho Panza, "as I take it, to have been exposed to shame in public."

"Just so," replied the galley slave, "and the offence for which they gave him that punishment was having been an ear-broker, nay body-broker; I mean, in short, that this gentleman goes as a pimp, and for having besides a certain touch of the sorcerer about him."

"If that touch had not been thrown in," said Don Quixote, "he would not deserve, for mere pimping, to row in the galleys, but rather to command and be admiral of them; for the office of pimp is no ordinary one, being the office of persons of discretion, one very necessary in a well-ordered state, and only to be exercised by persons of good birth; nay, there ought to be an inspector and overseer of them, as in other offices, and a fixed and recognized number, as with the brokers on change; in this way many of the evils would be avoided which are caused by this office and calling being in the hands of stupid and ignorant people, such as women more or less silly, and pages and jesters of little standing and experience, who on the most urgent occasions, and when ingenuity of contrivance is needed, let the crumbs freeze on the way to their mouths, and know not which is their right hand. I would go further, and give reasons to show that it is advisable to choose those who are to hold so necessary an office in the state, but this is not the fit place for it; some day I will expound the matter to some one able to see to and rectify it; all I say now is, that the additional fact of his being a sorcerer has removed the sorrow it gave me to see these white hairs and this venerable countenance in so painful a position on account of his being a pimp; though I know well there are no sorceries in the world that can move or compel the will as some simple folk fancy, for our will is free, nor is there herb or charm that can force it. All that certain silly women and quacks do is to turn men mad with potions and poisons, pretending that they have power to cause love, for, as I say, it is an impossibility to compel the will."

"It is true," said the good old man, "and indeed, sir, as far as the charge of sorcery goes I was not guilty; as to that of being a pimp I can not deny it; but I never thought I was doing any harm by it, for my only object was that all the world should enjoy itself and live in peace and quiet, without quarrels or troubles; but my good intentions were unavailing to save me from going where I never expect to come back from, with this weight of years upon me and a urinary ailment that never gives me a moment's ease"; and again he fell to weeping as before, and such compassion did Sancho feel for him that he took out a real of four from his bosom and gave it to him in alms.

Don Quixote went on and asked another what his crime was, and the man answered with no less but rather much more sprightliness than the last one, "I am here because I carried the joke too far with a couple of cousins of mine, and with a couple of other cousins who were none of mine; in short, I carried the joke so far with them all that it ended in such a complicated increase of kindred that no accountant could make it clear: it was all proved against me, I got no favor, I had no money, I was near having my neck stretched, they sentenced me to the galleys for six years, I accepted my fate, it is the punishment of my fault; I am a young man; let life only last, and with that all will come right. If you, sir, have anything wherewith to help the poor, God will repay it to you in heaven, and we on earth will take care in our petitions to Him to pray for the life and health of your worship, that they may be as long and as good as your amiable appearance deserves." This one was in the dress of a student, and one of the guards said he was a great talker and a very elegant Latin scholar.

Behind all these there came a man of thirty, a very personable fellow, except that when he looked his eyes turned in a little, one towards the other. He was bound differently from the rest, for he had to his leg a chain so long that it was wound all round his body, and two rings on his neck, one attached to the chain, the other to what they call a "keep-friend" or "friend's foot," from which hung two irons reaching to his waist with two manacles fixed to them in which his hands were secured by a big padlock, so that he could neither raise his hand to his mouth nor lower his head to his hands. Don Quixote asked why this man carried so many more chains than the others. The guard replied that it was because he alone had committed more crimes than all the rest put together, and was so daring and such a villain, that though they marched him in that fashion they did not feel sure of him, but were in dread of his making his escape.

"What crimes can he have committed," said Don Quixote, "if they have not deserved a heavier punishment than being sent to the galleys?"

"He goes for ten years," replied the guard, "which is the same thing as civil death, and all that need be said is that this good fellow is the famous Gines de Pasamonte, otherwise called Ginesillo de Parapilla."

"Gently, señor commissary," said the galley slave at this, "let us have no fixing of names or surnames; my name is Gines, not Ginesillo, and my family name is Pasamonte, not Parapilla as you say; let each one mind his own business, and he will be doing enough."

"Speak with less impertinence, master thief of extra measure," replied the commissary, "if you don't want me to make you hold your tongue in spite of your teeth."

"It is easy to see," returned the galley slave, "that man goes as God pleases, but some one shall know some day whether I am called Ginesillo de Parapilla or not."

"Don't they call you so, you liar?" said the guard.

"They do," returned Gines, "but I will make them give over calling me so with a vengeance; where, I won't say. If you, sir, have anything to give us, give it to us at once, and God speed you, for you are becoming tiresome with all this inquisitiveness about the lives of others; if you want to know about mine let me tell you I am Gines de Pasamonte, whose life is written by these fingers."

"He says true," said the commissary, "for he has himself written his story as grand as you please, and has left the book in the prison in pawn for two hundred reals."

"And I mean to take it out of pawn," said Gines, "though it were in for two hundred ducats."

"Is it so good?" said Don Quixote.

"So good is it," replied Gines, "that a fig for *Lazarillo de Tormes,* and all of that kind that have been written, or shall be written, compared with it; all I will say about it is that it deals with facts, and facts so neat and diverting that no lies could match them."

"And how is the book entitled?" asked Don Quixote.

"The Life of Gines de Pasamonte," replied the subject of it.

"And is it finished?" asked Don Quixote.

"How can it be finished," said the other, "when my life is not yet finished? All that is written is from my birth down to the point when they sent me to the galleys this last time."

"Then you have been there before?" said Don Quixote.

"In the service of God and the king I have been there for four years before now, and I know by this time what the biscuit and courbash are like," replied Gines; "and it is no great grievance to me to go back to them, for there I shall have time to finish my book; I have still many things left to say, and in the galleys of Spain there is more than enough leisure; though I do not want much for what I have to write, for I have it by heart."

"You seem a clever fellow," said Don Quixote.

"And an unfortunate one," replied Gines, "for misfortune always persecutes wit."

"It persecutes rogues," said the commissary.

"I told you already to go gently, master commissary," said Pasamonte; "their lordships yonder never gave you that staff to ill-treat us wretches here, but to conduct and take us where his majesty orders you; if not, by the life of—never mind—; it may be that some day the stains made in the inn will come out in the scouring; let every one hold his tongue and behave well and speak better; and now let us march on, for we have had quite enough of this entertainment."

The commissary lifted his staff to strike Pasamonte in return for his threats, but Don Quixote came between them, and begged him not to ill-use him, as it was not too much to allow one who had his hands tied to have his tongue a trifle free; and turning to the whole chain of them he said, "From all you have told me, dear brethren, I make out clearly that though they have punished you for your faults, the punishments you are about to endure do not give you much pleasure, and that you go to them very much against the grain and against your will, and that perhaps this one's want of courage under torture, that one's want of money, the other's

want of advocacy, and lastly the perverted judgment of the judge may have been the cause of your ruin and of your failure to obtain the justice you had on your side. All which presents itself now to my mind, urging, persuading, and even compelling me to demonstrate in your case the purpose for which Heaven sent me into the world and caused me to make profession of the order of chivalry to which I belong, and the vow I took therein to give aid to those in need and under the oppression of the strong. But as I know that it is a mark of prudence not to do by foul means what may be done by fair, I will ask these gentlemen, the guards and commissary, to be so good as to release you and let you go in peace, as there will be no lack of others to serve the king under more favorable circumstances; for it seems to me a hard case to make slaves of those whom God and nature have made free. Moreover, sirs of the guard," added Don Quixote, "these poor fellows have done nothing to you; let each answer for his own sins yonder; there is a God in heaven who will not forget to punish the wicked or reward the good; and it is not fitting that honest men should be the instruments of punishment to others, they being therein no way concerned. This request I make thus gently and quietly, that, if you comply with it, I may have reason for thanking you; and, if you will not voluntarily, this lance and sword together with the might of my arm shall compel you to comply with it by force."

"Nice nonsense!" said the commissary. "A fine piece of pleasantry he has come out with at last! He wants us to let the king's prisoners go, as if we had any authority to release them, or he to order us to do so! Go your way, sir, and good luck to you; put that basin straight that you've got on your head, and don't go looking for three feet on a cat."

" 'Tis you that are the cat, the rat, and the rascal," replied Don Quixote, and acting on the word he fell upon him so suddenly that without giving him time to defend himself he brought him to the ground sorely wounded with a lance-thrust, and lucky it was for him that it was the one that had the musket. The other guards stood thunderstruck and amazed at this unexpected event, but recovering presence of mind, those on horseback seized their swords, and those on foot their javelins, and attacked Don Quixote, who was waiting for them with great calmness; and no doubt it would have gone badly with him if the galley slaves seeing the chance before them of liberating themselves had not effected it by contriving to break the chain on which they were strung. Such was the confusion, that the guards, now rushing at the galley slaves who were breaking loose, now to attack Don Quixote who was waiting for them, did nothing at all that was of any use. Sancho, on his part, gave a helping hand to release Gines de Pasamonte, who was the first to leap forth upon the plain free and unfettered, and who, attacking the prostrate commissary, took from him his sword and the musket, with which, aiming at one and levelling at another, he, without ever discharging it, drove every one of the guards off the field, for they took to flight, as well to escape Pasamonte's musket, as the showers of stones the now released galley slaves were raining upon them. Sancho was greatly grieved at the affair, because he anticipated that those who had fled would report the matter to the Holy Brotherhood, who at the summons of the alarm-bell would at once sally forth in quest of the offenders; and he said so to his master, and entreated him to leave the place at once, and go into hiding in the sierra that was close by.

"That is all very well," said Don Quixote, "but I know what must be done now"; and calling together all the galley slaves, who were now running riot, and had stripped the commissary to the skin, he collected them round him to hear what he had to say, and addressed them as follows: "To be grateful for benefits received is the part of persons of good birth, and one of the sins most offensive to God is ingratitude; I say so because, sirs, ye have already seen by manifest proof the benefit ye have received from me; in return for which I desire, and it is my good pleasure that, laden with that chain which I have taken off your necks, ye at once set out and proceed to the city of El Toboso, and there present yourselves before the lady Dulcinea del Toboso, and say to her that her knight, he of the Rueful Countenance, sends to commend himself to her; and that ye recount to her in full detail all the particulars of this notable adventure, up to the recovery of your longed-for liberty; and this done ye may go where ye will, and good fortune attend you."

Gines de Pasamonte made answer for all, saying, "That which you, sir, our deliverer, demand of us, is of all impossibilities the most impossible to comply with, because we can not go together along the roads, but only singly and separate, and each one his own way, endeavoring to hide ourselves in the bowels of the earth to escape the Holy Brotherhood, which, no doubt, will come out in search of us. What your worship may do, and fairly do, is to change this service and tribute as regards the lady Dulcinea del Toboso for a certain quantity of *ave marias* and *credos* which we will say for your worship's intention, and this is a condition that can be complied with by night as well as by day, running or resting, in peace or in war; but to imagine that we are going now to return to the flesh-pots of Egypt, I mean to take up our chain and set out for El Toboso, is to imagine that it is now night, though it is not yet ten in the morning, and to ask this of us is like asking pears of the elm tree."

"Then by all that's good," said Don Quixote (now stirred to wrath), "Don son of a bitch, Don Ginesillo de Paropillo, or whatever your name is, you will have to go yourself alone, with your tail between your legs and the whole chain on your back."

Pasamonte, who was anything but meek (being by this time thoroughly convinced that Don Quixote was not quite right in his head as he had committed such a vagary as trying to set them free), finding himself abused in this fashion, gave the wink to his companions, and falling back they began to shower stones on Don Quixote at such a rate that he was quite unable to protect himself with his buckler, and poor Rocinante no more heeded the spur than if he had been made of brass. Sancho planted himself behind his ass, and with him sheltered himself from the hailstorm that poured on both of them. Don Quixote was unable to shield himself so well but that more pebbles than I could count struck him full on the body with such force that they brought him to the ground; and the instant he fell the student pounced upon him, snatched the basin from his head, and with it struck three or four blows on his shoulders, and as many more on the ground knocking it almost to pieces. They then stripped him of a jacket that he wore over his armor, and they would have stripped off his stockings if his greaves had not prevented them. From Sancho they took his coat, leaving him in his shirt-sleeves; and dividing among themselves the remaining spoils of the battle, they went each one his own way, more solicitous about keeping clear of the Holy Brotherhood they dreaded, than about burdening themselves with the chain, or going to present themselves before the lady Dulcinea del Toboso. The ass and Rocinante, Sancho and Don Quixote were all that were left upon the spot; the ass with drooping head, serious, shaking his ears from time to time as if he thought the storm of stones that assailed them was not yet over; Rocinante stretched beside his master, for he too had been brought to the ground by a stone; Sancho stripped, and trembling with fear of the Holy Brotherhood; and Don Quixote fuming to find himself so served by the very persons for whom he had done so much.

Chapter 23

Of what befell Don Quixote in the Sierra Morena, which was one of the rarest adventures related in this veracious history

SEEING himself served in this way, Don Quixote said to his squire, "I have always heard it said, Sancho, that to do good to boors is to throw water into the sea. If I had believed thy words, I should have avoided this trouble; but it is done now, it is only to have patience and take warning from this for the future."

"Your worship will take warning as much as I am a Turk," returned Sancho; "but, as you say this mischief might have been avoided if you had believed me, believe me now, and a still greater one will be avoided; for I tell you chivalry is of no account with the Holy Brotherhood, and they don't care two maravedís for all the knights-errant in the world; and I can tell you I fancy I hear their arrows whistling past my ears this minute."

"Thou art a coward by nature, Sancho," said Don Quixote, "but lest thou shouldst say I am obstinate, and that I never do as thou dost advise, this once I will take thy advice, and withdraw out of reach of that fury thou so dreadest; but it must be on one condition, that never, in life or in death, thou art to say to any one that I retired or withdrew from this danger out of fear, but only in compliance with thy entreaties; for if thou sayest otherwise thou wilt lie therein, and from this time to that, and from that to this, I give thee the lie, and say thou liest and wilt lie every time thou thinkest or sayest it; and answer me not again; for at the mere thought that I am withdrawing or retiring from any danger, above all from this, which does seem to carry some little shadow of fear with it, I am ready to take my stand here and wait alone, not only that Holy Brotherhood you talk of and dread, but the brothers of the twelve tribes of Israel, and the seven Maccabees, and Castor and Pollux, and all the brothers and brotherhoods in the world."

"Señor," replied Sancho, "to retire is not to flee, and there is no wisdom in waiting when danger outweighs hope, and it is the part of wise men to preserve themselves to-day for tomorrow, and not risk all in one day; and let me tell you, though I am a clown and a boor, I have got some notion of what they call safe conduct: so repent not of having taken my advice, but mount Rocinante if you can, and if not I will help you; and follow me, for my mother-wit tells me we have more need of legs than hands just now."

Don Quixote mounted without replying, and, Sancho leading the way on his ass, they entered the side of the Sierra Morena, which was close by, as it was Sancho's design to cross it entirely and come out again at El Viso or Almodóvar del Campo, and hide for some days among its crags so as to escape the search of the Brotherhood should they come to look for them. He was encouraged in this by perceiving that the stock of provisions carried by the ass had come safe out of the fray with the galley slaves, a circumstance that he regarded as a miracle, seeing how they pillaged and ransacked.

He on his part was rejoiced to the heart on entering the mountains, as they seemed to him to be just the place for the adventures he was in quest of. They brought back to his memory the marvellous adventures that had befallen knights-errant in like solitudes and wilds, and he went along reflecting on these things, so absorbed and carried away by them that he had no thought for anything else. Nor had Sancho any other care (now that he fancied he was travelling in a safe quarter) than to satisfy his appetite with such remains as were left of the clerical spoils, and so he marched behind his master laden with what Dapple used to carry, emptying the sack and packing his paunch, and so long as he could go that way, he would not have given a farthing to meet with another adventure.

While so engaged he raised his eyes and saw that his master had halted, and was trying with the point of his pike to lift some bulky object that lay upon the ground, on which he hastened to join him and help him if it were needful, and reached him just as with the point of the pike he was raising a saddle-pad with a valise attached to it, half or rather wholly rotten and torn; but so heavy were they that Sancho had to help to take them up, and his master directed him to see what the valise contained. Sancho did so with great alacrity, and though the valise was secured by a chain and padlock, from its torn and rotten condition he was able to see its contents, which were four shirts of fine holland, and other articles of linen no less curious than clean; and in a handkerchief he found a good lot of gold crowns, and as soon as he saw them he exclaimed, "Blessed be all Heaven for sending us an adventure that is good for something!" Searching further he found a little memorandum book richly bound; this Don Quixote asked of him, telling him to take the money and keep it for himself. Sancho kissed his hands for the favor, and cleared the valise of its linen, which he stowed away in the provision sack. Considering the whole matter, Don Quixote observed, "It seems to me, Sancho—and it is impossible it can be otherwise—that some strayed traveller must have crossed this sierra and been attacked and slain by footpads, who brought him to this remote spot to bury him."

"That can not be," answered Sancho, "because if they had been robbers they would not have left this money."

"Thou art right," said Don Quixote, "and I can not guess or explain what this may mean; but stay; let us see if in this memorandum book there is anything written by which we may be able to trace out or discover what we want to know."

He opened it, and the first thing he found in it, written roughly but in a very good hand, was a sonnet, and reading it aloud that Sancho might hear it, he found that it ran as follows:

Sonnet

Or Love is lacking in intelligence,
　Or to the height of cruelty attains,
　Or else it is my doom to suffer pains
Beyond the measure due to my offence.
But if Love be a God, it follows thence
　That he knows all, and certain it remains
　No God loves cruelty; then who ordains
This penance that enthralls while it torments?
It were a falsehood, Chloe, thee to name;
　Such evil with such goodness can not live;
And against Heaven I dare not charge the blame,
　I only know it is my fate to die.
To him who knows not whence his malady
　A miracle alone a cure can give.

"There is nothing to be learned from that rhyme," said Sancho, "unless by that clew there's in it, one may draw out the ball of the whole matter."

"What clew is there?" said Don Quixote.

"I thought your worship spoke of a clew in it," said Sancho.

"I only said Chloe," replied Don Quixote; "and that, no doubt, is the name of the lady of whom the author of the sonnet complains; and, faith, he must be a tolerable poet, or I know little of the craft."

"Then your worship understands rhyming too?" said Sancho.

"And better than thou thinkest," replied Don Quixote, "as thou shalt see when thou carriest a letter written in verse from beginning to end to my lady Dulcinea del Toboso, for I would have thee know, Sancho, that all or most of the knights-errant in days of yore were great troubadours and great musicians, for both of these accomplishments, or more properly speaking gifts, are the peculiar property of lovers-errant: true it is that the verses of the knights of old have more spirit than neatness in them."

"Read more, your worship," said Sancho, "and you will find something that will enlighten us."

Don Quixote turned the page and said, "This is prose and seems to be a letter."

"A correspondence letter, señor?" asked Sancho.

"From the beginning it seems to be a love-letter," replied Don Quixote.

"Then let your worship read it aloud," said Sancho, "for I am very fond of these love matters."

"With all my heart," said Don Quixote, and reading it aloud as Sancho had requested him, he found it ran thus:

Thy false promise and my sure misfortune carry me to a place whence the news of my death will reach thy ears before the words of my complaint. Ungrateful one, thou hast rejected me for one more wealthy, but not more worthy; but if virtue were esteemed wealth I should neither envy the fortunes of others nor weep for misfortunes of my own. What thy beauty raised up thy deeds have laid low; by it I believed thee to be an angel, by them I know thou art a woman. Peace be with thee who hast sent war to me, and Heaven grant that the deceit of thy husband be ever hidden from thee, so that thou repent not of what thou hast done, and I reap not a revenge I would not have.

When he had finished the letter, Don Quixote said, "There is less to be gathered from this than from the verses, except that he who wrote it is some rejected lover"; and turning over nearly all the pages of the book he found more verses and letters, some of which he could read, while others he could not: but they were all made up of complaints, laments, misgivings, desires and aversions, favors and rejections, some rapturous, some doleful. While Don Quixote examined the book, Sancho examined the valise, not leaving a corner in the whole of it or in the pad that he did not search, peer into, and explore, or seam that he did not rip, or tuft of wool that he did not pick to pieces, lest anything should escape for want of care and pains; so keen was the covetousness excited in him by the discovery of the crowns, which amounted to near a hundred; and though he found no more booty, he held the blanket flights, balsam vomits, stake benedictions, carriers' fisticuffs, missing *alforjas*, stolen coat, and all the hunger, thirst, and weariness he had endured in the service of his good master, cheap at the price; as he considered himself more than fully indemnified for all by the payment he received in the gift of the treasure-trove.

The Knight of the Rueful Countenance was still very anxious to find out who the owner of the valise could be, conjecturing from the sonnet and letter, from the money in gold, and from the fineness of the shirts, that he must be some lover of distinction whom the scorn and cruelty of his lady had driven to some desperate course; but as in that uninhabited and rugged spot there was no one to be seen of whom he could inquire, he saw nothing else for it but to push on taking whatever road Rocinante chose—which was where he could make his way—firmly persuaded that among these wilds he could not fail to meet some rare adventure. As he went along, then, occupied with these thoughts, he perceived on the summit of a height that rose before their eyes a man who went springing from rock to rock and from tussock to tussock with marvellous agility. As well as he could make out he was unclad, with a thick black beard, long tangled hair, and bare legs and feet, his thighs were covered by breeches apparently of tawny velvet but so ragged that they showed his skin in several places. He was bareheaded, and notwithstanding the swiftness with which he passed as has been described, the Knight of the Rueful Countenance observed and noted all these trifles, and though he made the attempt, he was unable to follow him, for it was not granted to the feebleness of Rocinante to make way over such rough ground, he being, moreover, slow-paced and sluggish by nature. Don Quixote at once came to the conclusion that this was the owner of the saddle-pad and of the valise, and made up his mind to go in search of him, even though he should have to wander a year in those mountains before he found him, and so he directed Sancho to take a short cut over one side of the mountain, while he himself went by the other, and perhaps by this means they might light upon this man who

had passed so quickly out of their sight.

"I could not do that," said Sancho, "for when I separate from your worship fear at once lays hold of me, and assails me with all sorts of panics and fancies; and let what I now say be a notice that from this time forth I am not going to stir a finger's length from your presence."

"It shall be so," said he of the Rueful Countenance, "and I am very glad that thou art willing to rely on my courage, which will never fail thee, even though the soul in thy body fail thee; so come on now behind me slowly as well as thou canst, and make lanterns of thine eyes; let us make the circuit of this ridge; perhaps we shall light upon this man that we saw, who no doubt is no other than the owner of what we found."

To which Sancho made answer, "Far better would it be not to look for him, for if we find him, and he happens to be the owner of the money, it is plain I must restore it; it would be better, therefore, that without taking this needless trouble, I should keep possession of it until in some other less meddlesome and officious way the real owner may be discovered; and perhaps that will be when I shall have spent it, and then the king will hold me harmless."

"Thou art wrong there, Sancho," said Don Quixote, "for now that we have a suspicion who the owner is, and have him almost before us, we are bound to seek him and make restitution; and if we do not seek him, the strong suspicion we have as to his being the owner makes us as guilty as if he were so; and so, friend Sancho, let not our search for him give thee any uneasiness, for if we find him it will relieve mine."

And so saying he gave Rocinante the spur, and Sancho followed him on foot and loaded, thanks to Ginesillo de Pasamonte, and after having partly made the circuit of the mountain they found lying in a ravine, dead and half devoured by dogs and pecked by crows, a mule saddled and bridled, all which still further strengthened their suspicion that he who had fled was the owner of the mule and the saddle-pad.

As they stood looking at it they heard a whistle like that of a shepherd watching his flock, and suddenly on their left there appeared a great number of goats, and behind them on the summit of the mountain the goatherd in charge of them, a man advanced in years. Don Quixote called aloud to him and begged him to come down to where they stood. He shouted in return, asking what had brought them to that spot, seldom or never trodden except by the feet of goats, or of the wolves and other wild beasts that roamed around. Sancho in return bade him come down, and they would explain all to him.

The goatherd descended, and reaching the place where Don Quixote stood, he said, "I will wager you are looking at that hack mule that lies dead in the hollow there, and, faith, it has been lying there now these six months; tell me, have you come upon its master about here?"

"We have come upon nobody," answered Don Quixote, "nor on anything except a saddle-pad and a little valise that we found not far from this."

"I found it too," said the goatherd, "but I would not lift it nor go near it for fear of some ill-luck or being charged with theft, for the devil is crafty, and things rise up under one's feet to make one stumble and fall without knowing why or wherefore."

"That's exactly what I say," said Sancho; "I found it too, and I would not go within a stone's throw of it; there I left it, and there it lies just as it was, for I don't want a dog with a bell."

"Tell me, good man," said Don Quixote, "do you know who is the owner of this property?"

"All I can tell you," said the goatherd, "is that about six months ago, more or less, there arrived at a shepherd's hut three leagues, perhaps, away from this, a youth of well-bred appearance and manners, mounted on that same mule which lies dead here, and with the same saddle-pad and valise which you say you found and did not touch. He asked us what part of this sierra was the most rugged and retired; we told him that it was where we now are; and so in truth it is, for if you push on half a league farther, perhaps you will not be able to find your way out; and I am wondering how you have managed to come here, for there is no road or path that leads to this spot. I say, then, that on hearing our answer the youth turned about and made for the place we pointed out to him, leaving us all charmed with his good looks, and wondering at his question and the haste with which we saw him depart in the direction of the sierra; and after that we saw him no more, until some days afterwards he crossed the path of one of our shepherds, and without saying a word to him, came up to him and gave him several cuffs and kicks, and then turned to the ass with our provisions and took all the bread and cheese it carried, and having done this made off back again into the sierra with extraordinary swiftness. When some of us goatherds learned this we went in search of him for about two days through the most remote portion of this sierra, at the end of which we found him lodged in the hollow of a large thick cork tree. He came out to meet us with great gentleness, with his dress now torn and his face so disfigured and burned by the sun, that we hardly recognized him but that his clothes, though torn, convinced us, from the recollection we had of them, that he was the person we were looking for. He saluted us courteously, and in a few well-spoken words he told us not to wonder at seeing him going about in this guise, as it was binding upon him in order that he might work out a penance which for his many sins had been imposed upon him. We asked him to tell us who he was, but we were never able to find out from him: we begged of him too, when he was in want of food, which he could not do without, to tell us where we should find him, as we would bring it to him with all good-will and readiness; or if this were not to his taste, at least to come and ask it of us and not take it by force from the shepherds. He thanked us for the offer, begged pardon for the late assault, and promised for the future to ask it in God's name without offering violence to anybody. As for fixed abode, he said he had no other than that which chance offered wherever night might overtake him; and his words ended in an outburst of weeping so bitter that we who listened to him must have been very stones had we not joined him in it, comparing what we saw of him the first time with what we saw now; for, as I said, he was a graceful and gracious youth, and in his courteous and polished language showed himself to be of good birth and courtly breeding, and rustics as we were that listened to him, even to our rusticity his gentle bearing sufficed to make it plain. But in the midst of his conversation he stopped and became silent, keeping his eyes fixed upon the ground for some time, during which we stood still waiting anxiously to see what would come of this abstraction; and with no little pity, for from his behavior, now staring at the ground with fixed gaze and eyes wide open without moving an eyelid, again closing them, compressing his lips and raising his eyebrows, we could perceive plainly that a fit of madness of some kind had come upon him; and before long he showed that what we imagined was the truth, for he arose in a fury from the ground where he had thrown himself, and attacked the first he found near him with such rage and fierceness that if we had not dragged him off him, he would have beaten or bitten him to death, all the while exclaiming, 'Oh faithless Fernan-

lo, here, here shalt thou pay the penalty of the
wrong thou hast done me; these hands shall tear
out that heart of thine, abode and dwelling of
all iniquity, but of deceit and fraud above all';
and to these he added other words all in effect
upbraiding this Fernando and charging him
with treachery and faithlessness. We forced
him to release his hold with no little difficulty,
and without another word he left us, and rushing off plunged in among these brakes and
brambles, so as to make it impossible for us to
follow him; from this we suppose that madness
comes upon him from time to time, and that
some one called Fernando must have done him
a wrong of a grievous nature such as the condition to which it had brought him seemed to
show. All this has been since then confirmed
on those occasions, and they have been many,
on which he has crossed our path, at one time
to beg the shepherds to give him some of the
food they carry, at another to take it from them
by force; for when there is a fit of madness upon him, even though the shepherds offer it freely, he will not accept it but snatches it from them
by dint of blows; but when he is in his senses
he begs it for the love of God, courteously and
civilly, and receives it with many thanks and
not a few tears. And to tell you the truth, sirs,"
continued the goatherd, "it was yesterday that
we resolved, I and four of the lads, two of them
our servants, and the other two friends of mine,
to go in search of him until we find him, and
when we do to take him, whether by force or of
his own consent, to the town of Almodóvar,
which is eight leagues from this, and there
strive to cure him (if indeed his malady admits
of a cure), or learn when he is in his senses who
he is, and if he has relatives to whom we may
give notice of his misfortune. This, sirs, is all
I can say in answer to what you have asked me;
and be sure that the owner of the articles you
found is he whom you saw pass by with such
nimbleness and so naked."

For Don Quixote had already described how
he had seen the man go bounding along the
mountain side, and he was now filled with
amazement at what he heard from the goatherd,
and more eager than ever to discover who the
unhappy madman was; and in his heart he resolved, as he had done before, to search for him
all over the mountain, not leaving a corner or
cave unexamined until he had found him. But
chance arranged matters better than he expected or hoped, for at that very moment, in a gorge
in the mountain that opened where they stood,
the youth he wished to find made his appear-

ance, coming along talking to himself in a way
that would have been unintelligible near at
hand, much more at a distance. His garb was
what has been described, save that as he drew
near, Don Quixote perceived that a tattered
doublet which he wore was amber-scented, from
which he concluded that one who wore such
garments could not be of very low rank. Approaching them, the youth greeted them in a
harsh and hoarse voice but with great courtesy.
Don Quixote returned his salutation with equal
politeness, and dismounting from Rocinante advanced with well-bred bearing and grace to embrace him, and held him for some time close in
his arms as if he had known him for a long
time. The other, whom we may call the Ragged
One of the Sorry Countenance, as Don Quixote
was of the Rueful, after submitting to the embrace pushed him back a little and, placing his
hands on Don Quixote's shoulders, stood gazing at him as if seeking to see whether he knew
him, not less amazed, perhaps, at the sight of
the face, figure, and armor of Don Quixote than
Don Quixote was at the sight of him. To be
brief, the first to speak after embracing was the
Ragged One, and he said what will be told
farther on.

Chapter 24

*In which is continued the adventure of the
Sierra Morena*

THE history relates that it was with the
greatest attention Don Quixote listened to the
ill-starred Knight of the Sierra, who began by
saying, "Of a surety, señor, whoever you are,
for I know you not, I thank you for the proofs
of kindness and courtesy you have shown me,
and would I were in a condition to requite with
something more than good-will that which you
have displayed towards me in the cordial reception you have given me; but my fate does not
afford me any other means of returning kindnesses done me save the hearty desire to repay
them."

"Mine," replied Don Quixote, "is to be of
service to you, so much so that I had resolved
not to quit these mountains until I had found
you, and learned of you whether there is any
kind of relief to be found for that sorrow under
which from the strangeness of your life you
seem to labor; and to search for you with all possible diligence, if search had been necessary.
And if your misfortune should prove to be one
of those that refuse admission to any sort of consolation, it was my purpose to join you in la-

menting and mourning over it, so far as I could; for it is still some comfort in misfortune to find one who can feel for it. And if my good intentions deserve to be acknowledged with any kind of courtesy, I entreat you, señor, by that which I perceive you possess in so high a degree, and likewise conjure you by whatever you love or have loved best in life, to tell me who you are and the cause that has brought you to live or die in these solitudes like a brute beast, dwelling among them in a manner so foreign to your condition as your garb and appearance show. And I swear," added Don Quixote, "by the order of knighthood which I, though unworthy and a sinner, have received, and by my vocation of knight-errant, if you gratify me in this, to serve you with all the zeal my calling demands of me, either in relieving your misfortune if it admits of relief, or in joining you in lamenting it as I promised to do."

The Knight of the Thicket, hearing him of the Rueful Countenance talk in this strain, did nothing but stare at him, and stare at him again, and again survey him from head to foot; and when he had thoroughly examined him, he said to him, "If you have anything to give me to eat, for God's sake give it me, and after I have eaten I will do all you ask in acknowledgment of the good-will you have displayed towards me."

Sancho from his sack, and the goatherd from his pouch, furnished the Ragged One with the means of appeasing his hunger, and what they gave him he ate like a half-witted being, so hastily that he took no time between mouthfuls, gorging rather than swallowing; and while he ate neither he nor they who observed him uttered a word. As soon as he had done he made signs to them to follow him, which they did, and he led them to a green plat which lay a little farther off around the corner of a rock. On reaching it he stretched himself upon the grass, and the others did the same, all keeping silence, until the Ragged One, settling himself in his place, said, "If it is your wish, sirs, that I should disclose in a few words the surpassing extent of my misfortunes, you must promise not to break the thread of my sad story with any question or other interruption, for the instant you do so the tale I tell will come to an end."

These words of the Ragged One reminded Don Quixote of the tale his squire had told him, when he failed to keep count of the goats that had crossed the river and the story remained unfinished; but to return to the Ragged One, he went on to say, "I give you this warning because I wish to pass briefly over the story of my misfortunes, for recalling them to memory only serves to add fresh ones, and the less you question me the sooner shall I make an end of the recital, though I shall not omit to relate anything of importance in order fully to satisfy your curiosity."

Don Quixote gave the promise for himself and the others, and with this assurance he began as follows:—

My name is Cardenio, my birthplace one of the best cities of this Andalusia, my family noble, my parents rich, my misfortune so great that my parents must have wept and my family grieved over it without being able by their wealth to lighten it; for the gifts of fortune can do little to relieve reverses sent by Heaven. In that same country there was a heaven in which love had placed all the glory I could desire; such was the beauty of Luscinda, a damsel as noble and as rich as I, but of happier fortunes, and of less firmness than was due to so worthy a passion as mine. This Luscinda I loved, worshipped, and adored from my earliest and tenderest years, and she loved me in all the innocence and sincerity of childhood. Our parents were aware of our feelings, and were not sorry to perceive them, for they saw clearly that as they ripened they must lead at last to a marriage between us, a thing that seemed almost pre-arranged by the equality of our families and wealth. We grew up, and with our growth grew the love between us, so that the father of Luscinda felt bound for propriety's sake to refuse me admission to his house, in this perhaps imitating the parents of that Thisbe so celebrated by the poets, and this refusal but added love to love and flame to flame; for though they enforced silence upon our tongues they could not impose it upon our pens, which can make known the heart's secrets to a loved one more freely than tongues; for many a time the presence of the object of love shakes the firmest will and strikes dumb the boldest tongue. Ah heavens! how many letters did I write her, and how many dainty modest replies did I receive! How many ditties and love-songs did I compose in which my heart declared and made known its feelings, described its ardent longings, revelled in its recollections and dallied with its desires! At length growing impatient and feeling my heart languishing with longing to see her, I resolved to put into execution and carry out what seemed to me the best mode of winning my desired and merited reward, to ask her of her father for my lawful wife, which I did. To this his answer was that he thanked me for the disposition I showed to do honor to him and to regard myself as honored by the bestowal of his treasure; but that as my father was alive it was his by right to make this demand, for if it were not in accordance with his full will and pleasure, Luscinda was not to be taken or given by stealth. I thanked him for his kindness, reflecting that there was rea son in what he said, and that my father would assent to it as soon as I should tell him, and with that view I went the very same instant to let him know what my desires were. When I entered the room where he was I found him with an open letter in his hand, which, before I could utter a word, he gave me, saying, "By this letter thou wilt see, Cardenio, the disposition the Duke Ricardo has to serve thee." This Duke Ricardo, as you, sirs, probably know already, is a grandee of Spain who has his seat in the best part of this Andalusia. I took and read the letter, which was couched in terms so flattering that even I myself felt it would be wrong in my father not to comply with the request the duke made in it, which was that he would send me immediately to him, as he wished me to become the companion, not servant, of his eldest son, and would take upon himself the charge of placing me in a position corresponding to the esteem in which he held me. On reading the letter my voice failed me, and still more when I heard my father say, "Two days hence thou wilt depart, Cardenio, in accordance with the duke's wish, and give thanks to God who is opening a road to thee by which thou mayest attain what I know thou dost deserve"; and to these words he added others of fatherly counsel. The time for my departure arrived; I spoke one night to Luscinda, I told her all that had occurred, as I did also to her father, entreating him to allow some delay, and to defer the disposal of her hand until I should see what the Duke Ricardo sought of me: he gave me the promise, and she confirmed it with vows and swoonings unnumbered. Finally, I presented myself to the duke, and was received and treated by him so kindly that very soon envy began to do its work, the old servants growing envious of me, and regarding the duke's inclination to show me favor as an injury to themselves. But the one to whom my arrival gave the greatest pleasure was the duke's second son, Fernando by name, a gallant youth, of noble, generous, and amorous disposition, who very soon made so intimate a friend of me that it was remarked by everybody; for though the elder was attached to me, and showed me kindness, he did not carry his affectionate treatment to the same length as Don Fernando. It so happened, then, that as between friends no secret remains unshared, and as the intimacy I enjoyed with Don Fernando had grown into friendship, he made all his thoughts known to me, and in particular a love affair which troubled his mind a little. He was deeply in love with a peasant girl, a vassal of his father's, the daughter of wealthy parents, and herself so beautiful, modest, discreet, and virtuous, that no one who knew her was able to decide in which of these respects she was most highly gifted or most excelled. The attractions of the fair peasant raised the passion of Don Fernando to such a point that, in order to gain his object and overcome her virtuous resolutions, he determined to pledge his word to her to become her husband, for to attempt it in any other way was to attempt an impossibility. Bound to him

as I was by friendship, I strove by the best arguments and the most forcible examples I could think of to restrain and dissuade him from such a course; but perceiving I produced no effect I resolved to make the Duke Ricardo, his father, acquainted with the matter; but Don Fernando, being sharp-witted and shrewd, foresaw and apprehended this, perceiving that by my duty as a good servant I was bound not to keep concealed a thing so much opposed to the honor of my lord the duke; and so, to mislead and deceive me, he told me he could find no better way of effacing from his mind the beauty that so enslaved him than by absenting himself for some months, and that he wished the absence to be effected by our going, both of us, to my father's house under the pretence, which he would make to the duke, of going to see and buy some fine horses that there were in my city, which produces the best in the world. When I heard him say so, even if his resolution had not been so good a one I should have hailed it as one of the happiest that could be imagined, prompted by my affection, seeing what a favorable chance and opportunity it offered me of returning to see my Luscinda. With this thought and wish I commended his idea and encouraged his design, advising him to put it into execution as quickly as possible, as, in truth, absence produced its effect in spite of the most deeply rooted feelings. But, as afterwards appeared, when he said this to me he had already enjoyed the peasant girl under the title of husband, and was waiting for an opportunity of making it known with safety to himself, being in dread of what his father the duke would do when he came to know of his folly. It happened, then, that as with young men love is for the most part nothing more than appetite, which, as its final object is enjoyment, comes to an end on obtaining it, and that which seemed to be love takes to flight, as it can not pass the limit fixed by nature, which fixes no limit to true love—what I mean is that after Don Fernando had enjoyed this peasant girl his passion subsided and his eagerness cooled, as if at first he feigned a wish to absent himself in order to cure his love, he was now in reality anxious to go to avoid keeping his promise.

The duke gave him permission, and ordered me to accompany him; we arrived at my city, and my father gave him the reception due to his rank; I saw Luscinda without delay, and, though it had not been dead or deadened, my love gathered fresh life. To my sorrow I told the story of it to Don Fernando, for I thought that in virtue of the great friendship he bore me I was bound to conceal nothing from him. I extolled her beauty, her gayety, her wit, so warmly, that my praises excited in him a desire to see a damsel adorned by such attractions. To my misfortune I yielded to it, showing her to him one night by the light of a taper at a window where we used to talk to one another. As she appeared to him in her dressing-gown, she drove all the beauties he had seen until then out of his recollection; speech failed him, his head turned, he was spellbound, and in the end love-smitten, as you will see in the course of the story of my misfortune; and to inflame still further his passion, which he hid from me and revealed to Heaven alone, it so happened that one day he found a note of hers entreating me to demand her of her father in marriage, so delicate, so modest, and so tender, that on reading it he told me that in Luscinda alone were combined all the charms of beauty and understanding that were distributed among all the other women in the world. It is true, and I own it now, that though I knew what good cause Don Fernando had to praise Luscinda, it gave me uneasiness to hear these praises from his mouth, and I began to fear, and with reason to feel distrust of him, for there was no moment when he was not ready to talk of Luscinda, and he would start the subject himself even though he dragged it in unseasonably, a circumstance that aroused in me a certain amount of jealousy; not that I feared any change in the constancy or faith of Luscinda; but still my fate led me to forebode what she assured me against. Don Fernando contrived always to read the letters I sent to Luscinda and her answers to me, under the pretence that he enjoyed the wit and sense of both. It so happened, then, that Luscinda having begged of me a book of chivalry to read, one that she was very fond of, *Amadis of Gaul*—

Don Quixote no sooner heard a book of chivalry mentioned, than he said, "Had your worship told me at the beginning of your story that the Lady Luscinda was fond of books of chivalry, no other laudation would have been requisite to impress upon me the superiority of her understanding, for it could not have been of the excellence you describe had a taste for such delightful reading been wanting; so, as far as I am concerned, you need waste no more words in describing her beauty, worth, and intelligence: for, on merely hearing what her taste was, I declare her to be the most beautiful and the most intelligent woman in the world; and I wish your worship had, along with Amadis of Gaul, sent her the worthy Don Rugel of Greece, for I know the Lady Luscinda would greatly relish Daraida and Garaya, and the shrewd sayings of the shepherd Darinel, and the admirable verses of his bucolics, sung and delivered by him with such sprightliness, wit, and ease; but a time may come when this omission can be remedied, and to rectify it nothing more is needed than for your worship to be so good as to come with me to my village, for there I can give you more than three hundred books which are the delight of my soul and the entertainment of my life—though it occurs to me that I have not got one of them now, thanks to the spite of wicked and envious enchanters—but

pardon me for having broken the promise we made not to interrupt your discourse; for when I hear chivalry or knights-errant mentioned, I can no more help talking about them than the rays of the sun can help giving heat, or those of the moon moisture; pardon me, therefore, and proceed, for that is more to the purpose now."

While Don Quixote was saying this, Cardenio allowed his head to fall upon his breast, and seemed plunged in deep thought; and though twice Don Quixote bade him go on with his story, he neither looked up nor uttered a word in reply; but after some time he raised his head and said, "I can not get rid of the idea, nor will any one in the world remove it, or make me think otherwise—and he would be a blockhead who would hold or believe anything else than that that arrant knave Master Elisabad made free with Queen Madasima."

"That is not true, by all that's good," said Don Quixote in high wrath, turning upon him angrily, as his way was; "and it is a very great slander, or rather villany. Queen Madasima was a very illustrious lady, and it is not to be supposed that so exalted a princess would have made free with a quack; and whoever maintains the contrary lies like a great scoundrel, and I will give him to know it, on foot or on horseback, armed or unarmed, by night or by day, or as he likes best."

Cardenio was looking at him steadily, and his mad fit having now come upon him, he had no disposition to go on with his story, nor would Don Quixote have listened to it, so much had what he had heard about Madasima disgusted him. Strange to say, he stood up for her as if she were in earnest his veritable born lady; to such a pass had his unholy books brought him. Cardenio, then, being, as I said, now mad, when he heard himself given the lie, and called a scoundrel and other insulting names, not relishing the jest, snatched up a stone that he found near him, and with it delivered such a blow on Don Quixote's breast that he laid him on his back. Sancho Panza, seeing his master treated in this fashion, attacked the madman with his closed fist; but the Ragged One received him in such a way that with a blow of his fist he stretched him at his feet, and then mounting upon him crushed his ribs to his own satisfaction; the goatherd, who came to the rescue, shared the same fate; and having beaten and pummelled them all he left them and quietly withdrew to his hiding-place on the mountain. Sancho rose, and with the rage he felt at finding himself so belabored without deserving t, ran to take vengeance on the goatherd, accusing him of not giving them warning that his man was at times taken with a mad fit, for f they had known it they would have been on heir guard to protect themselves. The goatherd replied that he had said so, and that if he had not heard him, that it was no fault of his. Sancho retorted, and the goatherd rejoined, and the altercation ended in seizing each other by the beard, and exchanging such fisticuffs hat if Don Quixote had not made peace beween them, they would have knocked one another to pieces. "Leave me alone, Sir Knight of the Rueful Countenance," said Sancho, grappling with the goatherd, "for of this fellow, who s a clown like myself, and no dubbed knight, I can safely take satisfaction for the affront he has offered me, fighting with him hand to hand ike an honest man."

"That is true," said Don Quixote, "but I know that he is not to blame for what has happened."

With this he pacified them, and again asked he goatherd if it would be possible to find Cardenio, as he felt the greatest anxiety to know the end of his story. The goatherd told him, as he had told him before, that there was no knowing of a certainty where his lair was; but that f he wandered about much in that neighborhood he could not fail to fall in with him either n or out of his senses.

Chapter 25

Which treats of the strange things that happened to the stout knight of La Mancha n the Sierra Morena, and of his imitation of the penance of Beltenebros

DON QUIXOTE took leave of the goatherd, and once more mounting Rocinante bade Sancho follow him, which he, having no ass, did very discontentedly. They proceeded slowly, making their way into the most rugged part of the mountain, Sancho all the while dying to have a talk with his master, and longing for him to begin, so that there should be no breach f the injunction laid upon him; but, unable to keep silence so long, he said to him, "Señor Don Quixote, give me your worship's blessing and dismissal, for I'd like to go home at once o my wife and children, with whom I can at any rate talk and converse as much as I like; for o want me to go through these solitudes day and night and not speak to you when I have a mind, is burying me alive. If luck would have t that animals spoke as they did in the days of

Guisopete, it would not be so bad, because I could talk to Rocinante about whatever came into my head, and so put up with my ill-fortune; but it is a hard case, and not to be borne with patience, to go seeking adventures all one's life, and get nothing but kicks and blanketings, brickbats and punches, and with all this, to have to sew up one's mouth without daring to say what is in one's heart, just as if one were dumb."

"I understand thee, Sancho," replied Don Quixote; "thou art dying to have the interdict I placed upon thy tongue removed; consider it removed, and say what thou wilt, on condition that the removal is not to last longer than while we are wandering in these mountains."

"So be it," said Sancho; "let me speak now, for God knows what will happen by-and-by; and to take advantage of the permit at once, I ask, what made your worship stand up so for that Queen Majimasa, or whatever her name is, or what did it matter whether that abbot was a friend of hers or not? For if your worship had let that pass—and you were not a judge in the matter—it is my belief the madman would have gone on with his story, and the blow of the stone, and the kicks, and more than half a dozen cuffs would have been escaped."

"In faith, Sancho," answered Don Quixote, "if thou knewest as I do what an honorable and illustrious lady Queen Madasima was, I know thou wouldst say I had great patience that I did not break in pieces the mouth that uttered such blasphemies, for a very great blasphemy it is to say or imagine that a queen has made free with a surgeon. The truth of the story is that that Master Elisabad whom the madman mentioned was a man of great prudence and sound judgment, and served as governor and physician to the queen, but to suppose that she was his mistress is nonsense deserving very severe punishment; and as a proof that Cardenio did not know what he was saying, remember when he said it he was out of his wits."

"That is what I say," said Sancho; "there was no occasion for minding the words of a madman; for if good luck had not helped your worship, and he had sent that stone at your head instead of at your breast, a fine way we should have been in for standing up for my lady yonder, God confound her! And then, would not Cardenio have gone free as a madman?"

"Against men in their senses or against madmen," said Don Quixote, "every knight-errant is bound to stand up for the honor of women, whoever they may be, much more for queens of such high degree and dignity as Queen Madasima, for whom I have a particular regard on account of her amiable qualities; for, besides being extremely beautiful, she was very wise, and very patient under her misfortunes, of which she had many; and the counsel and society of the Master Elisabad were a great help and support to her in enduring her afflictions with wisdom and resignation; hence the ignorant and ill-disposed vulgar took occasion to say and think that she was his mistress; and they lie, I say it once more, and will lie two hundred times more, all who think and say so."

"I neither say nor think so," said Sancho; "let them look to it; with their bread let them eat it; they have rendered account to God whether they misbehaved or not; I come from my vineyard, I know nothing; I am not fond of prying into other men's lives; he who buys and lies feels it in his purse; moreover, naked was I born, naked I find myself, I neither lose nor gain; but if they did, what is that to me? Many think there are flitches where there are no hooks; but who can put gates to the open plain? Moreover they said of God"—

"God bless me," said Don Quixote, "what a set of absurdities thou art stringing together! What has what we are talking about got to do with the proverbs thou art threading one after the other? For God's sake hold thy tongue, Sancho, and henceforward keep to prodding thy ass and don't meddle in what does not concern thee; and understand with all thy five senses that everything I have done, am doing, or shall do is well founded on reason and in conformity with the rules of chivalry, for I understand them better than all the knights in the world that profess them."

"Señor," replied Sancho, "is it a good rule of chivalry that we should go astray through these mountains without path or road, looking for a madman who when he is found will perhaps take a fancy to finish what he began, not his story, but your worship's head and my ribs, and end by breaking them altogether for us?"

"Peace, I say again, Sancho," said Don Quixote, "for let me tell thee it is not so much the desire of finding that madman that leads me into these regions as that which I have of performing among them an achievement wherewith I shall win eternal name and fame throughout the known world; and it shall be such that I shall thereby set the seal on all that can make a knight-errant perfect and famous."

"And is it very perilous, this achievement?" asked Sancho.

"No," replied he of the Rueful Countenance "though it may be in the dice that we may throw deuce-ace instead of sixes; but all will depend on thy diligence."

"On my diligence!" said Sancho.

"Yes," said Don Quixote, "for if thou dost return soon from the place where I mean to send thee, my penance will be soon over, and my glory will soon begin. But as it is not right to keep thee any longer in suspense, waiting to see what comes of my words, I would have thee know, Sancho, that the famous Amadis of Gaul was one of the most perfect knights-errant—I am wrong to say he was one; he stood alone, the first, the only one, the lord of all that were in the world in his time. A fig for Don Belianis and for all who say he equalled him in any respect, for, my oath upon it, they are deceiving themselves! I say, too, that when a painter desires to become famous in his art he endeavors to copy the originals of the rarest painters that he knows; and the same rule holds good for all the most important crafts and callings that serve to adorn a state; thus will he who would be esteemed prudent and patient imitate Ulysses, in whose person and labors Homer presents to us a lively picture of prudence and patience; as Virgil, too, shows us in the person of Æneas the virtue of a pious son and the sagacity of a brave and skilful captain; not representing or describing them as they were, but as they ought to be, so as to leave the example of their virtues to posterity. In the same way Amadis the pole-star, day-star, sun of valiant and devoted knights, whom all we who fight under the banner of love and chivalry are bound to imitate.

"This, then, being so, I consider, friend Sancho, that the knight-errant who shall imitate him most closely will come nearest to reaching the perfection of chivalry. Now one of the instances in which this knight most conspicuously showed his prudence, worth, valor, patience, fortitude and love was when he withdrew, rejected by the Lady Oriana, to do penance upon the Peña Pobre, changing his name into that of Beltenebros, a name assuredly significant and appropriate to the life which he had voluntarily adopted. So, as it is easier for me to imitate him in this than in cleaving giants asunder, cutting off serpents' heads, slaying dragons, routing armies, destroying fleets, and breaking enchantments, and as this place is so well suited for a similar purpose, I must not allow the opportunity to escape which now so conveniently offers me its forelock."

"What is it in reality," said Sancho, "that your worship means to do in such an out-of-the-way place as this?"

"Have I not told thee," answered Don Quixote, "that I mean to imitate Amadis here, playing the victim of despair, the madman, the maniac, so as at the same time to imitate the valiant Roland, when at the fountain he had evidence of the fair Angelica having disgraced herself with Medoro and through grief thereat went mad, and plucked up trees, troubled the waters of the clear springs, slew shepherds, destroyed flocks, burned down huts, levelled houses, dragged mares after him, and perpetrated a hundred thousand other outrages worthy of everlasting renown and record? And though I have no intention of imitating Roland, or Orlando, or Rotolando (for he went by all these names), step by step in all the mad things he did, said, and thought, I will make a rough copy to the best of my power of all that seems to me most essential; but perhaps I shall content myself with the simple imitation of Amadis, who, without giving way to any mischievous madness but merely to tears and sorrow, gained as much fame as the most famous."

"It seems to me," said Sancho, "that the knights who behaved in this way had provocation and cause for those follies and penances; but what cause has your worship for going mad? What lady has rejected you, or what evidence have you found to prove that the lady Dulcinea del Toboso has been trifling with Moor or Christian?"

"There is the point," replied Don Quixote, "and that is the beauty of this business of mine; no thanks to a knight-errant for going mad when he has a cause; the thing is to turn crazy without any provocation, and to let my lady know, if I do this in the dry, what I would do in the moist; moreover I have abundant cause in the long separation I have endured from my lady till death, Dulcinea del Toboso; for as thou didst hear that shepherd Ambrosio say the other day, in absence all ills are felt and feared; and so, friend Sancho, waste no time in advising me against so rare, so happy, and so unheard-of an imitation; mad I am, and mad I must be until thou returnest with the answer to a letter that I mean to send by thee to my lady Dulcinea; and if it be such as my constancy deserves, my insanity and penance will come to an end; and if it be to the opposite effect, I shall become mad in earnest, and, being so, I shall suffer no more; thus in whatever way she may answer I shall escape from the struggle and affliction in which thou wilt leave me, enjoying in my senses the boon thou bearest me, or as a madman not feeling the evil thou bringest me. But tell me, Sancho, hast thou got Mambrino's helmet safe; for I saw thee take it up from the ground when that wretch tried to break it in pieces but could not, by which the fineness of its temper may be seen?"

To which Sancho made answer, "By the living God, Sir Knight of the Rueful Countenance, I cannot endure or bear with patience some of the things that your worship says; and from them I begin to suspect that all you tell me about chivalry, and winning kingdoms and empires, and giving islands, and bestowing other rewards and dignities after the custom of knights-errant, must be all made up of wind and lies, and all pigments or figments, or whatever we may call them; for what would any one think that heard your worship calling a barber's basin Mambrino's helmet without ever seeing the mistake all this time, but that one who says and maintains such things must have his brains addled? I have the basin in my sack all dinted, and I am taking it home to have it mended, to trim my beard in it, if, by God's grace, I am allowed to see my wife and children some day or other."

"Look here, Sancho," said Don Quixote, "by him thou didst swear by just now I swear thou hast the most limited understanding that any squire in the world has or ever had. Is it possible that all this time thou hast been going about with me thou hast never found out that all things belonging to knights-errant seem to be illusions and nonsense and ravings, and to go always by contraries? And not because it really is so, but because there is always a swarm of enchanters in attendance upon us that change and alter everything with us, and turn things as they please, and according as they are disposed to aid or destroy us; thus what seems to thee a barber's basin seems to me Mambrino's helmet, and to another it will seem something else; and rare foresight it was in the sage who is on my side to make what is really and truly Mambrino's helmet seem a basin to everybody, for, being held in such estimation as it is, all the world would pursue me to rob me of it; but when they see it is only a barber's basin they do not take the trouble to obtain it; as was plainly shown by him who tried to break it, and left it on the ground without taking it, for, by my faith, had he known it he would never have left it behind. Keep it safe, my friend, for just now I have no need of it; indeed, I shall have to take off all this armor and remain as naked as I was born, if I have a mind to follow Roland rather than Amadis in my penance."

Thus talking they reached the foot of a high mountain which stood like an isolated peak among the others that surrounded it. Past its base there flowed a gentle brook, all around it spread a meadow so green and luxuriant that it was a delight to the eyes to look upon it, and forest trees in abundance, and shrubs and flowers, added to the charms of the spot. Upon this place the Knight of the Rueful Countenance fixed his choice for the performance of his penance, and as he beheld it exclaimed in a loud voice as though he were out of his senses, "This is the place, oh, ye heavens, that I select and choose for bewailing the misfortune in which ye yourselves have plunged me: this is the spot where the overflowings of mine eyes shall swell the waters of yon little brook, and my deep and endless sighs shall stir unceasingly the leaves of these mountain trees, in testimony and token of the pain my persecuted heart is suffering. Oh, ye rural deities, whoever ye be that haunt this lone spot, give ear to the complaint of a wretched lover whom long absence and brooding jealousy have driven to bewail his fate among these wilds and complain of the hard heart of that fair and ungrateful one, the end and limit of all human beauty! Oh, ye wood nymphs and dryads, that dwell in the thickets of the forest, so may the nimble wanton satyrs by whom ye are vainly wooed never disturb your sweet repose, help me to lament my hard fate or at least weary not at listening to it! Oh, Dulcinea del Toboso, day of my night, glory of my pain, guide of my path, star of my fortune, so may Heaven grant thee in full all thou seekest of it, bethink thee of the place and condition to which absence from thee has brought me, and make that return in kindness that is due to my fidelity! Oh, lonely trees, that from this day forward shall bear me company in my solitude, give me some sign by the gentle movement of your boughs that my presence is not distasteful to you! Oh, thou, my squire, pleasant companion in my prosperous and adverse fortunes, fix well in thy memory what thou shalt see me do here, so that thou mayest relate and report it to the sole cause of all," and so saying he dismounted from Rocinante, and in an instant relieved him of saddle and bridle, and giving him a slap on the croup, said, "He gives thee freedom who is bereft of it himself, oh steed as excellent in deed as thou art unfortunate in thy lot; begone where thou wilt, for thou bearest written on thy forehead that neither Astolfo's hippogriff, nor the famed Frontino that cost Bradamante so dear, could equal thee in speed."

Seeing this Sancho said, "Good luck to him who has saved us the trouble of stripping the pack-saddle off Dapple! By my faith he would not have gone without a slap on the croup and something said in his praise; though if he were here I would not let any one strip him, for there would be no occasion, as he had nothing of the lover or victim of despair about him, inasmuch as his master, which I was while it was God's pleasure, was nothing of the sort; and indeed, Sir Knight of the Rueful Countenance, if my departure and your worship's madness are to come off in earnest, it will be as well to saddle Rocinante again in order that he may supply the want of Dapple, because it will save me time in going and returning; for if I go on foot I don't know when I shall get there or when I shall get back, as I am, in truth, a bad walker."

"I declare, Sancho," returned Don Quixote, "it shall be as thou wilt, for thy plan does not seem to me a bad one, and three days hence thou wilt depart, for I wish thee to observe in the mean time what I do and say for her sake, that thou mayest be able to tell it."

"But what more have I to see besides what I have seen?" said Sancho.

"Much thou knowest about it!" said Don Quixote. "I have now got to tear up my garments, to scatter about my armor, knock my head against these rocks, and more of the same sort of thing, which thou must witness."

"For the love of God," said Sancho, "be careful, your worship, how you give yourself those knocks on the head, for you may come across such a rock, and in such a way, that the very first may put an end to the whole contrivance of this penance; and I should think, if indeed knocks on the head seem necessary to you, and this business can not be done without them, you might be content—as the whole thing is feigned, and counterfeit, and in joke—you might be content, I say, with giving them to yourself in the water, or against something soft, like cotton; and leave it all to me; for I'll tell my lady that your worship knocked your head against a point of rock harder than a diamond."

"I thank thee for thy good intentions, friend Sancho," answered Don Quixote, "but I would have thee know that all these things I am doing are not in joke, but very much in earnest, for anything else would be a transgression of the ordinances of chivalry, which forbid us to tell any lie whatever under the penalties due to

postasy; and to do one thing instead of another
s just the same as lying; so my knocks on the
ead must be real, solid, and valid, without any-
ning sophisticated or fanciful about them, and
: will be needful to leave me some lint to dress
ny wounds, since fortune has compelled us to
o without the balsam we lost."

"It was worse losing the ass," replied Sancho,
for with him lint and all were lost; but I beg
f your worship not to remind me again of that
ccursed liquor, for my soul, not to say my stom-
ch, turns at hearing the very name of it; and
beg of you, too, to reckon as past the three
ays you allowed me for seeing the mad things
ou do, for I take them as seen already and pro-
ounced upon, and I will tell wonderful stories
) my lady; so write the letter and send me off
t once, for I long to return and take your worhip out of this purgatory where I am leaving
ou."

"Purgatory dost thou call it, Sancho?" said
)on Quixote, "rather call it hell, or even worse
: there be anything worse."

"For one who is in hell," said Sancho, "nulla
st retentio, as I have heard say."

"I do not understand what retentio means,"
aid Don Quixote.

"Retentio," answered Sancho, "means that
vhoever is in hell never comes nor can come
ut of it, which will be the opposite case with
our worship or my legs will be idle, that is if I
ave spurs to enliven Rocinante: let me once
et to El Toboso and into the presence of my
ıdy Dulcinea, and I will tell her such things
f the follies and madnesses (for it is all one)
ıat your worship has done and is still doing,
ıat I will manage to make her softer than a
love though I find her harder than a cork tree;
ıd with her sweet and honeyed answer I will
ome back through the air like a witch, and
ıke your worship out of this purgatory that
eems to be hell but is not, as there is hope of
etting out of it; which, as I have said, those in
ell have not, and I believe your worship will
ot say anything to the contrary."

"That is true," said he of the Rueful Counte-
ance, "but how shall we manage to write the
etter?"

"And the ass-colt order too," added Sancho.

"All shall be included," said Don Quixote;
and as there is no paper, it would be well done
) write on the leaves of trees, as the ancients
id, or on tablets of wax; though that would be
s hard to find just now as paper. But it has
ıst occurred to me how it may be conveniently
ıd even more than conveniently written, and

that is in the note-book that belonged to Cardenio, and thou wilt take care to have it copied
on paper, in a good hand, at the first village
thou comest to where there is a schoolmaster, or
if not, any sacristan will copy it; but see thou
give it not to any notary to copy, for they write
a law hand that Satan could not make out."

"But what is to be done about the signature?"
said Sancho.

"The letters of Amadis were never signed,"
said Don Quixote.

"That is all very well," said Sancho, "but the
order must needs be signed, and if it is copied
they will say the signature is false, and I shall
be left without ass-colts."

"The order shall go signed in the same book,"
said Don Quixote, "and on seeing it my niece
will make no difficulty about obeying it; as to
the love-letter thou canst put by way of signature, 'Yours till death, the Knight of the Rueful
Countenance.' And it will be no great matter
if it is in some other person's hand, for as well
as I recollect Dulcinea can neither read nor
write, nor in the whole course of her life has
she seen handwriting or letter of mine, for my
love and hers have been always platonic, not going beyond a modest look, and even that so seldom that I can safely swear I have not seen her
four times in all these twelve years I have been
loving her more than the light of these eyes that
the earth will one day devour; and perhaps even
of those four times she has not once perceived
that I was looking at her: such is the retirement and seclusion in which her father Lorenzo Corchuelo and her mother Aldonza Nogales
have brought her up."

"So, so!" said Sancho; "Lorenzo Corchuelo's
daughter is the lady Dulcinea del Toboso, otherwise called Aldonza Lorenzo?"

"She it is," said Don Quixote, "and she it is
that is worthy to be lady of the universe."

"I know her well," said Sancho, "and let me
tell you she can fling a crowbar as well as the
lustiest lad in all the town. Giver of all good!
but she is a brave lass, and a right and stout
one, and fit to be helpmate to any knight-errant
that is or is to be, who may make her his lady: the
whoreson wench, what pith she has and what
a voice! I can tell you one day she posted herself
on the top of the belfry of the village to call
some laborers of theirs that were in a ploughed
field of her father's, and though they were better than half a league off they heard her as well
as if they were at the foot of the tower; and the
best of her is that she is not a bit prudish, for
she has plenty of affability, and jokes with

everybody, and has a grin and a jest for everything. So, Sir Knight of the Rueful Countenance, I say you not only may and ought to do mad freaks for her sake, but you have a good right to give way to despair and hang yourself; and no one who knows of it but will say you did well, though the devil should take you; and I wish I were on my road already, simply to see her, for it is many a day since I saw her, and she must be altered by this time, for going about the fields always, and the sun and the air spoil women's looks greatly. But I must own the truth to your worship, Señor Don Quixote; until now I have been under a great mistake, for I believed truly and honestly that the lady Dulcinea must be some princess your worship was in love with, or some person great enough to deserve the rich presents you have sent her, such as the Biscayan and the galley slaves, and many more no doubt, for your worship must have won many victories in the time when I was not yet your squire. But all things considered, what good can it do the lady Aldonza Lorenzo (I mean the lady Dulcinea del Toboso) to have the vanquished your worship sends or will send coming to her and going down on their knees before her? Because maybe when they came she'd be hackling flax or threshing on the threshing floor, and they'd be ashamed to see her, and she'd laugh, or resent the present."

"I have before now told thee many times, Sancho," said Don Quixote, "that thou art a mighty great chatterer, and that with a blunt wit thou art always striving at sharpness; but to show thee what a fool thou art and how rational I am, I would have thee listen to a short story. Thou must know that a certain widow, fair, young, independent, and rich, and above all free and easy, fell in love with a sturdy strapping young lay-brother; his superior came to know of it, and one day said to the worthy widow by way of brotherly remonstrance, 'I am surprised, señora, and not without good reason, that a woman of such high standing, so fair, and so rich as you are, should have fallen in love with such a mean, low, stupid fellow as So-and-so, when in this house there are so many masters, graduates and divinity students from among whom you might choose as if they were a lot of pears, saying, This one I'll take, that I won't take'; but she replied to him with great sprightliness and candor, 'My dear sir, you are very much mistaken, and your ideas are very old-fashioned, if you think that I have made a bad choice in So-and-so, fool as he seems; because for all I want with him he knows as much

and more philosophy than Aristotle.' In the same way, Sancho, for all I want with Dulcinea del Toboso she is just as good as the most exalted princess on earth. It is not to be supposed that all those poets who sang the praises of ladies under the fancy names they give them, had any such mistresses. Thinkest thou that the Amaryllises, the Phyllises, the Sylvias, the Dianas, the Galateas, the Filidas, and all the rest of them that the books, the ballads, the barbers' shops, the theatres are full of were really and truly ladies of flesh and blood, and mistresses of those that glorify and have glorified them? Nothing of the kind; they only invent them for the most part to furnish a subject for their verses, and that they may pass for lovers, or for men who have some pretensions to be so; and so it is enough for me to think and believe that the good Aldonza Lorenzo is fair and virtuous; and as to her pedigree it is very little matter, for no one will examine into it for the purpose of conferring any order upon her, and I, for my part, reckon her the most exalted princess in the world. For thou shouldst know, Sancho, if thou dost not know, that two things alone beyond all others are incentives to love, and these are great beauty and a good name, and these two things are to be found in Dulcinea in the highest degree, for in beauty no one equals her and in good name few approach her; and to put the whole thing in a nutshell, I persuade myself that all I say is as I say, neither more nor less, and I picture her in my imagination as I would have her to be, as well in beauty as in condition; Helen approaches her not, nor does Lucretia come up to her, nor any other of the famous women of times past, Greek, barbarian, or Latin; and let each say what he will, for if in this I am taken to task by the ignorant, I shall not be censured by the critical."

"I say that your worship is entirely right," said Sancho, "and that I am an ass. But I know not how the name of ass came into my mouth, for a rope is not to be mentioned in the house of him who has been hanged; but now for the letter, and then, God be with you, I am off."

Don Quixote took out the note-book, and, retiring to one side, very deliberately began to write the letter, and when he had finished it he called to Sancho, saying he wished to read it to him, so that he might commit it to memory, in case of losing it on the road; for with evil fortune like his anything might be apprehended. To which Sancho replied, "Write it two or three times there in the book and give it to me, and I will carry it very carefully, because to expect

ne to keep it in my memory is all nonsense, for
I have such a bad one that I often forget my
own name; but for all that repeat it to me, as I
shall like to hear it, for surely it will run as if
t was in print."

"Listen," said Don Quixote, "this is what it
says:

Don Quixote's Letter to Dulcinea del Toboso

SOVEREIGN AND EXALTED LADY, The pierced by
he point of absence, the wounded to the heart's
core, sends thee, sweetest Dulcinea del Toboso, the
health that he himself enjoys not. If thy beauty
despises me, if thy worth is not for me, if thy scorn
s my affliction, though I be sufficiently long-suffer-
ng, hardly shall I endure this anxiety, which, be-
ides being oppressive, is protracted. My good Squire
Sancho will relate to thee in full, fair ingrate, dear
enemy, the condition to which I am reduced on thy
account; if it be thy pleasure to give me relief, I am
hine; if not, do as may be pleasing to thee; for by
ending my life I shall satisfy thy cruelty and my
desire.

Thine till death,
THE KNIGHT OF THE RUEFUL COUNTENANCE

"By the life of my father," said Sancho, when
he heard the letter, "it is the loftiest thing I
ever heard. Body of me! how your worship says
everything as you like in it! And how well you
it in 'The Knight of the Rueful Countenance'
nto the signature. I declare your worship is indeed the very devil, and there is nothing you
don't know."

"Everything is needed for the calling I fol-
ow," said Don Quixote.

"Now then," said Sancho, "let your worship put the order for the three ass-colts on the
other side, and sign it very plainly, that they
may recognize it at first sight."

"With all my heart," said Don Quixote, and
as soon as he had written it he read it to this
effect:

MISTRESS NIECE, By this first of ass-colts please
pay to Sancho Panza, my squire, three of the five I
left at home in your charge: said three ass-colts to
be paid and delivered for the same number received
here in hand, which upon this and upon his receipt
shall be duly paid. Done in the heart of the Sierra
Morena, the twenty-seventh of August of this present year.

"That will do," said Sancho; "now let your
worship sign it."

"There is no need to sign it," said Don Quixote, "but merely to put my flourish, which is the
same as a signature, and enough for three asses,
or even three hundred."

"I can trust your worship," returned Sancho;

"let me go and saddle Rocinante, and be ready
to give me your blessing, for I mean to go at
once without seeing the fooleries your worship
is going to do; I'll say I saw you do so many
that she will not want any more."

"At any rate, Sancho," said Don Quixote, "I
should like—and there is reason for it—I should
like thee, I say, to see me stripped to the skin
and performing a dozen or two of insanities,
which I can get done in less than half an hour;
for having seen them with thine own eyes, thou
canst then safely swear to the rest that thou
wouldst add; and I promise thee thou wilt not
tell of as many as I mean to perform."

"For the love of God, master mine," said Sancho, "let me not see your worship stripped, for
it will sorely grieve me, and I shall not be able
to keep from tears, and my head aches so with
all I shed last night for Dapple, that I am not
fit to begin any fresh weeping; but if it is your
worship's pleasure that I should see some insanities, do them in your clothes, short ones,
and such as come readiest to hand; for I myself
want nothing of the sort, and, as I have said, it
will be a saving of time for my return, which
will be with the news your worship desires and
deserves. If not, let the lady Dulcinea look to it;
if she does not answer reasonably, I swear as
solemnly as I can that I will fetch a fair answer
out of her stomach with kicks and cuffs; for
why should it be borne that a knight-errant as
famous as your worship should go mad without
rhyme or reason for a—? Her ladyship had best
not drive me to say it, for by God I will speak
out and have done with it, though it stop the
sale: I am pretty good at that! She little knows
me; faith, if she knew me she'd be afraid of
me."

"In faith, Sancho," said Don Quixote, "to all
appearance thou art not sounder in thy wits
than I am."

"I am not so mad," answered Sancho, "but I
am more peppery; but apart from all this, what
has your worship to eat until I come back? Will
you sally out on the road like Cardenio to force
it from the shepherds?"

"Let not that anxiety trouble thee," replied
Don Quixote, "for even if I had it I should not
eat anything but the herbs and the fruits which
this meadow and these trees may yield me; the
beauty of this business of mine lies in not eating, and in performing other mortifications."

"Do you know what I am afraid of?" said
Sancho upon this; "that I shall not be able to
find my way back to this spot where I am leaving you, it is such an out-of-the-way place."

"Observe the landmarks well," said Don Quixote, "for I will try not to go far from this neighborhood, and I will even take care to mount the highest of these rocks to see if I can discover thee returning; however, not to miss me and lose thyself, the best plan will be to cut some branches of the broom that is so abundant about here, and as thou goest to lay them at intervals until thou hast come out upon the plain; these will serve thee, after the fashion of the clew in the labyrinth of Theseus, as marks and signs for finding me on thy return."

"So I will," said Sancho Panza, and having cut some, he asked his master's blessing, and not without many tears on both sides took his leave of him, and mounting Rocinante, of whom Don Quixote charged him earnestly to have as much care as of his own person, he set out for the plain, strewing at intervals the branches of broom as his master had recommended him; and so he went his way, though Don Quixote still entreated him to see him do were it only a couple of mad acts. He had not gone a hundred paces, however, when he returned and said, "I must say, señor, your worship said quite right, that in order to be able to swear without a weight on my conscience that I had seen you do mad things, it would be well for me to see if it were only one; though in your worship's remaining here I have seen a very great one."

"Did I not tell thee so?" said Don Quixote. "Wait, Sancho, and I will do them in the saying of a *credo*," and pulling off his breeches in all haste he stripped himself to his skin and his shirt, and then, without more ado, he cut a couple of *gambados* in the air, and a couple of somersaults, heels over head, making such a display that, not to see it a second time, Sancho wheeled Rocinante round, and felt easy, and satisfied in his mind that he could swear he had left his master mad; and so we will leave him to follow his road until his return, which was a quick one.

Chapter 26

In which are continued the refinements wherewith Don Quixote played the part of a lover in the Sierra Morena

RETURNING to the proceedings of him of the Rueful Countenance when he found himself alone, the history says that when Don Quixote had completed the performance of the somersaults or capers, naked from the waist down and clothed from the waist up, and saw that Sancho had gone off without waiting to see any more crazy feats, he climbed up to the top of a high rock, and there set himself to consider what he had several times before considered without ever coming to any conclusion on the point, namely, whether it would be better and more to his purpose to imitate the outrageous madness of Roland, or the melancholy madness of Amadis; and communing with himself he said, "What wonder is it if Roland was so good a knight and so valiant as every one says he was, when, after all, he was enchanted, and nobody could kill him save by thrusting a corking pin into the sole of his foot, and he always wore shoes with seven iron soles? Though cunning devices did not avail him against Bernardo del Carpio, who knew all about them, and strangled him in his arms at Roncesvalles. But putting the question of his valor aside, let us come to his losing his wits, for certain it is that he did lose them in consequence of the proofs he discovered at the fountain, and the intelligence the shepherd gave him of Angelica having slept more than two afternoons with Medoro, a little curly-headed Moor, and page to Agramante. If he was persuaded that this was true, and that his lady had wronged him, it is no wonder that he should have gone mad; but I, how am I to imitate him in his madness, unless I can imitate him in the cause of it? For my Dulcinea, I will venture to swear, never saw a Moor, as he is in his proper costume, in her life, and is this day as the mother that bore her, and I should plainly be doing her a wrong if, fancying anything else, I were to go mad with the same kind of madness as 'Roland the Furious.' On the other hand, I see that Amadis of Gaul, without losing his senses and without doing anything mad, acquired as a lover as much fame as the most famous; for, according to his history, on finding himself rejected by his lady Oriana, who had ordered him not to appear in her presence until it should be her pleasure, all he did was to retire to the Peña Pobre in company with a hermit, and there he took his fill of weeping until Heaven sent him relief in the midst of his great grief and need. And if this be true, as it is, why should I now take the trouble to strip stark naked, or do mischief to these trees which have done me no harm, or why am I to disturb the clear waters of these brooks which will give me to drink whenever I have a mind? Long live the memory of Amadis, and let him be imitated so far as is possible by Don Quixote of La Mancha, of whom it will be said, as was said of the other, that if he did not achieve great things, he died in attempting them; and if I am not repulsed or rejected by my Dulcinea, it is enough for me, as I have said, to be absent from her. And so, now to business; come to my memory ye deeds of Amadis, and show me how I am to begin to imitate you. I know already that what he chiefly did was to pray and commend himself to God; but what am I to do for a rosary, for I have not got one?" And then it occurred to him how he might make one, and that was by tearing a great strip off the tail of his shirt which hung down, and making eleven knots on it, one bigger than the rest, and this served him for a rosary all the time he was there, during which he repeated countless *ave marias*. But what distressed him greatly was not having another hermit there to confess him and receive consolation from; and so he solaced himself with pacing up and down the little meadow, and writing and carving on the bark of the trees and on the fine sand a multitude of verses all in harmony with his sadness, and some in praise of Dulcinea; but, when he was found there afterwards, the only ones completely legible that could be discovered were those that follow here:

Ye on the mountain side that grow,
  Ye green things all, trees, shrubs, and bushes,
Are ye aweary of the woe
    That this poor aching bosom crushes?
If it disturb you, and I owe
    Some reparation, it may be a
Defence for me to let you know
Don Quixote's tears are on the flow,
  And all for distant Dulcinea
          Del Toboso.

The lealest lover time can show,
  Doomed for a lady-love to languish,
Among these solitudes doth go,
  A prey to every kind of anguish.
Why Love should like a spiteful foe
    Thus use him, he hath no idea,
But hogsheads full—this doth he know—
Don Quixote's tears are on the flow,
  And all for distant Dulcinea
          Del Toboso.

Adventure-seeking doth he go
  Up ragged heights, down rocky valleys,
But hill or dale, or high or low,
  Mishap attendeth all his sallies:
Love still pursues him to and fro,
    And plies his cruel scourge—ah me! a
Relentless fate, an endless woe;
Don Quixote's tears are on the flow,
  And all for distant Dulcinea
          Del Toboso.

The addition of "Del Toboso" to Dulcinea's name gave rise to no little laughter among those who found the above lines, for they suspected Don Quixote must have fancied that unless he added "del Toboso" when he introduced the name of Dulcinea the verse would be unintelligible; which was indeed the fact, as he himself afterwards admitted. He wrote many more, but, as has been said, these three verses were all that could be plainly and perfectly deciphered. In this way, and in sighing and calling on the fauns and satyrs of the woods and the nymphs of the streams, and Echo, moist and mournful, to answer, console, and hear him, as well as in looking for herbs to sustain him, he passed his time until Sancho's return; and had that been delayed three weeks, as it was three days, the Knight of the Rueful Countenance would have worn such an altered countenance that the mother that bore him would not have known him: and here it will be well to leave him, wrapped up in sighs and verses, to relate how Sancho Panza fared on his mission.

As for him, coming out upon the high road, he made for El Toboso, and the next day reached the inn where the mishap of the blanket had befallen him. As soon as he recognized it he felt as if he were once more flying through the air, and he could not bring himself to enter it though it was an hour when he might well have done so, for it was dinner-time, and he longed to taste something hot as it had been all cold fare with him for many days past. This craving drove him to draw near to the inn, still undecided whether to go in or not, and as he was hesitating there came out two persons who at once recognized him, and said one to the other, "Señor licentiate, is not he on the horse there Sancho Panza who, our adventurer's housekeeper told us, went off with her master as esquire?"

"So it is," said the licentiate, "and that is our friend Don Quixote's horse"; and if they knew him so well it was because they were the curate and the barber of his own village, the same who had carried out the scrutiny and sentence upon the books; and as soon as they recognized Sancho Panza and Rocinante, being anxious to hear of Don Quixote, they approached, and calling him by his name the curate said, "Friend Sancho Panza, where is your master?"

Sancho recognized them at once, and determined to keep secret the place and circumstances where and under which he had left his master, so he replied that his master was engaged in a certain quarter on a certain matter of great importance to him which he could not disclose for the eyes in his head.

"Nay, nay," said the barber, "if you don't tell us where he is, Sancho Panza, we will suspect, as we suspect already, that you have murdered and robbed him, for here you are mounted on his horse; in fact, you must produce the master of the hack, or else take the consequences."

"There is no need of threats with me," said Sancho, "for I am not a man to rob or murder anybody; let his own fate, or God who made him, kill each one; my master is engaged very much to his taste doing penance in the midst of these mountains"; and then, offhand and without stopping, he told them how he had left him, what adventures had befallen him, and how he was carrying a letter to the lady Dulcinea del Toboso, the daughter of Lorenzo Corchuelo, with whom he was over head and ears in love. They were both amazed at what Sancho Panza told them; for though they were aware of Don Quixote's madness and the nature of it, each time they heard of it they were filled with fresh wonder. They then asked Sancho Panza to show them the letter he was carrying to the lady Dulcinea del Toboso. He said it was written in a note-book, and that his master's directions were that he should have it copied on paper at the first village he came to. On this the curate said if he showed it to him, he himself would make a fair copy of it. Sancho put his hand into his bosom in search of the note-book but could not find it, nor, if he had been searching until now, could he have found it, for Don Quixote had kept it, and had never given it to him, nor had he himself thought of asking for it. When Sancho discovered he could not find the book his face grew deadly pale, and in great haste he again felt his body all over, and seeing plainly it was not to be found, without more ado he seized his beard with both hands and plucked away half of it, and then, as quick as he could and without stopping, gave himself half a dozen cuffs on the face and nose till they were bathed in blood.

Seeing this, the curate and the barber asked him what had happened him that he gave himself such rough treatment.

"What should happen me" replied Sancho, "but to have lost from one hand to the other, in a moment, three ass-colts, each of them like a castle?"

"How is that?" said the barber.

"I have lost the note-book," said Sancho, "that contained the letter to Dulcinea, and an order signed by my master in which he directed his niece to give me three ass-colts out of four or five he had at home"; and he then told them about the loss of Dapple.

The curate consoled him, telling him that when his master was found he would get him to renew the order, and make a fresh draft on paper, as was usual and customary; for those made in note-books were never accepted or honored.

Sancho comforted himself with this, and said if that were so the loss of Dulcinea's letter did not trouble him much, for he had it almost by heart, and it could be taken down from him wherever and whenever they liked.

"Repeat it then, Sancho," said the barber, "and we will write it down afterwards."

Sancho Panza stopped to scratch his head to bring back the letter to his memory, and balanced himself now on one foot, now the other, one moment staring at the ground, the next at the sky, and after having half gnawed off the end of a finger and kept them in suspense waiting for him to begin, he said, after a long pause, "By God, señor licentiate, devil a thing can I recollect of the letter; but it said at the beginning, 'Exalted and scrubbing Lady.'"

"It cannot have said 'scrubbing,'" said the barber, "but 'superhuman' or 'sovereign.'"

"That is it," said Sancho; "then, as well as I remember, it went on, 'The wounded, and wanting of sleep, and the pierced, kisses your worship's hands, ungrateful and very unrecognized fair one'; and it said something or other about health and sickness that he was sending her; and from that it went tailing off until it ended with 'Yours till death, the Knight of the Rueful Countenance.'"

It gave them no little amusement, both of them, to see what a good memory Sancho had, and they complimented him greatly upon it, and begged him to repeat the letter a couple of times more, so that they too might get it by heart to write it out by-and-by. Sancho repeated it three times, and as he did, uttered three thousand more absurdities; then he told them more about his master; but he never said a word about the blanketing that had befallen himself in that inn, into which he refused to enter. He told them, moreover, how his lord, if he brought him a favorable answer from the lady Dulcinea del Toboso, was to put himself in the way of endeavoring to become an emperor, or at least a monarch; for it had been so settled between them, and with his personal worth and the might of his arm it was an easy matter to come to be one: and how on becoming one his lord was to make a marriage for him (for he would be a widower by that time, as a matter of course) and was to give him as a wife one of the damsels of the empress, the heiress of some rich and grand state on the mainland, having nothing to do with islands of any sort, for he did not care for them now. All this Sancho delivered with so much composure—wiping his nose from time to time—and with so little common-sense that his two hearers were again filled with wonder at the force of Don Quixote's madness that could run away with this poor man's reason. They did not care to take the trouble of disabusing him of his error, as they considered that since it did not in any way hurt his conscience it would be better to leave him in it, and they would have all the more amusement in listening to his simplicities; and so they bade him pray to God for his lord's health, as it was a very likely and a very feasible thing for him in course of time to come to be an emperor, as he said, or at least an archbishop or some other dignitary of equal rank.

To which Sancho made answer, "If fortune, sirs, should bring things about in such a way that my master should have a mind, instead of being an emperor, to be an archbishop, I should like to know what archbishops-errant commonly give their squires?"

"They commonly give them," said the curate, "some simple benefice or cure, or some place as sacristan which brings them a good fixed income, not counting the altar fees, which may be reckoned at as much more."

"But for that," said Sancho, "the squire must be unmarried, and must know, at any rate, how to help at Mass, and if that be so, woe is me, for I am married already and I don't know the first letter of the ABC. What will become of me if my master takes a fancy to be an archbishop and not an emperor, as is usual and customary with knights-errant?"

"Be not uneasy, friend Sancho," said the barber, "for we will entreat your master, and advise him, even urging it upon him as a case of conscience, to become an emperor and not an archbishop, because it will be easier for him as he is more valiant than lettered."

"So I have thought," said Sancho; "though I can tell you he is fit for anything: what I mean to do for my part is to pray to our Lord to place him where it may be best for him, and where he may be able to bestow most favors upon me."

"You speak like a man of sense," said the curate, "and you will be acting like a good Christian; but what must now be done is to take steps to coax your master out of that useless penance

you say he is performing; and we had best turn into this inn to consider what plan to adopt, and also to dine, for it is now time."

Sancho said they might go in, but that he would wait there outside, that he would tell them afterwards the reason why he was unwilling, and why it did not suit him to enter it; but he begged them to bring him out something to eat, and to let it be hot, and also to bring barley for Rocinante. They left him and went in, and presently the barber brought him out something to eat. By-and-by, after they had between them carefully thought over what they should do to carry out their object, the curate hit upon an idea very well adapted to humor Don Quixote, and effect their purpose; and his notion, which he explained to the barber, was that he himself should assume the disguise of a wandering damsel, while the other should try as best he could to pass for a squire, and that they should thus proceed to where Don Quixote was, and he, pretending to be an aggrieved and distressed damsel, should ask a favor of him, which as a valiant knight-errant he could not refuse to grant; and the favor he meant to ask him was that he should accompany her whither she would conduct him, in order to redress a wrong which a wicked knight had done her, while at the same time she should entreat him not to require her to remove her mask, nor ask her any question touching her circumstances until he had righted her with the wicked knight. And he had no doubt that Don Quixote would comply with any request made in these terms, and that in this way they might remove him and take him to his own village, where they would endeavor to find out if his extraordinary madness admitted of any kind of remedy.

Chapter 27

Of how the Curate and the Barber proceeded with their scheme; together with other matters worthy of record in this great history

THE curate's plan did not seem a bad one to the barber, but on the contrary so good that they immediately set about putting it in execution. They begged a petticoat and hood of the landlady, leaving her in pledge a new cassock of the curate's; and the barber made a beard out of a gray or red ox-tail in which the landlord used to stick his comb. The landlady asked them what they wanted these things for, and the curate told her in a few words about the madness of Don Quixote and how this disguise was intended to get him away from the mountain where he then was. The landlord and landlady immediately came to the conclusion that the madman was their guest, the balsam man and master of the blanketed squire, and they told the curate all that had passed between him and them, not omitting what Sancho had been so silent about. Finally the landlady dressed up the curate in a style that left nothing to be desired; she put on him a cloth petticoat with black velvet stripes a palm broad, all slashed, and a bodice of green velvet set off by a binding of white satin, which as well as the petticoat must have been made in the time of king Wamba. The curate would not let them cover him with the hood, but put on his head a little quilted linen cap which he used for a nightcap, and bound his forehead with a strip of black silk, while with another he made a mask with which he concealed his beard and face very well. He then put on his hat, which was broad enough to serve him for an umbrella, and enveloping himself in his cloak seated himself woman-fashion on his mule, while the barber mounted his with a beard down to the waist of mingled red and white, for it was, as has been said, the tail of a red ox. They took leave of all, and of the good Maritornes, who, sinner as she was, promised to pray a rosary of prayers that God might grant them success in such an arduous and Christian undertaking as that they had in hand. But hardly had he sallied forth from the inn when it struck the curate that he was doing wrong in rigging himself out in that fashion, as it was an indecorous thing for a priest to dress himself that way even though much might depend upon it; and saying so to the barber he begged him to change dresses, as it was fitter he should be the distressed damsel, while he himself would play the squire's part, which would be less derogatory to his dignity; otherwise he was resolved to have nothing more to do with the matter, and let the devil take Don Quixote. Just at this moment Sancho came up, and on seeing the pair in such a costume he was unable to restrain his laughter; the barber, however, agreed to do as the curate wished, and, altering their plan, the curate went on to instruct him how to play his part and what to say to Don Quixote to induce and compel him to come with them and give up his fancy for the place he had chosen for his idle penance. The barber told him he could manage it properly without any instruction, and as he did not care to dress himself up until they were near where Don Quixote was, he folded up the gar-

ments, and the curate adjusted his beard, and they set out under the guidance of Sancho Panza, who went along telling them of the encounter with the madman they met in the Sierra, saying nothing, however, about the finding of the valise and its contents; for with all his simplicity the lad was a trifle covetous.

The next day they reached the place where Sancho had laid the broom-branches as marks to direct him to where he had left his master, and recognizing it he told them that here was the entrance, and that they would do well to dress themselves, if that was required to deliver his master; for they had already told him that going in this guise and dressing in this way were of the highest importance in order to rescue his master from the pernicious life he had adopted; and they charged him strictly not to tell his master who they were, or that he knew them, and should he ask, as ask he would, if he had given the letter to Dulcinea, to say he had, and that, as she did not know how to read, she had given an answer by word of mouth, saying that she commanded him, on pain of her displeasure, to come and see her at once; and it was a very important matter for himself, because in this way and with what they meant to say to him they felt sure of bringing him back to a better mode of life and inducing him to take immediate steps to become an emperor or monarch, for there was no fear of his becoming an archbishop. All this Sancho listened to and fixed it well in his memory, and thanked them heartily for intending to recommend his master to be an emperor instead of an archbishop, for he felt sure that in the way of bestowing rewards on their squires emperors could do more than archbishops-errant. He said, too, that it would be as well for him to go on before them to find him, and give him his lady's answer; for that perhaps might be enough to bring him away from the place without putting them to all this trouble. They approved of what Sancho proposed, and resolved to wait for him until he brought back word of having found his master.

Sancho pushed into the glens of the Sierra, leaving them in one through which there flowed a little gentle rivulet, and where the rocks and trees afforded a cool and grateful shade. It was an August day with all the heat of one, and the heat in those parts is intense, and the hour was three in the afternoon, all which made the spot the more inviting and tempted them to wait there for Sancho's return, which they did. They were reposing, then, in the shade, when a voice unaccompanied by the notes of any instrument, but sweet and pleasing in its tone, reached their ears, at which they were not a little astonished, as the place did not seem to them likely quarters for one who sang so well; for though it is often said that shepherds of rare voice are to be found in the woods and fields, this is rather a flight of the poet's fancy than the truth. And still more surprised were they when they perceived that what they heard sung were the verses not of rustic shepherds, but of the polished wits of the city; and so it proved, for the verses they heard were these:

What makes my quest of happiness seem vain?
Disdain.
What bids me to abandon hope of ease?
Jealousies.
What holds my heart in anguish of suspense?
Absence.
If that be so, then for my grief
Where shall I turn to seek relief,
When hope on every side lies slain
By Absence, Jealousies, Disdain?
What the prime cause of all my woe doth prove?
Love.
What at my glory ever looks askance?
Chance.
Whence is permission to afflict me given?
Heaven.
If that be so, I but await
The stroke of a resistless fate,
Since, working for my woe, these three,
Love, Chance, and Heaven, in league I see.
What must I do to find a remedy?
Die.
What is the lure for love when coy and strange?
Change.
What, if all fail, will cure the heart of sadness?
Madness.
If that be so, it is but folly
To seek a cure for melancholy:
Ask where it lies; the answer saith
In Change, in Madness, or in Death.

The hour, the summer season, the solitary place, the voice and skill of the singer, all contributed to the wonder and delight of the two listeners, who remained still waiting to hear something more; finding, however, that the silence continued some little time, they resolved to go in search of the musician who sang with so fine a voice; but just as they were about to do so they were checked by the same voice, which once more fell upon their ears, singing this

Sonnet

When heavenward, holy Friendship, thou didst go
Soaring to seek thy home beyond the sky,
And take thy seat among the saints on high,
It was thy will to leave on earth below
Thy semblance, and upon it to bestow
Thy veil, wherewith at times hypocrisy,
Parading in thy shape, deceives the eye,
And makes its vileness bright as virtue show.
Friendship, return to us, or force the cheat
That wears it now, thy livery to restore,
By aid whereof sincerity is slain.
If thou wilt not unmask thy counterfeit,
This earth will be the prey of strife once more,
As when primeval discord held its reign.

The song ended with a deep sigh, and again the listeners remained waiting attentively for the singer to resume; but perceiving that the music had now turned to sobs and heart-rending moans they determined to find out who the unhappy being could be whose voice was as rare as his sighs were piteous, and they had not proceeded far when on turning the corner of a rock they discovered a man of the same aspect and appearance as Sancho had described to them when he told them the story of Cardenio. He, showing no astonishment when he saw them, stood still with his head bent down upon his breast like one in deep thought, without raising his eyes to look at them after the first glance when they suddenly came upon him. The curate, who was aware of his misfortune and recognized him by the description, being a man of good address, approached him and in a few sensible words entreated and urged him to quit a life of such misery, lest he should end it there, which would be the greatest of all misfortunes. Cardenio was then in his right mind, free from any attack of that madness which so frequently carried him away, and seeing them dressed in a fashion so unusual among the frequenters of those wilds, could not help showing some surprise, especially when he heard them speak of his case as if it were a well-known matter (for the curate's words gave him to understand as much); so he replied to them thus, "I see plainly, sirs, whoever you may be, that Heaven, whose care it is to succor the good, and even the wicked very often, here, in this remote spot, cut off from human intercourse, sends me, though I deserve it not, those who seek to draw me away from this to some better retreat, showing me by many and forcible arguments how unreasonably I act in leading the life I do; but as they know not what I know, that if I escape from this evil I shall fall into another still greater, perhaps they will set me down as a weak-minded man, or, what is worse, one devoid of reason; nor would it be any wonder, for I myself can perceive that the effect of the recollection of my misfortunes is so great and works so powerfully to my ruin, that in spite of myself I become at times like a stone, without feeling or consciousness; and I come to feel the truth of it when they tell me and show me proofs of the things I have done when the terrible fit overmasters me; and all I can do is bewail my lot in vain, and idly curse my destiny, and plead for my madness by telling how it was caused to any that care to hear it; for no reasonable beings on learning the cause will wonder at the effects; and if they can not help me at least they will not blame me, and the repugnance they feel at my wild ways will turn into pity for my woes. If it be, sirs, that you are here with the same design as others have come with, before you proceed with your wise arguments, I entreat you to hear the story of my countless misfortunes, for perhaps when you have heard it you will spare yourselves the trouble you would take in offering consolation to grief that is beyond the reach of it."

As they, both of them, desired nothing more than to hear from his own lips the cause of his suffering, they entreated him to tell it, promising not to do anything for his relief or comfort that he did not wish; and thereupon the unhappy gentleman began his sad story in nearly the same words and manner in which he had related it to Don Quixote and the goatherd a few days before, when, through Master Elisabad, and Don Quixote's scrupulous observance of what was due to chivalry, the tale was left unfinished, as this history has already recorded; but now fortunately the mad fit kept off, and allowed him to tell it to the end; and so, coming to the incident of the note which Don Fernando had found in the volume of *Amadis of Gaul*, Cardenio said that he remembered it perfectly and that it was in these words:

Luscinda to Cardenio

Every day I discover merits in you that oblige and compel me to hold you in higher estimation; so if you desire to relieve me of this obligation without cost to my honor, you may easily do so. I have a father who knows you and loves me dearly, who without putting any constraint on my inclination will grant what will be reasonable for you to have, if it be that you value me as you say and as I believe you do.

By this letter I was induced, as I told you, to demand Luscinda for my wife, and it was through it that Luscinda came to be regarded by Don Fernando as one of the most discreet and prudent women of the day, and this letter it was that suggested his design of ruining me before mine could be carried

into effect. I told Don Fernando that all Luscinda's father was waiting for was that mine should ask her of him, which I did not dare to suggest to him, fearing that he would not consent to do so; not because he did not know perfectly well the rank, goodness, virtue, and beauty of Luscinda, and that she had qualities that would do honor to any family in Spain, but because I was aware that he did not wish me to marry so soon, before seeing what the duke Ricardo would do for me. In short, I told him I did not venture to mention it to my father, as well on account of that difficulty, as of many others that discouraged me, though I knew not well what they were, only that it seemed to me that what I desired was never to come to pass. To all this Don Fernando answered that he would take it upon himself to speak to my father, and persuade him to speak to Luscinda's father. O, ambitious Marius! O, cruel Catiline! O, wicked Sulla! O, perfidious Ganelon! O, treacherous Vellido! O, vindictive Julian! O, covetous Judas! Traitor, cruel, vindictive, and perfidious, wherein had this poor wretch failed in his fidelity, who with such frankness showed thee the secrets and the joys of his heart? What offence did I commit? What words did I utter, or what counsels did I give that had not the furtherance of thy honor and welfare for their aim? But, woe is me, wherefore do I complain? For sure it is that when misfortunes spring from the stars, descending from on high they fall upon us with such fury and violence that no power on earth can check their course nor human device stay their coming. Who could have thought that Don Fernando, a high-born gentleman, intelligent, bound to me by gratitude for my services, one that could win the object of his love wherever he might set his affections, could have become so morbid, as they say, as to rob me of my one ewe lamb that was not even yet in my possession? But laying aside these useless and unavailing reflections, let us take up the broken thread of my unhappy story.

To proceed, then: Don Fernando finding my presence an obstacle to the execution of his treacherous and wicked design, resolved to send me to his elder brother under the pretext of asking money from him to pay for six horses which, purposely, and with the sole object of sending me away that he might the better carry out his infernal scheme, he had purchased the very day he offered to speak to my father, and the price of which he now desired me to fetch. Could I have anticipated this treachery? Could I by any chance have suspected it? Nay; so far from that, I offered with the greatest pleasure to go at once, in my satisfaction at the good bargain that had been made. That night I spoke with Luscinda, and told her what had been agreed upon with Don Fernando, and how I had strong hopes of our fair and reasonable wishes being realized. She, as unsuspicious as I was of the treachery of Don Fernando, bade me try to return speedily, as she believed the fulfilment of our desires would be delayed only so long as my father put off speaking to hers. I know not why it was that on saying this to me her eyes filled with tears, and there came a lump in her throat that prevented her from uttering a word of many more that it seemed to me she was striving to say to me. I was astonished at this unusual turn, which I never before observed in her, for we always conversed, whenever good fortune and my ingenuity gave us the chance, with the greatest gayety and cheerfulness, without mingling tears, sighs, jealousies, doubts, or fears with our words; it was all on my part a eulogy of my good fortune that Heaven should have given her to me for my mistress; I glorified her beauty, I extolled her worth and her understanding; and she paid me back by praising in me what in her love for me she thought worthy of praise; and besides we had a hundred thousand trifles and doings of our neighbors and acquaintances to talk about, and the utmost extent of my boldness was to take, almost by force, one of her fair white hands and carry it to my lips, as well as the closeness of the low grating that separated us allowed me. But the night before the unhappy day of my departure she wept, she moaned, she sighed, and she withdrew leaving me filled with perplexity and amazement, overwhelmed at the sight of such strange and affecting signs of grief and sorrow in Luscinda; but not to dash my hopes I ascribed it all to the depth of her love for me and the pain that separation gives those who love tenderly. At last I took my departure, sad and dejected, my heart filled with fancies and suspicions, but not knowing well what it was I suspected or fancied; plain omens pointing to the sad event and misfortune that was awaiting me.

I reached the place whither I had been sent, gave the letter to Don Fernando's brother, and was kindly received but not promptly dismissed, for he desired me to wait, very much against my will, eight days in some place where the duke his father was not likely to see me, as his brother wrote that the money was to be sent without his knowledge; all of which was a scheme of the treacherous Don Fernando, for his brother had no want of money to enable him to despatch me at once.

The command was one that exposed me to the temptation of disobeying it, as it seemed to me impossible to endure life for so many days separated from Luscinda, especially after leaving her in the sorrowful mood I have described to you; nevertheless as a dutiful servant I obeyed, though I felt it would be at the cost of my well-being. But four days later there came a man in quest of me with a letter which he gave me, and which by the address I perceived to be from Luscinda, as the writing was hers. I opened it with fear and trepidation, persuaded that it must be something serious that had impelled her to write to me when at a distance, as she seldom did so when I was near. Before reading it I asked the man who it was that had given it to him, and how long he had been upon the road; he told me that as he happened to be passing through one of the streets of the city at the hour of noon, a very beautiful lady called to him from a window, and with tears in her eyes said to him hurriedly, "Brother, if

you are, as you seem to be, a Christian, for the love of God I entreat you to have this letter despatched without a moment's delay to the person named in the address, all which is well known, and by this you will render a great service to our Lord; and that you may be at no inconvenience in doing so take what is in this handkerchief"; and said he, "with this she threw me a handkerchief out of the window in which were tied up a hundred reals and this gold ring which I bring here together with the letter I have given you. And then without waiting for any answer she left the window, though not before she saw me take the letter and the handkerchief, and I had by signs let her know that I would do as she bade me; and so, seeing myself so well paid for the trouble I would have in bringing it to you, and knowing by the address that it was to you it was sent (for, señor, I know you very well), and also unable to resist that beautiful lady's tears, I resolved to trust no one else, but to come myself and give it to you, and in sixteen hours from the time when it was given me I have made the journey, which, as you know, is eighteen leagues."

All the while the good-natured improvised courier was telling me this, I hung upon his words, my legs trembling under me so that I could scarcely stand. However, I opened the letter and read these words:

The promise Don Fernando gave you to urge your father to speak to mine, he has fulfilled much more to his own satisfaction than to your advantage. I have to tell you, señor, that he has demanded me for a wife, and my father, led away by what he considers Don Fernando's superiority over you, has favored his suit so cordially, that in two days hence the betrothal is to take place with such secrecy and so privately the only witnesses are to be the heavens above and a few of the household. Picture to yourself the state I am in; judge if it be urgent for you to come; the issue of the affair will show you whether I love you or not. God grant this may come to your hand before mine shall be forced to link itself with his who keeps so ill the faith that he has pledged.

Such, in brief, were the words of the letter, words that made me set out at once without waiting any longer for reply or money; for I now saw clearly that it was not the purchase of horses but of his own pleasure that had made Don Fernando send me to his brother. The exasperation I felt against Don Fernando, joined with the fear of losing the prize I had won by so many years of love and devotion, lent me wings; so that almost flying I reached home the same day, by the hour which served for speaking with Luscinda. I arrived unobserved, and left the mule on which I had come at the house of the worthy man who had brought me the letter, and fortune was pleased to be for once so kind that I found Luscinda at the grating that was the witness of our loves. She recognized me at once, and I her, but not as she ought to have recognized me, or I her. But who is there in the world that can boast of having fathomed or understood the wavering mind and unstable nature of a woman? Of a truth no one. To proceed: as soon as Luscinda saw me she said, "Cardenio, I am in my bridal dress, and the treacherous Don Fernando and my covetous father are waiting for me in the hall with the other witnesses, who shall be the witnesses of my death before they witness my betrothal. Be not distressed, my friend, but contrive to be present at this sacrifice, and if that can not be prevented by my words, I have a dagger concealed which will prevent more deliberate violence, putting an end to my life and giving thee a first proof of the love I have borne and bear thee." I replied to her distractedly and hastily, in fear lest I should not have time to reply, "May thy words be verified by thy deeds, lady; and if thou hast a dagger to save thy honor, I have a sword to defend thee or kill myself if fortune be against us."

I think she could not have heard all these words, for I perceived that they called her away in haste, as the bridegroom was waiting. Now the night of my sorrow set in, the sun of my happiness went down; I felt my eyes bereft of sight, my mind of reason. I could not enter the house, nor was I capable of any movement; but reflecting how important it was that I should be present at what might take place on the occasion, I nerved myself as best I could and went in, for I well knew all the entrances and outlets; and besides, with the confusion that in secret pervaded the house, no one perceived me, so, without being seen, I found an opportunity of placing myself in the recess formed by a window of the hall itself, and concealed by the ends and borders of two tapestries, from between which I could, without being seen, see all that took place in the room. Who could describe the agitation of heart I suffered as I stood there—the thoughts that came to me—the reflections that passed through my mind? They were such as can not be, nor were it well they should be, told. Suffice it to say that the bridegroom entered the hall in his usual dress, without ornament of any kind; as groomsman he had with him a cousin of Luscinda's, and except the servants of the house there was no one else in the chamber. Soon afterwards Luscinda came out from an ante-chamber, attended by her mother and two of her damsels, arrayed and adorned as became her rank and beauty, and in full festival and ceremonial attire. My anxiety and distraction did not allow me to observe or notice particularly what she wore; I could only perceive the colors, which were crimson and white, and the glitter of the gems and jewels on her head-dress and apparel, surpassed by the rare beauty of her lovely auburn hair that vying with the precious stones and the light of the four torches that stood in the hall shone with a brighter gleam than all. Oh memory, mortal foe of my peace! why bring before me now the incomparable beauty of that adored enemy of mine? Were it not better, cruel memory, to remind me and recall what she then did, that stirred by a wrong so glaring I may seek, if not vengeance now, at least to rid myself of life? Be not weary, sirs, of listening to these digressions: my sorrow is not one of those that can or should be told tersely and briefly, for to me each incident seems to call for many words.

To this the curate replied that not only were they not weary of listening to him, but that the details he mentioned interested them greatly, being of a kind by no means to be omitted and deserving of the same attention as the main story.

To proceed, then (continued Cardenio): all being assembled in the hall, the priest of the parish came in, and as he took the pair by the hand to perform the requisite ceremony, at the words, "Will you, Señora Luscinda, take Señor Don Fernando, here present, for your lawful husband, as the holy Mother Church ordains?" I thrust my head and neck out from between the tapestries, and with eager ears and throbbing heart set myself to listen to Luscinda's answer, awaiting in her reply the sentence of death or the grant of life. Oh, that I had but dared at that moment to rush forward crying aloud, "Luscinda, Luscinda! have a care what thou dost; remember what thou owest me; bethink thee thou art mine and canst not be another's; reflect that thy utterance of 'Yes' and the end of my life will come at the same instant. O, treacherous Don Fernando! robber of my glory, death of my life! what wouldst thou? What seekest thou? Remember that thou canst not as a Christian attain the object of thy wishes, for Luscinda is my bride, and I am her husband!" Fool that I am! now that I am far away, and out of danger, I say I should have done what I did not do: now that I have allowed my precious treasure to be robbed from me, I curse the robber, on whom I might have taken vengeance had I as much heart for it as I have for bewailing my fate; in short, as I was then a coward and a fool, little wonder is it if I am now dying shame-stricken, remorseful, and mad.

The priest stood waiting for the answer of Luscinda, who for a long time withheld it; and just as I thought she was taking out the dagger to save her honor, or struggling for words to make some declaration of the truth on my behalf, I heard her say in a faint and feeble voice, "I will": Don Fernando said the same, and giving her the ring they stood linked by a knot that could never be loosed. The bridegroom then approached to embrace his bride; and she, pressing her hand upon her heart, fell fainting in her mother's arms. It only remains now for me to tell you the state I was in when in that consent that I heard I saw all my hopes mocked, the words and promises of Luscinda proved falsehoods, and the recovery of the prize I had that instant lost rendered impossible forever. I stood stupefied, wholly abandoned, it seemed, by Heaven, declared the enemy of the earth that bore me, the air refusing me breath for my sighs, the water moisture for my tears; it was only the fire that gathered strength so that my whole frame glowed with rage and jealousy. They were all thrown into confusion by Luscinda's fainting, and as her mother was unlacing her to give her air, a sealed paper was discovered in her bosom, which Don Fernando seized at once and began to read by the light of one of the torches. As soon as he had read it he seated himself in a chair leaning his cheek on his hand in the attitude of one in deep thought, without taking any part in the efforts that were being made to recover his bride from her fainting fit.

Seeing all the household in confusion, I ventured to come out regardless whether I were seen or not, and determined if I were, to do some frenzied deed that would prove to all the world the righteous indignation of my breast in the punishment of the treacherous Don Fernando, and even in that of the fickle fainting traitress. But my fate, doubtless reserving me for greater sorrows, if such there be, so ordered it that just then I had enough and to spare of that reason which has since been wanting to me; and so, without seeking to take vengeance on my greatest enemies (which might have been easily taken, as all thought of me was so far from their minds), I resolved to take it upon myself, and on myself to inflict the pain they deserved, perhaps with even greater severity than I should have dealt out to them had I then slain them; for sudden pain is soon over, but that which is protracted by tortures is ever slaying without ending life. In a word, I quitted the house and reached that of the man with whom I had left my mule; I made him saddle it for me, mounted without bidding him farewell, and rode out of the city, like another Lot, not daring to turn my head to look back upon it; and when I found myself alone in the open country, screened by the darkness of the night, and tempted by the stillness to give vent to my grief without apprehension or fear of being heard or seen, then I broke silence and lifted up my voice in maledictions upon Luscinda and Don Fernando, as if I could thus avenge the wrong they had done me. I called her cruel, ungrateful, false, thankless, but above all covetous, since the wealth of my enemy had blinded the eyes of her affection, and turned it from me to transfer it to one to whom fortune had been more generous and liberal. And yet, in the midst of this outburst of execration and upbraiding, I found excuses for her, saying it was no wonder that a young girl in the seclusion of her parents' house, trained and schooled to obey them always, should have been ready to yield to their wishes when they offered her for a husband a gentleman of such distinction, wealth, and noble birth, that if she had refused to accept him she would have been thought out of her senses, or to have set her affection elsewhere, a suspicion injurious to her fair name and fame. But then again, I said, had she declared I was her husband, they would have seen that in choosing me she had not chosen so ill but that they might excuse her, for before Don Fernando had made his offer, they themselves could not have desired, if their desires had been ruled by reason, a more eligible husband for their daughter than I was; and she, before taking the last fatal step of giving her hand, might easily have said that I had already given her mine, for I should have come forward to support any assertion of hers to that effect. In short, I came to the conclusion that feeble love, little reflection, great ambition, and a craving for rank had made her forget the words with which she had deceived me, encouraged and supported by my firm hopes and honorable passion.

Thus soliloquizing and agitated, I journeyed onward for the remainder of the night, and by daybreak I reached one of the passes of these mountains, among which I wandered for three days more without taking any path or road, until I came to some meadows lying on I know not which side of the mountains, and there I inquired of some herdsmen in what direction the most rugged part of the range lay. They told me that it was in this quarter, and I at once directed my course hither, intending to end my life here; but as I was making my way among these crags, my mule dropped dead through fatigue and hunger, or, as I think more likely, in order to have done with such a worthless burden as it bore in me. I was left on foot, worn out, famished, without any one to help me or any thought of seeking help; and so thus I lay stretched on the ground, how long I know not, after which I rose up free from hunger, and found beside me some goatherds, who no doubt were the persons who had relieved me in my need, for they told me how they had found me, and how I had been uttering ravings that showed plainly I had lost my reason; and since then I am conscious that I am not always in full possession of it, but at times so deranged and crazed that I do a thousand mad things, tearing my clothes, crying aloud in these solitudes, cursing my fate, and idly calling on the dear name of her who is my enemy, and only seeking to end my life in lamentation; and when I recover my senses I find myself so exhausted and weary that I can scarcely move. Most commonly my dwelling is the hollow of a cork tree large enough to shelter this miserable body; the herdsmen and goatherds who frequent these mountains, moved by compassion, furnish me with food, leaving it by the wayside or on the rocks, where they think I may perhaps pass and find it; and so, even though I may be then out of my senses, the wants of nature teach me what is required to sustain me, and make me crave it and eager to take it. At other times, so they tell me when they find me in a rational mood, I sally out upon the road, and though they would gladly give it me, I snatch food by force from the shepherds bringing it from the village to their huts. Thus do I pass the wretched life that remains to me, until it be Heaven's will to bring it to a close, or so to order my memory that I no longer recollect the beauty or treachery of Luscinda, or the wrong done me by Don Fernando; for if it will do this without depriving me of life, I will turn my thoughts into some better channel; if not, I can only implore it to have full mercy on my soul, for in myself I feel no power or strength to release my body from this strait in which I have of my own accord chosen to place it.

Such, sirs, is the dismal story of my misfortune: say if it be one that can be told with less emotion than you have seen in me; and do not trouble yourselves with urging or pressing upon me what reason suggests as likely to serve for my relief, for it will avail me as much as the medicine prescribed by a wise physician avails the sick man who will not take it. I have no wish for health without Luscinda; and since it is her pleasure to be another's, when she is or should be mine, let it be mine to be a prey to misery when I might have enjoyed happiness. She by her fickleness strove to make my ruin irretrievable; I will strive to gratify her wishes by seeking destruction; and it will show generations to come that I alone was deprived of that of which all others in misfortune have a superabundance, for to them the impossibility of being consoled is itself a consolation, while to me it is the cause of greater sorrows and sufferings, for I think that even in death there will not be an end of them.

Here Cardenio brought to a close his long discourse and story, as full of misfortune as it was of love; but just as the curate was going to address some words of comfort to him, he was stopped by a voice that reached his ear, saying in melancholy tones what will be told in the Fourth Part of this narrative: for at this point the sage and sagacious historian, Cid Hamet Benengeli, brought the third to a conclusion.

Chapter 28

Which treats of the strange and delightful adventure that befell the Curate and the Barber in the same Sierra

HAPPY and fortunate were the times when that most daring knight Don Quixote of La Mancha was sent into the world; for by reason of his having formed a resolution so honorable as that of seeking to revive and restore to the world the long-lost and almost defunct order of knight-errantry, we now enjoy in this age of ours, so poor in light entertainment, not only the charm of his veracious history, but also of the tales and episodes contained in it, which are, in a measure, no less pleasing, ingenious, and truthful, than the history itself; which, resuming its thread, carded, spun, and wound, relates that just as the curate was going to offer consolation to Cardenio, he was interrupted by a voice that fell upon his ear saying in plaintive tones:

"O God! is it possible I have found a place that may serve as a secret grave for the weary load of this body that I support so unwillingly? If the solitude these mountains promise deceive me not, it is so; ah! woe is me! how much more grateful to my mind will be the society of these rocks and brakes that permit me to complain of my misfortune to Heaven, than that of any human being, for there is none on earth to look to for counsel in doubt, comfort in sorrow, or relief in distress!"

All this was heard distinctly by the curate and those with him, and as it seemed to them to be uttered close by, as indeed it was, they got up to look for the speaker, and before they had gone twenty paces they discovered behind a rock, seated at the foot of an ash tree, a youth in the dress of a peasant, whose face they were unable at the moment to see as he was leaning forward, bathing his feet in the brook that flowed past. They approached so silently that he did not perceive them, being fully occupied in bathing his feet, which were so fair that they looked like two pieces of shining crystal embedded among the stones of the brook. The whiteness and beauty of these feet struck them with surprise, for they did not seem to have been made to crush clods or to follow the plough and the oxen as their owner's dress suggested; and so, finding they had not been noticed, the curate, who was in front, made a sign to the other two to conceal themselves behind some fragments of rock that lay there; which they did, observing closely what the youth was about. He had on a loose double-skirted gray jacket bound tight to his body with a white cloth; he wore besides breeches and gaiters of gray cloth, and on his head a gray montera; and he had the gaiters turned up as far as the middle of the leg, which verily seemed to be of pure alabaster.

As soon as he had done bathing his beautiful feet, he wiped them with a towel he took from under the montera, on taking off which he raised his face, and those who were watching him had an opportunity of seeing a beauty so exquisite that Cardenio said to the curate in a whisper, "As this is not Luscinda, it is no human creature but a divine being."

The youth then took off the montera, and shaking his head from side to side there broke loose and spread out a mass of hair that the beams of the sun might have envied; by this they knew that what had seemed a peasant was a lovely woman, nay the most beautiful the eyes of two of them had ever beheld, or even Cardenio's if they had not seen and known Luscinda, for he afterwards declared that only the beauty of Luscinda could compare with this. The long auburn tresses not only covered her shoulders, but such was their length and abundance, concealed her all round beneath their masses, so that except the feet nothing of her form was visible. She now used her hands as a comb, and if her feet had seemed like bits of crystal in the water, her hands looked like pieces of driven snow among her locks; all which increased not only the admiration of the three beholders, but their anxiety to learn who she was. With this object they resolved to show themselves, and at the stir they made in getting upon their feet the fair damsel raised her head, and parting her hair from before her eyes with both hands, she looked to see who had made the noise, and the instant she perceived them she started to her feet, and without waiting to put on her shoes or gather up her hair, hastily snatched up a bundle as though of clothes that she had beside her, and, scared and alarmed, endeavored to take flight; but before she had gone six paces she fell to the ground, her delicate feet being unable to bear the roughness of the stones; seeing which, the three hastened towards her, and the curate addressing her first said, "Stay, señora, whoever you may be, for those whom you see here only desire to be of service to you; you have no need to attempt a flight so heedless, for neither can your feet bear it, nor we allow it."

Taken by surprise and bewildered, she made no reply to these words. They, however, came towards her, and the curate taking her hand went on to say, "What your dress would hide, señora, is made known to us by your hair; a clear proof that it can be no trifling cause that has disguised your beauty in a garb so unworthy of it, and sent it into solitudes like these where we have had the good fortune to find you, if not to relieve your distress, at least to offer you comfort; for no distress, as long as life lasts, can be so oppressive or reach such a height as to make the sufferer refuse to listen to comfort offered with good intention. And so, señora, or señor, or whatever you prefer to be, dismiss the fears that our appearance has caused you and make us acquainted with your good or evil fortunes, for from all of us together, or from each one of us, you will receive sympathy in your trouble."

While the curate was speaking, the disguised damsel stood as if spell-bound, looking at them without opening her lips or uttering a word, just like a village rustic to whom something strange that he has never seen before has been suddenly shown; but on the curate addressing some further words to the same effect to her, sighing deeply she broke silence and said, "Since the solitude of these mountains has been unable to conceal me, and the escape of my dishevelled tresses will not allow my tongue to deal in falsehoods, it would be idle for me now to make any further pretence of what, if you were to believe me, you would believe more out of courtesy than for any other reason. This being so, I say I thank you, sirs, for the offer you made me, which places me under the obligation of complying with the request you have made of me; though I fear the account I shall give you of my misfortunes will excite in you as much concern as compassion, for you will be unable to suggest anything to remedy them or any consolation to alleviate them. However, that my honor may not be left a matter of doubt in your minds, now that you have discovered me to be a woman, and see that I am young, alone, and in this dress, things that taken together or separately would be enough to destroy any good name, I feel bound to tell what I would willingly keep secret if I could."

All this she who was now seen to be a lovely woman delivered without any hesitation, with so much ease and in so sweet a voice that they were not less charmed by her intelligence than by her beauty, and as they again repeated their offers and entreaties to her to fulfil her promise, she without further pressing, first modestly covering her feet and gathering up her hair, seated herself on a stone with the three placed around her, and, after an effort to restrain some tears that came to her eyes, in a clear and steady voice began her story thus:

In this Andalusia there is a town from which a duke takes a title which makes him one of those that are called Grandees of Spain. This nobleman has two sons, the elder heir to his dignity and apparently to his good qualities; the younger heir to I know not what, unless it be the treachery of Vellido and the falsehood of Ganelon. My parents are this lord's vassals, lowly in origin, but so wealthy that if birth had conferred as much on them as fortune, they would have had nothing left to desire, nor should I have had reason to fear trouble like that in which I find myself now; for it may be that my ill-fortune came of theirs in not having been nobly born. It is true they are not so low that they have any reason to be ashamed of their condition, but neither are they so high as to remove from my mind the impression that my mishap comes of their humble birth. They are, in short, peasants, plain homely people, without any taint of disreputable blood, and, as the saying is, old rusty Christians, but so rich that by their wealth and free-handed way of life they are coming by degrees to be considered gentlefolk by birth, and even by position; though the wealth and nobility they thought most of was having me for their daughter; and as they have no other child to make their heir, and are affectionate parents, I was one of the most indulged daughters that ever parents indulged.

I was the mirror in which they beheld themselves, the staff of their old age, and the object in which, with submission to Heaven, all their wishes centred, and mine were in accordance with theirs, for I knew their worth; and as I was mistress of their hearts, so was I also of their possessions. Through me they engaged or dismissed their servants; through my hands passed the accounts and returns of what was sown and reaped; the oil-mills, the wine-presses, the count of the flocks and herds, the beehives, all in short that a rich farmer like my father has or can have, I had under my care, and I acted as steward and mistress with an assiduity on my part and satisfaction on theirs that I can not well describe to you. The leisure hours left to me after I had given the requisite orders to the shepherds, head men, and laborers, I passed in such employments as are not only allowable but necessary for young girls, those that the needle, embroidery cushion, and spinning wheel usually afford, and if to refresh my mind I quitted them for a while, I found recreation in reading some devotional book or playing the harp, for experience taught me that music soothes the troubled mind and relieves weariness of spirit. Such was the life I led in my parents' house, and if I have depicted it thus minutely, it is not out of ostentation, or to let you know that I am rich, but that you may see how, without any fault of mine, I have fallen from the happy condition I have described, to the misery I am in at present. The truth is that while I was leading this busy life, in a retirement that might compare with that of a monastery, and unseen as I thought by any except the servants of the house (for when I went to Mass it was so early in the morning, and I was so closely attended by my mother and the women of the household, and so thickly veiled and so shy, that my eyes scarcely saw more ground than I trod on), in spite of all this, the eyes of love, or idleness, more properly speaking, that the lynx's can not rival, discovered me, with the help of the assiduity of Don Fernando; for that is the name of the younger son of the duke I told you of.

The moment the speaker mentioned the name of Don Fernando, Cardenio changed color and broke into a sweat, with such signs of emotion that the curate and the barber, who observed it, feared that one of the mad fits which they heard attacked him sometimes was coming upon him; but Cardenio showed no further agitation and remained quiet, regarding the peasant girl with fixed attention, for he began to suspect who she was. She, however, without noticing the excitement of Cardenio, continuing her story, went on to say:

And they had hardly discovered me, when, as he owned afterwards, he was smitten with a violent love for me, as the manner in which it displayed itself plainly showed. But to shorten the long recital of my woes, I will pass over in silence all the artifices employed by Don Fernando for declaring his passion for me. He bribed all the household, he gave and offered gifts and presents to my parents; every day was like a holiday or a merrymaking in our street; by night no one could sleep for the music; the love letters that used to come to my hand no one knew how, were innumerable, full of tender pleadings and pledges, containing more promises and oaths than there were letters in them; all which not only did not soften me, but hardened my heart against him, as if he had been my mortal enemy, and as if everything he did to make me yield were done with the opposite intention. Not that the high-bred bearing of Don Fernando was disagreeable to me, or that I found his importunities wearisome; for it gave me a certain sort of satisfaction to find myself so sought and prized by a gentleman of such distinction, and I was not displeased at seeing my praises in his letters (for however ugly we women may be, it seems to me it always pleases us to hear ourselves called beautiful) but that my own sense of right was opposed to all this, as well as the repeated advice of my parents, who now very plainly perceived Don Fernando's purpose, for he cared very little if all the world knew it. They told me they trusted and confided their honor and good name to my virtue and rectitude alone, and bade me consider the disparity between Don Fernando and myself, from which I might conclude that his intentions, whatever he might say to the contrary, had for their aim his own pleasure rather than my advantage; and if I were at all desirous of opposing an obstacle to his unreasonable suit, they were ready, they said, to marry me at once to any one I preferred, either among the leading people of our own town, or of any of those in the neighborhood; for with their wealth and my good name, a match might be looked for in any quarter. This offer, and their sound advice, strengthened my resolution, and I never gave Don Fernando a word in reply that could hold out to him any hope of success, however remote.

All this caution of mine, which he must have taken for coyness, had apparently the effect of increasing his wanton appetite—for that is the name I give to his passion for me; had it been what he declared it to be, you would not know of it now, because there would have been no occasion to tell you of it. At length he learned that my parents were contemplating marriage for me in order to put an end to his hopes of obtaining possession of me, or at least to secure additional protectors to watch over me, and this intelligence or suspicion made him act as you shall hear. One night, as I was in my chamber with no other companion than a damsel who waited on me, with the doors carefully locked lest my honor should be imperilled through any carelessness, I know not nor can I conceive how it happened, but, with all this seclusion and these precautions, and in the solitude and silence of my retirement, I found him standing before me, a vision that so astounded me that it deprived my eyes of sight, and my tongue of speech. I had no power to utter a cry, nor, I think, did he give me time to utter one, as he immediately approached me, and taking me in his arms (for, overwhelmed as I was, I was powerless, I say, to help myself), he began to make such professions to me, that I know not how falsehood could have had the power of dressing them up to seem so like truth; and the traitor contrived that his tears should vouch for his words, and his sighs for his sincerity.

I, a poor young creature, the only daughter of the house, ill versed in such things, began, I know not how, to think all these lying protestations true, though without being moved by his sighs and tears to anything more than pure compassion; and so, as the first feeling of bewilderment passed away, and I began in some degree to recover myself, I said to him with more courage than I thought I could have possessed, "If, as I am now in your arms, señor, I were in the claws of a fierce lion, and my deliverance could be procured by doing or saying anything to the prejudice of my honor, it would no more be in my power to do it or say it, than it would be possible that what was should not have been; so then, if you hold my body clasped in your arms, I hold my soul secured by virtuous intentions, very different from yours, as you will see if you attempt to carry them into effect by force. I am your vassal, but I am not your slave; your nobility neither has nor should have any right to dishonor or degrade my humble birth; and low-born peasant as I am, I have my self-respect as much as you, a lord and gentleman: with me your violence will be to no purpose, your wealth will have no weight, your words will have no power to deceive me, nor your sighs or tears to soften me: were I to see any of the things I speak of in him whom my parents gave me as a husband, his will should be mine, and mine should be bounded by his; and my honor being preserved even though my inclinations were not gratified, I would willingly yield him what you, señor, would now obtain by force; and this I say lest you should suppose that any but my lawful husband shall ever win anything of me."—"If that," said this disloyal gentleman, "be the only scruple you feel, fairest Dorothea" (for that is the name of this unhappy being), "see here I give you my hand to be yours, and let Heaven, from which nothing is hid, and this image of Our Lady you have here, be witnesses of this pledge."

When Cardenio heard her say she was called Dorothea, he showed fresh agitation and felt convinced of the truth of his former suspicion, but he was unwilling to interrupt the story, and wished to hear the end of what he already all but knew, so he merely said, "What! is Dorothea your name, señora? I have heard of another of the same name who can perhaps match your misfortunes. But proceed; by-and-by I may tell you something that will astonish you as much as it will excite your compassion."

Dorothea was struck by Cardenio's words as well as by his strange and miserable attire, and begged him if he knew anything concerning her to tell it to her at once, for if fortune had left her any blessing it was courage to bear whatever calamity might fall upon her, as she felt sure in her own mind that none could reach her capable of increasing in any degree what she endured already.

"I would not let the occasion pass, señora," replied Cardenio, "of telling you what I think, if what I suspect were the truth, but so far there has been no opportunity, nor is it of any importance to you to know it."

"Be it as it may!" replied Dorothea. "To go on with my story":

Don Fernando, taking an image that stood in the chamber, placed it as a witness of our betrothal, and with the most binding words and extravagant oaths gave me his promise to become my husband; though before he had made an end of pledging himself I bade him consider well what he was doing, and think of the anger his father would feel at seeing him married to a peasant girl and one of his vassals; I told him not to let my beauty, such as it was, blind him, for that was not enough to furnish an excuse for his transgression; and if in the love he bore me he wished to do me any kindness, it would be to leave my lot to follow its course at the level my condition required; for marriages so unequal never brought happiness, nor did they continue long to afford the enoyment they began with.

All this that I have now repeated I said to him, and much more which I can not recollect; but it had no effect in inducing him to forego his purpose; he who has no intention of paying does not trouble himself about difficulties when he is striking the bargain. At the same time I argued the matter briefly in my own mind, saying to myself, "I shall not be the first who has risen through marriage from a lowly to a lofty station, nor will Don Fernando be the first whom beauty or, as is more likely, a blind attachment, has led to mate himself below his rank. Then, since I am introducing no new usage or practice, I may as well avail myself of the honor that chance offers me, for even though his inclination for me should not outlast the attainment of his wishes, I shall be, after all, his wife before God. And if I strive to repel him by scorn, I can see that, fair means failing, he is in a mood to use force, and I shall be left dishonored and without any means of proving my innocence to those who can not know how innocently I have come to be in this position; for what arguments would persuade my parents and others that this gentleman entered my chamber without my consent?"

All these questions and answers passed through my mind in a moment; but the oaths of Don Fernando, the witnesses he appealed to, the tears he shed, and lastly the charms of his person and his high-bred grace, which, accompanied by such signs of genuine love, might well have conquered a heart even more free and coy than mine—these were the things that more than all began to influence me and lead me unawares to my ruin. I called my waiting-maid to me, that there might be a witness on earth besides those in heaven, and again Don Fernando renewed and repeated his oaths, invoked as witnesses fresh saints in addition to the former ones, called down upon himself a thousand curses hereafter should he fail to keep his promise, shed more tears, redoubled his sighs and pressed me closer in his arms, from which he had never allowed me to escape; and so I was left by my maid, and ceased to be one, and he became a traitor and a perjured man.

The day which followed the night of my misfortune did not come so quickly, I imagine, as Don Fernando wished, for when desire had attained its object, the greatest pleasure is to fly from the scene of pleasure. I say so because Don Fernando made all haste to leave me, and by the adroitness of my maid, who was indeed the one who had admitted him, gained the street before daybreak; but on taking leave of me he told me, though not with as much earnestness and fervor as when he came, that I might rest assured of his faith and of the sanctity and sincerity of his oaths; and to confirm his words he drew a rich ring off his finger and placed it upon mine. He then took his departure and I was left, I know not whether sorrowful or happy; all I can say is, I was left agitated and troubled in mind and almost bewildered by what had taken place, and I had not the spirit, or else it did not occur to me, to chide my maid for the treachery she had been guilty of in concealing Don Fernando in my chamber; for as yet I was unable to make up my mind whether what had befallen me was for good or evil. I told Don Fernando at parting, that as I was now his, he might see me on other nights in the same way, until it should be his pleasure to let the matter become known; but, except the following night, he came no more, nor for more than a month could I catch a glimpse of him in the street or in church, while I wearied myself with watching for one; although I knew he was in the town, and almost every day went out hunting, a pastime he was very fond of. I remember well how sad and dreary those days and hours were to me; I remember well how I began to doubt as they went by, and even to lose confidence in the faith of Don Fernando; and I remember, too, how my maid heard those words in reproof of her audacity that she had not heard before, and how I was forced to put a constraint on my tears and on

the expression of my countenance, not to give my parents cause to ask me why I was so melancholy, and drive me to invent falsehoods in reply. But all this was suddenly brought to an end, for the time came when all such considerations were disregarded, and there was no further question of honor, when my patience gave way and the secret of my heart became known abroad. The reason was that a few days later it was reported in the town that Don Fernando had been married in a neighboring city to a maiden of rare beauty, the daughter of parents of distinguished position, though not so rich that her portion would entitle her to look for so brilliant a match; it was said, too, that her name was Luscinda, and that at the betrothal some strange things had happened.

Cardenio heard the name of Luscinda, but he only shrugged his shoulders, bit his lips, bent his brows, and before long two streams of tears escaped from his eyes. Dorothea, however, did not interrupt her story, but went on in these words:

This sad intelligence reached my ears, and, instead of being struck with a chill, with such wrath and fury did my heart burn that I scarcely restrained myself from rushing out into the streets, crying aloud and proclaiming openly the perfidy and treachery of which I was the victim; but this transport of rage was for the time checked by a resolution I formed, to be carried out the same night, and that was to assume this dress, which I got from a servant of my father's, one of the *zagals,* as they are called in farmhouses, to whom I confided the whole of my misfortune, and whom I entreated to accompany me to the city where I heard my enemy was. He, though he remonstrated with me for my boldness, and condemned my resolution, when he saw me bent upon my purpose, offered to bear me company, as he said, to the end of the world. I at once packed up in a linen pillow-case a woman's dress, and some jewels and money to provide for emergencies, and in the silence of the night, without letting my treacherous maid know, I sallied forth from the house, accompanied by my servant and abundant anxieties, and on foot set out for the city, but borne, as it were, on wings by my eagerness to reach it, if not to prevent what I presumed to be already done, at least to call upon Don Fernando to tell me with what conscience he had done it. I reached my destination in two days and a half, and on entering the city inquired for the house of Luscinda's parents. The first person I asked gave me more in reply than I sought to know; he showed me the house, and told me all that had occurred at the betrothal of the daughter of the family, an affair of such notoriety in the city that it was the talk of every knot of idlers in the street. He said that on the night of Don Fernando's betrothal with Luscinda, as soon as she had consented to be his bride by saying "Yes," she was taken with a sudden fainting fit, and that on the bridegroom approaching to unlace the bosom of her dress to give her air, he found a paper in her own handwriting, in which she said and declared that she could not be Don Fernando's bride, because she was already Cardenio's, who, according to the man's account, was a gentleman of distinction in the same city; and that if she had accepted Don Fernando, it was only in obedience to her parents. In short, he said, the words of the paper made it clear she meant to kill herself on the completion of the betrothal, and gave her reasons for putting an end to herself; all which was confirmed, it was said, by a dagger they found somewhere in her clothes. On seeing this, Don Fernando, persuaded that Luscinda had befooled, slighted, and trifled with him, assailed her before she had recovered from her swoon, and tried to stab her with the dagger that had been found, and would have succeeded had not her parents and those who were present prevented him. It was said, moreover, that Don Fernando went away at once, and that Luscinda did not recover from her prostration until the next day, when she told her parents how she was really the bride of that Cardenio I have mentioned. I learned besides that Cardenio, according to report, had been present at the betrothal; and that upon seeing her betrothed contrary to his expectation, he had quitted the city in despair, leaving behind him a letter declaring the wrong Luscinda had done him, and his intention of going where no one should ever see him again. All this was a matter of notoriety in the city, and every one spoke of it; especially when it became known that Luscinda was missing from her father's house and from the city, for she was not to be found anywhere, to the distraction of her parents, who knew not what steps to take to recover her. What I learned revived my hopes, and I was better pleased not to have found Don Fernando than to find him married, for it seemed to me that the door was not yet entirely shut upon relief in my case, and I thought that perhaps Heaven had put this impediment in the way of the second marriage, to lead him to recognize his obligations under the former one, and reflect that as a Christian he was bound to consider his soul above all human objects. All this passed through my mind, and I strove to comfort myself without comfort, indulging in faint and distant hopes of cherishing that life that I now abhor.

But while I was in the city, uncertain what to do, as I could not find Don Fernando, I heard notice given by the public crier offering a great reward to any one who should find me, and giving the particulars of my age and of the very dress I wore; and I heard it said that the lad who came with me had taken me away from my father's house; a thing that cut me to the heart, showing how low my good name had fallen, since it was not enough that I should lose it by my flight, but they must add with whom I had fled, and that one so much beneath me and so unworthy of my consideration. The instant I heard the notice I quitted the city

with my servant, who now began to show signs of wavering in his fidelity to me, and the same night, for fear of discovery, we entered the most thickly wooded part of these mountains. But, as is commonly said, one evil calls up another, and the end of one misfortune is apt to be the beginning of one still greater, and so it proved in my case; for my worthy servant, until then so faithful and trusty, when he found me in this lonely spot, moved more by his own villainy than by my beauty, sought to take advantage of the opportunity which these solitudes seemed to present him, and with little shame and less fear of God and respect for me, began to make overtures to me; and finding that I replied to the effrontery of his proposals with justly severe language, he laid aside the entreaties which he had employed at first, and began to use violence. But just Heaven, that seldom fails to watch over and aid good intentions, so aided mine that with my slight strength and with little exertion I pushed him over a precipice, where I left him, whether dead or alive I know not; and then, with greater speed than seemed possible in my terror and fatigue, I made my way into the mountains, without any other thought or purpose save that of hiding myself among them, and escaping my father and those despatched in search of me by his orders. It is now I know not how many months since with this object I came here, where I met a herdsman who engaged me as his servant at a place in the heart of this Sierra, and all this time I have been serving him as herd, striving to keep always afield to hide these locks which have now unexpectedly betrayed me. But all my care and pains were unavailing, for my master made the discovery that I was not a man, and harbored the same base designs as my servant; and as fortune does not always supply a remedy in cases of difficulty, and I had no precipice or ravine at hand down which to fling the master and cure his passion, as I had in the servant's case, I thought it a lesser evil to leave him and again conceal myself among these crags, than make trial of my strength and argument with him. So, as I say, once more I went into hiding to seek for some place where I might with sighs and tears implore Heaven to have pity on my misery, and grant me help and strength to escape from it, or let me die among the solitudes, leaving no trace of an unhappy being who, by no fault of hers, has furnished matter for talk and scandal at home and abroad.

Chapter 29

Which treats of the droll device and method adopted to extricate our love-stricken knight from the severe penance he had imposed upon himself

"Such, sirs, is the true story of my sad adventures; judge for yourselves now whether the sighs and lamentations you heard, and the tears that flowed from my eyes, had not sufficient

cause even if I had indulged in them more freely; and if you consider the nature of my misfortune you will see that consolation is idle, as there
is no possible remedy for it. All I ask of you is,
what you may easily and reasonably do, to show
me where I may pass my life unharassed by the
fear and dread of discovery by those who are in
search of me; for though the great love my parents bear me makes me feel sure of being kindly
received by them, so great is my feeling of shame
at the mere thought that I can not present myself before them as they expect, that I had rather
banish myself from their sight forever than look
them in the face with the reflection that they
beheld mine stripped of that purity that they
had a right to expect in me."

With these words she became silent, and the
color that overspread her face showed plainly
the pain and shame she was suffering at heart.
In theirs the listeners felt as much pity as wonder at her misfortunes; but as the curate was
just about to offer her some consolation and advice Cardenio forestalled him, saying, "So then,
señora, you are the fair Dorothea, the only daughter of the rich Clenardo?" Dorothea was astonished at hearing her father's name, and at the
miserable appearance of him who mentioned it,
for it has been already said how wretchedly clad
Cardenio was; so she said to him, "And who
may you be, brother, who seem to know my
father's name so well? For so far, if I remember
rightly, I have not mentioned it in the whole
story of my misfortunes."

"I am that unhappy being, señora," replied
Cardenio, "whom, as you have said, Luscinda
declared to be her husband; I am the unfortunate Cardenio, whom the wrong-doing of him
who has brought you to your present condition
has reduced to the state you see me in, bare,
ragged, bereft of all human comfort, and what
is worse, of reason, for I only possess it when
Heaven is pleased for some short space to restore it to me. I, Dorothea, am he who witnessed the wrong done by Don Fernando,
and waited to hear the 'Yes' uttered by which
Luscinda owned herself his betrothed: I am he
who had not courage enough to see how her
fainting fit ended, or what came of the paper
that was found in her bosom, because my heart
had not the fortitude to endure so many strokes
of ill-fortune at once; and so losing patience I
quitted the house, and leaving a letter with my
host, which I entreated him to place in Luscinda's hands, I betook myself to these solitudes,
resolved to end here the life I hated as if it were
my mortal enemy. But fate would not rid me of

it, contenting itself with robbing me of my reason, perhaps to preserve me for the good fortune
I have had in meeting you; for if that which you
have just told us be true, as I believe it to be, it
may be that Heaven has yet in store for both of
us a happier termination to our misfortunes than
we look for; because, seeing that Luscinda can
not marry Don Fernando, being mine, as she
has herself so openly declared, and that Don
Fernando can not marry her as he is yours, we
may reasonably hope that Heaven will restore
to us what is ours, as it is still in existence and
not yet alienated or destroyed. And as we have
this consolation springing from no very visionary hope or wild fancy, I entreat you, señora, to
form new resolutions in your better mind, as I
mean to do in mine, preparing yourself to look
forward to happier fortunes; for I swear to you
by the faith of a gentleman and a Christian not
to desert you until I see you in possession of
Don Fernando, and if I can not by words induce
him to recognize his obligation to you, in that
case to avail myself of the right which my rank
as a gentleman gives me, and with just cause
challenge him on account of the injury he has
done you, not regarding my own wrongs, which
I shall leave to Heaven to avenge, while I on
earth devote myself to yours."

Cardenio's words completed the astonishment
of Dorothea, and not knowing how to return
thanks for such an offer, she attempted to kiss
his feet; but Cardenio would not permit it, and
the licentiate replied for both, commended the
sound reasoning of Cardenio, and lastly, begged,
advised, and urged them to come with him to
his village, where they might furnish themselves
with what they needed, and take measures to
discover Don Fernando, or restore Dorothea to
her parents, or do what seemed to them most advisable. Cardenio and Dorothea thanked him,
and accepted the kind offer he made them; and
the barber, who had been listening to all attentively and in silence, on his part said some kindly words also, and with no less good-will than
the curate offered his services in any way that
might be of use to them. He also explained to
them in a few words the object that had brought
them there, and the strange nature of Don
Quixote's madness, and how they were waiting
for his squire, who had gone in search of him.
Like the recollection of a dream, the quarrel he
had had with Don Quixote came back to Cardenio's memory, and he described it to the
others; but he was unable to say what the
dispute was about.

At this moment they heard a shout, and recgnized it as coming from Sancho Panza, who, not finding them where he had left them, was calling aloud to them. They went to meet him, and in answer to their inquiries about Don Quixote, he told them how he had found him stripped to his shirt, lank, yellow, half dead with hunger, and sighing for his lady Dulcinea; and although he had told him that she commanded him to quit that place and come to El Toboso, where she was expecting him, he had answered that he was determined not to appear in the presence of her beauty until he had done deeds to make him worthy of her favor; and if this went on, Sancho said, he ran the risk of not becoming an emperor as in duty bound, or even an archbishop, which was the least he could be; for which reason they ought to consider what was to be done to get him away from there. The licentiate in reply told him not to be uneasy, for they would fetch him away in spite of himself. He then told Cardenio and Dorothea what they had proposed to do to cure Don Quixote, or at any rate take him home; upon which Dorothea said that she could play the distressed damsel better than the barber; especially as she had there the dress in which to do it to the life, and that they might trust to her acting the part in every particular requisite for carrying out their scheme, for she had read a great many books of chivalry, and knew exactly the style in which afflicted damsels begged boons of knights-errant.

"In that case," said the curate, "there is nothing more required than to set about it at once, for beyond a doubt, fortune is declaring itself in our favor, since it has so unexpectedly begun to open a door for your relief, and smoothed the way for us to our object."

Dorothea then took out of her pillow-case a complete petticoat of some rich stuff, and a green mantle of some other fine material, and a necklace and other ornaments out of a little box, and with these in an instant she so arrayed herself that she looked like a great and rich lady. All this, and more, she said, she had taken from home in case of need, but that until then she had had no occasion to make use of it. They were all highly delighted with her grace, air, and beauty, and declared Don Fernando to be a man of very little taste when he rejected such charms. But the one who admired her most was Sancho Panza, for it seemed to him (what indeed was true) that in all the days of his life he had never seen such a lovely creature; and he asked the curate with great eagerness who this beautiful lady was, and what she wanted in these out-of-the-way quarters.

"This fair lady, brother Sancho," replied the curate, "is no less a personage than the heiress in the direct male line of the great kingdom of Micomicon, who has come in search of your master to beg a boon of him, which is that he redress a wrong or injury that a wicked giant has done her; and from the fame as a good knight which your master has acquired far and wide, this princess has come from Guinea to seek him."

"A lucky seeking and a lucky finding!" said Sancho Panza at this. "Especially if my master has the good fortune to redress that injury, and right that wrong, and kill that son of a bitch of a giant your worship speaks of; as kill him he will if he meets him, unless, indeed, he happens to be a phantom; for my master has no power at all against phantoms. But one thing among others I would beg of you, señor licentiate, which is that, to prevent my master taking a fancy to be an archbishop, for that is what I'm afraid of, your worship would recommend him to marry this princess at once; for in this way he will be disabled from taking archbishop's orders, and will easily come into his empire, and I to the end of my desires; I have been thinking over the matter carefully, and by what I can make out I find it will not do for me that my master should become an archbishop, because I am no good for the Church, as I am married; and for me now, having as I have a wife and children, to set about obtaining dispensations to enable me to hold a place of profit under the Church, would be endless work; so that, señor, it all turns on my master marrying this lady at once—for as yet I do not know her grace, and so I can not call her by her name."

"She is called the Princess Micomicona," said the curate; "for as her kingdom is Micomicon, it is clear that must be her name."

"There's no doubt of that," replied Sancho, "for I have known many to take their name and title from the place where they were born and call themselves Pedro of Alcalá, Juan of Úbeda, and Diego of Valladolid; and it may be that over there in Guinea queens have the same way of taking the names of their kingdoms."

"So it may," said the curate; "and as for your master's marrying, I will do all in my power towards it": with which Sancho was as much pleased as the curate was amazed at his simplicity and at seeing what a hold the absurdities of his master had taken of his fancy, for he had evidently persuaded himself that he was going to be an emperor.

By this time Dorothea had seated herself upon the curate's mule, and the barber had fitted the ox-tail beard to his face, and they now told Sancho to conduct them to where Don Quixote was, warning him not to say that he knew either the licentiate or the barber, as his master's becoming an emperor entirely depended on his not recognizing them; neither the curate nor Cardenio, however, thought fit to go with them; Cardenio lest he should remind Don Quixote of the quarrel he had with him, and the curate as there was no necessity for his presence just yet, so they allowed the others to go on before them, while they themselves followed slowly on foot. The curate did not forget to instruct Dorothea how to act, but she said they might make their minds easy, as everything would be done exactly as the books of chivalry required and described.

They had gone about three-quarters of a league when they discovered Don Quixote in a wilderness of rocks, by this time clothed, but without his armor; and as soon as Dorothea saw him and was told by Sancho that that was Don Quixote, she whipped her palfrey, the well-bearded barber following her, and on coming up to him her squire sprang from his mule and came forward to receive her in his arms, and she dismounting with great ease of manner advanced to kneel before the feet of Don Quixote; and though he strove to raise her up, she without rising addressed him in this fashion, "From this spot I will not rise, O valiant and doughty knight, until your goodness and courtesy grant me a boon, which will redound to the honor and renown of your person and render a service to the most disconsolate and afflicted damsel the sun has seen; and if the might of your strong arm corresponds to the repute of your immortal fame, you are bound to aid the helpless being who, led by the savor of your renowned name, hath come from far distant lands to seek your aid in her misfortunes."

"I will not answer a word, beauteous lady," replied Don Quixote, "nor will I listen to anything further concerning you, until you rise from the earth."

"I will not rise, señor," answered the afflicted damsel, "unless of your courtesy the boon I ask is first granted me."

"I grant and accord it," said Don Quixote, "provided without detriment or prejudice to my king, my country, or her who holds the key of my heart and freedom, it may be complied with."

"It will not be to the detriment or prejudice of any of them, my worthy lord," said the afflicted damsel; and here Sancho Panza drew close to his master's ear and said to him very softly,

"Your worship may very safely grant the boon she asks; it's nothing at all; only to kill a big giant; and she who asks it is the exalted princess Micomicona, queen of the great kingdom of Micomicon of Ethiopia."

"Let her be who she may," replied Don Quixote, "I will do what is my bounden duty, and what my conscience bids me, in conformity with what I have professed"; and turning to the damsel he said, "Let your great beauty rise, for I grant the boon which you would ask of me."

"Then what I ask," said the damsel, "is that your magnanimous person accompany me at once whither I will conduct you, and that you promise not to engage in any other adventure or quest until you have avenged me of a traitor who, against all human and divine law, has usurped my kingdom."

"I repeat that I grant it," replied Don Quixote; "and so, lady, you may from this day forth lay aside the melancholy that distresses you, and let your failing hopes gather new life and strength, for with the help of God and of my arm you will soon see yourself restored to your kingdom, and seated upon the throne of your ancient and mighty realm, notwithstanding and despite of the felons who would gainsay it; and now hand to the work, for, as they say, in delay there is apt to be danger."

The distressed damsel strove with much pertinacity to kiss his hands; but Don Quixote, who was in all things a polished and courteous knight, would by no means allow it, but made her rise and embraced her with great courtesy and politeness, and ordered Sancho to look to Rocinante's girths, and to arm him without a moment's delay. Sancho took down the armor, which was hung up on a tree like a trophy, and having seen to the girths, armed his master in a trice, who as soon as he found himself in his armor exclaimed, "Let us be gone in the name of God to bring aid to this great lady."

The barber was all this time on his knees at great pains to hide his laughter and not let his beard fall, for had it fallen maybe their fine scheme would have come to nothing; but now seeing the boon granted, and the promptitude with which Don Quixote prepared to set out in compliance with it, he rose and took his lady's hand, and between them they placed her upon the mule. Don Quixote then mounted Rocinante, and the barber settled himself on his beast, Sancho being left to go on foot, which made him feel anew the loss of his Dapple, finding the want of him now. But he bore all with cheerfulness, being persuaded that his master had now fairly started and was just on the point of becoming an emperor; for he felt no doubt at all that he would marry this princess, and be king of Micomicon at least. The only thing that troubled him was the reflection that this kingdom was in the land of the blacks, and that the people they would give him for vassals would all be black; but for this he soon found a remedy in his fancy, and said he to himself, "What is it to me if my vassals are blacks? What more have I to do than make a cargo of them and carry them to Spain, where I can sell them and get ready money for them, and with it buy some title or some office in which to live at ease all the days of my life? Not unless you go to sleep and haven't the wit or skill to turn things to account and sell three, six, or ten thousand vassals while you would be talking about it! By God I will stir them up, big and little, or as best I can, and let them be ever so black I'll turn them into white or yellow. Come, come, what a fool I am!" And so he jogged on, so occupied with his thoughts and easy in his mind that he forgot all about the hardship of travelling on foot.

Cardenio and the curate were watching all this from among some bushes, not knowing how to join company with the others; but the curate, who was very fertile in devices, soon hit upon a way of effecting their purpose, and with a pair of scissors that he had in a case he quickly cut off Cardenio's beard, and putting on him a gray jerkin of his own he gave him a black cloak, leaving himself in his breeches and doublet, while Cardenio's appearance was so different from what it had been that he would not have known himself had he seen himself in a mirror. Having effected this, although the others had gone on ahead while they were disguising themselves, they easily came out on the high road before them, for the brambles and awkward places they encountered did not allow those on horseback to go as fast as those on foot. They then posted themselves on the level ground at the outlet of the Sierra, and as soon as Don Quixote and his companions emerged from it the curate began to examine him very deliberately, as though he were striving to recognize him, and after having stared at him for some time he hastened towards him with open arms exclaiming, "A happy meeting with the mirror of chivalry, my worthy compatriot Don Quixote of La Mancha, the flower and cream of high breeding, the protection and relief of the distressed, the quintessence of knights-errant!" And so saying he clasped in his arms the knee of Don Quixote's left leg. He, astonished at the stranger's words and behavior,

looked at him attentively, and at length recognized him, very much surprised to see him there, and made great efforts to dismount. This, however, the curate would not allow, on which Don Quixote said, "Permit me, señor licentiate, for it is not fitting that I should be on horseback and so reverend a person as your worship on foot."

"On no account will I allow it," said the curate; "your mightiness must remain on horseback, for it is on horseback you achieve the greatest deeds and adventures that have been beheld in our age; as for me, an unworthy priest, it will serve me well enough to mount on the haunches of one of the mules of these gentlefolk who accompany your worship, if they have no objection, and I will fancy I am mounted on the steed Pegasus, or on the zebra or charger that bore the famous Moor, Muzaraque, who to this day lies enchanted in the great hill of Zulema, a little distance from the great Complutum."

"Nor even that will I consent to, señor licentiate," answered Don Quixote, "and I know it will be the good pleasure of my lady the princess, out of love for me, to order her squire to give up the saddle of his mule to your worship, and he can sit behind if the beast will bear it."

"It will, I am sure," said the princess, "and I am sure, too, that I need not order my squire, for he is too courteous and too good a Christian to allow a Churchman to go on foot when he might be mounted."

"That he is," said the barber, and at once alighting, he offered his saddle to the curate, who accepted it without much entreaty; but unfortunately as the barber was mounting behind, the mule, being as it happened a hired one, which is the same thing as saying ill-conditioned, lifted its hind hoofs and let fly a couple of kicks in the air, which would have made Master Nicholas wish his expedition in quest of Don Quixote at the devil had they caught him on the breast or head. As it was, they so took him by surprise that he came to the ground, giving so little heed to his beard that it fell off, and all he could do when he found himself without it was to cover his face hastily with both his hands and moan that his teeth were knocked out. Don Quixote when he saw all that bundle of beard detached, without jaws or blood, from the face of the fallen squire, exclaimed, "By the living God, but this is a great miracle! It has knocked off and plucked the beard from his face as if it had been shaved off designedly."

The curate, seeing the danger of discovery

that threatened his scheme, at once pounced upon the beard and hastened with it to where Master Nicholas lay, still uttering moans, and drawing his head to his breast had it on in an instant, muttering over him some words which he said were a certain special charm for sticking on beards, as they would see; and as soon as he had it fixed he left him, and the squire appeared well bearded and whole as before, whereat Don Quixote was beyond measure astonished, and begged the curate to teach him that charm when he had an opportunity, as he was persuaded its virtue must extend beyond the sticking on of beards, for it was clear that where the beard had been stripped off the flesh must have remained torn and lacerated, and when it could heal all that it must be good for more than beards.

"And so it is," said the curate, and he promised to teach it to him on the first opportunity. They then agreed that for the present the curate should mount, and that the three should ride by turns until they reached the inn, which might be about six leagues from where they were.

Three then being mounted, that is to say, Don Quixote, the princess, and the curate, and three on foot, Cardenio, the barber, and Sancho Panza, Don Quixote said to the damsel, "Let your highness, lady, lead on whithersoever is most pleasing to you"; but before she could answer the licentiate said, "Towards what kingdom would your ladyship direct our course? Is it perchance towards that of Micomicon? It must be, or else I know little about kingdoms."

She, being ready on all points, understood that she was to answer "Yes," so she said, "Yes, señor, my way lies towards that kingdom."

"In that case," said the curate, "we must pass right through my village, and there your worship will take the road to Cartagena, where you will be able to embark, fortune favoring; and if the wind be fair and the sea smooth and tranquil, in somewhat less than nine years you may come in sight of the great lake Meona, I mean Meotides, which is little more than a hundred days' journey this side of your highness's kingdom."

"Your worship is mistaken, señor," said she; "for it is not two years since I set out from it, and though I never had good weather, nevertheless I am here to behold what I so longed for, and that is my Lord Don Quixote of La Mancha, whose fame came to my ears as soon as I set foot in Spain, and impelled me to go in search of him, to commend myself to his cour-

tesy, and intrust the justice of my cause to the might of his invincible arm."

"Enough; no more praise," said Don Quixote at this, "for I hate all flattery; and though this may not be so, still language of the kind is offensive to my chaste ears. I will only say, señora, that whether it has might or not, that which it may or may not have shall be devoted to your service even to death; and now, leaving this to its proper season, I would ask the señor licentiate to tell me what it is that has brought him into these parts, alone, unattended, and so lightly clad that I am filled with amazement."

"I will answer that briefly," replied the curate; "you must know then, Señor Don Quixote, that Master Nicholas, our friend and barber, and I were going to Seville to receive some money that a relative of mine who went to the Indies many years ago had sent me, and not such a small sum but that it was over sixty thousand pieces of eight, full weight, which is something; and passing by this place yesterday we were attacked by four footpads, who stripped us even to our beards, and them they stripped off so that the barber found it necessary to put on a false one, and even this young man here"—pointing to Cardenio—"they completely transformed. But the best of it is, the story goes in the neighborhood that those who attacked us belong to a number of galley slaves who, they say, were set free almost on the very same spot by a man of such valor that, in spite of the commissary and of the guards, he released the whole of them; and beyond all doubt he must have been out of his senses, or he must be as great a scoundrel as they, or some man without heart or conscience to let the wolf loose among the sheep, the fox among the hens, the fly among the honey. He has defrauded justice, and opposed his king and lawful master, for he opposed his just commands; he has, I say, robbed the galleys of their feet, stirred up the Holy Brotherhood which for many years past has been quiet, and, lastly, has done a deed by which his soul may be lost without any gain to his body." Sancho had told the curate and the barber of the adventure of the galley slaves, which, so much to his glory, his master had achieved, and hence the curate in alluding to it made the most of it to see what would be said or done by Don Quixote; who changed color at every word, not daring to say that it was he who had been the liberator of those worthy people. "These, then," said the curate, "were they who robbed us; and God in his mercy pardon him who would not let them go to the punishment they deserved."

Chapter 30

Which treats of the address displayed by the fair Dorothea, with other matters pleasant and amusing

THE curate had hardly ceased speaking, when Sancho said, "In faith, then, señor licentiate, he who did that deed was my master; and it was not for want of my telling him beforehand and and warning him to mind what he was about, and that it was a sin to set them at liberty, as they were all on the march there because they were special scoundrels."

"Blockhead!" said Don Quixote at this, "it is no business or concern of knights-errant to inquire whether any persons in affliction, in chains, or oppressed that they may meet on the highroads go that way and suffer as they do because of their faults or because of their misfortunes. It only concerns them to aid them as persons in need of help, having regard to their sufferings and not to their rascalities. I encountered a chaplet or string of miserable and unfortunate people, and did for them what my sense of duty demands of me, and as for the rest be that as it may; and whoever takes objection to it, saving the sacred dignity of the señor licentiate and his honored person, I say he knows little about chivalry and lies like a whoreson villain, and this I will give him to know to the fullest extent with my sword"; and so saying he settled himself in his stirrups and pressed down his morion; for the barber's basin, which according to him was Mambrino's helmet, he carried hanging at the saddlebow until he could repair the damage done to it by the galley slaves.

Dorothea, who was shrewd and sprightly, and by this time thoroughly understood Don Quixote's crazy turn, and that all except Sancho Panza were making game of him, not to be behind the rest said to him, on observing his irritation, "Sir Knight, remember the boon you have promised me, and that in accordance with it you must not engage in any other adventure, be it ever so pressing; calm yourself, for if the licentiate had known that the galley slaves had been set free by that unconquered arm he would have stopped his mouth thrice over, or even bitten his tongue three times before he would have said a word that tended towards disrespect of your worship."

"That I swear heartily," said the curate, "and would have even plucked off a mustache."

"I will hold my peace, señora," said Don Quixote, "and I will curb the natural anger that had arisen in my breast, and will proceed in peace and quietness until I have fulfilled my promise; but in return for this consideration I entreat you to tell me, if you have no objection to do so, what is the nature of your trouble, and how many, who, and what are the persons of whom I am to require due satisfaction, and on whom I am to take vengeance on your behalf?"

"That I will do with all my heart," replied Dorothea, "if it will not be wearisome to you to hear of miseries and misfortunes."

"It will not be wearisome, señora," said Don Quixote; to which Dorothea replied, "Well, if that be so, give me your attention." As soon as she said this, Cardenio and the barber drew close to her side, eager to hear what sort of story the quick-witted Dorothea would invent for herself; and Sancho did the same, for he was as much taken in by her as his master; and she having settled herself comfortably in the saddle, and with the help of coughing and other preliminaries taken time to think, began with great sprightliness of manner in this fashion:

"First of all, I would have you know, sirs, that my name is—" and here she stopped for a moment, for she forgot the name the curate had given her; but he came to her relief, seeing what her difficulty was, and said, "It is no wonder, señora, that your highness should be confused and embarrassed in telling the tale of your misfortunes; for such afflictions often have the effect of depriving the sufferers of memory, so that they do not even remember their own names, as is the case now with your ladyship, who has forgotten that she is called the Princess Micomicona, lawful heiress of the great kingdom of Micomicon; and with this cue your highness may now recall to your sorrowful recollection all you may wish to tell us."

"That is the truth," said the damsel; "but I think from this on I shall have no need of any prompting, and I shall bring my true story safe into port, and here it is. The king my father, who was called Tinacrio the Sapient, was very learned in what they call magic arts, and became aware by his craft that my mother, who was called Queen Jaramilla, was to die before he did, and that soon after he too was to depart this life, and I was to be left an orphan without father or mother. But all this, he declared, did not so much grieve or distress him as his certain knowledge that a prodigious giant, the lord of a great island close to our kingdom, Pandafilando of the Scowl by name—for it is averred that, though his eyes are properly placed and straight, he always looks askew as if he squinted, and this he does out of malignity, to strike fear and terror into those he looks at—that he knew, I say, that this giant on becoming aware of my orphan condition would overrun my kingdom with a mighty force and strip me of all, not leaving me even a small village to shelter me; but that I could avoid all this ruin and misfortune if I were willing to marry him; however, as far as he could see, he never expected that I would consent to a marriage so unequal; and he said no more than the truth in this, for it has never entered my mind to marry that giant, or any other, let him be ever so great or enormous. My father said, too, that when he was dead, and I saw Pandafilando about to invade my kingdom, I was not to wait and attempt to defend myself, for that would be destructive to me, but that I should leave the kingdom entirely open to him if I wished to avoid the death and total destruction of my good and loyal vassals, for there would be no possibility of defending myself against the giant's devilish power; and that I should at once with some of my followers set out for Spain, where I should obtain relief in my distress on finding a certain knight-errant whose fame by that time would extend over the whole kingdom, and who would be called, if I remember rightly, Don Azote or Don Gigote."

" 'Don Quixote,' he must have said, señora," observed Sancho at this, "otherwise called the Knight of the Rueful Countenance."

"That is it," said Dorothea; "he said, moreover, that he would be tall of stature and lank featured; and that on his right side under the left shoulder, or thereabouts, he would have a gray mole with hairs like bristles."

On hearing this, Don Quixote said to his squire, "Here, Sancho my son, bear a hand and help me to strip, for I want to see if I am the knight that sage king foretold."

"What does your worship want to strip for?" said Dorothea.

"To see if I have that mole your father spoke of," answered Don Quixote.

"There is no occasion to strip," said Sancho; "for I know your worship has just such a mole on the middle of your backbone, which is the mark of a strong man."

"That is enough," said Dorothea, "for with friends we must not look too closely into trifles; and whether it be on the shoulder or on the backbone matters little; it is enough if there is a mole, be it where it may, for it is all the same flesh; no doubt my good father hit the truth in every particular, and I have made a lucky hit in commending myself to Don Quixote; for he is the one my father spoke of, as the features of his countenance correspond with those assigned

to this knight by that wide fame he has acquired not only in Spain but in all La Mancha; for I had scarcely landed at Osuna when I heard such accounts of his achievements, that at once my heart told me he was the very one I had come in search of."

"But how did you land at Osuna, señora," asked Don Quixote, "when it is not a seaport?"

But before Dorothea could reply the curate anticipated her, saying, "The princess meant to say that after she had landed at Malaga the first place where she heard of your worship was Osuna."

"That is what I meant to say," said Dorothea.

"And that would be only natural," said the curate. "Will your majesty please proceed?"

"There is no more to add," said Dorothea, "save that in finding Don Quixote I have had such good fortune, that I already reckon and regard myself queen and mistress of my entire dominions, since of his courtesy and magnanimity he has granted me the boon of accompanying me whithersoever I may conduct him, which will be only to bring him face to face with Pandafilando of the Scowl, that he may slay him and restore to me what has been unjustly usurped by him; for all this must come to pass satisfactorily since my good father Tinacrio the Sapient foretold it, who likewise left it declared in writing in Chaldee or Greek characters (for I cannot read them) that if this predicted knight, after having cut the giant's throat, should be disposed to marry me, I was to offer myself at once without demur as his lawful wife, and yield him possession of my kingdom together with my person."

"What thinkest thou now, friend Sancho?" said Don Quixote at this. "Hearest thou that? Did I not tell thee so? See how we have already got a kingdom to govern and a queen to marry?"

"On my oath it is so," said Sancho; "and foul fortune to him who won't marry after slitting Señor Pandahilado's windpipe! And then, how ill-favored the queen is! I wish the fleas in my bed were that sort!" and so saying he cut a couple of capers in the air with every sign of extreme satisfaction, and then ran to seize the bridle of Dorothea's mule, and checking it fell on his knees before her, begging her to give him her hand to kiss in token of his acknowledgment of her as his queen and mistress. Which of the bystanders could have helped laughing to see the madness of the master and the simplicity of the servant? Dorothea therefore gave her hand, and promised to make him a great lord in her kingdom, when Heaven should be so good as to permit her to recover and enjoy it, for which Sancho returned hanks in words that set them all laughing again.

"This, sirs," continued Dorothea, "is my story; t only remains to tell you that of all the attendnts I took with me from my kingdom I have ione left except this well-bearded squire, for all vere drowned in a great tempest we encountered vhen in sight of port; and he and I came to land n a couple of planks as if by a miracle; and inleed the whole course of my life is a miracle nd a mystery as you may have observed; and if have been over minute in any respect or not s precise as I ought, let it be accounted for by vhat the licentiate said at the beginning of my ale, that constant and excessive troubles derive the sufferers of their memory."

"They shall not deprive me of mine, exalted nd worthy princess," said Don Quixote, "howver great and unexampled those which I shall ndure in your service may be; and here I conrm anew the boon I have promised you, and I wear to go with you to the end of the world ntil I find myself in the presence of your fierce nemy, whose haughty head I trust by the aid of God and of my arm to cut off with the edge of his—I will not say good sword, thanks to the Gines de Pasamonte who carried away mine"— this he said between his teeth, and then continied), "and when it has been cut off and you have een put in peaceful possession of your realm it hall be left to your own decision to dispose of our person as may be most pleasing to you; for o long as my memory is occupied, my will enlaved, and my understanding enthralled by her —I say no more—it is impossible for me for a moient to contemplate marriage, even with a Phœix."

The last words of his master about not wantng to marry were so disagreeable to Sancho that aising his voice he exclaimed with great irritaion, "By my oath, Señor Don Quixote, you are iot in your right senses; for how can your worhip possibly object to marrying such an exalted rincess as this? Do you think Fortune will ofer you behind every stone such a piece of luck s is offered you now? Is my lady Dulcinea fairr, perchance? Not she; nor half as fair; and I vill even go so far as to say she does not come p to the shoe of this one here. A poor chance I iave of getting that county I am waiting for if our worship goes looking for dainties in the botom of the sea. In the devil's name, marry, mary, and take this kingdom that comes to hand vithout any trouble, and when you are king iake me a marquis or governor of a province, nd for the rest let the devil take it all."

Don Quixote, when he heard such blasphe-

mies uttered against his lady Dulcinea, could not endure it, and lifting his pike, without saying anything to Sancho or uttering a word, he gave him two such thwacks that he brought him to the ground; and had it not been that Dorothea cried out to him to spare him he would have no doubt taken his life on the spot. "Do you think," he said to him after a pause, "you scurvy clown, that you are to be always interfering with me, and that you are to be always offending and I always pardoning? Don't fancy it, impious scoundrel, for that beyond a doubt thou art, since thou hast set thy tongue going against the peerless Dulcinea. Know you not, lout, vagabond, beggar, that were it not for the might which she infuses into my arm I should not have strength enough to kill a flea? Say, O scoffer with a viper's tongue, what think you has won this kingdom and cut off this giant's head and made you a marquis (for all this I count as already accomplished and decided), but the might of Dulcinea, employing my arm as the instrument of her achievements? She fights in me and conquers in me, and I live and breathe in her, and owe my life and being to her. O whoreson scoundrel, how ungrateful you are, you see yourself raised from the dust of the earth to be a titled lord, and the return you make for so great a benefit is to speak evil of her who has conferred it upon you!"

Sancho was not so stunned but that he heard all his master said, and rising with some degree of nimbleness he ran to place himself behind Dorothea's palfrey, and from that position he said to his master, "Tell me, señor; if your worship is resolved not to marry this great princess, it is plain the kingdom will not be yours; and not being so, how can you bestow favors upon me? That is what I complain of. Let your worship at any rate marry this queen, now that we have got her here as if showered down from heaven, and afterwards you may go back to my lady Dulcinea; for there must have been kings in the world who kept mistresses. As to beauty, I have nothing to do with it; and if the truth is to be told, I like them both; though I have never seen the lady Dulcinea."

"How! never seen her, blasphemous traitor!" exclaimed Don Quixote; "hast thou not just now brought me a message from her?"

"I mean," said Sancho, "that I did not see her so much at my leisure that I could take particular notice of her beauty, or of her charms piecemeal; but taken in the lump I like her."

"Now I forgive thee," said Don Quixote; "and do thou forgive me the injury I have done thee; for our first impulses are not in our control."

"That I see," replied Sancho, "and with me the wish to speak is always the first impulse, and I cannot help saying, once at any rate, what I have on the tip of my tongue."

"For all that, Sancho," said Don Quixote, "take heed of what thou sayest, for the pitcher goes so often to the well—I need say no more to thee."

"Well, well," said Sancho, "God is in heaven, and sees all tricks, and will judge who does most harm, I in not speaking right, or your worship in doing it."

"That is enough," said Dorothea; "run, Sancho, and kiss your lord's hand and beg his pardon, and henceforward be more circumspect with your praise and abuse; and say nothing in disparagement of that lady Tobosa, of whom I know nothing save that I am her servant; and put your trust in God, for you will not fail to obtain some dignity so as to live like a prince."

Sancho advanced hanging his head and begged his master's hand, which Don Quixote with dignity presented to him, giving him his blessing as soon as he had kissed it; he then bade him go on ahead a little, as he had questions to ask him and matters of great importance to discuss with him. Sancho obeyed, and when the two had gone some distance Don Quixote said to him, "Since thy return I have had no opportunity or time to ask thee many particulars touching thy mission and the answer thou hast brought back, and now that chance has granted us the time and opportunity, deny me not the happiness thou canst give me by such good news."

"Let your worship ask what you will," answered Sancho, "for I shall find a way out of all as easily as I found a way in; but I implore you, señor, not to be so revengeful in future."

"Why dost thou say that, Sancho?" said Don Quixote.

"I say it," he returned, "because those blows just now were more because of the quarrel the devil stirred up between us both the other night, than for what I said against my lady Dulcinea, whom I love and reverence as I would a relic—though there is nothing of that about her—merely as something belonging to your worship."

"Say no more on that subject for thy life, Sancho," said Don Quixote, "for it is displeasing to me; I have already pardoned thee for that, and thou knowest the common saying, 'For a fresh sin a fresh penance.'"

While this was going on they saw coming along the road they were following a man mounted on an ass, who when he came close seemed to be a gypsy; but Sancho Panza, whose eyes and heart were there wherever he saw asses, no sooner beheld the man than he knew him to be Gines de Pasamonte; and by the thread of the gypsy he got at the ball, his ass, for it was, in fact, Dapple that carried Pasamonte, who to escape recognition and to sell the ass had disguised himself as a gypsy, being able to speak the gypsy language, and many more, as well as if they were his own. Sancho saw him and recognized him, and the instant he did so he shouted to him "Ginesillo, you thief, give up my treasure, release my life, embarrass thyself not with my repose, quit my ass, leave my delight, be off, rip, get thee gone, thief, and give up what is not thine."

There was no necessity for so many words or objurgations, for at the first one Gines jumped down, and at a trot like racing speed made off and got clear of them all. Sancho hastened to his Dapple, and embracing him he said, "How hast thou fared, my blessing, Dapple of my eyes, my comrade?" all the while kissing him and caressing him as if he were a human being. The ass held his peace, and let himself be kissed and caressed by Sancho without answering a single word. They all came up and congratulated him on having found Dapple, Don Quixote especially, who told him that notwithstanding this he would not cancel the order for the three ass-colts, for which Sancho thanked him.

While the two had been going along conversing in this fashion, the curate observed to Dorothea that she had shown great cleverness, as well in the story itself as in its conciseness, and the resemblance it bore to those of the books of chivalry. She said that she had many times amused herself reading them; but that she did not know the situation of the provinces or seaports, and so she had said at hap-hazard that she had landed at Osuna.

"So I saw," said the curate, "and for that reason I made haste to say what I did, by which it was all set right. But is it not a strange thing to see how readily this unhappy gentleman believes all these figments and lies, simply because they are in the style and manner of the absurdities of his books?"

"So it is," said Cardenio; "and so uncommon and unexampled, that were one to attempt to invent and concoct it in fiction, I doubt if there be any wit keen enough to imagine it."

"But another strange thing about it," said the curate, "is that, apart from the silly things which this worthy gentleman says in connection with his craze, when other subjects are dealt with, he can discuss them in a perfectly rational manner, showing that his mind is quite clear and composed; so that, provided his chivalry is not touched upon, no one would take him to be anything but a man of thoroughly sound understanding."

While they were holding this conversation Don Quixote continued his with Sancho, saying, "Friend Panza, let us forgive and forget as to our quarrels, and tell me now, dismissing anger and irritation, where, how, and when didst thou find Dulcinea? What was she doing? What didst thou say to her? What did she answer? How did she look when she was reading my letter? Who copied it out for thee? and everything in the matter that seems to thee worth knowing, asking, and learning; neither adding nor falsifying to give me pleasure, nor yet curtailing lest you should deprive me of it."

"Señor," replied Sancho, "if the truth is to be told, nobody copied out the letter for me, for I carried no letter at all."

"It is as thou sayest," said Don Quixote, "for the note-book in which I wrote it I found in my own possession two days after thy departure, which gave me very great vexation, as I knew not what thou wouldst do on finding thyself without any letter; and I made sure thou wouldst return from the place where thou didst first miss it."

"So I should have done," said Sancho, "if I had not got it by heart when your worship read it to me, so that I repeated it to a sacristan, who copied it out for me from hearing it, so exactly that he said in all the days of his life, though he had read many a letter of excommunication, he had never seen or read so pretty a letter as that."

"And hast thou got it still in thy memory, Sancho?" said Don Quixote.

"No, señor," replied Sancho, "for as soon as I had repeated it, seeing there was no further use for it, I set about forgetting it; and if I recollect any of it, it is that about 'Scrubbing,' I mean to say 'Sovereign Lady,' and the end 'Yours till death, the Knight of the Rueful Countenance'; and between these two I put into it more than three hundred 'my souls' and 'my life's' and 'my eyes.'"

Chapter 31

Of the delectable discussion between
Don Quixote and Sancho Panza, his squire,
together with other incidents

"ALL that is not unsatisfactory to me," said Don Quixote. "Go on; thou didst reach her; and what was that queen of beauty doing? Surely thou didst find her stringing pearls, or embroi-

dering some device in gold thread for this her enslaved knight."

"I did not," said Sancho, "but I found her winnowing two bushels of wheat in the yard of her house."

"Then depend upon it," said Don Quixote, "the grains of that wheat were pearls when touched by her hands; and didst thou look, friend? was it white wheat or brown?"

"It was neither, but red," said Sancho.

"Then I promise thee," said Don Quixote, "that, winnowed by her hands, beyond a doubt the bread it made was of the whitest; but go on; when thou gavest her my letter, did she kiss it? Did she place it on her head? Did she perform any ceremony befitting such a letter, or what did she do?"

"When I went to give it to her," replied Sancho, "she was hard at it swaying from side to side with a lot of wheat she had in the sieve, and she said to me, 'Lay the letter, friend, on the top of that sack, for I can not read it until I have done sifting all this.'"

"Discreet lady!" said Don Quixote; "that was in order to read it at her leisure and enjoy it; proceed, Sancho; while she was engaged in her occupation what converse did she hold with thee? What did she ask about me, and what answer didst thou give? Make haste; tell me all, and let not an atom be left behind in the ink-bottle."

"She asked me nothing," said Sancho; "but I told her how your worship was left doing penance in her service, naked from the waist up, in among these mountains like a savage, sleeping on the ground, not eating bread off a tablecloth nor combing your beard, weeping and cursing your fortune."

"In saying I cursed my fortune thou saidst wrong," said Don Quixote; "for rather do I bless it and shall bless it all the days of my life for having made me worthy of aspiring to love so lofty a lady as Dulcinea del Toboso."

"And so lofty she is," said Sancho, "that she overtops me by more than a hand's-breadth."

"What! Sancho," said Don Quixote, "didst thou measure with her?"

"I measured in this way," said Sancho; "going to help her to put a sack of wheat on the back of an ass, we came so close together that I could see she stood more than a good palm over me."

"Well!" said Don Quixote, "and doth she not of a truth accompany and adorn this greatness with a thousand million charms of mind! But one thing thou wilt not deny, Sancho; when thou camest close to her didst thou not perceive a Sabæan odor, an aromatic fragrance, a, I know not what, delicious, that I can not find a name for; I mean a redolence, an exhalation, as if thou wert in the shop of some dainty glover?"

"All I can say is," said Sancho, "that I did perceive a little odor, something goaty; it must have been that she was all in a sweat with hard work."

"It could not be that," said Don Quixote, "but thou must have been suffering from cold in the head, or must have smelt thyself; for I know well what would be the scent of that rose among thorns, that lily of the field, that dissolved amber."

"Maybe so," replied Sancho; "there often comes from myself that same odor which then seemed to me to come from her grace the lady Dulcinea; but that's no wonder, for one devil is like another."

"Well then," continued Don Quixote, "now she has done sifting the corn and sent it to the mill; what did she do when she read the letter?"

"As for the letter," said Sancho, "she did not read it, for she said she could neither read nor write; instead of that she tore it up into small pieces, saying that she did not want to let any one read it lest her secrets should become known in the village, and that what I had told her by word of mouth about the love your worship bore her, and the extraordinary penance you were doing for her sake, was enough; and, to make an end of it, she told me to tell your worship that she kissed your hands, and that she had a greater desire to see you than to write to you; and that therefore she entreated and commanded you, on sight of this present, to come out of these thickets, and to have done with carrying on absurdities, and to set out at once for El Toboso, unless something else of greater importance should happen, for she had a great desire to see your worship. She laughed greatly when I told her how your worship was called the Knight of the Rueful Countenance; I asked her if that Biscayan the other day had been there; and she told me he had, and that he was a very honest fellow; I asked her too about the galley slaves, but she said she had not seen any yet."

"So far all goes well," said Don Quixote; "but tell me what jewel was it that she gave thee on taking thy leave, in return for thy tidings of me? For it is a usual and ancient custom with knights and ladies errant to give the squires, damsels, or dwarfs who bring tidings of their ladies to the knights, or of their knights to the ladies, some rich jewel as a guerdon for good news, and acknowledgment of the message."

"That is likely," said Sancho, "and a good custom it was, to my mind; but that must have been in days gone by, for now it would seem to be the custom only to give a piece of bread and cheese; because that was what my lady Dulcinea gave me over the top of the yard-wall when I took leave of her; and more by token it was sheep's-milk cheese."

"She is generous in the extreme," said Don Quixote, "and if she did not give thee a jewel of gold, no doubt it must have been because she had not one to hand there to give thee, but sleeves are good after Easter; I shall see her and all shall be made right. But knowest thou what amazes me, Sancho? It seems to me thou must have gone and come through the air, for thou hast taken but little more than three days to go to El Toboso and return, though it is more than thirty leagues from here to there. From which I am inclined to think that the sage magician who is my friend, and watches over my interest (for of necessity there is and must be one, or else I should not be a right knight-errant), that this same, I say, must have helped thee to travel without thy knowledge; for some of these sages will catch up a knight-errant sleeping in his bed, and without his knowing how or in what way it happened, he wakes up the next day more than a thousand leagues away from the place where he went to sleep. And if it were not for this, knights-errant would not be able to give aid to one another in peril, as they do at every turn. For a knight, maybe, is fighting in the mountains of Armenia with some dragon, or fierce serpent, or another knight, and gets the worst of the battle, and is at the point of death; but when he least looks for it, there appears over against him on a cloud, or chariot of fire, another knight, a friend of his, who just before had been in England, and who takes his part, and delivers him from death; and at night he finds himself in his own quarters supping very much to his satisfaction; and yet from one place to the other will have been two or three thousand leagues. And all this is done by the craft and skill of the sage enchanters who take care of those valiant knights. So that, friend Sancho, I find no difficulty in believing that thou mayest have gone from this place to El Toboso and returned in such a short time, since, as I have said, some friendly sage must have carried thee through the air without thee perceiving it."

"That must have been it," said Sancho, "for indeed Rocinante went like a gypsy's ass with quicksilver in his ears."

"Quicksilver!" said Don Quixote, "ay, and

what is more, a legion of devils, folk that can travel and make others travel without being weary, exactly as the whim seizes them. But putting this aside, what thinkest thou I ought to do about my lady's command to go and see her? For though I feel that I am bound to obey her mandate, I feel too that I am debarred by the boon I have accorded to the princess that accompanies us, and the law of chivalry compels me to have regard for my word in preference to my inclination; on the one hand the desire to see my lady pursues and harasses me, on the other my solemn promise and the glory I shall win in this enterprise urge and call me; but what I think I shall do is to travel with all speed and reach quickly the place where this giant is, and on my arrival I shall cut off his head, and establish the princess peacefully in her realm, and forthwith shall return, to behold the light that lightens my senses, to whom I shall make such excuses that she will be led to approve of my delay, for she will see that it entirely tends to increase her glory and fame; for all that I have won, am winning, or shall win by arms in this life, comes to me of the favor she extends to me, and because I am hers."

"Ah! what a sad state your worship's brains are in!" said Sancho. "Tell me, señor, do you mean to travel all that way for nothing, and to let slip and lose so rich and great a match as this where they give as a portion a kingdom that in sober truth I have heard say is more than twenty thousand leagues round about, and abounds with all things necessary to support human life, and is bigger than Portugal and Castile put together? Peace, for the love of God! Blush for what you have said, and take my advice, and forgive me, and marry at once in the first village where there is a curate; if not, here is our licentiate who will do the business beautifully; remember, I am old enough to give advice, and this I am giving comes pat to the purpose; for a sparrow in the hand is better than a vulture on the wing, and he who has the good to his hand and chooses the bad, that the good he complains of may not come to him."

"Look here, Sancho," said Don Quixote. "If thou art advising me to marry, in order that immediately on slaying the giant I may become king, and be able to confer favors on thee, and give thee what I have promised, let me tell thee I shall be able very easily to satisfy thy desires without marrying; for before going into battle I will make it a stipulation that, if I come out of it victorious, even if I do not marry, they shall give me a portion of the kingdom, that I may be-

stow it upon whomsoever I choose, and when they give it to me upon whom wouldst thou have me bestow it but upon thee?"

"That is plain speaking," said Sancho; "but let your worship take care to choose it on the sea-coast, so that if I don't like the life, I may be able to ship off my black vassals and deal with them as I have said; don't mind going to see my lady Dulcinea now, but go and kill this giant and let us finish off this business; for by God it strikes me it will be one of great honor and great profit."

"I hold thou art in the right of it, Sancho," said Don Quixote, "and I will take thy advice as to accompanying the princess before going to see Dulcinea; but I counsel thee not to say anything to any one, or to those who are with us, about what we have considered and discussed, for as Dulcinea is so decorous that she does not wish her thoughts to be known it is not right that I or any one for me should disclose them."

"Well then, if that be so," said Sancho, "how is it that your worship makes all those you overcome by your arm go to present themselves before my lady Dulcinea, this being the same thing as signing your name to it that you love her and are her lover? And as those who go must perforce kneel before her and say they come from your worship to submit themselves to her, how can the thoughts of both of you be hid?"

"O, how silly and simple thou art!" said Don Quixote; "seest thou not, Sancho, that this tends to her greater exaltation? For thou must know that according to our way of thinking in chivalry, it is a high honor to a lady to have many knights-errant in her service, whose thoughts never go beyond serving her for her own sake, and who look for no other reward for their great and true devotion than that she should be willing to accept them as her knights."

"It is with that kind of love," said Sancho, "I have heard preachers say we ought to love our Lord, for Himself alone, without being moved by the hope of glory or the fear of punishment; though for my part, I would rather love and serve Him for what He could do."

"The devil take thee for a clown!" said Don Quixote, "and what shrewd things thou sayest at times! One would think thou hadst studied."

"In faith, then, I can not even read," answered Sancho.

Master Nicholas here called out to them to wait a while, as they wanted to halt and drink at a little spring there was there. Don Quixote drew up, not a little to the satisfaction of Sancho, for he was by this time weary of telling so many lies, and in dread of his master catching him tripping, for though he knew that Dulcinea was a peasant girl of El Toboso, he had never seen her in all his life. Cardenio had now put on the clothes which Dorothea was wearing when they found her, and though they were not very good, they were far better than those he put off. They dismounted together by the side of the spring, and with what the curate had provided himself with at the inn they appeased, though not very well, the keen appetite they all of them brought with them.

While they were so employed there happened to come by a youth passing on his way, who stopping to examine the party at the spring, the next moment ran to Don Quixote and clasping him round the legs, began to weep freely, saying, "O señor, do you not know me? Look at me well; I am that lad Andres that your worship released from the oak tree where I was tied."

Don Quixote recognized him, and taking his hand he turned to those present and said: "That your worships may see how important it is to have knights-errant to redress the wrongs and injuries done by tyrannical and wicked men in this world, I may tell you that some days ago passing through a wood, I heard cries and piteous complaints as of a person in pain and distress; I immediately hastened, impelled by my bounden duty, to the quarter whence the plaintive accents seemed to me to proceed, and I found tied to an oak this lad who now stands before you, which in my heart I rejoice at, for his testimony will not permit me to depart from the truth in any particular. He was, I say, tied to an oak, naked from the waist up, and a clown, whom I afterwards found to be his master, was scarifying him by lashes with the reins of his mare. As soon as I saw him I asked the reason of so cruel a flagellation. The boor replied that he was flogging him because he was his servant and because of carelessness that proceeded rather from dishonesty than stupidity; on which this boy said, 'Señor, he flogs me only because I ask for my wages.' The master made I know not what speeches and explanations, which, though I listened to them, I did not accept. In short, I compelled the clown to unbind him, and to swear he would take him with him, and pay him real by real, and perfumed into the bargain. Is not all this true, Andres my son? Didst thou not mark with what authority I commanded him, and with what humility he promised to do all I enjoined, specified, and required of him? Answer without confusion or hesitation; tell these gentlemen what took place, that they may see and observe that it is as great an advantage as I

say to have knights-errant abroad."

"All that your worship has said is quite true, answered the lad; "but the end of the busines turned out just the opposite of what your wor ship supposes."

"How! the opposite?" said Don Quixote; "di not the clown pay thee then?"

"Not only did he not pay me," replied th lad, "but as soon as your worship had passed ou of the wood and we were alone, he tied me u again to the same oak and gave me a fresh flog ging, that left me like a flayed Saint Bartholo mew; and every stroke he gave me he followe up with some jest or gibe about having made fool of your worship, and but for the pain I wa suffering I should have laughed at the things h said. In short he left me in such a condition tha I have been until now in a hospital getting cure of the injuries which that rascally clown inflict ed on me then; for all which your worship is t blame; for if you had gone your own way an not come where there was no call for you, no meddled in other people's affairs, my maste would have been content with giving me one o two dozen lashes, and would have then loose me and paid me what he owed me; but whe your worship abused him so out of measure, an gave him so many hard words, his anger wa kindled; and as he could not revenge himself o you, as soon as he saw you had left him the stor burst upon me in such a way that I feel as if should never be a man again as long as I live."

"The mischief," said Don Quixote, "lay in m going away; for I should not have gone until had seen thee paid; because I ought to hav known well by long experience that there is n clown who will keep his word if he finds it wil not suit him to keep it; but thou rememberes Andres, that I swore if he did not pay thee would go and seek him, and find him though h were to hide himself in the whale's belly."

"That is true," said Andres; "but it was of n use."

"Thou shalt see now whether it is of use o not," said Don Quixote; and so saying, he go up hastily and bade Sancho bridle Rocinante who was browsing while they were eating. Dor othea asked him what he meant to do. He re plied that he meant to go in search of this clow and chastise him for such iniquitous conduct and see Andres paid to the last maravedí, des pite and in the teeth of all the clowns in th world. To which she replied that he must re member that in accordance with his promise h could not engage in any enterprise until he ha brought hers to a conclusion; and that as he kne this better than any one, he should restrain his ardor until his return from her kingdom.

"That is true," said Don Quixote, "and Andres must have patience until my return as you say, señora; but I once more swear and promise afresh not to stop until I have seen him avenged and paid."

"I have no faith in those oaths," said Andres; "I would rather have now something to help me to get to Seville than all the revenges in the world: if you have here anything to eat that I can take with me, give it me, and God be with your worship and all knights-errant; and may their errands turn out as well for themselves as they have for me."

Sancho took out from his store a piece of bread and another of cheese, and giving them to the lad he said, "Here, take this, brother Andres, for we have all of us a share in your misfortune."

"Why, what share have you got?" asked Andres.

"This share of bread and cheese I am giving you," answered Sancho; "and God knows whether I shall feel the want of it myself or not; for I would have you know, friend, that we squires to knights-errant have to bear a great deal of hunger and hard fortune, and even other things more easily felt than told."

Andres seized his bread and cheese, and seeing that nobody gave him anything more, bent his head, and took hold of the road, as the saying is. However, before leaving he said to Don Quixote, "For the love of God, sir knight-errant, if you ever meet me again, though you may see them cutting me to pieces, give me no aid or succor, but leave me to my misfortune, which will not be so great but that a greater will come to me by being helped by your worship, on whom and all the knights-errant that have ever been born God send his curse."

Don Quixote was getting up to chastise him, but he took to his heels at such a pace that no one attempted to follow him; and mightily chapfallen was Don Quixote at the story of Andres, and the others had to take great care to restrain their laughter so as not to put him entirely out of countenance.

Chapter 32

Which treats of what befell all Don Quixote's party at the inn

THEIR dainty repast being finished, they saddled at once, and without any adventure worth mentioning they reached next day the inn, the object of Sancho Panza's fear and dread;

but though he would have rather not entered it there was no help for it. The landlady, the landlord, their daughter, and Maritornes, when they saw Don Quixote and Sancho coming, went out to welcome them with signs of hearty satisfaction, which Don Quixote received with dignity and gravity, and bade them make up a better bed for him than the last time: to which the landlady replied that if he paid better than he did the last time she would give him one fit for a prince. Don Quixote said he would, so they made up a tolerable one for him in the same garret as before; and he lay down at once, being sorely shaken and in want of sleep.

No sooner was the door shut upon him than the landlady made at the barber, and seizing him by the beard, said, "By my faith you are not going to make a beard of my tail any longer; you must give me back my tail, for it is a shame the way that thing of my husband's goes tossing about on the floor; I mean the comb that I used to stick in my good tail." But for all she tugged at it the barber would not give it up until the licentiate told him to let her have it, as there was now no further occasion for that stratagem, because he might declare himself and appear in his own character, and tell Don Quixote that he had fled to this inn when those thieves the galley slaves robbed him; and should he ask for the princess's squire, they could tell him that she had sent him on before her to give notice to the people of her kingdom that she was coming, and bringing with her the deliverer of them all. On this the barber cheerfully restored the tail to the landlady, and at the same time they returned all the accessories they had borrowed to effect Don Quixote's deliverance. All the people of the inn were struck with astonishment at the beauty of Dorothea, and even at the comely figure of the shepherd Cardenio. The curate made them get ready such fare as there was in the inn, and the landlord, in hope of better payment, served them up a tolerably good dinner. All this time Don Quixote was asleep, and they thought it best not to awaken him, as sleeping would now do him more good than eating.

While at dinner, the company consisting of the landlord, his wife, their daughter, Maritornes, and all the travellers, they discussed the strange craze of Don Quixote and the manner in which he had been found; and the landlady told them what had taken place between him and the carrier; and then, looking round to see if Sancho was there, when she saw he was not, she gave them the whole story of his blanketing, which they received with no little amusement. But on the curate observing that it was the books of chivalry which Don Quixote had read that had turned his brain, the landlord said, "I can not understand how that can be, for in truth to my mind there is no better reading in the world, and I have here two or three of them, with other writings that are the very life, not only of myself but of plenty more; for when it is harvesttime the reapers flock here on holidays, and there is always one among them who can read and who takes up one of these books, and we gather round him, thirty or more of us, and stay listening to him with a delight that makes our gray hairs grow young again. At least I can say for myself that when I hear of what furious and terrible blows the knights deliver, I am seized with the longing to do the same, and I would like to be hearing about them night and day."

"And I just as much," said the landlady, "because I never have a quiet moment in my house except when you are listening to some one reading; for then you are so taken up that for the time being you forget to scold."

"That is true," said Maritornes; "and, faith, I relish hearing these things greatly too, for they are very pretty; especially when they describe some lady or another in the arms of her knight under the orange trees, and the duenna who is keeping watch for them half dead with envy and fright; all this I say is as good as honey."

"And you, what do you think, young lady?" said the curate turning to the landlord's daughter.

"I don't know indeed, señor," said she; "I listen too, and to tell the truth, though I do not understand it, I like hearing it; but it is not the blows that my father likes that I like, but the laments the knights utter when they are separated from their ladies; and indeed they sometimes make me weep with the compassion I feel for them."

"Then you would console them if it was for you they wept, young lady?" said Dorothea.

"I don't know what I should do," said the girl; "I only know that there are some of those ladies so cruel that they call their knights tigers and lions and a thousand other foul names: and, Jesus! I don't know what sort of folk they can be, so unfeeling and heartless, that rather than bestow a glance upon a worthy man they leave him to die or go mad. I don't know what is the good of such prudery; if it is for honor's sake, why not marry them? That's all they want."

"Hush, child," said the landlady; "it seems to me thou knowest a great deal about these things, and it is not fit for girls to know or talk so much."

"As the gentleman asked me, I could not help answering him," said the girl.

"Well then," said the curate, "bring me these books, señor landlord, for I should like to see them."

"With all my heart," said he, and going into his own room he brought out an old valise secured with a little chain, on opening which the curate found in it three large books and some manuscripts written in a very good hand. The first that he opened he found to be *Don Cirongílio of Thrace,* and the second *Don Felixmarte of Hircania,* and the other the *History of the Great Captain Gonzalo Hernandez de Cordova, with the Life of Diego García de Paredes.*

When the curate read the first two titles he looked over at the barber and said, "We want my friend's housekeeper and niece here now."

"Nay," said the barber, "I can do just as well to carry them to the yard or to the hearth, and there is a very good fire there."

"What! your worship would burn my books!" said the landlord.

"Only these two," said the curate, "Don Cirongílio and Felixmarte."

"Are my books, then, heretics or phlegmatics that you want to burn them?" said the landlord.

"Schismatics you mean, friend," said the barber, "not phlegmatics."

"That's it," said the landlord; "but if you want to burn any, let it be that about the Great Captain and that Diego García; for I would rather have a child of mine burnt than either of the others."

"Brother," said the curate, "those two books are made up of lies, and are full of folly and nonsense; but this of the Great Captain is a true history, and contains the deeds of Gonzalo Hernandez of Cordova, who by his many and great achievements earned the title all over the world of the Great Captain, a famous and illustrious name, and deserved by him alone; and this Diego García de Paredes was a distinguished knight of the city of Trujillo in Estremadura, a most gallant soldier, and of such bodily strength that with one finger he stopped a mill-wheel in full motion; and posted with a two-handed sword at the foot of a bridge he kept the whole of an immense army from passing over it, and achieved such other exploits that if, instead of his relating them himself with the modesty of a knight and of one writing his own history, some free and unbiased writer had recorded them, they would have thrown into the shade all the deeds of the Hectors, Achilleses, and Rolands."

"Tell that to my father," said the landlord.

"There's a thing to be astonished at! Stopping a mill-wheel! By God your worship should read what I have read of Felixmarte of Hircania, how with one single backstroke he cleft five giants asunder through the middle as if they had been made of bean-pods like the little friars the children make; and another time he attacked a very great and powerful army, in which there were more than a million six hundred thousand soldiers, all armed from head to foot, and he routed them all as if they had been flocks of sheep. And then, what do you say to the good Cirongílio of Thrace, that was so stout and bold; as may be seen in the book, where it is related that as he was sailing along a river there came up out of the midst of the water against him a fiery serpent, and he, as soon as he saw it, flung himself upon it and got astride of its scaly shoulders, and squeezed its throat with both hands with such force that the serpent, finding he was throttling it, had nothing for it but to let itself sink to the bottom of the river, carrying with it the knight who would not let go his hold; and when they got down there he found himself among palaces and gardens so pretty that it was a wonder to see; and then the serpent changed itself into an old ancient man, who told him such things as were never heard. Hold your peace, señor; for if you were to hear this you would go mad with delight. A couple of figs for your Great Captain and your Diego García!"

Hearing this Dorothea said in a whisper to Cardenio, "Our landlord is almost fit to play a second part to Don Quixote."

"I think so," said Cardenio, "for as he shows, he accepts it as a certainty that everything those books relate took place exactly as it is written down; and the barefooted friars themselves would not persuade him to the contrary."

"But consider, brother," said the curate once more, "there never was any Felixmarte of Hircania in the world, nor any Cirongílio of Thrace, or any of the other knights of the same sort, that the books of chivalry talk of; the whole thing is the fabrication and invention of idle wits, devised by them for the purpose you describe of beguiling the time, as your reapers do when they read: for I swear to you in all seriousness there never were any such knights in the world, and no such exploits or nonsense ever happened anywhere."

"Try that bone on another dog," said the landlord; "as if I did not know how many make five, and where my shoe pinches me; don't think to feed me with pap, for by God I am no fool. It is a good joke for your worship to try and persuade me that everything these good books say is non-

sense and lies, and they printed by the license of the Lords of the Royal Council, as if they were people who would allow such a lot of lies to be printed all together, and so many battle and enchantments that they take away one's senses."

"I have told you, friend," said the curate, "that this is done to divert our idle thoughts; and as in well-ordered states games of chess, fives, and billiards are allowed for the diversion of those who do not care, or are not obliged, or are unable to work, so books of this kind are allowed to be printed, on the supposition that, what indeed is the truth, there can be nobody so ignorant as to take any of them for true stories; and if it were permitted me now, and the present company desired it, I could say something about the qualities books of chivalry should possess to be good ones, that would be to the advantage and even to the taste of some; but I hope the time will come when I can communicate my ideas to some one who may be able to mend matters; and in the meantime, señor landlord, believe what I have said, and take your books, and make up your mind about their truth or falsehood, and much good may they do you; and God grant you may not fall lame of the same foot your guest Don Quixote halts on."

"No fear of that," returned the landlord; "I shall not be so mad as to make a knight-errant of myself; for I see well enough that things are not now as they used to be in those days, when they say those famous knights roamed about the world."

Sancho had made his appearance in the middle of this conversation, and he was very much troubled and cast down by what he heard said about knights-errant being now no longer in vogue, and all books of chivalry being folly and lies; and he resolved in his heart to wait and see what came of this journey of his master's, and if it did not turn out as happily as his master expected, he determined to leave him and go back to his wife and children and his ordinary labor.

The landlord was carrying away the valise and the books, but the curate said to him, "Wait; I want to see what those papers are that are written in such a good hand." The landlord taking them out handed them to him to read, and he perceived they were a work of about eight sheets of manuscript, with, in large letters at the beginning, the title of *Novel of the Ill-advised Curiosity*. The curate read three or four lines to himself, and said, "I must say the title of this novel does not seem to me a bad one, and I feel an inclination to read it all." To which the landlord replied, "Then your reverence will do well to read it, for I can tell you that some guests who have read it here have been much pleased with it, and have begged it of me very earnestly; but I would not give it, meaning to return it to the person who forgot the valise, books, and papers here, for maybe he will return here some time or other; and though I know I shall miss the books, faith I mean to return them; for though I am an innkeeper, still I am a Christian."

"You are very right, friend," said the curate; "but for all that, if the novel pleases me you must let me copy it."

"With all my heart," replied the host.

While they were talking Cardenio had taken up the novel and begun to read it, and forming the same opinion of it as the curate, he begged him to read it so that they might all hear it.

"I would read it," said the curate, "if the time would not be better spent in sleeping than in reading."

"It will be rest enough for me," said Dorothea, "to while away the time by listening to some tale, for my spirits are not yet tranquil enough to let me sleep when it would be seasonable."

"Well then, in that case," said the curate, "I will read it, if it were only out of curiosity; perhaps it may contain something pleasant."

Master Nicholas added his entreaties to the same effect, and Sancho too; seeing which, and considering that he would give pleasure to all, and receive it himself, the curate said, "Well then, attend to me every one, for the novel begins thus."

Chapter 33

In which is related The Novel of the Ill-advised Curiosity

IN Florence, a rich and famous city of Italy in the province called Tuscany, there lived two gentlemen of wealth and quality, Anselmo and Lothario, such great friends that by way of distinction they were called by all that knew them "The two Friends." They were unmarried, young, of the same age and of the same tastes, which was enough to account for the reciprocal friendship between them. Anselmo, it is true, was somewhat more inclined to seek pleasure in love than Lothario, for whom the pleasures of the chase had more attraction; but on occasion Anselmo would forego his own tastes to yield to those of Lothario, and Lothario would surrender his to fall in with those of Anselmo, and in this way their inclinations kept pace one with the other with a concord so perfect that the best regulated clock could not surpass it.

Anselmo was deep in love with a high-born and beautiful maiden of the same city, the daughter of parents so estimable, and so estimable herself, that

he resolved, with the approval of his friend Lothario, without whom he did nothing, to ask her of them in marriage, and did so, Lothario being the bearer of the demand, and conducting the negotiation so much to the satisfaction of his friend that in a short time he was in possession of the object of his desires, and Camilla so happy in having won Anselmo for her husband, that she gave thanks unceasingly to Heaven and to Lothario, by whose means such good fortune had fallen to her. The first few days, those of a wedding being usually days of merry-making, Lothario frequented his friend Anselmo's house as he had been wont, striving to do honor to him and to the occasion, and to gratify him in every way he could; but when the wedding days were over and the succession of visits and congratulations had slackened, he began purposely to leave off going to the house of Anselmo, for it seemed to him, as it naturally would to all men of sense, that friends' houses ought not to be visited after marriage with the same frequency as in their masters' bachelor days: because, though true and genuine friendship cannot and should not be in any way suspicious, still a married man's honor is a thing of such delicacy that it is held liable to injury from brothers, much more from friends. Anselmo remarked the cessation of Lothario's visits, and complained of it to him, saying that if he had known that marriage was to keep him from enjoying his society as he used, he would have never married; and that, if by the thorough harmony that subsisted between them while he was a bachelor they had earned such a sweet name as that of "The two Friends," he should not allow a title so rare and so delightful to be lost through a needless anxiety to act circumspectly; and so he entreated him, if such a phrase was allowable between them, to be once more master of his house and to come in and go out as formerly, assuring him that his wife Camilla had no other desire or inclination than that which he would wish her to have, and that knowing how sincerely they loved one another she was grieved to see such coldness in him.

To all this and much more that Anselmo said to Lothario to persuade him to come to his house as he had been in the habit of doing, Lothario replied with so much prudence, sense, and judgment, that Anselmo was satisfied of his friend's good intentions, and it was agreed that on two days in the week, and on holidays, Lothario should come to dine with him; but though this arrangement was made between them Lothario resolved to observe it no further than he considered to be in accordance with the honor of his friend, whose good name was more to him than his own. He said, and justly, that a married man upon whom Heaven had bestowed a beautiful wife should consider as carefully what friends he brought to his house as what female friends his wife associated with, for what can not be done or arranged in the market-place, in church, at public festivals or at stations (opportunities that husbands cannot always deny their wives) may be easily managed in the house of the female friend or relative in whom most confidence is reposed. Lothario said, too, that every married man should have some friend who would point out to him any negligence he might be guilty of in his conduct, for it will sometimes happen that owing to the deep affection the husband bears his wife either he does not caution her, or, not to vex her, refrains from telling her to do or not to do certain things, doing or avoiding which may be a matter of honor or reproach to him; and errors of this kind he could easily correct if warned by a friend. But where is such a friend to be found as Lothario would have, so judicious, so loyal, and so true?

Of a truth I know not; Lothario alone was such a one, for with the utmost care and vigilance he watched over the honor of his friend, and strove to diminish, cut down, and reduce the number of days for going to his house according to their agreement, lest the visits of a young man, wealthy, high-born, and with the attractions he was conscious of possessing, at the house of a woman as beautiful as Camilla, should be regarded with suspicion by the inquisitive and malicious eyes of the idle public. For though his integrity and reputation might bridle slanderous tongues, still he was unwilling to hazard either his own good name or that of his friend; and for this reason most of the days agreed upon he devoted to some other business which he pretended was unavoidable; so that a great portion of the day was taken up with complaints on one side and excuses on the other. It happened, however, that on one occasion when the two were strolling together through a meadow outside the city, Anselmo addressed the following words to Lothario.

"Thou mayest suppose, Lothario my friend, that I am unable to give sufficient thanks for the favors God has rendered me in making me the son of such parents as mine were, and bestowing upon me with no niggard hand what are called the gifts of nature as well as those of fortune, and above all for what he has done in giving me thee for a friend and Camilla for a wife—two treasures that I value, if not as highly as I ought, at least as highly as I am able. And yet, with all these good things, which are commonly all that men need to enable them to live happily, I am the most discontented and dissatisfied man in the whole world; for, I know not how long since, I have been harassed and oppressed by a desire so strange and so unusual, that I wonder at myself and blame and chide myself when I am alone, and strive to stifle it and hide it from my own thoughts, and with no better success than if I were endeavoring deliberately to publish it to all the world; and as, in short, it must come out, I would confide it to thy safekeeping, feeling sure that by this means, and by thy readiness as a true friend to afford me relief, I shall soon find myself freed from the distress it causes me, and that thy care will give me happiness in the same degree as my own folly has caused me misery."

The words of Anselmo struck Lothario with astonishment, unable as he was to conjecture the purport of such a lengthy prelude and preamble; and though he strove to imagine what desire it could be that so troubled his friend, his conjectures were all far from the truth, and to relieve the anxiety which this perplexity was causing him, he told him he was doing a flagrant injustice to their great friendship in seeking circuitous methods of confiding to him his most hidden thoughts, for he well knew he might reckon upon his counsel in diverting them, or his help in carrying them into effect.

"That is the truth," replied Anselmo, "and relying upon that I will tell thee, friend Lothario, that the desire which harasses me is that of knowing whether my wife Camilla is as good and as perfect as I think her to be; and I can not satisfy myself of the truth on this point except by testing her in such a way that the trial may prove the purity of her virtue as the fire proves that of gold; because I am persuaded, my friend, that a woman is virtuous only in proportion as she is or is not tempted; and that she alone is strong who does not yield to the promises, gifts, tears, and importunities of earnest lovers; for what thanks does a woman deserve for being good if no one urges her to be bad, and what wonder is it that she is reserved and circumspect to whom no opportunity is given of going wrong, and who knows she has a husband that will take her life the first time he detects her in an impropriety? I do not therefore hold her who is virtuous through fear or want of opportunity in the same estimation as her who comes out of temptation and trial with a crown of victory; and so, for these reasons and many others that I could give thee to justify and support the opinion I hold, I am desirous that my wife Camilla should pass this crisis, and be refined and tested by the fire of finding herself wooed and solicited, and by one worthy to set his affections upon her; and if she comes out, as I know she will, victorious from this struggle, I shall look upon my good fortune as unequaled, I shall be able to say that the cup of my desire is full, and that the virtuous woman of whom the sage says, 'Who shall find her?' has fallen to my lot. And if the result be the contrary of what I expect, in the satisfaction of knowing that I have been right in my opinion, I shall bear without complaint the pain which my so dearly bought experience will naturally cause me. And, as nothing of all thou wilt urge in opposition to my wish will avail to keep me from carrying it into effect, it is my desire, friend Lothario, that thou shouldst consent to become the instrument for effecting this purpose that I am bent upon, for I will afford thee opportunities to that end, and nothing shall be wanting that I may think necessary for the pursuit of a virtuous, honorable, modest, and high-minded woman. And among other reasons, I am induced to intrust this arduous task to thee by the consideration that if Camilla be conquered by thee the conquest will not be pushed to extremes, but only far enough to account that accomplished which from a sense of honor will be left undone;

thus I shall not be wronged in anything more than intention, and my wrong will remain buried in the integrity of thy silence, which I know well will be as lasting as that of death in what concerns me. If, therefore, thou wouldst have me enjoy what can be called life, thou wilt at once engage in this love struggle, not lukewarmly nor slothfully, but with the energy and zeal that my desire demands, and with the loyalty our friendship assures me of."

Such were the words Anselmo addressed to Lothario, who listened to them with such attention that, except to say what has been already mentioned, he did not open his lips until the other had finished. Then perceiving that he had no more to say, after regarding him for a while, as one would regard something never before seen that excited wonder and amazement, he said to him, "I can not persuade myself, Anselmo my friend, that what thou hast said to me is not in jest; if I thought that thou wert speaking seriously I would not have allowed thee to go so far; so as to put a stop to thy long harangue by not listening to thee. I verily suspect that either thou dost not know me, or I do not know thee; but no, I know well thou art Anselmo, and thou knowest that I am Lothario; the misfortune is, it seems to me, that thou are not the Anselmo thou wert, and must have thought that I am not the Lothario I should be; for the things that thou hast said to me are not those of that Anselmo who was my friend, nor are those that thou demandest of me what should be asked of the Lothario thou knowest. True friends will prove their friends and make use of them, as a poet has said, *usque ad aras;* whereby he meant that they will not make use of their friendship in things that are contrary to God's will. If this, then, was a heathen's feeling about friendship, how much more should it be a Christian's, who knows that the divine must not be forfeited for the sake of any human friendship? And if a friend should go so far as to put aside his duty to Heaven to fulfil his duty to his friend, it should not be in matters that are trifling or of little moment. but in such as affect the friend's life and honor. Now tell me, Anselmo, in which of these two art thou imperilled, that I should hazard myself to gratify thee, and do a thing so detestable as that thou seekest of me? Neither forsooth; on the contrary, thou dost ask of me, so far as I understand, to strive and labor to rob thee of honor and life, and to rob myself of them at the same time, for if I take away thy honor it is plain I take away thy life, as a man without honor is worse than dead; and being the instrument, as thou wilt have it so, of so much wrong to thee, shall not I, too, be left without honor, and consequently without life? Listen to me, Anselmo my friend, and be not impatient to answer me until I have said what occurs to me touching the object of thy desire, for there will be time enough left for thee to reply and for me to hear."

"Be it so," said Anselmo, "say what thou wilt."

Lothario then went on to say, "It seems to me, Anselmo, that thine is just now the temper of mind which is always that of the Moors, who can never be brought to see the error of their creed by quotations from the Holy Scriptures, or by reasons which depend upon the examination of the understanding or are founded upon the articles of faith, but must have examples that are palpable, easy, intelligible capable of proof, not admitting of doubt, with mathematical demonstrations that can not be denied, like, '*If equals be taken from equals, the remainders are equal*': and if they do not understand this in words, and indeed they do not, it has to be shown to them with the hands, and put before their eyes, and even with all this no one succeeds in convincing them of the truth of our holy religion. This same mode of proceeding I shall have to adopt with thee, for the desire which has sprung up in thee is so absurd and remote from everything that has a semblance of reason, that I feel it would be a waste of time to employ it in reasoning with thy simplicity, for at present I will call it by no other name; and I am even tempted to leave thee in thy folly as a punishment for thy pernicious desire; but the friendship I bear thee, which will not allow me to desert thee in such manifest danger of destruction, keeps me from dealing so harshly by thee. And that thou mayest clearly see this, say, Anselmo, hast thou not told me that I must force my suit upon a modest woman, decoy one that is virtuous, make overtures to one that is pure-minded, pay court to one that is prudent? Yes, thou hast told me so. Then, if thou knowest that thou hast a wife, modest, virtuous, pure-minded, and prudent, what is it that thou seekest? And if thou believest that she will come forth victorious from all my attacks—as doubtless she would—what higher titles than those she possesses now dost thou think thou canst bestow upon her then, or in what will she be better then than she is now? Either thou dost not hold her to be what thou sayest, or thou knowest not what thou dost demand. If thou dost not hold her to be what thou sayest, why dost thou seek to prove her instead of treating her as guilty in the way that may seem best to thee? But if she be as virtuous as thou believest, it is an uncalled-for proceeding to make trial of truth itself, for, after trial, it will but be in the same estimation as before. Thus, then, it is conclusive that to attempt things from which harm rather than advantage may come to us is the part of unreasoning and reckless minds, more especially when they are things which we are not forced or compelled to attempt, and which show from afar that it is plainly madness to attempt them.

"Difficulties are attempted either for the sake of God or for the sake of the world, or for both; those undertaken for God's sake are those which the saints undertake when they attempt to live the lives of angels in human bodies; those undertaken for the sake of the world are those of the men who traverse such a vast expanse of water, such a variety of climates, so many strange countries, to acquire what are called the blessings of fortune; and those undertaken for the sake of God and the world together are those of brave soldiers, who no sooner do they see in the enemy's wall a breach as wide as a cannon ball could make, than, casting aside all fear, without hesitating, or heeding the manifest peril that threatens them, borne onward by the desire of defending their faith, their country, and their king, they fling themselves dauntlessly into the midst of the thousand opposing deaths that await them. Such are the things that men are wont to attempt, and there is honor, glory, gain, in attempting them, however full of difficulty and peril they may be; but that which thou sayest it is thy wish to attempt and carry out will not win thee the glory of God nor the blessings of fortune nor fame among men; for even if the issue be as thou wouldst have it, thou wilt be no happier, richer, or more honored than thou art this moment; and if it be otherwise thou wilt be reduced to misery greater than can be imagined, for then it will avail thee nothing to reflect that no one is aware of the misfortune that has befallen thee; it will suffice to torture and crush thee that thou knowest it thyself. And in confirmation of the truth of what I say, let me repeat to thee a stanza made by the famous poet Luigi Tansillo at the end of the first part of his *Tears of Saint Peter*, which says thus:

The anguish and the shame but greater grew
   In Peter's heart as morning slowly came;
No eye was there to see him, well he knew,
   Yet he himself was to himself a shame;
Exposed to all men's gaze, or screened from view,
   A noble heart will feel the pang the same;
A prey to shame the sinning soul will be,
Though none but heaven and earth its shame can see.

Thus by keeping it secret thou wilt not escape thy sorrow, but rather thou wilt shed tears unceasingly, if not tears of the eyes, tears of blood from the heart, like those shed by that simple doctor our poet tells us of, that tried the test of the cup, which the wise Rinaldo, better advised, refused to do; for though this may be a poetic fiction it contains a moral lesson worthy of attention and study and imitation. Moreover by what I am about to say to thee thou wilt be led to see the great error thou wouldst commit.

"Tell me, Anselmo, if Heaven or good fortune had made thee master and lawful owner of a diamond of the finest quality, with the excellence and purity of which all the lapidaries that had seen it had been satisfied, saying with one voice and common consent that in purity, quality, and fineness, it was all that a stone of the kind could possibly be, thou thyself too being of the same belief, as knowing nothing to the contrary; would it be reasonable in thee to desire to take that diamond and place it between an anvil and a hammer, and by mere force of blows and strength of arm try if it were as hard and as fine as they said? And if thou didst, and if the stone should resist so silly a test, that would add nothing to its value or reputation; and if it were

broken, as it might be, would not all be lost? Undoubtedly it would, leaving its owner to be rated as a fool in the opinion of all. Consider, then Anselmo my friend, that Camilla is a diamond of the finest quality as well in thy estimation as in that of others, and that it is contrary to reason to expose her to the risk of being broken; for if she remain intact she can not rise to a higher value than she now possesses; and if she give way and be unable to resist, bethink thee now how thou wilt be deprived of her, and with what good reason thou wilt complain of thyself for having been the cause of her ruin and thine own. Remember there is no jewel in the world so precious as a chaste and virtuous woman, and that the whole honor of women consists in reputation; and since thy wife's is of that high excellence that thou knowest, wherefore shouldst thou seek to call that truth in question? Remember, my friend, that woman is an imperfect animal, and that impediments are not to be placed in her way to make her trip and fall, but that they should be removed, and her path left clear of all obstacles, so that without hinderance she may run her course freely to attain the desired perfection, which consists in being virtuous. Naturalists tell us that the ermine is a little animal which has a fur of purest white, and that when the hunters wish to take it, they make use of this artifice. Having ascertained the places which it frequents and passes, they stop the way to them with mud, and then rousing it, drive it towards the spot, and as soon as the ermine comes to the mud it halts, and allows itself to be taken captive rather than pass through the mire, and spoil and sully its whiteness, which it values more than life and liberty. The virtuous and chaste woman is an ermine, and whiter and purer than snow is the virtue of modesty; and he who wishes her not to lose it, but to keep and preserve it, must adopt a course different from that employed with the ermine; he must not put before her the mire of the gifts and attentions of persevering lovers, because perhaps—and even without a perhaps—she may not have sufficient virtue and natural strength in herself to pass through and tread under foot these impediments; they must be removed, and the brightness of virtue and the beauty of a fair fame must be put before her. A virtuous woman, too, is like a mirror of clear shining crystal, liable to be tarnished and dimmed by every breath that touches it. She must be treated as relics are; adored, not touched. She must be protected and prized as one protects and prizes a fair garden full of roses and flowers, the owner of which allows no one to trespass or pluck a blossom; enough for others that from afar and through the iron grating they may enjoy its fragrance and its beauty. Finally let me repeat to thee some verses that come to my mind; I heard them in a modern comedy, and it seems to me they bear upon the point we are discussing. A prudent old man was giving advice to another, the father of a young girl, to lock her up, watch over her and keep her in seclusion, and among other arguments he used these:

> *Woman is a thing of glass;*
> *But her brittleness 't is best*
> *Not too curiously to test:*
> *Who knows what may come to pass?*

> *Breaking is an easy matter,*
> *And it's folly to expose*
> *What you can not mend to blows;*
> *What you can't make whole to shatter.*

> *This, then, all may hold as true,*
> *And the reason's plain to see;*
> *For if Danaës there be,*
> *There are golden showers too.*

"All that I have said to thee so far, Anselmo, has had reference to what concerns thee; now it is right that I should say something of what regards myself; and if I be prolix, pardon me, for the labyrinth into which thou hast entered and from which thou wouldst have me extricate thee makes it necessary.

"Thou dost reckon me thy friend, and thou wouldst rob me of honor, a thing wholly inconsistent with friendship; and not only dost thou aim at this, but thou wouldst have me rob thee of it also. That thou wouldst rob me of it is clear, for when Camilla sees that I pay court to her as thou requirest, she will certainly regard me as a man without honor or right feeling, since I attempt and do a thing so much opposed to what I owe to my own position and thy friendship. That thou wouldst have me rob thee of it is beyond a doubt, for Camilla, seeing that I press my suit upon her, will suppose that I have perceived in her something light that has encouraged me to make known to her my base desire; and if she holds herself dishonored, her dishonor touches thee as belonging to her; and hence arises what so commonly takes place, that the husband of the adulterous woman, though he may not be aware of or have given any cause for his wife's failure in her duty, or (being careless or negligent) have had it in his power to prevent his dishonor, nevertheless is stigmatized by a vile and reproachful name, and in a manner regarded with eyes of contempt instead of pity by all who know of his wife's guilt, though they see that he is unfortunate not by his own fault, but by the lust of a vicious consort. But I will tell thee why with good reason dishonor attaches to the husband of the unchaste wife, though he know not that she is so, nor be to blame, nor have done anything, or given any provocation to make her so; and be not weary with listening to me, for it will be all for thy good.

"When God created our first parent in the earthly paradise, the Holy Scripture says that he infused sleep into Adam and while he slept took a rib from his left side of which he formed our mother Eve, and when Adam awoke and beheld her he said, 'This is flesh of my flesh, and bone of my bone.' And God said, 'For this shall a man leave his father and his mother, and they shall be two in one flesh'; and then was instituted the divine sacrament of marriage, with such ties that death alone can loose them. And such is the force and virtue of this miraculous sacrament that it makes two different persons one and the same flesh; and even more than this when the virtuous are married; for though they have two souls they have but one will. And hence it follows that as the flesh of the wife is one and the same with that of her husband, the stains that may come upon it, or the injuries it incurs fall upon the husband's flesh, though he, as has been said, may have given no cause for them; for as the pain of the foot or any member of the body is felt by the whole body, because all is one flesh, as the head feels the hurt to the ankle without having caused it, so the husband, being one with her, shares the dishonor of the wife; and as all worldly honor or dishonor comes of flesh and blood, and the erring wife's is of that kind, the husband must needs bear his part of it and be held dishonored without knowing it. See, then, Anselmo, the peril thou art encountering in seeking to disturb the peace of thy virtuous consort; see for what an empty and ill-advised curiosity thou wouldst rouse up passions that now repose in quiet in the breast of thy chaste wife; reflect that what thou art staking all to win is little, and what thou wilt lose so much that I leave it undescribed, not having the words to express it. But if all I have said be not enough to turn thee from thy vile purpose, thou must seek some other instrument for thy dishonor and misfortune; for such I will not consent to be, though by this I lose thy friendship, the greatest loss that I can conceive."

Having said this, the wise and virtuous Lotario was silent, and Anselmo, troubled in mind and deep in thought, was unable for a while to utter a word in reply; but at length he said, "I have listened, Lotario my friend, attentively, as thou hast seen, to what thou hast chosen to say to me, and in thy arguments, examples, and comparisons I have seen that high intelligence thou dost possess, and the perfection of true friendship thou hast reached; and likewise I see and confess that if I am not guided by thy opinion, but follow my own, I am flying from the good and pursuing the evil. This being so, thou must remember that I am now laboring under that infirmity which women sometime suffer from, when the craving seizes them to eat clay, plaster, charcoal, and things even worse, disgusting to look at, much more to eat; so that it will be necessary to have recourse to some artifice to cure me; and this can be easily effected if only thou wilt make a beginning, even though it be in a lukewarm and make-believe fashion, to pay court to Camilla, who will not be so yielding that her virtue will give way at the first attack: with this mere attempt I shall rest satisfied, and thou wilt have done what our friendship binds thee to do, not only in giving me life, but in persuading me not to discard my honor. And this thou art bound to do for one reason alone, that, being, as I am, resolved to apply this test, it is not for thee to permit me to reveal my weakness to another, and so imperil that honor thou art striving to keep me from losing; and if thine may not stand as high as it ought in the estimation of Camilla while thou art paying court to her, that is of little or no importance, because ere long, on finding in her that constancy which we expect, thou canst tell her the plain truth as regards our stratagem, and so regain thy place in her esteem; and as thou art venturing so little, and by the venture canst afford me so much satisfaction, refuse not to undertake it, even if further difficulties present themselves to thee; for, as I have said, if thou wilt only make a beginning I will acknowledge the issue decided."

Lotario seeing the fixed determination of Anselmo, and not knowing what further examples to offer or arguments to urge in order to dissuade him from it, and perceiving that he threatened to confide his pernicious scheme to someone else, to avoid a greater evil resolved to gratify him and do what he asked, intending to manage the business so as to satisfy Anselmo without corrupting the mind of Camilla; so in reply he told him not to communicate his purpose to any other, for he would undertake the task himself, and would begin it as soon as he pleased. Anselmo embraced him warmly and affectionately, and thanked him for his offer as if he had bestowed some great favor upon him; and it was agreed between them to set about it the next day, Anselmo affording opportunity and time to Lotario to converse alone with Camilla, and furnishing him with money and jewels to offer and present to her. He suggested, too, that he should treat her to music, and write verses in her praise, and if he was unwilling to take the trouble of composing them, he offered to do it himself. Lotario agreed to all with an intention very different from what Anselmo supposed, and with this understanding they returned to Anselmo's house, where they found Camilla awaiting her husband anxiously and uneasily, for he was later than usual in returning that day. Lotario repaired to his own house, and Anselmo remained in his, as well satisfied as Lotario was troubled in mind; for he could see no satisfactory way out of this ill-advised business. That night, however, he thought of a plan by which he might deceive Anselmo without any injury to Camilla. The next day he went to dine with his friend, and was welcomed by Camilla, who received and treated him with great cordiality, knowing the affection her husband felt for him. When dinner was over and the cloth removed, Anselmo told Lotario to stay there with Camilla while he attended to some pressing business, as he would return in an hour and a half. Camilla begged him not to go, and Lotario offered to accompany him, but nothing could persuade Anselmo, who on the contrary pressed Lotario to remain waiting for him as he had a matter of great importance to discuss with him. At the same time he bade Camilla not to leave Lotario alone until he came back. In short he contrived to put so good a face on the reason, or the folly, of his absence that no one could have suspected it was a pretence.

Anselmo took his departure, and Camilla and Lotario were left alone at the table, for the rest of the household had gone to dinner. Lotario saw himself in the lists according to his friend's wish, and facing an enemy that could by her beauty alone vanquish a squadron of armed knights; judge whether he had good reason to fear; but what he did was to lean his elbow on the arm of the chair, and his cheek upon his hand, and, asking Camilla's pardon for his ill manners, he said he wished to take a little sleep until Anselmo returned. Camilla in reply said he could repose more at his ease in the reception-room than in his chair, and begged of him to go in and sleep there; but Lotario declined, and there he remained asleep until the return of Anselmo, who finding Camilla in her own room, and Lotario asleep, imagined that he had stayed away so long as to have afforded them time enough for conversation and even for sleep, and was all impatience until Lotario should wake up, that he might go out with him and question him as to his success. Everything fell out as he wished; Lotario awoke, and the two at once left the house, and Anselmo asked what he was anxious to know, and Lotario in answer told him that he had not thought it advisable to declare himself entirely the first time, and therefore had only extolled the charms of Camilla, telling her that all the city spoke of nothing else but her beauty and wit, for this seemed to him an excellent way of beginning to gain her good-will, and render her disposed to listen to him with pleasure the next time, thus availing himself of the device the devil has recourse to when he would deceive one who is on the watch; for he being the angel of darkness transforms himself into an angel of light, and, under cover of a fair seeming, discloses himself at length, and effects his purpose if at the beginning his wiles are not discovered. All this gave great satisfaction to Anselmo, and he said he would afford the same opportunity every day, but without leaving the house, for he would find things to do at home so that Camilla should not detect the plot.

Thus, then, several days went by, and Lotario, without uttering a word to Camilla, reported to Anselmo that he had talked with her and that he had never been able to draw from her the slightest indication of consent to anything dishonorable, nor even a sign or shadow of hope; on the contrary, he said she threatened that if he did not abandon such a wicked idea she would inform her husband of it.

"So far well," said Anselmo; "Camilla has thus far resisted words; we must now see how she will resist deeds. I will give you to-morrow two thousand crowns in gold for you to offer or even present, and as many more to buy jewels to lure her, for women are fond of being becomingly attired and going gayly dressed, and all the more so if they are beautiful, however chaste they may be; and if she resists this temptation, I will rest satisfied and will give you no more trouble."

Lotario replied that now he had begun he would carry on the undertaking to the end, though he perceived he was to come out of it wearied and vanquished. The next day he received the four thousand crowns, and with them four thousand perplexities, for he knew not what to say by way of a new falsehood; but in the end he made up his mind to tell him that Camilla stood as firm against gifts and promises as against words, and that there was no use in taking any further trouble, for the time was all spent to no purpose.

But chance, directing things in a different manner, so ordered it that Anselmo, having left Lotario and Camilla alone as on other occasions, shut himself into a chamber and posted himself to watch and listen through the keyhole to what passed between them, and perceived that for more than half an hour Lotario did not utter a word to Camilla, nor would utter a word though he were to be there for an age; and he came to the conclusion that what his friend had told him about the replies of Camilla was all invention and falsehood, and to ascertain if it were so, he came out, and calling Lotario aside asked him what news he had and in what humor Camilla was. Lotario replied that he was not disposed to go on with the business, for she had answered him so angrily and harshly that he had no heart to say anything more to her.

"Ah, Lotario, Lotario," said Anselmo, "how ill dost thou meet thy obligations to me, and the great confidence I repose in thee! I have been just now watching through this keyhole, and I have seen that thou hast not said a word to Camilla, whence I conclude that on the former occasions thou hast not spoken to her either, and if this be so, as no doubt it is, why dost thou deceive me, or wherefore seekest thou by craft to deprive me of the means I might find of attaining my desire?"

Anselmo said no more, but he had said enough to cover Lotario with shame and confusion, and he, feeling as it were his honor touched by having been detected in a lie, swore to Anselmo that he would from that moment devote himself to satisfying him without any deception, as he would see if he had the curiosity to watch; though he need not take the trouble, for the pains he would take to satisfy him would remove all suspicions from his mind. Anselmo believed him, and to afford him an opportunity more free and less liable to surprise, he resolved to absent himself from his house for eight days, betaking himself to that of a friend of his who lived in a village not far from the city; and, the better to account for his departure to Camilla, he so arranged it that the friend should send him a very pressing invitation.

Unhappy, short-sighted Anselmo, what art thou doing, what art thou plotting, what art thou devising? Bethink thee thou art working against thyself, plotting thine own dishonor, devising thine own ruin. Thy wife Camilla is virtuous, thou dost possess her in peace and quietness, no one assails thy happiness, her thoughts wander not beyond the walls of thy house, thou art her heaven on earth, the object of her wishes, the fulfilment of her desires, the measure wherewith she measures her will, making it conform in all things to thine and Heaven's. If, then, the mine of her honor, beauty, virtue, and modesty yields thee without labor all the wealth it contains and thou canst wish for, why wilt thou dig the earth in search of fresh veins, of new unknown treasure, risking the collapse of all, since it but rests on the feeble props of her weak nature? Bethink thee that from him who seeks impossibilities that which is possible may with justice be withheld, as was better expressed by a poet who said:

> 'Tis mine to seek for life in death,
>   Health in disease seek I,
> I seek in prison freedom's breath,
>   In traitors loyalty.
>
> So Fate that ever scorns to grant
>   Or grace or boon to me,
> Since what can never be I want,
>   Denies me what might be.

The next day Anselmo took his departure for the village, leaving instructions with Camilla that during his absence Lotario would come to look after his house and to dine with her, and that she was to treat him as she would himself. Camilla was distressed, as a discreet and right-minded woman would be, at the orders her husband left her, and bade him remember that it was not becoming that any one should occupy his seat at the table during his absence, and if he acted thus from not feeling confident that she would be able to manage his house, let him try her this time, and he would find by experience that she was equal to greater responsibilities. Anselmo replied that it was his pleasure to have it so, and that she had only to submit and obey. Camilla said she would do so, though against her will.

Anselmo went, and the next day Lotario came to his house, where he was received by Camilla with a friendly and modest welcome; but she never suffered Lotario to see her alone, for she was always attended by her men and women servants, especially by a handmaid of hers, Leonela by name, to whom she was much attached (for they had been brought up together from childhood in her father's house), and whom she had kept with her after her marriage with Anselmo. The first three days Lotario did not speak to her, though he might have done so when they removed the cloth and the servants retired to dine hastily; for such were Camilla's orders; nay more, Leonela had directions to dine earlier than Camilla and never to leave her side. She, however, having her thoughts fixed upon other things more to her taste, and wanting that time and opportunity for her own pleasures, did not always obey her mistress's commands, but on the contrary left them alone, as if they had ordered her to do so; but the modest bearing of Camilla, the calmness of her countenance, the composure of her aspect, were enough to bridle the tongue of Lotario. But the influence which the many virtues of Camilla exerted in imposing silence on Lotario's tongue proved mischievous for both of them, for if his tongue was silent his thoughts were busy, and could dwell at leisure upon the perfections of Camilla's goodness and beauty one by one, charms enough to warm with love a marble statue, not to say a heart of flesh. Lothario gazed upon her when he might have been speaking to her, and thought how worthy of being loved she was; and thus reflection began little by little to assail his allegiance to Anselmo, and a thousand times he thought of withdrawing from the city and going where Anselmo should never see him nor he see Camilla. But already the delight he found in gazing on her interposed and held him fast. He put a constraint upon himself, and struggled to repel and repress the pleasure he found in contemplating Camilla; when alone he blamed himself for his weakness, called himself a bad friend, nay a bad Christian; then he argued the matter and compared himself with Anselmo; always coming to the conclusion that the folly and rashness of Anselmo had been worse than his faithlessness, and that if he could excuse his intentions as easily before God as with man, he need fear no punishment for his offence.

In short the beauty and goodness of Camilla, joined with the opportunity which the blind husband had placed in his hands, overthrew the loyalty of Lothario; and giving heed to nothing save the object towards which his inclinations led him, after Anselmo had been three days absent, during which he had been carrying on a continual struggle with his passion, he began to make love to Camilla with so much vehemence and warmth of language that she was overwhelmed with amazement, and could only rise from her place and retire to her room without answering him a word. But the hope which always springs up with love was not weakened in Lothario by this repelling demeanor; on the contrary his passion for Camilla increased, and she discovering in him what she had never expected, knew not what to do; and considering it neither safe nor right to give him the chance or opportunity of speaking to her again, she resolved to send, as she did that very night, one of her servants with a letter to Anselmo, in which she addressed the following words to him:

Chapter 34

In which is continued The Novel of the Ill-advised Curiosity

"IT is commonly said that an army looks ill without its general and a castle without its castellan, and I say that a young married woman looks still worse without her husband unless there are very good reasons for it. I find myself so ill at ease without you, and so incapable of enduring this separation, that unless you return quickly I shall have to go for relief to my parents' house, even if I leave yours without a protector; for the one you left me, if indeed he deserved that title, has, I think, more regard to his own pleasure than to what concerns you;

as you are possessed of discernment I need say no more to you, nor is it fitting I should say more."

Anselmo received this letter, and from it he gathered that Lothario had already begun his task and that Camilla must have replied to him as he would have wished; and delighted beyond measure at such intelligence he sent word to her not to leave his house on any account, as he would very shortly return. Camilla was astonished at Anselmo's reply, which placed her in greater perplexity than before, for she neither dared to remain in her own house, nor yet to go to her parents'; for in remaining her virtue was imperilled, and in going she was opposing her husband's commands. Finally she decided upon what was the worse course for her, to remain, resolving not to fly from the presence of Lothario, that she might not give food for gossip to her servants; and she now began to regret having written as she had to her husband, fearing he might imagine that Lothario had perceived in her some lightness which had impelled him to lay aside the respect he owed her; but confident of her rectitude she put her trust in God and in her own virtuous intentions, with which she hoped to resist in silence all the solicitations of Lothario, without saying anything to her husband so as not to involve him in any quarrel or trouble; and she even began to consider how to excuse Lothario to Anselmo when he should ask her what it was that induced her to write that letter. With these resolutions, more honorable than judicious or effectual, she remained the next day listening to Lothario, who pressed his suit so strenuously that Camilla's firmness began to waver, and her virtue had enough to do to come to the rescue of her eyes and keep them from showing signs of a certain tender compassion which the tears and appeals of Lothario had awakened in her bosom. Lothario observed all this, and it inflamed him all the more. In short he felt that while Anselmo's absence afforded time and opportunity he must press the siege of the fortress, and so he assailed her self-esteem with praises of her beauty, for there is nothing that more quickly reduces and levels the castle towers of fair women's vanity than vanity itself upon the tongue of flattery. In fact with the utmost assiduity he undermined the rock of her purity with such engines that had Camilla been of brass she must have fallen. He wept, he entreated, he promised, he flattered, he importuned, he pretended with so much feeling and apparent sincerity, that he overthrew the virtuous resolves of Camilla and won the triumph he least expected and most longed for. Camilla yielded, Camilla fell; but what wonder if the friendship of Lothario could not stand firm? A clear proof to us that the passion of love is to be conquered only by flying from it, and that no one should engage in a struggle with an enemy so mighty; for divine strength is needed to overcome his human power. Leonela alone knew of her mistress's weakness, for the two false friends and new lovers were unable to conceal it. Lothario did not care to tell Camilla the object Anselmo had in view, nor that he had afforded him the opportunity of attaining such a result, lest she should undervalue his love and think that it was by chance and without intending it and not of his own accord that he had made love to her.

A few days later Anselmo returned to his house and did not perceive what it had lost, that which he so lightly treated and so highly prized. He went at once to see Lothario, and found him at home; they embraced each other, and Anselmo asked for the tidings of his life or his death.

"The tidings I have to give thee, Anselmo my friend," said Lothario, "are that thou dost possess a wife that is worthy to be the pattern and crown of all good wives. The words that I have addressed to her were borne away on the wind, my promises have been despised, my presents have been refused, such feigned tears as I shed have been turned into open ridicule. In short, as Camilla is the essence of all beauty, so is she the treasure-house where purity dwells, and gentleness and modesty abide with all the virtues that can confer praise, honor, and happiness upon a woman. Take back thy money, my friend; here it is, and I have had no need to touch it, for the chastity of Camilla yields not to things so base as gifts or promises. Be content, Anselmo, and refrain from making further proof; and as thou hast passed dryshod through the sea of those doubts and suspicions that are and may be entertained of women, seek not to plunge again into the deep ocean of new embarrassments, or with another pilot make trial of the goodness and strength of the bark that Heaven has granted thee for thy passage across the sea of this world; but reckon thyself now safe in port, moor thyself with the anchor of sound reflection, and rest in peace until thou art called upon to pay that debt which no nobility on earth can escape paying."

Anselmo was completely satisfied by the words of Lothario, and believed them as fully as if they had been spoken by an oracle; nevertheless he begged of him not to relinquish the undertaking, were it but for the sake of curiosity and amusement; though thenceforward he need not make use of the same earnest endeavors as before; all he wished him to do was to write some verses to her, praising her under the name of Chloris, for he himself would give her to understand that he was in love with a lady to whom he had given that name to enable him to sing her praises with the decorum due to her modesty; and if Lothario were unwilling to take the trouble of writing the verses he would compose them himself.

"That will not be necessary," said Lothario, "for the muses are not such enemies of mine but that they visit me now and then in the course of the year. Do thou tell Camilla what thou hast proposed about a pretended amour of mine; as for the verses I will make them, and if not as good as the subject deserves, they shall be at least the best I can produce." An agreement to this effect was made between the friends, the ill-advised one and the treacherous, and Anselmo returning to his house asked Camilla the question she already wondered he had not asked before—what it was that had caused her to write the letter she had sent him. Camilla replied that it had seemed to her that Lothario looked at her somewhat more freely than when he had been at home; but that now she was undeceived and believed it to have been only her own imagination, for Lothario now avoided seeing her, or being alone with her. Anselmo told her she might be quite easy on the score of that suspicion, for he knew that Lothario was in love with a damsel of rank in the city whom he celebrated under the name of Chloris, and that even if he were not, his fidelity and their great friendship left no room for fear. Had not Camilla, however, been informed beforehand by Lothario that this love for Chloris was a pretence, and that he himself had told Anselmo of it in order to be able sometimes to give utterance to the praises of Camilla herself, no doubt she would have fallen into the despairing toils of jealousy; but being forewarned she received the startling news without uneasiness.

The next day as the three were at table Anselmo asked Lothario to recite something of what he had composed for his mistress Chloris; for, as Camilla did not know her, he might safely say what he liked.

"Even did she know her," returned Lothario, "I would hide nothing, for when a lover praises his lady's beauty, and charges her with cruelty, he casts no imputation upon her fair name; at any rate, all I can say is that yesterday I made a sonnet on the ingratitude of this Chloris, which goes thus:

Sonnet

At midnight, in the silence, when the eyes
Of happier mortals balmy slumbers close,
The weary tale of my unnumbered woes
To Chloris and to Heaven is wont to rise.
And when the light of day returning dyes
The portals of the east with tints of rose,
With undiminished force my sorrow flows
In broken accents and in burning sighs.
And when the sun ascends his star-girt throne,
And on the earth pours down his midday beams,
Noon but renews my wailing and my tears;
And with the night again goes up my moan.
Yet ever in my agony it seems
To me that neither Heaven nor Chloris hears."

The sonnet pleased Camilla, and still more Anselmo, for he praised it and said the lady was excessively cruel who made no return for sincerity so manifest. On which Camilla said, "Then all that love-smitten poets say is true?"

"As poets they do not tell the truth," replied Lothario; "but as lovers they are not more defective in expression that they are truthful."

"There is no doubt of that," observed Anselmo, anxious to support and uphold Lothario's ideas with Camilla, who was as regardless of his design as she was deep in love with Lothario; and so taking delight in anything that was his, and knowing that his thoughts and writings had her for their object, and that she herself was the real Chloris, she asked him to repeat some other sonnet or verses if he recollected any.

"I do," replied Lothario, "but I do not think it as good as the first one, or, more correctly speaking, less bad; but you can easily judge, for it is this.

Sonnet

I know that I am doomed; death is to me
As certain as that thou, ungrateful fair,
Dead at thy feet shouldst see me lying, ere
My heart repented of its love for thee.
If buried in oblivion I should be,
Bereft of life, fame, favor, even there
It would be found that I thy image bear
Deep graven in my breast for all to see.
This like some holy relic do I prize
To save me from the fate my truth entails,
Truth that to thy hard heart its vigor owes.
Alas for him that under lowering skies,
In peril o'er a trackless ocean sails,
Where neither friendly port
nor pole-star shows."

Anselmo praised this second sonnet too, as he had praised the first; and so he went on adding link after link to the chain with which he was binding himself and making his dishonor secure; for when Lothario was doing most to dishonor him he told him he was most honored; and thus each step that Camilla descended towards the depths of her abasement, she mounted, in the opinion of her husband, towards the summit of virtue and fair fame.

It so happened that finding herself on one occasion alone with her maid, Camilla said to her, "I am ashamed to think, my dear Leonela, how lightly I have valued myself that I did not compel Lothario to purchase by at least some expenditure of time that full possession of me that I so quickly yielded him of my own free will. I fear that he will think ill of my pliancy or lightness, not considering the irresistible influence he brought to bear upon me."

"Let not that trouble you, my lady," said Leonela, "for it does not take away the value of the thing given or make it the less precious to give it quickly if it be really valuable and worthy of being prized; nay, they are wont to say that he who gives quickly gives twice."

"They say also," said Camilla, "that what costs little is valued less."

"That saying does not hold good in your case," replied Leonela, "for love, as I have heard say, sometimes flies and sometimes walks; with this one it runs, with that it moves slowly; some it cools, others it burns; some it wounds, others it slays; it begins the course of its desires, and at the same moment completes and ends it; in the morning it will lay siege to a fortress and by night will have taken it, for there is no power that can resist it; so what are you in dread of, what do you fear, when the same

must have befallen Lothario, love having chosen the absence of my lord as the instrument for subduing you? and it was absolutely necessary to complete then what love had resolved upon, without affording the time to let Anselmo return and by his presence compel the work to be left unfinished; for love has no better agent for carrying out his designs than opportunity; and of opportunity he avails himself in all his feats, especially at the outset. All this I know well myself, more by experience than by hearsay, and some day, señora, I will enlighten you on the subject, for I am of young flesh and blood too. Moreover, Lady Camilla, you did not surrender yourself or yield so quickly but that first you saw Lothario's whole soul in his eyes, in his sighs, in his words, his promises and his gifts, and by it and his good qualities perceived how worthy he was of your love. This, then, being the case, let not these scrupulous and prudish ideas trouble your imagination, but be assured that Lothario prizes you as you do him, and rest content and satisfied that as you are caught in the noose of love it is one of worth and merit that has taken you, and one that has not only the four S's that they say true lovers ought to have, but a complete alphabet; only listen to me and you will see how I can repeat it by rote. He is, to my eyes and thinking, Amiable, Brave, Courteous, Distinguished, Elegant, Fond, Gay, Honorable, Illustrious, Loyal, Manly, Noble, Open, Polite, Quickwitted, Rich, and the S's according to the saying, and then Tender, Veracious: X does not suit him, for it is a rough letter; Y has been given already; and Z Zealous for your honor."

Camilla laughed at her maid's alphabet, and perceived her to be more experienced in love affairs than she said, which she admitted, confessing to Camilla that she had love passages with a young man of good birth of the same city. Camilla was uneasy at this, dreading lest it might prove the means of endangering her honor, and asked whether her intrigue had gone beyond words, and she with little shame and much effrontery said it had; for certain it is that ladies' imprudences make servants shameless, who, when they see their mistresses make a false step, think nothing of going astray themselves, or of its being known. All that Camilla could do was to entreat Leonela to say nothing about her doings to him whom she called her lover, and to conduct her own affairs secretly lest they should come to the knowledge of Anselmo or of Lothario. Leonela said she would, but kept her word in such a way that she confirmed Camilla's apprehension of losing her reputation through her means; for this abandoned and bold Leonela, as soon as she perceived that her mistress's demeanor was not what it was wont to be, had the audacity to introduce her lover into the house, confident that even if her mistress saw him she would not dare to expose him; for the sins of mistresses entail this mischief among others; they make themselves the slaves of their own servants, and are obliged to hide their laxities and depravities; as was the case with Camilla, who though she perceived, not once but many times, that Leonela was with her lover in some room of the house, not only did not dare to chide her, but afforded her opportunities for concealing him and removed all difficulties, lest he should be seen by her husband. She was unable, however, to prevent him from being seen on one occasion, as he sallied forth at daybreak, by Lothario, who, not knowing who he was, at first took him for a spectre; but, as soon as he saw him hasten away, muffling his face with his cloak and concealing himself carefully and cautiously, he rejected this foolish idea, and adopted another, which would have been the ruin of all had not Camilla found a remedy. It did not occur to Lothario that this man he had seen issuing at such an untimely hour from Anselmo's house could have entered it on Leonela's account, nor did he even remember there was such a person as Leonela; all he thought was that as Camilla had been light and yielding with him, so she had been with another; for this further penalty the erring woman's sin brings with it, that her honor is distrusted even by him to whose overtures and persuasions she has yielded; and he believes her to have surrendered more easily to others, and gives implicit credence to every suspicion that comes into his mind. All Lothario's good sense seems to have failed him at this juncture; all his prudent maxims escaped his memory; for without once reflecting rationally, and without more ado, in his impatience and in the blindness of the jealous rage that gnawed his heart, and dying to revenge himself upon Camilla, who had done him no wrong, before Anselmo had risen he hastened to him and said to him, "Know, Anselmo, that for several days past I have been struggling with myself, striving to withhold from thee what it is no longer possible or right that I should conceal from thee. Know that Camilla's fortress has surrendered and is ready to submit to my will; and if I have been slow to reveal this fact to thee, it was in order to see if it were some light caprice of hers, or if she sought to try me and ascertain if the love I began to make to her with thy permission was made with a serious intention. I thought, too, that she, if she were what she ought to be, and what we both believed her, would have ere this given the information of my addresses; but seeing that she delays, I believe the truth of the promise she has given me that the next time thou art absent from the house she will grant me an interview in the closet where thy jewels are kept (and it was true that Camilla used to meet him there); but I do not wish thee to rush precipitately to take vengeance, for the sin is as yet only committed in intention, and Camilla's may change perhaps between this and the appointed time, and repentance spring up in its place. As hitherto thou hast always followed my advice wholly or in part, follow and observe this that I will give thee now, so that, without mistake, and with mature deliberation, thou mayest satisfy thyself as to what may seem the best course; pretend to absent thyself for two or three days as thou hast been wont to do on other occasions, and contrive to hide thyself in the closet; for the tapestries and other things there afford great facilities for thy concealment, and then thou wilt see with thine own eyes and I with mine what Camilla's purpose may be. And if it be a guilty one, which may be feared rather than expected, with silence, prudence, and discretion thou canst thyself become the instrument of punishment for the wrong done thee."

Anselmo was amazed, overwhelmed, and astounded at the words of Lothario, which came upon him at a time when he least expected to hear them, for he now looked upon Camilla as having triumphed over the pretended attacks of Lothario, and was beginning to enjoy the glory of her victory. He remained silent for a considerable time, looking on the ground with fixed gaze, and at length said, "Thou hast behaved, Lothario, as I expected of thy friendship: I will follow thy advice in everything; do thou as thou wilt, and keep this secret as thou seest it should be kept in circumstances so unlooked for."

Lothario gave him his word, but after leaving him he repented altogether of what he had said to him, perceiving how foolishly he had acted, as he might have revenged himself upon Camilla in some less cruel and degrading way. He cursed his want of sense, condemned his hasty resolution, and knew not what course to take to undo the mischief or find some ready escape from it. At last he decided upon revealing all to Camilla, and, as there was no want of opportunity for doing so, he found her alone the same day; but she, as soon as she had the chance of speaking to him, said, "Lothario my friend, I must tell thee I have a sorrow in my heart which fills it so that it seems ready to burst; and it will be a wonder if it does not; for the audacity of Leonela has now reached such a pitch that every night she conceals a gallant of hers in this house and remains with him till morning, at the expense of my reputation; inasmuch as it is open to any one to question it who may see him quitting my house at such unseasonable hours; but what distresses me is that I cannot punish or chide her, for her privity to our intrigue bridles my mouth and keeps me silent about hers, while I am dreading that some catastrophe will come of it."

As Camilla said this Lothario at first imagined it was some device to delude him into the idea that the man he had seen going out was Leonela's lover and not hers; but when he saw how she wept and suffered, and begged him to help her, he became convinced of the truth, and the conviction completed his confusion and remorse; however, he told Camilla not to distress herself, as he would take measures to put a stop to the insolence of Leonela. At the same time he told her what, driven by the fierce rage of jealousy, he had said to Anselmo, and how he had arranged to hide himself in the closet that he might there see plainly how little she preserved her fidelity to him; and he entreated her pardon for this madness, and her advice as to how to repair it, and escape safely from the intricate labyrinth in which his imprudence had involved him. Camilla was struck with alarm at hearing what Lothario said, and with much anger, and great good sense, she reproved him and rebuked his base design and the foolish and mischievous resolution he had made; but as woman has by nature a nimbler wit than man for good and for evil, though it is apt to fail when she sets herself deliberately to reason, Camilla on the spur of the moment thought of a way to remedy what was to all appearance irremediable, and told Lothario to contrive that the next day Anselmo should conceal himself in the place he mentioned, for she hoped from his concealment to obtain the means of their enjoying themselves for the future without any apprehension; and without revealing her purpose to him entirely she charged him to be careful, as soon as Anselmo was concealed, to come to her when Leonela should call him, and to all she said to him to answer as he would have answered had he not known that Anselmo was listening. Lothario pressed her to explain her intention fully, so that he might with more certainty and precaution take care to do what he saw to be needful.

"I tell you," said Camilla, "there is nothing to take care of except to answer me what I shall ask you": for she did not wish to explain to him beforehand what she meant to do, fearing lest he should be unwilling to follow out an idea which seemed to her such a good one, and should try or devise some other less practicable plan.

Lothario then retired, and the next day Anselmo, under pretence of going to his friend's country house, took his departure, and then returned to conceal himself, which he was able to do easily, as Camilla and Leonela took care to give him the opportunity; and so he placed himself in hiding in the state of agitation that it may be imagined he would feel who expected to see the vitals of his honor laid bare before his eyes, and found himself on the point of losing the supreme blessing he thought he possessed in his beloved Camilla. Having made sure of Anselmo's being in his hiding-place, Camilla and Leonela entered the closet, and the instant she set foot within it Camilla said, with a deep sigh, "Ah! dear Leonela, would it not be better, before I do what I am unwilling you should know lest you should seek to prevent it, that you should take Anselmo's dagger that I have asked of you and with it pierce this vile heart of mine? But no; there is no reason why I should suffer the punishment of another's fault. I will first know what it is that the bold licentious eyes of Lothario have seen in me that could have encouraged him to reveal to me a design so base as that which he has disclosed regardless of his friend and of my honor. Go to the window, Leonela, and call him, for no doubt he is in the street waiting to carry out his vile project; but mine, cruel it may be, but honorable, shall be carried out first."

"Ah, señora," said the crafty Leonela, who knew her part, "what is it you want to do with this dagger? Can it be that you mean to take your own life,

or Lothario's? for whichever you mean to do, it will lead to the loss of your reputation and good name. It is better to dissemble your wrong and not give this wicked man the chance of entering the house now and finding us alone; consider, señora, we are weak women and he is a man, and determined, and as he comes with such a base purpose, blind and urged by passion, perhaps before you can put yours into execution he may do what will be worse for you than taking your life. Ill betide my master, Anselmo, for giving such authority in his house to this shameless fellow! And supposing you kill him, señora, as I suspect you mean to do, what shall we do with him when he is dead?"

"What, my friend?" replied Camilla, "we shall leave him for Anselmo to bury him; for in reason it will be to him a light labor to hide his own infamy under ground. Summon him, make haste, for all the time I delay in taking vengeance for my wrong seems to me an offence against the loyalty I owe my husband."

Anselmo was listening to all this, and every word that Camilla uttered made him change his mind; but when he heard that it was resolved to kill Lothario his first impulse was to come out and show himself to avert such a disaster; but in his anxiety to see the issue of a resolution so bold and virtuous he restrained himself, intending to come forth in time to prevent the deed. At this moment Camilla, throwing herself upon a bed that was close by, swooned away, and Leonela began to weep bitterly, exclaiming, "Woe is me! that I should be fated to have dying here in my arms the flower of virtue upon earth, the crown of true wives, the pattern of chastity!" with more to the same effect, so that any one who heard her would have taken her for the most tender-hearted and faithful handmaid in the world, and her mistress for another persecuted Penelope.

Camilla was not long in recovering from her fainting fit, and on coming to herself she said, "Why do you not go, Leonela, to call hither that friend, the falsest to his friend the sun ever shone upon or night concealed? Away, run, haste, speed! lest the fire of my wrath burn itself out with delay, and the righteous vengeance that I hope for melt away in menaces and maledictions."

"I am just going to call him, señora," said Leonela; "but you must first give me that dagger, lest while I am gone you should by means of it give cause to all who love you to weep all their lives."

"Go in peace, dear Leonela, I will not do so," said Camilla, "for rash and foolish as I may be, to your mind, in defending my honor, I am not going to be so much so as that Lucretia who they say killed herself without having done anything wrong, and without having first killed him on whom the guilt of her misfortune lay. I shall die, if I am to die; but it must be after full vengeance upon him who has brought me here to weep over audacity that no fault of mine gave birth to."

Leonela required much pressing before she would

go to summon Lothario, but at last she went, and while awaiting her return Camilla continued, as if speaking to herself, "Good God! would it not have been more prudent to have repulsed Lothario, as I have done many a time before, than to allow him, as I am now doing, to think me unchaste and vile, even for the short time I must wait until I undeceive him? No doubt it would have been better; but I should not be avenged, nor the honor of my husband vindicated, should he find so clear and easy an escape from the strait into which his depravity has led him. Let the traitor pay with his life for the temerity of his wanton wishes, let the world know (if haply it shall ever come to know) that Camilla not only preserved her allegiance to her husband, but avenged him of the man who dared to wrong him. Still, I think it might be better to disclose this to Anselmo. But then I have called his attention to it in the letter I wrote to him in the country, and, if he did nothing to prevent the mischief I there pointed out to him, I suppose it was that from pure goodness of heart and trustfulness he would not and could not believe that any thought against his honor could harbor in the breast of so stanch a friend; nor indeed did I myself believe it for many days, nor should I have ever believed it if his insolence had not gone so far as to make it manifest by open presents, lavish promises, and ceaseless tears. But why do I argue thus? Does a bold determination stand in need of arguments? Surely not. Then fears avaunt! Vengeance to my aid! Let the false one come, approach, advance, die, yield up his life, and then befall what may. Pure I came to him whom Heaven bestowed upon me, pure I shall leave him; and at the worst bathed in my own chaste blood and in the foul blood of the falsest friend that friendship ever saw"; and as she uttered these words she paced the room holding the unsheathed dagger, with such irregular and disordered steps, and such gestures that one would have supposed her to have lost her senses, and taken her for some violent desperado instead of a delicate woman.

Anselmo, concealed behind some tapestries where he had hidden himself, beheld and was amazed at all, and already felt that what he had seen and heard was a sufficient answer to even greater suspicions; and he would have been now well pleased if the proof afforded by Lothario's coming were dispensed with, as he feared some sudden mishap; but as he was on the point of showing himself and coming forth to embrace and undeceive his wife he paused as he saw Leonela returning, leading Lothario. Camilla when she saw him, drawing a long line in front of her on the floor with the dagger, said to him, "Lothario, pay attention to what I say to thee: if by any chance thou darest to cross this line thou seest, or even approach it, the instant I see thee attempt it that same instant will I pierce my bosom with this dagger that I hold in my hand; and before thou answerest me a word I desire thee to listen to a few from me, and afterwards thou shalt

reply as may please thee. First, I desire thee to tell me, Lothario, if thou knowest my husband Anselmo, and in what light thou regardest him; and secondly I desire to know if thou knowest me too. Answer me this, without embarrassment or reflecting deeply what thou wilt answer, for they are no riddles I put to thee."

Lothario was not so dull but that from the first moment when Camilla directed him to make Anselmo hide himself he understood what she intended to do, and therefore he fell in with her idea so readily and promptly that between them they made the imposture look more true than truth; so he answered her thus: "I did not think, fair Camilla, that thou wert calling me to ask questions so remote from the object with which I come; but if it is to defer the promised reward thou art doing so, thou mightest have put it off still longer, for the longing for happiness gives the more distress the nearer comes the hope of gaining it; but lest thou shouldst say that I do not answer thy questions, I say that I know thy husband Anselmo, and that we have known each other from our earliest years; I will not speak of what thou too knowest, of our friendship, that I may not compel myself to testify against the wrong that love, the mighty excuse for greater errors, makes me inflict upon him. Thee I know and hold in the same estimation as he does, for were it not so I had not for a lesser prize acted in opposition to what I owe to my station and the holy laws of true friendship, now broken and violated by me through that powerful enemy, love."

"If thou dost confess that," returned Camilla, "mortal enemy of all that rightly deserves to be loved, with what face dost thou dare to come before one whom thou knowest to be the mirror wherein he is reflected on whom thou shouldst look to see how unworthy thou wrongest him? But, woe is me, I now comprehend what has made thee give so little heed to what thou owest to thyself; it must have been some freedom of mine, for I will not call it immodesty, as it did not proceed from any deliberate intention, but from some heedlessness such as women are guilty of through inadvertence when they think they have no occasion for reserve. But tell me, traitor, when did I by word or sign give a reply to thy prayers that could awaken in thee a shadow of hope of attaining thy base wishes? When were not thy professions of love sternly and scornfully rejected and rebuked? When were thy frequent pledges and still more frequent gifts believed or accepted? But as I am persuaded that no one can long persevere in the attempt to win love unsustained by some hope, I am willing to attribute to myself the blame of thy assurance, for no doubt some thoughtlessness of mine has all this time fostered thy hopes; and therefore will I punish myself and inflict upon myself the penalty thy guilt deserves. And that thou mayest see that being so relentless to myself I cannot possibly be otherwise to thee, I have summoned thee to be a witness of the sacrifice I mean to offer to the injured honor of my honored husband, wronged by thee with all the assiduity thou wert capable of, and by me too through want of caution in avoiding every occasion, if I have given any, of encouraging and sanctioning thy base designs. Once more I say the suspicion in my mind that some imprudence of mine has engendered these lawless thoughts in thee, is what causes me most distress and what I desire most to punish with my own hands, for were any other instrument of punishment employed my error might become perhaps more widely known; but before I do so, in my death I mean to inflict death, and take with me one that will fully satisfy my longing for the revenge I hope for and have; for I shall see, wheresoever it may be that I go, the penalty awarded by inflexible, unswerving justice on him who has placed me in a position so desperate."

As she uttered these words, with incredible energy and swiftness she flew upon Lotario with the naked dagger, so manifestly bent on burying it in his breast that he was almost uncertain whether these demonstrations were real or feigned, for he was obliged to have recourse to all his skill and strength to prevent her from striking him; and with such reality did she act this strange farce and mystification that, to give it a color of truth, she determined to stain it with her own blood; for perceiving, or pretending, that she could not wound Lothario, she said, "Fate, it seems, will not grant my just desire complete satisfaction, but it will not be able to keep me from satisfying it partially at least"; and making an effort to free the hand with the dagger which Lothario held in his grasp, she released it, and directing the point to a place where it could not inflict a deep wound, she plunged it into her left side high up close to the shoulder, and then allowed herself to fall to the ground as if in a faint.

Leonela and Lotario stood amazed and astounded at the catastrophe, and seeing Camilla stretched on the ground and bathed in her blood they were uncertain as to the true nature of the act. Lotario, terrified and breathless, ran in haste to pluck out the dagger; but when he saw how slight the wound was he was relieved of his fears and once more admired the subtlety, coolness, and ready wit of the fair Camilla; and the better to support the part he had to play he began to utter profuse and doleful lamentations over her body as if she were dead, invoking maledictions not only on himself but also on him who had been the means of placing him in such a position: and knowing that his friend Anselmo heard him he spoke in such a way as to make a listener feel much more pity for him than for Camilla, even though he supposed her dead. Leonela took her up in her arms and laid her on the bed, entreating Lotario to go in quest of some one to attend to her wound in secret, and at the same time asking his advice and opinion as to what they should say to Anselmo about his lady's wound if he should chance to return before it was healed. He replied they might say what they liked, for he was not in a state to give advice that would be of any use; all he

could tell her was to try and stanch the blood, as he was going where he should never more be seen; and with every appearance of deep grief and sorrow he left the house; but when he found himself alone, and where there was nobody to see him, he crossed himself unceasingly, lost in wonder at the adroitness of Camilla and the consistent acting of Leonela. He reflected how convinced Anselmo would be that he had a second Portia for a wife, and he looked forward anxiously to meeting him in order to rejoice together over falsehood and truth the most craftily veiled that could possibly be imagined.

Leonela, as he told her, stanched her lady's blood, which was no more than sufficed to support her deception; and washing the wound with a little wine she bound it up to the best of her skill, talking all the time she was tending her in a strain that, even if nothing else had been said before, would have been enough to assure Anselmo that he had in Camilla a model of purity. To Leonela's words Camilla added her own, calling herself cowardly and wanting in spirit, since she had not enough at the time she had most need of it to rid herself of the life she so much loathed. She asked her attendant's advice as to whether or not she ought to inform her beloved husband of all that had happened, but the other bade her say nothing about it, as she would lay upon him the obligation of taking vengeance on Lothario, which he could not do but at great risk to himself; and it was the duty of a true wife not to give her husband provocation to quarrel, but, on the contrary, to remove it as far as possible from him.

Camilla replied that she believed she was right and that she would follow her advice, but at any rate it would be well to consider how she was to explain the wound to Anselmo, for he could not help seeing it; to which Leonela answered that she did not know how to tell a lie even in jest.

"How then can I know, my dear?" said Camilla, "for I should not dare to forge or keep up a falsehood if my life depended on it. If we can think of no escape from this difficulty, it will be better to tell him the plain truth than that he should find us out in an untrue story."

"Be not uneasy, señora," said Leonela; "between this and tomorrow I will think of what we must say to him, and perhaps the wound being where it is it can be hidden from his sight, and Heaven will be pleased to aid us in a purpose so good and honorable. Compose yourself, señora, and endeavor to calm your excitement lest my lord find you agitated; and leave the rest to my care and God's, who always supports good intentions."

Anselmo had with the deepest attention listened to and seen played out the tragedy of the death of his honor, which the performers acted with such wonderfully effective truth that it seemed as if they had become the realities of the parts they played. He longed for night and an opportunity of escaping from the house to go and see his good friend Lothario, and with him give vent to his joy over the precious pearl he had gained in having established his wife's purity. Both mistress and maid took care to give him time and opportunity to get away, and taking advantage of it he made his escape, and at once went in quest of Lothario, and it would be impossible to describe how he embraced him when he found him, and the things he said to him in the joy of his heart, and the praises he bestowed upon Camilla; all which Lothario listened to without being able to show any pleasure, for he could not forget how deceived his friend was and how dishonorably he had wronged him; and though Anselmo could see that Lothario was not glad, still he imagined it was only because he had left Camilla wounded and had been himself the cause of it; and so among other things he told him not to be distressed about Camilla's accident, for, as they had agreed to hide it from him, the wound was evidently trifling; and that being so, he had no cause for fear, but should henceforward be of good cheer and rejoice with him, seeing that by his means and adroitness he found himself raised to the greatest height of happiness that he could have ventured to hope for, and desired no better pastime than making verses in praise of Camilla that would preserve her name for all time to come. Lothario commended his purpose, and promised on his own part to aid him in raising a monument so glorious.

And so Anselmo was left the most charmingly hoodwinked man there could be in the world. He himself, persuaded he was conducting the instrument of his glory, led home by the hand him who had been the utter destruction of his good name; whom Camilla received with averted countenance, though with smiles in her heart. The deception was carried on for some time, until at the end of a few months Fortune turned her wheel and the guilt which had been until then so skilfully concealed was published abroad, and Anselmo paid with his life the penalty of his ill-advised curiosity.

Chapter 35

Which treats of the heroic and prodigious battle Don Quixote had with certain skins of red wine, and brings The Novel of the Ill-advised Curiosity *to a close*

THERE remained but little more of the novel to be read, when Sancho Panza burst forth in wild excitement from the garret where Don Quixote was lying, shouting, "Run, sirs! quick; and help my master, who is in the thick of the toughest and stiffest battle I ever laid eyes on. By the living God he has given the giant, the enemy of my lady the Princess Micomicona, such a slash that he has sliced his head clean off as if it were a turnip."

"What are you talking about, brother?" said the curate, pausing as he was about to read the remainder of the novel. "Are you in your senses, Sancho? How the devil can it be as you say, when the giant is two thousand leagues away?"

Here they heard a loud noise in the chamber, and Don Quixote shouting out, "Stand, thief, brigand, villain; now I have got thee and thy cimeter shall not avail thee!" And then it seemed as though he were slashing vigorously at the wall.

"Don't stop to listen," said Sancho, "but go in and part them or help my master: though there is no need of that now, for no doubt the giant is dead by this time and giving account to God of his past wicked life; for I saw the blood flowing on the ground, and the head cut off and fallen on one side, and it is as big as a large wineskin."

"May I die," said the landlord at this, "if Don Quixote or Don Devil has not been slashing some of the skins of red wine that stand full at his bed's head, and the spilt wine must be what this good fellow takes for blood"; and so saying he went into the room and the rest after him, and there they found Don Quixote in the strangest costume in the world. He was in his shirt, which was not long enough in front to cover his thighs completely and was six fingers shorter behind; his legs were very long and lean, covered with hair, and anything but clean; on his head he had a little greasy red cap that belonged to the host, round his left arm he had rolled the blanket of the bed, to which Sancho, for reasons best known to himself, owed a grudge, and in his right hand he held his unsheathed sword, with which he was slashing about on all sides, uttering exclamations as if he were actually fighting some giant: and the best of it was his eyes were not open, for he was fast asleep, and dreaming that he was doing battle with the giant. For his imagination was so wrought upon by the adventure he was going to accomplish, that it made him dream he had already reached the kingdom of Micomicon, and was engaged in combat with his enemy; and believing he was laying on to the giant, he had given so many sword cuts to the skins that the whole room was full of wine. On seeing this the landlord was so enraged that he fell on Don Quixote, and with his clinched fist began to pummel him in such a way, that if Cardenio and the curate had not dragged him off, he would have brought the war of the giant to an end. But in spite of all the poor gentleman never woke until the barber brought a great pot of cold water from the well and flung it with one dash all over his body, on which Don Quixote woke up, but not so completely as to understand what was the matter. Dorothea, seeing how short and slight his attire was, would not go in to witness the battle between her champion and her opponent. As for Sancho, he went searching all over the floor for the head of the giant, and not finding it he said, "I see now that it's all enchantment in this house; for the last time, on this very spot where I am now, I got ever so many thumps and thwacks without knowing who gave them to me, or being able to see anybody; and now this head is not to be seen anywhere about, though I saw it cut off with my own eyes and the blood running from the body as if from a fountain."

"What blood and fountains are you talking about, enemy of God and his saints?" said the landlord. "Don't you see, you thief, that the blood and the fountain are only these skins here that have been stabbed and the red wine swimming all over the room?—and I wish I saw the soul of him that stabbed them swimming in hell."

"I know nothing about that," said Sancho; "all I know is it will be my bad luck that through not finding this head my country will melt away like salt in water"—for Sancho awake was far worse than his master asleep, so much had his master's promises addled his wits.

The landlord was beside himself at the coolness of the squire and the mischievous doings of the master, and swore it should not be like the last time when they went without paying; and that their privileges of chivalry should not hold good this time to let one or other of them off without paying, even to the cost of the plugs that would have to be put to the damaged wineskins. The curate was holding Don Quixote's hands, who, fancying he had now ended the adventure and was in the presence of the Princess Micomicona, knelt before the curate and said, "Exalted and beauteous lady, your highness may live from this day forth fearless of any harm this base being could do you; and I too from this day forth am released from the promise I gave you, since by the help of God on high and by the favor of her by whom I live and breathe, I have fulfilled it so successfully."

"Did not I say so?" said Sancho on hearing this. "You see I wasn't drunk; there you see my master has already salted the giant; there's no doubt about the bulls: my country is all right!"

Who could have helped laughing at the absurdities of the pair, master and man? And laugh they did, all except the landlord, who cursed himself; but at length the barber, Cardenio, and the curate contrived with no small trouble to get Don Quixote on the bed, and he fell asleep with every appearance of excessive weariness. They

left him to sleep, and came out to the gate of the inn to console Sancho Panza on not having found the head of the giant; but much more work had they to appease the landlord, who was furious at the sudden death of his wine-skins; and said the landlady, half scolding, half crying, "At an evil moment and in an unlucky hour he came into my house, this knight-errant—would that I had never set eyes on him, for dear he has cost me; the last time he went off with the overnight score against him for supper, bed, straw, and barley, for himself and his squire and a hack and an ass, saying he was a knight adventurer—God send unlucky adventures to him and all the adventurers in the world—and therefore not bound to pay anything, for it was so settled by the knight-errantry tariff: and then, all because of him, came the other gentleman and carried off my tail, and gives it back more than two quartillos the worse, all stripped of its hair, so that it is no use for my husband's purpose; and then, for a finishing touch to all, to burst my wine-skins and spill my wine! I wish I saw his own blood spilt! But let him not deceive himself, for, by the bones of my father and the shade of my mother, they shall pay me down every quarto; or my name is not what it is, and I am not my father's daughter." All this and more to the same effect the landlady delivered with great irritation, and her good maid Maritornes backed her up, while the daughter held her peace and smiled from time to time. The curate smoothed matters by promising to make good all losses to the best of his power, not only as regarded the wine-skins but also the wine, and above all the depreciation of the tail which they set such store by. Dorothea comforted Sancho, telling him that she pledged herself, as soon as it should appear certain that his master had decapitated the giant, and she found herself peacefully established in her kingdom, to bestow upon him the best county there was in it. With this Sancho consoled himself, and assured the princess she might rely upon it that he had seen the head of the giant, and more by token it had a beard that reached to the girdle, and that if it was not to be seen now it was because everything that happened in that house went by enchantment, as he himself had proved the last time he had lodged there. Dorothea said she fully believed it, and that he need not be uneasy, for all would go well and turn out as he wished. All therefore being appeased, the curate was anxious to get on with the novel, as he saw there was but little more left to read. Dorothea and the others begged him to finish it, and he, as he was willing to please them, and enjoyed reading it himself, continued the tale in these words:

The result was, that from the confidence Anselmo felt in the virtue of Camilla, he lived happy and free from anxiety, and Camilla purposely looked coldly on Lothario, that Anselmo might suppose her feelings towards him to be the opposite of what they were; and the better to support the position, Lothario begged to be excused from coming to the house, as the displeasure with which Camilla regarded his presence was plain to be seen. But the befooled Anselmo said he would on no account allow such a thing, and so in a thousand ways he became the author of his own dishonor, while he believed he was insuring his happiness. Meanwhile the satisfaction with which Leonela saw herself empowered to carry on her amour reached such a height that, regardless of everything else, she followed her inclinations unrestrainedly, feeling confident that her mistress would screen her, and even show her how to manage it safely. At last one night Anselmo heard footsteps in Leonela's room, and on trying to enter to see who it was, he found that the door was held against him, which made him all the more determined to open it; and exerting his strength he forced it open, and entered the room in time to see a man leaping through the window into the street. He ran quickly to seize him or discover who he was, but he was unable to effect either purpose, for Leonela flung her arms around him crying, "Be calm, señor; do not give way to passion or follow him who has escaped from this; he belongs to me, and in fact he is my husband."

Anselmo would not believe it, but blind with rage drew a dagger and threatened to stab Leonela, bidding her tell the truth or he would kill her. She, in her fear, not knowing what she was saying, exclaimed, "Do not kill me, señor, for I can tell you things more important than any you can imagine."

"Tell me then at once or thou diest," said Anselmo.

"It would be impossible for me now," said Leonela, "I am so agitated: leave me till to-morrow, and then you shall hear from me what will fill you with astonishment; but rest assured that he who leaped through the window is a young man of this city, who has given me his promise to become my husband."

Anselmo was appeased with this, and was content to wait the time she asked of him, for he never expected to hear anything against Camilla, so satisfied and sure of her virtue was he; and so he quitted the room, and left Leonela locked in, telling her she should not come out until she had told him all she had to make known to him. He went at once to see Camilla, and tell her, as he did, all that had passed between him and her handmaid, and the promise she had given him to inform him of matters of serious importance.

There is no need of saying whether Camilla was agitated or not, for so great was her fear and dis[tress] may, that, making sure, as she had good reason t[o] do, that Leonela would tell Anselmo all she knew of her faithlessness, she had not the courage to wai[t] and see if her suspicions were confirmed; and tha[t] same night, as soon as she thought that Anselm[o] was asleep, she packed up the most valuable jewel[s] she had and some money, and without being ob[-] served by anybody escaped from the house and be[took] herself to Lothario's to whom she related wha[t] had occurred, imploring him to convey her to som[e] place of safety or fly with her where they might b[e] safe from Anselmo. The state of perplexity to whic[h] Camilla reduced Lothario was such that he was un[-] able to utter a word in reply, still less to decide up[on] what he should do. At length he resolved to con[-] duct her to a convent of which a sister of his wa[s] prioress; Camilla agreed to this, and with the spee[d] which the circumstances demanded, Lothario too[k] her to the convent and left her there, and then him[-] self quitted the city without letting any one kno[w] of his departure.

As soon as daylight came Anselmo, without miss[-] ing Camilla from his side, rose eager to learn wha[t] Leonela had to tell him, and hastened to the roo[m] where he had locked her in. He opened the doo[r] entered, but found no Leonela; all he found wa[s] some sheets knotted to the window, a plain proo[f] that she had let herself down from it and escaped[.] He returned, uneasy, to tell Camilla, but not find[-] ing her in bed or anywhere in the house he was los[t] in amazement. He asked the servants of the hous[e] about her, but none of them could give him an[y] explanation. As he was going in search of Camill[a] it happened by chance that he observed her boxe[s] were lying open, and that the greater part of he[r] jewels were gone; and now he became fully awar[e] of his disgrace, and that Leonela was not the caus[e] of his misfortune; and, just as he was, without d[e-] laying to dress himself completely, he repaired, sa[d] at heart and dejected, to his friend Lothario to mak[e] known his sorrow to him; but when he failed t[o] find him and the servants reported that he had bee[n] absent from his house all night and had taken wit[h] him all the money he had, he felt as though he wer[e] losing his senses; and to make all complete on r[e-] turning to his own house he found it deserted an[d] empty, not one of all his servants, male or femal[e,] remaining in it. He knew not what to think, or say[,] or do, and his reason seemed to be deserting hi[m] little by little. He reviewed his position, and sa[w] himself in a moment left without wife, friend, o[r] servants, abandoned, he felt, by the heaven abov[e] him, and more than all robbed of his honor, for i[n] Camilla's disappearance he saw his own ruin. Afte[r] long reflection he resolved at last to go to his friend['s] country house where he had been staying when h[e] afforded opportunities for the contrivance of th[is] complication of misfortune. He locked the doors o[f] his house, mounted his horse, and with a broke[n] spirit set out on his journey; but he had hardly gon[e] half-way when, harassed by his reflections, he ha[d] to dismount and tie his horse to a tree, at the foot of which he threw himself, giving vent to piteous heart-rending sighs; and there he remained till nearly nightfall, when he observed a man approaching on horseback from the city, of whom, after saluting him, he asked what was the news in Florence.

The citizen replied, "The strangest that have been heard for many a day; for it is reported abroad that Lothario, the great friend of the wealthy Anselmo, who lived at San Giovanni, carried off last night Camilla, the wife of Anselmo, who also has disappeared. All this has been told by a maid-servant of Camilla's, whom the governor found last night lowering herself by a sheet from the windows of Anselmo's house. I know not indeed, precisely, how the affair came to pass; all I know is that the whole city is wondering at the occurrence, for no one could have expected a thing of the kind, seeing the great and intimate friendship that existed between them, so great, they say, that they were called 'The two Friends.'"

"Is it known at all," said Anselmo, "what road Lothario and Camilla took?"

"Not in the least," said the citizen, "though the governor has been very active in searching for them."

"God speed you, señor," said Anselmo.

"God be with you," said the citizen, and went his way.

This disastrous intelligence almost robbed Anselmo not only of his senses, but of his life. He got up as well as he was able, and reached the house of his friend, who as yet knew nothing of his misfortune, but seeing him come pale, worn, and haggard, perceived that he was suffering some heavy affliction. Anselmo at once begged to be allowed to retire to rest, and to be given writing materials. His wish was complied with, and he was left lying down and alone, for he desired this, and even that the door should be locked. Finding himself alone, he so took to heart the thought of his misfortune that by the signs of death he felt within him, he knew well his life was drawing to a close, and therefore he resolved to leave behind him a declaration of the cause of his strange end. He began to write, but before he had put down all he meant to say, his breath failed him, and he yielded up his life, a victim to the suffering which his ill-advised curiosity had entailed upon him. The master of the house observing that it was now late and that Anselmo did not call, determined to go in and ascertain if his indisposition was increasing, and found him lying on his face, his body partly in the bed, partly on the writing-table, on which he lay with the written paper open and the pen still in his hand. Having first called to him without receiving any answer, his host approached him, and taking him by the hand, found that it was cold, and saw that he was dead. Greatly surprised and distressed he summoned the household to witness the sad fate which had befallen Anselmo; and then he read the paper, the handwriting of which he recognized as his, and which contained these words:

"A foolish and ill-advised desire has robbed me of life. If the news of my death should reach the ears of Camilla, let her know that I forgive her, for she was not bound to perform miracles, nor ought I to have required her to perform them; and since I have been the author of my own dishonor, there is no reason why"—

So far Anselmo had written, and thus it was plain that at this point, before he could finish what he had to say, his life came to an end. The next day his friend sent intelligence of his death to his relatives, who had already ascertained his misfortune, as well as the convent where Camilla lay almost on the point of accompanying her husband on that inevitable journey, not on account of the tidings of his death, but because of those she received of her lover's departure. Although she saw herself a widow, it is said she refused either to quit the convent or take the veil, until, not long afterwards, intelligence reached her that Lothario had been killed in a battle in which M. de Lautrec had been recently engaged with the Great Captain Gonzalo Fernandez de Cordova in the kingdom of Naples, whither her too late repentant lover had repaired. On learning this Camilla took the veil, and shortly afterwards died, worn out by grief and melancholy. This was the end of all three, an end that came of a thoughtless beginning.

"I like this novel," said the curate; "but I can not persuade myself of its truth; and if it has been invented, the author's invention is faulty, for it is impossible to imagine any husband so foolish as to try such a costly experiment as Anselmo's. If it had been represented as occurring between a gallant and his mistress it might pass; but between husband and wife there is something of an impossibility about it. As to the way in which the story is told, however, I have no fault to find."

Chapter 36

Which treats of more curious incidents that occurred at the inn

Just at that instant the landlord, who was standing at the gate of the inn, exclaimed, "Here comes a fine troop of guests; if they stop here we may say *gaudeamus.*"

"What are they?" said Cardenio.

"Four men," said the landlord, "riding *à la jineta,*[1] with lances and bucklers, and all with black veils, and with them there is a woman in white on a side-saddle, whose face is also veiled, and two attendants on foot."

"Are they very near?" said the curate.

"So near," answered the landlord, "that here they come."

[1] *i.e.* on high saddles with short stirrups.

Hearing this Dorothea covered her face, and Cardenio retreated into Don Quixote's room, and they hardly had time to do so before the whole party the host had described entered the inn, and the four that were on horseback, who were of highbred appearance and bearing, dismounted, and came forward to take down the woman who rode on the side-saddle, and one of them taking her in his arms placed her in a chair that stood at the entrance of the room where Cardenio had hidden himself. All this time neither she nor they had removed their veils or spoken a word, only on sitting down on the chair the woman gave a deep sigh and let her arms fall like one that was ill and weak. The attendants on foot then led the horses away to the stable. Observing this the curate, curious to know who these people in such a dress and preserving such silence were, went to where the servants were standing and put the question to one of them, who answered him, "Faith, sir, I can not tell you who they are, I only know they seem to be people of distinction, particularly he who advanced to take the lady you saw in his arms; and I say so because all the rest show him respect, and nothing is done except what he directs and orders."

"And the lady, who is she?" asked the curate.

"That I can not tell you either," said the servant, "for I have not seen her face all the way: I have indeed heard her sigh many times and utter such groans that she seems to be giving up the ghost every time: but it is no wonder if we do not know more than we have told you, as my comrade and I have only been in their company two days, for having met us on the road they begged and persuaded us to accompany them to Andalusia, promising to pay us well."

"And have you heard any of them called by his name?" asked the curate.

"No, indeed," replied the servant; "they all preserve a marvellous silence on the road, for not a sound is to be heard among them except the poor lady's sighs and sobs, which make us pity her; and we feel sure that wherever it is she is going, it is against her will, and as far as one can judge from her dress she is a nun or, what is more likely, about to become one; and perhaps it is because taking the vows is not of her own free will, that she is so unhappy as she seems to be."

"That may well be," said the curate, and leaving them he returned to where Dorothea was, who, hearing the veiled lady sigh, moved by natural compassion drew near to her and said, "What are you suffering from, señora? If it be anything that women are accustomed, and know how to relieve, I for my part offer you my services with all my heart."

To this the unhappy lady made no reply; and though Dorothea repeated her offers more earnestly she still kept silence, until the gentleman with the veil, who, the servant said, was obeyed by the rest, approached and said to Dorothea, "Do not give yourself the trouble, señora, of making any offers to that woman, for it is her way to give no thanks for anything that is done for her; and do not try to make her answer unless you want to hear some lie from her lips."

"I have never told a lie," was the immediate reply of her who had been silent until now; "on the contrary, it is because I am so truthful and so ignorant of lying devices that I am now in this miserable condition; and this I call you yourself to witness, for it is my unstained truth that has made you false and a liar."

Cardenio heard these words clearly and distinctly, being quite close to the speaker, for there was only the door of Don Quixote's room between them, and the instant he did so, uttering a loud exclamation he cried, "Good God! what is this I hear? What voice is this that has reached my ears?" Startled at the voice the lady turned her head; and not seeing the speaker she stood up and attempted to enter the room; observing which the gentleman held her back, preventing her from moving a step. In her agitation and sudden movement the silk with which she had covered her face fell off and disclosed a countenance of incomparable and marvellous beauty, but pale and terrified; for she kept turning her eyes, everywhere she could direct her gaze, with an eagerness that made her look as if she had lost her senses, and so marked that it excited the pity of Dorothea and all who beheld her, though they knew not what caused it. The gentleman grasped her firmly by the shoulders, and being so fully occupied with holding her back, he was unable to put a hand to his veil which was falling off, as it did at length entirely, and Dorothea, who was holding the lady in her arms, raising her eyes saw that he who likewise held her was her husband, Don Fernando. The instant she recognized him, with a prolonged plaintive cry drawn from the depths of her heart, she fell backwards fainting, and but for the barber being close by to catch her in his arms, she would have fallen completely to the ground. The curate at once hastened to uncover her face and throw water on it, and as he did so Don Fernando, for he it was who held the other in his arms, recognized her and stood as if death-stricken by the sight; not, however, relaxing his grasp of Luscinda, for it was she that was struggling to release herself from his hold, having recognized Cardenio by his voice, as he had recognized her. Cardenio also heard Dorothea's cry as she fell fainting, and imagining that it came from his Luscinda burst forth in terror from the room, and the first thing he saw was Don Fernando with Luscinda in his arms. Don Fernando, too, knew Cardenio at once; and all three, Luscinda, Cardenio, and Dorothea, stood in silent amazement scarcely knowing what had happened to them.

They gazed at one another without speaking, Dorothea at Don Fernando, Don Fernando at Cardenio, Cardenio at Luscinda, and Luscinda at Cardenio. The first to break silence was Luscinda, who thus addressed Don Fernando: "Leave me, Señor Don Fernando, for the sake of what you owe to yourself; if no other reason will induce you, leave me to cling to the wall of which I am the ivy, to the support from which neither your importunities, nor your threats, nor your promises, nor your gifts have been able to detach me. See how Heaven, by ways strange and hidden from our sight, has brought me face to face with my true husband; and well you know by dear-bought experience that death alone will be able to efface him from my memory. May this plain declaration, then, lead you, as you can do nothing else, to turn your love into rage, your affection into resentment, and so to take my life; for if I yield it up in the presence of my beloved husband I count it well bestowed; it may be by my death he will be convinced that I kept my faith to him to the last moment of life."

Meanwhile Dorothea had come to herself, and had heard Luscinda's words, by means of which she divined who she was; but seeing that Don Fernando did not yet release her or reply to her, summoning up her resolution as well as she could she rose and knelt at his feet, and with a flood of bright and touching tears addressed him thus:

"If, my lord, the beams of that sun that thou holdest eclipsed in thine arms did not dazzle and rob thine eyes of sight thou wouldst have seen by this time that she who kneels at thy feet is, so long as thou wilt have it so, the unhappy and unfortunate Dorothea. I am that lowly peasant girl whom thou in thy goodness or for thy pleasure wouldst raise high enough to call herself thine; I am she who in the seclusion of innocence led a contented life until at the voice of thy importunity, and thy true and tender passion, as it

seemed, she opened the gates of her modesty and surrendered to thee the keys of her liberty; a gift received by thee but thanklessly as is clearly shown by my forced retreat to the place where thou dost find me, and by thy appearance under the circumstances in which I see thee. Nevertheless, I would not have thee suppose that I have come here driven by my shame; it is only grief and sorrow at seeing myself forgotten by thee that have led me. It was thy will to make me thine, and thou didst so follow thy will, that now, even though thou repentest, thou canst not help being mine. Bethink thee, my lord, the unsurpassable affection I bear thee may compensate for the beauty and noble birth for which thou wouldst desert me. Thou canst not be the fair Luscinda's because thou art mine, nor can she be thine because she is Cardenio's; and it will be easier, remember, to bend thy will to love one who adores thee, than to lead one to love thee who abhors thee now. Thou didst address thyself to my simplicity, thou didst lay siege to my virtue, thou wert not ignorant of my station, well dost thou know how I yielded wholly to thy will; there is no ground or reason for thee to plead deception, and if it be so, as it is, and if thou art a Christian as thou art a gentleman, why dost thou by such subterfuges put off making me as happy at last as thou didst at first? And if thou wilt not have me for what I am, thy true and lawful wife, at least take and accept me as thy slave, for so long as I am thine I will count myself happy and fortunate. Do not by deserting me let my shame become the talk of the gossips in the streets; make not the old age of my parents miserable; for the loyal services they as faithful vassals have ever rendered thine are not deserving of such a return; and if thou thinkest it will debase thy blood to mingle it with mine, reflect that there is little or no nobility in the world that has not travelled the same road, and that in illustrious lineages it is not the woman's blood that is of account; and, moreover, that true nobility consists in virtue, and if thou art wanting in that, refusing me what in justice thou owest me, then even I have higher claims to nobility than thine. To make an end, señor, these are my last words to thee: whether thou wilt, or wilt not, I am thy wife; witness thy words, which must not and ought not to be false, if thou dost pride thyself on that for want of which thou scornest me; witness the pledge which thou didst give me, and witness Heaven, which thou thyself didst call to witness the promise thou hadst made me; and if all this fail, thy own conscience will not fail to lift up its silent voice in the midst of all thy gayety, and vindicate the truth of what I say and mar thy highest pleasure and enjoyment."

All this and more the injured Dorothea delivered with such earnest feeling and such tears that all present, even those who came with Don Fernando, were constrained to join her in them. Don Fernando listened to her without replying, until, ceasing to speak, she gave way to such sobs and sighs that it must have been a heart of brass that was not softened by the sight of so great sorrow. Luscinda stood regarding her with no less compassion for her sufferings than admiration for her intelligence and beauty, and would have gone to her to say some words of comfort to her, but was prevented by Don Fernando's grasp which held her fast. He, overwhelmed with confusion and astonishment, after regarding Dorothea for some moments with a fixed gaze, opened his arms, and, releasing Luscinda, exclaimed, "Thou hast conquered, fair Dorothea, thou hast conquered, for it is impossible to have the heart to deny the united force of so many truths."

Luscinda in her feebleness was on the point of falling to the ground when Don Fernando released her, but Cardenio, who stood near, having retreated behind Don Fernando to escape recognition, casting fear aside and regardless of what might happen, ran forward to support her, and said as he clasped her in his arms, "If Heaven in its compassion is willing to let thee rest at last, mistress of my heart, true, constant, and fair, nowhere canst thou rest more safely than in these arms that now receive thee, and received thee before when fortune permitted me to call thee mine."

At these words Luscinda looked up at Cardenio, at first beginning to recognize him by his voice and then satisfying herself by her eyes that it was he, and hardly knowing what she did, and heedless of all considerations of decorum, she flung her arms around his neck and pressing her face close to his, said, "Yes, my dear lord, you are the true master of this your slave, even though adverse fate interpose again, and fresh dangers threaten this life that hangs on yours."

A strange sight was this for Don Fernando and those that stood around, filled with surprise at an incident so unlooked for. Dorothea fancied that Don Fernando changed color and looked as though he meant to take vengeance on Cardenio, for she observed him put his hand to his sword; and the instant the idea struck her, with wonderful quickness she clasped him round the knees, and kissing them and holding him so as to prevent his moving, she said, while her tears continued to flow, "What is it thou wouldst do my only refuge, in this unforeseen event? Thou hast thy wife at thy feet, and she whom thou wouldst have for thy wife is in the arms of her husband: reflect whether it will be right for thee whether it will be possible for thee to undo what Heaven has done, or whether it will be becoming in thee to seek to raise her to be thy mate who in spite of every obstacle, and strong in her truth and constancy, is before thine eyes bathing with the tears of love the face and bosom of her lawful husband. For God's sake I entreat of thee, for thine own I implore thee let not this open manifestation rouse thy anger but rather so calm it as to allow these two lover to live in peace and quiet without any interference from thee so long as Heaven permit them; and in so doing thou wilt prove the generosity of thy lofty noble spirit, and the world shall see that with thee reason has more influence than passion."

All the while Dorothea was speaking Cardenio, though he held Luscinda in his arms never took his eyes off Don Fernando, determined, if he saw him make any hostile movement, to try and defend himself and resist a best he could all who might assail him, though it should cost him his life. But now Don Fernando's friends, as well as the curate and the barber, who had been present all the while, not forgetting the worthy Sancho Panza, ran forward and gathered round Don Fernando, entreating him to have regard for the tears of Dorothea and not suffer her reasonable hopes to be disappointed, since, as they firmly believed, what she said was but the truth; and bidding him observe that it was not, as it might seem, by accident but by a special disposition of Providence that they had all met in a place where no one could have expected a meeting. And the curate bade him remember that only death could part Luscinda from Cardenio; that even if some sword were to separate them they would think their death most happy; and that in a case that admitted of no remedy his wisest course was, by conquering and putting a constraint upon himself to show a generous mind, and of his own accord suffer these two to enjoy the happiness Heaven had granted them. He bade him, too, turn his eyes upon the beauty of Dorothea and he would see that few if any could equal much less exce her; while to that beauty should be added he modesty and the surpassing love she bore him. But besides all this, he reminded him that if he prided himself on being a gentleman and a Christian, he could not do otherwise than keep his plighted word; and that in doing so he would obey God and meet the approval of all sensible people, who know and recognize it to be the privilege of beauty, even in one of humble birth, provided virtue accompany it, to be able to raise itself to the level of any rank, without any slur upon him who places it upon an equality with himself; and furthermore that when the potent sway of passion asserts itself, so long as there be no mixture of sin in it, he is not to be blamed who gives way to it.

To be brief, they added to these such other forcible arguments that Don Fernando's manly heart, being after all nourished by noble blood, was touched, and yielded to the truth which, even had he wished it, he could not gainsay; and he showed his submission, and acceptance of the good advice that had been offered to him, by stooping down and embracing Dorothea, saying to her, "Rise, dear lady, it is not right that what I hold in my heart should be kneeling at my feet; and if until now I have shown no sign of what I own, it may have been by Heaven's decree in order that, seeing the constancy with which you love me, I may learn to value you as you deserve. What I entreat of you is that you reproach me not with my transgression and grievous wrong-doing; for the same cause and force that drove me to make you mine impelled me to struggle against being yours; and to prove this, turn and look at the eyes of the now happy Luscinda, and you will see in them an excuse for all my errors: and as she has found and gained the object of her desires, and I have found in you what satisfies all my wishes, may she live in peace and contentment as many happy years with her Cardenio, as on my knees I pray Heaven to allow me to live with my Dorothea"; and with these words he once more embraced her and pressed his face to hers with so much tenderness that he had to take great heed to keep his tears from completing the proof of his love and repentance in the sight of all. Not so Luscinda, and Cardenio, and almost all the others, for they shed so many tears, some in their own happiness, some at that of the others, that one would have supposed a heavy calamity had fallen upon them all. Even Sancho Panza was weeping; though afterwards he said he only wept because he saw that Dorothea was not as he fancied the queen Micomicona, of whom he expected such great favors. Their wonder as well as their weeping lasted some time, and then Cardenio and Luscinda went and fell on their knees before Don Fernando, returning him thanks for the favor he had rendered them in language so grateful that he knew not how to answer them, and raising them up embraced them with every mark of affection and courtesy.

He then asked Dorothea how she had managed to reach a place so far removed from her own home, and she in a few fitting words told all that she had previously related to Cardenio, with which Don Fernando and his companions were so delighted that they wished the story had been longer; so charmingly did Dorothea describe her misadventures. When she had finished Don Fernando recounted what had befallen him in the city after he had found in Luscinda's bosom the paper in which she declared that she was Cardenio's wife, and never could be his. He said he meant to kill her, and would have done so had he not been prevented by her parents, and that he quitted the house full of rage and shame, and resolved to avenge himself when a more convenient opportunity should offer. The next day he learned that Luscinda had disappeared from her father's house, and that no one could tell whither she had gone. Finally, at the end of some months he ascertained that she was in a convent and meant to remain there all the rest of her life, if she were not to share it with Cardenio; and as soon as he had learned this, taking these three gentlemen as his companions, he arrived at the place where she was, but avoided speaking to her, fearing that if it were known he was there stricter precautions would be taken in the convent; and watching a time when the porter's lodge was open he left two to guard the gate, and he and the other entered the convent in quest of Luscinda, whom they found in the cloisters in conversation with one of the nuns, and carrying her off without giving her time to resist, they reached a place with her where they provided themselves with what they required for taking her away; all which they were able to do in complete safety, as the convent was in the country at a considerable distance from the city. He added that when Luscinda found herself in his power she lost all consciousness, and after returning to herself did nothing but weep and sigh without speaking a word; and thus in silence and tears they reached that inn, which for him was reaching heaven where all the mischances of earth are over and at an end.

Chapter 37

*In which is continued the story of the famous
Princess Micomicona, with other droll
adventures*

To all this Sancho listened with no little sorrow at heart to see how his hopes of dignity were
fading away and vanishing in smoke, and how
the fair princess Micomicona had turned into
Dorothea, and the giant into Don Fernando,
while his master was sleeping tranquilly, totally
unconscious of all that had come to pass. Dorothea was unable to persuade herself that her
present happiness was not all a dream; Cardenio was in a similar state of mind, and Luscinda's
thoughts ran in the same direction. Don Fernando gave thanks to Heaven for the favor
shown to him and for having been rescued from
the intricate labyrinth in which he had been
brought so near the destruction of his good name
and of his soul; and in short everybody in the
inn was full of contentment and satisfaction at
the happy issue of such a complicated and hopeless business. The curate as a sensible man made
sound reflections upon the whole affair, and congratulated each upon his good fortune; but the
one that was in the highest spirits and good humor was the landlady, because of the promise
Cardenio and the curate had given her to pay
for all the losses and damage she had sustained
through Don Quixote's means. Sancho, as has
been already said, was the only one who was distressed, unhappy, and dejected; and so with a
long face he went in to his master, who had just
awoke, and said to him, "Sir Rueful Countenance, your worship may as well sleep on as
much as you like, without troubling yourself
about killing any giant or restoring her kingdom
to the princess; for that is all over and settled
now."

"I should think it was," replied Don Quixote,
"for I have had the most prodigious and stupendous battle with the giant that I ever remember
having had all the days of my life; and with one
back stroke—swish!—I brought his head tumbling to the ground, and so much blood gushed
forth from him that it ran in rivulets over the
earth like water."

"Like red wine, your worship had better say,"
replied Sancho; "for I would have you know, if
you don't know it, that the dead giant is a hacked
wine-skin, and the blood four-and-twenty gallons of red wine that it had in its belly, and the
cut-off head is the bitch that bore me; and the
devil take it all."

"What art thou talking about, fool?" said Don

Quixote; "art thou in thy senses?"

"Let your worship get up," said Sancho, "and
you will see the nice business you have made of
it, and what we have to pay; and you will see
the queen turned into a private lady called Dorothea, and other things that will astonish you,
if you understand them."

"I shall not be surprised at anything of the
kind," returned Don Quixote; "for if thou dost
remember the last time we were here I told thee
that everything that happened here was a matter of enchantment, and it would be no wonder if it were the same now."

"I could believe all that," replied Sancho, "if
my blanketing was the same sort of thing also;
only it wasn't, but real and genuine; for I saw
the landlord, who is here to-day, holding one
end of the blanket and jerking me up to the skies
very neatly and smartly, and with as much laughter as strength; and when it comes to be a case
of knowing people, I hold for my part, simple
and sinner as I am, that there is no enchantment
about it at all, but a great deal of bruising and
plenty of bad luck."

"Well, well, God will give a remedy," said
Don Quixote; "hand me my clothes and let me
go out, for I want to see these transformations
and things thou speakest of."

Sancho fetched him his clothes; and while he
was dressing, the curate gave Don Fernando and
the others present an account of Don Quixote's
madness and of the stratagem they had made
use of to withdraw him from that Peña Pobre
where he fancied himself stationed because of
his lady's scorn. He described to them also nearly
all the adventures that Sancho had mentioned,
at which they marvelled and laughed not a little,
thinking it, as all did, the strangest form of madness a crazy intellect could be capable of. But
now, the curate said, that the lady Dorothea's
good fortune prevented her from proceeding
with their purpose, it would be necessary to devise or discover some other way of getting him
home.

Cardenio proposed to carry out the scheme
they had begun, and suggested that Luscinda
would act and support Dorothea's part sufficiently well.

"No," said Don Fernando, "that must not be,
for I want Dorothea to follow out this idea of
hers; and if the worthy gentleman's village is
not very far off, I shall be happy if I can do anything for his relief."

"It is not more than two days' journey from
this," said the curate.

"Even if it were more," said Don Fernando,

"I would gladly travel so far for the sake of doing so good a work."

At this moment Don Quixote came out in full panoply, with Mambrino's helmet, all dinted as it was, on his head, his buckler on his arm, and leaning on his staff or pike. The strange figure he presented filled Don Fernando and the rest with amazement as they contemplated his lean yellow face half a league long, his armor of all sorts, and the solemnity of his deportment. They stood silent waiting to see what he would say, and he, fixing his eyes on the fair Dorothea, addressed her with great gravity and composure:

"I am informed, fair lady, by my squire here that your greatness has been annihilated and your being abolished, since, from a queen and lady of high degree as you used to be, you have been turned into a private maiden. If this has been done by the command of the magician king your father, through fear that I should not afford you the aid you need and are entitled to, I may tell you he did not know and does not know half the Mass, and was little versed in the annals of chivalry; for, if he had read and gone through them as attentively and deliberately as I have, he would have found at every turn that knights of less renown than mine, have accomplished things more difficult: it is no great matter to kill a whelp of a giant, however arrogant he may be; for it is not many hours since I myself was engaged with one, and—I will not speak of it, that they may not say I am lying; time, however, that reveals all, will tell the tale when we least expect it."

"You were engaged with a couple of wine-skins, and not a giant," said the landlord at this; but Don Fernando told him to hold his tongue and on no account interrupt Don Quixote, who continued, "I say in conclusion, high and disinherited lady, that if your father has brought about this metamorphosis in your person for the reason I have mentioned, you ought not to attach any importance to it; for there is no peril on earth through which my sword will not force a way, and with it, before many days are over, I will bring your enemy's head to the ground and place on yours the crown of your kingdom."

Don Quixote said no more, and waited for the reply of the princess, who, aware of Don Fernando's determination to carry on the deception until Don Quixote had been conveyed to his home, with great ease of manner and gravity made answer, "Whoever told you, valiant Knight of the Rueful Countenance, that I had undergone any change or transformation did not tell you the truth, for I am the same as I was yes-

terday. It is true that certain strokes of good fortune, that have given me more than I could have hoped for, have made some alteration in me; but I have not therefore ceased to be what I was before, or to entertain the same desire I have had all through of availing myself of the might of your valiant and invincible arm. And so, señor, let your goodness reinstate the father that begot me in your good opinion, and be assured that he was a wise and prudent man, since by his craft he found out such a sure and easy way of remedying my misfortune; for I believe, señor, that had it not been for you I should never have lit upon the good fortune I now possess; and in this I am saying what is perfectly true; as most of these gentlemen who are present can fully testify. All that remains is to set out on our journey to-morrow, for to-day we could not make much way; and for the rest of the happy result I am looking forward to, I trust to God and the valor of your heart."

So said the sprightly Dorothea, and on hearing her Don Quixote turned to Sancho, and said to him, with an angry air, "I declare now, little Sancho, thou art the greatest little villain in Spain. Say, thief and vagabond, hast thou not just now told me that this princess had been turned into a maiden called Dorothea, and that the head which I am persuaded I cut off from a giant was the bitch that bore thee, and other nonsense that put me in the greatest perplexity I have ever been in all my life? I vow" (and here he looked to heaven and ground his teeth) "I have a mind to play the mischief with thee, in a way that will teach sense for the future to all lying squires of knights-errant in the world."

"Let your worship be calm, señor," returned Sancho, "for it may well be that I have been mistaken as to the change of the lady princess Micomicona; but as to the giant's head, or at least as to the piercing of the wine-skins, and the blood being red wine, I make no mistake, as sure as there is a God; because the wounded skins are there at the head of your worship's bed, and the red wine has made a lake of the room; if not you will see when the eggs come to be fried; I mean when his worship the landlord here calls for all the damages: for the rest, I am heartily glad that her ladyship the queen is as she was, for it concerns me as much as any one."

"I tell thee again, Sancho, thou art a fool," said Don Quixote; "forgive me, and that will do."

"That will do," said Don Fernando; "let us say no more about it; and as her ladyship the princess proposes to set out to-morrow because it is too late to-day, so be it, and we will pass the night in pleasant conversation, and to-morrow we will all accompany Señor Don Quixote; for we wish to witness the valiant and unparalleled achievements he is about to perform in the course of this mighty enterprise which he has undertaken."

"It is I who shall wait upon and accompany you," said Don Quixote; "and I am much gratified by the favor that is bestowed upon me, and the good opinion entertained of me, which I shall strive to justify or it shall cost me my life, or even more, if it can possibly cost me more."

Many were the compliments and expressions of politeness that passed between Don Quixote and Don Fernando; but they were brought to an end by a traveller who at this moment entered the inn, and who seemed from his attire to be a Christian lately come from the country of the Moors, for he was dressed in a short-skirted coat of blue cloth with half-sleeves and without a collar; his breeches were also of blue cloth, and his cap of the same color, and he wore yellow buskins and had a Moorish cutlass slung from a baldric across his breast. Behind him, mounted upon an ass, there came a woman dressed in Moorish fashion, with her face veiled and a scarf on her head, and wearing a little brocaded cap, and a mantle that covered her from her shoulders to her feet. The man was of a robust and well-proportioned frame, in age a little over forty, rather swarthy in complexion, with long mustaches and a full beard, and, in short, his appearance was such that if he had been well dressed he would have been taken for a person of quality and good birth. On entering he asked for a room, and when they told him there was none in the inn he seemed distressed, and approaching her who by her dress seemed to be a Moor he took her down from the saddle in his arms. Luscinda, Dorothea, the landlady, her daughter, and Maritornes, attracted by the strange, and to them entirely new costume, gathered round her; and Dorothea, who was always kindly, courteous, and quick-witted, perceiving that both she and the man who had brought her were annoyed at not finding a room, said to her, "Do not be put out, señora, by the discomfort and want of luxuries here, for it is the way of road-side inns to be without them; still, if you will be pleased to share our lodging with us (pointing to Luscinda) perhaps you will have found worse accommodations in the course of your journey."

To this the veiled lady made no reply; all she did was to rise from her seat, crossing her hands upon her bosom, bowing her head and bending her body as a sign that she returned thanks. From her silence they concluded that she must be a Moor and unable to speak a Christian tongue.

At this moment the captive came up, having been until now otherwise engaged, and seeing that they all stood round his companion and that she made no reply to what they addressed to her, he said, "Ladies, this damsel hardly understands my language and can speak none but that of her own country, for which reason she does not and can not answer what has been asked of her."

"Nothing has been asked of her," returned Luscinda; "she has only been offered our company for this evening and a share of the quarters we occupy, where she shall be made as comfortable as the circumstances allow, with the good will we are bound to show all strangers that stand in need of it, especially if it be a woman to whom the service is rendered."

"On her part and my own, señora," replied the captive, "I kiss your hands, and I esteem highly, as I ought, the favor you have offered, which, on such an occasion and coming from persons of your appearance, is, it is plain to see, a very great one."

"Tell me, señor," said Dorothea, "is this lady a Christian or a Moor? for her dress and her silence lead us to imagine that she is what we could wish she was not."

"In dress and outwardly," said he, "she is a Moor, but at heart she is a thoroughly good Christian, for she has the greatest desire to become one."

"Then she has not been baptized?" returned Luscinda.

"There has been no opportunity for that," replied the captive, "since she left Algiers, her native country and home; and up to the present she has not found herself in any such imminent danger of death as to make it necessary to baptize her before she has been instructed in all the ceremonies our Holy Mother Church ordains; but, please God, ere long she shall be baptized with the solemnity befitting her quality, which is higher than her dress or mine indicates."

By these words he excited a desire in all who heard them to know who the Moorish lady and the captive were, but no one liked to ask just then, seeing that it was a fitter moment for helping them to rest themselves than for questioning them about their lives. Dorothea took the Moorish lady by the hand and leading her to a seat beside herself, requested her to remove her veil. She looked at the captive as if to ask him what they meant and what she was to do. He said to her in Arabic that they asked her to take off her veil, and thereupon she removed it and disclosed a countenance so lovely, that to Dorothea she seemed more beautiful than Luscinda, and to Luscinda more beautiful than Dorothea, and all the by-standers felt that if any beauty could compare with theirs it was the Moorish lady's, and there were even those who were inclined to give it somewhat the preference. And as it is the privilege and charm of beauty to win the heart and secure good-will, all forthwith became eager to show kindness and attention to the lovely Moor.

Don Fernando asked the captive what her name was, and he replied that it was Lela Zoraida; but the instant she heard him, she guessed what the Christian had asked, and said hastily, with some displeasure and energy, "No, not Zoraida; Maria, Maria!" giving them to understand that she was called "Maria" and not "Zoraida." These words, and the touching earnestness with which she uttered them, drew more than one tear from some of the listeners, particularly the women, who are by nature tenderhearted and compassionate. Luscinda embraced her affectionately, saying, "Yes, yes, Maria, Maria," to which the Moor replied, "Yes, yes, Maria; Zoraida *macange*," which means "not Zoraida."

Night was now approaching, and by the orders of those who accompanied Don Fernando the landlord had taken care and pains to prepare for them the best supper that was in his power. The hour, therefore, having arrived they all took their seats at a long table like a refectory one, for round or square table there was none in the inn, and the seat of honor at the head of it, though he was for refusing it, they assigned to Don Quixote, who desired the lady Micomicona to place herself by his side, as he was her protector. Luscinda and Zoraida took their places next her, opposite to them were Don Fernando and Cardenio, and next the captive and the other gentlemen, and by the side of the ladies, the curate and the barber. And so they supped in high enjoyment, which was increased when they observed Don Quixote leave off eating, and, moved by an impulse like that which made him deliver himself at such length when he supped with the goatherds, began to address them:

"Verily, gentlemen, if we reflect upon it, great and marvellous are the things they see, who make profession of the order of knight-errantry. Nay, what being is there in this world, who entering the gate of this castle at this mo-

ment, and seeing us as we are here, would suppose or imagine us to be what we are? Who would say that this lady who is beside me was the great queen that we all know her to be, or that I am that Knight of the Rueful Countenance, trumpeted far and wide by the mouth of Fame? Now, there can be no doubt that this art and calling surpasses all those that mankind has invented, and is the more deserving of being held in honor in proportion as it is the more exposed to peril. Away with those who assert that letters have the pre-eminence over arms; I will tell them, whosoever they may be, that they know not what they say. For the reason which such persons commonly assign, and upon which they chiefly rest, is, that the labors of the mind are greater than those of the body, and that arms give employment to the body alone; as if the calling were a porter's trade, for which nothing more is required than sturdy strength; or as if, in what we who profess them call arms, there were not included acts of vigor for the execution of which high intelligence is requisite; or as if the soul of the warrior, when he has an army, or the defence of a city under his care, did not exert itself as much by mind as by body. Nay; see whether by bodily strength it be possible to learn or divine the intentions of the enemy, his plans, stratagems, or obstacles, or to ward off impending mischief; for all these are the work of the mind, and in them the body has no share whatever. Since, therefore, arms have need of the mind, as much as letters, let us see now which of the two minds, that of the man of letters or that of the warrior, has most to do; and this will be seen by the end and goal that each seeks to attain; for that purpose is the more estimable which has for its aim the nobler object. The end and goal of letters—I am not speaking now of divine letters, the aim of which is to raise and direct the soul to Heaven; for with an end so infinite no other can be compared—I speak of human letters, the end of which is to establish distributive justice, give to every man that which is his, and see and take care that good laws are observed: an end undoubtedly noble, lofty, and deserving of high praise, but not such as should be given to that sought by arms, which have for their end and object peace, the greatest boon that men can desire in this life. The first good news the world and mankind received was that which the angels announced on the night that was our day, when they sang in the air, 'Glory to God in the highest, and peace on earth to men of good will'; and the salutation which the great Master of heaven and earth taught his disciples and chosen followers when they entered any house, was to say, 'Peace be on this house'; and many other times he said to them, 'My peace I give unto you, my peace I leave you, peace be with you'; a jewel and a precious gift given and left by such a hand: a jewel without which there can be no happiness either on earth or in heaven. This peace is the true end of war; and war is only another name for arms. This, then, being admitted, that the end of war is peace, and that so far it has the advantage of the end of letters, let us turn to the bodily labors of the man of letters, and those of him who follows the profession of arms, and see which are the greater."

Don Quixote delivered his discourse in such a manner and in such correct language, that for the time being he made it impossible for any of his hearers to consider him a madman; on the contrary, as they were mostly gentlemen, to whom arms are an appurtenance by birth, they listened to him with great pleasure as he continued: "Here, then, I say is what the student has to undergo; first of all poverty; not that all are poor, but to put the case as strongly as possible: and when I have said that he endures poverty, I think nothing more need be said about his hard fortune, for he who is poor has no share of the good things of life. This poverty he suffers from in various ways, hunger, or cold, or nakedness, or all together; but for all that it is not so extreme but that he gets something to eat, though it may be at somewhat unseasonable hours and from the leavings of the rich; for the greatest misery of the student is what they themselves call 'going out for soup,' and there is always some neighbor's brazier or hearth for them, which, if it does not warm, at least tempers the cold to them, and lastly, they sleep comfortably at night under a roof. I will not go into other particulars, as for example want of shirts, and no superabundance of shoes, thin and threadbare garments, and gorging themselves to surfeit in their voracity when good luck has treated them to a banquet of some sort. By this road that I have described, rough and hard, stumbling here, falling there, getting up again to fall again, they reach the rank they desire, and that once attained, we have seen many who have passed these Syrtes and Scyllas and Charybdises, as if borne flying on the wings of favoring fortune; we have seen them, I say, ruling and governing the world from a chair, their hunger turned into satiety, their cold into comfort, their nakedness into fine raiment, their sleep on a mat into repose in holland and damask, the justly earned reward of their virtue; but, contrasted and compared with what the warrior undergoes, all they have undergone falls short of it, as I am now about to show."

Chapter 38

Which treats of the curious discourse Don Quixote delivered on arms and letters

CONTINUING his discourse Don Quixote said: "As we began in the student's case with poverty and its accompaniments, let us see now if the soldier is richer, and we shall find that in poverty itself there is no one poorer; for he is dependent on his miserable pay, which comes late or never, or else on what he can plunder, seriously imperilling his life and conscience; and sometimes his nakedness will be so great that a slashed doublet serves him for uniform and shirt, and in the depth of winter he has to defend himself against the inclemency of the weather in the open field with nothing better than the breath of his mouth, which I need not say, coming from an empty place, must come out cold, contrary to the laws of nature. To be sure he looks forward to the approach of night to make up for all these discomforts on the bed that awaits him, which, unless by some fault of his, never sins by being over narrow, for he can easily measure out on the ground as many feet as he likes, and roll himself about in it to his heart's content without any fear of the sheets slipping away from him. Then, after all this, suppose the day and hour for taking his degree in his calling to have come; suppose the day of battle to have arrived, when they invest him with the doctor's cap made of lint, to mend some bullet-hole, perhaps, that has gone through his temples, or left him with a crippled arm or leg. Or if this does not happen, and merciful Heaven watches over him and keeps him safe and sound, it may be he will be in the same poverty he was in before, and he must go through more engagements and more battles, and come victorious out of all before he betters himself; but miracles of that sort are seldom seen. For tell me, sirs, if you have ever reflected upon it, by how much do those who have gained by war fall short of the number of those who have perished in it? No doubt you will reply that there can be no comparison, that the dead can not be numbered, while the living who have been rewarded may be summed up with three figures. All which is the reverse in the case of men of letters; for by skirts, to say nothing of sleeves, they all find means of support; so that though the soldier has more to endure, his reward is much less. But against all this it may be urged that it is easier o reward two thousand men of letters than thir-y thousand soldiers, for the former may be re-nunerated by giving them places, which must perforce be conferred upon men of their calling, while the latter can only be recompensed out of he very property of the master they serve; but his impossibility only strengthens my argument.

"Putting this, however, aside, for it is a puz-ling question for which it is difficult to find a olution, let us return to the superiority of arms over letters, a matter still undecided, so many re the arguments put forward on each side; for besides those I have mentioned, letters say that without them arms can not maintain themselves, or war, too, has its laws and is governed by hem, and laws belong to the domain of letters nd men of letters. To this arms make answer hat without them laws can not be maintained, or by arms states are defended, kingdoms pre-erved, cities protected, roads made safe, seas leared of pirates; and, in short, if it were not or them, states, kingdoms, monarchies, cities, vays by sea and land would be exposed to the violence and confusion which war brings with t, so long as it lasts and is free to make use of its privileges and powers. And then it is plain that whatever costs most is valued and deserves to be valued most. To attain to eminence in letters osts a man time, watching, hunger, nakedness, headaches, indigestions, and other things of the ort, some of which I have already referred to. But for a man to come in the ordinary course of hings to be a good soldier costs him all the stu-lent suffers, and in an incomparably higher de-ree, for at every step he runs the risk of losing his life. For what dread of want or poverty that an reach or harass the student can compare with what the soldier feels, who finds himself eleaguered in some stronghold mounting guard n some ravelin or cavalier, knows that the en-my is pushing a mine towards the post where he is stationed, and can not under any circum-tances retire or fly from the imminent danger hat threatens him? All he can do is to inform his captain of what is going on so that he may ry to remedy it by a counter-mine, and then tand his ground in fear and expectation of the noment when he will fly up to the clouds with-ut wings and descend into the deep against his will. And if this seems a trifling risk, let us see whether it is equalled or surpassed by the en-ounter of two galleys stem to stem, in the midst f the open sea, locked and entangled one with he other, when the soldier has no more stand-ng room than two feet of the plank of the spur; nd yet, though he sees before him threatening

him as many ministers of death as there are can-non of the foe pointed at him, not a lance length from his body, and sees too that with the first heedless step he will go down to visit the pro-fundities of Neptune's bosom, still with daunt-less heart, urged on by honor that nerves him, he makes himself a target for all that musketry, and struggles to cross that narrow path to the enemy's ship. And what is still more marvellous, no sooner has one gone down into the depths he will never rise from till the end of the world, than another takes his place; and if he too falls into the sea that waits for him like an enemy, another and another will succeed him without a moment's pause between their deaths: courage and daring the greatest that all the chances of war can show. Happy the blest ages that knew not the dread fury of those devilish engines of artillery, whose inventor I am persuaded is in hell receiving the reward of his diabolical inven-tion, by which he made it easy for a base and cowardly arm to take the life of a gallant gentle-man; and that, when he knows not how or whence, in the height of the ardor and enthu-siasm that fire and animate brave hearts, there should come some random bullet, discharged per-haps by one who fled in terror at the flash when he fired off his accursed machine, which in an instant puts an end to the projects and cuts off the life of one who deserves to live for ages to come. And thus when I reflect on this, I am al-most tempted to say that in my heart I repent of having adopted this profession of knight-errant in so detestable an age as we live in now; for though no peril can make me fear, still it gives me some uneasiness to think that powder and lead may rob me of the opportunity of making myself famous and renowned throughout the known earth by the might of my arm and the edge of my sword. But Heaven's will be done; if I succeed in my attempt I shall be all the more honored, as I have faced greater dangers than the knights-errant of yore exposed themselves to."

All this lengthy discourse Don Quixote de-livered while the others supped, forgetting to raise a morsel to his lips, though Sancho more than once told him to eat his supper, as he would have time enough afterwards to say all he wanted. It excited fresh pity in those who had heard him to see a man of apparently sound sense, and with rational views on every subject he discussed, so hopelessly wanting in all, when his wretched unlucky chivalry was in question. The curate told him he was quite right in all he had said in favor of arms, and that he himself, though a man of letters and a graduate, was of the same opinion.

They finished their supper, the cloth was removed, and while the hostess, her daughter, and Maritornes were getting Don Quixote of La Mancha's garret ready, in which it was arranged that the women were to be quartered by themselves for the night, Don Fernando begged the captive to tell them the story of his life, for it could not fail to be strange and interesting, to judge by the hints he had let fall on his arrival in company with Zoraida. To this the captive replied that he would very willingly yield to his request, only he feared his tale would not give them as much pleasure as he wished; nevertheless, not to be wanting in compliance, he would tell it. The curate and the others thanked him and added their entreaties, and he finding himself so pressed said there was no occasion to ask, where a command had such weight, and added, "If your worships will give me your attention you will hear a true story which, perhaps, fictitious ones constructed with ingenious and studied art can not come up to." These words made them settle themselves in their places and preserve a deep silence, and he seeing them waiting on his words in mute expectation, began thus in a pleasant quiet voice.

Chapter 39

Wherein the captive relates his life and adventures

My family had its origin in a village in the mountains of Leon, and nature had been kinder and more generous to it than fortune; though in the general poverty of those communities my father passed for being even a rich man; and he would have been so in reality had he been as clever in preserving his property as he was in spending it. This tendency of his to be liberal and profuse he had acquired from having been a soldier in his youth, for the soldier's life is a school in which the niggard becomes free-handed, and the free-handed prodigal; and if any soldiers are to be found who are misers, they are monsters of rare occurrence. My father went beyond liberality and bordered on prodigality, a disposition by no means advantageous to a married man who has children to succeed to his name and position. My father had three, all sons, and all of sufficient age to make choice of a profession. Finding, then, that he was unable to resist his propensity, he resolved to divest himself of the instrument and cause of his prodigality and lavishness, to divest himself of wealth, without which Alexander himself would have seemed parsimonious; and so calling us all three aside one day into a room, he addressed us in words somewhat to the following effect:

"My sons, to assure you that I love you, no mo[re] need be known or said than that you are my son[s] and to encourage a suspicion that I do not love yo[u] no more is needed than the knowledge that I hav[e] no self-control as far as preservation of your patr[i] mony is concerned; therefore, that you may for th[e] future feel sure that I love you like a father, an[d] have no wish to ruin you like a stepfather, I pr[o] pose to do with you what I have for some time bac[k] meditated, and after mature deliberation decide[d] upon. You are now of an age to choose your line [of] life or at least make choice of a calling that wi[ll] bring you honor and profit when you are older; an[d] what I have resolved to do is to divide my propert[y] into four parts; three I will give to you, to each h[is] portion without making any difference, and the oth[er] er I will retain to live upon and support myself f[or] whatever remainder of life Heaven may be please[d] to grant me. But I wish each of you on taking po[s] session of the share that falls to him to follow on[e] of the paths I shall indicate. In this Spain of ou[rs] there is a proverb, to my mind very true—as they a[re,] are, being short aphorisms drawn from long prac[ti] cal experience—and the one I refer to says, 'Th[e] church, or the sea, or the king's house'; as much [as] to say, in plainer language, whoever wants to flour[ish] ish and become rich, let him follow the church, [or] go to sea, adopting commerce as his calling, or [go] into the king's service in his household, for they sa[y] 'Better a king's crumb than a lord's favor.' I say [so] because it is my will and pleasure that one of yo[u] should follow letters, another trade, and the thir[d] serve the king in the wars, for it is a difficult matte[r] to gain admission to his service in his household[,] and if war does not bring much wealth it confe[rs] great distinction and fame. Eight days hence I wi[ll] give you your full shares in money, without d[e] frauding you of a farthing, as you will see in th[e] end. Now tell me if you are willing to follow o[ut] my idea and advice as I have laid it before you."

Having called upon me as the eldest to answe[r] I, after urging him not to strip himself of his pro[p] erty but to spend it all as he pleased, for we we[re] young men able to gain our living, consented [to] comply with his wishes, and said that mine we[re] to follow the profession of arms and thereby serv[e] God and my king. My second brother having mad[e] the same proposal, decided upon going to the I[n] dies, embarking the portion that fell to him in trad[e.] The youngest, and in my opinion the wisest, sai[d] he would rather follow the church, or go to com[] plete his studies at Salamanca. As soon as we ha[d] come to an understanding, and made choice of ou[r] professions, my father embraced us all, and in th[e] short time he mentioned carried into effect all h[e] had promised; and when he had given to each h[is] share, which as well as I remember was three thou[] sand ducats apiece in cash (for an uncle of ou[rs] bought the estate and paid for it down, not to let [it] go out of the family), we all three on the same da[y] took leave of our good father; and at the same tim[e,] as it seemed to me inhuman to leave my father wit[h] such scanty means in his old age, I induced him to take two of my three thousand ducats, as the remainder would be enough to provide me with all a soldier needed. My two brothers, moved by my example, gave him each a thousand ducats, so that there was left for me my father four thousand ducats in money, besides three thousand, the value of the portion that fell to him which he preferred to retain in land instead of selling it. Finally, as I said, we took leave of him, and of our uncle whom I have mentioned, not without sorrow and tears on both sides, they charging us to let them know whenever an opportunity offered how we fared, whether well or ill. We promised to do so, and when he had embraced us and given us his blessing, one set out for Salamanca, the other for Seville, and I for Alicante, where I had heard there was a Genoese vessel taking in a cargo of wool for Genoa.

It is now some twenty-two years since I left my father's house, and all that time, though I have written several letters, I have had no news whatever of him or of my brothers; my own adventures during that period I will now relate briefly. I embarked at Alicante, reached Genoa after a prosperous voyage, and proceeded thence to Milan, where I provided myself with arms and a few soldier's accoutrements; then it was my intention to go and take service in Piedmont, but as I was already on the road to Alessandria della Paglia, I learned that the great Duke of Alva was on his way to Flanders. I changed my plans, joined him, served under him in the campaigns he made, was present at the deaths of the Counts Egmont and Horn, and was promoted to be ensign under a famous captain of Guadalajara, Diego de Urbina by name. Some time after my arrival in Flanders news came of the league that his Holiness Pope Pius V of happy memory had made with Venice and Spain against the common enemy, the Turk, who had just then with his fleet taken the famous island of Cyprus, which belonged to the Venetians, a loss deplorable and disastrous. It was known as a fact that the Most Serene Don John of Austria, natural brother of our good king Don Philip, was coming as commander-in-chief of the allied forces, and rumors were abroad of the vast warlike preparations which were being made, all which stirred my heart and filled me with a longing to take part in the campaign which was expected; and though I had reason to believe, and most certain promises, that on the first opportunity that presented itself I should be promoted to be captain, I preferred to leave all and betake myself, as I did, to Italy; and it was my good fortune that Don John had just arrived at Genoa, and was going on to Naples to join the Venetian fleet, as he afterwards did at Messina. I may say, in short, that I took part in that glorious expedition, promoted by this time to be a captain of infantry, to which honorable charge my good luck rather than my merits raised me; and that day—so fortunate for Christendom, because then all the nations of the earth were disabused of the error under which they lay in imagining the Turks to be invincible on sea—on that day, I say, on which the Ottoman pride and arrogance were broken, among all that were there made happy (for the Christians who died that day were happier than those who remained alive and victorious) I alone was miserable; for, instead of some naval crown that I might have expected had it been in Roman times, on the night that followed that famous day I found myself with fetters on my feet and manacles on my hands.

It happened in this way: El Uchali, the King of Algiers, a daring and successful corsair, having attacked and taken the leading Maltese galley (only three knights being left alive in it, and they badly wounded), the chief galley of John Andrea Doria, on board of which I and my company were placed, came to its relief, and doing as I was bound to do in such a case, I leaped on board the enemy's galley, which, sheering off from that which had attacked it, prevented my men from following me, and so I found myself alone in the midst of my enemies, who were in such numbers that I was unable to resist; in short I was taken, covered with wounds; El Uchali, as you know, sirs, made his escape with his entire squadron, and I was left a prisoner in his power, the only sad being among so many filled with joy, and the only captive among so many free; for there were fifteen thousand Christians, all at the oar in the Turkish fleet, that regained their longed for liberty that day.

They carried me to Constantinople, where the Grand Turk, Selim, made my master general at sea for having done his duty in the battle and carried off as evidence of his bravery the standard of the Order of Malta. The following year, which was the year seventy-two, I found myself at Navarino rowing in the leading galley with the three lanterns. There I saw and observed how the opportunity of capturing the whole Turkish fleet in harbor was lost; for all the marines and janizzaries that belonged to it made sure that they were about to be attacked inside the very harbor, and had their kits and *pasamaques*, or shoes, ready to flee at once on shore without waiting to be assailed, in so great fear did they stand of our fleet. But Heaven ordered it otherwise, not for any fault or neglect of the general who commanded on our side, but for the sins of Christendom, and because it was God's will and pleasure that we should always have instruments of punishment to chastise us. As it was, El Uchali took refuge at Modon, which is an island near Navarino, and landing his forces fortified the mouth of the harbor and waited quietly until Don John retired. On this expedition was taken the galley called the *Prize,* whose captain was a son of the famous corsair Barbarossa. It was taken by the chief Neapolitan galley called the *She-Wolf,* commanded by that thunderbolt of war, that father of his men, that successful and unconquered captain Don Álvaro de Bazan, Marquis of Santa Cruz; and I cannot help telling you what took place at the capture of the *Prize.*

The son of Barbarossa was so cruel, and treated his slaves so badly, that, when those who were at the oars saw that the *She-Wolf* galley was bearing down upon them and gaining upon them, they all at once dropped their oars and seized their captain who stood on the stage at the end of the gangway shouting to them to row lustily; and passing him on from bench to bench, from the poop to the prow, they so bit him that before he had got much past the mast his soul had already got to hell; so great, as I said, was the cruelty with which he treated them, and the hatred with which they hated him.

We returned to Constantinople, and the following year, seventy-three, it became known that Don John had seized Tunis and taken the kingdom from the Turks, and placed Muley Hamet in possession, putting an end to the hopes which Muley Hamida, the cruelest and bravest Moor in the world, entertained of returning to reign there. The Grand Turk took the loss greatly to heart, and with the cunning which all his race possess, he made peace with the Venetians (who were much more eager for it than he was), and the following year, seventy-four, he attacked the Goletta, and the fort which Don John had left half built near Tunis. While all these events were occurring, I was laboring at the oar without any hope of freedom; at least I had no hope of obtaining it by ransom, for I was firmly resolved not to write to my father telling him of my misfortunes. At length the Goletta fell, and the fort fell, before which places there were seventy-five thousand regular Turkish soldiers, and more than four hundred thousand Moors and Arabs from all parts of Africa, and in the train of all this great host such munitions and engines of war, and so many pioneers that with their hand they might have covered the Goletta and the fort with handfuls of earth. The first to fall was the Goletta, until then reckoned impregnable, and it fell, not by any fault of its defenders, who did all that they could and should have done, but because experiment proved how easily intrenchments could be made in the desert sand there; for water used to be found at two palms depth, while the Turks found none at two yards; and so by means of a quantity of sandbags they raised their works so high that they commanded the walls of the fort, sweeping them as if from a cavalier, so that no one was able to make a stand or maintain the defence.

It was a common opinion that our men should not have shut themselves up in the Goletta, but should have waited in the open at the landing-place; but those who say so talk at random and with little knowledge of such matters; for if in the Goletta and in the fort there were barely seven thousand soldiers, how could such a small number, however resolute, sally out and hold their own against numbers like those of the enemy? And how is it possible to help losing a stronghold that is not relieved, above all when surrounded by a host of determined enemies in their own country? But many thought, and I thought so too, that it was a special favor and

mercy which Heaven showed to Spain in permitting the destruction of that source and hiding-place of mischief, that devourer, sponge, and moth of countless money, fruitlessly wasted there to no other purpose save preserving the memory of its capture by the invincible Charles V; as if to make that eternal, as it is and will be, these stones were needed to support it. The fort also fell; but the Turks had to win it inch by inch, for the soldiers who defended it fought so gallantly and stoutly that the number of the enemy killed in twenty-two general assaults exceeded twenty-five thousand. Of three hundred that remained alive not one was taken unwounded, a clear and manifest proof of their gallantry and resolution, and how sturdily they had defended themselves and held their post. A small fort or tower which was in the middle of the lagoon under the command of Don Juan Zanoguera, a Valencian gentleman and a famous soldier, capitulated upon terms. They took prisoner Don Pedro Puertocarrero, commandant of the Goletta, who had done all in his power to defend his fortress, and took the loss of it so much to heart that he died of grief on the way to Constantinople, where they were carrying him a prisoner. They also took the commandant of the fort, Gabrio Cerbellon by name, a Milanese gentleman, a great engineer and a very brave soldier. In these two fortresses perished many persons of note, among whom was Pagano Doria, knight of the Order of St. John, a man of generous disposition, as was shown by his extreme liberality to his brother, the famous John Andrea Doria; and what made his death the more sad was that he was slain by some Arabs to whom, seeing that the fort was now lost, he intrusted himself, and who offered to conduct him in the disguise of a Moor to Tabarca, a small fort or station on the coast held by the Genoese employed in the coral fishery. These Arabs cut off his head and carried it to the commander of the Turkish fleet, who proved on them the truth of our Castilian proverb, that "though the treason may please, the traitor is hated"; for they say he ordered those who brought him the present to be hanged for not having brought him alive.

Among the Christians who were taken in the fort was one named Don Pedro de Aguilar, a native of some place, I know not what, in Andalusia, who had been ensign in the fort, a soldier of great repute and rare intelligence, who had in particular a special gift for what they call poetry. I say so because his fate brought him to my galley and to my bench, and made him a slave to the same master; and before we left the port this gentleman composed two sonnets by way of epitaphs, one on the Goletta and the other on the fort; indeed, I may as well repeat them, for I have them by heart, and I think they will be liked rather than disliked.

The instant the captain mentioned the name of Don Pedro de Aguilar, Don Fernando looked at his companions and they all three smiled; and when he came to speak of the sonnets one of them said, "Before your worship proceeds any further I entreat you to tell me what became of that Don Pedro de Aguilar you have spoken of."

"All I know is," replied the captive, "that after having been in Constantinople two years, he escaped in the disguise of an Arnaut, in company with a Greek spy; but whether he regained his liberty or not I cannot tell, though I fancy he did, because a year afterwards I saw the Greek at Constantinople, though I was unable to ask him what the result of the journey was."

"Well then, you are right," returned the gentleman, "for that Don Pedro is my brother, and he is now in our village in good health, rich, married, and with three children."

"Thanks be to God for all the mercies he has shown him," said the captive; "for to my mind there is no happiness on earth to compare with recovering lost liberty."

"And what is more," said the gentleman, "I know the sonnets my brother made."

"Then let your worship repeat them," said the captive, "for you will recite them better than I can."

"With all my heart," said the gentleman; "that on the Goletta runs thus:

Chapter 40

In which the story of the captive is continued

Sonnet

"Blest souls, that, from this mortal husk set free,
 In guerdon of brave deeds beatified,
 Above this lowly orb of ours abide
Made heirs of heaven and immortality,
With noble rage and ardor glowing ye
 Your strength, while strength was yours, in
  battle plied,
 And with your own blood and the foeman's
  dyed
The sandy soil and the encircling sea.
It was the ebbing life-blood first that failed
The weary arms; the stout hearts never quailed.
 Though vanquished, yet ye earned the victor's
  crown:
Though mourned, yet still triumphant was your
 fall;
For there ye won, between the sword and wall,
 In Heaven glory and on earth renown."

"That is it exactly, according to my recollection," said the captive.

"Well then, that on the fort," said the gentleman, "if my memory serves me, goes thus:

Sonnet

"Up from this wasted soil, this shattered shell,
 Whose walls and towers here in ruin lie,
 Three thousand soldier souls took wing on high,
In the bright mansions of the blest to dwell.
The onslaught of the foeman to repel
 By might of arm all vainly did they try,
 And when at length 't was left them but to die,
Wearied and few the last defenders fell.
And this same arid soil hath ever been
A haunt of countless mournful memories,
 As well in our day as in days of yore.
But never yet to Heaven it sent, I ween,
From its hard bosom purer souls than these,
 Or braver bodies on its surface bore."

The sonnets were not disliked, and the captive was rejoiced at the tidings they gave him of his comrade, and continuing his tale, he went on to say:

The Goletta and the fort being thus in their hands, the Turks gave orders to dismantle the Goletta—for the fort was reduced to such a state that there was nothing left to level—and to do the work more quickly and easily they mined it in three places; but nowhere were they able to blow up the part which seemed to be the least strong, that is to say, the old walls, while all that remained standing of the new fortifications that the Fratin had made came to the ground with the greatest ease. Finally the fleet returned victorious and triumphant to Constantinople, and a few months later died my master, El Uchali, otherwise Uchali Fartax, which means in Turkish "the scabby renegade"; for that he was; it is the practice with the Turks to name people from some defect or virtue they may possess; the reason being that there are among them only four surnames belonging to families tracing their descent from the Ottoman house, and the others, as I have said, take their names and surnames either from bodily blemishes or moral qualities. This "scabby one" rowed at the oar as a slave of the Grand Signor's for fourteen years, and when over thirty-four years of age, in resentment at having been struck by a Turk while at the oar, turned renegade and renounced his faith in order to be able to revenge himself; and such was his valor that, without owing his advancement to the base ways and means by which most favorites of the Grand Signor rise to power, he came to be king of Algiers, and afterwards general-on-sea, which is the third place of trust in the realm. He was a Calabrian by birth, and a worthy man morally, and he treated his slaves with great humanity. He had three thousand of them, and after his death they were divided, as he directed by his will, between the Grand Signor (who is heir of all who die and shares with the children of the deceased) and his renegades. I fell to the lot of a Venetian renegade who, when a cabin-boy on board a ship, had been taken by Uchali and was so much beloved by him that he became one of his most favored youths.

He came to be the most cruel renegade I ever saw: his name was Hassan Aga, and he grew very rich and became king of Algiers. With him I went there from Constantinople, rather glad to be so near Spain, not that I intended to write to any one about my unhappy lot, but to try if fortune would be kinder to me in Algiers than in Constantinople, where I had attempted in a thousand ways to escape without ever finding a favorable time or chance; but in Algiers I resolved to seek for other means of effecting the purpose I cherished so dearly; for the hope of obtaining my liberty never deserted me; and when in my plots and schemes and attempts the result did not answer my expectations, without giving way to despair I immediately began to look out for or conjure up some new hope to support me, however faint or feeble it might be.

In this way I lived on immured in a building or prison called by the Turks a *baño,* in which they confine the Christian captives, as well those that are the king's as those belonging to private individuals, and also what they call those of the Almacen, which is as much as to say the slaves of the municipality, who serve the city in the public works and other employments; but captives of this kind recover their liberty with great difficulty, for, as they are public property and have no particular master, there is no one with whom to treat for their ransom, even though they may have the means. To these *baños,* as I have said, some private individuals of the town are in the habit of bringing their captives, especially when they are to be ransomed; because there they can keep them in safety and comfort until their ransom arrives. The king's captives also, that are on ransom, do not go out to work with the rest of the crew, unless when their ransom is delayed; for then, to make them write for it more pressingly, they compel them to work and go for wood, which is no light labor.

I, however, was one of those on ransom, for when it was discovered that I was a captain, although I declared my scanty means and want of fortune, nothing could dissuade them from including me among the gentlemen and those waiting to be ransomed. They put a chain on me, more as a mark of this than to keep me safe, and so I passed my life in that *baño* with several other gentlemen and persons of quality marked out as held to ransom; but though at times, or rather almost always, we suffered from hunger and scanty clothing, nothing distressed us so much as hearing and seeing at every turn the unexampled and unheard-of cruelties my master inflicted upon the Christians. Every day he hanged a man, impaled one, cut off the ears of another; and all with so little provocation, or so entirely without any, that the Turks acknowledged he did it merely for the sake of doing it, and because he was by nature murderously disposed towards the whole human race. The only one that fared at all well with him was a Spanish soldier, something de Saavedra[1] by name, to whom he never gave a blow himself, or

[1] Cervantes himself.

ordered a blow to be given, or addressed a hard word, although he had done things that will dwell in the memory of the people there for many a year, and all to recover his liberty; and for the least of the many things he did we all dreaded that he would be impaled, and he himself was in fear of it more than once; and only that time does not allow, I could tell you now something of what that soldier did, that would interest and astonish you much more than the narration of my own tale.

To go on with my story; the courtyard of our prison was overlooked by the windows of the house belonging to a wealthy Moor of high position; and these, as is usual in Moorish houses, were rather loopholes than windows, and besides were covered with thick and close blinds. It so happened, then, that as I was one day on the terrace of our prison with three other comrades, trying to pass away the time, how far we could leap with our chains, we being alone, for all the other Christians had gone out to work, I chanced to raise my eyes, and from one of these little closed windows I saw a reed appear with a cloth attached to the end of it, and it kept waving to and fro, and moving as if making signs to us to come and take it. We watched it, and one of those who were with me went and stood under the reed to see whether they would let it drop, or what they would do, but as he did so the reed was raised and moved from side to side, as if they meant to say "no" by a shake of the head. The Christian came back, and it was again lowered, making the same movements as before. Another of my comrades went, and with him the same happened as with the first, and then the third went forward, but with the same results as the first and second. Seeing this I did not like not to try my luck, and as soon as I came under the reed it was dropped and fell inside the *baño* at my feet. I hastened to untie the cloth, in which I perceived a knot, and in this were ten cianis, which are coins of base gold, current among the Moors, and each worth ten reals of our money. It is needless to say I rejoiced over this godsend, and my joy was not less than my wonder as I strove to imagine how this good fortune could have come to us, but to me specially; for the evident unwillingness to drop the reed for any but me showed that it was for me the favor was intended. I took my welcome money, broke the reed, and returned to the terrace, and looking up at the window, I saw a very white hand put out that opened and shut very quickly. From this we gathered or fancied that it must be some woman living in that house that had done us this kindness, and to show that we were grateful for it, we made salaams after the fashion of the Moors, bowing the head, bending the body, and crossing the arms on the breast. Shortly afterwards at the same window a small cross made of reeds was put out and immediately withdrawn. This sign led us to believe that some Christian woman was a captive in the house, and that it was she who had been so good to us; but the whiteness of the hand and the bracelets we had perceived made us dismiss that idea, hough we thought it might be one of the Christian enegades whom their masters very often take as awful wives, and gladly, for they prefer them to he women of their own nation. In all our conjectures we were wide of the truth; so from that time orward our sole occupation was watching and gazng at the window where the cross had appeared to us, as if it were our pole-star; but at least fifteen days passed without our seeing it or the hand, or ny other sign whatever; and though meanwhile we ndeavored with the utmost pains to ascertain who t was that lived in the house, and whether there vere any Christian renegade in it, nobody could ver tell us anything more than that he who lived here was a rich Moor of high position, Hadji Moato by name, formerly *alcaide* of La Pata, an ofce of high dignity among them. But when we least hought it was going to rain any more *cianis* from hat quarter, we saw the reed suddenly appear with nother cloth tied in a larger knot attached to it, nd this at a time when, as on the former occasion, he *baño* was deserted and unoccupied.

We made trial as before, each of the same three oing forward before I did; but the reed was delivred to none but me, and on my approach it was let rop. I untied the knot and I found forty Spanish old crowns with a paper written in Arabic, and t the end of the writing there was a large cross rawn. I kissed the cross, took the crowns and reurned to the terrace, and we all made our salaams; gain the hand appeared, I made signs that I would ead the paper, and then the window was closed. Ve were all puzzled, though filled with joy at what ad taken place; and as none of us understood Arac, great was our curiosity to know what the paper ontained, and still greater the difficulty of finding ome one to read it. At last I resolved to confide in renegade, a native of Murcia, who professed a ery great friendship for me, and had given pledges hat bound him to keep any secret I might intrust o him; for it is the custom with some renegades, vhen they intend to return to Christian territory, to arry about them certificates from captives of mark estifying, in whatever form they can, that such and uch a renegade is a worthy man who has always hown kindness to Christians, and is anxious to escape on the first opportunity that may present itself. Some obtain these testimonials with good intentions, others put them to a cunning use; for when they go o pillage on Christian territory, if they chance to be ast away, or taken prisoners, they produce their ertificates and say that from these papers may be seen the object they came for, which was to remain n Christian ground, and that it was to this end they oined the Turks in their foray. In this way they escape the consequences of the first outburst and make heir peace with the Church before it does them any narm, and then when they have the chance they eturn to Barbary to become what they were before. Others, however, there are who procure these papers and make use of them honestly, and remain on Christian soil. This friend of mine, then, was one

of these renegades that I have described; he had certificates from all our comrades, in which we testified in his favor as strongly as we could; and if the Moors had found the papers they would have burned him alive.

I knew that he understood Arabic very well, and could not only speak but also write it; but before I disclosed the whole matter to him, I asked him to read for me this paper which I had found by accident in a hole in my cell. He opened it and remained some time examining it and muttering to himself as he translated it. I asked him if he understood it, and he told me he did perfectly well, and that if I wished him to tell me its meaning word for word, I must give him pen and ink that he might do it more satisfactorily. We at once gave him what he required, and he set about translating it bit by bit, and when he had done he said, "All that is here in Spanish is what the Moorish paper contains, and you must bear in mind that when it says *Lela Marien* it means Our Lady the Virgin Mary." We read the paper and it ran thus:

"When I was a child my father had a slave who taught me to pray the Christian prayer in my own language, and told me many things about *Lela Marien*. The Christian died, and I know that she did not go to the fire, but to Allah, because since then I have seen her twice, and she told me to go to the land of the Christians to see *Lela Marien*, who had great love for me. I know not how to go. I have seen many Christians, but except thyself none has seemed to me to be a gentleman. I am young and beautiful, and have plenty of money to take with me. See if thou canst contrive how we may go, and if thou wilt thou shalt be my husband there, and if thou wilt not it will not distress me, for *Lela Marien* will find me some one to marry me. I myself have written this: have a care to whom thou givest it to read: trust no Moor, for they are all perfidious. I am greatly troubled on this account, for I would not have thee confide in any one, because if my father knew it he would at once fling me down a well and cover me with stones. I will put a thread to the reed; tie the answer to it, and if thou hast no one to write for thee in Arabic, tell it to me by signs, for *Lela Marien* will make me understand thee. She and Allah and this cross, which I often kiss as the captive bade me, protect thee."

Judge, sirs, whether we had reason for surprise and joy at the words of this paper; and both one and the other were so great, that the renegade perceived that the paper had not been found by chance, but had been in reality addressed to some one of us, and he begged us, if what he suspected were the truth, to trust him and tell him all, for he would risk his life for our freedom; and so saying he took out from his breast a metal crucifix, and with many tears swore by the God the image represented, in whom, sinful and wicked as he was, he truly and faithfully believed, to be loyal to us and keep secret whatever we chose to reveal to him; for he thought and almost foresaw that by means of her who had written that paper, he and all of us would obtain our liberty, and he himself obtain the object he so much desired, his restoration to the bosom of the Holy Mother Church, from which by his own sin and ignorance he was now severed like a corrupt limb. The renegade said this with so many tears and such signs of repentance, that with one consent we all agreed to tell him the whole truth of the matter, and so we gave him a full account of all, without hiding anything from him. We pointed out to him the window at which the reed appeared, and he by that means took note of the house, and resolved to ascertain with particular care who lived in it. We agreed also that it would be advisable to answer the Moorish lady's letter, and the renegade without a moment's delay took down the words I dictated to him, which were exactly what I shall tell you, for nothing of importance that took place in this affair has escaped my memory, or ever will while life lasts. This, then, was the answer returned to the Moorish lady:

"The true Allah protect thee, Lady, and that blessed *Marien* who is the true mother of God, and who has put it into thy heart to go to the land of the Christians, because she loves thee. Entreat her that she be pleased to show thee how thou canst execute the command she gives thee, for she will, such is her goodness. On my own part, and on that of all these Christians who are with me, I promise to do all that we can for thee, even to death. Fail not to write to me and inform me what thou dost mean to do, and I will always answer thee; for the great Allah has given us a Christian captive who can speak and write thy language well, as thou mayest see by this paper: without fear, therefore, thou canst inform us of all thou wouldst. As to what thou sayest, that if thou dost reach the land of the Christians thou wilt be my wife, I give thee my promise upon it as a good Christian; and know that the Christians keep their promises better than the Moors. Allah and *Marien* his mother watch over thee, my Lady."

The paper being written and folded I waited two days until the *baño* was empty as before, and immediately repaired to the usual walk on the terrace to see if there were any sign of the reed, which was not long in making its appearance. As soon as I saw it, although I could not distinguish who put it out, I showed the paper as a sign to attach the thread, but it was already fixed to the reed, and to it I tied the paper; and shortly afterwards our star once more made its appearance with the white flag of peace, the little bundle. It was dropped, and I picked it up, and found in the cloth, in gold and silver coins of all sorts, more than fifty crowns, which fifty times more doubled our joy and strengthened our hope of gaining our liberty. That very night our renegade returned and said he had learned that the Moor we had been told of lived in that house, that his name was Hadji Morato, that he was enormously rich, that he had one only daughter the heiress of all his wealth, and that it was the general opinion throughout the city that she was the most beautiful woman

in Barbary, and that several of the viceroys who came there had sought her for a wife, but that she had been always unwilling to marry; and he had learned, moreover, that she had a Christian slave who was now dead; all which agreed with the contents of the paper. We immediately took counsel with the renegade as to what means would have to be adopted in order to carry off the Moorish lady and bring us all to Christian territory; and in the end it was agreed that for the present we should wait for a second communication from Zoraida (for that was the name of her who now desires to be called Maria), because we saw clearly that she and no one else could find a way out of all these difficulties. When we had decided upon this the renegade told us not to be uneasy, for he would lose his life or restore us to liberty. For four days the *baño* was filled with people, for which reason the reed delayed its appearance for four days, but at the end of that time when the *baño* was, as it generally was, empty, it appeared with the cloth so bulky that it promised a happy birth. Reed and cloth came down to me, and I found another paper and a hundred crowns in gold, without any other coin. The renegade was present, and in our cell we gave him the paper to read, which he said was to this effect:

"I can not think of a plan, señor, for our going to Spain, nor has *Lela Marien* shown me one, though I have asked her. All that can be done is for me to give you plenty of money in gold from this window. With it ransom yourself and your friends, and let one of you go to the land of the Christians, and there buy a vessel and come back for the others; and he will find me in my father's garden, which is at the Babazoun gate near the sea-shore, where I shall be all this summer with my father and my servants. You can carry me away from there by night without any danger, and bring me to the vessel. And remember thou art to be my husband, else I will pray to *Marien* to punish thee. If thou canst not trust any one to go for the vessel, ransom thyself and do thou go, for I know thou wilt return more surely than any other, as thou art a gentleman and a Christian. Endeavor to make thyself acquainted with the garden; and when I see thee walking yonder I shall know that the *baño* is empty and I will give thee abundance of money. Allah protect thee, señor."

These were the words and contents of the second paper, and on hearing them, each declared himself willing to be the ransomed one, and promised to go and return with scrupulous good faith; and I too made the same offer; but to all this the renegade objected, saying that he would not on any account consent to one being set free before all went together, as experience had taught him how ill those who have been set free keep promises which they made in captivity; for captives of distinction frequently had recourse to this plan, paying the ransom of one who was to go to Valencia or Majorca with money to enable him to arm a bark and return for the others who had ransomed him; but who never came back; for recovered liberty and the dread of losing it again efface from the memory all the obligations in the world. And to prove the truth of what he said, he told us briefly what had happened to a certain Christian gentleman almost at that very time, the strangest case that had ever occurred even there, where astonishing and marvellous things are happening ev'ry instant. In short, he ended by saying that what could and ought to be done was to give the money intended for the ransom of one of us Christians to him, so that he might with it buy a vessel there in Algiers under the pretence of becoming a merchant and trading to Tetuan and along the coast; and when master of the vessel, it would be easy for him to hit on some way of getting us all out of the *baño* and putting us on board; especially if the Moorish lady gave, as she said, money enough to ransom all, because once free it would be the easiest thing in the world for us to embark even in open day; but the greatest difficulty was that the Moors do not allow any renegade to buy or own any craft, unless it be a large vessel for going on roving expeditions, because they are afraid that any one who buys a small vessel, especially if he be a Spaniard, only wants it for the purpose of escaping to Christian territory. This however he could get over by arranging with a Tagarin Moor to go shares with him in the purchase of the vessel and in the profit on the cargo; and under cover of this he could become master of the vessel, in which case he looked upon all the rest as accomplished. But though to me and my comrades it had seemed a better plan to send to Majorca for the vessel, as the Moorish lady suggested, we did not dare to oppose him, fearing that if we did not do as he said he would denounce us, and place us in danger of losing all our lives if he were to disclose our dealings with Zoraida, for whose life we would have all given our own. We therefore resolved to put ourselves in the hands of God and in the renegade's; and at the same time an answer was given to Zoraida, telling her that we would do all she recommended, for she had given as good advice as if *Lela Marien* had delivered it, and that it depended on her alone whether we were to defer the business or put it in execution at once. I renewed my promise to be her husband; and thus the next day that the *baño* chanced to be empty she at different times gave us by means of the reed and cloth two thousand gold crowns and a paper in which she said that the next *Jumá*, that is to say Friday, she was going to her father's garden, but that before she went she would give us more money; and if it were not enough we were to let her know, as she would give us as much as we asked, for her father had so much he would not miss it, and besides she kept all the keys.

We at once gave the renegade five hundred crowns to buy the vessel, and with eight hundred I ransomed myself, giving the money to a Valencian merchant who happened to be in Algiers at the time, and who had me released on his word, pledging it that on the arrival of the first ship from Valencia he would pay my ransom; for if he had given the money at once it would have made the king suspect that my ransom money had been for a long time in Algiers, and that the merchant had for his own advantage kept it secret. In fact my master was so difficult to deal with that I dared not on any account pay down the money at once. The Thursday before the Friday on which the fair Zoraida was to go to the garden she gave us a thousand crowns more, and warned us of her departure, begging me, if I were ransomed, to find out her father's garden at once, and by all means to seek an opportunity of going there to see her. I answered in a few words that I would do so, and that she must remember to commend us to *Lela Marien* with all the prayers the captive had taught her. This having been done, steps were taken to ransom our three comrades, so as to enable them to quit the *baño*, and lest, seeing me ransomed and themselves not, though the money was forthcoming, they should make a disturbance about it and the devil should prompt them to do something that might injure Zoraida; for though their position might be sufficient to relieve me from this apprehension, nevertheless I was unwilling to run any risk in the matter; and so I had them ransomed in the same way as I was, handing over all the money to the merchant so that he might with safety and confidence give security; without, however, confiding our arrangement and secret to him, which might have been dangerous.

Chapter 41

In which the captive still continues his adventures

BEFORE fifteen days were over our renegade had already purchased an excellent vessel with room for more than thirty persons; and to make the transaction safe and lend a color to it, he thought it well to make, as he did, a voyage to a place called Shershel, twenty leagues from Algiers on the Oran side, where there is an extensive trade in dried figs. Two or three times he made this voyage in company with the Tagarin already mentioned. The Moors of Aragon are called Tagarins in Barbary, and those of Granada Mudéjares; but in the Kingdom of Fez they call the Mudéjares Elches, and they are the people the king chiefly employs in war. To proceed: every time he passed with his vessel he anchored in a cove that was not two cross-bow shots from the garden where Zoraida was waiting; and there the renegade, together with the two Moorish lads that rowed, used purposely to station himself, either going through his prayers, or else practising as a part what he meant to perform in earnest. And thus he would go to Zoraida's garden and ask for fruit, which her father gave him, not knowing him; but though, as he afterwards told me, he sought to speak to Zoraida, and tell her who he was, and that by my orders he was to take her to the land of the Christians, so that she might feel satisfied and easy, he had never been able to do so; for the Moorish women do not allow themselves to be seen by any Moor or Turk, unless their husband or fathers bid them: with Christian captives they permit freedom of intercourse and communication, even more than might be considered proper. But for my part, I should have been sorry if he had spoken to her, for perhaps it might have alarmed her to find her affairs talked of by renegades. But God, who ordered it otherwise, afforded no opportunity for our renegade's well-meant purpose; and he, seeing how safely he could go to Shershel and return, and anchor when and how and where he liked, and that the Tagarin his partner had no will but his, and that, now I was ransomed, all we wanted was to find some Christians to row, told me to look out for any I should be willing to take with me, over and above those who had been ransomed, and to engage them for the next Friday, which he fixed upon for our departure. On this I spoke to twelve Spaniards, all stout rowers, and such as could most easily leave the city; but it was no easy matter to find so many just then, because there were twenty ships out on a cruise, and they had taken all the rowers with them; and these would not have been found were it not that their master remained at home that summer without going to sea, in order to finish a galliot that he had upon the stocks. To these men I said nothing more than that the next Friday in the evening, they were to come out stealthily one by one and hang about Hadji Morato's garden, waiting for me there until I came. These directions I gave each one separately, with orders that if they saw any other Christians there, they were not to say anything to them, except that I had directed them to wait at that spot.

This preliminary having been settled, another still more necessary step had to be taken, which was to let Zoraida know how matters stood that she might be prepared and forewarned, so as not to be taken by surprise if we were suddenly to seize upon her before she thought the Christians' vessel could have returned. I determined, therefore, to go to the garden and try if I could speak to her; and the day before my departure I went there under the pretence of gathering herbs. The first person I met was her father, who addressed me in the language that all over Barbary and even in Constantinople is the medium between captives and Moors, and is neither Morisco nor Castilian, nor of any other nation, but a mixture of all languages, by means of which we can all understand one another. In this sort of language, I say, he asked me what I wanted in his garden, and to whom I belonged. I replied that I was a slave of the Arnaut Mami (for I knew as a certainty that he was a very great friend of his), and that I wanted some herbs to make a salad. He asked me then whether I were on ransom or not, and what my master demanded for me. While these questions and answers were proceeding, the fair Zoraida, who had already perceived me some time before, came out of the house in the garden, and as Moorish women are by no means particular about letting themselves be seen by Christians, or, as I have said before, at all coy, she had no hesitation in coming to where her father stood with me; moreover her father, seeing her approaching slowly, called to her to come. It would be beyond my power now to describe to you the great beauty, the high-bred air, the rich, brilliant attire of my beloved Zoraida as she presented herself before my eyes. I will content myself with saying that more pearls hung from her fair neck, her ears, and her hair than she had hairs on her head. On her ankles, which as is customary were bare, she had *carcajes* (for so bracelets or anklets are called in Morisco) of the purest gold, set with so many diamonds that she told me afterwards her father valued them at ten thousand doubloons, and those she had on her wrists were worth as much more. The pearls were in profusion and very fine, for the highest display and adornment of the Moorish women is decking themselves with rich pearls and seed-pearls; and of these there are therefore more among the Moors than among any other people. Zoraida's father had the reputation of possessing a great number, and the purest in all Algiers, and of possessing also more than two hundred thousand Spanish crowns; and she, who is now mistress of me only, was mistress of all this. Whether thus adorned she would have been beautiful or not, and what she must have been in her prosperity, may be imagined from the beauty remaining to her after so many hardships; for, as every one knows, the beauty of some women has its times and its seasons, and is increased or diminished by chance causes; and naturally the emotions of the mind will heighten or impair it, though indeed more frequently they totally destroy it. In a word she presented herself before me that day attired with the utmost splendor, and supremely beautiful; at any rate, she seemed to me the most beautiful object I had ever seen; and when, besides, I thought of all I owed to her I felt as though I had before me some heavenly being come to earth to bring me relief and happiness.

As she approached, her father told her in his own language that I was a captive belonging to his friend the Arnaut Mami, and that I had come for salad.

She took up the conversation, and in that mixture of tongues I have spoken of she asked me if I was a gentleman, and why I was not ransomed.

I answered that I was already ransomed, and that by the price it might be seen what value my master set on me, as they had given one thousand five hundred *zoltanis* for me; to which she replied, "Hadst thou been my father's, I can tell thee, I would not have let him part with thee for twice as much, for you Christians always tell lies about yourselves and make yourselves out poor to cheat the Moors."

"That may be, lady," said I; "but indeed I dealt truthfully with my master, as I do and mean to do with everybody in the world."

"And when dost thou go?" said Zoraida.

"To-morrow, I think," said I, "for there is a vessel here from France which sails to-morrow, and I think I shall go in her."

"Would it not be better," said Zoraida, "to wait

or the arrival of ships from Spain and go with them, and not with the French who are not your friends?"

"No," said I; "though if there were intelligence that a vessel were now coming from Spain it is true I might, perhaps, wait for it; however, it is more likely I shall depart to-morrow, for the longing I feel to return to my country and to those I love is so great that it will not allow me to wait for another opportunity, however more convenient, if it be delayed."

"No doubt thou art married in thine own country," said Zoraida, "and for that reason thou art anxious to go and see thy wife."

"I am not married," I replied, "but I have given my promise to marry on my arrival there."

"And is the lady beautiful to whom thou hast given it?" said Zoraida.

"So beautiful," said I, "that, to describe her worthily and tell thee the truth, she is very like thee."

At this her father laughed very heartily and said, "By Allah, Christian, she must be very beautiful if she is like my daughter, who is the most beautiful woman in all this kingdom: only look at her well and thou wilt see I am telling the truth."

Zoraida's father as the better linguist helped to interpret most of these words and phrases, for though she spoke the bastard language, that, as I have said, is employed there, she expressed her meaning more by signs than by words.

While we were still engaged in this conversation, a Moor came running up, exclaiming that four Turks had leaped over the fence or wall of the garden, and were gathering the fruit, though it was not yet ripe. The old man was alarmed and Zoraida too, for the Moors commonly, and, so to speak, instinctively have a dread of the Turks, but particularly of the soldiers, who are so insolent and domineering to the Moors who are under their power that they treat them worse than if they were their slaves. So her father said to Zoraida, "Daughter, retire into the house and shut thyself in while I go and speak to these dogs; and thou, Christian, pick thy herbs, and go in peace, and Allah bring thee safe to thy own country."

I bowed, and he went away to look for the Turks, leaving me alone with Zoraida, who made as if she were about to retire as her father bade her; but the moment he was concealed by the trees of the garden, turning to me with her eyes full of tears she said, *"Tameji, cristiano, tameji?"* that is to say, "Art thou going, Christian, art thou going?"

I made answer, "Yes, lady, but not without thee, come what may: be on the watch for me on the next *Jumá*, and be not alarmed when thou seest us; for most surely we shall go to the land of the Christians."

This I said in such a way that she understood perfectly all that passed between us, and throwing her arm round my neck she began with feeble steps to move towards the house; but as fate would have it (and it might have been very unfortunate if Heaven had not otherwise ordered it), just as we were moving on in the manner and position I have described, with her arm round my neck, her father, as he returned after having sent away the Turks, saw how we were walking and we perceived that he saw us; but Zoraida, ready and quick-witted, took care not to remove her arm from my neck, but on the contrary drew closer to me and laid her head on my breast, bending her knees a little and showing all the signs and tokens of fainting, while I at the same time made it seem as though I were supporting her against my will. Her father came running up to where we were, and seeing his daughter in this state asked what was the matter with her; she, however, giving no answer, he said, "No doubt she has fainted in alarm at the entrance of those dogs," and taking her from mine he drew her to his own breast, while she sighing, her eyes still wet with tears, said again, *"Ameji, cristiano, ameji"*— "Go, Christian, go." To this her father replied, "There is no need, daughter, for the Christian to go, for he has done thee no harm, and the Turks have now gone; feel no alarm, there is nothing to hurt thee, for as I say, the Turks at my request have gone back the way they came."

"It was they who terrified her, as thou hast said, señor," said I to her father; "but since she tells me to go, I have no wish to displease her: peace be with thee, and with thy leave I will come back to this garden for herbs if need be, for my master says there are nowhere better herbs for salad than here."

"Come back for any thou hast need of," replied Hadji Morato; "for my daughter does not speak thus because she is displeased with thee or any Christian: she only meant that the Turks should go, not thou; or that it was time for thee to look for thy herbs."

With this I at once took my leave of both; and she, looking as though her heart were breaking, retired with her father. While pretending to look for herbs I made the round of the garden at my ease, and studied carefully all the approaches and outlets, and the fastenings of the house and everything that could be taken advantage of to make our task easy. Having done so I went and gave an account of all that had taken place to the renegade and my comrades, and looked forward with impatience to the hour when, all fear at an end, I should find myself in possession of the prize which fortune held out to me in the fair and lovely Zoraida. The time passed at length, and the appointed day we so longed for arrived; and, all following out the arrangement and plan which, after careful consideration and many a long discussion, we had decided upon, we succeeded as fully as we could have wished; for on the Friday following the day upon which I spoke to Zoraida in the garden, the renegade anchored his vessel at nightfall almost opposite the spot where she was. The Christians who were to row were ready and in hiding in different places round about, all waiting for me, anxious and elated, and eager to attack the vessel they had before their eyes; for they did not know the renegade's plan, but expected that they were to gain their liberty by force of arms and by killing the Moors who were on board the vessel. As soon, then, as I and my comrades made our appearance, all those that were in hiding seeing us came and joined us. It was now the time when the city gates are shut, and there was no one to be seen in all the space outside. When we were collected together we debated whether it would be better first to go for Zoraida, or to make prisoners of the Moorish rowers who rowed in the vessel; but while we were still uncertain our renegade came up asking us what kept us, as it was now the time, and all the Moors were off their guard and most of them asleep. We told him why we hesitated, but he said it was of more importance first to secure the vessel, which could be done with the greatest ease and without any danger, and then we could go for Zoraida. We all approved of what he said, and so without further delay, guided by him we made for the vessel, and he leaping on board first, drew his cutlass and said in Morisco, "Let no one stir from this if he does not want it to cost him his life." By this almost all the Christians were on board, and the Moors, who were faint-hearted, hearing their captain speak in this way, were cowed, and without any one of them taking to his arms (and indeed they had few or hardly any) they submitted without saying a word to be bound by the Christians, who quickly secured them, threatening them that if they raised any kind of outcry they would be all put to the sword. This having been accomplished, and half of our party being left to keep guard over them, the rest of us, again taking the renegade as our guide, hastened towards Hadji Morato's garden, and as good luck would have it, on trying the gate it opened as readily as if it had not been locked; and so, quite quietly and in silence, we reached the house without being perceived by anybody. The lovely Zoraida was watching for us at a window, and as soon as she perceived that there were people there, she asked in a low voice if we were *Nizarani*, as much as to say or ask if we were Christians. I answered that we were, and begged her to come down. As soon as she recognized me she did not delay an instant, but without answering a word came down immediately, opened the door and presented herself before us all, so beautiful and so richly attired that I cannot attempt to describe her. The moment I saw her I took her hand and kissed it, and the renegade and my two comrades did the same; and the rest, who knew nothing of the circumstances, did as they saw us do, for it only seemed as if we were returning thanks to her, and recognizing her as the giver of our liberty. The renegade asked her in the Morisco language if her father was in the house. She replied that he was and that he was asleep.

"Then it will be necessary to waken him and take him with us," said the renegade, "and everything of value in this fair mansion."

"Nay," said she, "my father must not on any account be touched, and there is nothing in the house except what I shall take, and that will be quite enough to enrich and satisfy all of you; wait a little and you shall see," and so saying she went in again,

telling us she would return immediately, and bidding us keep quiet without making any noise.

I asked the renegade what had passed between them, and when he told me, I declared that nothing should be done except in accordance with the wishes of Zoraida, who now came back with a little trunk so full of gold crowns that she could scarcely carry it. Unfortunately her father awoke while this was going on, and hearing a noise in the garden, came to the window, and at once perceiving that all those who were there were Christians, raising a prodigiously loud outcry, he began to call out in Arabic, "Christians, Christians! thieves, thieves!" by which cries we were all thrown into the greatest fear and embarrassment; but the renegade seeing the danger we were in and how important it was for him to effect his purpose before we were heard, mounted with the utmost quickness to where Hadji Morato was, and with him went some of our party; I, however, did not dare to leave Zoraida, who had fallen almost fainting in my arms. To be brief, those who had gone upstairs acted so promptly that in an instant they came down, carrying Hadji Morato with his hands bound and a napkin tied over his mouth, which prevented him from uttering a word, warning him at the same time that to attempt to speak would cost him his life. When his daughter caught sight of him she covered her eyes so as not to see him, and her father was horror-stricken, not knowing how willingly she had placed herself in our hands. But it was now most essential for us to be on the move, and carefully and quickly we regained the vessel, where those who had remained on board were waiting for us in apprehension of some mishap having befallen us. It was barely two hours after night set in when we were all on board the vessel, where the cords were removed from the hands of Zoraida's father, and the napkin from his mouth; but the renegade once more told him not to utter a word, or they would take his life. He, when he saw his daughter there, began to sigh piteously, and still more when he perceived that I held her closely embraced and that she lay quiet without resisting or complaining, or showing any reluctance; nevertheless he remained silent lest they should carry into effect the repeated threats the renegade had addressed to him.

Finding herself now on board, and that we were about to give way with the oars, Zoraida, seeing her father there, and the other Moors bound, bade the renegade ask me to do her the favor of releasing the Moors and setting her father at liberty, for she would rather drown herself in the sea than suffer a father that had loved her so dearly to be carried away captive before her eyes and on her account.

The renegade repeated this to me, and I replied that I was very willing to do so; but he replied that it was not advisable, because if they were left there they would at once raise the country and stir up the city, and lead to the despatch of swift cruisers in pursuit, and our being taken, by sea or land, without any possibility of escape; and that all that could be done was to set them free on the first Christian ground we reached. On this point we all agreed; and Zoraida, to whom it was explained, together with the reasons that prevented us from doing at once what she desired, was satisfied likewise; and then in glad silence and with cheerful alacrity each of our stout rowers took his oar, and commending ourselves to God with all our hearts, we began to shape our course for the island of Majorca, the nearest Christian land. Owing, however, to the Tramontana rising a little, and the sea growing somewhat rough, it was impossible for us to keep a straight course for Majorca, and we were compelled to coast in the direction of Oran, not without great uneasiness on our part lest we should be observed from the town of Shershel, which lies on that coast, not more than sixty miles from Algiers. Moreover we were afraid of meeting on that course one of the galliots that usually come with goods from Tetuan; although each of us for himself and all of us together felt confident that, if we were to meet a merchant galliot, so that it were not a cruiser, not only should we not be lost, but that we should take a vessel in which we could more safely accomplish our voyage. As we pursued our course Zoraida kept her head between my hands so as not to see her father, and I felt sure that she was praying to *Lela Marien* to help us.

We might have made about thirty miles when daybreak found us some three musket-shots off the land, which seemed to us deserted, and without any one to see us. For all that, however, by hard rowing we put out a little to sea, for it was now somewhat calmer, and having gained about two leagues the word was given to row by batches, while we ate something, for the vessel was well provided; but the rowers said it was not a time to take any rest; let food be served out to those who were not rowing, but they would not leave their oars on any account. This was done, but now a stiff breeze began to blow, which obliged us to leave off rowing and make sail at once and steer for Oran, as it was impossible to make any other course. All this was done very promptly, and under sail we ran more than eight miles an hour without any fear, except that of coming across some vessel out on a roving expedition. We gave the Moorish rowers some food, and the renegade comforted them by telling them that they were not held as captives, as we should set them free on the first opportunity.

The same was said to Zoraida's father, who replied, "Anything else, O Christian, I might hope for or think likely from your generosity and good behavior, but do not think me so simple as to imagine you will give me my liberty; for you would have never exposed yourselves to the danger of depriving me of it only to restore it to me so generously, especially as you know who I am and the sum you may expect to receive on restoring it; and if you will only name that, I here offer you all you require for myself and for my unhappy daughter there; or else for her alone, for she is the greatest and most precious part of my soul."

As he said this he began to weep so bitterly that he filled us all with compassion and forced Zoraida to look at him, and when she saw him weeping she was so moved that she rose from my feet and ran to throw her arms round him, and pressing her face to his, they both gave way to such an outburst of tears that several of us were constrained to keep them company.

But when her father saw her in full dress and with all her jewels about her, he said to her in his own language, "What means this, my daughter? Last night, before this terrible misfortune in which we are plunged befell us, I saw thee in thy everyday and indoor garments; and now, without having had time to attire thyself, and without my bringing thee any joyful tidings to furnish an occasion for adorning and bedecking thyself, I see thee arrayed in the finest attire it would be in my power to give thee when fortune was most kind to us. Answer me this; for it causes me greater anxiety and surprise than even this misfortune itself."

The renegade interpreted to us what the Moor said to his daughter; she, however, returned him no answer. But when he observed in one corner of the vessel the little trunk in which she used to keep her jewels, which he well knew he had left in Algiers and had not brought to the garden, he was still more amazed, and asked her how that trunk had come into our hands, and what there was in it. To which the renegade, without waiting for Zoraida to reply, made answer, "Do not trouble thyself by asking thy daughter Zoraida so many questions, señor, for the one answer I will give thee will serve for all; I would have thee know that she is a Christian, and that it is she who has been the file for our chains and our deliverer from captivity. She is here of her own free will, as glad, I imagine, to find herself in this position as he who escapes from darkness into the light, from death to life, and from suffering to glory."

"Daughter, is this true, what he says?" cried the Moor.

"It is," replied Zoraida.

"That thou art in truth a Christian," said the old man, "and that thou hast given thy father into the power of his enemies?"

To which Zoraida made answer, "A Christian I am, but it is not I who have placed thee in this position, for it never was my wish to leave thee or do thee harm, but only to do good to myself."

"And what good hast thou done thyself, daughter?" said he.

"Ask thou that," said she, "of *Lela Marien,* for she can tell thee better than I."

The Moor had hardly heard these words when with marvellous quickness he flung himself headforemost into the sea, where no doubt he would have been drowned had not the long and full dress he wore held him up for a little on the surface of the water. Zoraida cried aloud to us to save him, and we all hastened to help, and seizing him by his robe we drew him in half-drowned and insensible, at which Zoraida was in such distress that she wept over him as piteously and bitterly as though he were already dead. We turned him upon his face and he voided a great quantity of water, and at the end of two hours came to himself. Meanwhile, the wind having changed we were compelled to head for the land, and ply our oars to avoid being driven on shore; but it was our good fortune to make a cove that lies on one side of a small promontory or cape, called by the Moors that of the *Cava rumia,* which in our language means "the wicked Christian woman"; for it is a tradition among them that La Cava, through whom Spain was lost, lies buried at that spot; *cava* in their language meaning "wicked woman," and *rumia* "Christian"; moreover, they count it unlucky to anchor there when necessity compels them, and they never do so otherwise. For us, however, it was not the resting-place of the wicked woman but a haven of safety for our relief, so much had the sea now got up. We posted a look-out on shore, and never let the oars out of our hands, and ate of the stores the renegade had laid in, imploring God and Our Lady with all our hearts to help and protect us, that we might give a happy ending to a beginning so prosperous. At the entreaty of Zoraida orders were given to set on shore her father and the other Moors who were still bound, for she could not endure, nor could her tender heart bear to see her father in bonds and her fellow-countrymen prisoners before her eyes. We promised her to do this at the moment of departure, for as it was uninhabited we ran no risk in releasing them at that place.

Our prayers were not so far in vain as to be unheard by Heaven, for the wind immediately changed in our favor, and the sea grew calm, inviting us once more to resume our voyage with a good heart. Seeing this we unbound the Moors, and one by one put them on shore, at which they were filled with amazement; but when we came to land Zoraida's father, who had now completely recovered his senses, he said, "Why is it, think ye, Christians, that this wicked woman is rejoiced at your giving me my liberty? Think ye it is because of the affection she bears me? Nay verily, it is only because of the hindrance my presence offers to the execution of her base designs. And think not that it is her belief that yours is better than ours that has led her to change her religion; it is only because she knows that immodesty is more freely practised in your country than in ours." Then turning to Zoraida, while I and another of the Christians held him fast by both arms, lest he should do some mad act, he said to her, "Infamous girl, misguided maiden, whither in thy blindness and madness art thou going in the hands of these dogs, our natural enemies? Cursed be the hour when I begot thee! Cursed the luxury and indulgence in which I reared thee!" But seeing that he was not likely soon to cease I made haste to put him on shore, and thence he continued his maledictions and lamentations aloud; calling on Mohammed to pray to Allah to destroy us, to confound us, to make an end of us; and when, in consequence

of having made sail, we could no longer hear what he said we could see what he did; how he plucked out his beard and tore his hair and lay writhing on the ground. But once he raised his voice to such a pitch that we were able to hear what he said. "Come back, dear daughter, come back to shore; I forgive thee all; let those men have the money, for it is theirs now, and come back to comfort thy sorrowing father, who will yield up his life on this barren strand if thou dost leave him."

All this Zoraida heard, and heard with sorrow and tears, and all she could say in answer was, "Allah grant that *Lela Marien,* who has made me become a Christian, give thee comfort in thy sorrow, O my father. Allah knows that I could not do otherwise than I have done, and that these Christians owe nothing to my will; for even had I wished not to accompany them, but remain at home, it would have been impossible for me, so eagerly did my soul urge me on to the accomplishment of this purpose, which I feel to be as righteous as to thee, dear father, it seems wicked."

But neither could her father hear her nor we see him when she said this; and so, while I consoled Zoraida, we turned our attention to our voyage, in which a breeze from the right point so favored us that we made sure of finding ourselves off the coast of Spain on the morrow by daybreak. But, as good seldom or never comes pure and unmixed, without being attended or followed by some disturbing evil that gives a shock to it, our fortune, or perhaps the curses which the Moor had hurled at his daughter (for whatever kind of father they may come from these are always to be dreaded), brought it about that when we were now in mid-sea, and the night about three hours spent, as we were running with all sail set and oars lashed, for the favoring breeze saved us the trouble of using them, we saw by the light of the moon, which shone brilliantly, a square-rigged vessel in full sail close to us, luffing up and standing across our course, and so close that we had to strike sail to avoid running foul of her, while they too put the helm hard up to let us pass. They came to the side of the ship to ask who we were, whither we were bound, and whence we came, but as they asked this in French our renegade said, "Let no one answer, for no doubt these are French corsairs who plunder all comers." Acting on this warning no one answered a word, but after we had gone a little ahead, and the vessel was now lying to leeward, suddenly they fired two guns, and apparently both loaded with chainshot, for with one they cut our mast in half and brought down both it and the sail into the sea, and the other, discharged at the same moment, sent a ball into our vessel amidships, staving her in completely, but without doing any further damage. We, however, finding ourselves sinking began to shout for help and call upon those in the ship to pick us up as we were beginning to fill. They then lay to, and lowering a skiff or boat, as many as a dozen Frenchmen, well armed with matchlocks, and their matches burning, got into it and

me alongside; and seeing how few we were, and
aat our vessel was going down, they took us in,
lling us that this had come to us through our in-
vility in not giving then an answer. Our renegade
ook the trunk containing Zoraida's wealth and
ropped it into the sea without any one perceiving
hat he did. In short we went on board with the
renchmen, who, after having ascertained all they
anted to know about us, rifled us of everything
e had, as if they had been our bitterest enemies,
nd from Zoraida they took even the anklets she
ore on her feet; but the distress they caused her
id not distress me so much as the fear I was in that
om robbing her of her rich and precious jewels
ey would proceed to rob her of the most precious
ewel that she valued more than all. The desires,
owever, of those people do not go beyond money,
ut of that their covetousness is insatiable, and on
iis occasion it was carried to such a pitch that they
ould have taken even the clothes we wore as cap-
ves if they had been worth anything to them. It
as the advice of some of them to throw us all in-
o the sea wrapped up in a sail; for their purpose
as to trade at some of the ports of Spain, giving
emselves out as Bretons, and if they brought us
live they would be punished as soon as the rob-
ery was discovered; but the captain (who was the
ne who had plundered my beloved Zoraida) said
e was satisfied with the prize he had got, and that
e would not touch at any Spanish port, but pass
he Straits of Gibraltar by night, or as best he could,
nd make for Rochelle, from which he had sailed.
o they agreed by common consent to give us the
kiff belonging to their ship and all we required for
he short voyage that remained to us, and this they
lid the next day on coming in sight of the Spanish
oast, with which, and the joy we felt, all our suf-
erings and miseries were as completely forgotten
s if they had never been endured by us, such is
he delight of recovering lost liberty.

It may have been about mid-day when they placed
is in the boat, giving us two kegs of water and some
iscuit; and the captain, moved by I know not what
ompassion, as the lovely Zoraida was about to em-
ark gave her some forty gold crowns, and would
ot permit his men to take from her those same garments which she has on now. We got into the boat,
eturning them thanks for their kindness to us, and
howing ourselves grateful rather than indignant.
They stood out to sea, steering for the straits; we,
vithout looking to any compass save the land we
iad before us, set ourselves to row with such energy
hat by sunset we were so near that we might easily,
ve thought, land before the night was far advanced.
3ut as the moon did not show that night, and the
ky was clouded, and as we knew not whereabouts
ve were, it did not seem to us a prudent thing to
nake for the shore, as several of us advised, saying
ve ought to run ourselves ashore even if it were on
ocks and far from any habitation, for in this way
ve should be relieved from the apprehensions we
aaturally felt of the prowling vessels of the Tetuan

corsairs, who leave Barbary at nightfall and are on
the Spanish coast by daybreak, where they commonly take some prize, and then go home to sleep in
their own houses. But of the conflicting counsels the
one which was adopted was that we should approach gradually, and land where we could if the
sea were calm enough to permit us. This was done,
and a little before midnight we drew near to the
foot of a huge and lofty mountain, not so close to
the sea but that it left a narrow space on which to
land conveniently. We ran our boat up on the sand,
and all sprang out and kissed the ground, and with
tears of joyful satisfaction returned thanks to God
our Lord for all his incomparable goodness to us on
our voyage. We took out of the boat the provisions
it contained, and drew it up on the shore, and then
climbed a long way up the mountain, for even there
we could not feel easy in our hearts, or thoroughly
persuade ourselves that it was Christian soil that
was now under our feet.

The dawn came, more slowly, I think, than we
could have wished; we completed the ascent in order to see if from the summit any habitation or any
shepherd's huts could be discovered, but strain our
eyes as we might, neither dwelling, nor human being, nor path nor road could we perceive. However,
we determined to push on farther, as it could not
but be that ere long we must see some one who
could tell us where we were. But what distressed
me most was to see Zoraida going on foot over that
rough ground; for though I once carried her on my
shoulders, she was more wearied by my weariness
than rested by the rest; and so she would never
again allow me to undergo the exertion, and went on
very patiently and cheerfully, while I led her by
the hand. We had gone rather less than a quarter
of a league when the sound of a little bell fell on
our ears, a clear proof that there were flocks hard
by, and looking about carefully to see if any were
within view, we observed a young shepherd tranquilly and unsuspiciously trimming a stick with his
knife, at the foot of a cork tree. We called to him,
and he, raising his head, sprang nimbly to his feet,
for, as we afterwards learned, the first who presented
themselves to his sight were the renegade and Zoraida, and seeing them in Moorish dress he imagined
that all the Moors of Barbary were upon him; and
plunging with marvellous swiftness into the thicket
in front of him, he began to raise a prodigious outcry, exclaiming, "The Moors—the Moors have landed!" We were all thrown into perplexity by these
cries, not knowing what to do; but reflecting that
the shouts of the shepherd would raise the country
and that the mounted coast-guard would come at
once to see what was the matter, we agreed that the
renegade must strip off his Turkish garments and
put on a captive's jacket or coat, which one of our
party gave him at once, though he himself was reduced to his shirt; and so commending ourselves to
God, we followed the same road which we saw the
shepherd take, expecting every moment that the
coast-guard would be down upon us. Nor did our

expectation deceive us, for two hours had not passed when, coming out of the brushwood into the open ground, we perceived some fifty mounted men swiftly approaching us at a hand-gallop. As soon as we saw them we stood still, waiting for them; but as they came close and, instead of the Moors they were in quest of, saw a set of poor Christians, they were taken aback, and one of them asked if it could be we who were the cause of the shepherd having raised the call to arms. I said yes, and as I was about to explain to him what had occurred, and whence we came and who we were, one of the Christians of our party recognized the horseman who had put the question to us, and before I could say anything more he exclaimed, "Thanks be to God, sirs, for bringing us to such good quarters; for, if I do not deceive myself, the ground we stand on is that of Velez Malaga; unless, indeed, all my years of captivity have made me unable to recollect that you, señor, who ask who we are, are Pedro de Bustamente, my uncle."

The Christian captive had hardly uttered these words, when the horseman threw himself off his horse, and ran to embrace the young man, crying, "Nephew of my soul and life! I recognize thee now; and long have I mourned thee as dead, I, and my sister, thy mother, and all thy kin that are still alive, and whom God has been pleased to preserve that they may enjoy the happiness of seeing thee. We knew long since that thou wert in Algiers, and from the appearance of thy garments and those of all this company, I conclude that ye have had a miraculous restoration to liberty."

"It is true," replied the young man, "and by and by we will tell you all."

As soon as the horsemen understood that we were Christian captives, they dismounted from their horses, and each offered his to carry us to the city of Velez Malaga, which was a league and a half distant. Some of them went to bring the boat to the city, we having told them where we had left it; others took us up behind them, and Zoraida was placed on the horse of the young man's uncle. The whole town came out to meet us, for they had by this time heard of our arrival from one who had gone on in advance. They were not astonished to see liberated captives or Moorish captives, for people on that coast are well used to see both one and the other; but they were astonished at the beauty of Zoraida, which was just then heightened, as well by the exertion of travelling as by joy at finding herself on Christian soil, and relieved of all fear of being lost; for this had brought such a glow upon her face, that, unless my affection for her were deceiving me, I would venture to say that there was not a more beautiful creature in the world—at least, that I had ever seen.

We went straight to the church to return thanks to God for the mercies we had received, and when Zoraida entered it she said there were faces there like Lela Marien's. We told her they were her images; and as well as he could the renegade explained to her what they meant, that she might adore them as if each of them were the very same Lela Marien that had spoken to her; and she, having great intelligence and a quick and clear instinct, understood at once all he said to her about them. Thence they took us away and distributed us all in different houses in the town; but as for the renegade, Zoraida, and myself, the Christian who came with us brought us to the house of his parents, who had a fair share of the gifts of fortune, and treated us with as much kindness as they did their own son.

We remained six days in Velez, at the end of which the renegade, having informed himself of all that was requisite for him to do, set out for the city of Granada to restore himself to the sacred bosom of the Church through the medium of the Holy Inquisition. The other released captives took their departures, each the way that seemed best to him, and Zoraida and I were left alone, with nothing more than the crowns which the courtesy of the Frenchman had bestowed upon Zoraida, out of which I bought the beast on which she rides; and, I for the present attending her as her father and squire and not as her husband, we are now going to ascertain if my father is living, or if any of my brothers has had better fortune than mine has been; though as Heaven has made me the companion of Zoraida, I think no other lot could be assigned to me, however happy, that I would rather have. The patience with which she endures the hardships that poverty brings with it, and the eagerness she shows to become a Christian, are such that they fill me with admiration, and bind me to serve her all my life; though the happiness I feel in seeing myself hers, and her mine, is disturbed and marred by not knowing whether I shall find any corner to shelter her in my own country, or whether time and death may not have made such changes in the fortunes and lives of my father and brothers, that I shall hardly find any one who knows me, if they are not to be found.

I have no more of my story to tell you, gentlemen; whether it be an interesting or a curious one, let your better judgments decide; all I can say is I would gladly have told it to you more briefly; although my fear of wearying you has made me leave out more than one circumstance.

Chapter 42

Which treats of what further took place in the inn, and of several other things worth knowing

WITH these words the captive held his peace, and Don Fernando said to him, "In truth, Captain, the manner in which you have related this remarkable adventure has been such as befitted the novelty and strangeness of the matter. The whole story is curious and uncommon, and abounds with incidents that fill the hearers with wonder and astonishment; and so great is the pleasure we have found in listening to it that we should be glad if it were to begin again, even though to-morrow were to find us still occupied with the same tale." And while he said this Cardenio and the rest of them offered to be of service to him in any way that lay in their power, and in words and language so kindly and sincere that the captain was much gratified by their good-will. In particular Don Fernando offered, if he would go back with him, to get his brother, the marquis, to become godfather at the baptism of Zoraida, and on his own part to provide him with the means of making his appearance in his own country with the credit and comfort he was entitled to. For all this the captive returned thanks very courteously, but would not accept any of their generous offers.

By this time night closed in, and as it did, there came up to the inn a coach attended by some men on horseback, who demanded accommodation; to which the landlady replied that there was not a hand's breadth of the whole inn unoccupied.

"Still, for all that," said one of those who had entered on horseback, "room must be found for his lordship the judge here."

At this name the landlady was taken aback, and said, "Señor, the fact is I have no beds; but if his lordship the judge carries one with him, as no doubt he does, let him come in and welcome; for my husband and I will give up our room to accommodate his worship."

"Very good, so be it," said the squire; but in the meantime a man had got out of the coach whose dress indicated at a glance the office and post he held, for the long robe with ruffled sleeves that he wore showed that he was, as his servant said, a Judge of Appeal. He led by the hand a young girl in a travelling dress, apparently about sixteen years of age, and of such a high-bred air, so beautiful and so graceful, that all were filled with admiration when she made her appearance, and but for having seen Dorothea, Luscinda, and Zoraida, who were there in the inn, they would have fancied that a beauty like that of this maiden's would have been hard to find. Don Quixote was present at the entrance of the judge with the young lady, and as soon as he saw him he said, "Your worship may with confidence enter and take your ease in this castle; for though the accommodation be scanty and poor, there are no quarters so cramped or inconvenient that they cannot make room for arms and letters; above all if arms and letters have beauty for a guide and leader, as letters represented by your worship have in this

fair maiden, to whom not only ought castles to throw themselves open and yield themselves up, but rocks should rend themselves asunder and mountains divide and bow themselves down to give her a reception. Enter, your worship, I say, into this paradise, for here you will find stars and suns to accompany the heaven your worship brings with you; here you will find arms in their supreme excellence, and beauty in its highest perfection."

The judge was struck with amazement at the language of Don Quixote, whom he scrutinized very carefully, no less astonished by his figure than by his talk; and before he could find words to answer him he had a fresh surprise, when he saw opposite to him Luscinda, Dorothea, and Zoraida, who, having heard of the new guests and of the beauty of the young lady, had come to see her and welcome her; Don Fernando, Cardenio, and the curate, however, greeted him in a more intelligible and polished style. In short, the judge made his entrance in a state of bewilderment, as well with what he saw as what he heard, and the fair ladies of the inn gave the fair damsel a cordial welcome. On the whole he could perceive that all who were there were people of quality; but with the figure, countenance, and bearing of Don Quixote he was at his wits' end; and all civilities having been exchanged, and the accommodation of the inn inquired into, it was settled, as it had been before settled, that all the women should retire to the garret that has been already mentioned, and that the men should remain outside as if to guard them; the judge, therefore, was very well pleased to allow his daughter, for such the damsel was, to go with the ladies, which she did very willingly; and with part of the host's narrow bed and half of what the judge had brought with him they made a more comfortable arrangement for the night than they had expected.

The captive, whose heart had leaped within him the instant he saw the judge, telling him somehow that this was his brother, asked one of the servants who accompanied him what his name was, and whether he knew from what part of the country he came. The servants replied that he was called the Licentiate Juan Perez de Viedma, and that he had heard it said he came from a village in the mountains of Leon. From this statement, and what he himself had seen, he felt convinced that this was his brother who had adopted letters by his father's advice; and excited and rejoiced, he called Don Fernando and Cardenio and the curate aside, and told them how the matter stood, assuring them that the judge was his brother. The servant had further informed him that he was now going to the Indies with the appointment of judge of the Supreme Court of Mexico; and he had learned, likewise, that the young lady was his daughter, whose mother had died in giving birth to her, and that he was very rich in consequence of the dowry left to him with the daughter. He asked their advice as to what means he should adopt to make himself known, or to ascertain beforehand whether, when he had made himself known, his brother, seeing him so poor, would be ashamed of him, or would receive him with a warm heart.

"Leave it to me to find out that," said the curate; "though there is no reason for supposing, Captain, that you will not be kindly received, because the worth and wisdom that your brother's bearing shows him to possess do not make it likely that he will prove haughty or insensible, or that he will not know how to estimate the accidents of fortune at their proper value."

"Still," said the captain, "I would not make myself known abruptly, but in some indirect way."

"I have told you already," said the curate, "that I will manage it in a way to satisfy us all."

By this time supper was ready, and they all took their seats at the table, except the captive, and the ladies, who supped by themselves in their own room. In the middle of supper the curate said, "I had a comrade of your worship's name, Señor Judge, in Constantinople, where I was a captive for several years, and the same comrade was one of the stoutest soldiers and captains in the whole Spanish infantry; but he had as large a share of misfortune as he had of gallantry and courage."

"And how was the captain called, señor?" asked the judge.

"He was called Ruy Perez de Viedma," replied the curate, "and he was born in a village in the mountains of Leon; and he mentioned a circumstance connected with his father and his brothers which, had it not been told me by so truthful a man as he was, I should have set down as one of those fables the old women tell over the fire in winter; for he said his father had divided his property among his three sons and had addressed words of advice to them sounder than any of Cato's. But I can say this much, that the choice he made of going to the wars was attended with such success, that by his gallant conduct and courage, and without any help save his own merit, he rose in a few

years to be captain of infantry, and to see himself on the high-road and in position to be given the command of a corps before long; but Fortune was against him, for where he might have expected her favor he lost it, and with it his liberty, on that glorious day when so many recovered theirs, at the battle of Lepanto. I lost mine at the Goletta, and after a variety of adventures we found ourselves comrades at Constantinople. Thence we went to Algiers, where we met with one of the most extraordinary adventures that ever befell any one in this world."

Here the curate went on to relate briefly his brother's adventure with Zoraida; to all which the judge gave such an attentive hearing as he had never yet given to any cause he heard. The curate, however, only went so far as to describe how the Frenchmen plundered those who were in the boat, and the poverty and distress in which his comrade and the fair Moor were left; of whom he said he had not been able to learn what became of them, or whether they had reached Spain, or been carried to France by the Frenchmen.

The captain, standing a little to one side, was listening to all the curate said, and watching every movement of his brother, who, as soon as he perceived the curate had made an end of his story, gave a deep sigh and said with his eyes full of tears, "Oh, señor, if you only knew what news you have given me and how it comes home to me, making me show how I feel it with these tears that spring from my eyes in spite of all my worldly wisdom and self-restraint! That brave captain that you speak of is my eldest brother, who, being of a bolder and loftier mind than my other brother or myself, chose the honorable and worthy calling of arms, which was one of the three careers our father proposed to us, as your comrade mentioned in that fable you thought he was telling you. I followed that of letters, in which God and my own exertions have raised me to the position in which you see me. My second brother is in Peru, so wealthy that with what he has sent to my father and to me he has fully repaid the portion he took with him, and has even furnished my father's hands with the means of gratifying his natural generosity, while I too have been enabled to pursue my studies in a more becoming and creditable fashion, and so to attain my present standing. My father is still alive, though dying with anxiety to hear of his eldest son, and he prays God unceasingly that death may not close his eyes until he has looked upon those of his son; but with regard to him what surprises me is, that

aving so much common sense as he had, he
ould have neglected to give any intelligence
bout himself, either in his troubles and suffer-
gs, or in his prosperity, for if his father or any
us had known of his condition he need not
ave waited for that miracle of the reed to ob-
in his ransom; but what now disquiets me is
e uncertainty whether those Frenchmen may
ave restored him to liberty, or murdered him
hide the robbery. All this will make me con-
nue my journey, not with the satisfaction in
hich I began it, but in the deepest melancholy
nd sadness. Oh dear brother! that I only knew
here thou art now, and I would hasten to seek
ee out and deliver thee from thy sufferings,
ough it were to cost me suffering myself! Oh
at I could bring news to our old father that
ou art alive, even wert thou in the deepest
ungeon of Barbary; for his wealth and my
rother's and mine would rescue thee thence!
h beautiful and generous Zoraida, that I could
pay thy goodness to a brother! That I could
e present at the new birth of thy soul, and at
y bridal that would give us all such happi-
ess!"

All this and more the judge uttered with
ch deep emotion at the news he had received
f his brother that all who heard him shared in
, showing their sympathy with his sorrow.
he curate, seeing, then, how well he had suc-
eeded in carrying out his purpose and the cap-
in's wishes, had no desire to keep them un-
appy any longer, so he rose from the table and
ping into the room where Zoraida was he took
er by the hand, Luscinda, Dorothea, and the
dge's daughter following her. The captain
as waiting to see what the curate would do,
hen the latter, taking him with the other
and, advanced with both of them to where the
dge and the others were, and said, "Let your
ears cease to flow, Señor Judge, and the wish
f your heart be gratified as fully as you could
esire, for you have before you your worthy
rother and your good sister-in-law. He whom
ou see here is the Captain Viedma, and this is
e fair Moor who has been so good to him.
he Frenchmen I told you of have reduced
em to the state of poverty you see that you
ay show the generosity of your kind heart."

The captain ran to embrace his brother, who
laced both hands on his breast so as to have a
ood look at him, holding him a little way off;
ut as soon as he had fully recognized him he
lasped him in his arms so closely, shedding such
ears of heartfelt joy, that most of those present
ould not but join in them. The words the

brothers exchanged, the emotion they showed
can scarcely be imagined, I fancy, much less
put down in writing. They told each other in a
few words the events of their lives; they showed
the true affection of brothers in all its strength;
then the judge embraced Zoraida, putting all
he possessed at her disposal; then he made his
daughter embrace her, and the fair Christian
and the lovely Moor drew fresh tears from every
eye. And there was Don Quixote observing all
these strange proceedings attentively without
uttering a word, and attributing the whole to
chimeras of knight-errantry. Then they agreed
that the captain and Zoraida should return with
his brother to Seville, and send news to his father of his having been delivered and found,
so as to enable him to come and be present at
the marriage and baptism of Zoraida, for it was
impossible for the judge to put off his journey,
as he was informed that in a month from that
time the fleet was to sail from Seville for New
Spain, and to miss the passage would have been
a great inconvenience to him. In short, everybody was well pleased and glad at the captive's
good fortune; and as now almost two-thirds of
the night were past they resolved to retire to
rest for the remainder of it. Don Quixote offered to mount guard over the castle lest they
should be attacked by some giant or other malevolent scoundrel, covetous of the great treasure
of beauty the castle contained. Those who understood him returned him thanks for this service, and they gave the judge an account of his
extraordinary humor, with which he was not a
little amused. Sancho Panza alone was fuming
at the lateness of the hour for retirement to
rest; and he of all was the one that made himself most comfortable, as he stretched himself
on the trappings of his ass, which, as will be
told farther on, cost him so dear.

The ladies, then, having retired to their
chamber, and the others having disposed themselves with as little discomfort as they could,
Don Quixote sallied out of the inn to act as
sentinel of the castle as he had promised. It
happened, however, that a little before the approach of dawn a voice so musical and sweet
reached the ears of the ladies that it forced them
all to listen attentively, but especially Dorothea,
who had been awake, and by whose side Doña
Clara de Viedma, for so the judge's daughter
was called, lay sleeping. No one could imagine
who it was that sang so sweetly, and the voice
was unaccompanied by any instrument. At one
moment it seemed to them as if the singer were
in the court-yard, at another in the stable; and

as they were all attention, wondering, Cardenio came to the door and said, "Listen, whoever is not alseep, and you will hear a muleteer's voice that enchants as it chants."

"We are listening to it already, señor," said Dorothea; on which Cardenio went away; and Dorothea, giving all her attention to it, made out the words of the song to be these:

Chapter 43

Wherein is related the pleasant story of the muleteer, together with other strange things that came to pass in the inn

Ah me, Love's mariner am I
On Love's deep ocean sailing;
I know not where the haven lies,
I dare not hope to gain it.

One solitary distant star
Is all I have to guide me,
A brighter orb than those of old
That Palinurus lighted.

And vaguely drifting am I borne,
I know not where it leads me;
I fix my gaze on it alone,
Of all beside it heedless.

But over-cautious prudery,
And coyness cold and cruel,
When most I need it, these, like clouds,
Its longed-for light refuse me.

Bright star, goal of my yearning eyes
As thou above me beamest,
When thou shalt hide thee from my sight
I'll know that death is near me.

The singer had got so far when it struck Dorothea that it was not fair to let Clara miss hearing such a sweet voice, so, shaking her from side to side, she woke her, saying, "Forgive me, child, for waking thee, but I do so that thou mayest have the pleasure of hearing the best voice thou hast ever heard, perhaps, in all thy life." Clara awoke quite drowsy, and not understanding at the moment what Dorothea said, asked her what it was; she repeated what she had said, and Clara became attentive at once; but she had hardly heard two lines, as the singer continued, when a strange trembling seized her, as if she were suffering from a severe attack of quartan ague, and throwing her arms round Dorothea she said, "Ah, dear lady of my soul and life! why did you wake me? The greatest kindness fortune could do me now would be to close my eyes and ears so as neither to see nor hear that unhappy musician."

"What art thou talking about, child?" said Dorothea. "Why, they say this singer is a muleteer."

"Nay, he is the lord of many places," replied Clara, "and that one in my heart which he holds so firmly shall never be taken from him, unless he be willing to surrender it."

Dorothea was amazed at the ardent language of the girl, for it seemed to be far beyond such experience of life as her tender years gave any promise of, so she said to her, "You speak in such a way that I cannot understand you Señora Clara; explain yourself more clearly, and tell me what is this you are saying about hearts and places and this musician whose voice has so moved you? But do not tell me anything now; I do not want to lose the pleasure I get from listening to the singer by giving my attention to your transports, for I perceive he is beginning to sing a new strain and a new air."

"Let him, in Heaven's name," returned Clara and not to hear him she stopped both ears with her hands, at which Dorothea was again surprised; but turning her attention to the song she found that it ran in this fashion:

Sweet Hope, my stay,
That onward to the goal of thy intent
Dost make thy way,
Heedless of hinderance or impediment,
Have thou no fear
If at each step thou findest death is near.

No victory,
No joy of triumph doth the faint heart know;
Unblest is he
That a bold front to Fortune dares not show,
But soul and sense
In bondage yieldeth up to indolence.

If Love his wares
Do dearly sell, his right must be confest;
What gold compares
With that whereon his stamp he hath imprest?
And all men know
What costeth little that we rate but low.

Love resolute
Knows not the word "impossibility";
And though my suit
Beset by endless obstacles I see,
Yet no despair
Shall hold me bound to earth while heaven is there.

Here the voice ceased and Clara's sobs began afresh, all which excited Dorothea's curiosity to know what could be the cause of singing so sweet and weeping so bitter, so she again asked her what it was she was going to say be-ore. On this Clara, afraid that Luscinda might overhear her, winding her arms tightly round Dorothea put her mouth so close to her ear that he could speak safely without fear of being heard by any one else, and said, "This singer, dear señora, is the son of a gentleman of Aragon, lord of two villages, who lives opposite my father's house at Madrid; and though my father had curtains to the windows of his house in winter, and blinds in summer, in some way—I know not how—this gentleman, who was pursuing his studies, saw me—whether in church or elsewhere, I can not tell—and, in fact, fell in love with me, and gave me to know it from the windows of his house, with so many signs and tears that I was forced to believe him, and even to love him, without knowing what it was he wanted of me. One of the signs he used to make me was to link one hand in the other, to show me he wished to marry me; and, though I should have been glad if that could be, being alone and motherless I knew not whom to open my mind to, and so I left it as it was, showing him no favor, except when my father, and his too, were from home, to raise the curtain or the blind a little and let him see me plainly, at which he would show such delight that he seemed as if he were going mad. Meanwhile the time for my father's departure arrived, which he became aware of, but not from me, for I had never been able to tell him of it. He fell sick, of grief I believe, and so the day we were going away I could not see him to take farewell of him, were it only with the eyes. But after we had been two days on the road, on entering the posada of a village a day's journey from this, I saw him at the inn door in the dress of a muleteer, and so well disguised, that if I did not carry his image graven on my heart it would have been impossible for me to recognize him. But I knew him, and I was surprised, and glad; he watched me, unsuspected by my father, from whom he always hides himself when he crosses my path on the road, or in the posadas where we halt; and, as I know what he is, and reflect that for love of me he makes this journey on foot in all this hardship, I am ready to die of sorrow; and where he sets foot there I set my eyes. I know not with what object he has come; or how he could have got away from his father, who loves him beyond measure, having no other heir, and because he deserves it, as you will perceive when you see him. And moreover, I can tell you, all that he sings is out of his own head; for I have heard them say he is a great scholar and poet; and what is more, every time I see him or hear him sing I tremble all over, and am terrified lest my father should recognize him and come to know of our loves. I have never spoken a word to him in my life, and for all that I love him so that I could not live without him. This, dear señora, is all I have to tell you about the musician whose voice has delighted you so much; and from it alone you might easily perceive he is no muleteer, but a lord of hearts and towns, as I told you already."

"Say no more, Doña Clara," said Dorothea at this, at the same time kissing her a thousand times over, "say no more, I tell you, but wait till day comes; when I trust in God to arrange this affair of yours so that it may have the happy ending such an innocent beginning deserves."

"Ah, señora," said Doña Clara, "what end can be hoped for when his father is of such lofty position, and so wealthy, that he would think I was not fit to be even a servant to his son, much less wife? And as to marrying without the knowledge of my father, I would not do it for all the world. I would not ask anything more than that this youth should go back and leave me; perhaps with not seeing him, and the long distance we shall have to travel, the pain I suffer now may become easier; though I dare say the remedy I propose will do me very little good. I don't know by what deviltry this has come about, or how this love I have for him got in; I such a young girl, and he such a mere boy; for I verily believe we are both of an age, and I am not sixteen yet; for I shall be sixteen Michaelmas Day next, my father says."

Dorothea could not help laughing to hear how like a child Doña Clara spoke. "Let us go to sleep now, señora," said she, "for the little of the night that I fancy is left to us: God will soon send us daylight, and we will set all to rights, or it will go hard with me."

With this they fell asleep, and deep silence reigned all through the inn. The only persons not asleep were the landlady's daughter and her servant Maritornes, who, knowing the weak point of Don Quixote's humor, and that he was outside the inn mounting guard in armor and on horseback, resolved, the pair of them, to play some trick upon him, or at any rate to amuse themselves for a while by listening to his nonsense. As it so happened there was not a window in the whole inn that looked outwards except a hole in the wall of a straw-loft through which they used to throw out the straw. At this hole the two demi-damsels posted themselves, and observed Don Quixote on his horse, leaning on his pike and from time to time sending forth such deep and doleful sighs, that he seemed to pluck up his soul by the roots with each of them; and they could hear him, too, saying in a soft, tender, loving tone, "Oh my lady Dulcinea del Toboso, perfection of all beauty, summit and crown of discretion, treasure house of grace, depository of virtue, and, finally, ideal of all that is good, honorable, and delectable in this world! What is thy grace doing now? Art thou, perchance, mindful of thy enslaved knight who of his own free will hath exposed himself to so great perils, and all to serve thee? Give me tidings of her, oh luminary of the three faces! Perhaps at this moment, envious of hers, thou art regarding her, either as she paces to and fro some gallery of her sumptuous palaces, or leans over some balcony, meditating how, whilst preserving her purity and greatness, she may mitigate the tortures this wretched heart of mine endures for her sake, what glory should recompense my sufferings, what repose my toil, and lastly what death my life, and what reward my services? And thou, oh sun, that art now doubtless harnessing thy steeds in haste to rise betimes and come forth to see my lady; when thou seest her I entreat of thee to salute her on my behalf: but have a care, when thou shalt see her and salute her, that thou kiss not her face; for I shall be more jealous of thee than thou wert of that light-footed ingrate that made thee sweat and run so on the plains of Thessaly, or on the banks of the Peneus (for I do not exactly recollect where it was thou didst run on that occasion) in thy jealousy and love."

Don Quixote had got so far in his pathetic speech when the landlady's daughter began to signal to him, saying, "Señor, come over here, please."

At these signals and voice Don Quixote turned his head and saw by the light of the moon, which then was in its full splendor, that some one was calling to him from the hole in the wall, which seemed to him to be a window, and what is more, with a gilt grating, as rich castles, such as he believed the inn to be, ought to have; and it immediately suggested itself to his imagination that, as on the former occasion, the fair damsel, the daughter of the lady of the castle, overcome by love for him, was once more endeavoring to win his affections; and with this idea, not to show himself discourteous, or ungrateful, he turned Rocinante's head and approached the hole, and as he perceived the two wenches he said, "I pity you, beauteous lady, that you should have directed your thoughts of

love to a quarter from whence it is impossib[le] that such a return can be made to you as is d[ue] to your great merit and gentle birth, for whic[h] you must not blame this unhappy knight-erra[nt] whom love renders incapable of submission [to] any other than her whom, the first moment h[is] eyes beheld her, he made absolute mistress [of] his soul. Forgive me, noble lady, and retire [to] your apartment, and do not, by any furth[er] declaration of your passion, compel me to sho[w] myself more ungrateful; and if, of the love yo[u] bear me, you should find that there is anythi[ng] else in my power wherein I can gratify yo[u,] provided it be not love itself, demand it of m[e,] for I swear to you by that sweet absent enem[y] of mine to grant it this instant, though it [be] that you require of me a lock of Medusa's ha[ir,] which was all snakes, or even the very bea[ms] of the sun shut up in a vial."

"My mistress wants nothing of that sort, s[ir] knight," said Maritornes at this.

"What then, discreet dame, is it that yo[ur] mistress wants?" replied Don Quixote.

"Only one of your fair hands," said Ma[ri]tornes, "to enable her to vent over it the gre[at] passion which has brought her to this loopho[le,] so much to the risk of her honor; for if the lo[rd] her father had heard her, the least slice he wou[ld] cut off her would be her ear."

"I should like to see that tried," said D[on] Quixote; "but he had better beware of that, [if] he does not want to meet the most disastro[us] end that ever father in the world met for ha[v]ing laid hands on the tender limbs of a lo[ve]stricken daughter."

Maritornes felt sure that Don Quixote wou[ld] present the hand she had asked, and makin[g] up her mind what to do, she got down from th[e] hole and went into the stable, where she too[k] the halter of Sancho Panza's ass, and in [a] haste returned to the hole, just as Don Quixo[te] had planted himself standing on Rocinant[e's] saddle in order to reach the grated windo[w] where he supposed the love-lorn damsel to b[e;] and giving her his hand, he said, "Lady, ta[ke] this hand, or rather this scourge of the ev[il] doers of the earth; take, I say, this hand whic[h] no other hand of woman has ever touched, n[ot] even hers who has complete possession of m[y] entire body. I present it to you, not that yo[u] may kiss it, but that you may observe the co[n]texture of the sinews, the close network of th[e] muscles, the breadth and capacity of the vein[s,] whence you may infer what must be the streng[th] of the arm that has such a hand."

"That we shall see presently," said Ma[ri]

tornes, and making a running knot on the halter, she passed it over his wrist and coming down from the hole tied the other end very firmly to the bolt of the door of the straw-loft.

Don Quixote, feeling the roughness of the rope on his wrist, exclaimed, "Your grace seems to be grating rather than caressing my hand; treat it not so harshly, for it is not to blame for the offence my resolution has given you, nor is it just to wreak all your vengeance on so small a part; remember that one who loves so well should not revenge herself so cruelly."

But there was nobody now to listen to these words of Don Quixote's, for as soon as Maritornes had tied him she and the other made off, ready to die with laughing, leaving him fastened in such a way that it was impossible for him to release himself.

He was, as has been said, standing on Rocinante, with his arm passed through the hole and his wrist tied to the bolt of the door, and in mighty fear and dread of being left hanging by the arm if Rocinante were to stir one side or the other; so he did not dare to make the least movement, although from the patience and imperturbable disposition of Rocinante, he had good reason to expect that he would stand without budging for a whole century. Finding himself fast, then, and that the ladies had retired, he began to fancy that all this was done by enchantment, as on the former occasion when in that same castle that enchanted Moor of a carrier had belabored him; and he cursed in his heart his own want of sense and judgment in venturing to enter the castle again, after having come off so badly the first time; it being a settled point with knights-errant that when they have tried an adventure, and have not succeeded in it, it is a sign that it is not reserved for them but for others, and that therefore they need not try it again. Nevertheless he pulled his arm to see if he could release himself, but it had been made so fast that all his efforts were in vain. It is true he pulled it gently lest Rocinante should move, but try as he might to seat himself in the saddle, he had nothing for it but to stand upright or pull his hand off. Then it was he wished for the sword of Amadis, against which no enchantment whatever had any power; then he cursed his ill fortune; then he magnified the loss the world would sustain by his absence while he remained there enchanted, for that he believed he was beyond all doubt; then he once more took to thinking of his beloved Dulcinea del Toboso; then he called to his worthy squire Sancho Panza, who, buried

in sleep and stretched upon the pack-saddle of his ass, was oblivious, at that moment, of the mother that bore him; then he called upon the sages Lirgandeo and Alquife to come to his aid; then he invoked his good friend Urganda to succor him; and then, at last, morning found him in such a state of desperation and perplexity that he was bellowing like a bull, for he had no hope that day would bring any relief to his suffering, which he believed would last forever, inasmuch as he was enchanted; and of this he was convinced by seeing that Rocinante never stirred, much or little, and he felt persuaded that he and his horse were to remain in this state, without eating or drinking or sleeping, until the malign influence of the stars was overpast, or until some other more sage enchanter should disenchant him.

But he was very much deceived in this conclusion, for daylight had hardly begun to appear when there came up to the inn four men on horseback, well equipped and accoutred, with firelocks across their saddle-bows. They called out and knocked loudly at the gate of the inn, which was still shut; on seeing which, Don Quixote, even there where he was, did not forget to act as sentinel, and said in a loud and imperious tone, "Knights, or squires, or whatever ye be, ye have no right to knock at the gates of this castle; for it is plain enough that they who are within are either asleep, or else are not in the habit of throwing open the fortress until the sun's rays are spread over the whole surface of the earth. Withdraw to a distance, and wait till it is broad daylight, and then we shall see whether it will be proper or not to open to you."

"What the devil fortress or castle is this," said one, "to make us stand on such ceremony? If you are the innkeeper bid them open to us; we are travellers who only want to feed our horses and go on, for we are in haste."

"Do you think, gentlemen, that I look like an innkeeper?" said Don Quixote.

"I don't know what you look like," replied the other; "but I know that you are talking nonsense when you call this inn a castle."

"A castle it is," returned Don Quixote, "nay, more, one of the best in this whole province, and it has within it people who have had the sceptre in the hand and the crown on the head."

"It would be better if it were the other way," said the traveller, "the sceptre on the head and the crown in the hand; but if so, maybe there is within some company of players, with whom it is a common thing to have those crowns and sceptres you speak of; for in such a small inn as this, and where such silence is kept, I do not believe any people entitled to crowns and sceptres can have taken up their quarters."

"You know but little of the world," returned Don Quixote, "since you are ignorant of what commonly occurs in knight-errantry."

But the comrades of the spokesman growing weary of the dialogue with Don Quixote, renewed their knocks with great vehemence, so much so that the host, and not only he but everybody in the inn, awoke, and he got up to ask who knocked. It happened at this moment that one of the horses of the four who were seeking admittance went to smell Rocinante, who melancholy, dejected, and with drooping ears, stood motionless, supporting his sorely stretched master; and as he was, after all, flesh, though he looked as if he were made of wood, he could not help giving way and in return smelling the one who had come to offer him attentions. But he had hardly moved at all when Don Quixote lost his footing; and slipping off the saddle, he would have come to the ground, but for being suspended by the arm, which caused him such agony that he believed either his wrist would be cut through or his arm torn off; and he hung so near the ground that he could just touch it with his feet, which was all the worse for him; for, finding how little was wanted to enable him to plant his feet firmly, he struggled and stretched himself as much as he could to gain a footing; just like those undergoing the torture of the *strappado*, when they are fixed at "touch and no touch," who aggravate their own sufferings by their violent efforts to stretch themselves, deceived by the hope which makes them fancy that with a very little more they will reach the ground.

Chapter 44

In which are continued the unheard-of adventures of the inn

So loud, in fact, were the shouts of Don Quixote, that the landlord opening the gate of the inn in all haste, came out in dismay, and ran to see who was uttering such cries, and those who were outside joined him. Maritornes, who had been by this time roused up by the same outcry, suspecting what it was, ran to the loft and, without any one seeing her, untied the halter by which Don Quixote was suspended, and down he came to the ground in the sight of the landlord and the travellers, who approaching asked him what was the matter with him that he shouted so. He without replying a word took the rope off his wrist, and rising to his feet leaped upon Rocinante, braced his buckler on his arm, put his lance in rest, and making a considerable circuit of the plain came back at a half gallop exclaiming, "Whoever shall say that I have been enchanted with just cause, provided my lady the Princess Micomicona grants me permission to do so, I give him the lie, challenge him and defy him to single combat."

The newly arrived travellers were amazed at the words of Don Quixote; but the landlord removed their surprise by telling them who he was, and not to mind him as he was out of his senses. They then asked the landlord if by any chance a youth of about fifteen years of age had come to that inn, one dressed like a muleteer, and of such and such an appearance, describing that of Doña Clara's lover. The landlord replied that there were so many people in the inn he had not noticed the person they were inquiring for; but one of them observing the coach in which the judge had come, said, "He is here no doubt, for this is the coach he is following: let one of us stay at the gate, and the rest go in to look for him; or indeed it would be as well if one of us went round the inn, lest he should escape over the wall of the yard." "So be it," said another; and while two of them went in, one remained at the gate and the other made the circuit of the inn; observing all which, the landlord was unable to conjecture for what reason they were taking all these precautions, though he understood they were looking for the youth whose description they had given him.

It was by this time broad daylight; and for that reason, as well as in consequence of the noise Don Quixote had made, everybody was awake and up, but particularly Doña Clara and Dorothea; for they had been able to sleep but badly that night, the one from agitation at having her lover so near her, the other from curiosity to see him. Don Quixote, when he saw that not one of the four travellers took any notice of him or replied to his challenge, was furious and ready to die with indignation and wrath; and if he could have found in the ordinances of chivalry that it was lawful for a knight-errant to undertake or engage in another enterprise when he had plighted his word and faith not to involve himself in any until he had made an end of the one to which he was pledged, he would have attacked the whole of them, and would have made them return an answer in spite of themselves. But considering that it would not become him, nor be right, to begin any new emprise until he had established Miomicona in her kingdom, he was constrained to hold his peace and wait quietly to see what would be the upshot of the proceedings of those same travellers; one of whom found the youth they were seeking lying asleep by the side of a muleteer, without a thought of any one coming in search of him, much less finding him.

The man laid hold of him by the arm, saying, It becomes you well indeed, Señor Don Luis, to be in the dress you wear, and well the bed in which I find you agrees with the luxury in which your mother reared you."

The youth rubbed his sleepy eyes and stared for a while at him who held him, but presently recognized him as one of his father's servants, at which he was so taken aback that for some time he could not find or utter a word; while the servant went on to say, "There is nothing for it now, Señor Don Luis, but to submit quietly and return home, unless it is your wish that my lord, your father, should take his departure for the other world, for nothing else can be the consequence of the grief he is in at your absence."

"But how did my father know that I had gone this road and in this dress?" said Don Luis.

"It was a student to whom you confided your intentions," answered the servant, "that disclosed them, touched with pity at the distress he saw your father suffer on missing you; he therefore despatched four of his servants in quest of you, and here we all are at your service, better pleased than you can imagine that we shall return so soon and restore you to those eyes that so yearn for you."

"That shall be as I please, or as Heaven orders," returned Don Luis.

"What can you please or Heaven order," said the other, "except to agree to go back? Anything else is impossible."

All this conversation between the two was overheard by the muleteer at whose side Don Luis lay, and rising, he went to report what had taken place to Don Fernando, Cardenio, and the others, who had by this time dressed themselves; and told them how the man had addressed the youth as "Don," and what words had passed, and how he wanted him to return to his father, which the youth was unwilling to do. With this, and what they already knew of the rare voice that Heaven had bestowed upon him, they all felt very anxious to know more particularly who he was, and even to help him if it was attempted to employ force against him; so they hastened to where he was still talking and arguing with his servant. Dorothea at this in-

stant came out of her room, followed by Doña Clara all in a tremor; and calling Cardenio aside, she told him in a few words the story of the musician and Doño Clara, and he at the same time told what had happened, how his father's servants had come in search of him; but in telling her so, he did not speak low enough but that Doña Clara heard what he said, at which she was so much agitated that had not Dorothea hastened to support her she would have fallen to the ground. Cardenio then bade Dorothea return to her room, as he would endeavor to make the whole matter right, and they did as he desired. All the four who had come in quest of Don Luis had now come into the inn and surrounded him, urging him to return and console his father and at once without a moment's delay. He replied that he could not do so on any account until he had concluded some business in which his life, honor, and heart were at stake. The servants pressed him, saying that most certainly they would not return without him, and that they would take him away whether he liked it or not.

"You shall not do that," replied Don Luis, "unless you take me dead; though however you take me, it will be without life."

By this time most of those in the inn had been attracted by the dispute, but particularly Cardenio, Don Fernando, his companions, the judge, the curate, the barber, and Don Quixote; for he now considered there was no necessity for mounting guard over the castle any longer. Cardenio being already acquainted with the young man's story, asked the men who wanted to take him, what object they had in seeking to carry off this youth against his will.

"Our object," said one of the four, "is to save the life of his father, who is in danger of losing it through this gentleman's disappearance."

Upon this Don Luis exclaimed, "There is no need to make my affairs public here; I am free, and I will return if I please; and if not, none of you shall compel me."

"Reason will compel your worship," said the man, "and if it has no power over you, it has power over us, to make us do what we came for, and what it is our duty to do."

"Let us hear what the whole affair is about," said the judge at this; but the man, who knew him as a neighbor of theirs, replied, "Do you not know this gentleman, Señor Judge? He is the son of your neighbor, who has run away from his father's house in a dress so unbecoming his rank, as your worship may perceive."

The judge on this looked at him more carefully and recognized him, and embracing him said, "What folly is this, Señor Don Luis, or what can have been the cause that could have induced you to come here in this way, and in this dress, which so ill becomes your condition?"

Tears came into the eyes of the young man, and he was unable to utter a word in reply to the judge, who told the four servants not to be uneasy, for all would be satisfactorily settled; and then taking Don Luis by the hand, he drew him aside and asked the reason of his having come there.

But while he was questioning him they heard a loud outcry at the gate of the inn, the cause of which was that two of the guests who had passed the night there, seeing everybody busy about finding out what it was the four men wanted, had conceived the idea of going off without paying what they owed; but the landlord, who minded his own affairs more than other people's, caught them going out of the gate and demanded his reckoning, abusing them for their dishonesty with such language that he drove them to reply with their fists, and so they began to lay on him in such a style that the poor man was forced to cry out, and call for help. The landlady and her daughter could see no one more free to give aid than Don Quixote, and to him the daughter said, "Sir knight, by the virtue God has given you, help my poor father, for there are two wicked men beating him to a mummy."

To which Don Quixote very deliberately and phlegmatically replied, "Fair damsel, at the present moment your request is inopportune, for I am debarred from involving myself in any adventure until I have brought to a happy conclusion one to which my word has pledged me; but that which I can do for you is what I will now mention: run and tell your father to stand his ground as well as he can in this battle, and on no account to allow himself to be vanquished, while I go and request permission of the Princess Micomicona to enable me to succor him in his distress; and if she grants it, rest assured I will relieve him from it."

"Sinner that I am," exclaimed Maritornes, who stood by; "before you have got your permission my master will be in the other world."

"Give me leave, señora, to obtain the permission I speak of," returned Don Quixote; "and if I get it, it will matter very little if he is in the other world; for I will rescue him thence in spite of all the same world can do; or at any rate I will give you such a revenge over those who shall have sent him there that you will be

more than moderately satisfied"; and withou saying anything more he went and knelt befor Dorothea, requesting her Highness in knight and errant phrase to be pleased to grant hi permission to aid and succor the castellan of th castle, who now stood in grievous jeopardy The princess granted it graciously, and he once, bracing his buckler on his arm and draw ing his sword, hastened to the inn-gate, whe the two guests were handling the landlord rough ly; but as soon as he reached the spot he stoppe short and stood still, though Maritornes and th landlady asked him why he hesitated to hel their master and husband.

"I hesitate," said Don Quixote, "because it not lawful for me to draw sword against pe sons of squirely condition; but call my squi Sancho to me; for this defence and vengeanc are his affair and business."

Thus matters stood at the inn-gate, whe there was a very lively exchange of fisticuffs an punches, to the sore damage of the landlord an to the wrath of Maritornes, the landlady, an her daughter, who were furious when they sa the pusillanimity of Don Quixote, and the har treatment their master, husband, and father w undergoing. But let us leave him there; for h will surely find some one to help him, and not, let him suffer and hold his tongue who a tempts more than his strength allows him to d and let us go back fifty paces to see what Do Luis said in reply to the judge whom we le questioning him privately as to his reasons f coming on foot and so meanly dressed.

To which the youth, pressing his hand in way that showed his heart was troubled by som great sorrow, and shedding a flood of tears, ma answer: "Señor, I have no more to tell you tha that for the moment when, through Heaven will and our being near neighbors, I first sa Doña Clara, your daughter and my lady, fro that instant I made her the mistress of my wil and if yours, my true lord and father, offers r impediment, this very day she shall become m wife. For her I left my father's house, and f her I assumed this disguise, to follow her whit ersoever she may go, as the arrow seeks its ma or the sailor the pole-star. She knows nothi more of my passion than what she may hav learned from having sometimes seen from a di tance that my eyes were filled with tears. Yo know already, señor, the wealth and noble bir of my parents, and that I am their sole heir; this be a sufficient inducement for you to ve ture to make me completely happy, accept n at once as your son; for if my father, influence by other objects of his own, should disapprove of this happiness I have sought for myself, time has more power to alter and change things, than human will."

With this the love-smitten youth was silent, while the judge, after hearing him, was astonished, perplexed, and surprised, as well at the manner and intelligence with which Don Luis had confessed the secret of his heart, as at the position in which he found himself, not knowing what course to take in a matter so sudden and unexpected. All the answer, therefore, he gave him was to bid him to make his mind easy for the present, and arrange with his servants not to take him back that day, so that there might be time to consider what was best for all parties. Don Luis kissed his hands by force, nay, bathed them with his tears, in a way that would have touched a heart of marble, not to say that of the judge, who as a shrewd man, had already perceived how advantageous the marriage would be to his daughter; though, were it possible, he would have preferred that it should be brought about with the consent of the father of Don Luis, who he knew looked for a title for his son.

The guests had by this time made peace with the landlord, for, by persuasion and Don Quixote's fair words more than by threats, they had paid him what he demanded, and the servants of Don Luis were waiting for the end of the conversation with the judge and their master's decision, when the devil, who never sleeps, contrived that the barber, from whom Don Quixote had taken Mambrino's helmet, and Sancho Panza the trappings of his ass in exchange for those of his own, should at this instant enter the inn; which said barber, as he led his ass to the stable, observed Sancho Panza engaged in repairing something or other belonging to the pack-saddle; and the moment he saw it he knew it, and made bold to attack Sancho, exclaiming, "Ho, sir thief, I have caught you! hand over my basin and my pack-saddle, and all my trappings that you robbed me of."

Sancho, finding himself so unexpectedly assailed, and hearing the abuse poured upon him, seized the pack-saddle with one hand, and with the other gave the barber a cuff that bathed his teeth in blood. The barber, however, was not so ready to relinquish the prize he had made in the pack-saddle; on the contrary, he raised such an outcry that every one in the inn came running to know what the noise and quarrel meant. "Here, in the name of the king and justice!" he cried, "this thief and highwayman wants to kill me for trying to recover my property."

"You lie," said Sancho, "I am no highwayman; it was in fair war my master Don Quixote won these spoils."

Don Quixote was standing by at the time, highly pleased to see his squire's stoutness, both offensive and defensive, and from that time forth he reckoned him a man of mettle, and in his heart resolved to dub him a knight on the first opportunity that presented itself, feeling sure that the order of chivalry would be fittingly bestowed upon him.

In the course of the altercation, among other things the barber said, "Gentlemen, this packsaddle is mine as surely as I owe God a death, and I know it as well as if I had given birth to it, and here is my ass in the stable who will not let me lie; only try it, and if it does not fit him like a glove, call me a rascal; and what is more, the same day I was robbed of this, they robbed me likewise of a new brass basin, never yet handselled, that would fetch a crown any day."

At this Don Quixote could not keep himself from answering; and interposing between the two, and separating them, he placed the pack-saddle on the ground, to lie there in sight until the truth was established, and said, "Your worships may perceive clearly and plainly the error under which this worthy squire lies when he calls that a basin which was, is, and shall be the helmet of Mambrino, which I won from him in fair war, and made myself master of by legitimate and lawful possession. With the pack-saddle I do not concern myself; but I may tell you on that head that my squire Sancho asked my permission to strip off the caparison of this vanquished poltroon's steed, and with it adorn his own; I allowed him, and he took it; and as to its having been changed from a caparison into a pack-saddle, I can give no explanation except the usual one, that such transformations will take place in adventures of chivalry. To confirm all which, run, Sancho my son, and fetch hither the helmet which this good fellow calls a basin."

"Egad, master," said Sancho, "if we have no other proof of our case than what your worship puts forward, Mambrino's helmet is just as much a basin as this good fellow's caparison is a pack-saddle."

"Do as I bid thee," said Don Quixote; "it can not be that everything in this castle goes by enchantment."

Sancho hastened to where the basin was, and brought it back with him, and when Don Quixote saw it, he took hold of it and said, "Your worships may see with what a face this squire can assert that this is a basin and not the helmet I told you of; and I swear by the order of chivalry I profess, that this helmet is the identical one I took from him, without anything added to or taken from it."

"There is no doubt of that," said Sancho, "for from the time my master won it until now he has only fought one battle in it, when he let loose those unlucky men in chains; and if it had not been for this basin-helmet he would not have come off over well that time, for there was plenty of stone-throwing in that affair."

Chapter 45

In which the doubtful question of Mambrino's helmet and the pack-saddle is finally settled, with other adventures that occurred in truth and earnest

"What do you think now, gentlemen," said the barber, "of what these gentles say, when they even want to make out that this is not a basin but a helmet?"

"And whoever says the contrary," said Don Quixote, "I will let him know he lies if he is a knight, and if he is a squire that he lies again a thousand times."

Our own barber, who was present at all this, and understood Don Quixote's humor so thoroughly, took it into his head to back up his delusion and carry on the joke for the general amusement; so addressing the other barber he said, "Señor barber, or whatever you are, you must know that I belong to your profession too, and have had a license to practise for more than twenty years, and I know the implements of the barber craft, every one of them, perfectly well; and I was likewise a soldier for some time in the days of my youth, and I know also what a helmet is, and a morion, and a headpiece with a visor, and other things pertaining to soldiering, I mean to say to soldiers' arms; and I say—saving better opinions and always with submission to sounder judgments—that this piece we have now before us, which this worthy gentleman has in his hands, not only is no barber's basin, but is as far from being one as white is from black, and truth from falsehood; I say, moreover, that this, although it is a helmet, is not a complete helmet."

"Certainly not," said Don Quixote, "for half of it is wanting, that is to say the beaver."

"It is quite true," said the curate, who saw the object of his friend the barber; and Cardenio, Don Fernando and his companions agreed with him, and even the judge, if his thoughts had not been so full of Don Luis's affair, would have helped to carry on the joke; but he was so taken up with the serious matters he had on his mind that he paid little or no attention to these facetious proceedings.

"God bless me!" exclaimed their butt the barber at this; "is it possible that such an honorable company can say that this is not a basin but a helmet? Why, this is a thing that would astonish a whole university, however wise it might be! That will do; if this basin is a helmet, why then the pack-saddle must be a horse's caparison as this gentleman has said."

"To me it looks like a pack-saddle," said Don Quixote; "but I have already said that with that question I do not concern myself."

"As to whether it be pack-saddle or caparison," said the curate, "it is only for Señor Don Quixote to say; for in these matters of chivalry all these gentlemen and I bow to his authority."

"By God, gentlemen," said Don Quixote, "so many strange things have happened to me in this castle on the two occasions on which I have sojourned in it, that I will not venture to assert anything positively in reply to any question touching anything it contains; for it is my belief that everything that goes on within it goes by enchantment. The first time, an enchanted Moor that is in there gave me sore trouble, nor did Sancho fare well among certain followers of his; and last night I was kept hanging by this arm for nearly two hours, without knowing how or why I came by such a mishap. So that now, for me to come forward to give an opinion in such a puzzling matter, would be to risk a rash decision. As regards the assertion that this is a basin and not a helmet I have already given an answer; but as to the question whether this is a pack-saddle or a caparison I will not venture to give a positive opinion, but will leave it to your worship's better judgment. Perhaps as you are not dubbed knights like myself, the enchantments of this place have nothing to do with you, and your faculties are unfettered, and you can see things in this castle as they really and truly are, and not as they appear to me."

"There can be no question," said Don Fernando on this, "but that Señor Don Quixote has spoken very wisely, and that with us rest the decision of this matter; and that we may have surer ground to go on, I will take the votes of the gentlemen in secret, and declare the result clearly and fully."

To those who were in the secret of Don Quixote's humor all this afforded great amusement; but to those who knew nothing about it it seemed the greatest nonsense in the world, in particular to the four servants of Don Luis, as well as to Don Luis himself, and to three other travellers who had by chance come to the inn, and had the appearance of officers of the Holy Brotherhood, as indeed they were; but the one who above all was at his wits' end was the barber whose basin, there before his very eyes, had been turned into Mambrino's helmet, and whose pack-saddle he had no doubt whatever was about to become a rich caparison for a horse. All laughed to see Don Fernando going from one to another collecting the votes, and whispering to them to give him their private opinion whether the treasure over which there had been so much fighting was a pack-saddle or a caparison; but after he had taken the votes of those who knew Don Quixote, he said aloud, "The fact is, my good fellow, that I am tired collecting such a number of opinions, for I find that there is not one of whom I ask what I desire to know, who does not tell me that it is absurd to say that this is the pack-saddle of an ass, and not the caparison of a horse, nay, of a thoroughbred horse; so you must submit, for, in spite of you and your ass, this is a caparison and no pack-saddle, and you have stated and proved your case very badly."

"May I never share heaven," said the poor barber, "if your worships are not all mistaken; and may my soul appear before God as that appears to me a pack-saddle and not a caparison; but 'laws go,'—I say no more; and indeed I am not drunk, for I am fasting, except it be from sin."

The simple talk of the barber did not afford less amusement than the absurdities of Don Quixote, who now observed, "There is no more to be done now than for each to take what belongs to him, and to whom God has given it, may St. Peter add his blessing."

But said one of the four servants, "Unless, indeed, this is a deliberate joke, I can not bring myself to believe that men so intelligent as those present are, or seem to be, can venture to declare and assert that this is not a basin, and that not a pack-saddle; but as I perceive that they do assert and declare it, I can only come to the conclusion that there is some mystery in this persistence in what is so opposed to the evidence of experience and truth itself; for I swear by" —and here he rapped out a round oath—"all the people in the world will not make me believe that this is not a barber's basin and that a jack-ass's pack-saddle."

"It might easily be a she-ass's," observed the curate.

"It is all the same," said the servant; "that is not the point; but whether it is or is not a pack-saddle, as your worships say."

On hearing this one of the newly arrived officers of the Brotherhood, who had been listening to the dispute and controversy, unable to restrain his anger and impatience, exclaimed, "It is a pack-saddle as sure as my father is my father, and whoever has said or will say anything else must be drunk."

"You lie like a rascally clown," returned Don Quixote; and lifting his pike, which he had never let out of his hand, he delivered such a blow at his head that, had not the officer dodged it, it would have stretched him at full length. The pike was shivered in pieces against the ground, and the rest of the officers, seeing their comrade assaulted, raised a shout, calling for help for the Holy Brotherhood. The landlord, who was of the fraternity, ran at once to fetch his staff of office and his sword, and ranged himself on the side of his comrades; the servants of Don Luis clustered round him, lest he should escape from them in the confusion; the barber, seeing the house turned upside down, once more laid hold of his pack-saddle and Sancho did the same; Don Quixote drew his sword, and charged the officers; Don Luis cried out to his servants to leave him alone and go and help Don Quixote, and Cardenio and Don Fernando, who were supporting him; the curate was shouting at the top of his voice, the landlady was screaming, her daughter was wailing, Maritornes was weeping, Dorothea was aghast, Luscinda terror-stricken, and Doña Clara in a faint. The barber cudgelled Sancho, and Sancho pommelled the barber; Don Luis gave one of his servants, who ventured to catch him by the arm to keep him from escaping, a cuff that bathed his teeth in blood; the judge took his part; Don Fernando had got one of the officers down and was belaboring him heartily; the landlord raised his voice again calling for help for the Holy Brotherhood; so that the whole inn was nothing but cries, shouts, shrieks, confusion, terror, dismay, mishaps, sword-cuts, fisticuffs, cudgellings, kicks, and bloodshed; and in the midst of all this chaos, complication, and general entanglement, Don Quixote took it into his head that he had been plunged into the thick of the discord of Agramante's camp; and, in a voice that shook the inn like thunder, he cried out, "Hold all, let all sheathe their swords, let all be calm and attend to me as they value their lives!"

All paused at his mighty voice, and he went

on to say, "Did I not tell you, sirs, that this castle was enchanted, and that a legion or so of devils dwelt in it? In proof whereof I call upon you to behold with your own eyes how the discord of Agramante's camp has come hither, and been transferred into the midst of us. See how they fight, there for the sword, here for the horse, on that side for the eagle, on this for the helmet; we are all fighting, and all at cross purposes. Come then, you, Señor Judge, and you, Señor Curate; let the one represent King Agramante and the other King Sobrino, and make peace among us; for by God Almighty it is a sorry business that so many persons of quality as we are should slay one another for such trifling cause."

The officers, who did not understand Don Quixote's mode of speaking, and found themselves roughly handled by Don Fernando, Cardenio, and their companions, were not to be appeased; the barber was, however, for both his beard and his pack-saddle were the worse for the struggle; Sancho like a good servant obeyed the slightest word of his master; while the four servants of Don Luis kept quiet when they saw how little they gained by not being so. The landlord alone insisted upon it that they must punish the insolence of this madman, who at every turn raised a disturbance in the inn; but at length the uproar was stilled for the present; the pack-saddle remained a caparison till the day of judgment, and the basin a helmet and the inn a castle in Don Quixote's imagination.

All having been now pacified and made friends by the persuasion of the judge and the curate, the servants of Don Luis began again to urge him to return with them at once; and while he was discussing the matter with them, the judge took counsel with Don Fernando, Cardenio, and the curate as to what he ought to do in the case, telling them how it stood, and what Don Luis had said to him. It was agreed at length that Don Fernando should tell the servants of Don Luis who he was, and that it was his desire that Don Luis should accompany him to Andalusia, where he would receive from the marquis his brother the welcome his quality entitled him to; for, otherwise, it was easy to see from the determination of Don Luis that he would not return to his father at present, though they tore him to pieces. On learning the rank of Don Fernando and the resolution of Don Luis the four then settled it between themselves that three of them should return to tell his father how matters stood, and that the other should remain to wait upon Don Luis and not leave him

until they came back for him, or his father's orders were known. Thus by the authority of Agramante and the wisdom of King Sobrino all this complication of disputes was arranged; but the enemy of concord and hater of peace, feeling himself slighted and made a fool of, and seeing how little he had gained after having involved them all in such an elaborate entanglement, resolved to try his hand once more by stirring up fresh quarrels and disturbances.

It came about in this wise: the officers were pacified on learning the rank of those with whom they had been engaged, and withdrew from the contest, considering that whatever the result might be they were likely to get the worst of the battle; but one of them, the one who had been thrashed and kicked by Don Fernando, recollected that among some warrants he carried for the arrest of certain delinquents, he had one against Don Quixote, whom the Holy Brotherhood had ordered to be arrested for setting the galley slaves free, as Sancho had, with very good reason, apprehended. Suspecting how it was, then, he wished to satisfy himself as to whether Don Quixote's features corresponded; and taking a parchment out of his bosom he lit upon what he was in search of, and setting himself to read it deliberately, for he was not a quick reader, as he made out each word he fixed his eyes on Don Quixote, and went on comparing the description in the warrant with his face, and discovered that beyond all doubt he was the person described in it. As soon as he had satisfied himself, folding up the parchment, he took the warrant in his left hand and with his right seized Don Quixote by the collar so tightly that he did not allow him to breathe, and shouted aloud, "Help for the Holy Brotherhood! and that you may see I demand it in earnest, read this warrant which says this highwayman is to be arrested."

The curate took the warrant and saw that what the officer said was true, and that it agreed with Don Quixote's appearance, who, on his part, when he found himself roughly handled by this rascally clown, worked up to the highest pitch of wrath, and all his joints cracking with rage, with both hands seized the officer by the throat with all his might, so that had he not been helped by his comrades he would have yielded up his life ere Don Quixote released his hold. The landlord, who had perforce to support his brother officers, ran at once to aid them. The landlady, when she saw her husband engaged in a fresh quarrel, lifted up her voice afresh, and its note was immediately caught up by

Maritornes and her daughter, calling upon Heaven and all present for help; and Sancho, seeing what was going on, exclaimed, "By the Lord, it is quite true what my master says about the enchantments of this castle, for it is impossible to live an hour in peace in it!"

Don Fernando parted the officer and Don Quixote, and to their mutual contentment made them relax the grip by which they held, the one the coat collar, the other the throat of his adversary; for all this, however, the officers did not cease to demand their prisoner and call on them to help, and deliver him over bound into their power, as was required for the service of the King and of the Holy Brotherhood, on whose behalf they again demanded aid and assistance to effect the capture of this robber and footpad of the highways and byways.

Don Quixote smiled when he heard these words, and said very calmly, "Come now, base, ill-born brood; call ye it highway robbery to give freedom to those in bondage, to release the captives, to succor the miserable, to raise up the fallen, to relieve the needy? Infamous beings, who by your vile grovelling intellects deserve that Heaven should not make known to you the virtue that lies in knight-errantry, or show you the sin and ignorance in which ye lie when ye refuse to respect the shadow, not to say the presence, of any knight-errant! Come now; band, not of officers, but of thieves; footpads with the license of the Holy Brotherhood; tell me who was the ignoramus who signed a warrant of arrest against such a knight as I am? Who was he that did not know that knights-errant are independent of all jurisdictions, that their law is their sword, their charter their prowess, and their edicts their will? Who, I say again, was the fool that knows not that there are no letters patent of nobility that confer such privileges or exemptions as a knight-errant acquires the day he is dubbed a knight, and devotes himself to the arduous calling of chivalry? What knight-errant ever paid poll-tax, duty, queen's pin-money, king's dues, toll or ferry? What tailor ever took payment of him for making his clothes? What castellan that received him in his castle ever made him pay his shot? What king did not seat him at his table? What damsel was not enamoured of him and did not yield herself up wholly to his will or pleasure? And, lastly, what knight-errant has there been, is there, or will there ever be in the world, not bold enough to give, single-handed, four hundred cudgellings to four hundred officers of the Holy Brotherhood if they come in his way?"

Chapter 46

Of the end of the notable adventure of the officers of the Holy Brotherhood; and of the great ferocity of our worthy Knight, Don Quixote

WHILE Don Quixote was talking in this strain, the curate was endeavoring to persuade the officers that he was out of his senses, as they might perceive by his deeds and his words, and that they need not press the matter any further, for even if they arrested him and carried him off, they would have to release him by and by as a madman; to which the holder of the warrant replied that he had nothing to do with inquiring into Don Quixote's madness, but only to execute his superior's orders, and that once taken they might let him go three hundred times if they liked.

"For all that," said the curate, "you must not take him away this time, nor will he, it is my opinion, let himself be taken away."

In short, the curate used such arguments, and Don Quixote did such mad things, that the officers would have been more mad than he was if they had not perceived his want of wits, and so they thought it best to allow themselves to be pacified, and even to act as peacemakers between the barber and Sancho Panza, who still continued their altercation with much bitterness. In the end they, as officers of justice, settled the question by arbitration in such a manner that both sides were, if not perfectly contented, at least to some extent satisfied; for they changed the pack-saddles, but not the girths or headstalls; and as to Mambrino's helmet, the curate, under the rose and without Don Quixote's knowing it, paid eight reals for the basin, and the barber executed a full receipt and engagement to make no further demand then or thenceforth for evermore, amen. These two disputes, which were the most important and gravest, being settled, it only remained for the servants of Don Luis to consent that three of them should return while one was left to accompany him whither Don Fernando desired to take him; and good luck and better fortune, having already begun to solve difficulties and remove obstructions in favor of the lovers and warriors of the inn, were pleased to persevere and bring everything to a happy issue; for the servants agreed to do as Don Luis wished; which gave Doña Clara such happiness that no one could have looked into her face just then without seeing the joy of her heart. Zoraida, though she did not fully comprehend all she saw, was grave or gay without knowing why, as she watched and studied the various countenances, but particularly her Spaniard's, whom she followed with her eyes and clung to with her soul. The gift and compensation which the curate gave the barber had not escaped the landlord's notice, and he demanded Don Quixote's reckoning, together with the amount of the damage to his wine-skins, and the loss of his wine, swearing that neither Rocinante nor Sancho's ass should leave the inn until he had been paid to the very last farthing. The curate settled all amicably, and Don Fernando paid; though the judge had also very readily offered to pay the score; and all became so peaceful and quiet that the inn no longer reminded one of the discord of Agramante's camp, as Don Quixote said, but of the peace and tranquillity of the days of Octavianus: for all which it was the universal opinion that their thanks were due to the great zeal and eloquence of the curate, and to the unexampled generosity of Don Fernando.

Finding himself now clear and quit of all quarrels, his squire's as well as his own, Don Quixote considered that it would be advisable to continue the journey he had begun, and bring to a close that great adventure for which he had been called and chosen; and with this high resolve he went and knelt before Dorothea, who, however, would not allow him to utter a word until he had risen; so to obey her he rose, and said, "It is a common proverb, fair lady, that 'diligence is the mother of good fortune,' and experience has often shown in important affairs that the earnestness of the negotiator brings the doubtful case to a successful termination; but in nothing does this truth show itself more plainly than in war, where quickness and activity forestall the devices of the enemy, and win the victory before the foe has time to defend himself. All this I say, exalted and esteemed lady, because it seems to me that for us to remain any longer in this castle now is useless, and may be injurious to us in a way that we shall find out some day; for who knows but that your enemy the giant may have learned by means of secret and diligent spies that I am going to destroy him, and if the opportunity be given him he may seize it to fortify himself in some impregnable castle or stronghold, against which all my efforts and the might of my indefatigable arm may avail but little? Therefore, lady, let us, as I say, forestall his schemes by our activity, and let us depart at once in quest of fair fortune; for your highness is only kept from enjoying it as fully as you could desire by

my delay in encountering your adversary."

Don Quixote held his peace and said no more, calmly awaiting the reply of the beauteous princess, who, with commanding dignity and in a style adapted to Don Quixote's own, replied to him in these words, "I give you thanks, sir knight, for the eagerness you, like a good knight to whom it is a natural obligation to succor the orphan and the needy, display to afford me aid in my sore trouble; and Heaven grant that your wishes and mine may be realized, so that you may see that there are women in this world capable of gratitude; as to my departure, let it be forthwith, for I have no will but yours; dispose of me entirely in accordance with your good pleasure; for she who has once intrusted to you the defence of her person, and placed in your hands the recovery of her dominions, must not think of offering opposition to that which your wisdom may ordain."

"On, then, in God's name," said Don Quixote; "for, when a lady humbles herself to me, I will not lose the opportunity of raising her up, and placing her on the throne of her ancestors. Let us depart at once, for the common saying, that in delay there is danger, lends spurs to my eagerness to take the road; and as neither Heaven has created nor hell seen any that can daunt or intimidate me, saddle Rocinante, Sancho, and get ready thy ass and the queen's palfrey, and let us take leave of the castellan and these gentlemen, and go hence this very instant."

Sancho, who was standing by all the time, said, shaking his head, "Ah! master, master, there is more mischief in the village than one hears of, begging all good bodies' pardon."

"What mischief can there be in any village, or in all the cities of the world, you booby, that can hurt my reputation?" said Don Quixote.

"If your worship is angry," replied Sancho, "I will hold my tongue and leave unsaid what as a good squire, I am bound to say, and what a good servant should tell his master."

"Say what thou wilt," returned Don Quixote, "provided thy words be not meant to work upon my fears; for thou, when thou fearest, art behaving like thyself; but I like myself, when I fear not."

"It is nothing of the sort, as I am a sinner before God," said Sancho, "but that I take it to be sure and certain that this lady, who calls herself queen of the great kingdom of Micomicon, is no more so than my mother; for, if she was what she says, she would not go rubbing noses with one that is here every instant and behind every door."

Dorothea turned red at Sancho's words, for the truth was that her husband, Don Fernando, had now and then, when the others were not looking, gathered from her lips some of the reward his love had earned, and Sancho seeing this, had considered that such freedom was more like a courtesan than a queen of a great kingdom; she, however, being unable or not caring to answer him, allowed him to proceed, and he continued, "This I say, señor, because, if after we have travelled roads and highways, and passed bad nights and worse days, one who is now enjoying himself in this inn is to reap the fruit of our labors, there is no need for me to be in a hurry to saddle Rocinante, put the pad on the ass, or get ready the palfrey; for it will be better for us to stay quiet, and let every jade mind her spinning, and let us go to dinner."

Good God, what was the indignation of Don Quixote when he heard the audacious words of his squire! So great was it, that in a voice inarticulate with rage, with a stammering tongue, and eyes that flashed living fire, he exclaimed, "Rascally clown, boorish, insolent, and ignorant, ill-spoken, foul-mouthed, impudent backbiter and slanderer! Hast thou dared to utter such words in my presence and in that of these illustrious ladies? Hast thou dared to harbor such gross and shameless thoughts in thy muddled imagination? Begone from my presence, thou born monster, storehouse of lies, hoard of untruths, garner of knaveries, inventor of scandals, publisher of absurdities, enemy of the respect due to royal personages! Begone, show thyself no more before me under pain of my wrath"; and so saying he knitted his brows, puffed out his cheeks, gazed around him, and stamped on the ground violently with his right foot, showing in every way the rage that was pent up in his heart; and at his words and furious gestures Sancho was so scared and terrified that he would have been glad if the earth had opened that instant and swallowed him, and his only thought was to turn round and make his escape from the angry presence of his master.

But the ready-witted Dorothea, who by this time so well understood Don Quixote's humor, said, to mollify his wrath, "Be not irritated at the absurdities your good squire has uttered, Sir Knight of the Rueful Countenance, for perhaps he did not utter them without cause, and from his good sense and Christian conscience it is not likely that he would bear false witness against any one. We may therefore believe, without any hesitation, that since, as you say, sir knight, everything in this castle goes and is brought about by means of enchantment, Sancho, I say, may possibly have seen, through this diabolical medium, what he says he saw so much to the detriment of my modesty."

"I swear by God Omnipotent," exclaimed Don Quixote at this, "your highness has hit the point; and that some vile illusion must have come before this sinner of a Sancho, that made him see what it would have been impossible to see by any other means than enchantments; for I know well enough, from the poor fellow's goodness and harmlessness, that he is incapable of bearing false witness against anybody."

"True, no doubt," said Don Fernando, "for which reason, Señor Don Quixote, you ought to forgive him and restore him to the bosom of your favor, *sicut erat in principio*, before illusions of this sort had taken away his senses."

Don Quixote said he was ready to pardon him, and the curate went for Sancho, who came in very humbly, and falling on his knees begged for the hand of his master, who having presented it to him and allowed him to kiss it, gave him his blessing and said, "Now, Sancho my son, thou wilt be convinced of the truth of what I have many a time told thee, that everything in this castle is done by means of enchantment."

"So it is, I believe," said Sancho, "except the affair of the blanket, which came to pass in reality by ordinary means."

"Believe it not," said Don Quixote, "for had it been so, I would have avenged thee that instant, or even now; but neither then nor now could I, nor have I seen any one upon whom to avenge thy wrong."

They were all eager to know what the affair of the blanket was, and the landlord gave them a minute account of Sancho's flights, at which they laughed not a little, and at which Sancho would have been no less out of countenance had not his master once more assured him it was all enchantment. For all that his simplicity never reached so high a pitch that he could persuade himself it was not the plain and simple truth, without any deception whatever about it, that he had been blanketed by beings of flesh and blood, and not by visionary and imaginary phantoms, as his master believed and protested.

The illustrious company had now been two days in the inn; and as it seemed to them time to depart, they devised a plan so that, without giving Dorothea and Don Fernando the trouble of going back with Don Quixote to his village under pretence of restoring Queen Micomicona, the curate and the barber might carry him away with them as they proposed, and the curate be able to take his madness in hand at home; and in pursuance of their plan they arranged with the owner of an ox-cart who happened to be passing that way to carry him after this fashion. They constructed a kind of cage with wooden bars, large enough to hold Don Quixote comfortably; and then Don Fernando and his companions, the servants of Don Luis, and the officers of the Brotherhood, together with the landlord, by the directions and advice of the curate, covered their faces and disguised themselves, some in one way, some in another, so as to appear to Don Quixote quite different from the persons he had seen in the castle. This done, in profound silence they entered the room where he was asleep, taking his rest after the past frays, and advancing to where he was sleeping tranquilly, not dreaming of anything of the kind happening, they seized him firmly and bound him fast hand and foot, so that, when he awoke startled, he was unable to move, and could only marvel and wonder at the strange figures he saw before him; upon which he at once gave way to the idea which his crazed fancy invariably conjured up before him, and took it into his head that all these shapes were phantoms of the enchanted castle, and that he himself was unquestionably enchanted as he could neither move nor help himself; precisely what the curate, the concocter of the scheme, expected would happen. Of all that were there Sancho was the only one who was at once in his senses and in his own proper character, and he, though he was within very little of sharing his master's infirmity, did not fail to perceive who all these disguised figures were; but he did not dare to open his lips until he saw what came of this assault and capture of his master; nor did the latter utter a word, waiting to see the upshot of his mishap; which was that, bringing in the cage, they shut him up in it and nailed the bars so firmly that they could not be easily burst open. They then took him on their shoulders, and as they passed out of the room an awful voice—as much so as the barber, not he of the packsaddle but the other, was able to make it—was heard to say, "O Knight of the Rueful Countenance, let not this captivity in which thou art placed afflict thee, for this must needs be, for the more speedy accomplishment of the adventure in which thy great heart has engaged thee; the which shall be accomplished when the raging Manchegan lion and the white Tobosan dove shall be linked together, having first humbled their haughty necks to the gentle yoke of matrimony. And from this marvellous union shall come forth to the light of the world brave whelps, that shall rival the ravening claws of their valiant father; and this shall come to pass ere the pursuer of the flying nymph shall in his swift natural course have twice visited the starry signs. And thou, O most noble and obedient squire that ever bore sword at side, beard on face, or nose to smell with, be not dismayed or grieved to see the flower of knight-errantry carried away thus before thy very eyes; for soon, if it so please the Framer of the universe, thou shalt see thyself exalted to such a height that thou shalt not know thyself, and the promises which thy good master has made thee shall not prove false; and I assure thee, on the authority of the sage Mentironiana,[1] that thy wages shall be paid thee as thou shalt see in due season. Follow then the footsteps of the valiant enchanted knight, for it is expedient that thou shouldst go to the destination assigned to both of you; and as it is not permitted to me to say more, God be with thee; for I return to that place I wot of"; and as he brought the prophecy to a close he raised his voice to a high pitch, and then lowered it to such a soft tone, that even those who knew it was all a joke were almost inclined to take what they heard seriously.

Don Quixote was comforted by the prophecy he heard, for he at once comprehended its meaning perfectly and perceived it was promised to him that he should see himself united in holy and lawful matrimony with his beloved Dulcinea del Toboso, from whose blessed womb should proceed the whelps, his sons, to the eternal glory of La Mancha; and being thoroughly and firmly persuaded of this, he lifted up his voice, and with a deep sigh exclaimed, "O thou, whoever thou art, who hast foretold me so much good, I implore of thee that on my part thou entreat that sage enchanter who takes charge of my interests, that he leave me not to perish in this captivity in which they are now carrying me away, ere I see fulfilled promises so joyful and incomparable as those which have been now made me; for, let this but come to pass, and I shall glory in the pains of my prison, find comfort in these chains wherewith they bind me, and regard this bed whereon they stretch me, not as a hard battlefield, but as a soft and happy nuptial couch; and touching the consolation of Sancho Panza, my squire, I rely upon his goodness and rectitude that he will not desert me in good or evil fortune; for if, by his ill luck or mine, it may not happen to be in my

[1] A name formed from *mentir*, to tell lies.

ower to give him the island I have promised, or ny equivalent for it, at least his wages shall ot be lost; for in my will, which is already ade, I have declared the sum that shall be aid to him, measured, not by his many faithful rvices, but by the means at my disposal."

Sancho bowed his head very respectfully and issed both his hands, for being tied together, e could not kiss one; and then the apparitions fted the cage upon their shoulders and fixed upon the ox-cart.

Chapter 47

f the strange manner in which Don Quixote La Mancha was carried away enchanted, gether with other remarkable incidents

WHEN Don Quixote saw himself caged and oisted on the cart in this way, he said, "Many ave histories of knights-errant have I read; but ever yet have I read, seen, or heard of their arrying off enchanted knights-errant in this shion, or at the slow pace that these lazy, uggish animals promise; for they always take em away through the air with marvellous viftness, enveloped in a dark thick cloud, or a chariot of fire, or it may be on some hippo-iff or other beast of the kind; but to carry me F like this on an ox-cart! By God, it puzzles e! But perhaps the chivalry and enchantments our day take a different course from that of ose in days gone by; and it may be, too, that, I am a new knight in the world, and the first revive the already forgotten calling of knight-dventurers, they may have newly invented her kinds of enchantments and other modes carrying off the enchanted. What thinkest ou of the matter, Sancho my son?"

"I don't know what to think," answered San-ho, "not being as well read as your worship in rant writings; but for all that I venture to say d swear that these apparitions that are about are not quite Catholic."

"Catholic!" said Don Quixote. "Father of me! ow can they be Catholic when they are all vils that have taken fantastic shapes to come d do this, and bring me to this condition? nd if thou wouldst prove it, touch them, and el them, and thou wilt find they have only dies of air, and no consistency except in ap-earance."

"By God, master," returned Sancho, "I have uched them already; and that devil, that goes out there so busily, has firm flesh, and another roperty very different from what I have heard y devils have, for by all accounts they all smell

of brimstone and other bad smells; but this one smells of amber half a league off." Sancho was here speaking of Don Fernando, who, like a gentleman of his rank, was very likely perfumed as Sancho said.

"Marvel not at that, Sancho my friend," said Don Quixote; "for let me tell thee devils are crafty; and even if they do carry odors about with them, they themselves have no smell, be-cause they are spirits; or, if they have any smell, they can not smell of anything sweet, but of something foul and fetid; and the reason is that as they carry hell with them wherever they go, and can get no ease whatever from their tor-ments, and as a sweet smell is a thing that gives pleasure and enjoyment, it is impossible that they can smell sweet; if, then, this devil thou speakest of seems to thee to smell of amber, ei-ther thou art deceiving thyself, or he wants to deceive thee by making thee fancy he is not a devil."

Such was the conversation that passed be-tween master and man; and Don Fernando and Cardenio, apprehensive of Sancho's making a complete discovery of their scheme, towards which he had already gone some way, resolved to hasten their departure, and calling the land-lord aside, they directed him to saddle Roci-nante and put the pack-saddle on Sancho's ass, which he did with great alacrity. In the mean-time the curate had made an arrangement with the officers that they should bear them company as far as his village, he paying them so much a day. Cardenio hung the buckler on one side of the bow of Rocinante's saddle and the basin on the other, and by signs commanded Sancho to mount his ass and take Rocinante's bridle, and at each side of the cart he placed two officers with their muskets; but before the cart was put in motion, out came the landlady and her daughter and Maritornes to bid Don Quixote farewell, pretending to weep with grief at his misfortune; and to them Don Quixote said, "Weep not, good ladies, for all these mishaps are the lot of those who follow the profession I profess; and if these reverses did not befall me I should not esteem myself a famous knight-errant; for such things never happen to knights of little renown and fame, because nobody in the world thinks about them; to valiant knights they do, for these are envied for their virtue and valor by many princes and other knights who compass the destruction of the worthy by base means. Nevertheless, vir-tue is of herself so mighty, that, in spite of all the magic that Zoroastes its first inventor knew, she will come victorious out of every trial, and shed her light upon the earth as the sun does upon the heavens. Forgive me, fair ladies, if, through inadvertence, I have in aught offended you; for intentionally and wittingly I have never done so to any; and pray to God that he deliver me from this captivity to which some malevolent enchanter has consigned me; and should I find myself released therefrom, the favors that ye have bestowed upon me in this castle shall be held in memory by me, that I may acknowledge, recognize, and requite them as they deserve."

While this was passing between the ladies of the castle and Don Quixote, the curate and the barber bade farewell to Don Fernando and his companions, to the captain, his brother, and the ladies, now all made happy, and in particular to Dorothea and Luscinda. They all embraced one another, and promised to let each other know how things went with them, and Don Fernando directed the curate where to write to him, to tell him what became of Don Quixote, assuring him that there was nothing that could give him more pleasure than to hear, and that he too, on his part, would send him word of everything he thought he would like to know, about his marriage, Zoraida's baptism, Don Luis's affair, and Luscinda's return to her home. The curate promised to comply with his request carefully, and they embraced once more, and renewed their promises.

The landlord approached the curate and handed him some papers, saying he had discovered them in the lining of the valise in which the *Novel of the Ill-advised Curiosity* had been found, and that he might take them all away with him as their owner had not since returned; for, as he could not read, he did not want them himself. The curate thanked him, and opening them he saw at the beginning of the manuscript the words, *Novel of Rinconete and Cortadillo*, by which he perceived that it was a novel, and as that of *The Ill-advised Curiosity* had been good he concluded this would be so too, as they were both probably by the same author; so he kept it, intending to read it when he had an opportunity. He then mounted and his friend the barber did the same, both masked, so as not to be recognized by Don Quixote, and set out following in the rear of the cart. The order of march was this: first went the cart with the owner leading it; at each side of it marched the officers of the Brotherhood, as has been said, with their muskets; then followed Sancho Panza on his ass, leading Rocinante by the bridle; and behind all came the curate and the barber

on their mighty mules, with faces covered, a aforesaid, and a grave and serious air, measu ing their pace to suit the slow steps of the oxer Don Quixote was seated in the cage, with h hands tied and his feet stretched out, leanin against the bars as silent and as patient as if h were a stone statue and not a man of flesh. Thu slowly and silently they made, it might be, tw leagues, until they reached a valley which th carter thought a convenient place for restin and feeding his oxen, and he said so to the c rate, but the barber was of opinion that the ought to push on a little farther, as at the othe side of a hill which appeared close by he kne there was a valley that had more grass an much better than the one where they propose to halt; and his advice was taken and they con tinued their journey.

Just at that moment the curate, looking bacl saw coming on behind them six or seven moun ed men, well found and equipped, who soo overtook them, for they were travelling, not the sluggish, deliberate pace of oxen, but lik men who rode canons' mules, and in haste t take their noontide rest as soon as possible at th inn which was in sight not a league off. Th quick travellers came up with the slow, an courteous salutations were exchanged; and on of the new comers, who was, in fact, a canon Toledo and master of the others who accom panied him, observing the regular order of th procession, the cart, the officers, Sancho, Roc nante, the curate and the barber, and above a Don Quixote caged and confined, could n help asking what was the meaning of carryin the man in that fashion; though, from th badges of the officers, he already conclude that he must be some desperate highwayman other malefactor whose punishment fell withi the jurisdiction of the Holy Brotherhood. On of the officers to whom he had put the question replied, "Let the gentleman himself tell you th meaning of his going this way, señor, for we d not know."

Don Quixote overheard the conversation an said, "Haply, gentlemen, you are versed an learned in matters of chivalry? Because if yo are I will tell you my misfortunes; if not, the is no good in my giving myself the trouble relating them"; but here the curate and the ba ber, seeing that the travellers were engaged i conversation with Don Quixote, came forwar in order to answer in such a way as to save the stratagem from being discovered.

The canon, replying to Don Quixote, sai "In truth, brother, I know more about books o

hivalry than I do about Villalpando's elements
f logic; so if that be all, you may safely tell me
vhat you please."

"In God's name, then, señor," replied Don
Quixote; "if that be so, I would have you know
hat I am held enchanted in this cage by the
nvy and fraud of wicked enchanters; for vir-
ue is more persecuted by the wicked than loved
·y the good. I am a knight-errant, and not one
f those whose names Fame has never thought
f immortalizing in her record, but of those who,
n defiance and in spite of envy itself, and all
he magicians that Persia, or Brahmans that
ndia, or Gymnosophists that Ethiopia ever pro-
·uced, will place their names in the temple of
mmortality, to serve as examples and patterns
or ages to come, whereby knights-errant may
·ee the footsteps in which they must tread if
·hey would attain the summit and crowning
·oint of honor in arms."

"What Señor Don Quixote of La Mancha
·ays," observed the curate, "is the truth; for he
·oes enchanted in this cart, not from any fault
·r sins of his, but because of the malevolence of
·hose to whom virtue is odious and valor hate-
·ul. This, señor, is the Knight of the Rueful
Countenance, if you have ever heard him
·amed, whose valiant achievements and mighty
·eeds shall be written on lasting brass and im-
·erishable marble, notwithstanding all the ef-
·orts of envy to obscure them and malice to
·ide them."

When the canon heard both the prisoner and
·he man who was at liberty talk in such a strain
·e was ready to cross himself in his astonish-
·nent, and could not make out what had befal-
·en him; and all his attendants were in the same
·tate of amazement.

At this point Sancho Panza, who had drawn
·ear to hear the conversation, said, in order to
·nake everything plain, "Well, sirs, you may
·ike or dislike what I am going to say, but the
·act of the matter is, my master, Don Quixote,
·s just as much enchanted as my mother. He is
·n his full senses, he eats and he drinks, and he
·as his calls like other men and as he had yes-
·erday, before they caged him. And if that's the
·ase, what do they mean by wanting me to be-
·ieve that he is enchanted? For I have heard
·nany a one say that enchanted people neither
·at, nor sleep, nor talk; and my master, if you
·lon't stop him, will talk more than thirty law-
·ers." Then turning to the curate he exclaimed,
·And, Señor Curate, Señor Curate! do you
·hink I don't know you? Do you think I don't
·uess and see the drift of these new enchant-

ments? Well, then, I can tell you I know you,
for all your face is covered, and I can tell you
I am up to you, however you may hide your
tricks. After all, where envy reigns virtue cannot live, and where there is niggardliness there
can be no liberality. Ill betide the devil! if it
had not been for your worship my master would
be married to the Princess Micomicona this
minute, and I should be a count at least; for
no less was to be expected, as well from the
goodness of my master, him of the Rueful
Countenance, as from the greatness of my services. But I see now how true it is what they say
in these parts, that the wheel of fortune turns
faster than a mill-wheel, and that those who
were up yesterday are down to-day. I am sorry
for my wife and children, for when they might
fairly and reasonably expect to see their father
return to them a governor or viceroy of some
island or kingdom, they will see him come back
a horse-boy. I have said all this, Señor Curate,
only to urge your paternity to lay to your conscience your ill-treatment of my master; and
have a care that God does not call you to account in another life for making a prisoner of
him in this way, and charge against you all the
succors and good deeds that my lord Don Quixote leaves undone while he is shut up."

"Trim those lamps there!" exclaimed the barber at this; "so you are of the same fraternity as
your master, too, Sancho? By God, I begin to
see that you will have to keep him company in
the cage, and be enchanted like him for having
caught some of his humor and chivalry. It was
an evil hour when you let yourself be got with
child by his promises, and that island you long
so much for found its way into your head."

"I am not with child by any one," returned
Sancho, "nor am I a man to let myself be got
with child, if it was by the King himself.
Though I am poor I am an old Christian, and
I owe nothing to nobody, and if I long for an
island, other people long for worse. Each of us
is the son of his own works; and being a man I
may come to be pope, not to say governor of an
island, especially as my master may win so
many that he will not know whom to give them
to. Mind how you talk, master barber; for shaving is not everything, and there is some difference between Peter and Peter. I say this because we all know one another, and it will not
do to throw false dice with me; and as to the enchantment of my master, God knows the truth;
leave it as it is; it will only make it worse to stir
it."

The barber did not care to answer Sancho

lest by his plain speaking he should disclose what the curate and he himself were trying so hard to conceal; and under the same apprehension the curate had asked the canon to ride on a little in advance, so that he might tell him the mystery of this man in the cage, and other things that would amuse him. The canon agreed, and going on ahead with his servants, listened with attention to the account of the character, life, madness, and ways of Don Quixote, given him by the curate, who described to him briefly the beginning and origin of his craze, and told him the whole story of his adventures up to his being confined in the cage, together with the plan they had of taking him home to try if by any means they could discover a cure for his madness. The canon and his servants were surprised anew when they heard Don Quixote's strange story, and when it was finished he said, "To tell the truth, Señor Curate, I for my part consider what they call books of chivalry to be mischievous to the State; and though, led by idle and false taste, I have read the beginnings of almost all that have been printed, I never could manage to read any one of them from beginning to end; for it seems to me they are all more or less the same thing; and one has nothing more in it than another; this no more than that. And in my opinion this sort of writing and composition is of the same species as the fables they call the Milesian, nonsensical tales that aim solely at giving amusement and not instruction, exactly the opposite of the apologue fables which amuse and instruct at the same time. And though it may be the chief object of such books to amuse, I do not know how they can succeed, when they are so full of such monstrous nonsense. For the enjoyment the mind feels must come from the beauty and harmony which it perceives or contemplates in the things that the eye or the imagination brings before it; and nothing that has any ugliness or disproportion about it can give any pleasure. What beauty, then, or what proportion of the parts to the whole, or of the whole to the parts, can there be in a book or fable where a lad of sixteen cuts down a giant as tall as a tower and makes two halves of him as if he was an almond cake? And when they want to give us a picture of a battle, after having told us that there are a million of combatants on the side of the enemy, let the hero of the book be opposed to them, and we have perforce to believe, whether we like it or not, that the said knight wins the victory by the single might of his strong arm. And then, what shall we say of the facility with which a born

queen or empress will give herself over into th[e] arms of some unknown wandering knigh[t?] What mind, that is not wholly barbarous an[d] uncultured, can find pleasure in reading of ho[w] a great tower full of knights sails away acro[ss] the sea like a ship with a fair wind, and will b[e] to-night in Lombardy and to-morrow mornin[g] in the land of Prester John of the Indies, [or] some other that Ptolemy never described n[or] Marco Polo saw? And if, in answer to this, [I] am told that the authors of books of the kin[d] write them as fiction, and therefore are n[ot] bound to regard niceties of truth, I would repl[y] that fiction is all the better the more it loo[ks] like truth, and gives the more pleasure the mo[re] probability and possibility there is about it. Plo[ts] in fiction should be wedded to the understan[d]ing of the reader, and be constructed in such [a] way that, reconciling impossibilities, smoothin[g] over difficulties, keeping the mind on the aler[t,] they may surprise, interest, divert, and ente[r]tain, so that wonder and delight joined ma[y] keep pace one with the other; all which he wi[ll] fail to effect who shuns verisimilitude and trut[h] to nature, wherein lies the perfection of wri[t]ing. I have never yet seen any book of chivalr[y] that puts together a connected plot complete i[n] all its numbers, so that the middle agrees wit[h] the beginning, and the end with the beginnin[g] and middle; on the contrary, they constru[ct] them with such a multitude of members th[at] it seems as though they meant to produce [a] chimera or monster rather than a well-propo[r]tioned figure. And besides all this they a[re] harsh in their style, incredible in their achieve[-]ments, licentious in their amours, uncouth i[n] their courtly speeches, prolix in their battle[s,] silly in their arguments, absurd in their travel[s,] and, in short, wanting in everything like inte[l]ligent art; for which reason they deserve to b[e] banished from the Christian commonwealth a[s] a worthless breed."

The curate listened to him attentively an[d] felt that he was a man of sound understandin[g,] and that there was good reason in what he sai[d;] so he told him that, being of the same opinio[n] himself, and bearing a grudge to books of chi[v]alry, he had burned all Don Quixote's, whic[h] were many; and gave him an account of th[e] scrutiny he had made of them, and of those h[e] had condemned to the flames and those he ha[d] spared, with which the canon was not a littl[e] amused, adding that though he had said s[o] much in condemnation of these books, still h[e] found one good thing in them, and that was th[e] opportunity they afforded to a gifted intellec[t] for displaying itself; for they presented a wide and spacious field over which the pen might range freely, describing shipwrecks, tempests, combats, battles, portraying a valiant captain with all the qualifications requisite to make one, showing him sagacious in foreseeing the wiles of the enemy, eloquent in speech to encourage or restrain his soldiers, ripe in counsel, rapid in resolve, as bold in biding his time as in pressing the attack; now picturing some sad tragic incident, now some joyful and unexpected event; here a beauteous lady, virtuous, wise, and modest; there a Christian knight, brave and gentle; here a lawless, barbarous braggart; there a courteous prince, gallant and gracious; setting forth the devotion and loyalty of vassals, the greatness and generosity of nobles. "Or again," said he, "the author may show himself to be an astronomer, or a skilled cosmographer, or musician, or one versed in affairs of state, and sometimes he will have a chance of coming forward as a magician if he likes. He can set forth the craftiness of Ulysses, the piety of Æneas, the valor of Achilles, the misfortunes of Hector, the treachery of Sinon, the friendship of Euryalus, the generosity of Alexander, the boldness of Cæsar, the clemency and truth of Trajan, the fidelity of Zopyrus, the wisdom of Cato, and in short all the faculties that serve to make an illustrious man perfect, now uniting them in one individual, again distributing them among many; and if this be done with charm of style and ingenious invention, aiming at the truth as much as possible, he will assuredly weave a web of bright and varied threads that, when finished, will display such perfection and beauty that it will attain the worthiest object any writing can seek, which, as I said before, is to give instruction and pleasure combined; for the unrestricted range of these books enables the author to show his powers, epic, lyric, tragic, or comic, and all the moods the sweet and winning arts of poesy and oratory are capable of; for the epic may be written in prose just as well as in verse."

Chapter 48

In which the Canon pursues the subject of the books of chivalry, with other matters worthy of his wit

"It is as you say, Señor Canon," said the curate; "and for that reason those who have hitherto written books of the sort deserve all the more censure for writing without paying any attention to good taste or to the rules of art, by which they might guide themselves and become as famous in prose as the two princes of Greek and Latin poetry are in verse."

"I myself, at any rate," said the canon, "was once tempted to write a book of chivalry in which all the points I have mentioned were to be observed; and if I must own the truth I have more than a hundred sheets written; and to try if it came up to my own opinion of it, I showed them to persons who were fond of this kind of reading, to learned and intelligent men as well as to ignorant people who cared for nothing but the pleasure of listening to nonsense, and from all I obtained flattering approval; nevertheless I proceeded no further with it, as well because it seemed to me an occupation inconsistent with my profession, as because I perceived that the fools are more numerous than the wise; and, though it is better to be praised by the wise few than applauded by the foolish many, I have no mind to submit myself to the stupid judgment of the silly public, to whom the reading of such books falls for the most part.

"But what most of all made me hold my hand and even abandon all idea of finishing it was an argument I put to myself taken from the plays that are acted now-a-days, which was in this wise: if those that are now in vogue, as well those that are pure invention as those founded on history, are, all or most of them, downright nonsense and things that have neither head nor tail, and yet the public listens to them with delight, and regards and cries them up as perfection when they are so far from it; and if the authors who write them, and the players who act them, say that this is what they must be, for the public wants this and will have nothing else; and that those that go by rule and work out a plot according to the laws of art will only find some half-dozen intelligent people to understand them, while all the rest remain blind to the merit of their composition; and that for themselves it is better to get bread from the many than praise from the few; then my book will fare the same way, after I have burnt off my eyebrows in trying to observe the principles I have spoken of, and I shall be 'the tailor of El Campillo.' [1] And though I have sometimes endeavored to convince actors that they are mistaken in this notion they have adopted, and that they would attract more people, and get more credit, by producing plays in accordance with the rules of art, than by absurd ones, they are so thoroughly wedded to their own opinion

[1] Alluding to the proverb: "The tailor of El Campillo, who stitched for nothing and had to provide the thread."

that no argument or evidence can wean them from it.

"I remember saying one day to one of these obstinate fellows, 'Tell me, do you not recollect that a few years ago, there were three tragedies acted in Spain, written by a famous poet of these kingdoms, which were such that they filled all who heard them with admiration, delight, and interest, the ignorant as well as the wise, the masses as well as the higher orders, and brought in more money to the performers, these three alone, than thirty of the best that have been since produced?' "

" 'No doubt,' replied the actor in question, 'you mean the *Isabella,* the *Phyllis,* and the *Alexandra.*' "

" 'Those are the ones I mean,' said I; 'and see if they did not observe the principles of art, and if, by observing them, they failed to show their superiority and please all the world; so that the fault does not lie with the public that insists upon nonsense, but with those who don't know how to produce something else. *The Ingratitude Revenged* was not nonsense, nor was there any in *The Numantia,* nor any to be found in *The Merchant Lover,* nor yet in *The Friendly Fair Foe,* nor in some others that have been written by certain gifted poets, to their own fame and renown, and to the profit of those that brought them out'; some further remarks I added to these, with which, I think, I left him rather dumbfoundered, but not so satisfied or convinced that I could disabuse him of his error."

"You have touched upon a subject, Señor Canon," observed the curate here, "that has awakened an old enmity I have against the plays in vogue at the present day, quite as strong as that which I bear to the books of chivalry; for while the drama, according to Tully, should be the mirror of human life, the model of manners, and the image of the truth, those which are presented now-a-days are mirrors of nonsense, models of folly, and images of lewdness. For what greater nonsense can there be in connection with what we are now discussing than for an infant to appear in swaddling clothes in the first scene of the first act, and in the second a grown-up, bearded man? Or what greater absurdity can there be than putting before us an old man as a swashbuckler, a young man as a poltroon, a lackey using fine language, a page giving sage advice, a king plying as a porter, a princess who is a kitchen-maid? And then what shall I say of their attention to the time in which the action they represent may or can take place,

save that I have seen a play where the first act began in Europe, the second in Asia, the third finished in Africa, and no doubt, had it been in four acts, the fourth would have ended in America, and so it would have been laid in all four quarters of the globe? And if truth to life is the main thing the drama should keep in view, how is it possible for any average understanding to be satisfied when the action is supposed to pass in the time of King Pepin or Charlemagne, and the principal personage in it they represent to be the Emperor Heraclius who entered Jerusalem with the cross and won the Holy Sepulchre, like Godfrey of Bouillon, there being years innumerable between the one and the other? or, if the play is based on fiction and historical facts are introduced, or bits of what occurred to different people and at different times mixed up with it, all, not only without any semblance of probability, but with obvious errors that from every point of view are inexcusable? And the worst of it is, there are ignorant people who say that this is perfection, and that anything beyond this is affected refinement. And then if we turn to sacred dramas—what miracles they invent in them! What apocryphal, ill-devised incidents, attributing to one saint the miracles of another! And even in secular plays they venture to introduce miracles without any reason or object except that they think some such miracle, or transformation as they call it, will come in well to astonish stupid people and draw them to the play. All this tends to the prejudice of the truth and the corruption of history, nay more, to the reproach of the wits of Spain; for foreigners who scrupulously observe the laws of the drama look upon us as barbarous and ignorant, when they see the absurdity and nonsense of the plays we produce. Nor will it be a sufficient excuse to say that the chief object well-ordered governments have in view when they permit plays to be performed in public, is to entertain the people with some harmless amusement occasionally, and keep it from those evil humors which idleness is apt to engender; and that, as this may be attained by any sort of play, good or bad, there is no need to lay down laws, or bind those who write or act them to make them as they ought to be made, since, as I say, the object sought for may be secured by any sort. To this I would reply that the same end would be, beyond all comparison, better attained by means of good plays than by those that are not so; for after listening to an artistic and properly constructed play, the hearer will come away enlivened by the jests, instructed by the serious parts, full of admiration at the incidents, his wits sharpened by the arguments, warned by the tricks, all the wiser for the examples, inflamed against vice, and in love with virtue; for in all these ways a good play will stimulate the mind of the hearer, be he ever so boorish or dull; and of all impossibilities the greatest is that a play endowed with all these qualities will not entertain, satisfy, and please much more than one wanting in them, like the greater number of those which are commonly acted now-a-days. Nor are the poets who write them to be blamed for this; for some there are among them who are perfectly well aware of their faults, and know thoroughly what they ought to do; but as plays have become a salable commodity, they say, and with truth, that the actors will not buy them unless they are after this fashion; and so the poet tries to adapt himself to the requirements of the actor who is to pay him for his work. And that this is the truth may be seen by the countless plays that a most fertile wit of these kingdoms has written, with so much brilliancy, so much grace and gayety, such polished versification, such choice language, such profound reflections, and in a word, so rich in eloquence and elevation of style, that he has filled the world with his fame; and yet, in consequence of his desire to suit the taste of the actors, they have not all, as some of them have, come as near perfection as they ought. Others write plays with such heedlessness that after they have been acted, the actors have to fly and abscond, afraid of being punished, as they often have been, for having acted something offensive to some king or other, or insulting to some noble family. All which evils, and many more that I say nothing of, would be removed if there were some intelligent and sensible person at the capital to examine all plays before they were acted, not only those produced in the capital itself, but all that were intended to be acted in Spain; without whose approval, seal, and signature, no local magistracy should allow any play to be acted. In that case actors would take care to send their plays to the capital, and could act them in safety, and those who write them would be more careful and take more pains with their work, standing in awe of having to submit it to the strict examination of one who understood the matter; and so good plays would be produced and the objects they aim at happily attained; as well the amusement of the people, as the credit of the wits of Spain, the interest and safety of the actors, and the saving of trouble in inflicting punishment

on them. And if the same or some other person were authorized to examine the newly written books of chivalry, no doubt some would appear with all the perfections you have described, enriching our language with the gracious and precious treasure of eloquence, and driving the old books into obscurity before the light of the new ones that would come out for the harmless entertainment, not merely of the idle but of the very busiest; for the bow can not be always bent, nor can weak human nature exist without some lawful amusement."

The canon and the curate had proceeded thus far with their conversation, when the barber, coming forward, joined them, and said to the curate, "This is the spot, Señor Licentiate, that I said was a good one for fresh and plentiful pasture for the oxen, while we take our noontide rest."

"And so it seems," returned the curate, and he told the canon what he proposed to do, on which he too made up his mind to halt with them, attracted by the aspect of the fair valley that lay before their eyes; and to enjoy it as well as the conversation of the curate, to whom he had begun to take a fancy, and also to learn more particulars about the doings of Don Quixote, he desired some of his servants to go on to the inn, which was not far distant, and fetch from it what eatables there might be for the whole party, as he meant to rest for the afternoon where he was; to which one of his servants replied that the sumpter mule, which by this time ought to have reached the inn, carried provisions enough to make it unnecessary to get anything from the inn except barley.

"In that case," said the canon, "take all the beasts there, and make the sumpter mule come back."

While this was going on, Sancho, perceiving that he could speak to his master without having the curate and the barber, of whom he had his suspicions, present all the time, approached the cage in which Don Quixote was placed, and said, "Señor, to ease my conscience I want to tell you the state of the case as to your enchantment, and that is that these two here, with their faces covered, are the curate of our village and the barber; and I suspect they have hit upon this plan of carrying you off in this fashion, out of pure envy because your worship surpasses them in doing famous deeds; and if this be the truth it follows that you are not enchanted, but hoodwinked and made a fool of. And to prove this I want to ask you one thing; and if you answer me as I believe you will answer, you will be able to lay your finger on the trick, and you will see that you are not enchanted but gone wrong in your wits."

"Ask what thou wilt, Sancho my son," returned Don Quixote, "for I will satisfy thee and answer all thou requirest. As to what thou sayest, that these who accompany us yonder are the curate and the barber, our neighbors and acquaintances, it is very possible that they may seem to be those same persons; but that they are so in reality and in fact, believe it not on any account; what thou art to believe and think is that, if they look like them, as thou sayest, it must be that those who have enchanted me have taken this shape and likeness; for it is easy for enchanters to take any form they please, and they may have taken those of our friends in order to make thee think as thou dost, and lead thee into a labyrinth of fancies from which thou wilt find no escape though thou hadst the ford of Theseus; and they may also have done it to make me uncertain in my mind, and unable to conjecture whence this evil comes to me; for if on the one hand thou dost tell me that the barber and curate of our village are here in company with us, and on the other I find myself shut up in a cage, and know in my heart that no power on earth that was not supernatural would have been able to shut me in, what wouldst thou have me say or think, but that my enchantment is of a sort that transcends all I have ever read of in all the histories that deal with knights-errant that have been enchanted? So thou mayst set thy mind at rest as to the idea that they are what thou sayest, for they are as much so as I am a Turk. But touching thy desire to ask me something, say on, and I will answer thee, though thou shouldst ask questions from this till to-morrow morning."

"May Our Lady be good to me!" said Sancho, lifting up his voice; "and is it possible that your worship is so thick of skull and so short of brains that you cannot see that what I say is the simple truth, and that malice has more to do with your imprisonment and misfortune than enchantment? But as it is so, I will prove plainly to you that you are not enchanted. Now tell me, so may God deliver you from this affliction, and so may you find yourself when you least expect it in the arms of my lady Dulcinea"—

"Leave off conjuring me," said Don Quixote, "and ask what thou wouldst know; I have already told thee I will answer with all possible precision."

"That is what I want," said Sancho; "and what I would know, and have you tell me without adding or leaving out anything, but tellin the whole truth as one expects it to be told and as it is told, by all who profess arms, as you worship professes them, under the title of knights-errant"—

"I tell thee I will not lie in any particular, said Don Quixote: "finish thy question; fo in truth thou weariest me with all these asseveral tions, requirements, and precautions, Sancho.

"Well, I rely on the goodness and truth of my master," said Sancho; "and so, because i bears upon what we are talking about, I woul ask, speaking with all reverence, whether sinc your worship has been shut up and, as you think enchanted in this cage, you have felt any desir or inclination to go anywhere, as the saying is?

"I do not understand 'going anywhere,'" sai Don Quixote; "explain thyself more clearly Sancho, if thou wouldst have me give an answe to the point."

"Is it possible," said Sancho, "that your wor ship does not understand 'going anywhere' Why, the schoolboys know that from the tim they were babes. Well then, you must know mean have you had any desire to do what ca not be avoided?"

"Ah! now I understand thee, Sancho," sai Don Quixote; "yes, often, and even this minute get me out of this strait, or all will not go right.

Chapter 49

Which treats of the shrewd conversation which Sancho Panza held with his master, Don Quixote

"Aha, I have caught you," said Sancho "this is what in my heart and soul I was longin to know. Come now, señor, can you deny wha is commonly said around us, when a person i out of humor, 'I don't know what ails so-and-so that he neither eats, nor drinks, nor sleeps, no gives a proper answer to any question; one woul think he was enchanted'? From which it is t be gathered that those who do not eat, or drink or sleep, or do any of the natural acts I am speak ing of—that such persons are enchanted; but no those that have the desire your worship has, an drink when drink is given them, and eat whe there is anything to eat, and answer every ques tion that is asked them."

"What thou sayest is true, Sancho," replie Don Quixote; "but I have already told thee there are many sorts of enchantments, and i may be that in the course of time they have bee changed one for another, and that now it ma be the way with enchanted people to do all tha

I do, though they did not do so before; so it is vain to argue or draw inferences against the usage of the time. I know and feel that I am enchanted, and that is enough to ease my conscience; for it would weigh heavily on it if I thought that I was not enchanted, and that in a faint-hearted and cowardly way I allowed myself to lie in this cage, defrauding multitudes of the succor I might afford to those in need and distress, who at this very moment may be in sore want of my aid and protection."

"Still for all that," replied Sancho, "I say that, for your greater and fuller satisfaction, it would be well if your worship were to try to get out of this prison (and I promise to do all in my power to help, and even to take you out of it), and see if you could once more mount your good Rocinante, who seems to be enchanted too, he is so melancholy and dejected; and then we might try our chance in looking for adventures again; and if we have no luck there will be time enough to go back to the cage; in which, on the faith of a good and loyal squire, I promise to shut myself up along with your worship, if so be you are so unfortunate, or I so stupid, as not to be able to carry out my plan."

"I am content to do as thou sayest, brother Sancho," said Don Quixote, "and when thou seest an opportunity for effecting my release I will obey thee absolutely; but thou wilt see, Sancho, how mistaken thou art in thy conception of my misfortune."

The knight-errant and the ill-errant squire kept up their conversation till they reached the place where the curate, the canon, and the barber, who had already dismounted, were waiting for them. The carter at once unyoked the oxen and left them to roam at large about the pleasant green spot, the freshness of which seemed to invite, not enchanted people like Don Quixote, but wide-awake, sensible folk like his squire, who begged the curate to allow his master to leave the cage for a little; for if they did not let him out, the prison might not be as clean as the propriety of such a gentleman as his master required. The curate understood him, and said he would very gladly comply with his request, only that he feared his master, finding himself at liberty, would take to his old courses and make off where nobody could ever find him again.

"I will answer for his not running away," said Sancho.

"And I for everything," said the canon, "especially if he gives me his word as a knight not to leave us without our consent."

Don Quixote, who was listening to all this, said he would give it; and that moreover one who was enchanted as he was could not do as he liked with himself; for he who had enchanted him could prevent his moving from one place for three ages, and if he attempted to escape would bring him back flying; and that being so, they might as well release him, particularly as it would be to the advantage of all; for, if they did not let him out, he protested he would be unable to avoid offending their nostrils unless they kept their distance.

The canon took his hand, tied together as they both were, and on his word and promise they unbound him, and rejoiced beyond measure he was to find himself out of the cage. The first thing he did was to stretch himself all over, and then he went to where Rocinante was standing and giving him a couple of slaps on the haunches said, "I still trust in God and in his blessed mother, O flower and mirror of steeds, that we shall soon see ourselves, both of us, as we wish to be, thou with thy master on thy back, and I mounted upon thee, following the calling for which God sent me into the world." And so saying, accompanied by Sancho, he withdrew to a retired spot, from which he came back much relieved and more eager than ever to put his squire's scheme into execution.

The canon gazed at him, wondering at the extraordinary nature of his madness, and that in all his remarks and replies he should show such excellent sense, and only lose his stirrups, as has been already said, when the subject of chivalry was broached. And so, moved by compassion, he said to him, as they all sat on the green grass awaiting the arrival of the provisions, "Is it possible, gentle sir, that the nauseous and idle reading of books of chivalry can have had such an effect on your worship as to upset your reason so that you fancy yourself enchanted, and the like, all as far from the truth as falsehood itself is? How can there be any human understanding that can persuade itself there ever was all that infinity of Amadises in the world, or all that multitude of famous knights, all those emperors of Trebizond, all those Felixmartes of Hircania, all those palfreys, and damsels-errant, and serpents, and monsters, and giants, and marvellous adventures, and enchantments of every kind, and battles, and prodigious encounters, splendid costumes, love-sick princesses, squires made counts, droll dwarfs, love-letters, billings and cooings, swashbuckler women, and, in a word, all that nonsense the books of chivalry contain? For myself, I can only say that when I read them, so long as I do not stop to think that they are all lies and frivolity, they give me a certain amount of pleasure; but when I come to consider what they are, I fling the very best of them at the wall, and would fling it into the fire if there were one at hand, as richly deserving such punishment as cheats and impostors out of the range of ordinary toleration, and as founders of new sects and modes of life, and teachers that lead the ignorant public to believe and accept as truth all the folly they contain. And such is their audacity, they even dare to unsettle the wits of gentlemen of birth and intelligence, as is shown plainly by the way they have served your worship, when they have brought you to such a pass that you have to be shut up in a cage and carried on an ox-cart as one would carry a lion or a tiger from place to place to make money by showing it. Come, Señor Don Quixote, have some compassion for yourself, return to the bosom of common sense, and make use of the liberal share of it that Heaven has been pleased to bestow upon you, employing your abundant gifts of mind in some other reading that may serve to benefit your conscience and add to your honor. And if, still led away by your natural bent, you desire to read books of achievements and of chivalry, read the Book of Judges in the Holy Scriptures, for there you will find grand reality, and deeds as true as they are heroic. Lusitania had a Viriatus, Rome a Cæsar, Carthage a Hannibal, Greece an Alexander, Castile a Count Fernan Gonzalez, Valencia a Cid, Andalusia a Gonzalo Fernandez, Estremadura a Diego García de Paredes, Jerez a Garci Perez de Vargas, Toledo a Garcilaso, Seville a Don Manuel de Leon, to read of whose valiant deeds will entertain and instruct the loftiest minds and fill them with delight and wonder. Here, Señor Don Quixote, will be reading worthy of your sound understanding; from which you will rise learned in history, in love with virtue, strengthened in goodness, improved in manners, brave without rashness, prudent without cowardice; and all to the honor of God, your own advantage and the glory of La Mancha, whence, I am informed, your worship derives your birth and origin."

Don Quixote listened with the greatest attention to the canon's words, and when he found he had finished, after regarding him for some time, he replied to him, "It appears to me, gentle sir, that your worship's discourse is intended to persuade me that there never were any knights-errant in the world, and that all the books of chivalry are false, lying, mischievous, and useless to the State, and that I have done wrong in reading them, and worse in believing them, and still worse in imitating them, when I undertook to follow the arduous calling of knight-errantry which they set forth; for you deny that there ever were Amadises of Gaul or of Greece, or any other of the knights of whom the books are full."

"It is all exactly as you state it," said the canon; to which Don Quixote returned, "You also went on to say that books of this kind had done me much harm, inasmuch as they had upset my senses, and shut me up in a cage, and that it would be better for me to reform and change my studies, and read other truer books which would afford more pleasure and instruction."

"Just so," said the canon.

"Well then," returned Don Quixote, "to my mind it is you who are the one that is out of his wits and enchanted, as you have ventured to utter such blasphemies against a thing so universally acknowledged and accepted as true that whoever denies it, as you do, deserves the same punishment which you say you inflict on the books that irritate you when you read them. For to try to persuade anybody that Amadis, and all the other knights-adventurers with whom the books are filled, never existed, would be like trying to persuade him that the sun does not yield light, or ice cold, or earth nourishment. What wit in the world can persuade another that the story of the Princess Floripes and Guy of Burgundy is not true, or that of Fierabras and the bridge of Mantible, which happened in the time of Charlemagne? For by all that is good it is as true as that it is daylight now; and if it be a lie, it must be a lie too that there was a Hector, or Achilles, or Trojan war, or Twelve Peers of France, or Arthur of England, who still lives changed into a raven, and is unceasingly looked for in his kingdom. One might just as well try to make out that the history of Guarino Mezquino, or of the quest of the Holy Grail, is false, or that the loves of Tristram and the Queen Yseult are apocryphal, as well of those of Guinevere and Lancelot, when there are persons who can almost remember having seen the Dame Quintañona, who was the best cup-bearer in Great Britain. And so true is this, that I recollect a grandmother of mine on the father's side, whenever she saw any dame in a venerable hood, used to say to me, 'Grandson, that one is like Dame Quintañona'; from which I conclude that she must have known her, or at least had managed to see some portrait of her.

Then who can deny that the story of Pierres and the fair Magalona is true, when even to this day may be seen in the king's armory the pin with which the valiant Pierres guided the wooden horse he rode through the air, and it is a trifle bigger than the pole of a cart? And alongside of the pin is Babieca's saddle, and at Roncesvalles there is Roland's horn, as large as a large beam; whence we may infer that there were Twelve Peers, and a Pierres, and a Cid, and other knights like them, of the sort people commonly call adventurers. Or perhaps I shall be told, too, that there was no such knight-errant as the valiant Lusitanian Juan de Merlo, who went to Burgundy and in the city of Arras fought with the famous lord of Charny, Mosen Pierres by name, and afterwards in the city of Basle with Mosen Enrique de Remestan, coming out of both encounters covered with fame and honor; or adventures and challenges achieved and delivered, also in Burgundy, by the valiant Spaniards Pedro Barba and Gutierre Quixada (of whose family I come in the direct male line), when they vanquished the sons of the Count of San Polo. I shall be told, too, that Don Fernando de Guevara did not go in quest of adventures to Germany, where he engaged in combat with Micer George, a knight of the house of the Duke of Austria. I shall be told that the jousts of Suero de Quiñones, him of the 'Paso,' and the emprise of Mosen Luis de Falces against the Castilian knight, Don Gonzalo de Guzman, were mere mockeries; as well as many other achievements of Christian knights of these and foreign realms, which are so authentic and true, that, I repeat, he who denies them must be totally wanting in reason and good sense."

The canon was amazed to hear the medley of truth and fiction Don Quixote uttered, and to see how well acquainted he was with everything relating or belonging to the achievements of his knight-errantry; so he said in reply, "I cannot deny, Señor Don Quixote, that there is some truth in what you say, especially as regards the Spanish knights-errant; and I am willing to grant too that the Twelve Peers of France existed, but I am not disposed to believe that they did all the things that the Archbishop Turpin relates of them. For the truth of the matter is they were knights chosen by the kings of France, and called 'Peers' because they were all equal in worth, rank, and prowess (at least if they were not they ought to have been), and it was a kind of religious order like those of Santiago and Calatrava in the present day, in which it is assumed that those who take it are valiant knights of distinction and good birth; and just as we say now a knight of St. John, or of Alcántara, they used to say then a Knight of the Twelve Peers, because twelve equals were chosen for the military order. That there was a Cid, as well as a Bernardo del Carpio, there can be no doubt; but that they did the deeds people say they did, I hold to be very doubtful. In that other matter of the pin of Count Pierres that you speak of, and say is near Babieca's saddle in the Armory, I confess my sin; for I am either so stupid or so short-sighted, that, though I have seen the saddle, I have never been able to see the pin, in spite of it being as big as your worship says it is."

"For all that it is there, without any manner of doubt," said Don Quixote; "and more by token they say it is enclosed in a sheath of cowhide to keep it from rusting."

"All that may be," replied the canon; "but, by the orders I have received, I do not remember seeing it. However, granting it is there, that is no reason why I am bound to believe the stories of all those Amadises and of all that multitude of knights they tell us about, nor is it reasonable that a man like your worship, so worthy, and with so many good qualities, and endowed with such a good understanding, should allow himself to be persuaded that such wild crazy things as are written in those absurd books of chivalry are really true."

Chapter 50

Of the shrewd controversy which Don Quixote and the Canon held, together with other incidents

"A GOOD joke, that!" returned Don Quixote. "Books that have been printed with the king's license, and with the approbation of those to whom they have been submitted, and read with universal delight, and extolled by great and small, rich and poor, learned and ignorant, gentle and simple, in a word by people of every sort, of whatever rank or condition they may be —that these should be lies! And above all when they carry such an appearance of truth with them; for they tell us the father, mother, country, kindred, age, place, and the achievements, step by step, and day by day, performed by such and such a knight or knights! Hush, sir; utter not such blasphemy; trust me I am advising you now to act as a sensible man should; only read them, and you will see the pleasure you will derive from them. For, come, tell me, can there be anything more delightful than to see, as it were, here now displayed before us a vast lake of bubbling pitch with a host of snakes and serpents and lizards, and ferocious and terrible creatures of all sorts swimming about in it, while from the middle of the lake there comes a plaintive voice saying: 'Knight, whosoever thou art who beholdest this dread lake, if thou wouldst win the prize that lies hidden beneath these dusky waves, prove the valor of thy stout heart and cast thyself into the midst of its dark burning waters, else thou shalt not be worthy to see the mighty wonders contained in the seven castles of the seven Fays that lie beneath this black expanse'; and then the knight, almost ere the awful voice has ceased, without stopping to consider, without pausing to reflect upon the danger to which he is exposing himself, without even relieving himself of the weight of his massive armor, commending himself to God and to his lady, plunges into the mist of the boiling lake, and when he little looks for it, or knows what his fate is to be, he finds himself among flowery meadows, with which the Elysian fields are not to be compared. The sky seems more transparent there, and the sun shines with a strange brilliancy, and a delightful grove of green leafy trees presents itself to the eyes and charms the sight with its verdure, while the ear is soothed by the sweet untutored melody of the countless birds of gay plumage that flit to and fro among the interlacing branches. Here he sees a brook whose limpid waters, like liquid crystal, ripple over fine sands and white pebbles that look like sifted gold and purest pearls. There he perceives a cunningly wrought fountain of many-colored jasper and polished marble; here another of rustic fashion where the little mussel-shells and the spiral white and yellow mansions of the snail disposed in studious disorder, mingled with fragments of glittering crystal and mock emeralds, make up a work of varied aspect, where art, imitating nature, seems to have outdone it. Suddenly there is presented to his sight a strong castle or gorgeous palace with walls of massy gold, turrets of diamond and gates of jacinth; in short, so marvellous is its structure that though the materials of which it is built are nothing less than diamonds, carbuncles, rubies, pearls, gold, and emeralds, the workmanship is still more rare. And after having seen all this, what can be more charming than to see how a bevy of damsels comes forth from the gate of the castle in gay and gorgeous attire, such that, were I to set myself now to depict it as the histories describe it to us, I should never

have done; and then how she who seems to be the first among them all takes the bold knight who plunged into the boiling lake by the hand and without addressing a word to him leads him into the rich palace or castle, and strips him as naked as when his mother bore him, and bathes him in lukewarm water, and anoints him all over with sweet-smelling unguents, and clothes him in a shirt of the softest sendal, all scented and perfumed, while another damsel comes and throws over his shoulders a mantle which is said to be worth at the very least a city, and even more? How charming it is, then, when they tell us how, after all this, they lead him to another chamber where he finds the tables set out in such style that he is filled with amazement and wonder; to see how they pour out water for his hands distilled from amber and sweet-scented flowers; how they seat him on an ivory chair; to see how the damsels wait on him all in profound silence; how they bring him such a variety of dainties so temptingly prepared that the appetite is at a loss which to select; to hear the music that resounds while he is at table, by whom or whence produced he knows not. And then when the repast is over and the tables removed, for the knight to recline in the chair, picking his teeth perhaps as usual, and a damsel, much lovelier than any of the others, to enter unexpectedly by the chamber door, and seat herself by his side, and begin to tell him what the castle is, and how she is held enchanted there, and other things that amaze the knight and astonish the readers who are perusing his history. But I will not expatiate any further upon this, as it may be gathered from it that whatever part of whatever history of a knight-errant one reads, it will fill the reader, whoever he be, with delight and wonder; and take my advice, sir, and, as I said before, read these books and you will see how they will banish any melancholy you may feel and raise your spirits should they be depressed. For myself I can say that since I have been a knight-errant I have become valiant, polite, generous, well-bred, magnanimous, courteous, dauntless, gentle, patient, and have learned to bear hardships, imprisonments, and enchantments; and though it be such a short time since I have seen myself shut up in a cage like a madman, I hope by the might of my arm, if Heaven aid me and fortune thwart me not, to see myself king of some kingdom where I may be able to show the gratitude and generosity that dwell in my heart; for by my faith, señor, the poor man is incapacitated from showing the virtue of generosity to any one, though he may possess it in the highest degree; and gratitude that consists of disposition only is a dead thing, just as faith without works is dead. For this reason I should be glad were fortune soon to offer me some opportunity of making myself an emperor, so as to show my heart in doing good to my friends, particularly to this poor Sancho Panza, my squire, who is the best fellow in the world; and I would gladly give him a county I have promised him this ever so long, only that I am afraid he has not the capacity to govern his realm."

Sancho partly heard these last words of his master, and said to him, "Strive hard you, Señor Don Quixote, to give me that county so often promised by you and so long looked for by me, for I promise you there will be no want of capacity in me to govern it; and even if there is, I have heard say there are men in the world who farm seigniories, paying so much a year, and they themselves taking charge of the government, while the lord, with his legs stretched out, enjoys the revenue they pay him, without troubling himself about anything else. That's what I'll do, and not stand haggling over trifles, but wash my hands at once of the whole business, and enjoy my rents like a duke, and let things go their own way."

"That, brother Sancho," said the canon, "only holds good as far as the enjoyment of the revenue goes; but the lord of the seigniory must attend to the administration of justice, and here capacity and sound judgment come in, and above all a firm determination to find out the truth; for if this be wanting in the beginning, the middle and the end will always go wrong; and God as commonly aids the honest intentions of the simple as he frustrates the evil designs of the crafty."

"I don't understand those philosophies," returned Sancho Panza; "all I know is I would I had the county as soon as I shall know how to govern it; for I have as much soul as another, and as much body as any one, and I shall be as much king of my realm as any other of his; and being so I should do as I liked, and doing as I liked I should please myself, and pleasing myself I should be content, and when one is content he has nothing more to desire, and when one has nothing more to desire there is an end of it; so let the county come, and God be with you, and let us see one another, as one blind man said to the other."

"That is not bad philosophy thou art talking, Sancho," said the canon; "but for all that there is a good deal to be said on this matter of counties."

To which Don Quixote returned, "I know not what more there is to be said; I only guide myself by the example set me by the great Amadis of Gaul, when he made his squire count of the Insula Firme; and so, without any scruples of conscience, I can make a count of Sancho Panza, for he is one of the best squires that ever knight-errant had."

The canon was astonished at the methodical nonsense (if nonsense be capable of method) that Don Quixote uttered, at the way in which he had described the adventure of the knight of the lake, at the impression that the deliberate lies of the books he read had made upon him, and lastly he marvelled at the simplicity of Sancho, who desired so eagerly to obtain the county his master had promised him.

By this time the canon's servants, who had gone to the inn to fetch the sumpter mule, had returned, and making a carpet and the green grass of the meadow serve as a table, they seated themselves in the shade of some trees and made their repast there, that the carter might not be deprived of the advantage of the spot, as has been already said. As they were eating they suddenly heard a loud noise and the sound of a bell that seemed to come from among some brambles and thick bushes that were close by, and the same instant they observed a beautiful goat, spotted all over black, white, and brown, spring out of the thicket with a goatherd after it, calling to it and uttering the usual cries to make it stop or turn back to the fold. The fugitive goat, scared and frightened, ran towards the company as if seeking their protection and then stood still, and the goatherd coming up seized it by the horns and began to talk to it as if it were possessed of reason and understanding: "Ah wanderer, wanderer, Spotty, Spotty; how have you gone limping all this time? What wolves have frightened you, my daughter? Won't you tell me what is the matter, my beauty? But what else can it be except that you are a she, and can not keep quiet? A plague on your humors and the humors of those you take after! Come back, come back, my darling; and if you will not be so happy, at any rate you will be safe in the fold or with your companions; for if you who ought to keep and lead them, go wandering astray in this fashion, what will become of them?"

The goatherd's talk amused all who heard it, but especially the canon, who said to him, "As you live, brother, take it easy, and be not in such a hurry to drive this goat back to the fold; for, being a female, as you say, she will follow her natural instinct in spite of all you can do to prevent it. Take this morsel and drink a sup, and that will soothe your irritation, and in the mean time the goat will rest herself," and so saying, he handed him the loins of a cold rabbit on a fork.

The goatherd took it with thanks, and drank and calmed himself, and then said, "I should be sorry if your worships were to take me for a simpleton for having spoken so seriously as I did to this animal; but the truth is there is a certain mystery in the words I used. I am a clown, but not so much of one but that I know how to behave to men and to beasts."

"That I can well believe," said the curate, "for I know already by experience that the woods breed men of learning, and shepherds' huts harbor philosophers."

"At all events, señor," returned the goatherd, "they shelter men of experience; and that you may see the truth of this and grasp it, though I may seem to put myself forward without being asked, I will, if it will not tire you, gentlemen, and you will give me your attention for a little, tell you a true story which will confirm this gentleman's words (and he pointed to the curate) as well as my own."

To this Don Quixote replied, "Seeing that this affair has a certain color of chivalry about it, I for my part, brother, will hear you most gladly, and so will all these gentlemen, from the high intelligence they possess and their love of curious novelties that interest, charm, and entertain the mind, as I feel quite sure your story will do. So begin, friend, for we are all prepared to listen."

"I draw my stakes," said Sancho, "and will retreat with this pasty to the brook there, where I mean to victual myself for three days; for I have heard my lord, Don Quixote, say that a knight-errant's squire should eat until he can hold no more, whenever he has the chance, because it often happens them to get by accident into a wood so thick that they can not find a way out of it for six days; and if the man is not well filled or his *alforjas* well stored, there he may stay, as very often he does, turned into a dried mummy."

"Thou art in the right of it, Sancho," said Don Quixote; "go where thou wilt and eat all thou canst, for I have had enough, and only want to give my mind its refreshment, as I shall by listening to this good fellow's story."

"It is what we shall all do," said the canon; and then begged the goatherd to begin the promised tale.

The goatherd gave the goat which he held by the horns a couple of slaps on the back, saying, "Lie down here beside me, Spotty, for we have time enough to return to our fold." The goat seemed to understand him, for as her master seated himself, she stretched herself quietly beside him and looked up in his face to show him she was all attention to what he was going to say, and then in these words he began his story.

Chapter 51

Which deals with what the goatherd told those who were carrying off Don Quixote

THREE leagues from this valley there is a village which, though small, is one of the richest in all this neighborhood, and in it there lived a farmer, a very worthy man, and so much respected that, although to be so is the natural consequence of being rich, he was even more respected for his virtue than for the wealth he had acquired. But what made him still more fortunate, as he said himself, was having a daughter of such exceeding beauty, rare intelligence, gracefulness, and virtue, that everyone who knew her and beheld her marvelled at the extraordinary gifts with which heaven and earth had endowed her. As a child she was beautiful, she continued to grow in beauty, and at the age of sixteen she was most lovely. The fame of her beauty began to spread abroad through all the villages around—but why do I say the villages around, merely, when it spread to distant cities, and even made its way into the halls of royalty and reached the ears of people of every class, who came from all sides to see her as if to see something rare and curious, or some wonder-working image?

Her father watched over her and she watched over herself; for there are no locks, or guards, or bolts that can protect a young girl better than her own modesty. The wealth of the father and the beauty of the daughter led many neighbors as well as strangers to seek her for a wife; but he, as one might well be who had the disposal of so rich a jewel, was perplexed and unable to make up his mind to which of her countless suitors he should intrust her. I was one among the many who felt a desire so natural, and, as her father knew who I was, and I was of the same town, of pure blood, in the bloom of life, and very rich in possessions, I had great hopes of success. There was another of the same place and qualifications who also sought her, and this made her father's choice hang in the balance, for he felt that on either of us his daughter would be well bestowed; so to escape from this state of perplexity he resolved to refer the matter to Leandra (for that is the name of the rich damsel who has reduced me to misery), reflecting that as we were both equal it would be best to leave it to his dear daughter to choose according to her inclination —a course that is worthy of imitation by all fathers who wish to settle their children in life. I do not mean that they ought to leave them to make a choice of what is contemptible and bad, but that they should place before them what is good and then allow them to make a good choice as they please. I do not know which Leandra chose; I only know her father put us off with the tender age of his daughter and vague words that neither bound him nor dismissed us. My rival is called Anselmo and I myself Eugenio—that you may know the names of the personages that figure in this tragedy, the end of which is still in suspense, though it is plain to see it must be disastrous.

About this time there arrived in our town one Vicente de la Roca, the son of a poor peasant of the same town, the said Vicente having returned from service as a soldier in Italy and divers other parts. A captain who chanced to pass that way with his company had carried him off from our village when he was a boy of about twelve years, and now twelve years later the young man came back in a soldier's uniform, arrayed in a thousand colors, and all over glass trinkets and fine steel chains. To-day he would appear in one gay dress, to-morrow in another; but all flimsy and gaudy, of little substance and less worth. The peasant folk, who are naturally malicious, and when they have nothing to do can be malice itself, remarked all this, and took note of his finery and jewellery, piece by piece, and discovered that he had three suits of different colors, with garters and stockings to match; but he made so many arrangements and combinations out of them, that if they had not counted them, any one would have sworn that he had made a display of more than ten suits of clothes and twenty plumes. Do not look upon all this that I am telling you about the clothes as uncalled for or spun out, for they have a great deal to do with the story. He used to seat himself on a bench under the great poplar in our plaza; and there he would keep us all hanging open-mouthed on the stories he told us of his exploits. There was no country on the face of the globe he had not seen, nor battle he had not been engaged in; he had killed more Moors than there are in Morocco and Tunis, and fought more single combats, according to his own account, than Garcilaso, Diego García de Paredes and a thousand others he named, and out of all he had come victorious without losing a drop of blood. On the other hand he showed marks of wounds, which, though they could not be made out, he said were gunshot wounds received in divers encounters and actions. Lastly, with monstrous impudence he used to say "you" to his equals and even those who knew what he was, and declare that his arm was his father and his deeds his pedigree, and that being a soldier he was as good as the king himself. And to add to these swaggering ways he was a trifle of a musician, and played the guitar with such a flourish that some said he made it speak; nor did his accomplishments end here, for he was something of a poet too, and on every trifle that happened in the town he made a ballad a league and a half long.

This soldier, then, that I have described, this Vicente de la Roca, this bravo, gallant, musician, poet, was often seen and watched by Leandra from a window of her house which looked out on the plaza. The glitter of his showy attire took her fancy, his ballads bewitched her (for he gave away twenty copies of every one he made), the tales of his exploits which he told about himself came to her ears; and in short, as the devil no doubt had arranged it, she fell in love with him before the presumption of making love to her had suggested itself to him; and as in love-affairs none are more easily brought to an issue than those which have the inclination of the lady for an ally, Leandra and Vicente came to an understanding without any difficulty; and before any of her numerous suitors had any suspicion of her design, she had already carried it into effect, having left the house of her dearly beloved father (for mother she had none), and disappeared from the village with the soldier, who came more triumphantly out of this enterprise than out of any of the large number he laid claim to. All the village and all who heard of it were amazed at the affair; I was aghast, Anselmo thunderstruck, her father full of grief, her relations indignant, the authorities all in a ferment, the officers of the Brotherhood all in arms. They scoured the roads, they searched the woods and all quarters, and at the end of three days they found the flighty Leandra in a mountain cave, strip to her shift, and robbed of all the money and precious jewels she had carried away from home with her. They brought her back to her unhappy father, and questioned her as to her misfortune, and she confessed without pressure that Vicente de la Roca had deceived her, and under promise of marrying her had induced her to leave her father's house, as he meant to take her to the richest and most delightful city in the whole world, which was Naples; and that she, ill-advised and deluded, had believed him, and robbed her father, and handed over all to him the night she disappeared; and that he had carried her away to a rugged mountain and shut her up in the cave where they had found her. She said, moreover, that the soldier, without robbing her of her honor, had taken from her everything she had, and made off, leaving her in the cave, a thing that still further surprised everybody. It was not easy for us to credit the young man's continence, but she asserted it with such earnestness that it helped to console her distressed father, who thought nothing of what had been taken since the jewel that once lost can never be recovered had been left to his daughter. The same day that Leandra made her appearance her father removed her from our sight and took her away to shut her up in a convent in a town near this, in the hope that time may wear away some of the disgrace she has incurred. Leandra's youth furnished an excuse for her fault, at least with those to whom it was of no consequence whether she was good or bad; but those who knew her shrewdness and intelligence did not attribute her misdemeanor to ignorance but to wantonness and the natural disposition of women, which is for the most part flighty and ill-regulated.

Leandra withdrawn from sight, Anselmo's eyes grew blind, or at any rate found nothing to look at that gave them any pleasure, and mine were in darkness without a ray of light to direct them to anything enjoyable while Leandra was away. Our melancholy grew greater, our patience grew less; we cursed the soldier's finery and railed at the carelessness of Leandra's father. At last Anselmo and I agreed to leave the village and come to this valley; and, he feeding a great flock of sheep of his own, and I a large herd of goats of mine, we pass our life among the trees, giving vent to our sorrows, together singing the fair Leandra's praises, or upbraiding her, or else sighing alone, and to Heaven pouring forth our complaints in solitude. Following our example, many more of Leandra's lovers have come to these rude mountains and adopted our mode of life, and they are so numerous that one would fancy the place had been turned into the pastoral Arcadia, so full it is of shepherds and sheepfolds; nor is there a spot in it where the name of the fair Leandra is not heard. Here one curses her and calls her capricious, fickle, and immodest, there another condemns her as frail and frivolous; this pardons and absolves her, that spurns and reviles her; one extols her beauty, another assails her character, and in short, all abuse her, and all adore her, and to such a pitch has this general infatuation gone that there are some who complain of her scorn without ever having exchanged a word with her, and even some that bewail and mourn the raging fever of jealousy, for which she never gave any one cause, for, as I have already said, her misconduct was known before her passion. There is no nook among the rocks, no brookside, no shade beneath the trees that is not haunted by some shepherd telling his woes to the breezes; wherever there is an echo it repeats the name of Leandra; the mountains ring with "Leandra," "Leandra" murmur the brooks, and Leandra keeps us all bewildered and bewitched, hoping without hope and fearing without knowing what we fear. Of all this silly set the one that shows the least and also the most sense is my rival Anselmo, for having so many other things to complain of, he only complains of separation, and to the accompaniment of a rebeck, which he plays admirably, he sings his complaints in verses that show his ingenuity. I follow another easier, and to my mind wiser course, and that is to rail at the frivolity of women, at their inconstancy, their double dealing, their broken promises, their unkept pledges, and in short the want of reflection they show in fixing their affections and inclinations. This, sirs, was the reason of words and expressions I made use of to this goat when I came up just now; for as she is a female I have a contempt for her, though she is the best in all my fold. This is the story I promised to tell you, and if I have been tedious in telling it, I will not be slow to serve you; my hut is close by, and I hav fresh milk and dainty cheese there, as well as variety of toothsome fruit, no less pleasing to th eye than to the palate.

Chapter 52

Of the quarrel that Don Quixote had with th goatherd, together with the rare adventure of the penitents, which with an expenditure of sweat he brought to a happy conclusion

THE goatherd's tale gave great satisfaction to all the hearers, and the canon especially enjoyed it, for he had remarked with particular attention the manner in which it had been told which was as unlike the manner of a clownisl goatherd as it was like that of a polished city wit and he observed that the curate had been quite right in saying that the woods bred men of learning. They all offered their services to Eugenio but he who showed himself most liberal in thi way was Don Quixote, who said to him, "Mos assuredly, brother goatherd, if I found mysel in a position to attempt any adventure, I would this very instant, set out on your behalf, anc would rescue Leandra from that convent (where no doubt she is kept against her will), in spite of the abbess and all who might try to preven me, and would place her in your hands to dea with her according to your will and pleasure observing, however, the laws of chivalry whicl lay down that no violence of any kind is to be offered to any damsel. But I trust in God ou Lord that the might of one malignant enchante may not prove so great but that the power of an other better disposed may prove superior to it and then I promise you my support and assist ance, as I am bound to do by my profession which is none other than to give aid to the weak and needy."

The goatherd eyed him, and noticing Dor Quixote's sorry appearance and looks, he wa filled with wonder and asked the barber, who was next him, "Señor, who is this man who makes such a figure and talks in such a strain?"

"Who should it be," said the barber, "but the famous Don Quixote of La Mancha, the undoer of injustice, the righter of wrongs, the protecto of damsels, the terror of giants, and the winne of battles?"

"That," said the goatherd, "sounds like wha one reads in the books of the knights-errant, who did all that you say this man does; though it i my belief that either you are joking, or else thi gentleman has empty lodgings in his head."

"You are a great scoundrel," said Don Quixote, "and it is you who are empty and a fool. I am fuller than ever was the whoreson bitch that bore you"; and passing from words to deeds, he caught up a loaf that was near him and sent it full in the goatherd's face, with such force that he flattened his nose; but the goatherd, who did not understand jokes, and found himself roughly handled in such good earnest, paying no respect to carpet, table-cloth, or diners, sprang upon Don Quixote, and seizing him by the throat with both hands would no doubt have throttled him, had not Sancho Panza that instant come to the rescue, and grasping him by the shoulders flung him down on the table, smashing plates, breaking glasses, and upsetting and scattering everything on it. Don Quixote, finding himself free, strove to get on top of the goatherd, who, with his face covered with blood, and soundly kicked by Sancho, was on all fours feeling about for one of the table-knives to take a bloody revenge with. The canon and the curate, however, prevented him, but the barber so contrived it that the goatherd got Don Quixote under, and rained down upon him such a shower of fisticuffs that the poor knight's face streamed with blood as freely as his own. The canon and the curate were bursting with laughter, the officers were capering with delight, and both the one and the other hissed them on as they do dogs that are worrying one another in a fight. Sancho alone was frantic, for he could not free himself from the grasp of one of the canon's servants, who kept him from going to his master's assistance.

At last, while they were all, with the exception of the two bruisers who were mauling each other, in high glee and enjoyment, they heard a trumpet sound a note so doleful that it made them all look in the direction whence the sound seemed to come. But the one that was most excited by hearing it was Don Quixote, who, though sorely against his will he was under the goatherd, and something more than pretty well pummelled, said to him, "Brother devil (for it is impossible but that thou must be one since thou hast had might and strength enough to overcome mine), I ask thee to agree to a truce for but one hour, for the solemn note of yonder trumpet that falls on our ears seems to me to summon me to some new adventure." The goatherd, who was by this time tired of pummelling and being pummelled, released him at once, and Don Quixote rising to his feet and turning his eyes to the quarter where the sound had been heard, suddenly saw coming down the slope of a hill several men clad in white like penitents.

The fact was that the clouds had that year withheld their moisture from the earth, and in all the villages of the district they were organizing processions, rogations, and penances, imploring God to open the hands of his mercy and send them rain; and to this end the people of a village that was hard by were going in procession to a holy hermitage that was on one side of that valley. Don Quixote, when he saw the strange garb of the penitents, without reflecting how often he had seen it before, took it into his head that this was a case of adventure, and that it fell to him alone as a knight-errant to engage in it; and he was all the more confirmed in this notion, by the idea that an image draped in black they had with them was some illustrious lady that these villains and discourteous thieves were carrying off by force. As soon as this occurred to him he ran with all speed to Rocinante who was grazing at large, and taking the bridle and the buckler from the saddle-bow, he had him bridled in an instant, and calling to Sancho for his sword he mounted Rocinante, braced his buckler on his arm, and in a loud voice exclaimed to those who stood by, "Now, noble company, ye shall see how important it is that there should be knights in the world professing the order of knight-errantry; now, I say, ye shall see, by the deliverance of that worthy lady who is borne captive there, whether knights-errant deserve to be held in estimation," and so saying he brought his legs to bear on Rocinante—for he had no spurs—and at a full canter (for in all this veracious history we never read of Rocinante fairly galloping) set off to encounter the penitents, though the curate, the canon, and the barber ran to prevent him. But it was out of their power, nor did he even stop for the shouts of Sancho calling after him, "Where are you going, Señor Don Quixote? What devils have possessed you to set you on against our Catholic faith? Plague take me! mind, that is a procession of penitents, and the lady they are carrying on that stand there is the blessed image of the immaculate Virgin. Take care what you are doing, señor, for this time it may be safely said you don't know what you are about." Sancho labored in vain, for his master was so bent on coming to quarters with these sheeted figures and releasing the lady in black that he did not hear a word; and even had he heard, he would not have turned back if the king had ordered him. He came up with the procession and reined in Rocinante, who was already anxious enough to slacken speed a little, and in a hoarse, excited voice he exclaimed, "You who hide your faces, perhaps because you are not good subjects, pay attention and listen to what I am about to say to you." The first to halt were those who were carrying the image, and one of the four ecclesiastics who were chanting the Litany, struck by the strange figure of Don Quixote, the leanness of Rocinante, and the other ludicrous peculiarities he observed, said in reply to him, "Brother, if you have anything to say to us say it quickly, for these brethren are whipping themselves, and we cannot stop, nor is it reasonable we should stop to hear anything, unless indeed it is short enough to be said in two words."

"I will say it in one," replied Don Quixote, "and it is this; that at once, this very instant, ye release that fair lady whose tears and sad aspect show plainly that ye are carrying her off against her will, and that ye have committed some scandalous outrage against her; and I, who was born into the world to redress all such like wrongs, will not permit you to advance another step until you have restored to her the liberty she pines for and deserves."

From these words all the hearers concluded that he must be a madman, and began to laugh heartily, and their laughter acted like gunpowder on Don Quixote's fury, for drawing his sword without another word he made a rush at the stand. One of those who supported it, leaving the burden to his comrades, advanced to meet him, flourishing a forked stick that he had for propping up the stand when resting, and with this he caught a mighty cut Don Quixote made at him that severed it in two; but with the portion that remained in his hand he dealt such a thwack on the shoulder of Don Quixote's sword arm (which the buckler could not protect against the clownish assault) that poor Don Quixote came to the ground in a sad plight.

Sancho Panza, who was coming on close behind puffing and blowing, seeing him fall, cried out to his assailant not to strike him again, for he was a poor enchanted knight, who had never harmed any one all the days of his life; but what checked the clown was, not Sancho's shouting, but seeing that Don Quixote did not stir hand or foot; and so, fancying he had killed him, he hastily hitched up his tunic under his girdle and took to his heels across the country like a deer.

By this time all Don Quixote's companions had come up to where he lay; but the processionists seeing them come running, and with them the officers of the Brotherhood with their crossbows, apprehended mischief, and clustering round the image, raised their hoods, and grasped their scourges, as the priests did their tapers, and awaited the attack, resolved to defend themselves and even to take the offensive against their assailants if they could. Fortune, however, arranged the matter better than they expected, for all Sancho did was to fling himself on his master's body, raising over him the most doleful and laughable lamentation that ever was heard, for he believed he was dead. The curate was known to another curate who walked in the procession, and their recognition of one another set at rest the apprehensions of both parties; the first then told the other in two words who Don Quixote was, and he and the whole troop of penitents went to see if the poor gentleman was dead, and heard Sancho Panza saying, with tears in his eyes, "Oh flower of chivalry, that with one blow of a stick hast ended the course of thy well-spent life! Oh pride of thy race, honor and glory of all La Mancha, nay, of all the world, that for want of thee will be full of evildoers, no longer in fear of punishment for their misdeeds! Oh thou, generous above all the Alexanders, since for only eight months of service thou hast given me the best island the sea girds or surrounds! Humble with the proud, haughty with the humble, encounterer of dangers, endurer of outrages, enamoured without reason, imitator of the good, scourge of the wicked, enemy of the mean, in short, knight-errant, which is all that can be said!"

At the cries and moans of Sancho, Don Quixote came to himself, and the first word he said was, "He who lives separated from you, sweetest Dulcinea, has greater miseries to endure than these. Aid me, friend Sancho, to mount the enchanted cart, for I am not in a condition to press the saddle of Rocinante, as this shoulder is all knocked to pieces."

"That I will do with all my heart, señor," said Sancho; "and let us return to our village with these gentlemen, who seek your good, and there we will prepare for making another sally, which may turn out more profitable and creditable to us."

"Thou art right, Sancho," returned Don Quixote; "it will be wise to let the malign influence of the stars which now prevails pass off."

The canon, the curate, and the barber told him he would act very wisely in doing as he said; and so, highly amused at Sancho Panza's simplicities, they placed Don Quixote in the cart as before. The procession once more formed itself in order and proceeded on its road; the goatherd took his leave of the party; the officers of the Brotherhood declined to go any farther, and the curate paid them what was due to them; the canon begged the curate to let him know how Don Quixote did, whether he was cured of his madness or still suffered from it, and then begged leave to continue his journey; in short, they all separated and went their ways, leaving to themselves the curate and the barber, Don Quixote, Sancho Panza, and the good Rocinante, who regarded everything with as great resignation as his master. The carter yoked his oxen and made Don Quixote comfortable on a truss of hay, and at his usual deliberate pace took the road the curate directed, and at the end of six days they reached Don Quixote's village, and entered it about the middle of the day, which it so happened was a Sunday, and the people were all in the plaza, through which Don Quixote's cart passed. They all flocked to see what was in the cart, and when they recognized their townsman they were filled with amazement, and a boy ran off to bring the news to his housekeeper and his niece that their master and uncle had come back all lean and yellow and stretched on a truss of hay on an ox-cart. It was piteous to hear the cries the two good ladies raised, how they beat their breasts and poured out fresh maledictions on those accursed books of chivalry; all which was renewed when they saw Don Quixote coming in at the gate.

At the news of Don Quixote's arrival Sancho Panza's wife came running, for she by this time knew that her husband had gone away with him as his squire, and on seeing Sancho, the first thing she asked him was if the ass was well. Sancho replied that he was, better than his master was.

"Thanks be to God," said she, "for being so good to me; but now tell me, my friend, what have you made by your squirings? What gown have you brought me back? What shoes for your children?"

"I bring nothing of that sort, wife," said Sancho; "though I bring other things of more consequence and value."

"I am very glad of that," returned his wife; "show me these things of more value and consequence, my friend; for I want to see them to cheer my heart that has been so sad and heavy all these ages that you have been away."

"I will show them to you at home, wife," said Sancho; "be content for the present; for if it please God that we should again go on our travels in search of adventures, you will soon see me a count, or governor of an island, and that not one of those everyday ones, but the best that is to be had."

"Heaven grant it, husband," said she, "for indeed we have need of it. But tell me, what's this about islands, for I don't understand it?"

"Honey is not for the mouth of the ass," returned Sancho; "all in good time thou shalt see, wife—nay, thou wilt be surprised to hear thyself called 'your ladyship,' by all thy vassals."

"What are you talking about, Sancho, with your ladyships, islands, and vassals?" returned Teresa Panza—for so Sancho's wife was called, though they were not relations, for in La Mancha it is customary for wives to take their husbands' surnames.

"Don't be in such a hurry to know all this, Teresa," said Sancho; "it is enough that I am telling you the truth, so shut your mouth. But I may tell you this much by the way, that there is nothing in the world more delightful than to be a person of consideration, squire to a knight-errant, and a seeker of adventures. To be sure most of those one finds do not end as pleasantly as one could wish, for out of a hundred that one meets with, ninety-nine will turn out cross and contrary. I know it by experience, for out of some I came blanketed, and out of others belabored. Still, for all that, it is a fine thing to be on the lookout for what may happen, crossing mountains, searching woods, climbing rocks, visiting castles, putting up at inns, all at free quarters, and devil take the maravedí to pay."

While this conversation passed between Sancho Panza and his wife, Don Quixote's housekeeper and niece took him in and undressed him and laid him in his old bed. He eyed him askance, and could not make out where he was. The curate charged his niece to be very careful to make her uncle comfortable and to keep a watch over him lest he should make his escape from them again, telling her what they had been obliged to do to bring him home. On this the pair once more lifted up their voices and renewed their maledictions upon the books of chivalry, and implored Heaven to plunge the authors of such lies and nonsense into the midst of the bottomless pit. They were, in short, kept in anxiety and dread lest their uncle and master should give them the slip the moment he found himself somewhat better, and as they feared so it fell out.

But the author of this history, though he has devoted research and industry to the discovery of the deeds achieved by Don Quixote in his third sally, has been unable to obtain any information respecting them, at any rate derived from authentic documents; tradition has merely preserved in the memory of La Mancha the fact that

Don Quixote, the third time he sallied forth from his home, betook himself to Saragossa, where he was present at some famous jousts which came off in that city, and that he had adventures there worthy of his valor and high intelligence. Of his end and death he could learn no particulars, nor would he have ascertained it or known of it, if good fortune had not produced an old physician for him who had in his possession a leaden box, which, according to his account, had been discovered among the crumbling foundations of an ancient hermitage that was being rebuilt; in which box were found certain parchment manuscripts in Gothic character, but in Castilian verse, containing many of his achievements, and setting forth the beauty of Dulcinea, the form of Rocinante, the fidelity of Sancho Panza, and the burial of Don Quixote himself, together with sundry epitaphs and eulogies on his life and character; but all that could be read and deciphered were those which the trustworthy author of this new and unparalleled history here presents. And the said author asks of those that shall read it nothing in return for the vast toil which it has cost him in examining and searching the Manchegan archives in order to bring it to light, save that they give him the same credit that people of sense give to the books of chivalry that pervade the world and are so popular; for with this he will consider himself amply paid and fully satisfied, and will be encouraged to seek out and produce other histories, if not as truthful, at least equal in invention and not less entertaining. The first words written on the parchment found in the leaden box were these:

THE ACADEMICIANS OF ARGAMASILLA A VILLAGE OF LA MANCHA

ON THE LIFE AND DEATH OF DON QUIXOTE OF LA MANCHA

HOC SCRIPSERUNT

MONICONGO, ACADEMICIAN OF ARGAMASILLA, ON THE TOMB OF DON QUIXOTE

Epitaph

The scatterbrain that gave La Mancha more
  Rich spoils than Jason's; who a point so keen
  Had to his wit, and happier far had been
If his wit's weathercock a blunter bore;
The arm renowned far as Gaeta's shore,
  Cathay, and all the lands that lie between;
  The muse discreet and terrible in mien
As ever wrote on brass in days of yore;
He who surpassed the Amadises all,

And who as naught the Galaors accounted,
  Supported by his love and gallantry:
Who made the Belianises sing small,
  And sought renown on Rocinante mounted;
  Here, underneath this cold stone, doth he
  lie.

PANIAGUADO, ACADEMICIAN OF ARGAMASILLA, IN PRAISE OF DULCINEA DEL TOBOSO

Sonnet

She, whose full features may be here descried,
  High-bosomed, with a bearing of disdain,
  Is Dulcinea, she for whom in vain
The great Don Quixote of La Mancha sighed.
For her, Toboso's queen, from side to side
  He traversed the grim sierra, the champaign
  Of Aranjuez, and Montiel's famous plain:
On Rocinante oft a weary ride.
Malignant planets, cruel destiny,
  Pursued them both, the fair Manchegan dame,
And the unconquered star of chivalry.
  Nor youth nor beauty saved her from the claim
Of death; he paid love's bitter penalty,
  And left the marble to preserve his name.

CAPRICHOSO, A MOST ACUTE ACADEMICIAN OF ARGAMASILLA, IN PRAISE OF ROCINANTE, STEED OF DON QUIXOTE OF LA MANCHA

Sonnet

On that proud throne of diamantine sheen,
  Which the blood-reeking feet of Mars degrade,
The mad Manchegan's banner now hath been
  By him in all its bravery displayed.
  There hath he hung his arms and trenchant
  blade
Wherewith, achieving deeds till now unseen,
  He slays, lays low, cleaves, hews; but art hath
  made
A novel style for our new paladin.
If Amadis be the proud boast of Gaul,
  If by his progeny the fame of Greece
  Through all the regions of the earth be
  spread,
Great Quixote crowned in grim Bellona's hall
  To-day exalts La Mancha over these,
  And above Greece or Gaul she holds her
  head.
Nor ends his glory here, for his good steed
Doth Brillador and Bayard far exceed;
As mettled steeds compared with Rocinante,
The reputation they have won is scanty.

BURLADOR, ACADEMICIAN OF ARGAMASILLA, ON SANCHO PANZA

Sonnet

The worthy Sancho Panza here you see;
  A great soul once was in that body small,
  Nor was there squire upon this earthly ball
So plain and simple, or of guile so free.
Within an ace of being Count was he,

And would have been but for the spite and
    gall
Of this vile age, mean and illiberal,
That can not even let a donkey be.
For mounted on an ass (excuse the word),
    By Rocinante's side this gentle squire
      Was wont his wandering master to attend.
Delusive hopes that lure the common herd
    With promises of ease, the heart's desire,
     In shadows, dreams, and smoke ye always
      end.

CACHIDIABLO, ACADEMICIAN OF ARGAMASILLA, ON THE TOMB OF DON QUIXOTE

Epitaph

The knight lies here below,
    Ill-errant and bruisèd sore,
    Whom Rocinante bore
In his wanderings to and fro.
By the side of the knight is laid
    Stolid man Sancho too,
    Than whom a squire more true
Was not in the esquire trade.

TIQUITOC, ACADEMICIAN OF ARGAMASILLA, ON THE TOMB OF DULCINEA DEL TOBOSO

Epitaph

Here Dulcinea lies.
    Plump was she and robust:
    Now she is ashes and dust:
The end of all flesh that dies.
A lady of high degree,
    With the port of a lofty dame,
    And the great Don Quixote's flame,
And the pride of her village was she.

These were all the verses that could be deciphered; the rest, the writing being worm-eaten, were handed over to one of the Academicians to make out their meaning conjecturally. We have been informed that at the cost of many sleepless nights and much toil he has succeeded, and that he means to publish them in hopes of Don Quixote's third sally.

Forse altro canterà con miglior plettro.[1]
[1] Perhaps another will sing with a better voice.

PREFACE TO THE SECOND PART

God bless me, gentle (or it may be plebeian) reader, how eagerly must thou be looking forward to this preface, expecting to find there retaliation, scolding, and abuse against the author of the second Don Quixote—I mean him who was, they say, begotten at Tordesillas and born at Tarragona! [1] Well then, the truth is, I am not going to give thee that satisfaction; for, though injuries stir up anger in humbler breasts, in mine the rule must admit of an exception. Thou wouldst have me call him ass, fool, and malapert, but I have no such intention; let his offence be his punishment, with his bread let him eat it, and there's an end of it. What I can not help taking amiss is, that he charges me with being old and one-handed, as if it had been in my power to keep time from passing over me, or as if the loss of my hand had been brought about in some tavern, and not on the grandest occasion the past or present has seen, or the future can hope to see. If my wounds have no beauty to the beholder's eye, they are, at least, honorable in the estimation of those who know where they were received; for the soldier shows to greater advantage dead in battle than alive in flight; and so strongly is this my feeling, that if now it were proposed to perform an impossibility for me, I would rather have had my share in that mighty action, than be free from my wounds this minute without having been present at it. Those the soldier shows on his face and breast, are stars that direct others to the heaven of honor and ambition of merited praise; and moreover it is to be observed that it is not with gray hairs that one writes, but with the understanding, and that commonly improves with years. I take it amiss, too, that he calls me envious, and explains to me, as if I were ignorant, what envy is; for really and truly, of the two kinds there are, I only know that which is holy, noble, and high-minded; and if that be so, as it is, I am not likely to attack a priest, above all if, in addition, he holds the rank of familiar of the Holy Office. And if he said what he did on account of him on whose

behalf it seems he spoke, he is entirely mistaken; for I worship the genius of that person, and admire his works and his unceasing and strenuous industry. After all, however, I am grateful to this gentleman, the author, for saying that my novels are more satirical than exemplary, but that they are good; for they could not be that unless there was a little of everything in them.

I suspect thou wilt say that I am taking a very humble line, and keeping myself too much within the bounds of my moderation, from a feeling that additional suffering should not be inflicted upon a sufferer, and that what this gentleman has to endure must doubtless be very great, as he does not dare to come out into the open field and broad daylight, but hides his name and disguises his country as if he had been guilty of some lese majesty. If perchance thou shouldst come to know him, tell him from me that I do not hold myself aggrieved; for I know well what the temptations of the devil are, and that one of the greatest is putting it into a man's head that he can write and print a book by which he will get as much fame as money, and as much money as fame; and to prove it I will beg of you, in your own sprightly, pleasant way, to tell him this story.

There was a madman in Seville who took to one of the drollest absurdities and vagaries that ever madman in the world gave way to. It was this: he made a tube of reed sharp at one end, and catching a dog in the street, or wherever it might be, he with his foot held one of its legs fast, and with his hand lifted up the other, and as best he could fixed the tube where, by blowing, he made the dog as round as a ball; then holding it in this position, he gave it a couple of slaps on the belly, and let it go, saying to the bystanders (and there were always plenty of them): "Do your worships think, now, that it is an easy thing to blow up a dog?"—Does your worship think now, that it is an easy thing to write a book?

And if this story does not suit him, you may, dear reader, tell him this one, which is likewise of a madman and a dog.

In Cordova there was another madman, whose way it was to carry a piece of marble slab or a

---

[1] This refers to the spurious *Second Part*, written by someone who described himself as Alonso Fernandez de Avellaneda, of Tordesillas.

stone, not of the lightest, on his head, and when he came upon any unwary dog he used to draw close to him and let the weight fall right on top of him; on which the dog in a rage, barking and howling, would run three streets without stopping. It so happened, however, that one of the dogs he discharged his load upon was a cap-maker's dog, of which his master was very fond. The stone came down hitting it on the head, the dog raised a yell at the blow, the master saw the affair and was wroth, and snatching up a measuring-yard rushed out at the madman and did not leave a sound bone in his body, and at every stroke he gave him he said, "You dog, you thief! my lurcher! Don't you see, you brute, that my dog is a lurcher?" and so, repeating the word "lurcher" again and again, he sent the madman away beaten to a jelly. The madman took the lesson to heart, and vanished, and for more than a month never once showed himself in public; but after that he came out again with his old trick and a heavier load than ever. He came up to where there was a dog, and, examining it very carefully without venturing to let the stone fall, he said: "This is a lurcher; ware!" In short, all the dogs he came across, be they mastiffs or terriers, he said were lurchers; and he discharged no more stones. May be it will be the same with this historian; that he will not venture another time to discharge the weight of his wit in books, which, being bad, are harder than stones. Tell him, too, that I do not care a farthing for the threat he holds out to me of depriving me of my profit by means of his book; for, to borrow from the famous interlude of *The Perendenga,* I say in answer to him, "Long life to my lord the *Veintiquatro,* and Christ be with us all." Long life to the great Conde de Lemos, whose Christian charity and well-known generosity support me against all the strokes of my curst fortune; and long life to the supreme benevolence of His Eminence of Toledo, Don Bernardo de Sandoval y Rojas; and what matter if there be no printing-presses in the world, or if they print more books against me than there are letters in the verses of Mingo Revulgo! These two princes, unsought by any adulation or flattery of mine, of their own goodness alone, have taken it upon them to show me kindness and protect me, and in this I consider myself happier and richer than if Fortune had raised me to her greatest height in the ordinary way. The poor man may retain honor, but not the vicious; poverty may cast a cloud over nobility, but can not hide it altogether; and as virtue of itself sheds a certain light, even though it be through the straits and chinks of penury, it wins the esteem of lofty and noble spirits, and in consequence their protection. Thou needst say no more to him, nor will I say anything more to thee, save to tell thee to bear in mind that this Second Part of *Don Quixote* which I offer thee is cut by the same craftsman and from the same cloth as the First, and that in it I present thee Don Quixote continued, and at length dead and buried, so that no one may dare to bring forward any further evidence against him, for that already produced is sufficient, and suffice it, too, that some reputable person should have given an account of all these shrewd lunacies of his without going into the matter again; for abundance, even of good things, prevents them from being valued; and scarcity, even in the case of what is bad, confers a certain value. I was forgetting to tell thee that thou mayest expect the *Persiles,* which I am now finishing, and also the Second Part of *Galatea.*

THE SECOND PART

Chapter 1

Of the interview the Curate and the Barber had with Don Quixote about his malady

CID HAMET BENENGELI, in the Second Part of this history, and third sally of Don Quixote, says that the curate and the barber remained nearly a month without seeing him, lest they should recall or bring back to his recollection what had taken place. They did not, however, omit to visit his niece and housekeeper, and charge them to be careful to treat him with attention, and give him comforting things to eat, and such as were good for the heart and the brain, whence, it was plain to see, all his misfortune proceeded. The niece and housekeeper replied that they did so, and meant to do so with all possible care and assiduity, for they could perceive that their master was now and then beginning to show signs of being in his right mind. This gave great satisfaction to the curate and the barber, for they concluded they had taken the right course in carrying him off enchanted in the ox-cart, as has been described in the First Part of this great as well as accurate history, in the last chapter thereof. So they resolved to pay him a visit and test the improvement in his condition, although they thought it almost impossible that there could be any; and they agreed not to touch upon any point connected with knight-errantry, so as not to run the risk of re-opening wounds which were still so tender.

They came to see him consequently, and found him sitting up in bed in a green baize waistcoat and a red Toledo cap, and so withered and dried up that he looked as if he had been turned into a mummy. They were very cordially received by him; they asked him after his health, and he talked to them about it and about himself very naturally and in very well chosen language. In the course of their conversation they fell to discussing what they call Statecraft and systems of government, correcting this abuse and con-demning that, reforming one practice and abolishing another, each of the three setting up for a new legislator, a modern Lycurgus, or a brand-new Solon; and so completely did they remodel the State, that they seemed to have thrust it into a furnace and taken out something quite different from what they had put in; and on all the subjects they dealt with, Don Quixote spoke with such good sense that the pair of examiners were fully convinced that he was quite recovered and in his full senses.

The niece and housekeeper were present at the conversation and could not find words enough to express their thanks to God at seeing their master so clear in his mind; the curate, however, changing his original plan, which was to avoid touching upon matters of chivalry, resolved to test Don Quixote's recovery thoroughly, and see whether it were genuine or not; and so, from one subject to another, he came at last to talk of the news that had come from the capital, and, among other things, he said it was considered certain that the Turk was coming down with a powerful fleet, and that no one knew what his purpose was, or when the great storm would burst; and that all Christendom was in apprehension of this, which almost every year calls us to arms, and that his Majesty had made provision for the security of the coasts of Naples and Sicily and the island of Malta.

To this Don Quixote replied, "His Majesty has acted like a prudent warrior in providing for the safety of his realms in time, so that the enemy may not find him unprepared; but if my advice were taken I would recommend him to adopt a measure which at present, no doubt, his Majesty is very far from thinking of."

The moment the curate heard this he said to himself, "God keep thee in his hand, poor Don Quixote, for it seems to me thou are precipitating thyself from the height of thy madness into the profound abyss of thy simplicity."

But the barber, who had the same suspicion as the curate, asked Don Quixote what would be his advice as to the measures that he said ought to be adopted; for perhaps it might prove to be one that would have to be added to the list of the many impertinent suggestions that people were in the habit of offering to princes.

"Mine, master shaver," said Don Quixote, "will not be impertinent, but, on the contrary, pertinent."

"I don't mean that," said the barber, "but that experience has shown that all or most of the expedients which are proposed to his Majesty are either impossible, or absurd, or injurious to the King and to the kingdom."

"Mine, however," replied Don Quixote, "is neither impossible nor absurd, but the easiest, the most reasonable, the readiest and most expeditious that could suggest itself to any projector's mind."

"You take a long time to tell it, Señor Don Quixote," said the curate.

"I don't choose to tell it here, now," said Don Quixote, "and have it reach the ears of the lords of the council to-morrow morning, and some other carry off the thanks and rewards of my trouble."

"For my part," said the barber, "I give my word here and before God that I will not repeat what your worship says, to King, Rook, or earthly man—an oath I learned from the ballad of the curate, who, in the prelude, told the king of the thief who had robbed him of the hundred gold crowns and his pacing mule."

"I am not versed in stories," said Don Quixote; "but I know the oath is a good one, because I know the barber to be an honest fellow."

"Even if he were not," said the curate, "I will go bail and answer for him that in this matter he will be as silent as a dummy, under pain of paying any penalty that may be pronounced."

"And who will be security for you, señor curate?" said Don Quixote.

"My profession," replied the curate, "which is to keep secrets."

"Ods body!" said Don Quixote at this, "what more has his Majesty to do but to command, by public proclamation, all the knights-errant that are scattered over Spain to assemble on a fixed day in the capital, for even if no more than half a dozen come, there may be one among them who alone will suffice to destroy the entire might of the Turk. Give me your attention and follow me. Is it, pray, any new thing for a single knight-errant to demolish an army of two hundred thousand men, as if they all had but one throat or were made of sugar-paste? Nay, tell me, how many histories are there filled with these mar-

vels? If only (in an evil hour for me: I don't speak for any one else) the famous Don Belianis were alive now, or any one of the innumerable progeny of Amadis of Gaul! If any of these were alive to-day, and were to come face to face with the Turk, by my faith, I would not give much for the Turk's chance. But God will have regard for his people, and will provide some one who, if not so valiant as the knights-errant of yore, at least will not be inferior to them in spirit; but God knows what I mean, and I say no more."

"Alas!" exclaimed the niece at this, "may I die if my master does not want to turn knight-errant again"; to which Don Quixote replied, "A knight-errant I shall die, and let the Turk come down or go up when he likes, and in as strong force as he can, once more I say, God knows what I mean." But here the barber said, "I ask your worships to give me leave to tell a short story of something that happened in Seville, which comes so pat to the purpose just now that I should like greatly to tell it." Don Quixote gave him leave, and the rest prepared to listen, and he began thus:

"In the madhouse at Seville there was a man whom his relations had placed there as being out of his mind. He was a graduate of Osuna in canon law; but even if he had been of Salamanca, it was the opinion of most people that he would have been mad all the same. This graduate, after some years of confinement, took it into his head that he was sane and in his full senses, and under this impression wrote to the Archbishop entreating him earnestly, and in very correct language, to have him released from the misery in which he was living; for by God's mercy he had now recovered his lost reason, though his relations, in order to enjoy his property, kept him there, and, in spite of the truth, would make him out to be mad until his dying day. The Archbishop, moved by repeated sensible, well-written letters, directed one of his chaplains to make inquiry of the governor of the madhouse as to the truth of the licentiate's statements, and to have an interview with the madman himself, and, if it should appear that he was in his senses, to take him out and restore him to liberty. The chaplain did so, and the governor assured him that the man was still mad, and that though he often spoke like a highly intelligent person, he would in the end break out into nonsense that in quantity and quality counterbalanced all the sensible things he had said before, as might be easily tested by talking to him. The chaplain resolved to try the experiment, and obtaining access to the madman conversed with him for an hour or more, during the whole of which time he never uttered a word that was incoherent or absurd, but, on the contrary, spoke so rationally that the chaplain was compelled to believe him to be sane. Among other things, he said the governor was against him, not to lose the presents his relations made him for reporting him still mad but with lucid intervals; and that the worst foe he had in his misfortune was his large property; for in order to enjoy it his enemies disparaged and threw doubts upon the mercy our Lord had shown him in turning him from a brute beast into a man. In short, he spoke in such a way that he cast suspicion on the governor, and made his relations appear covetous and heartless, and himself so rational that the chaplain determined to take him away with him that the Archbishop might see him, and ascertain for himself the truth of the matter. Yielding to this conviction, the worthy chaplain begged the governor to have the clothes in which the licentiate had entered the house given to him. The governor again bade him beware of what he was doing, as the licentiate was beyond a doubt still mad; but all his cautions and warnings were unavailing to dissuade the chaplain from taking him away. The governor, seeing that it was the order of the Archbishop, obeyed, and they dressed the licentiate in his own clothes, which were new and decent. He, as soon as he saw himself clothed like one in his senses, and divested of the appearance of a madman, entreated the chaplain to permit him in charity to go and take leave of his comrades the madmen. The chaplain said he would go with him to see what madmen there were in the house; so they went upstairs, and with them some of those who were present. Approaching a cage in which there was a furious madman, though just at that moment calm and quiet, the licentiate said to him, 'Brother, think if you have any commands for me, for I am going home, as God has been pleased, in his infinite goodness and mercy, without any merit of mine, to restore me my reason. I am now cured and in my senses, for with God's power nothing is impossible. Have strong hope and trust in him, for as he has restored me to my original condition, so likewise he will restore you if you trust in him. I will take care to send you some good things to eat; and be sure you eat them; for I would have you know I am convinced, as one who has gone through it, that all this madness of ours comes of having the stomach empty and the brains full of wind. Take courage! take courage! for despondency in misfortune breaks down

health and brings on death.'

"To all these words of the licentiate another madman in a cage opposite that of the furious one was listening; and raising himself up from an old mat on which he lay stark naked, he asked in a loud voice who it was that was going away cured and in his senses. The licentiate answered, 'It is I, brother, who am going; I have now no need to remain here any longer, for which I return infinite thanks to Heaven that has had so great mercy upon me.'

" 'Mind what you are saying, licentiate; don't let the devil deceive you,' replied the madman. 'Keep quiet, stay where you are, and you will save yourself the trouble of coming back.'

" 'I know I am cured,' returned the licentiate, 'and that I shall not have to go stations again.'

" 'You cured!' said the madman; 'well, we shall see; God be with you; but I swear to you by Jupiter, whose majesty I represent on earth, that for this crime alone, which Seville is committing to-day in releasing you from this house, and treating you as if you were in your senses, I shall have to inflict such a punishment on it as will be remembered for ages and ages, amen. Dost thou not know, thou miserable little licentiate, that I can do it, being, as I say, Jupiter the Thunderer, who hold in my hands the fiery bolts with which I am able and am wont to threaten and lay waste the world? But in one way only will I punish this ignorant town, and that is by not raining upon it, nor on any part of its district or territory, for three whole years, to be reckoned from the day and moment when this threat is pronounced. Thou free, thou cured, thou in thy senses! and I mad, I disordered, I bound! I will as soon think of sending rain as of hanging myself.'

"Those present stood listening to the words and exclamations of the madman; but our licentiate, turning to the chaplain and seizing him by the hands, said to him, 'Be not uneasy, señor; attach no importance to what this madman has said; for if he is Jupiter and will not send rain, I, who am Neptune, the father and god of the waters, will rain as often as it pleases me and may be needful.'

"The governor and the bystanders laughed, and at their laughter the chaplain was half ashamed, and he replied, 'For all that, Señor Neptune, it will not do to vex Señor Jupiter; remain where you are, and some other day, when there is a better opportunity and more time, we will come back for you.' So they stripped the licentiate, and he was left where he was; and that's the end of the story."

"So that's the story, master barber," said Don Quixote, "which came in so pat to the purpose that you could not help telling it? Master shaver, master shaver! how blind is he who can not see through a sieve. Is it possible that you do not know that comparisons of wit with wit, valor with valor, beauty with beauty, birth with birth, are always odious and unwelcome? I, master barber, am not Neptune the god of the waters, nor do I try to make any one take me for an astute man, for I am not one. My only endeavor is to convince the world of the mistake it makes in not reviving in itself the happy time when the order of knight-errantry was in the field. But our depraved age does not deserve to enjoy such a blessing as those ages enjoyed when knights-errant took upon their shoulders the defence of kingdoms, the protection of damsels, the succor of orphans and minors, the chastisement of the proud, and the recompense of the humble. With the knights of these days, for the most part, it is the damask, brocade, and rich stuffs they wear, that rustle as they go, not the chain mail of their armor; no knight now-a-days sleeps in the open field exposed to the inclemency of heaven, and in full panoply from head to foot; no one now takes a nap, as they call it, without drawing his feet out of the stirrups, and leaning upon his lance, as the knights-errant used to do; no one now, issuing from the wood, penetrates yonder mountains, and then treads the barren, lonely shore of the sea—mostly a tempestuous and stormy one—and finding on the beach a little bark without oars, sail, mast, or tackling of any kind, in the intrepidity of his heart flings himself into it and commits himself to the wrathful billows of the deep sea, that one moment lift him up to heaven and the next plunge him into the depths; and opposing his breast to the irresistible gale, finds himself, when he least expects it, three thousand leagues and more away from the place where he embarked; and leaping ashore in a remote and unknown land has adventures that deserve to be written, not on parchment, but on brass. But now sloth triumphs over energy, indolence over exertion, vice over virtue, arrogance over courage, and theory over practice in arms, which flourished and shone only in the golden ages and in knights-errant. For tell me, who was more virtuous and more valiant than the famous Amadis of Gaul? Who more discreet than Palmerin of England? Who more gracious and easy than Tirante el Blanco? Who more courtly than Lisuarte of Greece? Who more slashed or slashing than Don Belianis? Who more intrepid than Perion of Gaul? Who more

ready to face danger than Felixmarte of Hi cania? Who more sincere than Esplandian? Wh more impetuous than Don Cirongilio of Thrace Who more bold than Rodamonte? Who mo prudent than King Sobrino? Who more darin than Reinaldos? Who more invincible than R land? and who more gallant and courteous tha Ruggiero, from whom the dukes of Ferrara the present day are descended, according to Tu pin in his *Cosmography*? All these knights, an many more that I could name, señor curate, we knights-errant, the light and glory of chivalr These, or such as these, I would have to carr out my plan, and in that case his Majesty woul find himself well served and would save grea expense, and the Turk would be left tearing h beard. And so I will stay where I am, as the cha lain does not take me away; and if Jupiter, the barber has told us, will not send rain, he am I, and I will rain when I please. I say th that Master Basin may know that I understan him."

"Indeed, Señor Don Quixote," said the ba ber, "I did not mean it in that way, and, so hel me God, my intention was good, and your wo ship ought not to be vexed."

"As to whether I ought to be vexed or not returned Don Quixote, "I myself am the be judge."

Hereupon the curate observed, "I have har ly said a word as yet; and I would gladly be r lieved of a doubt, arising from what Don Qui ote has said, that worries and works my co science."

"The señor curate has leave for more tha that," returned Don Quixote, "so he may decla his doubt, for it is not pleasant to have a doul on one's conscience."

"Well then, with that permission," said th curate, "I say my doubt is that, all I can do, can not persuade myself that the whole pack knights-errant you, Señor Quixote, have me tioned, were really and truly persons of fles and blood, that ever lived in the world; on th contrary, I suspect it to be all fiction, fable, an falsehood, and dreams told by men awakene from sleep, or rather still half asleep."

"That is another mistake," replied Don Qui ote, "into which many have fallen who do not b lieve that there ever were such knights in th world, and I have often, with divers people an on divers occasions, tried to expose this almo universal error to the light of truth. Sometim I have not been successful in my purpose, som times I have, supporting it upon the shoulde of the truth; which truth is so clear that I ca almost say I have with my own eyes seen Amadis of Gaul, who was a man of lofty stature, fair complexion, with a handsome though black beard, of a countenance between gentle and stern in expression, sparing of words, slow to anger, and quick to put it away from him; and as I have depicted Amadis, so I could, I think, portray and describe all the knights-errant that are in all the histories in the world; for by the perception I have that they were what their histories describe, and by the deeds they did and the dispositions they displayed, it is possible, with the aid of sound philosophy, to deduce their features, complexion, and stature."

"How big, in your worship's opinion, may the giant Morgante have been, Señor Don Quixote?" asked the barber.

"With regard to giants," replied Don Quixote, "opinions differ as to whether there ever were any or not in the world; but the Holy Scripture, which can not err by a jot from the truth, shows us that there were, when it gives us the history of that big Philistine, Goliath, who was seven cubits and a half in height, which is a huge size. Likewise, in the island of Sicily, there have been found leg-bones and arm-bones so large that their size makes it plain that their owners were giants, and as tall as great towers; geometry puts this fact beyond a doubt. But, for all that, I can not speak with certainty as to the size of Morgante, though I suspect he can not have been very tall; and I am inclined to be of this opinion because I find in the history in which his deeds are particularly mentioned, that he frequently slept under a roof; and as he found houses to contain him, it is clear that his bulk could not have been anything excessive."

"That is true," said the curate, and yielding to the enjoyment of hearing such nonsense, he asked him what was his notion of the features of Reinaldos of Montalban, and Don Roland and the rest of the Twelve Peers of France, for they were all knights-errant.

"As for Reinaldos," replied Don Quixote, "I venture to say that he was broad-faced, of ruddy complexion, with roguish and somewhat prominent eyes, excessively punctilious and touchy, and given to the society of thieves and scapegraces. With regard to Roland, or Rotolando, or Orlando (for the histories call him by all these names), I am of opinion, and hold, that he was of middle height, broad-shouldered, rather bow-legged, swarthy-complexioned, red-bearded, with a hairy body and a severe expression of countenance, a man of few words, but very polite and well-bred."

"If Roland was not a more graceful person than your worship has described," said the curate, "it is no wonder that the fair Lady Angelica rejected him and left him for the gayety, liveliness, and grace of that budding-bearded little Moor to whom she surrendered herself; and she showed her sense in falling in love with the gentle softness of Medoro rather than the roughness of Roland."

"That Angelica, señor curate," returned Don Quixote, "was a giddy damsel, flighty and somewhat wanton, and she left the world as full of her vagaries as of the fame of her beauty. She treated with scorn a thousand gentlemen, men of valor and wisdom, and took up with a smooth-faced sprig of a page, without fortune or fame, except such reputation for gratitude as the affection he bore his friend got for him. The great poet who sang her beauty, the famous Ariosto, not caring to sing her adventures after her contemptible surrender (which probably were not over and above creditable), dropped her where he says:

How she received the sceptre of Cathay,
Some bard of defter quill may sing some day;

and this was no doubt a kind of prophecy, for poets are also called *vates*, that is to say diviners; and its truth was made plain; for since then a famous Andalusian poet has lamented and sung her tears, and another famous and rare poet, a Castilian, has sung her beauty."

"Tell me, Señor Don Quixote," said the barber here, "among all those who praised her, has there been no poet to write a satire on this Lady Angelica?"

"I can well believe," replied Don Quixote, "that if Sacripante or Roland had been poets they would have given the damsel a trimming; for it is naturally the way with poets who have been scorned and rejected by their ladies, whether fictitious or not, in short by those whom they select as the ladies of their thoughts, to avenge themselves in satires and libels—a vengeance, to be sure, unworthy of generous hearts; but up to the present I have not heard of any defamatory verse against the Lady Angelica, who turned the world upside down."

"Strange," said the curate; but at this moment they heard the housekeeper and the niece, who had previously withdrawn from the conversation, exclaiming aloud in the courtyard, and at the noise they all ran out.

Chapter 2

*Which treats of the notable altercation which
Sancho Panza had with Don Quixote's niece
and housekeeper, together with other
droll matters*

THE history relates that the outcry Don
Quixote, the curate, and the barber heard came
from the niece and the housekeeper exclaiming
to Sancho, who was striving to force his way in
to see Don Quixote while they held the door
against him, "What does the vagabond want in
this house? Be off to your own, brother, for it is
you, and no one else, that delude my master, and
lead him astray, and take him tramping about
the country."

To which Sancho replied, "Devil's own housekeeper! it is I who am deluded, and led astray,
and taken tramping about the country, and not
thy master! He has carried me all over the world,
and you are mightily mistaken. He enticed me
away from home by a trick, promising me an island, which I am still waiting for."

"May evil islands choke thee, thou detestable
Sancho," said the niece; "what are islands? Is it
something to eat, glutton and gormandizer that
thou art?"

"It is not something to eat," replied Sancho,
"but something to govern and rule, and better
than four cities or four judgeships at court."

"For all that," said the housekeeper, "you
don't enter here, you bag of mischief and sack of
knavery; go govern your house and dig your seed-
patch, and give over looking for islands or shy-
lands."

The curate and the barber listened with great
amusement to the words of the three; but Don
Quixote, uneasy lest Sancho should blab and
blurt out a whole heap of mischievous stupidities, and touch upon points that might not be
altogether to his credit, called to him and made
the other two hold their tongues and let him
come in. Sancho entered, and the curate and the
barber took their leave of Don Quixote, of whose
recovery they despaired when they saw how
wedded he was to his crazy ideas, and how saturated with the nonsense of his unlucky chivalry; and said the curate to the barber, "You will
see, gossip, that when we are least thinking of
it, our gentleman will be off once more for another flight."

"I have no doubt of it," returned the barber;
"but I do not wonder so much at the madness
of the knight as at the simplicity of the squire,
who has such a firm belief in all that about the
island, that I suppose all the exposures that
could be imagined would not get it out of his
head."

"God help them," said the curate; "and let us
be on the look-out to see what comes of all these
absurdities of the said knight and squire, for it
seems as if they had both been cast in the same
mould, and the madness of the master without
the simplicity of the man would not be worth a
farthing."

"That is true," said the barber, "and I should
like very much to know what the pair are talking about at this moment."

"I promise you," said the curate, "the niece or
the housekeeper will tell us by-and-by, for they
are not the ones to forget to listen."

Meanwhile Don Quixote shut himself up in
his room with Sancho, and when they were
alone he said to him, "It grieves me greatly, Sancho, that thou shouldst have said, and sayest
that I took thee out of thy cottage, when thou
knowest I did not remain in my house. We sallied forth together, we took the road together,
we wandered abroad together; we have had the
same fortune and the same luck; if they blanketed thee once, they belabored me a hundred
times, and that is the only advantage I have of
thee."

"That was only reasonable," replied Sancho,
"for, by what your worship says, misfortunes belong more properly to knights-errant than to
their squires."

"Thou art mistaken, Sancho," said Don Quixote, "according to the maxim *quando caput dolet*
etc."

"I don't understand any language but my
own," said Sancho.

"I mean to say," said Don Quixote, "that when
the head suffers all the members suffer; and so
being thy lord and master, I am thy head, and
thou a part of me as thou art my servant; and
therefore any evil that affects or shall affect me
should give thee pain, and what affects thee
give pain to me."

"It should be so," said Sancho; "but when I
was blanketed as a member, my head was on the
other side of the wall, looking on while I was
flying through the air, and did not feel any pain
whatever; and if the members are obliged to feel
the suffering of the head, it should be obliged
to feel their sufferings."

"Dost thou mean to say now, Sancho," said
Don Quixote, "that I did not suffer when they
were blanketing thee? If thou dost, thou must
not say so or think so, for I felt more pain then
in spirit than thou didst in body. But let us put
that aside for the present, for we shall have op-

portunities enough for considering and settling the point; tell me, Sancho my friend, what do they say about me in the village here? What do the common people think of me? What do the hidalgos? What do the caballeros? What do they say of my valor; of my achievements; of my courtesy? How do they treat the task I have undertaken in reviving and restoring to the world the now forgotten order of chivalry? In short, Sancho, I would have thee tell me all that has come to thine ears on this subject; and thou art to tell me, without adding anything to the good or taking away anything from the bad; for it is the duty of loyal vassals to tell the truth to their lords just as it is and in its proper shape, not allowing flattery to add to it or any idle deference to lessen it. And I would have thee know, Sancho, that if the naked truth, undisguised by flattery, came to the ears of princes, times would be different, and other ages would be reckoned iron ages more than ours, which I hold to be the golden of these latter days. Profit by this advice, Sancho, and report to me clearly and faithfully the truth of what thou knowest touching what I have demanded of thee."

"That I will do with all my heart, master," replied Sancho, "provided your worship will not be vexed at what I say, as you wish me to say it out in all its nakedness, without putting any more clothes on it than it came to my knowledge in."

"I will not be vexed at all," returned Don Quixote; "thou mayest speak freely, Sancho, and without any beating about the bush."

"Well then," said he, "first of all, I have to tell you that the common people consider your worship a mighty great madman, and me no less a fool. The hidalgos say that, not keeping within the bounds of your quality of gentleman, you have assumed the 'Don,' and made a knight of yourself at a jump, with four vine-stocks and a couple of acres of land, and never a shirt to your back. The caballeros say they do not want to have hidalgos setting up in opposition to them, particularly squire hidalgos who polish their own shoes and darn their black stockings with green silk."

"That," said Don Quixote, "does not apply to me, for I always go well dressed and never patched, ragged I may be, very likely, but ragged more from the wear and tear of arms than of time."

"As to your worship's valor, courtesy, achievements, and task, there is a variety of opinions. Some say, 'mad but droll'; others, 'valiant but unlucky'; others, 'courteous but meddling'; and

then they go into such a number of things that they don't leave a whole bone either in your worship or in myself."

"Recollect, Sancho," said Don Quixote, "that wherever virtue exists in an eminent degree it is persecuted. Few or none of the famous men that have lived escaped being calumniated by malice. Julius Cæsar, the boldest, wisest, and bravest of captains, was charged with being ambitious, and not particularly cleanly in his dress, or pure in his morals. Of Alexander, whose deeds won him the name of Great, they say that he was somewhat of a drunkard. Of Hercules, him of the many labors, it is said that he was lewd and luxurious. Of Don Galaor, the brother of Amadis of Gaul, it was whispered that he was over quarrelsome, and of his brother that he was lachrymose. So that, O Sancho, amongst all these calumnies against good men, mine may be let pass, since they are no more than thou hast said."

"That's just where it is, body of my father!" returned Sancho.

"Is there more, then?" asked Don Quixote.

"There's the tail to be skinned yet," said Sancho; "all so far is cakes and fancy bread; but if your worship wants to know all about the calumnies they bring against you, I will fetch you one this instant who can tell you the whole of them without missing an atom; for last night the son of Bartholomew Carrasco, who has been studying at Salamanca, came home after having been made a bachelor, and when I went to welcome him, he told me that your worship's history is already abroad in books, with the title of THE INGENIOUS GENTLEMAN DON QUIXOTE OF LA MANCHA; and he says they mention me in it by my own name of Sancho Panza, and the lady Dulcinea del Toboso too, and divers things that happened to us when we were alone; so that I crossed myself in my wonder how the historian who wrote them down could have known them."

"I promise thee, Sancho," said Don Quixote, "the author of our history will be some sage enchanter; for to such nothing that they choose to write about is hidden."

"What!" said Sancho, "a sage and an enchanter! Why, the bachelor Samson Carrasco (that is the name of him I spoke of) says the author of the history is called Cid Hamet Berengena."

"That is a Moorish name," said Don Quixote.

"May be so," replied Sancho; "for I have heard say that the Moors are mostly great lovers of *berengenas.*"[1]

"Thou must have mistaken the surname of

[1] The egg plant.

this 'Cid'—which means in Arabic 'Lord'—Sancho," observed Don Quixote.

"Very likely," replied Sancho, "but if your worship wishes me to fetch the bachelor I will go for him in a twinkling."

"Thou wilt do me a great pleasure, my friend," said Don Quixote, "for what thou hast told me has amazed me, and I shall not eat a morsel that will agree with me until I have heard all about it."

"Then I am off for him," said Sancho; and leaving his master he went in quest of the bachelor, with whom he returned in a short time, and, all three together, they had a very droll colloquy.

Chapter 3

Of the laughable conversation that passed between Don Quixote, Sancho Panza, and the Bachelor Samson Carrasco

DON QUIXOTE remained very deep in thought, waiting for the bachelor Carrasco, from whom he was to hear how he himself had been put into a book as Sancho said; and he could not persuade himself that any such history could be in existence, for the blood of the enemies he had slain was not yet dry on the blade of his sword, and now they wanted to make out that his mighty achievements were going about in print. For all that, he fancied some sage, either a friend or an enemy, might, by the aid of magic, have given them to the press; if a friend, in order to magnify and exalt them above the most famous ever achieved by any knight-errant; if an enemy, to bring them to naught and degrade them below the meanest ever recorded of any low squire, though, as he said to himself, the achievements of squires never were recorded. If, however, it were the fact that such a history were in existence, it must necessarily, being the story of a knight-errant, be grandiloquent, lofty, imposing, grand and true. With this he comforted himself somewhat, though it made him uncomfortable to think that the author was a Moor, judging by the title of "Cid"; and that no truth was to be looked for from Moors, as they are all impostors, cheats, and schemers. He was afraid he might have dealt with his love affairs in some indecorous fashion, that might tend to the discredit and prejudice of the purity of his lady Dulcinea del Toboso; he would have had him set forth the fidelity and respect he had always observed towards her, spurning queens, empresses, and damsels of all sorts, and keeping in check the

impetuosity of his natural impulses. Absorbed and wrapped up in these and divers other cogitations, he was found by Sancho and Carrasco, whom Don Quixote received with great courtesy.

The bachelor, though he was called Samson, was of no great bodily size, but he was a very great wag; he was of a sallow complexion, but very sharp-witted, somewhere about four-and-twenty years of age, with a round face, flat nose, and a large mouth, all indications of a mischievous disposition and a love of fun and jokes; and of this he gave a sample as soon as he saw Don Quixote, by falling on his knees before him and saying, "Let me kiss your mightiness's hand, Señor Don Quixote of La Mancha, for, by the habit of St. Peter that I wear, though I have no more than the first four orders, your worship is one of the most famous knights-errant that have ever been, or will be, all the world over. A blessing on Cid Hamet Benengeli, who has written the history of your great deeds, and a double blessing on that connoisseur who took the trouble of having it translated out of the Arabic into our Castilian vulgar tongue for the universal entertainment of the people!"

Don Quixote made him rise, and said, "So then, it is true that there is a history of me, and that it was a Moor and a sage who wrote it?"

"So true is it, señor," said Samson, "that my belief is there are more than twelve thousand volumes of the said history in print this very day. Only ask Portugal, Barcelona, and Valencia, where they have been printed, and moreover there is a report that it is being printed at Antwerp, and I am persuaded there will not be a country or language in which there will not be a translation of it."

"One of the things," here observed Don Quixote, "that ought to give most pleasure to a virtuous and eminent man is to find himself in his lifetime in print and in type, familiar in people's mouths with a good name; I say with a good name, for if it be the opposite, then there is no death to be compared to it."

"If it goes by good name and fame," said the bachelor, "your worship alone bears away the palm from all the knights-errant; for the Moor in his own language, and the Christian in his, have taken care to set before us your gallantry, your high courage in encountering dangers, your fortitude in adversity, your patience under misfortunes as well as wounds, the purity and continence of the platonic loves of your worship and my lady Doña Dulcinea del Toboso"—

"I never heard my lady Dulcinea called Doña,

observed Sancho here; "nothing more than the lady Dulcinea del Toboso; so here already the history is wrong."

"That is not an objection of any importance," replied Carrasco.

"Certainly not," said Don Quixote; "but tell me, señor bachelor, what deeds of mine are they that are made most of in this history?"

"On that point," replied the bachelor, "opinions differ, as tastes do; some swear by the adventure of the windmills that your worship took to be Briareuses and giants; others by that of the fulling mills; one cries up the description of the two armies that afterwards took the appearance of two droves of sheep; another that of the dead body on its way to be buried at Segovia; a third says the liberation of the galley slaves is the best of all, and a fourth that nothing comes up to the affair with the Benedictine giants, and the battle with the valiant Biscayan."

"Tell me, señor bachelor," said Sancho at this point, "does the adventure with the Yanguesans come in, when our good Rocinante went hankering after dainties?"

"The sage has left nothing in the ink-bottle," replied Samson; "he tells all and sets down everything, even to the capers the worthy Sancho cut in the blanket."

"I cut no capers in the blanket," returned Sancho; "in the air I did, and more of them than I liked."

"There is no human history in the world, I suppose," said Don Quixote, "that has not its ups and downs, but more than others such as deal with chivalry, for they can never be entirely made up of prosperous adventures."

"For all that," replied the bachelor, "there are those who have read the history who say they would have been glad if the author had left out some of the countless cudgellings that were inflicted on Señor Don Quixote in various encounters."

"That's where the truth of the history comes in," said Sancho.

"At the same time they might fairly have passed them over in silence," observed Don Quixote; "for there is no need of recording events which do not change or affect the truth of a history, if they tend to bring the hero of it into contempt. Æneas was not in truth and earnest so pious as Virgil represents him, nor Ulysses so wise as Homer describes him."

"That is true," said Samson; "but it is one thing to write as a poet, another to write as a historian; the poet may describe or sing things, not as they were, but as they ought to have been; but the historian has to write them down, not as they ought to have been, but as they were, without adding anything to the truth or taking anything from it."

"Well then," said Sancho, "if this señor Moor goes in for telling the truth, no doubt among my master's drubbings mine are to be found; for they never took the measure of his worship's shoulders without doing the same for my whole body; but I have no right to wonder at that, for, as my master himself says, the members must share the pain of the head."

"You are a sly dog, Sancho," said Don Quixote; "i' faith, you have no want of memory when you choose to remember."

"If I were to try to forget the thwacks they gave me," said Sancho, "my weals would not let me, for they are still fresh on my ribs."

"Hush, Sancho," said Don Quixote, "and don't interrupt the bachelor, whom I entreat to go on and tell me all that is said about me in this same history."

"And about me," said Sancho, "for they say, too, that I am one of the principal presonages in it."

"Personages, not presonages, friend Sancho," said Samson.

"What! Another word-catcher!" said Sancho; "if that's to be the way we shall not make an end in a lifetime."

"May God shorten mine, Sancho," returned the bachelor, "if you are not the second person in the history, and there are even some who would rather hear you talk than the cleverest in the whole book; though there are some, too, who say you showed yourself over-credulous in believing there was any possibility in the government of that island offered you by Señor Don Quixote here."

"There is still sunshine on the wall," said Don Quixote; "and when Sancho is somewhat more advanced in life, with the experience that years bring, he will be fitter and better qualified for being a governor than he is at present."

"By God, master," said Sancho, "the island that I can not govern with the years I have, I'll not be able to govern with the years of Methuselam; the difficulty is that the said island keeps its distance somewhere, I know not where; and not that there is any want of head in me to govern it."

"Leave it to God, Sancho," said Don Quixote, "for all will be well, and perhaps better than you think; no leaf on the tree stirs but by God's will."

"That is true," said Samson; "and if it be God's will, there will not be any want of a thousand islands, much less one, for Sancho to govern."

"I have seen governors in these parts," said Sancho, "that are not to be compared to my shoe-sole; and for all that they are called 'your lord-ship' and served on silver."

"Those are not governors of islands," observed Samson, "but of other governments of an easier kind: those that govern islands must at least know grammar."

"I could manage the gram well enough," said Sancho; "but for the mar I have neither leaning nor liking, for I don't know what it is; but leav-ing this matter of the government in God's hands, to send me wherever it may be most to his service, I may tell you, señor bachelor Sam-son Carrasco, it has pleased me beyond measure that the author of this history should have spok-en of me in such a way that what is said of me gives no offence; for, on the faith of a true squire, if he had said anything about me that was at all unbecoming an old Christian, such as I am, the deaf would have heard of it."

"That would be working miracles," said Sam-son.

"Miracles or no miracles," said Sancho, "let every one mind how he speaks or writes about people, and not set down at random the first thing that comes into his head."

"One of the faults they find with this history," said the bachelor, "is that its author inserted in it a novel called *The Ill-advised Curiosity;* not that it is bad or ill-told, but that it is out of place and has nothing to do with the history of his worship Señor Don Quixote."

"I will bet the son of a dog has mixed the cab-bages and the baskets," said Sancho.

"Then, I say," said Don Quixote, "the author of my history was no sage, but some ignorant chatterer, who, in a haphazard and heedless way, set about writing it, let it turn out as it might, just as Orbaneja, the painter of Úbeda, used to do, who, when they asked him what he was painting, answered 'What it may turn out.' Sometimes he would paint a cock in such a fashion, and so unlike, that he had to write alongside of it in Gothic letters, 'This is a cock'; and so it will be with my history, which will re-quire a commentary to make it intelligible."

"No fear of that," returned Samson, "for it is so plain that there is nothing in it to puzzle over; the children turn its leaves, the young people read it, the grown men understand it, the old folk praise; in a word, it is so thumbed, and read, and got by heart by people of all sorts, that the instant they see any lean hack, they say, 'There goes Rocinante.' And those that are most given to reading it are the pages, for there is not a lord's ante-chamber where there is not a *Don Quixote* to be found; one takes it up if another lays it down; this one pounces upon it, and that begs for it. In short, the said history is the most delightful and least injurious entertainment that has been hitherto seen, for there is not to be found in the whole of it even the semblance of an immodest word, or a thought that is other than Catholic."

"To write in any other way," said Don Quix-ote, "would not be to write truth, but falsehood, and historians who have recourse to falsehood, ought to be burned, like those who coin false money; and I know not what could have led the author to have recourse to novels and irrelevant stories, when he had so much to write about in mine; no doubt he must have gone by the prov-erb 'with straw or with hay, etc.,' for by merely setting forth my thoughts, my sighs, my tears, my lofty purposes, my enterprises, he might have made a volume as large, or larger than all the works of El Tostado would make up. In fact, the conclusion I arrive at, señor bachelor, is, that to write histories, or books of any kind, there is need of great judgment and a ripe understand-ing. To give expression to humor, and write in a strain of graceful pleasantry, is the gift of great geniuses. The cleverest character in comedy is the clown, for he who would make people take him for a fool, must not be one. History is in a measure a sacred thing, for it should be true, and where the truth is, there God is, so far as truth is concerned; but notwithstanding this, there are some who write and fling books broadcast on the world as if they were fritters."

"There is no book so bad but it has something good in it," said the bachelor.

"No doubt of that," replied Don Quixote; "but it often happens that those who have ac-quired and attained a well-desired reputation by their writings, lose it entirely, or damage it in some degree, when they give them to the press."

"The reason of that," said Samson, "is, that as printed works are examined leisurely, their faults are easily seen; and the greater the fame of the writer, the more closely are they scruti-nized. Men famous for their genius, great poets, illustrious historians, are always, or most com-monly, envied by those who take a particular de-light and pleasure in criticising the writings of others, without having produced any of their own."

"That is no wonder," said Don Quixote; "for there are many divines who are no good for the pulpit, but excellent in detecting the defects or excesses of those who preach."

"All that is true, Señor Don Quixote," said Carrasco; "but I wish such fault-finders were more lenient and less exacting, and did not pay so much attention to the spots on the bright sun of the work they grumble at; for if *aliquando bonus dormitat Homerus*, they should remember how long he remained awake to shed the light of his work with as little shade as possible; and perhaps it may be that what they find fault with may be moles, that sometimes heighten the beauty of the face that bears them; and so I say very great is the risk to which he who prints a book exposes himself, for of all impossibilities the greatest is to write one that will satisfy and please all readers."

"That which treats of me must have pleased few," said Don Quixote.

"Quite the contrary," said the bachelor; "for, as *stultorum infinitus est numerus,* innumerable are those who have relished the said history; but some have brought a charge against the author's memory, inasmuch as he forgot to say who the thief was who stole Sancho's Dapple; for it is not stated there, but only to be inferred from what is set down, that he was stolen, and a little farther on we see Sancho mounted on the same ass, without any re-appearance of it. They say, too, that he forgot to state what Sancho did with those hundred crowns that he found in the valise in the Sierra Morena, as he never alludes to them again, and there are many who would be glad to know what he did with them, or what he spent them on, for it is one of the serious omissions of the work."

"Señor Samson, I am not in a humor now for going into accounts or explanations," said Sancho; "for there's a sinking of the stomach come over me, and unless I doctor it with a couple of sups of the old stuff it will put me on the thorn of Santa Lucia. I have it at home, and my old woman is waiting for me; after dinner I'll come back, and will answer you and all the world every question you may choose to ask, as well about the loss of the ass as about the spending of the hundred crowns"; and without another word or waiting for a reply he made off home.

Don Quixote begged and entreated the bachelor to stay and do penance with him. The bachelor accepted the invitation and remained, a couple of young pigeons were added to the ordinary fare, at dinner they talked chivalry, Carrasco fell in with his host's humor, the banquet came to an end, they took their afternoon sleep, Sancho returned, and the previous conversation was resumed.

Chapter 4

In which Sancho Panza gives a satisfactory reply to the doubts and questions of the bachelor Samson Carrasco, together with other matters worth knowing and mentioning

SANCHO came back to Don Quixote's house, and returning to the late subject of conversation, he said, "As to what Señor Samson said, that he would like to know by whom, or how, or when my ass was stolen, I say in reply that the same night we went into the Sierra Morena, flying from the Holy Brotherhood after that unlucky adventure of the galley slaves, and the other of the corpse that was going to Segovia, my master and I ensconced ourselves in a thicket, and there, my master leaning on his lance, and I seated on my Dapple, battered and weary with the late frays we fell asleep as if it had been on four feather beds; and I in particular slept so sound, that, whoever he was, he was able to come and prop me up on four stakes, which he put under the four corners of the pack-saddle in such a way that he left me mounted on it, and took away Dapple from under me without my feeling it."

"That is an easy matter," said Don Quixote, "and it is no new occurrence, for the very same thing happened to Sacripante, when, at the siege of Albracca, the famous thief called Brunello, by the same contrivance, took his horse from between his legs."

"Day came," continued Sancho, "and the moment I stretched myself the stakes gave way and I fell to the ground with a mighty come down; I looked about for the ass, but could not see him; the tears rushed to my eyes and I raised such a lamentation that, if the author of our history has not put it in, he may depend upon it he has left out a good thing. Some days after, I know not how many, travelling with her ladyship the Princess Micomicona, I saw my ass, and mounted upon him, in the dress of a gypsy, was that Gines de Pasamonte, the great rogue and rascal that my master and I freed from the chain."

"That is not where the mistake is," replied Samson; "it is, that before the ass has turned up, the author speaks of Sancho as being mounted on it."

"I don't know what to say to that," said Sancho, "unless that the historian made a mistake, or perhaps it might be a blunder of the printer's."

"No doubt that's it," said Samson; "but what became of the hundred crowns?"

"They vanished," said Sancho; "I spent them for my own good, and my wife's, and my children's, and it is they have made my wife bear so patiently all my wanderings on highways and byways, in the service of my master, Don Quixote; for if after all this time I had come back to the house without a rap and without the ass, it would have been a poor look-out for me; and if any one wants to know anything more about me, here I am, ready to answer the king himself in person; and it is no affair of any one's, whether I took or did not take, whether I spent or did not spend; for if the whacks that were given me in these journeys were to be paid for in money, even if they were valued at no more than four maravedís apiece, another hundred crowns would not pay me for half of them. Let each look to himself and not try to make out white black, and black white; for each of us is as God made him, ay, and often worse."

"I will take care," said Carrasco, "to impress upon the author of the history that, if he prints it again, he must not forget what worthy Sancho has said, for it will raise it a good span higher than it is."

"Is there anything else to correct in the history, señor bachelor?" asked Don Quixote.

"No doubt there is," replied he; "but not anything that will be of the same importance as those I have mentioned."

"Does the author promise a second part at all?" said Don Quixote.

"He does promise one," replied Samson; "but he says he has not found it, nor does he know who has got it; and we can not say whether it will appear or not; and so, on that head, as some say that no second part has ever been good, and others that enough has been already written about Don Quixote, it is thought there will be no second part; though some, who are jovial rather than saturnine, say, 'Let us have more Quixotades, let Don Quixote charge and Sancho chatter, and no matter what it may turn out, we shall be satisfied with that.'"

"And what does the author mean to do?" said Don Quixote.

"What?" replied Samson; "why, as soon as he has found the history which he is now searching for with extraordinary diligence, he will at once give it to the press, moved more by the profit that may accrue to him from doing so than by any thought of praise."

Whereat Sancho observed, "The author looks for money and profit, does he? It will be a wonder if he succeeds, for it will be only hurry, hurry, with him, like the tailor on Easter Eve; and works done in a hurry are never finished as perfectly as they ought to be. Let Master Moor, or whatever he is, pay attention to what he is doing, and I and my master will give him as much grouting ready to his hand, in the way of adventures and accidents of all sorts, as would make up not only one second part, but a hundred. The good man fancies, no doubt, that we are fast asleep in the straw here, but let him hold up our feet to be shod and he will see which foot it is we go lame on. All I say is, that if my master would take my advice, we would be now afield, redressing outrages and righting wrongs, as is the use and custom of good knights-errant."

Sancho had hardly uttered these words when the neighing of Rocinante fell upon their ears, which neighing Don Quixote accepted as a happy omen, and he resolved to make another sally in three or four days from that time. Announcing his intention to the bachelor, he asked his advice as to the quarter in which he ought to commence his expedition, and the bachelor replied that in his opinion he ought to go to the kingdom of Aragon, and the city of Saragossa, where there were to be certain solemn joustings at the festival of St. George, at which he might win renown above all the knights of Aragon, which would be winning it above all the knights of the world. He commended his very praiseworthy and gallant resolution, but admonished him to proceed with greater caution in encountering dangers, because his life did not belong to him, but to all those who had need of him to protect and aid them in their misfortunes.

"There's where it is, what I abominate, Señor Samson," said Sancho here; "my master will attack a hundred armed men as a greedy boy would half a dozen melons. Body of the world, señor bachelor! there is a time to attack and a time to retreat, and it is not to be always 'Santiago, and close Spain!' Moreover, I have heard it said (and I think by my master himself, if I remember rightly) that the mean of valor lies between the extremes of cowardice and rashness; and if that be so, I don't want him to fly without having good reason, or to attack when the odds make it better not. But, above all things, I warn my master that if he is to take me with him it must be on the condition that he is to do all the fighting, and that I am not to be called upon to do anything except what concerns keeping him clean and comfortable; in this I will dance attendance on him readily; but to expect me to draw sword, even against rascally churls of the hatchet and hood, is idle. I don't set up to be a fighting man, Señor Samson, but only the best and most loyal squire that ever served knight-errant; and if my master Don Quixote, in consideration of my many faithful services, is pleased to give me some island of the many his worship says one may stumble on in these parts, I will take it as a great favor; and if he does not give it to me, I was born like every one else, and a man must not live in dependence on any one except God; and what is more, my bread will taste as well, and perhaps even better, without a government than if I were a governor; and how do I know but that in these governments the devil may have prepared some trip for me, to make me lose my footing and fall and knock my grinders out? Sancho I was born and Sancho I mean to die. But for all that, if Heaven were to make me a fair offer of an island or something else of the kind, without much trouble and without much risk, I am not such a fool as to refuse it; for they say, too, 'when they offer thee a heifer, run with a halter'; and 'when good luck comes to thee, take it in.' "

"Brother Sancho," said Carrasco, "you have spoken like a professor; but, for all that, put your trust in God and in Señor Don Quixote, for he will give you a kingdom, not to say an island."

"It is all the same, be it more or be it less," replied Sancho; "though I can tell Señor Carrasco that my master would not throw the kingdom he might give me into a sack all in holes; for I have felt my own pulse and I find myself sound enough to rule kingdoms and govern islands; and I have before now told my master as much."

"Take care, Sancho," said Samson; "honors change manners, and perhaps when you find yourself a governor you won't know the mother that bore you."

"That may hold good of those that are born in the ditches," said Sancho, "not of those who have the fat of an old Christian four fingers deep on their souls, as I have. Nay, only look at my disposition, is that likely to show ingratitude to any one?"

"God grant it," said Don Quixote; "we shall see when the government comes; and I seem to see it already."

He then begged the bachelor, if he were a poet, to do him the favor of composing some verses for him conveying the farewell he meant to take of his lady Dulcinea del Toboso, and to see that a letter of her name was placed at the beginning of each line, so that, at the end of the verses, "Dulcinea del Toboso" might be read by putting together the first letters. The bachelor replied that although he was not one of the famous poets of Spain, who were, they said, only

three and a half, he would not fail to compose the required verses; though he saw a great difficulty in the task, as the letters which made up the name were seventeen; so, if he made four ballad stanzas of four lines each, there would be a letter over, and if he made them of five, what they called *decimas* or *redondillas,* there were three letters short; nevertheless he would try to drop a letter as well as he could, so that the name "Dulcinea del Toboso" might be got into four ballad stanzas.

"It must be, by some means or other," said Don Quixote, "for unless the name stands there plain and manifest, no woman would believe the verses were made for her."

They agreed upon this, and that the departure should take place in three days from that time. Don Quixote charged the bachelor to keep it a secret, especially from the curate and Master Nicholas, and from his niece and the housekeeper, lest they should prevent the execution of his praiseworthy and valiant purpose. Carrasco promised all, and then took his leave, charging Don Quixote to inform him of his good or evil fortunes whenever he had an opportunity; and thus they bade each other farewell, and Sancho went away to make the necessary preparations for their expedition.

Chapter 5

Of the shrewd and droll conversation that passed between Sancho Panza and his wife Teresa Panza, and other matters worthy of being duly recorded

THE translator of this history, when he comes to write this fifth chapter, says that he considers it apocryphal, because in it Sancho Panza speaks in a style unlike that which might have been expected from his limited intelligence, and says things so subtle that he does not think it possible he could have conceived them; however, desirous of doing what his task imposed upon him, he was unwilling to leave it untranslated, and therefore he went on to say:

Sancho came home in such glee and spirits that his wife noticed his happiness a bowshot off, so much so that it made her ask him, "What have you got, Sancho friend, that you are so glad?"

To which he replied, "Wife, if it were God's will, I should be very glad not to be so well pleased as I show myself."

"I don't understand you, husband," said she, "and I don't know what you mean by saying you would be glad, if it were God's will, not to be well pleased; for, fool as I am, I don't know how one can find pleasure in not having it."

"Hark ye, Teresa," replied Sancho, "I am glad because I have made up my mind to go back to the service of my master Don Quixote, who means to go out a third time to seek for adventures; and I am going with him again, for my necessities will have it so, and also the hope that cheers me with the thought that I may find another hundred crowns like those we have spent; though it makes me sad to have to leave thee and the children; and if God would be pleased to let me have my daily bread, dry-shod and at home, without taking me out into the byways and cross-roads—and he could do it at small cost by merely willing it—it is clear my happiness would be more solid and lasting, for the happiness I have is mingled with sorrow at leaving thee; so that I was right in saying I would be glad, if it were God's will, not to be well pleased."

"Look here, Sancho," said Teresa; "ever since you joined on to a knight-errant you talk in such a roundabout way that there is no understanding you."

"It is enough that God understands me, wife," replied Sancho; "for he is the understander of all things; that will do; but mind, sister, you must look to Dapple carefully for the next three days, so that he may be fit to take arms; double his feed and see to the pack-saddle and other harness, for it is not to a wedding we are bound, but to go round the world, and play at give and take with giants and dragons and monsters, and hear hissings and roarings and bellowings and howlings; and even all this would be lavender, if we had not to reckon with Yanguesans and enchanted Moors."

"I know well enough, husband," said Teresa, "that squires-errant don't eat their bread for nothing, and so I will be always praying to our Lord to deliver you speedily from all that hard fortune."

"I can tell you, wife," said Sancho, "if I did not expect to see myself governor of an island before long, I would drop down dead on the spot."

"Nay, then, husband," said Teresa, "let the hen live, though it be with her pip; live, and let the devil take all the governments in the world; you came out of your mother's womb without a government, you have lived until now without a government, and when it is God's will you will go, or be carried, to your grave without a government. How many there are in the world who live without a government, and continue to live

all the same, and are reckoned in the number of the people. The best sauce in the world is hunger, and as the poor are never without that, they always eat with a relish. But mind, Sancho, if by good luck you should find yourself with some government, don't forget me and your children. Remember that Sanchico is now full fifteen, and it is right he should go to school, if his uncle the abbot has a mind to have him trained for the Church. Consider, too, that your daughter Mari Sancha will not die of grief if we marry her; for I have my suspicions that she is as eager to get a husband as you to get a government; and, after all, a daughter looks better ill-married than well kept."

"By my faith," replied Sancho, "if God brings me to get any sort of a government, I intend wife, to make such a high match for Mari Sancha that there will be no approaching her without calling her 'my lady.'"

"Nay, Sancho," returned Teresa, "marry her to her equal, that is the safest plan; for if you put her out of wooden clogs into high-heeled shoes, out of her gray flannel petticoat into hoops and silk gowns, out of the plain 'Marica' and 'thou,' into 'Doña So-and-so' and 'my lady,' the girl won't know where she is, and at every turn she will fall into a thousand blunders that will show the thread of her coarse homespun stuff."

"Tut, you fool," said Sancho; "it will be only to practise it for two or three years; and then dignity and decorum will fit her as easily as a glove; and if not, what matter? Let her be 'my lady,' and never mind what happens."

"Keep to your own station, Sancho," replied Teresa; "don't try to raise yourself higher, and bear in mind the proverb that says, 'wipe the nose of your neighbor's son, and take him into your house.' A fine thing it would be, indeed, to marry our Maria to some great count or grand gentleman, who, when the humor took him, would abuse her and call her clown-bred and clodhopper's daughter and spinning wench. I have not been bringing up my daughter for that all this time, I can tell you, husband. Do you bring home money, Sancho, and leave marrying her to my care; there is Lope Tocho, Juan Tocho's son, a stout, sturdy young fellow that we know, and I can see he does not look sour at the girl; and with him, one of our own sort, she will be well married, and we shall have her always under our eyes, and be all one family, parents and children, grandchildren and sons-in-law, and the peace and blessing of God will dwell among us; so don't you go marrying her in those courts and grand palaces where they won't know what to make of her, or she what to make of herself."

"Why, you idiot and wife for Barabbas," said Sancho, "what do you mean by trying, without why or wherefore, to keep me from marrying my daughter to one who will give me grandchildren that will be called 'your lordship?' Look ye, Teresa, I have always heard my elders say that he who does not know how to take advantage of luck when it comes to him, has no right to complain if it gives him the go-by; and now that it is knocking at our door, it will not do to shut it out; let us go with the favoring breeze that blows upon us." (It is this sort of talk, and what Sancho says lower down, that made the translator of the history say he considered this chapter apocryphal.) "Don't you see, you animal," continued Sancho, "that it will be well for me to drop into some profitable government that will lift us out of the mire, and marry Mari-Sancha to whom I like; and you yourself will find yourself called 'Doña Teresa Panza,' and sitting in church on a fine carpet and cushions and draperies, in spite and in defiance of all the born ladies of the town? No, stay as you are, growing neither greater nor less, like a tapestry figure—Let us say no more about it, for Sanchia shall be a countess, say what you will."

"Are you sure of all you say, husband?" replied Teresa. "Well, for all that, I am afraid this rank of countess for my daughter will be her ruin. You do as you like, make a duchess or a princess of her, but I can tell you it will not be with my will and consent. I was always a lover of equality, brother, and I can't bear to see people give themselves airs without any right. They called me Teresa at my baptism, a plain, simple name, without any additions or tags or fringes of Dons or Doñas; Cascajo was my father's name, and as I am your wife, I am called Teresa Panza, though by right I ought to be called Teresa Cascajo; but 'kings go where laws like,' and I am content with this name without having the 'Don' put on top of it to make it so heavy that I can not carry it; and I don't want to make people talk about me when they see me go dressed like a countess or governor's wife; for they will say at once, 'See what airs the slut gives herself! Only yesterday she was always spinning flax, and used to go to Mass with the tail of her petticoat over her head instead of a mantle, and there she goes today in a hooped gown with her brooches and airs, as if we didn't know her!' If God keeps me in my seven senses, or five, or whatever number I have, I am not going to bring myself to such a pass; go you, brother, and be a govern-

ment or an island man, and swagger as much as you like; for by the soul of my mother, neither my daughter nor I are going to stir a step from our village; a respectable woman should have a broken leg and keep at home; and to be busy at something is a virtuous damsel's holiday; be off to your adventures along with your Don Quixote, and leave us to our misadventures, for God will mend them for us according as we deserve it. I don't know, I'm sure, who fixed the 'Don' to him, what neither his father nor grandfather ever had."

"I declare thou hast a devil of some sort in thy body!" said Sancho. "God help thee, woman, what a lot of things thou hast strung together, one after the other, without head or tail! What have Cascajo, and the brooches and the proverbs and the airs, to do with what I say? Look here, fool and dolt (for so I may call you, when you don't understand my words, and run away from good fortune), if I had said that my daughter was to throw herself down from a tower, or go roaming the world, as the Infanta Doña Urraca wanted to do, you would be right in not giving way to my will; but if in an instant, in less than the twinkling of an eye, I put the 'Don' and 'my lady' on her back, and take her out of the stubble, and place her under the canopy, on a daïs, and on a couch, with more velvet cushions than all the Almohades of Morocco ever had in their family, why won't you consent and fall in with my wishes?"

"Do you know why, husband?" replied Teresa; "because of the proverb that says 'who covers thee, discovers thee.' At the poor man people only throw a hasty glance; on the rich man they fixed their eyes; and if the said rich man was once on a time poor, it is then there is the sneering and the tattle and spite of backbiters; and in the streets here they swarm as thick as bees."

"Look here, Teresa," said Sancho, "and listen to what I am now going to say to you; maybe you never heard it in all your life; and I do not give my own notions, for what I am about to say are the opinions of his reverence the preacher, who preached in this town last Lent, and who said, if I remember rightly, that all things present that our eyes behold, bring themselves before us, and remain and fix themselves on our memory much better and more forcibly than things past." (These observations which Sancho makes here are the other ones on account of which the translator says he regards this chapter as apocryphal, inasmuch as they are beyond Sancho's capacity.) "Whence it arises," he continued, "that when we see any person well-dressed and making a figure with rich garments and retinue of servants, it seems to lead and impel us perforce to respect him, though memory may at the same moment recall to us some lowly condition in which we have seen him, but which, whether it may have been poverty or low birth, being now a thing of the past, has no existence; while the only thing that has any existence is what we see before us; and if this person whom fortune has raised from his original lowly state (these were the very words the padre used) to his present height of prosperity, be well bred, generous, courteous to all, without seeking to vie with those whose nobility is of ancient date, depend upon it, Teresa, no one will remember what he was, and every one will respect what he is, except indeed the envious, from whom no fair fortune is safe."

"I do not understand you, husband," replied Teresa; "do as you like, and don't break my head with any more speechifying and rhetoric; and if you have revolved to do what you say"—

"Resolved, you should say, woman," said Sancho, "not revolved."

"Don't set yourself to wrangle with me, husband," said Teresa; "I speak as God pleases, and don't deal in out-of-the-way phrases; and I say if you are bent upon having a government, take your son Sancho with you, and teach him from this time on how to hold a government; for sons ought to inherit and learn the trades of their fathers."

"As soon as I have the government," said Sancho, "I will send for him by post, and I will send thee money, of which I shall have no lack, for there is never any want of people to lend it to governors when they have not got it; and do thou dress him so as to hide what he is and make him look what he is to be."

"You send the money," said Teresa, "and I'll dress him up for you as fine as you please."

"Then we are agreed that our daughter is to be a countess," said Sancho.

"The day that I see her a countess," replied Teresa, "it will be the same to me as if I was burying her; but once more I say do as you please, for we women are born to this burden of being obedient to our husbands, though they be blockheads"; and with this she began to weep in downright earnest, as if she already saw Sanchica dead and buried.

Sancho consoled her by saying that though he must make her a countess, he would put it off as long as possible. Here their conversation came to an end, and Sancho went back to see Don Quixote, and make arrangements for their departure.

Chapter 6

Of what took place between Don Quixote and his niece and housekeeper; one of the most important chapters in the whole history

WHILE Sancho Panza and his wife, Teresa Cascajo, held the above irrelevant conversation, Don Quixote's niece and housekeeper were not idle, for by a thousand signs they began to perceive that their uncle and master meant to give them the slip for the third time, and once more betake himself to his, for them, ill-errant chivalry. They strove by all the means in their power to divert him from such an unlucky scheme; but it was all preaching in the desert and hammering cold iron.

Nevertheless, among many other representations made to him, the housekeeper said to him, "In truth, master, if you do not keep still and stay quiet at home, and give over roaming mountains and valleys like a troubled spirit, looking for what they say are called adventures, but what I call misfortunes, I shall have to make complaint to God and the king with loud supplication to send some remedy."

To which Don Quixote replied, "What answer God will give to your complaints, housekeeper, I know not, nor what his Majesty will answer either; I only know that if I were king I should decline to answer the numberless silly petitions they present every day; for one of the greatest among the many troubles kings have is being obliged to listen to all and answer all, and therefore I should be sorry that any affairs of mine should worry him."

Whereupon the housekeeper said, "Tell us, señor, at his Majesty's court are there no knights?"

"There are," replied Don Quixote, "and plenty of them; and it is right there should be, to set off the dignity of the prince, and for the greater glory of the king's majesty."

"Then might not your worship," said she, "be one of those that, without stirring a step, serve their king and lord in his court?"

"Recollect, my friend," said Don Quixote, "not all knights can be courtiers, nor can all courtiers be knights-errant, nor need they be. There must be all sorts in the world; and though we may be all knights, there is a great difference between one and another; for the courtiers, without quitting their chambers, or the threshold of the court, range the world over by looking at a map, without its costing them a farthing, and without suffering heat or cold, hunger or thirst; but we, the true knights-errant, measure the whole earth with our own feet, exposed to the sun, to the cold, to the air, to the inclemencies of heaven, by day and night, on foot and on horseback; nor do we only know enemies in pictures, but in their own real shapes; and at all risks and on all occasions we attack them, without any regard to childish points or rules of single combat, whether one has or has not a shorter lance or sword, whether one carries relics or any secret contrivance about him, whether or not the sun is to be divided and portioned out,[1] and other niceties of the sort that are observed in set combats of man to man, that you know nothing about, but I do. And you must know besides, that the true knight-errant, though he may see ten giants, that not only touch the clouds with their heads but pierce them, and that go, each of them, on two tall towers by way of legs, and whose arms are like the masts of mighty ships, and each eye like a great mill-wheel, and glowing brighter than a glass furnace, must not on any account be dismayed by them. On the contrary, he must attack and fall upon them with a gallant bearing and a fearless heart, and, if possible, vanquish and destroy them, even though they have for armor the shells of a certain fish, that they say are harder than diamonds, and in place of swords wield trenchant blades of Damascus steel, or clubs studded with spikes also of steel, such as I have more than once seen. All this I say, housekeeper, that you may see the difference there is between the one sort of knight and the other; and it would be well if there were no prince who did not set a higher value on this second, or more properly speaking first, kind of knights-errant; for, as we read in their histories, there have been some among them who have been the salvation, not merely of one kingdom, but of many."

"Ah, señor," here exclaimed the niece, "remember that all this you are saying about knights-errant is fable and fiction; and their histories, if indeed they were not burned, would deserve, each of them, to have a *sanbenito*[2] put on it, or some mark by which it might be known as infamous and a corrupter of good manners."

"By the God that gives me life," said Don Quixote, "if thou wert not my full niece, being daughter of my own sister, I would inflict a chas-

tisement upon thee for the blasphemy thou hast uttered that all the world should ring with. What! can it be that a young hussy that hardly knows how to handle a dozen lace-bobbins dares to wag her tongue and criticise the histories of knights-errant! What would Señor Amadis say if he heard of such a thing? He, however, no doubt would forgive thee, for he was the most humble-minded and courteous knight of his time, and moreover a great protector of damsels; but some there are that might have heard thee, and it would not have been well for thee in that case; for they are not all courteous or mannerly; some are ill-conditioned scoundrels; nor is it every one that calls himself a gentleman, that is so in all respects; some are gold, others pinchbeck, and all look like gentlemen, but not all can stand the touchstone of truth. There are men of low rank who strain themselves to bursting to pass for gentlemen, and high gentlemen who, one would fancy, were dying to pass for men of low rank; the former raise themselves by their ambition or by their virtues, the latter debase themselves by their lack of spirit or by their vices; and one has need of experience and discernment to distinguish these two kinds of gentlemen, so much alike in name and so different in conduct."

"God bless me!" said the niece, "that you should know so much, uncle—enough, if need be, to get up into a pulpit and go preach in the streets—and yet that you should fall into a delusion so great and a folly so manifest as to try to make yourself out vigorous when you are old, strong when you are sickly, able to put straight what is crooked when you yourself are bent by age, and, above all, a caballero when you are not one; for though gentlefolk may be so, poor men are nothing of the kind!"

"There is a great deal of truth in what you say, niece," returned Don Quixote, "and I could tell you somewhat about birth that would astonish you; but not to mix up things humane and divine, I refrain. Look you, my dears, all the lineages in the world (attend to what I am saying) can be reduced to four sorts, which are these: those that had humble beginnings, and went on spreading and extending themselves until they attained surpassing greatness; those that had great beginnings and maintained them, and still maintain and uphold the greatness of their origin; those, again, that from a great beginning have ended in a point like a pyramid, having reduced and lessened their original greatness till it has come to naught, like the point of a pyramid, which, relatively to its base or foundation, is nothing; and then there are those—and it is

---

[1] In a formal combat the men were so placed that neither should be at a disadvantage by having the sun in his eyes.

[2] The garment worn by penitents, who have been tried by the Inquisition and have confessed.

they that are the most numerous—that have had neither an illustrious beginning nor a remarkable mid-course, and so will have an end without a name, like an ordinary plebeian line. Of the first, those that had an humble origin and rose to the greatness they still preserve, the Ottoman house may serve as an example, which from an humble and lowly shepherd, its founder, has reached the height at which we now see it. For examples of the second sort of lineage, that began with greatness and maintains it still without adding to it, there are the many princes who have inherited the dignity, and maintain themselves in their inheritance, without increasing or diminishing it, keeping peacefully within the limits of their states. Of those that began great and ended in a point, there are thousands of examples, for all the Pharaohs and Ptolemys of Egypt, the Cæsars of Rome, and the whole herd (if I may apply such a word to them) of countless princes, monarchs, lords, Medes, Assyrians, Persians, Greeks, and barbarians, all these lineages and lordships have ended in a point and come to nothing, they themselves as well as their founders, for it would be impossible now to find one of their descendants, and, even should we find one, it would be in some lowly and humble condition. Of plebeian lineages I have nothing to say, save that they merely serve to swell the number of those that live, without any eminence to entitle them to any fame or praise beyond this. From all I have said I would have you gather, my poor innocents, that great is the confusion among lineages, and that only those are seen to be great and illustrious that show themselves so by the virtue, wealth, and generosity of their possessors. I have said virtue, wealth, and generosity, because a great man who is vicious will be a great example of vice, and a rich man who is not generous will be merely a miserly beggar; for the possessor of wealth is not made happy by possessing it, but by spending it, and not by spending as he pleases, but by knowing how to spend it well. The poor gentleman has no way of showing that he is a gentleman but by virtue, by being affable, well-bred, courteous, gentle-mannered and kindly, not haughty, arrogant, or censorious, but above all by being charitable; for by two maravedís given with a cheerful heart to the poor, he will show himself as generous as he who distributes alms with bell-ringing, and no one that perceives him to be endowed with the virtues I have named, even though he know him not, will fail to recognize and set him down as one of good blood; and it would be strange were it not so; praise has ever

been the reward of virtue, and those who are virtuous can not fail to receive commendation. There are two roads, my daughters, by which men may reach wealth and honors; one is that of letters, the other that of arms. I have more of arms than of letters in my composition, and, judging by my inclination to arms, was born under the influence of the planet Mars. I am, therefore, in a measure constrained to follow that road, and by it I must travel in spite of all the world, and it will be labor in vain for you to urge me to resist what Heaven wills, fate ordains, reason requires, and, above all, my own inclination favors; for knowing as I do the countless toils that are the accompaniments of knight-errantry, I know, too, the infinite blessings that are attained by it; I know that the path of virtue is very narrow, and the road of vice broad and spacious; I know their ends and goals are different, for the broad and easy road of vice ends in death, and the narrow and toilsome one of virtue in life, and not transitory life, but in that which has no end; I know, as our great Castilian poet says, that—

It is by rugged paths like these they go
That scale the heights of immortality,
Unreached by those that falter here below."

"Woe is me!" exclaimed the niece, "my lord is a poet, too! He knows everything, and he can do everything; I will bet, if he chose to turn mason, he could make a house as easily as a cage."

"I can tell you, niece," replied Don Quixote, "if these chivalrous thoughts did not engage all my faculties, there would be nothing that I could not do, nor any sort of knick-knack that would not come from my hands, particularly cages and tooth-picks."

At this moment there came a knocking at the door, and when they asked who was there, Sancho Panza made answer that it was he. The instant the housekeeper knew who it was, she ran to hide herself so as not to see him; in such abhorrence did she hold him. The niece let him in, and his master Don Quixote came forward to receive him with open arms, and the pair shut themselves up in his room, where they had another conversation not inferior to the previous one.

Chapter 7

Of what passed between Don Quixote and his squire, together with other very notable incidents

THE instant the housekeeper saw Sancho Panza shut himself in with her master, she guessed what they were about; and suspecting that the result of the consultation would be a resolve to undertake a third sally, she seized her mantle, and, in deep anxiety and distress, ran to find the bachelor Samson Carrasco, as she thought that, being a well-spoken man, and a new friend of her master's, he might be able to persuade him to give up any such crazy notion. She found him pacing the patio of his house, and, the moment she saw him, she fell at his feet perspiring and flurried.

Carrasco, seeing how distressed and overcome she was, said to her, "What is this, mistress housekeeper? What has happened you? One would think you heart-broken."

"Nothing, Señor Samson," said she, "only that my master is breaking out, plainly breaking out."

"Whereabouts is he breaking out, señora?" asked Samson; "has any part of his body burst?"

"He is only breaking out at the door of his madness," she replied; "I mean, dear señor bachelor, that he is going to break out again (and this will be the third time) to hunt all over the world for what he calls ventures, though I can't make out why he gives them that name. The first time he was brought back to us slung across the back of an ass, and belabored all over; and the second time he came in an ox-cart, shut up in a cage, in which he persuaded himself he was enchanted, and the poor creature was in such a state that the mother that bore him would not have known him; lean, yellow, with eyes sunk deep in the cells of his skull; so that to bring him round again, ever so little, cost me more than six hundred eggs, as God knows, and all the world, and my hens too, that won't let me tell a lie."

"That I can well believe," replied the bachelor, "for they are so good and so fat, and so well-bred, that they would not say one thing for another, though they were to burst for it. In short then, mistress housekeeper, that is all, and there is nothing the matter, except what it is feared Don Quixote may do?"

"No, señor," said she.

"Well then," returned the bachelor, "don't be uneasy, but go home in peace; get me ready something hot for breakfast, and while you are on the way say the prayer of Santa Apollonia, that is if you know it; for I will come presently and you will see miracles."

"Woe is me," cried the housekeeper, "is it the prayer of Santa Apollonia you would have me say? That would do if it was the toothache my master had; but it is in the brains, what he has got."

"I know what I am saying, mistress housekeeper; go, and don't set yourself to argue with me, for you know I am a bachelor of Salamanca, and one can't be more of a bachelor than that," replied Carrasco; and with this the housekeeper retired, and the bachelor went at once to look for the curate, and arrange with him what will be told in its proper place.

While Don Quixote and Sancho were shut up together, they had a discussion which the history records with great precision and scrupulous exactness. Sancho said to his master, "Señor, I have educed my wife to let me go with your worship wherever you choose to take me."

"Induced, you should say, Sancho," said Don Quixote; "not educed."

"Once or twice, as well as I remember," replied Sancho, "I have begged of your worship not to mend my words, if so be as you understand what I mean by them; and if you don't understand them to say, 'Sancho,' or 'devil, I don't understand thee'; and if I don't make my meaning plain, then you may correct me, for I am so focile"—

"I don't understand thee, Sancho," said Don Quixote at once; "for I know not what 'I am so focile' means."

"'So focile' means I am so much that way," replied Sancho.

"I understand thee still less now," said Don Quixote.

"Well, if you can't understand me," said Sancho, "I don't know how to put it; I know no more, God help me."

"Oh, now I have hit it," said Don Quixote; "thou wouldst say thou art so docile, tractable, and gentle that thou wilt take what I say to thee, and submit to what I teach thee."

"I would bet," said Sancho, "that from the very first you understood me, and knew what I meant, but you wanted to put me out that you might hear me make another couple of dozen blunders."

"May be so," replied Don Quixote; "but to come to the point, what does Teresa say?"

"Teresa says," replied Sancho, "that I should make sure with your worship, and 'let papers speak and beards be still,' for 'he who binds does not wrangle,' since one 'take' is better than two 'I'll give thee's'; and I say a woman's advice is no great things, and he who won't take it is a fool."

"And so say I," said Don Quixote; "continue, Sancho my friend; go on; you talk pearls to-day."

"The fact is," continued Sancho, "that, as your worship knows better than I do, we are all of us liable to death, and to-day we are, and to-morrow we are not, and the lamb goes as soon as the sheep, and nobody can promise himself more hours of life in this world than God may be pleased to give him; for death is deaf, and when it comes to knock at our life's door, it is always urgent, and neither prayers, nor struggles, nor sceptres, nor mitres, can keep it back, as common talk and report say, and as they tell us from the pulpits every day."

"All that is very true," said Don Quixote; "but I can not make out what thou art driving at."

"What I am driving at," said Sancho, "is that your worship settle some fixed wages for me, to be paid monthly while I am in your service, and that the same be paid me out of your estate; for I don't care to stand on rewards which either come late, or ill, or never at all; God help me with my own. In short, I would like to know what I am to get, be it much or little; for the hen will lay on one egg, and many littles make a much, and so long as one gains something there is nothing lost. To be sure, if it should happen (what I neither believe nor expect) that your worship were to give me that island you have promised me, I am not so ungrateful nor so grasping but that I would be willing to have the revenue of such island valued and stopped out of my wages in due promotion."

"Sancho, my friend," replied Don Quixote, "sometimes proportion may be as good as promotion."

"I see," said Sancho; "I'll bet I ought to have said proportion, and not promotion; but it is no matter, as your worship has understood me."

"And so well understood," returned Don Quixote, "that I have seen into the depths of thy thoughts, and know the mark thou art shooting at with the countless shafts of thy proverbs. Look here, Sancho, I would readily fix thy wages if I had ever found any instance in the histories of the knights-errant to show or indicate, by the slightest hint, what their squires used to get monthly or yearly; but I have read all or the best part of their histories, and I can not remember reading of any knight-errant having assigned fixed wages to his squire; I only know that they all served on reward, and that when they least expected it, if good luck attended their masters, they found themselves recompensed with an island or something equivalent to it, or at the least they were left with a title and lordship. If with these hopes and additional inducements you, Sancho, please to return to my service, well and good; but to suppose that I am going to disturb or unhinge the ancient usage of knight-errantry, is all nonsense. And so, my Sancho, get you back to your house and explain my intentions to your Teresa, and if she likes and you like to be on reward with me, *bene quidem;* if not, we remain friends; for if the pigeon-house does not lack food, it will not lack pigeons; and bear in mind, my son, that a good hope is better than a bad holding, and a good grievance better than a bad compensation. I speak in this way, Sancho, to show you that I can shower down proverbs just as well as yourself; and in short I mean to say, and I do say, that if you don't like to come on reward with me, and run the same chance that I run, God be with you and make a saint of you; for I shall find plenty of squires more obedient and painstaking, and not so thick-headed or talkative as you are."

When Sancho heard his master's firm, resolute language, a cloud came over the sky with him and the wings of his heart dropped, for he had made sure that his master would not go without him for all the wealth of the world; and as he stood there dumbfounded and moody, Samson Carrasco came in with the housekeeper and niece, who were anxious to hear by what arguments he was about to dissuade their master from going to seek adventures. The arch wag Samson came forward, and embracing him as he had done before, said with a loud voice, "O flower of knight-errantry! O shining light of arms! O honor and mirror of the Spanish nation! may God Almighty in his infinite power grant that any person or persons, who would impede or hinder thy third sally, may find no way out of the labyrinth of their schemes, nor ever accomplish what they most desire!" And then, turning to the housekeeper, he said, "Mistress Housekeeper may just as well give over saying the prayer of Santa Apollonia, for I know it is the positive determination of the spheres that Señor Don Quixote shall proceed to put into execution his new and lofty designs; and I should lay a heavy burden on my conscience did I not urge and persuade this knight not to keep the might of his strong arm and the virtue of his valiant spirit any longer curbed and checked, for by his inactivity he is defrauding the world of the redress of wrongs, of the protection of orphans, of the honor of virgins, of the aid of widows, and of the support of wives, and other matters of this kind appertaining, belonging, proper and peculiar to the order of knight-errantry. On, then, my Lord Don Quixote, beautiful and brave, let your worship and highness set out to-day rather than to-morrow; and if anything be needed for the execution of your purpose, here am I ready in person and purse to supply the want; and were it requisite to attend your magnificence as squire, I should esteem it the rarest good fortune."

At this, Don Quixote, turning to Sancho, said "Did I not tell thee, Sancho, there would be squires enough and to spare for me? See now who offers to become one; no less than the illustrious bachelor Samson Carrasco, the perpetual joy and delight of the courts of the Salamancan schools, sound in body, discreet, patient under heat or cold, hunger or thirst, with all the qualifications requisite to make a knight-errant's squire! But Heaven forbid that, to gratify my own inclination, I should shake or shatter this pillar of letters and vessel of the sciences, and cut down this towering palm of the fair and liberal arts. Let this new Samson remain in his own country, and, bringing honor to it, bring honor at the same time on the gray heads of his venerable parents; for I will be content with any squire that comes to hand, as Sancho does not deign to accompany me."

"I do deign," said Sancho, deeply moved and with tears in his eyes; "it shall not be said of me, master mine," he continued, " 'the bread eaten and the company dispersed.' Nay, I come of no ungrateful stock, for all the world knows, but particularly my own town, who the Panzas from whom I am descended were; and, what is more, I know and have learned, by many good words and deeds, your worship's desire to show me favor; and if I have been bargaining more or less about my wages, it was only to please my wife, who, when she sets herself to press a point, no hammer drives the hoops of a cask as she drives one to do what she wants; but, after all, a man must be a man, and a woman a woman; and as I am a man anyhow, which I can't deny, I will be one in my own house too, let who will take it amiss; and so there's nothing more to do but for your worship to make your will with its codicil in such a way that it can't be provoked, and let us set out at once, to save Señor Samson's soul from suffering, as he says his conscience obliges him to persuade your worship to sally out upon the world a third time; so I offer again to serve your worship faithfully and loyally, as well and better than all the squires that served knights-errant in times past or present."

The bachelor was filled with amazement when he heard Sancho's phraseology and style of talk, for though he had read the first part of his master's history he never thought that he could be so droll as he was there described; but now, hearing him talk of a will and codicil that could not be provoked, instead of will and codicil that could not be revoked, he believed all he had read of him, and set him down as one of the greatest simpletons of modern times; and he said to himself that two such lunatics as master and man the world had never seen. In fine, Don Quixote and Sancho embraced one another and made friends, and by the advice and with the approval of the great Carrasco, who was now their oracle, it was arranged that their departure should take place three days thence, by which time they could have all that was requisite for the journey ready, and procure a closed helmet, which Don Quixote said he must by all means take. Samson offered him one, as he knew a friend of his who had it would not refuse it to him, though it was more dingy with rust and mildew than bright and clean like burnished steel.

The curses which both housekeeper and niece poured out on the bachelor were past counting; they tore their hair, they clawed their faces, and in the style of the hired mourners that were once in fashion, they raised a lamentation over the departure of their master and uncle, as if it had been his death. Samson's intention in persuading him to sally forth once more was to do what the history relates farther on; all by the advice of the curate and barber, with whom he had previously discussed the subject. Finally, then, during those three days, Don Quixote and Sancho provided themselves with what they considered necessary, and Sancho having pacified his wife, and Don Quixote his niece and housekeeper, at nightfall, unseen by any one except the bachelor, who thought fit to accompany them half a league out of the village, they set out for El Toboso, Don Quixote on his good Rocinante and Sancho on his old Dapple, his *alforjas* furnished with certain matters in the way of victuals, and his purse, with money that Don Quixote gave him to meet emergencies. Samson embraced him, and entreated him to let him hear of his good or evil fortunes, so that he might rejoice over the former or condole with him over the latter, as the laws of friendship required. Don Quixote promised him he would do so, and Samson returned to the village, and the other two took the road for the great city of El Toboso.

Chapter 8

Wherein is related what befell Don Quixote on his way to see his lady Dulcinea del Toboso

"Blessed be Allah the all-powerful!" says Hamet Benengeli on beginning this eighth chapter; "blessed be Allah!" he repeats three times; and he says he utters these thanksgivings at seeing that he has now got Don Quixote and Sancho fairly afield, and that the readers of his delightful history may reckon that the achievements and humors of Don Quixote and his squire are now about to begin; and he urges them to forget the former chivalries of the ingenious gentleman and to fix their eyes on those that are to come, which now begin on the road to El Toboso, as the others began on the plains of Montiel; nor is it much that he asks in consideration of all he promises, and so he goes on to say:

Don Quixote and Sancho were left alone, and the moment Samson took his departure, Rocinante began to neigh, and Dapple to sigh, which, by both knight and squire, was accepted as a good sign and a very happy omen; though, if the truth is to be told, the sighs and brays of Dapple were louder than the neighings of the hack, from which Sancho inferred that his good fortune was to exceed and overtop that of his master, building, perhaps, upon some judicial astrology that he may have known, though the history says nothing about it; all that can be said is, that when he stumbled or fell, he was heard to say he wished he had not come out, for by stumbling or falling there was nothing to be got but a damaged shoe or a broken rib; and, fool as he was, he was not much astray in this.

Said Don Quixote, "Sancho, my friend, night is drawing on upon us as we go, and more darkly than will allow us to reach El Toboso by daylight; for there I am resolved to go before I engage in another adventure, and there I shall obtain the blessing and generous permission of the peerless Dulcinea, with which permission I expect and feel assured that I shall conclude and bring to a happy termination every perilous adventure; for nothing in life makes knights-errant more valorous than finding themselves favored by their ladies."

"So I believe," replied Sancho; "but I think it will be difficult for your worship to speak with her or see her, at any rate where you will be able to receive her blessing; unless, indeed, she throws it over the wall of the yard where I saw her the time before, when I took her the letter that told of the follies and mad things your worship was doing in the Sierra Morena."

"Didst thou take that for a yard wall, Sancho?" said Don Quixote, "where or at which thou sawest that never sufficiently extolled grace and beauty? It must have been the gallery, corridor, or portico of some rich and royal palace."

"It might have been all that," returned Sancho, "but to me it looked like a wall, unless I am short of memory."

"At all events, let us go there, Sancho," said Don Quixote; "for, so that I see her, it is the same to me whether it be over a wall, or at a window, or through the chink of a door, or the grate of a garden; for any beam of the sun of her beauty that reaches my eyes will give light to my reason and strength to my heart, so that I shall be unmatched and unequalled in wisdom and valor."

"Well, to tell the truth, señor," said Sancho, "when I saw that sun of the lady Dulcinea del Toboso, it was not bright enough to throw out any beams at all; it must have been, that as her grace was sifting that wheat I told you of, the thick dust she raised came before her face like a cloud and dimmed it."

"What! dost thou still persist, Sancho," said Don Quixote, "in saying, thinking, believing, and maintaining that my lady Dulcinea was sifting wheat, that being an occupation and task entirely at variance with what is and should be the employment of persons of distinction, who are constituted and reserved for other avocations and pursuits that show their rank a bow-shot off? Thou hast forgotten, O Sancho, those lines of our poet wherein he paints for us how, in their crystal abodes, those four nymphs employed themselves who rose from their loved Tagus and seated themselves in a verdant meadow to embroider those tissues which the ingenious poet there describes to us, how they were worked and woven with gold and silk and pearls; and something of this sort must have been the employment of my lady when thou sawest her, only that the spite which some wicked enchanter seems to have against everything of mine changes all those things that give me pleasure, and turns them into shapes unlike their own; and so I fear that in that history of my achievements which they say is now in print, if haply its author was some sage who is an enemy of mine, he will have put one thing for another, mingling a thousand lies with one truth, and amusing himself by relating transactions which have nothing to do with the sequence of a true history. O envy, root of all countless evils, and canker-worm of the virtues! All the vices, Sancho, bring some kind of pleasure with them; but envy brings nothing but irritation, bitterness, and rage."

"So I say too," replied Sancho; "and I suspect in that legend or history of us that the bachelor Samson Carrasco told us he saw, my honor goes dragged in the dirt, knocked about, up and down, sweeping the streets, as they say. And yet, on the faith of an honest man, I never spoke ill of any enchanter, and I am not so well off that I am to be envied; to be sure, I am rather sly, and I have a certain spice of the rogue in me; but all is covered by the great cloak of my simplicity, always natural and never acted; and if I had no other merit save that I believe, as I always do, firmly and truly in God, and all the holy Roman Catholic Church holds and believes, and that I am a mortal enemy of the Jews, as I am, the historians ought to have mercy on me and treat me well in their writings. But let them say what they like; naked was I born, naked I find myself, I neither lose nor gain; nay, while I see myself put into a book and passed on from hand to hand all over the world, I don't care a fig, let them say what they like of me."

"That, Sancho," returned Don Quixote, "reminds me of what happened to a famous poet of our own day, who, having written a bitter satire against all the court ladies, did not insert or name in it a certain lady of whom it was questionable whether she was one or not. She, seeing she was not in the list of the ladies, complained to the poet, asking him what he had seen in her that he did not include her in the number of the others, and telling him he must add to his satire and put her in the new part, or else look out for the consequences. The poet did as she bade him, and left her without a shred of reputation, and she was satisfied by getting fame though it was infamy. In keeping with this is what they relate of that shepherd who set fire to the famous temple of Diana, by repute one of the seven wonders of the world, and burned it with the sole object of making his name live in after ages; and, though it was forbidden to name him, or mention his name by word of mouth or in writing, lest the object of his ambition should be attained, nevertheless it became known that he was called Erostratus. And something of the same sort is what happened in the case of the great emperor Charles V and a gentleman in Rome. The emperor was anxious to see that famous temple of the Rotondo, called in ancient times the temple 'of all the gods,' but now-a-days, by a better nomenclature, 'of all the saints,' which is the best preserved building of all those of pagan construction in Rome, and the one which best sustains the reputation of the mighty works and magnificence of its founders. It is in the form of a half orange, of enormous dimensions, and well lighted, though no light penetrates it save that which is admitted by a window, or rather round skylight, at the top; and it was from this that the emperor examined the building. A Roman gentleman stood by his side and explained to him the skilful construction and ingenuity of the vast fabric and its wonderful architecture, and when they had left the skylight he said to the emperor, 'A thousand times, your Sacred Majesty, the impulse came upon me to seize your Majesty in my arms and fling myself down from yonder skylight, so as to leave behind me in the world a name that would last forever.' 'I am thankful to you for not carrying such an evil thought into effect,' said the emperor, 'and I shall give you no opportunity in future of again putting your loyalty to the test; and I therefore forbid you ever to speak to me or to be where I am'; and he followed up these words by bestowing a liberal bounty upon him. My meaning is, Sancho, that the desire of acquiring fame is a very powerful motive. What, thinkest thou, was it that flung Horatius in full armor down from the bridge into the depths of the Tiber? What burned the hand and arm of Mutius? What impelled Curtius to plunge into the deep burning gulf that opened in the midst of Rome? What, in opposition to all the omens that declared against him, made Julius Cæsar cross the Rubicon? And to come to more modern examples, what scuttled the ships, and left stranded and cut off the gallant Spaniards under the command of the courteous Cortés in the New World? All these and a variety of other great exploits are, were, and will be, the work of fame that mortals desire as a reward and a portion of the immortality their famous deeds deserve; though we Catholic Christians and knights-errant look more to that future glory that is everlasting in the ethereal regions of heaven, than to the vanity of the fame that is to be acquired in this present transitory life; a fame that, however long it may last, must after all end with the world itself, which has its own appointed end. So that, O Sancho, in what we do we must not overpass the bounds which the Christian religion we profess has assigned to us. We have to slay pride in giants, envy by generosity and nobleness of heart, anger by calmness of demeanor and equanimity, gluttony and sloth by the spareness of our diet and the length of our vigils, lust and lewdness by the loyalty we preserve to those whom we have made the mistresses of our thoughts, indolence by traversing the world in all directions seeking opportunities of making ourselves, besides Christians, famous knights. Such, Sancho, are the means by which we reach those extremes of praise that fair fame carries with it."

"All that your worship has said so far," said Sancho, "I have understood quite well; but still I would be glad if your worship would dissolve a doubt for me, which has just this minute come into my mind."

"Solve, thou meanest, Sancho," said Don Quixote; "say on, in God's name, and I will answer as well as I can."

"Tell me, señor," Sancho went on to say, "those Julys or Augusts, and all those venturous knights that you say are now dead—where are they now?"

"The heathens," replied Don Quixote, "are, no doubt, in hell; the Christians, if they were good Christians, are either in purgatory or in heaven."

"Very good," said Sancho; "but now I want to know—the tombs where the bodies of those great lords are, have they silver lamps before them, or are the walls of their chapels ornamented with crutches, winding-sheets, tresses of hair, legs and eyes in wax? Or, if not, what are they ornamented with?"

To which Don Quixote made answer: "The tombs of the heathens were generally sumptuous temples; the ashes of Julius Cæsar's body were placed on the top of a stone pyramid of vast size, which they now call in Rome Saint Peter's needle. The emperor Hadrian had for a tomb a castle as large as a good-sized village, which they called the *Moles Adriani,* and is now the castle of St. Angelo in Rome. The queen Artemisia buried her husband Mausolus in a tomb which was reckoned one of the seven wonders of the world; but none of these tombs, or of the many others of the heathens, were ornamented with winding-sheets or any of those other offerings and tokens that show that they who are buried there are saints."

"That's the point I'm coming to," said Sancho; "and now tell me, which is the greater work, to bring a dead man to life or to kill a giant?"

"The answer is easy," replied Don Quixote; "it is a greater work to bring to life a dead man."

"Now I have got you," said Sancho; "in that case the fame of them who bring the dead to life, who give sight to the blind, cure cripples, restore health to the sick, and before whose tombs there are lamps burning, and whose chapels are filled with devout folk on their knees adoring their relics, will be a better fame in this life and in the other, than that which all the heathen emperors and knights-errant that have ever been in the world have left or may leave behind them?"

"That I grant, too," said Don Quixote.

"Then this fame, these favors, these privileges, or whatever you call it," said Sancho, "belong to the bodies and relics of the saints who, with the approbation and permission of our holy moth-er Church, have lamps, tapers, winding-sheets, crutches, pictures, eyes and legs, by means of which they increase devotion and add to their own Christian reputation. Kings carry the bodies or relics of saints on their shoulders, and kiss bits of their bones, and enrich and adorn their oratories and favorite altars with them."

"What wouldst thou have me infer from all thou hast said, Sancho?" asked Don Quixote.

"My meaning is," said Sancho, "let us set about becoming saints, and we shall obtain more quickly the fair fame we are striving after; for you know, señor, yesterday or the day before yesterday (for it is so lately one may say so) they canonized and beatified two little barefoot friars, and it is now reckoned the greatest good luck to kiss or touch the iron chains with which they girt and tortured their bodies, and they are held in greater veneration, so it is said, than the sword of Roland in the armory of our lord the King, whom God preserve. So that, señor, it is better to be an humble little friar of no matter what order, than a valiant knight-errant; with God a couple of dozen of penance lashings are of more avail than two thousand lance-thrusts, be they given to giants, or monsters, or dragons."

"All that is true," returned Don Quixote, "but we can not all be friars, and many are the ways by which God takes his own to heaven; chivalry is a religion, there are sainted knights in glory."

"Yes," said Sancho, "but I have heard say that there are more friars in heaven than knights-errant."

"That," said Don Quixote, "is because those in religious orders are more numerous than knights."

"The errants are many," said Sancho.

"Many," replied Don Quixote, "but few they who deserve the name of knights."

With these, and other discussions of the same sort, they passed that night and the following day, without anything worth mention happening to them, whereat Don Quixote was not a little dejected; but at length the next day, at daybreak, they descried the great city of El Toboso, at the sight of which Don Quixote's spirits rose and Sancho's fell, for he did not know Dulcinea's house, nor in all his life had he ever seen her, any more than his master; so that they were both uneasy, the one to see her, the other at not having seen her, and Sancho was at a loss to know what he was to do when his master sent him to El Toboso. In the end, Don Quixote made up his mind to enter the city at nightfall, and they waited until the time came among some oak trees that were near El Toboso; and when the moment they had agreed upon arrived, they made their entrance into the city, where something happened to them that may fairly be called something.

Chapter 9

Wherein is related what will be seen there

'T was at the very midnight hour—more or less—when Don Quixote and Sancho quitted the wood and entered El Toboso. The town was in deep silence, for all the inhabitants were asleep, and stretched on the broad of their backs, as the saying is. The night was darkish, though Sancho would have been glad had it been quite dark, so as to find in the darkness an excuse for his blundering. All over the place nothing was to be heard except the barking of dogs, which deafened the ears of Don Quixote and troubled the heart of Sancho. Now and then an ass brayed, pigs grunted, cats mewed, and the various noises they made seemed louder in the silence of the night; all which the enamoured knight took to be of evil omen; nevertheless he said to Sancho, "Sancho, my son, lead on to the palace of Dulcinea, it may be that we shall find her awake."

"Body of the sun! what palace am I to lead to," said Sancho, "when what I saw her highness in was only a very little house?"

"Most likely she had then withdrawn into some small apartment of her palace," said Don Quixote, "to amuse herself with her damsels, as great ladies and princesses are accustomed to do."

"Señor," said Sancho, "if your worship will have it in spite of me that the house of my lady Dulcinea is a palace, is this an hour, think you, to find the door open; and will it be right for us to go knocking till they hear us and open the door; making a disturbance and confusion all through the household? Are we going, do you fancy, to the house of our wenches, like gallants who come and knock and go in at any hour, however late it may be?"

"Let us first of all find out the palace for certain," replied Don Quixote, "and then I will tell thee, Sancho, what we had best do; but look, Sancho, for either I see badly, or that great dark mass that one sees from here should be Dulcinea's palace."

"Then let your worship lead the way," said Sancho; "perhaps it may be so; though I see it with my eyes and touch it with my hands, I'll believe it as much as I believe it is daylight now."

Don Quixote took the lead, and having gone a matter of two hundred paces he came upon the mass that produced the shade, and found it was a great tower, and then he perceived that the building in question was no palace, but the chief church of the town, and said he, "It's the church we have lit upon, Sancho."

"So I see," said Sancho, "and God grant we may not light upon our graves; it is no good sign to find one's self wandering in a graveyard at this time of night; and that, after my telling your worship, if I don't mistake, that the house of this lady will be in an alley without an outlet."

"The curse of God on thee for a blockhead!" said Don Quixote; "where hast thou ever heard of castles and royal palaces being built in alleys without an outlet?"

"Señor," replied Sancho, "every country has a way of its own; perhaps here in El Toboso it is the way to build palaces and grand buildings in alleys; so I entreat your worship to let me search about among these streets or alleys before me, and perhaps, in some corner or other, I may stumble on this palace—and I wish I saw the dogs eating it for leading us such a dance."

"Speak respectfully of what belongs to my lady, Sancho," said Don Quixote; "let us keep the feast in peace, and not throw the rope after the bucket."

"I'll hold my tongue," said Sancho, "but how am I to take it patiently when your worship wants me, with only once seeing the house of our mistress, to know it always, and find it in the middle of the night, when your worship can't find it, who must have seen it thousands of times?"

"Thou wilt drive me to desperation, Sancho," said Don Quixote. "Look here, heretic, have I not told thee a thousand times that I have never once in my life seen the peerless Dulcinea or crossed the threshold of her palace, and that I am enamoured solely by hearsay and by the great reputation she bears for beauty and discretion?"

"I hear it now," returned Sancho; "and I may tell you that if you have not seen her, no more have I."

"That can not be," said Don Quixote, "for, at any rate, thou saidst, on bringing back the answer to the letter I sent by thee, that thou sawest her sifting wheat."

"Don't mind that, señor," said Sancho; "I must tell you that my seeing her and the answer I brought you back were by hearsay too, for I can no more tell who the lady Dulcinea is than I can hit the sky."

"Sancho, Sancho," said Don Quixote, "there are times for jests, and times when jests are out of place; if I tell thee that I have neither seen nor spoken to the lady of my heart, it is no reason why thou shouldst say thou hast not spoken to her or seen her, when the contrary is the case, as thou well knowest."

While the two were engaged in this conversation, they perceived some one with a pair of mules approaching the spot where they stood, and from the noise the plough made as it dragged along the ground they guessed him to be some laborer who had got up before daybreak to go to his work, and so it proved to be. He came along singing the ballad that says—

Ill did ye fare, ye men of France,
In Roncesvalles chase—

"May I die, Sancho," said Don Quixote, when he heard him, "if any good will come to us tonight! Dost thou not hear what that clown is singing?"

"I do," said Sancho, "but what has Roncesvalles chase to do with what we have in hand? He might just as well be singing the ballad of Calainos, for any good or ill that can come to us in our business."

By this time the laborer had come up, and Don Quixote asked him, "Can you tell me, worthy friend, and God speed you, whereabouts here is the palace of the peerless princess Doña Dulcinea del Toboso?"

"Señor," replied the lad, "I am a stranger, and I have been only a few days in the town, doing farm work for a rich farmer. In that house opposite there live the curate of the village and the sacristan, and both or either of them will be able to give your worship some account of this lady princess, for they have a list of all the people of El Toboso; though it is my belief there is not a princess living in the whole of it; many ladies there are, of quality, and in her own house each of them may be a princess."

"Well, then, she I am inquiring for will be one of these, my friend," said Don Quixote.

"May be so," replied the lad; "God be with you, for here comes the daylight"; and without waiting for any more of his questions, he whipped on his mules.

Sancho, seeing his master downcast and somewhat dissatisfied, said to him, "Señor, daylight will be here before long, and it will not do for us to let the sun find us in the street; it will be better for us to quit the city, and for your worship to hide in some forest in the neighborhood, and I will come back in the daytime, and I won't leave a nook or corner of the whole village that I won't search for the house, castle, or palace, of

my lady, and it will be hard luck for me if I don't find it; and as soon as I have found it I will speak to her grace, and tell her where and how your worship is waiting for her to arrange some plan for you to see her without any damage to her honor and reputation."

"Sancho," said Don Quixote, "thou hast delivered a thousand sentences condensed in the compass of a few words; I thank thee for the advice thou hast given me, and take it most gladly. Come, my son, let us go look for some place where I may hide, while thou dost return, as thou sayest, to seek, see, and speak with my lady, from whose discretion and courtesy I look for favors more than miraculous."

Sancho was in a fever to get his master out of the town, lest he should discover the falsehood of the reply he had brought to him in the Sierra Morena on behalf of Dulcinea; so he hastened their departure, which they took at once; and two miles out of the village they found a forest or thicket wherein Don Quixote ensconced himself, while Sancho returned to the city to speak to Dulcinea, in which embassy things befell him which demand fresh attention and a new chapter.

Chapter 10

Wherein is related the crafty device Sancho
adopted to enchant the Lady Dulcinea,
and other incidents as ludicrous as
they are true

THE history relates that as soon as Don Quixote had ensconced himself in the forest, oak grove, or wood near El Toboso, he bade Sancho return to the city, and not come into his presence again without having first spoken on his behalf to his lady, and begged of her that it might be her good pleasure to permit herself to be seen by her enslaved knight, and deign to bestow her blessing upon him, so that he might thereby hope for a happy issue in all his encounters and difficult enterprises. Sancho undertook to execute the task according to the instructions, and to bring back an answer as good as the one he brought back before.

"Go, my son," said Don Quixote, "and be not dazed when thou findest thyself exposed to the light of that sun of beauty thou art going to seek. Happy thou, above all the squires in the world! Bear in mind, and let it not escape thy memory, how she receives thee; if she changes color while thou art giving her my message; if she is agitated and disturbed at hearing my name; if she cannot rest upon her cushion, shouldst thou haply find her seated in the sumptuous state-chamber proper to her rank; and should she be standing, observe if she poises herself now on one foot, now on the other; if she repeats two or three times the reply she gives thee; if she passes from gentleness to austerity, from asperity to tenderness; if she raises her hand to smooth her hair though it be not disarranged. In short, my son, observe all her actions and motions, for if thou wilt report them to me as they were, I will gather what she hides in the recesses of her heart as regards my love; for I would have thee know, Sancho, if thou knowest it not, that with lovers the outward actions and motions they give way to when their loves are in question, are the faithful messengers that carry the news of what is going on in the depths of their hearts. Go, my friend, may better fortune than mine attend thee, and bring thee a happier issue than that which I await in dread in this dreary solitude."

"I will go and return quickly," said Sancho; 'cheer up that little heart of yours, master mine, for at the present moment you seem to have got one no bigger than a hazel nut; remember what they say, that a stout heart breaks bad luck, and that where there are no flitches there are no pegs; and moreover they say, the hare jumps up where it's not looked for. I say this because, if we could not find my lady's palaces or castle tonight, now that it is daylight I count upon finding them when I least expect it, and once found, leave it to me to manage her."

"Verily, Sancho," said Don Quixote, "thou dost always bring in thy proverbs happily, whatever we deal with; may God give me better luck in what I am anxious about."

With this, Sancho wheeled about and gave Dapple the stick, and Don Quixote remained behind, seated on his horse, resting in his stirrups and leaning on the end of his lance, filled with sad and troubled forebodings; and there we will leave him, and accompany Sancho, who went off no less serious and troubled than he left his master; so much so, that as soon as he had got out of the thicket, and looking round saw that Don Quixote was not within sight, he dismounted from his ass, and seating himself at the foot of a tree began to commune with himself, saying, "Now, brother Sancho, let us know where your worship is going. Are you going to look for some ass that has been lost? Not at all. Then what are you going to look for? I am going to look for a princess, that's all; and in her for the sun of beauty and the whole heaven at once. And where do you expect to find all this, Sancho? Where? Why, in the great city of El Tobo-

so. Well, and for whom are you going to look for her? For the famous knight Don Quixote of La Mancha, who rights wrongs, gives food to those who thirst and drink to the hungry. That's all very well, but do you know her house, Sancho? My master says it will be some royal palace or grand castle. And have you ever seen her by any chance? Neither I nor my master ever saw her. And does it strike you that it would be just and right if the El Toboso people, finding out that you were here with the intention of going to tamper with their princesses and trouble their ladies, were to come and cudgel your ribs, and not leave a whole bone in you? They would, indeed, have very good reason, if they did not see that I am under orders, and that 'you are a messenger, my friend, no blame belongs to you.' Don't you trust to that, Sancho, for the Manchegan folk are as hot-tempered as they are honest, and won't put up with liberties from anybody. By the Lord, if they get scent of you, it will be worse for you, I promise you. Be off, you scoundrel! Let the bolt fall. Why should I go looking for three feet on a cat, to please another man; and what is more, when looking for Dulcinea will be like looking for Marica in Rabena, or the bachelor in Salamanca? The devil, the devil and nobody else, has mixed me up in this business!"

Such was the soliloquy Sancho held with himself, and all the conclusion he could come to was to say to himself again, "Well, there's a remedy for everything except death, under whose yoke we have all to pass, whether we like it or not, when life's finished. I have seen by a thousands signs that this master of mine is a madman fit to be tied, and for that matter, I too, am not behind him; for I'm a greater fool than he is when I follow him and serve him, if there's any truth in the proverb that says, 'Tell me what company thou keepest, and I'll tell thee what thou art,' or in that other, 'Not with whom thou art bred, but with whom thou art fed.' Well then, if he be mad, as he is, and with a madness that mostly takes one thing for another, and white for black, and black for white, as was seen when he said the windmills were giants, and the monks' mules dromedaries, and the flocks of sheep armies of enemies, and much more to the same tune, it will not be very hard to make him believe that some country girl, the first I come across here, is the lady Dulcinea; and if he does not believe it, I'll swear it; and if he should swear, I'll swear again; and if he persists, I'll persist still more, so as, come what may, to have my quoit always over the peg. Maybe, by holding out in this way, I may put a stop to his sending me on messages of this kind another time; or maybe he will think, as I suspect he will, that one of those wicked enchanters, who he says have a spite against him, has changed her form for the sake of doing him an ill turn and injuring him."

With this reflection Sancho made his mind easy, counting the business as good as settled, and stayed there till the afternoon so as to make Don Quixote think he had time enough to go to El Toboso and return; and things turned out so luckily for him that as he got up to mount Dapple, he spied, coming from El Toboso towards the spot where he stood, three peasant girls on three colts, or fillies—for the author does not make the point clear, though it is more likely they were she-asses, the usual mount with village girls; but as it is of no great consequence, we need not stop to prove it.

To be brief, the instant Sancho saw the peasant girls, he returned full speed to seek his master, and found him sighing and uttering a thousand passionate lamentations. When Don Quixote saw him he exclaimed, "What news, Sancho my friend? Am I to mark this day with a white stone or a black?"

"Your worship," replied Sancho, "had better mark it with ruddle, like the lists on the professors' chairs, that those who see it may see it plain."

"Then thou bringest good news," said Don Quixote.

"So good," replied Sancho, "that your worship has only to spur Rocinante and get out into the open field to see the lady Dulcinea del Toboso, who, with two others, damsels of hers, is coming to see your worship."

"Holy God! what art thou saying, Sancho my friend?" exclaimed Don Quixote. "Take care thou art not deceiving me, or seeking by false joy to cheer my real sadness."

"What could I get by deceiving your worship," returned Sancho, "especially when it will so soon be shown whether I tell the truth or not? Come, señor, push on, and you will see the princess our mistress coming, robed and adorned—in fact, like what she is. Her damsels and she are all one glow of gold, all bunches of pearls, all diamonds, all rubies, all cloth of brocade of more than ten borders; with their hair loose on their shoulders like so many sunbeams playing with the wind; and moreover, they come mounted on three piebald cackneys, the finest sight ever you saw."

"Hackneys, you mean, Sancho," said Don Quixote.

"There is not much difference between cackneys and hackneys," said Sancho; "but no matter what they come on, there they are, the finest ladies one could wish for, especially my lady the princess Dulcinea, who staggers one's senses."

"Let us go, Sancho my son," said Don Quixote, "and in guerdon of this news, as unexpected as it is good, I bestow upon thee the best spoil I shall win in the first adventure I may have; or if that does not satisfy thee, I promise thee the foals I shall have this year from my three mares that thou knowest are in foal on our village common."

"I'll take the foals," said Sancho; "for it is not quite certain that the spoils of the first adventure will be good ones."

By this time they had cleared the wood, and saw the three village lasses close at hand. Don Quixote looked all along the road to El Toboso, and as he could see nobody except the three peasant girls, he was completely puzzled, and asked Sancho if it was outside the city he had left them.

"How outside the city?" returned Sancho. "Are your worship's eyes in the back of your head, that you can't see that they are these who are coming here, shining like the very sun at noonday?"

"I see nothing, Sancho," said Don Quixote, "but three country girls on three jackasses."

"Now, may God deliver me from the devil!" returned Sancho, "and can it be that your worship takes three hackneys—or whatever they're called—as white as the driven snow, for jackasses? By the Lord, I could tear my beard if that was the case!"

"Well, I can only say, Sancho my friend," said Don Quixote, "that it is as plain they are jackasses—or jennyasses—as that I am Don Quixote and thou Sancho Panza: at any rate, they seem to me to be so."

"Hush, señor," said Sancho, "don't talk that way, but open your eyes, and come and pay your respects to the lady of your thoughts, who is close upon us now"; and with these words he advanced to receive the three village lasses, and dismounting from Dapple, caught hold of one of the asses of the three country girls by the halter, and dropping on both knees on the ground he said, "Queen and princess and duchess of beauty, may it please your haughtiness and greatness to receive into your favor and good-will your captive knight who stands there turned into marble stone, and quite stupefied and benumbed at finding himself in your magnificent presence. I am Sancho Panza, his squire, and he the vagabond knight Don Quixote of La Mancha, otherwise called 'The Knight of the Rueful Countenance.'"

Don Quixote had by this time placed himself on his knees beside Sancho, and, with eyes starting out of his head and a puzzled gaze, was regarding her whom Sancho called queen and lady; and as he could see nothing in her except a village lass, and not a very well-favored one, for she was platter-faced and snub-nosed, he was perplexed and bewildered, and did not venture to open his lips. The country girls, at the same time, were astonished to see these two men, so different in appearance, on their knees, preventing their companion from going on. She, however, who had been stopped, breaking silence, said angrily and testily, "Get out of the way, bad luck to you, and let us pass, for we are in a hurry."

To which Sancho returned, "Oh, princess and universal lady of El Toboso, is not your magnanimous heart softened by seeing the pillar and prop of knight-errantry on his knees before your sublimated presence?"

On hearing this, one of the others exclaimed, "Woa then! why, I'm rubbing thee down, she-ass of my father-in-law! See how the lordlings come to make game of the village girls now, as if we here could not chaff as well as themselves. Go your own way, and let us go ours, and it will be better for you."

"Get up, Sancho," said Don Quixote at this; "I see that fortune, 'with evil done to me unsated still,' has taken possession of all the roads by which any comfort may reach this wretched soul that I carry in my flesh. And thou, O highest perfection of excellence that can be desired, utmost limit of grace in human shape, sole relief of this afflicted heart that adores thee, though the malign enchanter that persecutes me has brought clouds and cataracts on my eyes, and to them, and them only, transformed thy unparagoned beauty and changed thy features into those of a poor peasant girl, if so be he has not at the same time changed mine into those of some monster to render them loathsome in thy sight, refuse not to look upon me with tenderness and love; seeing in this submission that I make on my knees to thy transformed beauty, the humility with which my soul adores thee."

"Hey-day! My grandfather!" cried the girl; "much I care for your love-making! Get out of the way and let us pass, and we'll thank you."

Sancho stood aside and let her go, very well pleased to have got so well out of the hobble he was in. The instant the village lass who had done duty for Dulcinea found herself free, prodding her cackney with a spike she had at the end of a stick, she set off at full speed across the field. The ass, however, feeling the point more acutely than usual, began cutting such capers, that it flung the lady Dulcinea to the ground; seeing which, Don Quixote ran to raise her up, and Sancho to fix and girth the pack-saddle, which also had slipped under the ass's belly. The pack-saddle being secured, as Don Quixote was about to lift up his enchanted mistress in his arms and put her upon her beast, the lady, getting up from the ground, saved him the trouble, for, going back a little, she took a short run, and putting both hands on the croup of the ass she dropped into the saddle more lightly than a falcon, and sat astride like a man, whereat Sancho said, "Roque! but our lady is lighter than a lanner, and might teach the cleverest Cordovan or Mexican how to mount; she cleared the back of the saddle in one jump, and without spurs she is making the hackney go like a zebra; and her damsels are no way behind her, for they all fly like the wind"; which was the truth, for as soon as they saw Dulcinea mounted, they pushed on after her, and sped away without looking back, for more than half a league.

Don Quixote followed them with his eyes, and when they were no longer in sight, he turned to Sancho and said, "How now, Sancho? thou seest how I am hated by enchanters! And see to what a length the malice and spite they bear me go, when they seek to deprive me of the happiness it would give me to see my lady in her own proper form. The fact is, I was born to be an example of misfortune, and the target and mark at which the arrows of adversity are aimed and directed. Observe too, Sancho, that these traitors were not content with changing and transforming my Dulcinea, but they transformed and changed her into a shape as mean and ill-favored as that of the village girl yonder; and at the same time they robbed her of that which is such a peculiar property of ladies of distinction, that is to say, the sweet fragrance that comes of being always among perfumes and flowers. For I must tell thee, Sancho, that when I approached to put Dulcinea upon her hackney (as thou sayest it was, though to me it appeared a she-ass), she gave me a whiff of raw garlic that made my head reel, and poisoned my very heart."

"O scum of the earth!" cried Sancho at this, "O miserable, spiteful enchanters! O that I could see you all strung by the gills, like sardines on a twig! Ye know a great deal, ye can do a great deal, and ye do much harm. It ought to have been enough for you, ye scoundrels, to have changed the pearls of my lady's eyes into oak galls, and her hair of purest gold into the bristles of a red ox's tail, and, in short, all her features from fair to foul, without meddling with her smell; for by that we might somehow have found out what was hidden underneath that ugly rind; though, to tell the truth, I never perceived her ugliness, but only her beauty, which was raised to the highest pitch of perfection by a mole she had on her right lip, like a mustache, with seven or eight red hairs like threads of gold, and more than a palm long."

"From the correspondence which exists between those of the face and those of the body," said Don Quixote, "Dulcinea must have another mole resembling that on the thick of the thigh on that side on which she has the one on her face; but hairs of the length thou hast mentioned are very long for moles."

"Well, all I can say is there they were as plain as could be," replied Sancho.

"I believe it, my friend," returned Don Quixote; "for nature bestowed nothing on Dulcinea that was not perfect and well-finished; and so, if she had a hundred moles like the one thou hast described, in her they would not be moles, but moons and shining stars. But tell me, Sancho, that which seemed to me to be a pack-saddle as thou wert fixing it, was it a flat-saddle or a side-saddle?"

"It was neither," replied Sancho, "but a *jineta* saddle, with a field covering worth half a kingdom, so rich is it."

"And that I could not see all this, Sancho!" said Don Quixote; "once more I say, and will say a thousand times, I am the most unfortunate of men."

Sancho, the rogue, had enough to do to hide his laughter, at hearing the simplicity of the master he had so nicely befooled. At length, after a good deal more conversation had passed between them, they remounted their beasts, and followed the road to Saragossa, which they expected to reach in time to take part in a certain grand festival which is held every year in that illustrious city; but before they got there things happened to them, so many, so important, and so strange, that they deserve to be recorded and read, as will be seen farther on.

Chapter 11

Of the strange adventure which the valiant Don Quixote had with the car or cart of The Cortes of Death

DEJECTED beyond measure did Don Quixote pursue his journey, turning over in his mind the cruel trick the enchanters had played him in changing his lady Dulcinea into the vile shape of the village lass, nor could he think of any way of restoring her to her original form; and these reflections so absorbed him, that without being aware of it he let go Rocinante's bridle, and he, perceiving the liberty that was granted him, stopped at every step to crop the fresh grass which the plain abounded.

Sancho recalled him from his revery. "Melancholy, señor," said he, "was made, not for beasts, but for men; but if men give way to it overmuch they turn to beasts; control yourself, your worship; be yourself again; gather up Rocinante's reins; cheer up, rouse yourself and show that gallant spirit that knights-errant ought to have. What the devil is this? What weakness is this? Are we here or in France? The devil fly away with all the Dulcineas in the world; for the well-being of a single knight-errant is of more consequence than all the enchantments and transformations on earth."

"Hush, Sancho," said Don Quixote in a weak and faint voice, "hush, I say, and utter no blasphemies against that enchanted lady; for I alone am to blame for her misfortune and hard fate; her calamity has come of the hatred the wicked bear me."

"So say I," returned Sancho; "his heart 'twould rend in twain, I trow, who saw her once, to see her now."

"Thou mayest well say that, Sancho," replied Don Quixote, "as thou sawest her in the full perfection of her beauty; for the enchantment does not go so far as to pervert thy vision or hide her loveliness from thee; against me alone and against my eyes is the strength of its venom directed. Nevertheless, there is one thing which has occurred to me, and that is that thou didst ill describe her beauty to me, for, as well as I recollect, thou saidst that her eyes were pearls; but eyes that are like pearls are rather the eyes of a sea-bream than of a lady, and I am persuaded that Dulcinea's must be green emeralds, full and soft, with two rainbows for eyebrows; take away those pearls from her eyes and transfer them to her teeth; for beyond a doubt, Sancho, thou hast taken the one for the other, the eyes for the teeth."

"Very likely," said Sancho; "for her beauty bewildered me as much as her ugliness did your worship; but let us leave it all to God, who alone knows what is to happen in this vale of tears, in this evil world of ours, where there is hardly a thing to be found without some mixture of wickedness, roguery, and rascality. But one thing, señor, troubles me more than all the rest, and that is thinking what is to be done when your worship conquers some giant, or some other knight, and orders him to go and present himself before the beauty of the lady Dulcinea. Where is this poor giant, or this poor wretch of a vanquished knight, to find her? I think I can see them wandering all over El Toboso, looking like noddies, and asking for my lady Dulcinea; and even if they meet her in the middle of the street they won't know her any more than they would my father."

"Perhaps, Sancho," returned Don Quixote, "the enchantment does not go so far as to deprive conquered and presented giants and knights of the power of recognizing Dulcinea; we will try by experiment with one or two of the first I vanquish and send to her, whether they see her or not, by commanding them to return and give me an account of what happened to them in this respect."

"I declare, I think what your worship has proposed is excellent," said Sancho; "and that by this plan we shall find out what we want to know; and if it be that it is only from your worship she is hidden, the misfortune will be more yours than hers; but so long as the lady Dulcinea is well and happy, we on our part will make the best of it, and get on as well as we can, seeking our adventures, and leaving Time to take his own course; for he is the best physician for these and greater ailments."

Don Quixote was about to reply to Sancho Panza, but he was prevented by a cart crossing the road full of the most diverse and strange personages and figures that could be imagined. He who led the mules and acted as carter was a hideous demon; the cart was open to the sky, without a tilt or cane roof, and the first figure that presented itself to Don Quixote's eyes was that of Death itself with a human face; next to it was an angel with large painted wings, and at one side an emperor, with a crown, to all appearance of gold, on his head. At the feet of Death was the god called Cupid, without his bandage, but with his bow, quiver, and arrows; there was also a knight in full armor, except that he had no morion or helmet, but only a hat decked with plumes of divers colors; and along with these there were others with a variety of costumes and faces. All this, unexpectedly encountered, took Don Quixote somewhat aback, and struck terror into the heart of Sancho; but the next instant Don Quixote was glad of it, believing that some new perilous adventure was presenting itself to him, and under this impression, and with a spirit prepared to face any danger, he planted himself in front of the cart, and in a loud and menacing tone, exclaimed, "Carter, or coachman, or devil, or whatever thou art, tell me at once who thou art, whither thou art going, and who these folk are thou carriest in thy wagon, which looks more like Charon's boat than an ordinary cart."

To which the devil, stopping the cart, answered quietly, "Señor, we are players of Angulo el Malo's company; we have been acting the play of *The Cortes of Death* this morning, which is the octave of Corpus Christi, in a village behind that hill, and we have to act it this afternoon in that village which you can see from this; and as it is so near, and to save the trouble of undressing and dressing again, we go in the costumes in which we perform. That lad there appears as Death, that other as an angel, that woman, the manager's wife, plays the queen, this one the soldier, that the emperor, and I the devil; and I am one of the principal characters of the play, for in this company I take the leading parts. If you want to know anything more about us, ask me and I will answer with the utmost exactitude, for as I am a devil I am up to everything."

"By the faith of a knight-errant," replied Don Quixote, "when I saw this cart I fancied some great adventure was presenting itself to me; but I declare one must touch with the hand what appears to the eye, if illusions are to be avoided. God speed you, good people; keep your festival, and remember, if you demand of me ought wherein I can render you a service, I will do it gladly and willingly, for from a child I was fond of the play, and in my youth a keen lover of the actor's art."

While they were talking, fate so willed it that one of the company in a mummer's dress with a great number of bells, and armed with three blown ox-bladders at the end of a stick, joined them, and this merry-andrew approaching Don Quixote, began flourishing his stick and banging the ground with the bladders and cutting capers with great jingling of the bells, which untoward apparition so startled Rocinante that, in spite of Don Quixote's efforts to hold him in, taking the bit between his teeth he set off across the plain with greater speed than the bones of his anatomy ever gave any promise of. Sancho, who thought his master was in danger of being thrown, jumped off Dapple, and ran in all haste to help him; but by the time he reached him he was already on the ground, and beside him was Rocinante, who had come down with his master, the usual end and upshot of Rocinante's vivacity and high spirits. But the moment Sancho quitted his beast to go and help Don Quixote, the dancing devil with the bladders jumped up on Dapple, and beating him with them, more by the fright and the noise than by the pain of the blows, made him fly across the fields towards the village where they were going to hold their festival. Sancho witnessed Dapple's career and his master's fall, and did not know which of the two cases of need he should attend to first; but in the end, like a good squire and good servant, he let his love for his master prevail over his affection for his ass; though every time he saw the bladders rise in the air and come down on the hind quarters of his Dapple he felt the pains and terrors of death, and he would have rather had the blows fall on the apples of his own eyes than on the least hair of his ass's tail. In this trouble and perplexity he came to where Don Quixote lay in a far sorrier plight than he liked, and having helped him to mount Rocinante, he said to him, "Señor, the devil has carried off my Dapple."

"What devil?" asked Don Quixote.

"The one with the bladders," said Sancho.

"Then I will recover him," said Don Quixote, "even if he be shut up with him in the deepest and darkest dungeons of hell. Follow me, Sancho, for the cart goes slowly, and with the mules of it I will make good the loss of Dapple."

"You need not take the trouble, señor," said Sancho; "keep cool, for as I now see, the devil has let Dapple go and he is coming back to his old quarters"; and so it turned out, for, having come down with Dapple, in imitation of Don Quixote and Rocinante, the devil made off on foot to the town, and the ass came back to his master.

"For all that," said Don Quixote, "it will be well to visit the discourtesy of that devil upon some of those in the cart, even if it were the emperor himself."

"Don't think of it, your worship," returned Sancho; "take my advice and never meddle with actors, for they are a favored class; I myself have known an actor taken up for two murders, and yet come off scot-free; remember that, as they are merry folk who give pleasure, every one fa-

vors and protects them, and helps and make much of them, above all when they are those o the royal companies and under patent, all o most of whom in dress and appearance look lik princes."

"Still, for all that," said Don Quixote, "th player devil must not go off boasting, even if th whole human race favors him."

So saying, he made for the cart, which wa now very near the town, shouting out as he went "Stay! halt! ye merry, jovial crew! I want to teacl you how to treat asses and animals that serve th squires of knights-errant for steeds."

So loud were the shouts of Don Quixote, tha those in the cart heard and understood them and, guessing by the words what the speaker' intention was, Death in an instant jumped ou of the cart, and the emperor, the devil carter an the angel after him, nor did the queen or th god Cupid stay behind; and all armed them selves with stones and formed in line, prepare to receive Don Quixote on the points of thei pebbles. Don Quixote, when he saw them draw up in such a gallant array with uplifted arm ready for a mighty discharge of stones, checke Rocinante and began to consider in what wa he could attack them with the least danger to him self. As he halted Sancho came up, and seein him disposed to attack this well-ordered squad ron, said to him, "It would be the height of mad ness to attempt such an enterprise; remember señor, that against sops from the brook, and plen ty of them, there is no defensive armor in th world, except to stow one's self away under brass bell; and besides, one should remembe that it is rashness, and not valor, for a singl man to attack an army that has Death in it, an where emperors fight in person, with angels good and bad, to help them; and if this reflec tion will not make you keep quiet, perhaps it wil to know for certain that among all these, thoug they look like kings, princes, and emperors, ther is not a single knight-errant."

"Now, indeed thou hast hit the point, San cho," said Don Quixote, "which may and shoul turn me from the resolution I had alread formed. I can not and must not draw sword, a I have many a time before told thee, agains any one who is not a dubbed knight; it is fo thee, Sancho, if thou wilt, to take vengeanc for the wrong done to thy Dapple; and I will hel thee from here by shouts and salutary counsels."

"There is no occasion to take vengeance o any one, señor," replied Sancho; "for it is no the part of good Christians to revenge wrongs and besides, I will arrange it with my ass to leave his grievance to my good-will and pleasure, and that is to live in peace as long as Heaven grants me life."

"Well," said Don Quixote, "if that be thy determination, good Sancho, sensible Sancho, Christian Sancho, honest Sancho, let us leave these phantoms alone and turn to the pursuit of better and worthier adventures; for, from what I see of this country, we can not fail to find plenty of marvellous ones in it."

He at once wheeled about, Sancho ran to take possession of his Dapple, Death and his whole flying squadron returned to their cart and pursued their journey, and thus the dread adventure of the cart of Death ended happily, thanks to the sound advice Sancho gave his master; who had, the following day, a fresh adventure, of no less thrilling interest than the last, with an enamoured knight-errant.

Chapter 12

Of the strange adventure which befell the
valiant Don Quixote with the bold
Knight of the Mirrors

THE night succeeding the day of the encounter with Death, Don Quixote and his squire passed under some tall shady trees, and Don Quixote at Sancho's persuasion ate a little from the store carried by Dapple, and over their supper Sancho said to his master, "Señor, what a fool I should have looked if I had chosen for my reward the spoils of the first adventure your worship achieved, instead of the foals of the three mares. After all, after all, 'a sparrow in the hand is better than a vulture on the wing.' "

"At the same time, Sancho," replied Don Quixote, "if thou hadst let me attack them as I wanted, at the very least the emperor's gold crown and Cupid's painted wings would have fallen to thee as spoils, for I should have taken them by force and given them into thy hands."

"The sceptres and crowns of those play-actor emperors," said Sancho, "were never yet pure gold, but only brass foil or tin."

"That is true," said Don Quixote, "for it would not be right that the accessories of the drama should be real, instead of being mere fictions and semblances, like the drama itself; towards which, Sancho—and, as a necessary consequence, towards those who represent and produce it—I would that thou wert favorably disposed, for they are all instruments of great good to the State, placing before us at every step a mirror in which we may see vividly displayed what goes on in human life; nor is there any similitude that shows us more faithfully what we are and ought to be, than the play and the players. Come, tell me, hast thou not seen a play acted in which kings, emperors, pontiffs, knights, ladies, and divers other personages were introduced? One plays the villain, another the knave, this one the merchant, that the soldier, one the sharp-witted fool, another the foolish lover; and when the play is over, and they have put off the dresses they wore in it, all the actors become equal."

"Yes, I have seen that," said Sancho.

"Well, then," said Don Quixote, "the same thing happens in the comedy and life of this world, where some play emperors, others popes, and, in short, all the characters that can be brought into a play; but when it is over, that is to say when life ends, death strips them all of the garments that distinguish one from the other, and all are equal in the grave."

"A fine comparison!" said Sancho; "though not so new but that I have heard it many and many a time, as well as that other one of the game of chess; how, so long as the game lasts, each piece has its own particular office, and when the game is finished they are all mixed, jumbled up and shaken together, and stowed away in the bag, which is much like ending life in the grave."

"Thou art growing less doltish and more shrewd every day, Sancho," said Don Quixote.

"Ay," said Sancho; "it must be that some of your worship's shrewdness sticks to me; land that, of itself, is barren and dry will come to yield good fruit if you dung it and till it; what I mean is that your worship's conversation has been the dung that has fallen on the barren soil of my dry wit, and the time I have been in your service and society has been the tillage; and with the help of this I hope to yield fruit in abundance that will not fall away or slide from those paths of good breeding that your worship has made in my parched understanding."

Don Quixote laughed at Sancho's affected phraseology, and perceived that what he said about his improvement was true, for now and then he spoke in a way that surprised him; though always, or mostly, when Sancho tried to talk fine and attempted polite language, he wound up by toppling over from the summit of his simplicity into the abyss of his ignorance; and where he showed his culture and his memory to the greatest advantage was in dragging in proverbs, no matter whether they had any bearing or not upon the subject in hand, as may have been seen already and will be noticed in the course of this history.

In conversation of this kind they passed a good part of the night, but Sancho felt a desire to let down the curtains of his eyes, as he used to say when he wanted to go to sleep; and stripping Dapple he left him at liberty to graze his fill. He did not remove Rocinante's saddle, as his master's express orders were, that so long as they were in the field or not sleeping under a roof Rocinante was not to be stripped—the ancient usage established and observed by knights-errant being to take off the bridle and hang it on the saddle-bow, but to remove the saddle from the horse—never! Sancho acted accordingly, and gave him the same liberty he had given Dapple, between whom and Rocinante there was a friendship so unequalled and so strong, that it is handed down by tradition from father to son, that the author of this veracious history devoted some special chapters to it, which, in order to preserve the propriety and decorum due to a history so heroic, he did not insert therein; although at times he forgets this resolution of his and describes how eagerly the two beasts would scratch one another when they were together, and how, when they were tired or full, Rocinante would lay his neck across Dapple's, stretching half a yard or more on the other side, and the pair would stand thus, gazing thoughtfully on the ground, for three days, or at least so long as they were left alone, or hunger did not drive them to go and look for food. I may add that they say the author left it on record that he likened their friendship to that of Nisus and Euryalus, and Pylades and Orestes; and if that be so, it may be perceived, to the admiration of mankind, how firm the friendship must have been between these two peaceful animals, shaming men, who preserve friendships with one another so badly. This was why it was said—

For friend no longer is there friend;
The reeds turn lances now.

And some one else has sung—

Friend to friend the bug, etc.

and let no one fancy that the author was at all astray when he compared the friendship of these animals to that of men; for men have received many lessons from beasts, and learned many important things, as, for example, the clyster from the stork, emetics and gratitude from the dog, watchfulness from the crane, foresight from the ant, modesty from the elephant, and loyalty from the horse.

Sancho at last fell asleep at the foot of a cork tree, while Don Quixote dozed at that of a sturdy oak; but a short time only had elapsed when a noise he heard behind him awoke him, and rising up startled, he listened and looked in the direction the noise came from, and perceived two men on horseback, one of whom, letting himself drop from the saddle, said to the other, "Dismount, my friend, and take the bridles off the horses, for, so far as I can see, this place will furnish grass for them, and the solitude and silence my love-sick thoughts have need of." As he said this he stretched himself upon the ground, and as he flung himself down, the armor in which he was clad rattled, whereby Don Quixote perceived that he must be a knight-errant; and going over to Sancho, who was asleep, he shook him by the arm and with no small difficulty brought him back to his senses, and said in a low voice to him, "Brother Sancho, we have got an adventure."

"God send us a good one," said Sancho; "and where, señor, may her ladyship the adventure be?"

"Where, Sancho?" replied Don Quixote; "turn thine eyes and look, and thou wilt see stretched there a knight-errant, who, it strikes me, is not over and above happy, for I saw him fling himself off his horse and throw himself on the ground with a certain air of dejection, and his armor rattled as he fell."

"Well," said Sancho, "how does your worship make out that to be an adventure?"

"I do not mean to say," returned Don Quixote, "that it is a complete adventure, but that it is the beginning of one, for it is in this way adventures begin. But listen, for it seems he is tuning a lute or guitar, and from the way he is spitting and clearing his chest he must be getting ready to sing something."

"Faith, you are right," said Sancho, "and no doubt he is some enamoured knight."

"There is no knight-errant that is not," said Don Quixote; "but let us listen to him, for, if he sings, by that thread we shall extract the ball of his thoughts; because out of the abundance of the heart the mouth speaketh."

Sancho was about to reply to his master, but the Knight of the Grove's voice, which was neither very bad nor very good, stopped him, and listening attentively the pair heard him sing this:

Sonnet

Your pleasure, prithee, lady mine, unfold;
Declare the terms that I am to obey;
My will to yours submissively I mould,

And from your law my feet shall never stray.
Would you I die, to silent grief a prey?
Then count me even now as dead and cold;
Would you I tell my woes in some new way?
Then shall my tale by love itself be told.
The unison of opposites to prove,
Of the soft wax and diamond hard am I;
But still, obedient to the laws of love,
Here, hard or soft, I offer you my breast,
Whate'er you grave or stamp thereon shall rest
Indelible for all eternity.

With an "Ah me!" that seemed to be drawn from he inmost recesses of his heart, the Knight of he Grove brought his lay to an end, and shortly afterwards exclaimed in a melancholy and piteous voice, "O fairest and most ungrateful woman on earth! What! can it be, most serene Casildea de Vandalia, that thou wilt suffer this thy captive knight to waste away and perish in ceaseless wanderings and rude and arduous toils? Is it not enough that I have compelled all the knights of Navarre, all the Leonese, all the Tartesians, all the Castilians, and finally all the knights of La Mancha, to confess thee the most beautiful in the world?"

"Not so," said Don Quixote at this, "for I am of La Mancha, and I have never confessed anything of the sort, nor could I nor should I confess a thing so much to the prejudice of my lady's beauty; thou seest how this knight is raving, Sancho. But let us listen, perhaps he will tell us more about himself."

"That he will," returned Sancho, "for he seems in a mood to bewail himself for a month at a stretch."

But this was not the case, for the Knight of the Grove, hearing voices near him, instead of continuing his lamentation, stood up and exclaimed in a distinct but courteous tone, "Who goes there? What are you? Do you belong to the number of the happy or of the miserable?"

"Of the miserable," answered Don Quixote.

"Then come to me," said he of the Grove, "and rest assured that it is to woe itself and affliction itself you come."

Don Quixote, finding himself answered in such a soft and courteous manner, went over to him, and so did Sancho.

The doleful knight took Don Quixote by the arm, saying, "Sit down here, sir knight; for, that you are one, and of those that profess knight-errantry, it is to me a sufficient proof to have found you in this place, where solitude and night, the natural couch and proper retreat of knights-errant, keep you company." To which Don Quixote made

answer, "A knight I am of the profession you mention; and though sorrows, misfortunes, and calamities have made my heart their abode, the compassion I feel for the misfortunes of others has not been thereby banished from it. From what you have just now sung I gather that yours spring from love, I mean from the love you bear that fair ingrate you named in your lament."

In the mean time, they had seated themselves together on the hard ground peaceably and socially, just as if, as soon as day broke, they were not going to break one another's heads.

"Are you, sir knight, in love perchance?" asked he of the Grove of Don Quixote.

"By mischance I am," replied Don Quixote; "though the ills arising from well-bestowed affections should be esteemed favors rather than misfortunes."

"That is true," returned he of the Grove, "if scorn did not unsettle our reason and understanding, for if it be excessive it looks like revenge."

"I was never scorned by my lady," said Don Quixote.

"Certainly not," said Sancho, who stood close by, "for my lady is as gentle as a lamb, and softer than a roll of butter."

"Is this your squire?" asked he of the Grove.

"He is," said Don Quixote.

"I never yet saw a squire," said he of the Grove, "who ventured to speak when his master was speaking; at least, there is mine, who is as big as his father, and it can not be proved that he has ever opened his lips when I am speaking."

"By my faith, then," said Sancho, "I have spoken, and am fit to speak, in the presence of one as much, or even—but never mind—it only makes it worse to stir it."

The Squire of the Grove took Sancho by the arm, saying to him, "Let us two go where we can talk in squire style as much as we please, and leave these gentlemen our masters to fight it out over the story of their loves; and, depend upon it, daybreak will find them at it without having made an end of it."

"So be it by all means," said Sancho; "and I will tell your worship who I am, that you may see whether I am to be reckoned among the number of the most talkative squires."

With this the two squires withdrew to one side, and between them there passed a conversation as droll as that which passed between their masters was serious.

Chapter 13

In which is continued the adventure of the Knight of the Grove, together with the sensible, original, and tranquil colloquy that passed between the two squires

THE knights and the squires made two parties, these telling the story of their lives, the others the story of their loves; but the history relates first of all the conversation of the servants, and afterwards takes up that of the masters; and it says that, withdrawing a little from the others, he of the Grove said to Sancho, "A hard life it is we lead and live, señor, we that are squires to knights-errant; verily, we eat our bread in the sweat of our faces, which is one of the curses God laid on our first parents."

"It may be said, too," added Sancho, "that we eat it in the chill of our bodies; for who gets more heat and cold than the miserable squires of knight-errantry? Even so it would not be so bad if we had something to eat, for woes are lighter if there's bread; but sometimes we go a day or two without breaking our fast, except with the wind that blows."

"All that," said he of the Grove, "may be endured and put up with when we have hopes of reward; for, unless the knight-errant he serves is excessively unlucky, after a few turns the squire will at least find himself rewarded with a fine government of some island or some fair country."

"I," said Sancho, "have already told my master that I shall be content with the government of some island, and he is so noble and generous that he has promised it to me ever so many times."

"I," said he of the Grove, "shall be satisfied with a canonry for my services, and my master has already assigned me one."

"Your master," said Sancho, "no doubt is a knight in the Church line, and can bestow rewards of that sort on his good squire; but mine is only a layman; though I remember some clever, but, to my mind, designing people, strove to persuade him to try and become an archbishop. He, however, would not be anything but an emperor; but I was trembling all the time lest he should take a fancy to go into the Church, not finding myself fit to hold office in it; for I may tell you, though I seem a man, I am no better than a beast for the Church."

"Well, then, you are wrong there," said he of the Grove; "for those island governments are not all satisfactory; some are awkward, some are poor, some are dull, and, in short, the highest and choicest brings with it a heavy burden of cares and troubles which the unhappy wight to whose lot it has fallen bears upon his shoulders. Far better would it be for us who have adopted this accursed service, to go back to our own houses, and there employ ourselves in pleasanter occupations—in hunting or fishing, for instance; for what squire in the world is there so poor as not to have a hack and a couple of greyhounds and a fishing-rod to amuse himself within his own village?"

"I am not in want of any of those things," said Sancho; "to be sure I have no hack, but I have an ass that is worth my master's horse twice over; God send me a bad Easter, and that the next one I am to see, if I would swap, even if I got four bushels of barley to boot. You will laugh at the value I put on my Dapple—for dapple is the color of my beast. As to greyhounds, I can't want for them, for there are enough and to spare in my town; and, moreover, there is more pleasure in sport when it is at other people's expense."

"In truth and earnest, sir squire," said he of the Grove, "I have made up my mind and determined to have done with these drunken vagaries of these knights, and go back to my village, and bring up my children; for I have three, like three Oriental pearls."

"I have two," said Sancho, "that might be presented before the Pope himself, especially a girl whom I am breeding up for a countess, please God, though in spite of her mother."

"And how old is this lady that is being bred up for a countess?" asked he of the Grove.

"Fifteen, a couple of years more or less," answered Sancho; "but she is as tall as a lance, and as fresh as an April morning, and as strong as a porter."

"Those are gifts to fit her to be not only a countess but a nymph of the greenwood," said he of the Grove; "whoreson strumpet! what pith the rogue must have!"

To which Sancho made answer, somewhat sulkily, "She's no strumpet, nor was her mother, nor will either of them be, please God, while I live; speak more civilly; for one bred up among knights-errant, who are courtesy itself, your words don't seem to me to be very becoming."

"O how little you know about compliments, sir squire," returned he of the Grove. "What! don't you know that when a horseman delivers a good lance thrust at the bull in the plaza, or when any one does anything very well, the people are wont to say, 'Ha, whoreson rip! how well he has done it!' and that what seems to be abuse in the expression is high praise? Disown sons and daughters, señor, who don't do what deserves that compliments of this sort should be paid to their parents."

"I do disown them," replied Sancho, "and in this way, and by the same reasoning, you might call me and my children and my wife all the trumpets in the world, for all they do and say is of a kind that in the highest degree deserves the same praise; and to see them again I pray God to deliver me from mortal sin, or, what comes to the same thing, to deliver me from this perilous calling of squire into which I have fallen a second time, decoyed and beguiled by a purse with a hundred ducats that I found one day in the heart of the Sierra Morena; and the devil is always putting a bag full of doubloons before my eyes, here, there, everywhere, until I fancy at every step I am putting my hand on it, and hugging it, and carrying it home with me, and making investments, and getting interest, and living like a prince; and so long as I think of this I make light of all the hardships I endure with this simpleton of a master of mine, who, I well know, is more of a madman than a knight."

"There's why they say that 'covetousness bursts the bag,'" said he of the Grove; "but if you come to talk of that sort, there is not a greater one in the world than my master, for he is one of those of whom they say, 'The cares of others kill the ass;' for, in order that another knight may recover the senses he has lost, he makes a madman of himself and goes looking for what, when found, may, for all I know, fly in his own face."

"And is he in love, now?" asked Sancho.

"He is," said he of the Grove, "with one Casildea de Vandalia, the rawest and best roasted lady the whole world could produce; but the rawness is not the only foot he limps on, for he has greater schemes rumbling in his bowels, as will be seen before many hours are over."

"There's no road so smooth but it has some hole or hinderance in it," said Sancho; "in other houses they cook beans, but in mine it's by the potful; madness will have more followers and hangers-on than sound sense; but if there be any truth in the common saying, that to have companions in trouble gives some relief, I may take consolation from you, inasmuch as you serve a master as crazy as my own."

"Crazy but valiant," replied he of the Grove, "and more roguish than crazy or valiant."

"Mine is not that," said Sancho; "I mean he has nothing of the rogue in him; on the contrary, he has the soul of a pitcher; he has no thought of doing harm to any one, only good to all, nor has he any malice whatever in him; a child might persuade him that it is night at noonday; and for this simplicity I love him as the core of my heart, and I can't bring myself to leave him, let him do ever such foolish things."

"For all that, brother and señor," said he of the Grove, "if the blind lead the blind both are in danger of falling into the pit. It is better for us to beat a quiet retreat and get back to our own quarters; for those who seek adventures don't always find good ones."

Sancho kept spitting from time to time, and his spittle seemed somewhat ropy and dry, observing which the compassionate Squire of the Grove said, "It seems to me that with all this talk of ours our tongues are sticking to the roofs of our mouths; but I have a pretty good loosener hanging from the saddle-bow of my horse," and getting up he came back the next minute with a large bota of wine and a pasty half a yard across; and this is no exaggeration, for it was made of a house rabbit so big that Sancho, as he handled it, took it to be made of a goat, not to say a kid, and looking at it he said, "And do you carry this with you, señor?"

"Why, what are you thinking about?" said the other; "do you take me for some paltry squire? I carry a better larder on my horse's croup than a general takes with him when he goes on a march."

Sancho ate without requiring to be pressed, and in the dark bolted mouthfuls like the knots on a tether, and said he, "You are a proper trusty squire, one of the right sort, sumptuous and grand, as this banquet shows, which, if it has not come here by magic art, at any rate has the look of it; not like me, unlucky beggar, that have nothing more in my *alforjas* than a scrap of cheese, so hard that one might brain a giant with it, and, to keep it company, a few dozen carobs and as many more filberts and walnuts; thanks to the austerity of my master, and the idea he has and the rule he follows, that knights-errant must not live or sustain themselves on anything except dried fruits and the herbs of the field."

"By my faith, brother," said he of the Grove, "my stomach is not made for thistles, or wild pears, or roots out of the woods; let our masters do as they like, with their chivalry notions and laws, and eat what those enjoin; I carry my prog-basket and this bota hanging to the saddle-bow, whatever they may say; and it is such an object of worship with me, and I love it so, that there is hardly a moment but I am kissing and embracing it over and over again"; and so saying he thrust it into Sancho's hands, who raising it aloft pressed to his mouth, gazed at the stars for a quarter of an hour; and when he had done drinking let his head fall on one side, and giving a deep sigh, exclaimed, "Ah, whoreson rogue, how catholic it is!"

"There, you see," said he of the Grove as he heard Sancho's exclamation, "how you have called this wine whoreson by way of praise."

"Well," said Sancho, "I own it, and I grant it is no dishonor to call any one whoreson when it is to be understood in the sense of praise. But tell me, señor, by what you love best, is this Ciudad Real wine?"

"O rare wine-taster!" said he of the Grove; "nowhere else indeed does it come from, and it has some years' age too."

"Leave me alone for that," said Sancho; "never fear but I'll hit upon the place it came from somehow. What would you say, sir squire, to my having such a great natural instinct in judging wines that you have only to let me smell one and I can tell positively its country, its kind, its flavor and soundness, the changes it will undergo, and everything that appertains to a wine? But it is no wonder, for I have had in my family, on my father's side, the two best wine-tasters that have been known in La Mancha for many a long year, and to prove it I'll tell you now a thing that happened them. They gave the two of them some wine out of a cask, to try, asking their opinion as to the condition, quality, goodness or badness of the wine. One of them tried it with the tip of his tongue, the other did no more than bring it to his nose. The first said the wine had a flavor of iron, the second said it had a stronger flavor of cordovan. The owner said the cask was clean, and that nothing had been added to the wine from which it could have got a flavor of either iron or leather. Nevertheless, these two great wine-tasters held to what they had said. Time went by, the wine was sold, and when they came to clean out the cask, they found in it a small key hanging to a thong of cordovan; see now if one who comes of the same stock has not a right to give his opinion in such like cases."

"Therefore, I say," said he of the Grove, "let us give up going in quest of adventures, and as we have loaves let us not go looking for cakes, but return to our cribs, for God will find us there if it be his will."

"Until my master reaches Saragossa," said Sancho, "I'll remain in his service; after that we'll see."

The end of it was that the two squires talked so much and drank so much that sleep had to tie their tongues and moderate their thirst, for to quench it was impossible; and so the pair of them fell asleep clinging to the now nearly empty bota and with half-chewed morsels in their mouths; and there we will leave them for the present, to relate what passed between the Knight of the Grove and him of the Rueful Countenance.

Chapter 14

Wherein is continued the adventure of the Knight of the Grove

AMONG the many things that passed between Don Quixote and the Knight of the Wood, the history tells us he of the Grove said to Don Quixote, "In fine, sir knight, I would have you know that my destiny, or, more properly speaking, my choice led me to fall in love with the peerless Casildea de Vandalia. I call her peerless because she has no peer, whether it be in bodily stature or in the supremacy of rank and beauty. This same Casildea, then, that I speak of, requited my honorable passion and gentle aspirations by compelling me, as his stepmother did Hercules, to engage in many perils of various sorts, at the end of each promising me that, with the end of the next, the object of my hopes should be attained; but my labors have gone on increasing link by link until they are past counting, nor do I know what will be the last one that is to be the beginning of the accomplishment of my chaste desires. On one occasion she bade me go and challenge the famous giantess of Seville, La Giralda by name, who is as mighty and strong as if made of brass, and though never stirring from one spot, is the most restless and changeable woman in the world.[1] I came, I saw, I conquered, and I made her stay quiet and behave herself, for nothing but north winds blew for more than a week. Another time I was ordered to lift those ancient stones, the mighty bulls of Guisando,[2] an enterprise that might more fitly be intrusted to porters than to knights. Again, she bade me fling myself into the cavern of Cabra—an unparalleled and awful peril—and bring her a

[1] The colossal statue of Faith that acts as weathercock on top of the bell-tower of the Cathedral at Seville.

[2] Rude stone figures.

minute account of all that is concealed in those gloomy depths. I stopped the motion of the Giralda, I lifted the bulls of Guisando, I flung myself into the cavern and brought to light the secrets of its abyss; and my hopes are as dead as dead can be, and her scorn and her commands as lively as ever. To be brief, last of all she has commanded me to go through all the province of Spain and compel all the knights-errant wandering therein to confess that she surpasses all women alive to-day in beauty, and that I am the most valiant and the most deeply enamoured knight on earth; in support of which claim I have already travelled over the greater part of Spain, and have there vanquished several knights who have dared to contradict me; but what I most plume and pride myself upon is having vanquished in single combat that so famous knight Don Quixote of La Mancha, and made him confess that my Casildea is more beautiful than his Dulcinea; and in this one victory I hold myself to have conquered all the knights in the world; for this Don Quixote that I speak of has vanquished them all, and I having vanquished him, his glory, his fame, and his honor have passed and are transferred to my person; for

The more the vanquished hath of fair renown,
The greater glory gilds the victor's crown.

Thus the innumerable achievements of the said Don Quixote are now set down to my account and have become mine."

Don Quixote was amazed when he heard the Knight of the Grove, and was a thousand times on the point of telling him he lied, and had the lie direct already on the tip of his tongue; but he restrained himself as well as he could, in order to force him to confess the lie with his own lips; so he said to him quietly, "As to what you say, sir knight, about having vanquished most of the knights of Spain, or even of the whole world, I say nothing; but that you have vanquished Don Quixote of La Mancha I consider doubtful; it may have been some other that resembled him, although there are few like him."

"How! not vanquished?" said he of the Grove; "by the heaven that is above us I fought Don Quixote and overcame him and made him yield; and he is a man of tall stature, gaunt features, long, lank limbs, with hair turning gray, an aquiline nose rather hooked, and large black drooping mustaches; he does battle under the name of 'The Knight of the Rueful Countenance,' and he has for squire a peasant called Sancho Panza; he presses the loins and rules the reins of a famous steed called Rocinante; and lastly, he has for the mistress of his will a certain Dulcinea del Toboso, once upon a time called Aldonza Lorenzo, just as I call mine Casildea de Vandalia because her name is Casilda and she is of Andalusia. If all these tokens are not enough to vindicate the truth of what I say, here is my sword, that will compel incredulity itself to give credence to it."

"Calm yourself, sir knight," said Don Quixote, "and give ear to what I am about to say to you. I would have you know that this Don Quixote you speak of is the greatest friend I have in the world; so much so that I may say I regard him in the same light as my own person; and from the precise and clear indications you have given I can not but think that he must be the very one you have vanquished. On the other hand, I see with my eyes and feel with my hands that it is impossible it can have been the same; unless indeed it be that, as he has many enemies who are enchanters, and one in particular who is always persecuting him, some one of these may have taken his shape in order to allow himself to be vanquished, so as to defraud him of the fame that his exalted achievements as a knight have earned and acquired for him throughout the known world. And in confirmation of this, I must tell you, too, that it is but ten hours since these said enchanters his enemies transformed the shape and person of the fair Dulcinea del Toboso into a foul and mean village lass, and in the same way they must have transformed Don Quixote; and if all this does not suffice to convince you of the truth of what I say, here is Don Quixote himself, who will maintain it by arms, on foot or on horseback or in any way you please."

And so saying he stood up and laid his hand on his sword, waiting to see what the Knight of the Grove would do, who in an equally calm voice said in reply, "Pledges don't distress a good paymaster; he who has succeeded in vanquishing you once when transformed, Sir Don Quixote, may fairly hope to subdue you in your own proper shape; but as it is not becoming for knights to perform their feats of arms in the dark, like highwaymen and bullies, let us wait till daylight, that the sun may behold our deeds; and the conditions of our combat shall be that the vanquished shall be at the victor's disposal, to do all that he may enjoin, provided the injunction be such as shall be becoming a knight."

"I am more than satisfied with these conditions and terms," replied Don Quixote; and so saying, they betook themselves to where their squires lay, and found them snoring, and in the same posture they were in when sleep fell upon them. They roused them up, and bade them get the horses ready, as at sunrise they were to engage in a bloody and arduous single combat; at which intelligence Sancho was aghast and thunderstruck, trembling for the safety of his master because of the mighty deeds he had heard the Squire of the Grove ascribe to his; but without a word the two squires went in quest of their cattle; for by this time the three horses and the ass had smelt one another out, and were all together.

On the way, he of the Grove said to Sancho, "You must know, brother, that it is the custom with the fighting men of Andalusia, when they are godfathers in any quarrel, not to stand idle with folded arms while their godsons fight; I say so to remind you that while our masters are fighting, we, too, have to fight, and knock one another to shivers."

"That custom, sir squire," replied Sancho, "may hold good among those bullies and fighting men you talk of, but certainly not among the squires of knights-errant; at least, I have never heard my master speak of any custom of the sort, and he knows all the laws of knight-errantry by heart; but granting it true that there is an express law that squires are to fight while their masters are fighting, I don't mean to obey it, but to pay the penalty that may be laid on peacefully minded squires like myself; for I am sure it can not be more than two pounds of wax, and I would rather pay that, for I know it will cost me less than the lint I shall be at the expense of to mend my head, which I look upon as broken and split already; there's another thing that makes it impossible for me to fight, that I have no sword, for I never carried one in my life."

"I know a good remedy for that," said he of the Grove; "I have here two linen bags of the same size; you shall take one, and I the other, and we will fight at bag blows with equal arms."

"If that's the way, so be it with all my heart," said Sancho, "for that sort of battle will serve to knock the dust out of us instead of hurting us."

"That will not do," said the other, "for we must put into bags, to keep the wind from blowing them away, half a dozen nice smooth pebbles, all of the same weight; and in this way we shall be able to baste one another without doing ourselves any harm or mischief."

"Body of my father!" said Sancho, "see what marten and sable, and pads of carded cotton he is putting into the bags, that our heads may not be broken and our bones beaten to jelly! But even if they are filled with floss silk, I can tell you, señor, I am not going to fight; let our masters fight, that's their lookout, and let us drink and live; for time will take care to ease us of our lives, without our going to look for fillips so that they may be finished off before their proper time comes and they drop from ripeness."

"Still," returned he of the Grove, "we must fight, if it be only for half an hour."

"By no means," said Sancho; "I am not going to be so discourteous or so ungrateful as to have any quarrel, be it ever so small, with one I have eaten and drunk with; besides, who the devil could bring himself to fight in cold blood, without anger or provocation?"

"I can remedy that entirely," said he of the Grove, "and in this way: before we begin the battle, I will come up to your worship fair and softly, and give you three or four buffets, with which I shall stretch you at my feet and rouse your anger, though it were sleeping sounder than a dormouse."

"To match that plan," said Sancho, "I have another that is not a whit behind it; I will take a cudgel, and before your worship comes near enough to waken my anger I will send yours so sound to sleep with whacks, that it won't waken unless it be in the other world, where it is known that I am not a man to let my face be handled by any one; let each look out for the arrow—though the surer way would be to let every one's anger sleep, for nobody knows the heart of any one, and a man may come for wool and go back shorn; God gave his blessing to peace and his curse to quarrels; if a hunted cat, surrounded and hard pressed, turns into a lion, God knows what I, who am a man, may turn into; and so from this time forth I warn you, sir squire, that all the harm and mischief that may come of our quarrel will be put down to your account."

"Very good," said he of the Grove; "God will send the dawn and we shall be all right."

And now gay-plumaged birds of all sorts began to warble in the trees, and with their varied and gladsome notes seemed to welcome and salute the fresh morn that was beginning to show the beauty of her countenance at the gates and balconies of the east, shaking from her locks a profusion of liquid pearls, in which dulcet moisture bathed; the plants, too, seemed to shed and shower down a pearly spray, the willows distilled sweet manna, the fountains laughed, the brooks babbled, the woods rejoiced, and the meadows arrayed themselves in all their glory at her coming. But hardly had the light of day made it possible to see and distinguish things, when the first object that presented itself to the eyes of Sancho Panza was the Squire of the Grove's nose, which was so big that it almost overshadowed his whole body. It is, in fact, stated, that it was of enormous size, hooked in the middle, covered with warts, and of a mulberry color like an egg-plant; it hung down two fingers'-lengths below his mouth, and the size, the color, the warts, and the bend of it, made his face so hideous, that Sancho, as he looked at him, began to tremble hand and foot like a child in convulsions, and he vowed in his heart to let himself be given two hundred buffets, sooner than be provoked to fight that monster. Don Quixote examined his adversary, and found that he already had his helmet on and the visor lowered, so that he could not see his face; he observed, however, that he was a sturdily built man, but not very tall in stature. Over his armor he wore a surcoat or cassock of what seemed to be the finest cloth of gold, all bespangled with glittering mirrors like little moons, which gave him an extremely gallant and splendid appearance; above his helmet fluttered a great quantity of plumes, green, yellow, and white, and his lance, which was leaning against a tree, was very long and stout, and had a steel point more than a palm in length.

Don Quixote observed all, and took note of all, and from what he saw and observed he concluded that the said knight must be a man of great strength, but he did not for all that give way to fear, like Sancho Panza; on the contrary, with a composed and dauntless air, he said to the Knight of the Mirrors, "If, sir knight, your great eagerness to fight has not banished your courtesy, by it I would entreat you to raise your visor a little, in order that I may see if the comeliness of your countenance corresponds with that of your equipment."

"Whether you come victorious or vanquished out of this emprise, sir knight," replied he of the Mirrors, "you will have more than enough time and leisure to see me; and if now I do not comply with your request, it is because it seems to me I should do a serious wrong to the fair Casildea de Vandalia in wasting time while I stopped to raise my visor before compelling you to confess what you are already aware I maintain."

"Well then," said Don Quixote, "while we are mounting you can at least tell me if I am that Don Quixote whom you said you vanquished."

"To that we answer you," said he of the Mirrors, "that you are as like the very knight I vanquished as one egg is like another, but as you say enchanters persecute you, I will not venture to say positively whether you are the said person or not."

"That," said Don Quixote, "is enough to convince me that you are under a deception; however, entirely to relieve you of it, let our horses be brought, and in less time than it would take you to raise your visor, if God, my lady, and my arm stand me in good stead, I shall see your face, and you shall see that I am not the vanquished Don Quixote you take me to be."

With this, cutting short the colloquy, they mounted, and Don Quixote wheeled Rocinante round in order to take a proper distance to charge back upon his adversary, and he of the Mirrors did the same; but Don Quixote had not moved away twenty paces when he heard himself called by the other, and, each returning half-way, he of the Mirrors said to him, "Remember, sir knight, that the terms of our combat are, that the vanquished, as I said before, shall be at the victor's disposal."

"I am aware of it already," said Don Quixote; "provided what is commanded and imposed upon the vanquished be things that do not transgress the limits of chivalry."

"That is understood," replied he of the Mirrors.

At that moment the extraordinary nose of the squire presented itself to Don Quixote's view, and he was no less amazed than Sancho at the sight; insomuch that he set him down as a monster of some kind, or a human being of some new species or unearthly breed. Sancho, seeing his master retiring to run his course, did not like to be left alone with the nosey man, fearing that with one flap of that nose on his own face the battle would be all over for him and he would be left stretched on the ground, either by the blow or with fright; so that he ran after his master, holding on to Rocinante's stirrup-leather, and when it seemed to him time to turn about, he said, "I implore of your worship, señor, before you turn to charge, to help me up into this cork tree, from which I will be able to witness the gallant encounter your worship is going to have with this knight, more to my taste and better than from the ground."

"It seems to me rather, Sancho," said Don Quixote, "that thou wouldst mount a scaffold in order to see the bulls without danger."

"To tell the truth," returned Sancho, "the monstrous nose of that squire has filled me with fear and terror, and I dare not stay near him."

"It is," said Don Quixote, "such a one that were I not what I am it would terrify me too; so, come, I will help thee up where thou wilt."

While Don Quixote waited for Sancho to mount into the cork tree he of the Mirrors took as much ground as he considered requisite, and, supposing Don Quixote to have done the same, without waiting for any sound of trumpet or other signal to direct them, he wheeled his horse, which was not more agile or better looking than Rocinante, and at his top speed, which was an easy trot, he proceeded to charge his enemy; seeing him, however, engaged in putting Sancho up, he drew rein, and halted in mid career, for which his horse was very grateful, as he was already unable to go. Don Quixote, fancying that his foe was coming down upon him flying, drove his spurs vigorously into Rocinante's lean flanks and made him scud along in such style that the history tells us that on this occasion only was he known to make something like running, for on all others it was a simple trot with him; and with this unparalleled fury he bore down where he of the Mirrors stood digging his spurs into his horse up to the buttons, without being able to make him stir a finger's length from the spot where he had come to a standstill in his course. At this lucky moment and crisis, Don Quixote came upon his adversary, in trouble with his horse, and embarrassed with his lance, which he either could not manage, or had no time to lay in rest. Don Quixote, however, paid no attention to these difficulties, and in perfect safety to himself and without any risk encountered him of the Mirrors with such force that he brought him to the ground in spite of himself over the haunches of his horse, and with so heavy a fall that he lay to all appearance dead, not stirring hand or foot. The instant Sancho saw him fall he slid down from the cork tree, and made all haste to where his master was, who, dismounting from Rocinante, went and stood over him of the Mirrors, and unlacing his helmet to see if he was dead, and to give him air if he should happen to be alive, he saw—who can say what he saw, without filling all who hear it with astonishment, wonder, and awe? He saw, the history says, the very countenance, the very face, the very look, the very physiognomy, the very effigy, the very image of the bachelor Samson Carrasco! As soon as he saw it he called out in a loud voice, "Make haste here, Sancho, and behold what thou art to see but not to believe; quick, my son, and learn what magic can do, and wizards and enchanters are capable of."

Sancho came up, and when he saw the countenance of the bachelor Carrasco, he fell to crossing himself a thousand times, and blessing himself as many more. All this time the prostrate knight showed no signs of life, and Sancho said to Don Quixote, "It is my opinion, señor, that in any case your worship should take and thrust your sword into the mouth of this one here that looks like the bachelor Samson Carrasco; perhaps in him you will kill one of your enemies, the enchanters."

"Thy advice is not bad," said Don Quixote, "for of enemies the fewer the better"; and he was drawing his sword to carry into effect Sancho's counsel and suggestion, when the Squire of the Mirrors came up, now without the nose which had made him so hideous, and cried out in a loud voice, "Mind what you are about, Señor Don Quixote; that is your friend, the bachelor Samson Carrasco, you have at your feet, and I am his squire."

"And the nose?" said Sancho, seeing him without the hideous feature he had before; to which he replied, "I have it here in my pocket," and putting his hand into his right pocket, he pulled out a masquerade nose of varnished pasteboard of the make already described; and Sancho, examining him more and more closely, exclaimed aloud in a voice of amazement, "Holy Mary be good to me! Isn't it Tom Cecial, my neighbor and gossip?"

"Why, to be sure I am!" returned the now unnosed squire; "Tom Cecial I am, gossip and friend Sancho Panza; and I'll tell you presently the means and tricks and falsehoods by which I have been brought here; but in the meantime beg and entreat of your master not to touch, maltreat, wound, or slay the Knight of the Mirrors whom he has at his feet; because, beyond all dispute, it is the rash and ill-advised bachelor Samson Carrasco, our fellow townsman."

At this moment he of the Mirrors came to himself, and Don Quixote perceiving it, held the naked point of his sword over his face, and said to him, "You are a dead man, knight, unless you confess that the peerless Dulcinea del Toboso excels your Casildea de Vandalia in beauty; and in addition to this you must promise, if you should survive this enounter and fall, to go to the city of El Toboso and present yourself before her on my behalf, that she deal with you according to her good pleasure; and if she leaves you free to do yours, you are in like manner to return and seek me out (for the trail of my mighty deeds will serve you as a guide to lead you to where I may be), and tell me what may have passed between you and her—conditions which, in accordance with what we stipulated before our combat, do not transgress the just limits of knight-errantry."

"I confess," said the fallen knight, "that the dirty tattered shoe of the lady Dulcinea del Toboso is better than the ill-combed though clean beard of Casildea; and I promise to go and to return from her presence to yours, and to give you a full and particular account of all you demand of me."

"You must also confess and believe," added Don Quixote, "that the knight you vanquished was not and could not be Don Quixote of La Mancha, but some one else in his likeness, just as I confess and believe that you, though you seem to be the bachelor Samson Carrasco, are not so, but some other resembling him, whom my enemies have here put before me in his shape, in order that I may restrain and moderate the vehemence of my wrath, and make a gentle use of the glory of my victory."

"I confess, hold, and think everything to be as you believe, hold, and think it," replied the crippled knight; "let me rise, I entreat you; if, indeed, the shock of my fall will allow me, for it has left me in a sorry plight enough."

Don Quixote helped him to rise, with the assistance of his squire Tom Cecial; from whom Sancho never took his eyes, and to whom he put questions, the replies to which furnished clear proof that he was really and truly the Tom Cecial he said; but the impression made on Sancho's mind by what his master said about the enchanters having changed the face of the Knight of the Mirrors into that of the bachelor Samson Carrasco, would not permit him to believe what he saw with his eyes. In fine, both master and man remained under the delusion; and, down in the mouth, and out of luck, he of the Mirrors and his squire parted from Don Quixote and Sancho, he meaning to go look for some village where he could plaster and strap his ribs. Don Quixote and Sancho resumed their journey to Saragossa, and on it the history leaves them in order that it may tell who the Knight of the Mirrors and his long-nosed squire were.

Chapter 15

Wherein it is told and made known who the Knight of the Mirrors and his squire were

Don Quixote went off satisfied, elated, and vain-glorious in the highest degree at hav-

ing won a victory over such a valiant knight as he fancied him of the Mirrors to be, and one from whose knightly word he expected to learn whether the enchantment of his lady still continued; inasmuch as the said vanquished knight was bound, under the penalty of ceasing to be one, to return and render him an account of what took place between him and her. But Don Quixote was of one mind, he of the Mirrors of another, for he just then had no thought of anything but finding some village where he could plaster himself, as has been said already. The history goes on to say, then, that when the bachelor Samson Carrasco recommended Don Quixote to resume his knight-errantry which he had laid aside, it was in consequence of having been previously in conclave with the curate and the barber on the means to be adopted to induce Don Quixote to stay at home in peace and quiet without worrying himself with his ill-starred adventures; at which consultation it was decided by the unanimous vote of all, and on the special advice of Carrasco, that Don Quixote should be allowed to go, as it seemed impossible to restrain him, and that Samson should sally forth to meet him as a knight-errant, and do battle with him, for there would be no difficulty about a cause, and vanquish him, that being looked upon as an easy matter; and that it should be agreed and settled that the vanquished was to be at the mercy of the victor. Then Don Quixote being vanquished, the bachelor knight was to command him to return to his village and his house, and not quit it for two years, or until he received further orders from him; all which it was clear Don Quixote would unhesitatingly obey, rather than contravene or fail to observe the laws of chivalry; and during the period of his seclusion he might perhaps forget his folly, or there might be an opportunity of discovering some ready remedy for his madness. Carrasco undertook the task, and Tom Cecial, a gossip and neighbor of Sancho Panza's, a lively, feather-headed fellow, offered himself as his squire. Carrasco armed himself in the fashion described, and Tom Cecial, that he might not be known by his gossip when they met, fitted on over his own natural nose the false masquerade one that has been mentioned; and so they followed the same route Don Quixote took, and almost came up with him in time to be present at the adventure of the cart of Death; and finally encountered them in the grove, where all that the sagacious reader has been reading about took place; and had it not been for the extraordinary fancies of Don Quixote, and his conviction that the bachelor was not the bachelor, señor bachelor would have been incapacitated forever from taking his degree of licentiate, all through not finding nests where he thought to find birds.

Tom Cecial, seeing how ill they had succeeded, and what a sorry end their expedition had come to, said to the bachelor, "Sure enough, Señor Samson Carrasco, we are served right; it is easy enough to plan and set about an enterprise, but it is often a difficult matter to come well out of it. Don Quixote a madman, and we sane; he goes off laughing, safe, and sound, and you are left sore and sorry! I'd like to know now which is the madder, he who is so because he can not help it, or he who is so of his own choice?"

To which Samson replied, "The difference between the two sorts of madmen is, that he who is so will he nill he, will be one always, while he who is so of his own accord can leave off being one whenever he likes."

"In that case," said Tom Cecial, "I was a madman of my own accord when I volunteered to become your squire, and, of my own accord, I'll leave off being one and go home."

"That's your affair," returned Samson, "but to suppose that I am going home until I have given Don Quixote a thrashing is absurd; and it is not any wish that he may recover his senses that will make me hunt him out now, but a wish for revenge; for the sore pain I am in with my ribs won't let me entertain more charitable thoughts."

Thus discoursing, the pair proceeded until they reached a town where it was their good luck to find a bone-setter, with whose help the unfortunate Samson was cured. Tom Cecial left him and went home, while he stayed behind meditating vengeance; and the history will return to him again at the proper time, so as not to omit making merry with Don Quixote now.

Chapter 16

Of what befell Don Quixote with a discreet gentleman of La Mancha

DON QUIXOTE pursued his journey in the high spirits, satisfaction, and self-complacency already described, fancying himself the most valorous knight-errant of the age in the world because of his late victory. All the adventures that could befall him from that time forth he regarded as already done and brought to a happy issue; he made light of enchantments and enchanters;

he thought no more of the countless drubbing that had been administered to him in the course of his knight-errantry, nor of the volley of stone that had levelled half his teeth, nor of the in gratitude of the galley slaves, nor of the audac ity of the Yanguesans and the shower of stakes that fell upon him; in short, he said to himsel that could he discover any means, mode, or way of disenchanting his lady Dulcinea, he woulc not envy the highest fortune that the most for tunate knight-errant of yore ever reached o could reach.

He was going along entirely absorbed in these fancies, when Sancho said to him, "Isn't it odd señor, that I have still before my eyes that mon strous enormous nose of my gossip, Tom Ce cial?"

"And dost thou, then, believe, Sancho," saic Don Quixote, "that the Knight of the Mirror was the bachelor Carrasco, and his squire Ton Cecial thy gossip?"

"I don't know what to say to that," repliec Sancho; "all I know is that the tokens he gave me about my own house, wife and children, no body else but himself could have given me and the face, once the nose was off, was the very face of Tom Cecial, as I have seen it many a time in my town and next door to my owr house; and the sound of the voice was just the same."

"Let us reason the matter, Sancho," said Dor Quixote. "Come now, by what process of think ing can it be supposed that the bachelor Sam son Carrasco would come as a knight-errant, ir arms offensive and defensive, to fight with me Have I ever been by any chance his enemy Have I ever given him any occasion to owe me a grudge? Am I his rival, or does he profess arms that he should envy the fame I have acquirec in them?"

"Well, but what are we to say, señor," re turned Sancho, "about that knight, whoever he is, being so like the bachelor Carrasco, and hi squire so like my gossip, Tom Cecial? And i that be enchantment, as your worship says, was there no other pair in the world for them to take the likeness of?"

"It is all," said Don Quixote, "a scheme anc plot of the malignant magicians that persecute me, who, foreseeing that I was to be victorious in the conflict, arranged that the vanquishec knight should display the countenance of my friend the bachelor, in order that the friendship I bear him should interpose to stay the edge o my sword and might of my arm, and temper the just wrath of my heart; so that he who sough to take my life by fraud and falsehood should save his own. And to prove it, thou knowest already, Sancho, by experience which can not lie or deceive, how easy it is for enchanters to change one countenance into another, turning fair into foul, and foul into fair; for it is not two days since thou sawest with thine own eyes the beauty and elegance of the peerless Dulcinea in all its perfection and natural harmony, while I saw her in the repulsive and mean form of a coarse country wench, with cataracts in her eyes and a foul smell in her mouth; and when the perverse enchanter ventured to effect so wicked a transformation, it is no wonder if he effected that of Samson Carrasco and thy gossip in order to snatch the glory of victory out of my grasp. For all that, however, I console myself, because, after all, in whatever shape he may have been, I have been victorious over my enemy."

"God knows what's the truth of it all," said Sancho; and knowing as he did that the transformation of Dulcinea had been a device and imposition of his own, his master's illusions were not satisfactory to him; but he did not like to reply lest he should say something that might disclose his trickery.

As they were engaged in this conversation they were overtaken by a man who was following the same road behind them, mounted on a very handsome flea-bitten mare, and dressed in a gaban of fine green cloth, with tawny velvet facings, and a montera of the same velvet. The trappings of the mare were of the field and jineta fashion, and of mulberry color and green. He carried a Moorish cutlass hanging from a broad green and gold baldric; the buskins were of the same make as the baldric; the spurs were not gilt, but lacquered green, and so brightly polished that, matching as they did the rest of his apparel, they looked better than if they had been of pure gold.

When the traveller came up with them he saluted them courteously, and spurring his mare was passing them without stopping, but Don Quixote called out to him, "Gallant sir, if so be your worship is going our road, and has no occasion for speed, it would be a pleasure to me if we were to join company."

"In truth," replied he on the mare, "I would not pass you so hastily but for fear that horse might turn restive in the company of my mare."

"You may safely hold in your mare, señor," said Sancho in reply to this, "for our horse is the most virtuous and well-behaved horse in the world; he never does anything wrong on such occasions, and the only time he misbehaved, my master and I suffered for it sevenfold; I say again your worship may pull up if you like; for if she was offered to him between two plates the horse would not hanker after her."

The traveller drew rein, amazed at the trim and features of Don Quixote, who rode without his helmet, which Sancho carried like a valise in front of Dapple's pack-saddle; and if the man in green examined Don Quixote closely, still more closely did Don Quixote examine the man in green, who struck him as being a man of intelligence. In appearance he was about fifty years of age, with but few gray hairs, an aquiline cast of features, and an expression between grave and gay; and his dress and accoutrements showed him to be a man of good condition. What he in green thought of Don Quixote of La Mancha was that a man of that sort and shape he had never yet seen; he marvelled at the length of his hair, his lofty stature, the lankness and sallowness of his countenance, his armor, his bearing and his gravity—a figure and picture such as had not been seen in those regions for many a long day.

Don Quixote saw very plainly the attention with which the traveller was regarding him, and read his curiosity in his astonishment; and courteous as he was and ready to please everybody, before the other could ask him any question he anticipated him by saying, "The appearance I present to your worship being so strange and so out of the common, I should not be surprised if it filled you with wonder; but you will cease to wonder when I tell you, as I do, that I am one of those knights who, as people say, go seeking adventures. I have left my home, I have mortgaged my estate, I have given up my comforts, and committed myself to the arms of Fortune, to bear me whithersoever she may please. My desire was to bring to life again knight-errantry, now dead, and for some time past, stumbling here, falling there, now coming down headlong, now raising myself up again, I have carried out a great portion of my design, succoring widows, protecting maidens, and giving aid to wives, orphans, and minors, the proper and natural duty of knights-errants; and, therefore, because of my many valiant and Christian achievements, I have been already found worthy to make my way in print to well-nigh all, or most, of the nations of the earth. Thirty-thousand volumes of my history have been printed, and it is on the high-road to be printed thirty-thousand thousands of times, if Heaven does not put a stop to it. In short to sum up all in a few words, or in a single one, I may tell you I am Don Quixote of

La Mancha, otherwise called 'The Knight of the Rueful Countenance'; for though self-praise is degrading, I must perforce sound my own sometimes, that is to say, when there is no one at hand to do it for me. So that, gentle sir, neither this horse, nor this lance, nor this shield, nor this squire, nor all these arms put together, nor the sallowness of my countenance, nor my gaunt leanness, will henceforth astonish you, now that you know who I am and what profession I follow."

With these words Don Quixote held his peace, and, from the time he took to answer, the man in green seemed to be at a loss for a reply; after a long pause, however, he said to him, "You were right when you saw curiosity in my amazement, sir knight; but you have not succeeded in removing the astonishment I feel at seeing you; for although you say, señor, that knowing who you are ought to remove it, it has not done so; on the contrary, now that I know, I am left more amazed and astonished than before. What! is it possible that there are knights-errant in the world in these days, and histories of real chivalry printed? I can not realize the fact that there can be any one on earth now-a-days who aids widows, or protects maidens, or defends wives, or succors orphans; nor should I believe it had I not seen it in your worship with my own eyes. Blessed be Heaven! for by means of this history of your noble and genuine chivalrous deeds, which you say has been printed, the countless stories of fictitious knights-errant with which the world is filled, so much to the injury of morality and the prejudice and discredit of good histories, will have been driven into oblivion."

"There is a good deal to be said on that point," said Don Quixote, "as to whether the histories of the knights-errant are fiction or not."

"Why, is there any one who doubts that those histories are false?" said the man in green.

"I doubt it," said Don Quixote, "but never mind that just now; if our journey lasts long enough, I trust in God I shall show your worship that you do wrong in going with the stream of those who regard it as a matter of certainty that they are not true."

From this last observation of Don Quixote's, the traveller began to have a suspicion that he was some crazy being, and was waiting him to confirm it by something further; but before they could turn to any new subject Don Quixote begged him to tell him who he was, since he himself had rendered account of his station and life. To this, he in the green gaban replied, "I,

Sir Knight of the Rueful Countenance, am a gentleman by birth, native of the village where, please God, we are going to dine to-day; I am more than fairly well off, and my name is Don Diego de Miranda. I pass my life with my wife, children, and friends; my pursuits are hunting and fishing, but I keep neither hawks nor greyhounds, nothing but a tame partridge or a bold ferret or two; I have six dozen or so of books, some in our mother tongue, some Latin, some of them history, others devotional; those of chivalry have not as yet crossed the threshold of my door; I am more given to turning over the profane than the devotional, so long as they are books of honest entertainment that charm by their style and attract and interest by the invention they display, though of these there are very few in Spain. Sometimes I dine with my neighbors and friends, and often invite them; my entertainments are neat and well served without stint of anything. I have no taste for tattle, nor do I allow tattling in my presence; I pry not into my neighbors' lives, nor have I lynx-eyes for what others do. I hear Mass every day; I share my substance with the poor, making no display of good works, lest I let hypocrisy and vainglory, those enemies that subtly take possession of the most watchful heart, find an entrance into mine. I strive to make peace between those whom I know to be at variance; I am the devoted servant of Our Lady, and my trust is ever in the infinite mercy of God our Lord."

Sancho listened with the greatest attention to the account of the gentleman's life and occupations; and thinking it a good and a holy life, and that he who led it ought to work miracles, he threw himself off Dapple, and running in haste seized his right stirrup and kissed his foot again and again with a devout heart and almost with tears.

Seeing this the gentleman asked him, "What are you about, brother? What are these kisses for?"

"Let me kiss," said Sancho, "for I think your worship is the first saint in the saddle I ever saw all the days of my life."

"I am no saint," replied the gentleman, "but a great sinner; but you are, brother, for you must be a good fellow, as your simplicity shows."

Sancho went back and regained his pack-saddle, having extracted a laugh from his master's profound melancholy, and excited fresh amazement in Don Diego. Don Quixote then asked him how many children he had, and observed that one of the things wherein the ancient philosophers, who were without the true knowledge of God, placed the *summum bonum* was in the gifts of nature, in those of fortune, in having many friends, and many and good children.

"I, Señor Don Quixote," answered the gentleman, "have one son, without whom, perhaps, I should count myself happier than I am, not because he is a bad son, but because he is not so good as I could wish. He is eighteen years of age; he has been for six at Salamanca studying Latin and Greek, and when I wished him to turn to the study of other sciences I found him so wrapped up in that of poetry (if that can be called a science) that there is no getting him to take kindly to the law, which I wished him to study, or to theology, the queen of them all. I would like him to be an honor to his family, as we live in days when our kings liberally reward learning that is virtuous and worthy; for learning without virtue is a pearl on a dunghill. He spends the whole day in settling whether Homer expressed himself correctly or not in such and such a line of the *Iliad,* whether Martial was indecent or not in such and such an epigram, whether such and such lines of Virgil are to be understood in this way or in that; in short, all his talk is of the works of these poets, and those of Horace, Persius, Juvenal, and Tibullus; for of the moderns in our language he makes no great account; but with all his seeming indifference to Spanish poetry, just now his thoughts are absorbed in making a gloss on four lines that have been sent him from Salamanca, which I suspect are for some poetical tournament."

To all this Don Quixote said in reply, "Children, señor, are portions of their parents' bowels, and therefore, be they good or bad, are to be loved as we love the souls that give us life; it is for the parents to guide them from infancy in the ways of virtue, propriety, and worthy Christian conduct, so that when grown up they may be the staff of their parents' old age, and the glory of their posterity; and to force them to study this or that science I do not think wise, though it may be no harm to persuade them; and when there is no need to study for the sake of *pane lucrando,* and it is the student's good fortune that Heaven has given him parents who provide him with it, it would be my advice to them to let him pursue whatever science they may see him most inclined to; and though that of poetry is less useful than pleasurable, it is not one of those that bring discredit upon the possessor. Poetry, gentle sir, is, as I take it, like a tender young maiden of supreme beauty, to array, bedeck, and adorn whom is the task of several other maidens, who are all the rest of the sciences; and she must avail herself of the help of all, and all derive their lustre from her. But this maiden will not bear to be handled, nor dragged through the streets, nor exposed either at the corners of the market-places, or in the closets of palaces. She is the product of an Alchemy of such virtue that he who is able to practise it, will turn her into pure gold of inestimable worth. He that possesses her must keep her within bounds, not permitting her to break out in ribald satires or soulless sonnets. She must on no account be offered for sale, unless, indeed, it be in heroic poems, moving tragedies, or sprightly and ingenious comedies. She must not be touched by the buffoons, nor by the ignorant vulgar, incapable of comprehending or appreciating her hidden treasures. And do not suppose, señor, that I apply the term vulgar here merely to plebeians and the lower orders; for every one who is ignorant, be he lord or prince, may and should be included among the vulgar. He, then, who shall embrace and cultivate poetry under the conditions I have named, shall become famous, and his name honored throughout all the civilized nations of the earth. And with regard to what you say, señor, of your son having no great opinion of Spanish poetry, I am inclined to think that he is not quite right there, and for this reason: the great poet Homer did not write in Latin, because he was a Greek, nor did Virgil write in Greek, because he was a Latin; in short, all the ancient poets wrote in the language they imbibed with their mother's milk, and never went in quest of foreign ones to express their sublime conceptions; and that being so, the usage should in justice extend to all nations, and the German poet should not be undervalued because he writes in his own language, nor the Castilian, nor even the Biscayan, for writing in his. But your son, señor, I suspect, is not prejudiced against Spanish poetry, but against those poets who are mere Spanish verse writers, without any knowledge of other languages or sciences to adorn and give life and vigor to their natural inspiration; and yet even in this he may be wrong; for, according to a true belief, a poet is born one; that is to say, the poet by nature comes forth a poet from his mother's womb; and following the bent that Heaven has bestowed upon him, without the aid of study or art, he produces things that show how truly he spoke who said, '*Est Deus in nobis,*' etc. At the same time, I say that the poet by nature who calls in art to his aid will be a far better poet, and will surpass him who tries to be one relying upon his knowledge of art alone. The reason is, that art does not surpass nature, but only brings it to perfection; and thus, nature combined with art, and art with nature, will produce a perfect poet. To bring my argument to a close, I would say then, gentle sir, let your son go on as his star leads him, for being so studious as he seems to be, and having already successfully surmounted the first step of the sciences, which is that of the languages, with their help he will by his own exertions reach the summit of polite literature, which so well becomes an independent gentleman, and adorns, honors, and distinguishes him, as much as the mitre does the bishop, or the gown the learned counsellor. If your son write satires reflecting on the honor of others, chide and correct him, and tear them up; but if he compose discourses in which he rebukes vice in general, in the style of Horace, and with elegance like his, commend him; for it is legitimate for a poet to write against envy and lash the envious in his verse, and the other vices too, provided he does not single out individuals; there are, however, poets who, for the sake of saying something spiteful, would run the risk of being banished to the coast of Pontus. If the poet be pure in his morals, he will be pure in his verses too; the pen is the tongue of the mind, and as the thought engendered there, so will be the things that it writes down. And when kings and princes observe this marvellous science of poetry in wise, virtuous, and thoughtful subjects, they honor, value, exalt them, and even crown them with the leaves of that tree which the thunderbolt strikes not, as if to show that they whose brows are honored and adorned with such a crown are not to be assailed by any one."

He of the green gaban was filled with astonishment at Don Quixote's argument, so much so that he began to abandon the notion he had taken up about his being crazy. But in the middle of the discourse, it being not very much to his taste, Sancho had turned aside out of the road to beg a little milk from some shepherds, who were milking their ewes hard by; and just as the gentleman, highly pleased with Don Quixote's sound sense and intelligence, was about to renew the conversation, Don Quixote, raising his head, perceived a cart covered with royal flags coming along the road they were travelling; and persuaded that this must be some new adventure, he called aloud to Sancho to come and bring him helmet. Sancho, hearing himself called, quitted the shepherds, and, prodding Dapple vigorously, came up to his master, to whom there fell a terrific and desperate adventure.

Chapter 17

Wherein is shown the furthest and highest point which the unexampled courage of Don Quixote reached or could reach; together with the happily achieved adventure of the lions

WHEN the author of this great history comes to relate what is set down in this chapter he says he would have preferred to pass it over in silence, fearing it would not be believed, because here Don Quixote's madness reaches the confines of the greatest that can be conceived, and even goes a couple of bowshots beyond the greatest. But after all, though still under the same fear and apprehension, he has recorded it without adding to the story or leaving out a particle of the truth, and entirely disregarding the charges of falsehood that might be brought against him; and he was right, for the truth may run fine but will not break, and always rises above falsehood as oil above water; and so, going on with his story, he says that when Don Quixote called out to Sancho to bring him his helmet, Sancho was buying some curds the shepherds agreed to sell him, and flurried by the great haste his master was in did not know what to do with them or what to carry them in; so, not to lose them, for he had already paid for them, he thought it best to throw them into his master's helmet, and acting on this bright idea he went to see what his master wanted with him. He, as he approached, exclaimed to him, "Give me that helmet, my friend, for either I know little of adventures, or what I observe yonder is one that will, and does, call upon me to arm myself." He of the green gaban, on hearing this, looked in all directions, but could perceive nothing, except a cart coming towards them with two or three small flags, which led him to conclude it must be carrying treasure of the King's, and he said so to Don Quixote. He, however, would not believe him, being always persuaded and convinced that all that happened to him must be adventures and still more adventures; so he replied to the gentleman, "He who is prepared has his battle half fought; nothing is lost by my preparing myself, for I know by experience that I have enemies, visible and invisible, and I know not when, or where, or at what moment, or in what shapes they will attack me"; and turning to Sancho he called for his helmet; and Sancho, as he had no time to take out the curds, had to give it just as it was. Don Quixote took it, and without perceiving what was in it thrust it down in hot haste upon his head; but as the curds were pressed and squeezed the whey began to run all over his face and beard, whereat he was so startled that he cried out to Sancho, "Sancho, what's this? I think my head is softening, or my brains are melting, or I am sweating from head to foot! If I am sweating it is not indeed from fear. I am convinced beyond a doubt that the adventure which is about to befall me is a terrible one. Give me something to wipe myself with, if thou hast it, for this profuse sweat is blinding me."

Sancho held his tongue, and gave him a cloth, and gave thanks to God at the same time that his master had not found out what was the matter. Don Quixote then wiped himself, and took off his helmet to see what it was that made his head feel so cool, and seeing all that white mash inside his helmet he put it to his nose, and as soon as he had smelt it he exclaimed, "By the life of my lady Dulcinea del Toboso, but it is curds thou hast put here, thou treacherous, impudent, ill-mannered squire!"

To which, with great composure and pretended innocence, Sancho replied, "If they are curds let me have them, your worship, and I'll eat them; but let the devil eat them, for it must have been he who put them there. I dare to dirty your worship's helmet! You have guessed the offender finely! Faith, sir, by the light God gives me, it seems I must have enchanters too, that persecute me as a creature and limb of your worship, and they must have put that nastiness there in order to provoke your patience to anger, and make you baste my ribs as you are wont to do. Well, this time, indeed, they have missed their aim, for I trust to my master's good sense to see that I have got no curds or milk, or anything of the sort; and that if I had, it is in my stomach I would put it and not in the helmet."

"May be so," said Don Quixote. All this the gentleman was observing, and with astonishment, more especially when, after having wiped himself clean, his head, face, beard, and helmet, Don Quixote put it on, and settling himself firmly in his stirrups, easing his sword in the scabbard, and grasping his lance, he cried, "Now, come who will, here am I, ready to try conclusions with Satan himself in person!"

By this time the cart with the flags had come up, unattended by any one except the carter on a mule, and a man sitting in front. Don Quixote planted himself before it and said, "Whither are you going, brothers? What cart is this? What have you got in it? What flags are those?"

To this the carter replied, "The cart is mine; what is in it is a pair of fine caged lions, which the governor of Oran is sending to court as a present to his Majesty; and the flags are our lord the King's, to show that what is here is his property."

"And are the lions large?" asked Don Quixote.

"So large," replied the man who sat at the door of the cart, "that larger, or as large, have never crossed from Africa to Spain; I am the keeper, and I have brought over others, but never any like these. They are male and female; the male in that first cage and the female in the one behind, and they are hungry now, for they have eaten nothing to-day, so let your worship stand aside, for we must make haste to the place where we are to feed them."

Hereupon, smiling slightly, Don Quixote exclaimed, "Lion-whelps to me! to me whelps of lions, and at such a time! Then, by God! those gentlemen who send them here shall see if I am a man to be frightened by lions. Get down, my good fellow, and as you are the keeper open the cages, and turn me out those beasts, and in the midst of this plain I will let them know who Don Quixote of La Mancha is, in spite and in the teeth of the enchanters who send them to me."

"So, so," said the gentleman to himself at this; "our worthy knight has shown of what sort he is; the curds, no doubt, have softened his skull and brought his brains to a head."

At this instant Sancho came up to him, saying, "Señor, for God's sake do something to keep my master, Don Quixote, from tackling these lions; for if he does they'll tear us all to pieces here."

"Is your master then so mad," asked the gentleman, "that you believe and are afraid he will engage such fierce animals?"

"He is not mad," said Sancho, "but he is venturesome."

"I will prevent it," said the gentleman; and going over to Don Quixote, who was insisting upon the keeper's opening the cages, he said to him, "Sir knight, knights-errant should attempt adventures which encourage the hope of a successful issue, not those which entirely withhold it; for valor that trenches upon temerity savors rather of madness than of courage; moreover, these lions do not come to oppose you, nor do they dream of such a thing; they are going as presents to his Majesty, and it will not be right to stop them or delay their journey."

"Gentle sir," replied Don Quixote, "you go and mind your tame partridge and your bold ferret, and leave every one to manage his own business; this is mine, and I know whether these gentlemen the lions come to me or not"; and then turning to the keeper he exclaimed, "By all that's good, sir scoundrel, if you don't open the cages this very instant, I'll pin you to the cart with this lance."

The carter, seeing the determination of this apparition in armor, said to him, "Please your worship, for charity's sake, señor, let me unyoke the mules and place myself in safety along with them before the lions are turned out; for if they kill them on me I am ruined for life, for all I possess is this cart and mules."

"O man of little faith," replied Don Quixote, "get down and unyoke; you will soon see that you are exerting yourself for nothing, and that you might have spared yourself the trouble."

The carter got down and with all speed unyoked the mules, and the keeper called out at the top of his voice, "I call all here to witness that against my will and under compulsion I open the cages and let the lions loose, and that I warn this gentleman that he will be accountable for all the harm and mischief which these beasts may do, and for my salary and dues as well. You, gentlemen, place yourselves in safety before I open, for I know they will do me no harm."

Once more the gentleman strove to persuade Don Quixote not to do such a mad thing, as it was tempting God to engage in such a piece of folly. To this, Don Quixote replied that he knew what he was about. The gentleman in return entreated him to reflect, for he knew he was under a delusion.

"Well, señor," answered Don Quixote, "if you do not like to be a spectator of this tragedy, as in your opinion it will be, spur your flea-bitten mare and place yourself in safety."

Hearing this, Sancho with tears in his eyes entreated him to give up an enterprise compared with which the one of the windmills, and the awful one of the fulling mills, and, in fact, all the feats he had attempted in the whole course of his life, were cakes and fancy bread. "Look ye, señor," said Sancho, "there's no enchantment here, nor anything of the sort, for between the bars and chinks of the cage I have seen the paw of a real lion, and judging by that I reckon the lion such a paw could belong to must be bigger than a mountain."

"Fear, at any rate," replied Don Quixote, "will make him look bigger to thee than half the world. Retire, Sancho, and leave me; and if I die here thou knowest our old compact; thou wilt repair to Dulcinea—I say no more." To these he added some further words that banished all hope of his giving up his insane project. He of the green gaban would have offered resistance, but he found himself ill-matched as to arms, and did not think it prudent to come to blows with a madman, for such Don Quixote had shown himself to be in every respect; and the latter, renewing his commands to the keeper and repeating his threats, gave warning to the gentleman to spur his mare, Sancho his Dapple, and the carter his mules, all striving to get away from the cart as far as they could before the lions broke loose. Sancho was weeping over his master's death, for this time he firmly believed it was in store for him from the claws of the lions; and he cursed his fate and called it an unlucky hour when he thought of taking service with him again; but with all his tears and lamentations he did not forget to thrash Dapple so as to put a good space between himself and the cart. The keeper, seeing that the fugitives were now some distance off, once more entreated and warned Don Quixote as he had entreated and warned him before; but he replied that he heard him, and that he need not trouble himself with any further warnings or entreaties, as they would be fruitless, and bade him make haste.

During the delay that occurred while the keeper was opening the first cage, Don Quixote was considering whether it would not be well to do battle on foot, instead of on horseback, and finally resolved to fight on foot, fearing that Rocinante might take fright at the sight of the lions; he therefore sprang off his horse, flung his lance aside, braced his buckler on his arm, and drawing his sword, advanced slowly with marvellous intrepidity and resolute courage, to plant himself in front of the cart, commending himself with all his heart, first to God, and then to his lady Dulcinea.

It is to be observed, that on coming to this passage, the author of this veracious history breaks out into exclamations. "O doughty Don Quixote! high mettled past extolling! Mirror, wherein all the heroes of the world may see themselves! Second and modern Don Manuel de Leon, once the glory and honor of Spanish knighthood! In what words shall I describe this dread exploit, by what language shall I make it credible to ages to come, what eulogies are there unmeet for thee, though they be hyperboles piled on hyperboles! On foot, alone, undaunted, high-souled, with but a simple sword, and that no trenchant blade of the Perrillo brand, a shield, but no bright polished steel one, there stoodst thou, biding and awaiting the two fiercest lions that Afric's forests ever bred! Thy own deeds be thy praise, O valiant Manchegan, and here I leave them as they stand, wanting the words wherewith to glorify them!"

Here the author's outburst came to an end, and he proceeded to take up the thread of his story, saying that the keeper, seeing that Don Quixote had taken up his position, and that it was impossible for him to avoid letting out the male without incurring the enmity of the fiery and daring knight, flung open the doors of the first cage, containing, as has been said, the lion, which was now seen to be of enormous size, and grim and hideous mien. The first thing he did was to turn round in the cage in which he lay, and protrude his claws, and stretch himself thoroughly; he next opened his mouth, and yawned very leisurely, and with near two palms'-length of tongue that he had thrust forth, he licked the dust out of his eyes and washed his face; having done this, he put his head out of the cage and looked all round with eyes like glowing coals, a spectacle and demeanor to strike terror into temerity itself. Don Quixote merely observed him steadily, longing for him to leap from the cart and come to close quarters with him, when he hoped to hew him in pieces.

So far did his unparalleled madness go; but the noble lion, more courteous than arrogant, not troubling himself about silly bravado, after having looked all round, as has been said, turned about and presented his hind-quarters to Don Quixote, and very coolly and tranquilly lay down again in the cage. Seeing this, Don Quixote ordered the keeper to take a stick to him and provoke him to make him come out.

"That I won't," said the keeper; "for if I anger him, the first he'll tear to pieces will be myself. Be satisfied, sir knight, with what you have done, which leaves nothing more to be said on the score of courage, and do not seek to tempt fortune a second time. The lion has the door open; he is free to come out or not to come out; but as he has not come out so far, he will not come out to-day. The greatness of your worship's courage has been fully manifested already; no brave champion, so it strikes me, is bound to do more than challenge his enemy and wait for him on the field; if his adversary does not come, on him lies the disgrace, and he who waits for him carries off the crown of victory."

"That is true," said Don Quixote; "close the door, my friend, and let me have, in the best form thou canst, what thou hast seen me do, by way of certificate; to wit, that thou didst open for the lion, that I waited for him, that he did not come out, that I still waited for him, and that still he did not come out, and lay down again. I am not bound to do more; enchantments avaunt, and God uphold the right, the truth, and true chivalry! Close the door as I bade thee, while I make signals to the fugitives that have left us, that they may learn this exploit from my lips."

The keeper obeyed, and Don Quixote, fixing on the point of his lance the cloth he had wiped his face with after the deluge of curds, proceeded to recall the others, who still continued to fly, looking back at every step, all in a body, the gentleman bringing up the rear. Sancho, however, happening to observe the signal of the white cloth, exclaimed, "May I die, if my master has not overcome the wild beasts, for he is calling to us."

They all stopped, and perceived that it was Don Quixote who was making signals, and shaking off their fears to some extent, they approached slowly until they were near enough to hear distinctly Don Quixote's voice calling to them. They returned at length to the cart, and as they came up, Don Quixote said to the carter, "Put your mules to once more, brother, and continue your journey; and do thou, Sancho, give him two gold crowns for himself and the keeper, to compensate for the delay they have incurred through me."

"That will I give with all my heart," said Sancho; "but what has become of the lions? Are they dead or alive?"

The keeper, then, in full detail, and bit by bit, described the end of the contest, exalting to the best of his power and ability the valor of Don Quixote, at the sight of whom the lion quailed, and would not and dared not come out of the cage, although he had held the door open ever so long; and showing how, in consequence of his having represented to the knight that it was tempting God to provoke the lion in order to force him out, which he wished to have done, he very reluctantly, and altogether against his will, had allowed the door to be closed.

"What dost thou think of this, Sancho?" said Don Quixote. "Are there any enchantments that can prevail against true valor? The enchanters may be able to rob me of good fortune, but of fortitude and courage they can not."

Sancho paid the crowns, the carter put to, the keeper kissed Don Quixote's hands for the bounty bestowed upon him, and promised to give an account of the valiant exploit to the King himself, as soon as he saw him at court.

"Then," said Don Quixote, "if his Majesty should happen to ask who performed it, you must say THE KNIGHT OF THE LIONS; for it is my desire that into this the name I have hitherto borne of Knight of the Rueful Countenance be from this time forward changed, altered, transformed, and turned; and in this I follow the ancient usage of knights-errant, who changed their names when they pleased, or when it suited their purpose."

The cart went its way, and Don Quixote, Sancho, and he of the green gaban went theirs. All this time, Don Diego de Miranda had not spoken a word, being entirely taken up with observing and noting all that Don Quixote did and said, and the opinion he formed was that he was a man of brains gone mad, and a madman on the verge of rationality. The first part of his history had not yet reached him, for, had he read it, the amazement with which his words and deeds filled him would have vanished, as he would then have understood the nature of his madness; but knowing nothing of it, he took him to be rational one moment, and crazy the next, for what he said was sensible, elegant, and well expressed, and what he did, absurd, rash, and foolish; and said he to himself, "What could be madder than putting on a helmet full of curds, and then persuading one's self that enchanters are softening one's skull? or what could be greater rashness and folly than wanting to fight lions tooth and nail?"

Don Quixote roused him from these reflections and this soliloquy by saying, "No doubt, Señor Don Diego de Miranda, you set me down in your mind as a fool and a madman, and it would be no wonder if you did, for my deeds do not argue anything else. But for all that, I would have you take notice that I am neither so mad nor so foolish as I must have seemed to you. A gallant knight shows to advantage bringing his lance to bear adroitly upon a fierce bull under the eyes of his sovereign, in the midst of a spacious plaza; a knight shows to advantage arrayed in glittering armor, pacing the lists before the ladies in some joyous tournament, and all those knights show to advantage that entertain, divert, and, if we may say so, honor the courts of their princes by warlike exercises, or what resemble them; but to greater advantage than all these does a knight-errant show when he traverses deserts, solitudes, cross-roads, forests, and mountains, in quest of perilous adventures, bent on bringing them to a happy and successful issue, all to win a glorious and lasting renown. To greater advantage, I maintain, does the knight-errant show bringing aid to some widow in some lonely waste, than the court knight dallying with some city damsel. All knights have their own special parts to play, let the courtier devote himself to the ladies, let him add lustre to his sovereign's court by his liveries, let him entertain poor gentlemen with the sumptuous fare of his table, let him arrange joustings, marshal tournaments, and prove himself noble, generous, and magnificent, and above all a good Christian, and so doing he will fulfil the duties that are especially his; but let the knight-errant explore the corners of the earth and penetrate the most intricate labyrinths, at each step let him attempt impossibilities, on desolate heaths let him endure the burning rays of the midsummer sun, and the bitter inclemency of the winter winds and frosts; let no lions daunt him, no monsters terrify him, no dragons make him quail; for to seek these, to attack those, and to vanquish all, are in truth his main duties. I, then, as it has fallen to my lot to be a member of knight-errantry, can not avoid attempting all that to me seems to come within the sphere of my duties; thus it was my bounden duty to attack those lions that I just now attacked, although I knew it to be the height of rashness; for I know well what valor is, that it is a virtue that occupies a place between two vicious extremes, cowardice and temerity; but it will be a lesser evil for him who is valiant to rise till he reaches the point of rashness, than to sink until he reaches the point of cowardice; for, as it is easier for the prodigal than for the miser to become generous, so it is easier for a rash man to prove truly valiant than for a coward to rise to true valor; and believe me, Señor Don Diego, in attempting adventures it is better to lose by a card too many than by a card too few; for to hear it said, 'such a knight is rash and daring,' sounds better than 'such a knight is timid and cowardly.'"

"I protest, Señor Don Quixote," said Don Diego, "everything you have said and done is proved correct by the test of reason itself; and I believe, if the laws and ordinances of knight-errantry should be lost, they might be found in your worship's breast as in their own proper depository and muniment-house; but let us make haste, for it grows late, and reach my village and house, where you shall take rest after your late exertions; for if they have not been of the body they have been of the spirit, and these sometimes tend to produce bodily fatigue."

"I take the invitation as a great favor and honor, Señor Don Diego," replied Don Quixote; and pressing forward at a better pace than before, at about two in the afternoon they reached the village and house of Don Diego, or, as Don Quixote called him, "The Knight of the Green Gaban."

Chapter 18

Of what happened to Don Quixote in the castle or house of the Knight of the Green Gaban, together with other matters out of the common

DON QUIXOTE found Don Diego de Miranda's house built in village style, with his arms in rough stone over the street door; in the patio was the store-room, and at the entrance the cellar, with plenty of wine-jars standing round, which, coming from El Toboso, brought back to his memory his enchanted and transformed Dulcinea; and with a sigh, and not thinking of what he was saying, or in whose presence he was, he exclaimed—

*"O ye sweet treasures, to my sorrow found!
Once sweet and welcome when 'twas Heaven's
good-will.*

O ye Tobosan jars, how ye bring back to my memory the sweet object of my bitter regrets!"

The student poet, Don Diego's son, who had come out with his mother to receive him, heard this exclamation, and both mother and son were filled with amazement at the extraordinary figure he presented; he, however, dismounting from Rocinante, advanced with great politeness to ask permission to kiss the lady's hand, while Don Diego said, "Señora, pray receive with your wonted kindness Señor Don Quixote of La Mancha, whom you see before you, a knight-errant, and the bravest and wisest in the world."

The lady, whose name was Doña Cristina, received him with every sign of good-will and great courtesy, and Don Quixote placed himself at her service with an abundance of well-chosen and polished phrases. Almost the same civilities were exchanged between him and the student, who, listening to Don Quixote, took him to be a sensible, clear-headed person.

Here the author describes minutely everything belonging to Don Diego's mansion, putting before us in his picture the whole contents of a rich gentleman-farmer's house; but the translator of the history thought it best to pass over these and other details of the same sort in silence, as they are not in harmony with the main purpose of the story, the strong point of which is truth rather than dull digressions.

They led Don Quixote into a room, and Sancho removed his armor, leaving him in his loose Walloon breeches and chamois-leather doublet, all stained with the rust of his armor; his collar was a falling one of scholastic cut, without starch or lace, his buskins buff-colored, and his shoes polished. He wore his good sword, which hung in a baldric of sea-wolf's skin, for he had suffered for many years, they say, from an ailment of the kidneys; and over all he threw a long cloak of good gray cloth. But first of all, with five or six buckets of water (for as regards the number of buckets there is some dispute) he washed his head and face, and still the water remained whey-colored, thanks to Sancho's greediness and purchase of those unlucky curds that turned his master so white. Thus arrayed, and with an easy, sprightly, and gallant air, Don Quixote passed out into another room, where the student was waiting to entertain him while the table was being laid; for on the arrival of so distinguished a guest, Doña Cristina was anxious to show that she knew how and was able to give a becoming reception to those who came to her house.

While Don Quixote was taking off his armor, Don Lorenzo (for so Don Diego's son was called) took the opportunity to say to his father, "What are we to make of this gentleman you have brought home to us, sir? For his name, his appearance, and your describing him as a knight-errant have completely puzzled my mother and me."

"I don't know what to say, my son," replied Don Diego; "all I can tell thee is that I have seen him act the acts of the greatest madman in the world, and heard him make observations so sensible that they efface and undo all he does; do thou talk to him and feel the pulse of his wits, and as thou art shrewd, form the most reasonable conclusion thou canst as to his wisdom or folly; though, to tell the truth, I am more inclined to take him to be mad than sane."

With this Don Lorenzo went away to entertain Don Quixote as has been said, and in the course of the conversation that passed between them Don Quixote said to Don Lorenzo, "Your father, Señor Don Diego de Miranda, has told me of the rare abilities and subtle intellect you possess, and, above all, that you are a great poet."

"A poet, it may be," replied Don Lorenzo,

"but a great one, by no means. It is true that I am somewhat given to poetry and to reading good poets, but not so much so as to justify the title of 'great' which my father gives me."

"I do not dislike that modesty," said Don Quixote; "for there is no poet who is not conceited and does not think he is the best poet in the world."

"There is no rule without an exception," said Don Lorenzo; "there may be some who are poets and yet do not think they are."

"Very few," said Don Quixote; "but tell me, what verses are those which you have now in hand, and which your father tells me keep you somewhat restless and absorbed? If it be some gloss, I know something about glosses, and I should like to hear them; and if they are for a poetical tournament, contrive to carry off the second prize; for the first always goes by favor or personal standing, the second by simple justice; and so the third comes to be the second, and the first, reckoning in this way, will be third, in the same way as licentiate degrees are conferred at the universities; but, for all that, the title of first is a great distinction."

"So far," said Don Lorenzo to himself, "I should not take you to be a madman; but let us go on." So he said to him, "Your worship has apparently attended the schools; what sciences have you studied?"

"That of knight-errantry," said Don Quixote, "which is as good as that of poetry, and even a finger or two above it."

"I do not know what science that is," said Don Lorenzo, "and until now I have never heard of it."

"It is a science," said Don Quixote, "that comprehends in itself all or most of the sciences in the world, for he who professes it must be a jurist, and must know the rules of justice, distributive and equitable, so as to give to each one what belongs to him and is due to him. He must be a theologian, so as to be able to give a clear and distinctive reason for the Christian faith he professes, wherever it may be asked of him. He must be a physician, and above all a herbalist, so as in wastes and solitudes to know the herbs that have the property of healing wounds, for a knight-errant must not go looking for some one to cure him at every step. He must be an astronomer, so as to know by the stars how many hours of the night have passed, and what clime and quarter of the world he is in. He must know mathematics, for at every turn some occasion for them will present itself to him; and, putting it aside that he must be

adorned with all the virtues, cardinal and theological, to come down to minor particulars, he must, I say, be able to swim as well as Nicholas or Nicolao the Fish could, as the story goes; he must know how to shoe a horse, and repair his saddle and bridle; and, to return to higher matters, he must be faithful to God and to his lady; he must be pure in thought, decorous in words, generous in works, valiant in deeds, patient in suffering, compassionate towards the needy, and, lastly, an upholder of the truth though its defence should cost him his life. Of all these qualities, great and small, is a true knight-errant made up; judge then, Señor Don Lorenzo, whether it be a contemptible science which the knight who studies and professes it has to learn, and whether it may not compare with the very loftiest that are taught in the schools."

"If that be so," replied Don Lorenzo, "this science, I protest, surpasses all."

"How, if that be so?" said Don Quixote.

"What I mean to say," said Don Lorenzo, "is, that I doubt whether there are now, or ever were, any knights-errant, and adorned with such virtues."

"Many a time," replied Don Quixote, "have I said what I now say once more, that the majority of the world are of opinion that there never were any knights-errant in it; and as it is my opinion that, unless Heaven by some miracle brings home to them the truth that there were and are, all the pains one takes will be in vain (as experience has often proved to me), I will not now stop to disabuse you of the error you share with the multitude. All I shall do is to pray to Heaven to deliver you from it, and show you how beneficial and necessary knights-errant were in days of yore, and how useful they would be in these days were they but in vogue; but now, for the sins of the people, sloth and indolence, gluttony and luxury are triumphant."

"Our guest has broken out on our hands," said Don Lorenzo to himself at this point; "but, for all that, he is a glorious madman, and I should be a dull blockhead to doubt it."

Here, being summoned to dinner, they brought their colloquy to a close. Don Diego asked his son what he had been able to make out as to the wits of their guest. To which he replied, "All the doctors and clever scribes in the world will not make sense of the scrawl of his madness; he is a madman in streaks, full of lucid intervals."

They went in to dinner, and the repast was such as Don Diego said on the road he was in the habit of giving to his guests, neat, plentiful, and tasty; but what pleased Don Quixote most was the marvellous silence that reigned throughout the house, for it was like a Carthusian monastery.

When the cloth had been removed, grace said, and their hands washed, Don Quixote earnestly pressed Don Lorenzo to repeat to him his verses for the poetical tournament, to which he replied, "Not to be like those poets who, when they are asked to recite their verses, refuse, and when they are not asked for them vomit them up, I will repeat my gloss, for which I do not expect any prize, having composed it merely as an exercise of ingenuity."

"A discerning friend of mine," said Don Quixote, "was of opinion that no one ought to waste labor in glossing verses; and the reason he gave was that the gloss can never come up to the text, and that often or most frequently it wanders away from the meaning and purpose aimed at in the glossed lines; and besides, that the laws of the gloss were too strict, as they did not allow interrogations, nor 'said he,' nor 'I say,' nor turning verbs into nouns, or altering the construction, not to speak of other restrictions and limitations that fetter gloss-writers, as you no doubt know."

"Verily, Señor Don Quixote," said Don Lorenzo, "I wish I could catch your worship tripping at a stretch, but I can not, for you slip through my fingers like an eel."

"I don't understand what you say or mean by slipping," said Don Quixote.

"I will explain myself another time," said Don Lorenzo; "for the present pray attend to the glossed verses and the gloss, which run thus:

"Could 'was' become an 'is' for me,
  Then would I ask no more than this;
  Or could, for me, the time that is
Become the time that is to be!—

Gloss

"Dame Fortune once upon a day
  To me was bountiful and kind;
  But all things change; she changed her
    mind,
And what she gave she took away.
O Fortune, long I've sued to thee;
  The gifts thou gavest me restore,
  For, trust me, I would ask no more,
Could 'was' become an 'is' for me.

"No other prize I seek to gain,
  No triumph, glory, or success,
  Only the long-lost happiness,
The memory whereof is pain.

One taste, methinks, of bygone bliss
  The heart-consuming fire might stay;
  And, so it come without delay,
Then would I ask no more than this.

"I ask what can not be, alas!
  That time should ever be, and then
  Come back to us, and be again,
No power on earth can bring to pass;
For fleet of foot is he, I wis,
  And idly, therefore, do we pray
  That what for aye hath left us may
Become for us the time that is.

"Perplexed, uncertain, to remain
  'Twixt hope and fear, is death, not life;
  'T were better, sure, to end the strife,
And dying, seek release from pain.
And yet, though 't were the best for me,
  Anon the thought aside I fling,
  And to the present fondly cling,
And dread the time that is to be."

When Don Lorenzo had finished reciting his gloss, Don Quixote stood up, and in a loud voice, almost a shout, exclaimed as he grasped Don Lorenzo's right hand in his, "By the highest heavens, O noble youth, but you are the best poet on earth, and deserve to be crowned with laurel, not by Cyprus or by Gaeta—as a certain poet, God forgive him, said—but by the Academies of Athens, if they still flourished, and by those that flourish now, Paris, Bologna, and Salamanca. Heaven grant that the judges who rob you of the first prize—that Phœbus may pierce them with his arrows, and the Muses never cross the thresholds of their doors. Repeat me some of your long-measure verses, señor, if you will be so good, for I want thoroughly to feel the pulse of your rare genius."

Is there any need to say that Don Lorenzo enjoyed hearing himself praised by Don Quixote, albeit he looked upon him as a madman? O power of flattery, how far-reaching art thou, and how wide are the bounds of thy pleasant jurisdiction! Don Lorenzo gave a proof of it, for he complied with Don Quixote's request and entreaty, and repeated to him this sonnet on the fable or story of Pyramus and Thisbe.

Sonnet

The lovely maid, she pierces now the wall;
  Heart-pierced by her young Pyramus doth lie;
  And Love spreads wing from Cyprus isle to fly,
A chink to view so wondrous great and small.
There silence speaketh, for no voice at all
  Can pass so strait a strait; but love will ply
  Where to all other power 'twere vain to try;
For love will find a way whate'er befall.
Impatient of delay, with reckless pace

*The rash maid wins the fatal spot where she
Sinks not in lover's arms but death's embrace.
So runs the strange tale, how the lovers twain
One sword, one sepulchre, one memory,
Slays, and entombs, and brings to life again.*

"Blessed be God," said Don Quixote when he had heard Don Lorenzo's sonnet, "that among the hosts there are of irritable poets I have found one consummate one, which, señor, the art of this sonnet proves to me that you are!"

For four days was Don Quixote most sumptuously entertained in Don Diego's house, at the end of which time he asked his permission to depart, telling him he thanked him for the kindness and hospitality he had received in his house, but that, as it did not become knights-errant to give themselves up for long to idleness and luxury, he was anxious to fulfil the duties of his calling in seeking adventures, of which he was informed there was an abundance in that neighborhood, where he hoped to employ his time until the day came round for the jousts at Saragossa, for that was his proper destination; and that, first of all, he meant to enter the cave of Montesinos, of which so many marvellous things were reported all through the country, and at the same time to investigate and explore the origin and true source of the seven lakes commonly called the lakes of Ruidera.

Don Diego and his son commended his laudable resolution, and bade him furnish himself with all he wanted from their house and belongings, as they would most gladly be of service to him; which, indeed, his personal worth and his honorable profession made it incumbent upon them to be.

The day of his departure came at length, as welcome to Don Quixote as it was sad and sorrowful to Sancho Panza, who was very well satisfied with the abundance of Don Diego's house, and objected to return to the starvation of the woods and wilds and the short-commons of his ill-stocked *alforjas*; these, however, he filled and packed with what he considered most needful. On taking leave, Don Quixote said to Don Lorenzo, "I know not whether I have told you already, but if I have I tell you once more, that if you wish to spare yourself fatigue and toil in reaching the inaccessible summit of the temple of fame, you have nothing to do but to turn aside out of the somewhat narrow path of poetry and take the still narrower one of knight-errantry, wide enough, however, to make you an emperor in the twinkling of an eye."

In this speech Don Quixote wound up the evidence of his madness, but still better in what he added when he said, "God knows, I would gladly take Don Lorenzo with me to teach him how to spare the humble, and trample the proud under foot, virtues that are part and parcel of the profession I belong to; but since his tender age does not allow of it, nor his praiseworthy pursuits permit it, I will simply content myself with impressing it upon your worship that you will become famous as a poet if you are guided by the opinion of others rather than by your own; because no fathers or mothers ever think their own children ill-favored, and this sort of deception prevails still more strongly in the case of the children of the brain."

Both father and son were amazed afresh at the strange medley Don Quixote talked, at one moment sense, at another nonsense, and at the pertinacity and persistence he displayed in going through thick and thin in quest of his unlucky adventures, which he made the end and aim of his desires. There was a renewal of offers of service and civilities, and then, with the gracious permission of the lady of the castle, they took their departure, Don Quixote on Rocinante, and Sancho on Dapple.

Chapter 19

In which is related the adventure of the enamored shepherd, together with other truly droll incidents

Don Quixote had gone but a short distance beyond Don Diego's village, when he fell in with a couple of either priests or students, and a couple of peasants, mounted on four beasts of the ass kind. One of the students carried, wrapped up in a piece of green buckram by way of a portmanteau, what seemed to be a little linen and a couple of pair of ribbed stockings; the other carried nothing but a pair of new fencing-foils with buttons. The peasants carried divers articles that showed they were on their way from some large town where they had bought them, and were taking them home to their village; and both students and peasants were struck with the same amazement that everybody felt who saw Don Quixote for the first time, and were dying to know who this man, so different from ordinary men, could be. Don Quixote saluted them, and after ascertaining that their road was the same as his, made them an offer of his company, and begged them to slacken their pace, as their young asses travelled faster than his horse; and then, to gratify them, he told them in a few words who he was and the calling and profession he followed, which was that of a knight-errant seeking adventures in all parts of the world. He informed them that his name was properly Don Quixote of La Mancha, and that he was called, by way of surname, the Knight of the Lions.

All this was Greek or gibberish to the peasants, but not so to the students, who very soon perceived the crack in Don Quixote's pate; for all that, however, they regarded him with admiration and respect, and one of them said to him, "If you, sir knight, have no fixed road, as it is the way with those who seek adventures not to have any, let your worship come with us; you will see one of the finest and richest weddings that up to this day have ever been celebrated in La Mancha, or for many a league round."

Don Quixote asked him if it was some prince's, that he spoke of it in this way. "Not at all," said the student; "it is the wedding of a farmer and a farmer's daughter, he the richest in all this country, and she the fairest mortal ever set eyes on. The display with which it is to be attended will be something rare and out of the common, for it will be celebrated in a meadow adjoining the town of the bride, who is called, *par excellence*, Quiteria the fair, as the bridegroom is called Camacho the rich. She is eighteen, and he twenty-two, and they are fairly matched, though some knowing ones, who have all the pedigrees in the world by heart, will have it that the family of the fair Quiteria is better than Camacho's; but no one minds that now-a-days, for wealth can solder a great many flaws. At any rate, Camacho is free-handed, and it is his fancy to screen the whole meadow with boughs and cover it in overhead, so that the sun will have hard work if he tries to get in to reach the grass that covers the soil. He has provided dancers too, not only sword- but also bell-dancers, for in his own town there are those who ring the changes and jingle the bells to perfection; of shoe-dancers I say nothing, for of them he has engaged a host. But none of these things, nor of the many others I have omitted to mention, will do more to make this a memorable wedding than the part which I suspect the despairing Basilio will play in it. This Basilio is a youth of the same village as Quiteria, and he lived in the house next door to that of her parents, of which circumstance Love took advantage to reproduce to the world the long-forgotten loves of Pyramus and Thisbe; for Basilio loved Quiteria from his earliest years, and she responded to his passion with countless modest proofs of affection, so that the loves of the two children, Basilio and Quiteria, were the talk and the amusement of the town. As they grew up, the father of Quiteria made up his mind to refuse Basilio his wonted freedom of access to the house, and, to relieve himself of constant doubts and suspicions, he arranged a match for his daughter with the rich Camacho, as he did not approve of marrying her to Basilio, who had not so large a share of the gifts of fortune as of nature; for if the truth be told ungrudgingly, he is the most agile youth we know, a mighty thrower of the bar, a first-rate wrestler, and a great ball-player; he runs like a deer, and leaps better than a goat, bowls over the nine-pins as if by magic, sings like a lark, plays the guitar so as to make it speak, and, above all, handles a sword as well as the best."

"For that excellence alone," said Don Quixote at this, "the youth deserves to marry, not merely the fair Quiteria, but Queen Guinevere herself, were she alive now, in spite of Launcelot and all who would try to prevent it."

"Say that to my wife," said Sancho, who had until now listened in silence, "for she won't hear of anything but each one marrying his equal, holding with the proverb 'each ewe to her like.' What I would like is that this good Basilio (for I am beginning to take a fancy to him already) should marry this lady Quiteria; and a blessing and good luck—I meant to say the opposite—on people who would prevent those who love one another from marrying."

"If all those who love one another were to marry," said Don Quixote, "it would deprive parents of the right to choose, and marry their children to the proper person and at the proper time; and if it was left to daughters to choose husbands as they pleased, one would be for choosing her father's servant, and another, some one she has seen passing in the street and fancies gallant and dashing, though he may be a drunken bully; for love and fancy easily blind the eyes of the judgment, so much wanted in choosing one's way of life; and the matrimonial choice is very liable to error, and it needs great caution and the special favor of Heaven to make it a good one. He who has to make a long journey will, if he is wise, look out for some trusty and pleasant companion to accompany him before he sets out. Why, then, should not he do the same who has to make the whole journey of life down to the final halting-place of death, more especially when the companion has to be his companion in bed, at board, and everywhere, as the wife is to her husband? The companionship of one's wife is no article of merchandise, that, after it has been bought, may be returned, or bartered, or changed; for it is an inseparable accident that lasts as long as life lasts; it is a noose that, once you put it round your neck, turns into a Gordian knot, which, if the scythe of Death does not cut it, there is no untying. I could say a great deal more on this subject, were I not prevented by the anxiety I feel to know if the señor licentiate has anything more to tell about the story of Basilio."

To this the student, bachelor, or, as Don Quixote called him, licentiate, replied, "I have nothing whatever to say further, but that from the moment Basilio learned that the fair Quiteria was to be married to Camacho the rich, he has never been seen to smile, or heard to utter a rational word, and he always goes about moody and dejected, talking to himself in a way that shows plainly he is out of his senses. He eats little and sleeps little, and all he eats is fruit, and when he sleeps, if he sleeps at all, it is in the field on the hard earth like a brute beast. Sometimes he gazes at the sky, at other times he fixes his eyes on the earth in such an abstracted way that he might be taken for a clothed statue, with its drapery stirred by the wind. In short, he shows such signs of a heart crushed by suffering, that all we who know him believe that when tomorrow the fair Quiteria says 'yes' it will be his sentence of death."

"God will guide it better," said Sancho, "for God who gives the wound gives the salve; nobody knows what will happen; there are a good many hours between this and to-morrow, and any one of them, or any moment, the house may fall; I have seen the rain coming down and the sun shining all at one time; many a one goes to bed in good health who can't stir the next day. And tell me, is there any one who can boast of having driven a nail into the wheel of fortune? No, faith; and between a woman's 'yes' and 'no' I wouldn't venture to put the point of a pin, for there would not be room for it; if you tell me Quiteria loves Basilio heart and soul, then I'll give him a bag of good luck, for love, I have heard say, looks through spectacles that make copper seem gold, poverty, wealth; and blear eyes pearls."

"What art thou driving at, Sancho, curses on thee?" said Don Quixote; "for when thou takest to stringing proverbs and sayings together, no one can understand thee but Judas himself, and I wish he had thee. Tell me, thou animal, what dost thou know about nails or wheels, or anything else?"

"Oh, if you don't understand me," replied Sancho, "it is no wonder my words are taken for nonsense; but no matter; I understand myself, and I know I have not said anything very fool-ish in what I have said; only your worship, señor, is always gravelling at everything I say, nay, everything I do."

"Cavilling, not gravelling," said Don Quixote, "thou prevaricator of honest language, God confound thee!"

"Don't find fault with me, your worship," returned Sancho, "for you know I have not been bred up at court or trained at Salamanca, to know whether I am adding or dropping a letter or so in my words. Why! God bless me, it's not fair to force a Sayago-man to speak like a Toledan; and may be there are Toledans who do not hit it off when it comes to polished talk."

"That is true," said the licentiate, "for those who have been bred up in the Tanneries and the Zocodover, can not talk like those who are almost all day pacing the cathedral cloisters, and yet they are all Toledans. Pure, correct, elegant, and lucid language will be met with in men of courtly breeding and discrimination, though they may have been born in Majalahonda; I say of discrimination, because there are many who are not so, and discrimination is the grammar of good language, if it be accompanied by practice. I, sirs, for my sins have been a student of canon law at Salamanca, and I rather pique myself on expressing my meaning in clear, plain, and intelligible language."

"If you did not pique yourself more on your dexterity with those foils you carry than on dexterity of tongue," said the other student, "you would have been head of the degrees, where you are now tail."

"Look here, bachelor Corchuelo," returned the licentiate, "you have the most mistaken idea in the world about skill with the sword, if you think it useless."

"It is no idea on my part, but an established truth," replied Corchuelo; "and if you wish me to prove it to you by experiment, you have swords there, and it is a good opportunity; I have a steady hand and a strong arm, and these joined with my resolution, which is not small, will make you confess that I am not mistaken. Dismount and put in practice your positions and circles and angles and science, for I hope to make you see stars at noonday with my rude raw swordsmanship, in which, next to God, I place my trust that the man is yet to be born who will make me turn my back, and that there is not one in the world I will not compel to give ground."

"As to whether you turn your back or not, I do not concern myself," replied the master of fence; "though it might be that your grave would be dug on the spot where you planted your foot the first time; I mean that you would be stretched dead there for despising skill with the sword."

"We shall soon see," replied Corchuelo, and getting off his ass briskly, he drew out furiously one of the swords the licentiate carried on his beast.

"It must not be that way," said Don Quixote at this point; "I will be the director of this fencing match, and judge of this often disputed question"; and dismounting from Rocinante and grasping his lance, he planted himself in the middle of the road, just as the licentiate, with an easy, graceful bearing and step, advanced towards Corchuelo, who came on against him, darting fire from his eyes, as the saying is. The other two of the company, the peasants, without dismounting from their asses, served as spectators of the mortal tragedy. The cuts, thrusts, down strokes, back strokes and doubles, that Corchuelo delivered were past counting, and came thicker than hops or hail. He attacked like an angry lion, but he was met by a tap on the mouth from the button of the licentiate's sword that checked him in the midst of his furious onset, and made him kiss it as it had been a relic, though not as devoutly as relics are and ought to be kissed. The end of it was that the licentiate reckoned up for him by thrusts every one of the buttons of the short cassock he wore, tore the skirts into strips, like the tails of a cuttle-fish, knocked off his hat twice, and so completely tired him out, that in vexation, anger, and rage, he took the sword by the hilt and flung it away with such force, that one of the peasants that were there, who was a notary, and who went for it, made an affidavit afterwards that he sent it nearly three-quarters of a league, which testimony will serve, and has served, to show and establish with all certainty that strength is overcome by skill.

Corchuelo sat down wearied, and Sancho approaching him said, "By my faith, señor bachelor, if your worship takes my advice, you will never challenge any one to fence again, only to wrestle and throw the bar, for you have the youth and strength for that; but as for these fencers as they all call them, I have heard say they can put the point of a sword through the eye of a needle."

"I am satisfied with having tumbled off my donkey," said Corchuelo, "and with having had the truth I was so ignorant of proved to me by experience"; and getting up he embraced the licentiate, and they were better friends than ever; and not caring to wait for the notary who had

gone for the sword, as they saw he would be a long time about it, they resolved to push on so as to reach the village of Quiteria, to which they all belonged, in good time.

During the remainder of the journey the licentiate held forth to them on the excellences of the sword, with such conclusive arguments, and such figures and mathematical proofs, that all were convinced of the value of the science, and Corchuelo cured of his dogmatism.

It grew dark; but before they reached the town it seemed to them all as if there was a heaven full of countless glittering stars in front of it. They heard, too, the pleasant mingled notes of a variety of instruments, flutes, drums, psalteries, pipes, tabors, and timbrels, and as they drew near they perceived that the trees of a leafy arcade that had been constructed at the entrance of the town were filled with lights unaffected by the wind, for the breeze at the time was so gentle that it had not power to stir the leaves on the trees. The musicians were the life of the wedding, wandering through the pleasant grounds in separate bands, some dancing, others singing, others playing the various instruments already mentioned. In short, it seemed as though mirth and gayety were frisking and gambolling all over the meadow. Several other persons were engaged in erecting raised benches from which people might conveniently see the plays and dances that were to be performed the next day on the spot dedicated to the celebration of the marriage of Camacho the rich and the obsequies of Basilio. Don Quixote would not enter the village, although the peasant as well as the bachelor pressed him; he excused himself, however, on the grounds, amply sufficient in his opinion, that it was the custom of knights-errant to sleep in the fields and woods in preference to towns, even were it under gilded ceilings; and so he turned aside a little out of the road, very much against Sancho's will, as the good quarters he had enjoyed in the castle or house of Don Diego came back to his mind.

Chapter 20

Wherein an account is given of the wedding of Camacho the rich, together with the incident of Basilio the poor

Scarce had the fair Aurora given bright Phœbus time to dry the liquid pearls upon her golden locks with the heat of his fervent rays, when Don Quixote, shaking off sloth from his limbs, sprang to his feet and called to his squire Sancho, who was still snoring; seeing which

Don Quixote ere he roused him thus addressed him: "Happy thou, above all the dwellers on the face of the earth, that, without envying or being envied, sleepest with tranquil mind, and that neither enchanters persecute nor enchantments affright. Sleep, I say, and will say a hundred times, without any jealous thoughts of thy mistress to make thee keep ceaseless vigils, or any cares as to how thou are to pay the debts thou owest, or find to-morrow's food for thyself and thy needy little family, to interfere with thy repose. Ambition breaks not thy rest, nor doth this world's empty pomp disturb thee, for the utmost reach of thy anxiety is to provide for thy ass, since upon my shoulders thou hast laid the support of thyself, the counterpoise and burden that nature and custom have imposed upon masters. The servant sleeps and the master lies awake thinking how he is to feed him, advance him, and reward him. The distress of seeing the sky turn brazen, and withhold its needful moisture from the earth, is not felt by the servant, but by the master, who in time of scarcity and famine must support him who has served him in times of plenty and abundance."

To all this Sancho made no reply because he was asleep, nor would he have wakened up so soon as he did had not Don Quixote brought him to his senses with the butt of his lance. He awoke at last, drowsy and lazy, and casting his eyes about in every direction, observed, "There comes, if I don't mistake, from the direction of that arcade a steam and a smell a great deal more like fried rashers than galingale or thyme; a wedding that begins with smells like that, by my faith, ought to be plentiful and unstinting."

"Have done, thou glutton," said Don Quixote; "come, let us go and witness this bridal, and see what the rejected Basilio does."

"Let him do what he likes," returned Sancho; "he'd be poor and yet marry Quiteria. To make a grand match for himself, and he without a farthing; is that all he wants? Faith, señor, it's my opinion the poor man should be content with what he can get, and not go looking for dainties in the bottom of the sea. I will bet my arm that Camacho could bury Basilio in reals; and if that be so, as no doubt it is, what a fool Quiteria would be to refuse the fine dresses and jewels Camacho must have given her and will give her, and take Basilio's bar-throwing and sword-play. They won't give a pint of wine at the tavern for a good cast of the bar or a neat thrust of the sword. Talents and accomplishments that can't be turned into money, let Count Dirlos have them; but when such gifts fall to one that has

hard cash, I wish my condition of life was as becoming as they are. On a good foundation you can raise a good building, and the best foundation and groundwork in the world is money."

"For God's sake, Sancho," said Don Quixote here, "stop that harangue; it is my belief, if thou wert allowed to continue all thou beginnest every instant, thou wouldst have no time left for eating or sleeping; for thou wouldst spend it all in talking."

"If your worship had a good memory," replied Sancho, "you would remember the articles of our agreement before we started from home this last time; one of them was that I was to be let say all I liked, so long as it was not against my neighbor or your worship's authority; and so far, it seems to me, I have not broken the said article."

"I remember no such article, Sancho," said Don Quixote; "and even if it were so, I desire you to hold your tongue and come along; for the instruments we heard last night are already beginning to enliven the valleys again, and no doubt the marriage will take place in the cool of the morning, and not in the heat of the afternoon."

Sancho did as his master bade him, and putting the saddle on Rocinante and the pack-saddle on Dapple, they both mounted and at a leisurely pace entered the arcade. The first thing that presented itself to Sancho's eyes was a whole ox spitted on a whole elm tree, and in the fire at which it was to be roasted there was burning a middling-sized mountain of fagots, and six stewpots that stood round the blaze had not been made in the ordinary mould of common pots, for they were six half wine-jars, each fit to hold the contents of a slaughter-house; they swallowed up whole sheep and hid them away in their insides without showing any more sign of them than if they were pigeons. Countless were the hares ready skinned and the plucked fowls that hung on the trees for burial in the pots, numberless the wildfowl and game of various sorts suspended from the branches that the air might keep them cool. Sancho counted more than sixty wine-skins of over six gallons each, and all filled, as it proved afterwards, with generous wines. There were, besides, piles of the whitest bread, like the heaps of corn one sees on the threshing-floors. There was a wall made of cheeses arranged like open brick-work, and two caldrons full of oil, bigger than those of a dyer's shop, served for cooking fritters, which when fried were taken out with two mighty shovels, and plunged into another caldron of prepared honey that stood close by. Of cooks and cook-maids there were over fifty, all clean, brisk, and blithe. In the capacious belly of the ox were a dozen soft little sucking-pigs, which, sewn up there, served to give it tenderness and flavor. The spices of different kinds did not seem to have been bought by the pound, but by the quarter, and all lay open to view in a great chest. In short, all the preparations made for the wedding were in rustic style, but abundant enough to feed an army.

Sancho observed all, contemplated all, and everything won his heart. The first to captivate and take his fancy were the pots, out of which he would have very gladly helped himself to a moderate pipkinful; then the wine-skins secured his affections; and lastly, the produce of the frying-pans, if, indeed, such imposing caldrons may be called frying-pans; and unable to control himself or bear it any longer, he approached one of the busy cooks and civilly but hungrily begged permission to soak a scrap of bread in one of the pots; to which the cook made answer, "Brother, this is not a day on which hunger is to have any sway, thanks to the rich Camacho; get down and look about for a ladle and skim off a hen or two, and much good may they do you."

"I don't see one," said Sancho.

"Wait a bit," said the cook; "sinner that I am! how particular and bashful you are!" and so saying, he seized a bucket and plunging it into one of the half jars took up three hens and a couple of geese, and said to Sancho, "Fall to, friend, and take the edge off your appetite with these skimmings until dinner-time comes."

"I have nothing to put them in," said Sancho.

"Well, then," said the cook, "take spoon and all; for Camacho's wealth and happiness furnish everything."

While Sancho fared thus, Don Quixote was watching the entrance, at one end of the arcade, of some twelve peasants, all in holiday and gala dress, mounted on twelve beautiful mares with rich handsome field trappings and a number of little bells attached to their petrals, who, marshalled in regular order, ran not one but several courses over the meadow, with jubilant shouts and cries of "Long live Camacho and Quiteria! he as rich as she is fair, and she the fairest on earth!"

Hearing this, Don Quixote said to himself, 'It is easy to see these folk have never seen my Dulcinea del Toboso; for if they had they would be more moderate in their praises of this Quiteria of theirs."

Shortly after this, several bands of dancers of various sorts began to enter the arcade at different points, and among them one of sword-dancers composed of some four-and-twenty lads of gallant and high-spirited mien, clad in the finest and whitest of linen, and with handkerchiefs embroidered in various colors with fine silk; and one of those on the mares asked an active youth who led them if any of the dancers had been wounded. "As yet, thank God, no one has been wounded," said he, "we are all safe and sound"; and he at once began to execute complicated figures with the rest of his comrades, with so many turns and so great dexterity, that although Don Quixote was well used to see dances of the same kind, he thought he had never seen any so good as this. He also admired another that came in composed of fair young maidens, none of whom seemed to be under fourteen or over eighteen years of age, all clad in green stuff, with their locks partly braided, partly flowing loose, but all of such bright gold as to vie with the sunbeams, and over them they wore garlands of jessamine, roses, amaranth, and honeysuckle. At their head were a venerable old man and an ancient dame, more brisk and active, however, than might have been expected from their years. The notes of a Zamora bagpipe accompanied them, and with modesty in their countenances and in their eyes, and lightness in their feet, they looked the best dancers in the world.

Following these there came an artistic dance of the sort they call "speaking dances." It was composed of eight nymphs in two files, with the god Cupid leading one and Interest the other, the former furnished with wings, bow, quiver and arrows, the latter in a rich dress of gold and silver of divers colors. The nymphs that followed Love bore their names written on white parchment in large letters on their backs. "Poetry" was the name of the first, "Wit" of the second, "Birth" of the third, and "Valour" of the fourth. Those that followed Interest were distinguished in the same way; the badge of the first announced "Liberality," that of the second "Largess," the third "Treasure," and the fourth "Peaceful Possession." In front of them all came a wooden castle drawn by four wild men, all clad in ivy and hemp stained green, and looking so natural that they nearly terrified Sancho. On the front of the castle and on each of the four sides of its frame it bore the inscription, "Castle of Caution." Four skilful tabor and flute players accompanied them, and the dance having been opened, Cupid, after executing two figures, raised his eyes and bent his bow against a damsel who stood between the turrets of the castle, and thus addressed her:

> I am the mighty God whose sway
>   Is potent over land and sea.
> The heavens above us own me; nay,
>   The shades below acknowledge me.
> I know not fear, I have my will,
>   Whate'er my whim or fancy be;
> For me there's no impossible,
>   I order, bind, forbid, set free.

Having concluded the stanza, he discharged an arrow at the top of the castle, and went back to his place. Interest then came forward and went through two more figures, and as soon as the tabors ceased, he said:

> But mightier than Love am I,
>   Though Love it be that leads me on,
> Than mine no lineage is more high,
>   Or older, underneath the sun.
> To use me rightly few know how
>   To act without me fewer still,
> For I am Interest, and I vow
>   For evermore to do thy will.

Interest retired, and Poetry came forward, and when she had gone through her figures like the others, fixing her eyes on the damsel of the castle, she said:

> With many a fanciful conceit,
>   Fair Lady, winsome Poesy
> Her soul, an offering at thy feet,
>   Presents in sonnets unto thee.
> If thou my homage wilt not scorn,
>   Thy fortune, watched by envious eyes,
> On wings of poesy upborne
>   Shall be exalted to the skies.

Poetry withdrew, and on the side of Interest, Liberality advanced, and after having gone through her figures, said:

> To give, while shunning each extreme,
>   The sparing hand, the over-free,
> Therein consists, so wise men deem,
>   The virtue Liberality.
> But thee, fair lady, to enrich,
>   Myself a prodigal I'll prove,
> A vice not wholly shameful, which
>   May find its fair excuse in love.

In the same manner all the characters of the two bands advanced and retired, and each executed its figures, and delivered its verses, some of them graceful, some burlesque, but Don Quixote's memory (though he had an excellent one) only carried away those that have been just quoted. All then mingled together, forming chains and breaking off again with graceful, unconstrained gayety; and whenever Love passed in front of the castle he shot his arrows up at it, while Interest broke gilded pellets against it. At length, after they had danced a good while, Interest drew out a great purse, made of the skin of a large brindled cat and to all appearance full of money, and flung it at the castle, and with the force of the blow the boards fell asunder and tumbled down, leaving the damsel exposed and unprotected. Interest and the characters of his band advanced, and throwing a great chain of gold over her neck pretended to take her and lead her away captive, on seeing which, Love and his supporters made as though they would release her, the whole action being to the accompaniment of the tabors and in the form of a regular dance. The wild men made peace between them, and with great dexterity readjusted and fixed the boards of the castle, and the damsel once more ensconced herself within; and with this the dance wound up, to the great enjoyment of the beholders.

Don Quixote asked one of the nymphs who it was that had composed and arranged it. She replied that it was a beneficiary of the town who had a nice taste in devising things of the sort.

"I will lay a wager," said Don Quixote, "that the same bachelor or beneficiary is a greater friend of Camacho's than of Basilio's, and that he is better at satire than at vespers; he has introduced the accomplishments of Basilio and the riches of Camacho very neatly into the dance."

Sancho Panza, who was listening to all this, exclaimed, "The king is my cock; I stick to Camacho."

"It is easy to see thou art a clown, Sancho," said Don Quixote, "and one of that sort that cry 'Long life to the conqueror.'"

"I don't know of what sort I am," returned Sancho, "but I know very well I'll never get such elegant skimmings off Basilio's pots as these I have got off Camacho's"; and he showed him the bucketful of geese and hens, and seizing one began to eat with great gayety and appetite, saying, "A fig for the accomplishments of Basilio! As much as thou hast so much art thou worth, and as much as thou art worth so much hast thou. As a grandmother of mine used to say, there are only two families in the world, the Haves and the Haven'ts; and she stuck to the Haves; and to this day, Señor Don Quixote, people would sooner feel the pulse of 'Have' than of 'Know'; an ass covered with gold looks better than a horse with a pack-saddle. So once more I say I stick to Camacho, the bountiful skimmings of whose pots are geese and hens, hares and rabbits; but of Basilio's, if any ever come to hand, or even to foot, they'll be only rinsings."

"Hast thou finished thy harangue, Sancho?" said Don Quixote.

"Of course I have finished it," replied Sancho, "because I see your worship takes offence at it; but if it was not for that, there was work enough cut out for three days."

"God grant I may see thee dumb before I die, Sancho," said Don Quixote.

"At the rate we are going," said Sancho, "I'll be chewing clay before your worship dies; and then, maybe, I'll be so dumb that I'll not say a word until the end of the world, or, at least, till the day of judgment."

"Even should that happen, O Sancho," said Don Quixote, "thy silence will never come up to all thou hast talked, art talking, and wilt talk all thy life; moreover, it naturally stands to reason, that my death will come before thine; so I never expect to see thee dumb, not even when thou art drinking or sleeping, and that is the utmost I can say."

"In good faith, señor," replied Sancho, "there's no trusting that fleshless one, I mean Death, who devours the lamb as soon as the sheep, and, as I have heard our curate say, treads with equal foot upon the lofty towers of kings and the lowly huts of the poor. That lady is more mighty than dainty, she is no way squeamish, she devours all and is ready for all, and fills her *alforjas* with people of all sorts, ages, and ranks. She is no reaper that sleeps out the noontide; at all times she is reaping and cutting down, as well the dry grass as the green; she never seems to chew, but bolts and swallows all that is put before her, for she has a canine appetite that is never satisfied; and though she has no belly, she shows she has a dropsy and is athirst to drink the lives of all that live, as one would drink a jug of cold water."

"Say no more, Sancho," said Don Quixote at this; "don't try to better it, and risk a fall; for in truth what thou hast said about death in thy rustic phrase is what a good preacher might have said. I tell thee, Sancho, if thou hadst discretion equal to thy mother wit, thou mightst take a pulpit in hand, and go about the world preaching fine sermons."

"He preaches well who lives well," said Sancho, "and I know no more th'ology than that."

"Nor needst thou," said Don Quixote; "but I cannot conceive or make out how it is that, the fear of God being the beginning of wisdom, thou, who art more afraid of a lizard than of him, knowest so much."

"Pass judgment on your chivalries, señor," returned Sancho, "and don't set yourself up to judge of other men's fears or braveries, for I am as good a fearer of God as my neighbors; but leave me to despatch these skimmings, for all the rest is only idle talk that we shall be called to account for in the other world"; and so saying, he began a fresh attack on the bucket, with such a hearty appetite that he aroused Don Quixote's, who no doubt would have helped him had he not been prevented by what must be told farther on.

Chapter 21

In which Camacho's wedding is continued, with other delightful incidents

WHILE Don Quixote and Sancho were engaged in the discussion set forth in the last chapter, they heard loud shouts and a great noise, which were uttered and made by the men on the mares as they went at full gallop, shouting, to receive the bride and bridegroom, who were approaching with musical instruments and pageantry of all sorts around them, and accompanied by the priest and the relatives of both, and all the most distinguished people of the surrounding villages. When Sancho saw the bride, he exclaimed, "By my faith, she is not dressed like a country girl, but like some fine court lady; egad, as well as I can make out, the *patena* she wears is rich coral, and her green Cuenca stuff is thirty-pile velvet; and then the white linen trimming —by my oath, but it's satin! Look at her hands— jet rings on them! May I never have luck if they're not gold rings, and real gold, and set with pearls as white as curdled milk, and every one of them worth an eye of one's head! Whoreson baggage, what hair she has! if it's not a wig, I never saw longer or brighter all the days of my life. See how bravely she bears herself—and her shape! Wouldn't you say she was like a walking palm-tree loaded with clusters of dates? for the trinkets she has hanging from her hair and neck look just like them. I swear in my heart she is a brave lass, and fit to pass the banks of Flanders." [1]

Don Quixote laughed at Sancho's boorish eulogies, and thought that, saving his lady Dulcinea del Toboso, he had never seen a fairer woman. The fair Quiteria appeared somewhat pale, which was, no doubt, because of the bad night brides always pass dressing themselves out for their wedding on the morrow. They advanced towards a theatre that stood on one side of the meadow, decked with carpets and boughs, where they were to plight their troth, and from which

[1] Fit for any enterprise; the shoals of the Flemish coast being regarded with great awe by the Spanish sailors.

they were to behold the dances and plays; but at the moment of their arrival at the spot they heard a loud outcry behind them, and a voice exclaiming, "Wait a little, ye, as inconsiderate as ye are hasty!"

At these words all turned round, and perceived that the speaker was a man clad in what seemed to be a loose black coat garnished with crimson patches like flames. He was crowned (as was presently seen) with a crown of gloomy cypress, and in his hand he held a long staff. As he approached he was recognized by every one as the gay Basilio, and all waited anxiously to see what would come of his words, in dread of some catastrophe in consequence of his appearance at such a moment. He came up at last weary and breathless, and planting himself in front of the bridal pair, drove his staff, which had a steel spike at the end, into the ground, and, with a pale face and eyes fixed on Quiteria, he thus addressed her in a hoarse, trembling voice: "Well dost thou know, ungrateful Quiteria, that, according to the holy law we acknowledge, so long as I live thou canst take no husband; nor art thou ignorant either that, in my hopes that time and my own exertions would improve my fortunes, I have never failed to observe the respect due to thy honor; but thou, casting behind thee all thou owest to my true love, wouldst surrender what is mine to another whose wealth serves to bring him not only good fortune, but supreme happiness; and now to complete it (not that I think he deserves it, but inasmuch as Heaven is pleased to bestow it upon him), I will, with my own hands, do away with the obstacle that may interfere with it, and remove myself from between you. Long live the rich Camacho! many a happy year may he live with the ungrateful Quiteria! and let the poor Basilio die, Basilio whose poverty clipped the wings of his happiness, and brought him to the grave!" and so saying, he seized the staff he had driven into the ground, and leaving one half of it fixed there, showed it to be a sheath that concealed a tolerably long rapier; and, what may be called its hilt being planted in the ground, he swiftly, coolly, and deliberately threw himself upon it, and in an instant the bloody point and half the steel blade appeared at his back, the unhappy man falling to the earth bathed in his blood, and transfixed by his own weapon.

His friends at once ran to his aid, filled with grief at his misery and sad fate, and Don Quixote, dismounting from Rocinante, hastened to support him, and took him in his arms, and found he had not yet ceased to breathe. They were about to draw out the rapier, but the priest who was standing by objected to its being withdrawn before he had confessed him, as the instant of its withdrawal would be that of his death. Basilio, however, reviving slightly, said in a weak voice, as though in pain, "If thou wouldst consent, cruel Quiteria, to give me thy hand as my bride in this last fatal moment, I might still hope that my rashness would find pardon, as by its means I attained the bliss of being thine."

Hearing this the priest bade him think of the welfare of his soul rather than of the cravings of the body, and in all earnestness implore God's pardon for his sins and for his rash resolve; to which Basilio replied that he was determined not to confess unless Quiteria first gave him her hand in marriage, for that happiness would compose his mind and give him courage to make his confession.

Don Quixote, hearing the wounded man's entreaty, exclaimed aloud that what Basilio asked was just and reasonable, and moreover a request that might be easily complied with; and that it would be as much to Señor Camacho's honor to receive the lady Quiteria as the widow of the brave Basilio as if he received her direct from her father. "In this case," said he "it will be only to say 'yes,' and no consequences can follow the utterance of the word, for the nuptial couch of this marriage must be the grave."

Camacho was listening to all this, perplexed and bewildered and not knowing what to say or do; but so urgent were the entreaties of Basilio's friends, imploring him to allow Quiteria to give him her hand, so that his soul, quitting this life in despair, should not be lost, that they moved, nay, forced him, to say that if Quiteria were willing to give it he was satisfied, as it was only putting off the fulfilment of his wishes for a moment. At once all assailed Quiteria and pressed her, some with prayers, and others with tears, and others with persuasive arguments, to give her hand to poor Basilio; but she, harder than marble and more unmoved than any statue, seemed unable or unwilling to utter a word, nor would she have given any reply had not the priest bade her decide quickly what she meant to do, as Basilio now had his soul at his teeth, and there was no time for hesitation.

On this the fair Quiteria, to all appearance distressed, grieved, and repentant, advanced without a word to where Basilio lay, his eyes already turned in his head, his breathing short and painful, murmuring the name of Quiteria between his teeth, and apparently about to die like a neathen and not like a Christian. Quiteria approached him, and kneeling, demanded his hand by signs without speaking. Basilio opened his eyes and gazing fixedly at her, said, "O Quiteria, why hast thou turned compassionate at a moment when thy compassion will serve as a dagger to rob me of life, for I have not now the strength left either to bear the happiness thou givest me in accepting me as thine, or to suppress the pain that is rapidly drawing the dread shadow of death over my eyes? What I entreat of thee, O thou fatal star to me, is that the hand thou demandest of me and wouldst give me, be not given out of complaisance or to deceive me afresh, but that thou confess and declare that without any constraint upon thy will thou givest it to me as to thy lawful husband; for it is not meet that thou shouldst trifle with me at such a moment as this, or have recourse to falsehoods with one who has dealt so truly by thee."

While uttering these words he showed such weakness that the bystanders expected each return of faintness would take his life with it. Then Quiteria, overcome with modesty and shame, holding in her right hand the hand of Basilio, said, "No force would bend my will; as freely, therefore, as it is possible for me to do so, I give thee the hand of a lawful wife, and take thine if thou givest it to me of thine own free will, untroubled and unaffected by the calamity thy hasty act has brought upon thee."

"Yes, I give it," said Basilio, "not agitated or distracted, but with the unclouded reason that Heaven is pleased to grant me, thus do I give myself to be thy husband."

"And I give myself to be thy wife," said Quiteria, "whether thou livest many years, or they carry thee from my arms to the grave."

"For one so badly wounded," observed Sancho at this point, "this young man has a great deal to say; they should make him leave off billing and cooing, and attend to his soul; for to my thinking he has it more on his tongue than at his teeth."

Basilio and Quiteria having thus joined hands, the priest, deeply moved and with tears in his eyes, pronounced the blessing upon them, and implored Heaven to grant an easy passage to the soul of the newly wedded man, who, the instant he received the blessing, started nimbly to his feet and with unparalleled effrontery pulled out the rapier that had been sheathed in his body. All the bystanders were astounded, and some, more simple than inquiring, began shouting, "A miracle, a miracle!" But Basilio replied, "No miracle, no miracle; only a trick, a trick!" The

priest, perplexed and amazed, made haste to examine the wound with both hands, and found that the blade had passed, not through Basilio's flesh and ribs, but through a hollow iron tube full of blood, which he had adroitly fixed at the place, the blood, as was afterwards ascertained, having been so prepared as not to congeal. In short, the priest and Camacho and most of those present saw they were tricked and made fools of. The bride showed no signs of displeasure at the deception; on the contrary, hearing them say that the marriage, being fraudulent, would not be valid, she said that she confirmed it afresh, whence they all concluded that the affair had been planned by agreement and understanding between the pair, whereat Camacho and his supporters were so mortified that they proceeded to revenge themselves by violence, and a great number of them drawing their swords attacked Basilio, in whose protection as many more swords were in an instant unsheathed, while Don Quixote taking the lead on horseback, with his lance over his arm and well covered with his shield, made all give way before him. Sancho, who never found any pleasure or enjoyment in such doings, retreated to the wine-jars from which he had taken his delectable skimmings, considering that, as a holy place, that spot would be respected. "Hold, sirs, hold!" cried Don Quixote in a loud voice; "we have no right to take vengeance for wrongs that love may do to us: remember love and war are the same thing, and as in war it is allowable and common to make use of wiles and stratagems to overcome the enemy, so in the contests and rivalries of love the tricks and devices employed to attain the desired end are justifiable, provided they be not to the discredit or dishonor of the loved object. Quiteria belonged to Basilio and Basilio to Quiteria by the just and beneficent disposal of Heaven. Camacho is rich, and can purchase his pleasure when, where, and as it pleases him. Basilio has but this ewe-lamb, and no one, however powerful he may be, shall take her from him; these two whom God hath joined man can not separate; and he who attempts it must first pass the point of this lance"; and so saying he brandished it so stoutly and dexterously that he overawed all who did not know him.

But so deep an impression had the rejection of Quiteria made on Camacho's mind that it banished her at once from his thoughts; and so the counsels of the priest, who was a wise and kindly disposed man, prevailed with him, and by their means he and his partisans were pacified and tranquillized, and to prove it put up their swords again, inveighing against the pliancy of Quiteria rather than the craftiness of Basilio; Camacho maintaining that, if Quiteria as a maiden had such a love for Basilio, she would have loved him too as a married woman, and that he ought to thank Heaven more for having taken her than for having given her.

Camacho and those of his following, therefore, being consoled and pacified, those on Basilio's side were appeased; and the rich Camacho, to show that he felt no resentment for the trick, and did not care about it, desired the festival to go on just as if he were married in reality. Neither Basilio, however, nor his bride, nor their followers would take any part in them, and they withdrew to Basilio's village; for the poor, if they are persons of virtue and good sense, have those who follow, honor, and uphold them, just as the rich have those who flatter and dance attendance on them. With them they carried Don Quixote, regarding him as a man of worth and a stout one. Sancho alone had a cloud on his soul, for he found himself debarred from waiting for Camacho's splendid feast and festival, which lasted until night; and thus dragged away, he moodily followed his master, who accompanied Basilio's party, and left behind him the fleshpots of Egypt; though in his heart he took them with him, and their now nearly finished skimmings that he carried in the bucket conjured up visions before his eyes of the glory and abundance of the good cheer he was losing. And so, vexed and dejected though not hungry, without dismounting from Dapple he followed in the footsteps of Rocinante.

Chapter 22

Wherein is related the grand adventure of the cave of Montesinos in the heart of La Mancha, which the valiant Don Quixote brought to a happy termination

MANY and great were the attentions shown to Don Quixote by the newly married couple, who felt themselves under an obligation to him for coming forward in defence of their cause; and they exalted his wisdom to the same level with his courage, rating him as a Cid in arms and a Cicero in eloquence. Worthy Sancho enjoyed himself for three days at the expense of the pair, from whom they learned that the sham wound was not a scheme arranged with the fair Quiteria, but a device of Basilio's, who counted on exactly the result they had seen; he confessed, it is true, that he had confided his idea to some of his friends, so that at the proper time they might aid him in his purpose and insure the success of the deception.

"That," said Don Quixote, "is not and ought not to be called deception which aims at virtuous ends"; and the marriage of lovers he maintained to be a most excellent end, reminding them, however, that love has no greater enemy than hunger and constant want; for love is all gayety, enjoyment, and happiness, especially when the lover is in the possession of the object of his love, and poverty and want are the the declared enemies of all these; which he said to urge Señor Basilio to abandon the practice of those accomplishments he was skilled in, for though they brought him fame, they brought him no money, and apply himself to the acquisition of wealth by legitimate industry, which will never fail those who are prudent and persevering. The poor man who is a man of honor (if indeed a poor man can be a man of honor) has a jewel when he has a fair wife, and if she is taken from him, his honor is taken from him and slain. The fair woman who is a woman of honor, and whose husband is poor, deserves to be crowned with the laurels and crowns of victory and triumph. Beauty by itself attracts the desires of all who behold it, and the royal eagles and birds of towering flight stoop on it as on a dainty lure; but if beauty be accompanied by want and penury, then the ravens and the kites and other birds of prey assail it, and she who stands firm against such attacks well deserves to be called the crown of her husband. "Remember, O prudent Basilio," added Don Quixote, "it was the opinion of a certain sage, I know not whom, that there was not more than one good woman in the whole world; and his advice was that each one should think and believe that this one good woman was his own wife, and in this way he would live happy. I myself am not married, nor, so far, has it ever entered my thoughts to be so; nevertheless I would venture to give advice to any one who might ask it, as to the mode in which he should seek a wife such as he would be content to marry. The first thing I would recommend him would be to look to good name rather than to wealth, for a good woman does not win a good name merely by being good, but by letting it be seen that she is so; and open looseness and freedom do much more damage to a woman's honor than secret depravity. If you take a good woman into your house it will be an easy matter to keep her good, and even to make her still better; but if you take a bad one you will find it hard work to mend her, for it is no very easy matter to pass from one extreme to another. I do not say it is impossible, but I look upon it as difficult."

Sancho, listening to all this, said to himself, "This master of mine, when I say anything that has weight and substance, says I might take a pulpit in hand, and go about the world preaching fine sermons; but I say of him that, when he begins stringing maxims together and giving advice, not only might he take a pulpit in hand, but two on each finger, and go into the market-places to his heart's content. Devil take you for a knight-errant, what a lot of things you know! I used to think in my heart that the only thing he knew was what belonged to his chivalry; but there is nothing he won't have a finger in."

Sancho muttered this somewhat aloud, and his master overheard him, and asked, "What art thou muttering there, Sancho?"

"I'm not saying anything or muttering anything," said Sancho; "I was only saying to myself that I wish I had heard what your worship has said just now before I married; perhaps I'd say now, 'The ox that's loose licks himself well.'"

"Is thy Teresa so bad then, Sancho?" said Don Quixote.

"She is not very bad," replied Sancho; "but she is not very good; at least she is not as good as I could wish."

"Thou dost wrong, Sancho," said Don Quixote, "to speak ill of thy wife; for after all she is the mother of thy children."

"We are quits," returned Sancho; "for she speaks ill of me whenever she takes it into her head, especially when she is jealous; and Satan himself could not put up with her then."

In fine, they remained three days with the newly married couple, by whom they were entertained and treated like kings. Don Quixote begged the fencing licentiate to find him a guide to show him the way to the cave of Montesinos, as he had a great desire to enter it and see with his own eyes if the wonderful tales that were told of it all over the country were true. The licentiate said he would get him a cousin of his own, a famous scholar, and one very much given to reading books of chivalry, who would have great pleasure in conducting him to the mouth of the very cave, and would show him the lakes of Ruidera, which were likewise famous all over La Mancha, and even all over Spain; and he assured him he would find him entertaining, for he was a youth who could write books good enough to be printed and dedicated to princes. The cousin arrived at last, leading an ass in foal, with a pack-saddle covered with a party-colored carpet or sackcloth; Sancho saddled Rocinante,

got Dapple ready, and stocked his *alforjas*, along with which went those of the cousin, likewise well filled; and so, commending themselves to God and bidding farewell to all, they set out, taking the road for the famous cave of Montesinos.

On the way Don Quixote asked the cousin of what sort and character his pursuits, avocations, and studies were, to which he replied that he was by profession a humanist, and that his pursuits and studies were making books for the press, all of great utility and no less entertainment to the nation. One was called *The Book of Liveries,* in which he described seven hundred and three liveries, with their colors, mottoes, and ciphers, from which gentlemen of the court might pick and choose any they fancied for festivals and revels, without having to go a begging for them from any one, or puzzling their brains, as the saying is, to have them appropriate to their objects and purposes; "for," said he, "I give the jealous, the rejected, the forgotten, the absent, what will suit them, and fit them without fail. I have another book, too, which I shall call *Metamorphoses, or the Spanish Ovid,* one of rare and original invention; for, imitating Ovid in burlesque style, I show in it who the Giralda of Seville and the Angel of the Magdalena were, what the sewer of Vecinguerra at Cordova was, what the bulls of Guisando, the Sierra Morena, the Leganitos and Lavapiés fountains at Madrid, not forgetting those of el Piojo, of the Caño Dorado, and of the Priora; and all with their allegories, metaphors, and changes, so that they are amusing, interesting, and instructive, all at once. Another book I have which I call *The Supplement to Polydore Vergil,* which treats of the invention of things, and is a work of great erudition and research, for I establish and elucidate elegantly some things of great importance which Polydore omitted to mention. He forgot to tell us who was the first man in the world that had a cold in his head, and who was the first to try salivation for the French disease, but I give it accurately set forth, and quote more than five-and-twenty authors in proof of it, so your worship may perceive I have labored to good purpose and that the book will be of service to the whole world."

Sancho, who had been very attentive to the cousin's words, said to him, "Tell me, señor,—and God give you luck in printing your books, —can you tell me (for of course you know, as you know everything) who was the first man that scratched his head? For to my thinking it must have been our father Adam."

"So it must," replied the cousin; "for there is no doubt but Adam had a head and hair; and being the first man in the world he would have scratched himself sometimes."

"So I think," said Sancho; "but now tell me, who was the first tumbler in the world?"

"Really, brother," answered the cousin, "I could not at this moment say positively without having investigated it; I will look it up when I go back to where I have my books, and will satisfy you the next time we meet, for this will not be the last time."

"Look here, señor," said Sancho, "don't give yourself any trouble about it, for I have just this minute hit upon what I asked you. The first tumbler in the world, you must know, was Lucifer, when they cast or pitched him out of heaven; for he came tumbling into the bottomless pit."

"You are right, friend," said the cousin; and said Don Quixote, "Sancho, that question and answer are not thine own; thou hast heard them from some one else."

"Hold your peace, señor," said Sancho; "faith, if I take to asking questions and answering, I'll go on from this till tomorrow morning. Nay! to ask foolish things and answer nonsense I needn't go looking for help from my neighbors."

"Thou hast said more than thou art aware of, Sancho," said Don Quixote; "for there are some who weary themselves out in learning and proving things that, after they are known and proved, are not worth a farthing to the understanding or memory."

In this and other pleasant conversation the day went by, and that night they put up at a small hamlet whence it was not more than two leagues to the cave of Montesinos, so the cousin told Don Quixote, adding that if he was bent upon entering it, it would be requisite for him to provide himself with ropes, so that he might be tied and lowered into its depths. Don Quixote said that even if it reached to the bottomless pit he meant to see where it went to; so they bought about a hundred fathoms of rope, and next day at two in the afternoon they arrived at the cave, the mouth of which is spacious and wide, but full of thorn and wild-fig bushes and brambles and briers, so thick and matted that they completely close it up and cover it over.

On coming within sight of it the cousin, Sancho, and Don Quixote dismounted, and the first two immediately tied the latter very firmly with the ropes, and as they were girding and swathing him Sancho said to him, "Mind what you are about, master mine; don't go burying yourself alive, or putting yourself where you'll be like a bottle put to cool in a well; it's no affair or

business of your worship's to become the explorer of this, which must be worse than a Moorish dungeon."

"Tie me and hold thy peace," said Don Quixote, "for an emprise like this, friend Sancho, was reserved for me"; and said the guide, "I beg of you, Señor Don Quixote, to observe carefully and examine with a hundred eyes everything that is within there; perhaps there may be some things for me to put into my book of transformations."

"The drum is in hands that will know how to beat it well enough," said Sancho Panza.

When he had said this and finished the tying (which was not over the armor, but only over the doublet) Don Quixote observed, "It was careless of us not to have provided ourselves with a small cattle-bell to be tied on the rope close to me, the sound of which would show that I was still descending and alive; but as this is out of the question now, in God's hand be it to guide me"; and forthwith he fell on his knees and in a low voice offered up a prayer to Heaven, imploring God to aid him and grant him success in this to all appearance perilous and untried adventure, and then exclaimed aloud, "O mistress of my actions and movements, illustrious and peerless Dulcinea del Toboso, if so be the prayers and supplications of this thy fortunate lover can reach thy ears, by thy incomparable beauty I entreat thee to listen to them, for they but ask thee not to refuse me thy favor and protection now that I stand in such need of them. I am about to precipitate, to sink, to plunge myself into the abyss that is here before me, only to let the world know that while thou dost favor me there is no impossibility I will not attempt and accomplish." With these words he approached the cavern, and perceived that it was impossible to let himself down or effect an entrance except by sheer force or cleaving a passage; so drawing his sword he began to demolish and cut away the brambles at the mouth of the cave, at the noise of which a vast multitude of crows and choughs flew out of it so thick and so fast that they knocked Don Quixote down; and if he had been as much of a believer in augury as he was a Catholic Christian he would have taken it as a bad omen and declined to bury himself in such a place. He got up, however, and as there came no more crows, or night birds like the bats that flew out at the same time with the crows, the cousin and Sancho giving him rope, he lowered himself into the depths of the dread cavern; and as he entered it Sancho sent his blessing after him, making a thousand crosses over him and saying, "God, and the Peña de Francia, and the Trinity of Gaeta guide thee, O flower and cream of knights-errant. There thou goest, thou dare-devil of the earth, heart of steel, arm of brass; once more, God guide thee and send thee back safe, and sound, and unhurt to the light of this world thou art leaving to bury thyself in the darkness thou art seeking there"; and the cousin offered up almost the same prayers and supplications.

Don Quixote kept calling to them to give him rope and more rope, and they gave it out little by little, and by the time the calls, which came out of the cave as out of a pipe, ceased to be heard they had let down the hundred fathoms of rope. They were inclined to pull Don Quixote up again, as they could give him no more rope; however, they waited about half an hour, at the end of which time they began to gather in the rope again with great ease and without feeling any weight, which made them fancy Don Quixote was remaining below; and persuaded that it was so, Sancho wept bitterly, and hauled away in great haste in order to settle the question. When, however, they had come to, as it seemed, rather more than eighty fathoms they felt a weight, at which they were greatly delighted; and at last, at ten fathoms more, they saw Don Quixote distinctly, and Sancho called out to him, saying, "Welcome back, señor, for we had begun to think you were going to stop there to found a family." But Don Quixote answered not a word, and drawing him out entirely they perceived he had his eyes shut and every appearance of being fast asleep.

They stretched him on the ground and untied him, but still he did not awake; however, they rolled him back and forwards and shook and pulled him about, so that after some time he came to himself, stretching himself just as if he were waking up from a deep and sound sleep, and looking about him as if scared he said, "God forgive you, friends; ye have taken me away from the sweetest and most delightful existence and spectacle that ever human being enjoyed or beheld. Now indeed do I know that all the pleasures of this life pass away like a shadow and a dream, or fade like the flower of the field. O ill-fated Montesinos! O sore-wounded Durandarte! O unhappy Belerma! O tearful Guadiana, and ye O hapless daughters of Ruidera who show in your waves the tears that flowed from your beauteous eyes!"

The cousin and Sancho Panza listened with deep attention to the words of Don Quixote, who uttered them as though with immense pain he drew them up from his very bowels. They begged of him to explain himself, and tell them what he had seen in that hell down there.

"Hell do you call it?" said Don Quixote; "call it by no such name, for it does not deserve it, as ye shall soon see."

He then begged them to give him something to eat, as he was very hungry. They spread the cousin's sack-cloth on the grass, and put the stores of the *alforjas* into requisition, and all three sitting down lovingly and sociably, they made a luncheon and a supper of it all in one; and when the sackcloth was removed, Don Quixote of La Mancha said, "Let no one rise; and attend to me, my sons, both of you."

Chapter 23

Of the wonderful things the incomparable Don Quixote said he saw in the profound cave of Montesinos, the impossibility and magnitude of which cause this adventure to be deemed apocryphal

IT was about four in the afternoon when the sun, veiled in clouds, with subdued light and tempered beams, enabled Don Quixote to relate, without heat or inconvenience, what he had seen in the cave of Montesinos to his two illustrious hearers, and he began as follows:

"A matter of some twelve or fourteen times a man's height down in this pit, on the left-hand side, there is a recess or space, roomy enough to contain a large cart with its mules. A little light reaches it through some chinks or crevices, communicating with it and open to the surface of the earth. This recess or space I perceived when I was already growing weary and disgusted at finding myself hanging suspended by the rope, travelling downwards into that dark region without any certainty or knowledge of where I was going to, so I resolved to enter it and rest myself for a while. I called out, telling you not to let out more rope until I bade you, but you can not have heard me. I then gathered in the rope you were sending me, and making a coil or pile of it I seated myself upon it, ruminating and considering what I was to do to lower myself to the bottom, having no one to hold me up; and as I was thus deep in thought and perplexity, suddenly and without provocation a profound sleep fell upon me, and when I least expected it, I know not how, I awoke and found myself in the midst of the most beautiful, delicious, delightful meadow that nature could produce or the most lively human imagination conceive. I opened my eyes, I rubbed them, and found I was not asleep, but thoroughly awake. Nevertheless, I felt my head and breast to satisfy myself whether it was I myself who was there or some empty delusive phantom; but touch, feeling, the collected thoughts that passed through my mind, all convinced me that I was the same then and there that I am this moment. Next there presented itself to my sight a stately royal palace or castle, with walls that seemed built of clear transparent crystal; and through two great doors that opened wide therein, I saw coming forth and advancing towards me a venerable old man, clad in a long gown of mulberry-colored serge that trailed upon the ground. On his shoulders and breast he had a green satin collegiate hood, and covering his head a black Milanese bonnet, and his snow-white beard fell below his girdle. He carried no arms whatever, nothing but a rosary of beads bigger than fair-sized filberts, each tenth bead being like a moderate ostrich egg; his bearing, his gait, his dignity and imposing presence held me spellbound and wondering. He approached me, and the first thing he did was to embrace me closely, and then he said to me, 'For a long time now, O valiant knight Don Quixote of La Mancha, we who are here enchanted in these solitudes have been hoping to see thee, that thou mayest make known to the world what is shut up and concealed in this deep cave, called the cave of Montesinos, which thou hast entered, an achievement reserved for thy invincible heart and stupendous courage alone to attempt. Come with me, illustrious sir, and I will show thee the marvels hidden within this transparent castle, whereof I am the *alcalde* and perpetual warden; for I am Montesinos himself, from whom the cave takes its name.' [1]

"The instant he told me he was Montesinos, I asked him if the story they told in the world above here was true, that he had taken out the heart of his great friend Durandarte from his breast with a little dagger, and carried it to the lady Belerma, as his friend when at the point of death had commanded him. He said in reply that they spoke the truth in every respect except as to the dagger, for it was not a dagger, nor little, but a burnished poniard sharper than an awl."

"That poniard must have been made by Ramon de Hoces the Sevillian," said Sancho.

"I do not know," said Don Quixote; "it could not have been by that poniard maker, however, because Ramon de Hoces was a man of yester-

[1] Montesinos is the hero of half a dozen ballads, according to which he was one of the Peers, and a grandson of Charlemagne.

day, and the affair of Roncesvalles, where this mishap occurred, was long ago; but the question is of no great importance, nor does it affect or make any alteration in the truth or substance of the story."

"That is true," said the cousin; "continue, Señor Don Quixote, for I am listening to you with the greatest pleasure in the world."

"And with no less do I tell the tale," said Don Quixote; "and so, to proceed—the venerable Montesinos led me into the palace of crystal, where, in a lower chamber, strangely cool and entirely of alabaster, was an elaborately wrought marble tomb, upon which I beheld stretched at full length, a knight, not of bronze, or marble, or jasper, as are seen on other tombs, but of actual flesh and bone. His right hand (which seemed to me somewhat hairy and sinewy, a sign of great strength in its owner) lay on the side of his heart; but before I could put any question to Montesinos, he, seeing me gazing at the tomb in amazement, said to me, 'This is my friend Durandarte, flower and mirror of the true lovers and valiant knights of his time. He is held enchanted here, as I myself and many others are, by that French enchanter Merlin, who, they say, was the devil's son; but my belief is, not that he was the devil's son, but that he knew, as the saying is, a point more than the devil. How or why he enchanted us no one knows, but time will tell, and I suspect that time is not far off. What I marvel at is, that I know it to be as sure as that it is now day, that Durandarte ended his life in my arms, and that after his death, I took out his heart with my own hands; and indeed it must have weighed more than two pounds, for, according to naturalists, he who has a large heart is more largely endowed with valor than he who has a small one. Then, as this is the case, and as the knight did really die, how comes it that he now moans and sighs from time to time, as if he were still alive?'

"As he said this, the wretched Durandarte cried out in a loud voice:

> O cousin Montesinos!
> 'Twas my last request of thee,
> When my soul hath left the body,
> And that lying dead I be,
> With thy poniard or thy dagger
> Cut the heart from out my breast,
> And bear it to Belerma.
> This was my last request.

On hearing which, the venerable Montesinos fell on his knees before the unhappy knight and with tearful eyes exclaimed, 'Long since

O Señor Durandarte, my beloved cousin, long since have I done what you bade me on that sad day when I lost you; I took out your heart as well as I could, not leaving an atom of it in your breast, I wiped it with a lace handkerchief, and I took the road to France with it, having first laid you in the bosom of the earth with tears enough to wash and cleanse my hands of the blood that covered them after wandering among your bowels; and more by token, O cousin of my soul, at the first village I came to after leaving Roncesvalles, I sprinkled a little salt upon your heart to keep it sweet, and bring it, if not fresh, at least pickled, into the presence of the lady Belerma, whom, together with you, myself, Guadiana your squire, the duenna Ruidera and her seven daughters and two nieces, and many more of your friends and acquaintances, the sage Merlin has been keeping enchanted here these many years; and although more than five hundred have gone by, not one of us has died; Ruidera and her daughters and nieces alone are missing, and these, because of the tears they shed, Merlin, out of the compassion he seems to have felt for them, changed into so many lakes, which to this day in the world of the living, and in the province of La Mancha, are called the lakes of Ruidera. The seven daughters belong to the kings of Spain, and the two nieces to the knights of a very holy order called the Order of St. John. Guadiana your squire, likewise bewailing your fate, was changed into a river of his own name, but when he came to the surface and beheld the sun of another heaven, so great was his grief at finding he was leaving you, that he plunged into the bowels of the earth; however, as he can not help following his natural course, he from time to time comes forth and shows himself to the sun and the world. The lakes aforesaid send him their waters, and with these, and others that come to him, he makes a grand and imposing entrance into Portugal; but for all that, go where he may, he shows his melancholy and sadness, and takes no pride in breeding dainty choice fish, only coarse and tasteless sorts, very different from those of the golden Tagus. All this that I tell you now, O cousin mine, I have told you many times before, and as you make no answer, I fear that either you believe me not, or do not hear me, whereat I feel God knows what grief. I have now news to give you, which, if it serves not to alleviate your sufferings, will not in any wise increase them. Know that you have here before you (open your eyes and you will see) that great knight of whom the sage Merlin has prophesied such great things; that Don Quixote of La Mancha I mean, who has again, and to better purpose than in past times, revived in these days knight-errantry, long since forgotten, and by whose intervention and aid it may be we shall be disenchanted; for great deeds are reserved for great men.'

" 'And if that may not be,' said the wretched Durandarte in a low and feeble voice, 'if that may not be, then, O my cousin, I say "patience and shuffle" '; and turning over on his side, he relapsed into his former silence without uttering another word.

"And now there was heard a great outcry and lamentation, accompanied by deep sighs and bitter sobs. I looked round, and through the crystal wall I saw passing through another chamber a procession of two lines of fair damsels all clad in mourning, and with white turbans of Turkish fashion on their heads. Behind, in the rear of these, there came a lady, for so from her dignity she seemed to be, also clad in black, with a white veil so long and ample that it swept the ground. Her turban was twice as large as the largest of any of the others; her eyebrows met, her nose was rather flat, her mouth was large but with ruddy lips, and her teeth, of which at times she allowed a glimpse, were seen to be sparse and ill-set, though as white as peeled almonds. She carried in her hands a fine cloth, and in it, as well as I could make out, a heart that had been mummied, so parched and dried was it. Montesinos told me that all those forming the procession were the attendants of Durandarte and Belerma, who were enchanted there with their master and mistress, and that the last, she who carried the heart in the cloth, was the lady Belerma, who, with her damsels, four days in the week went in procession singing, or rather weeping, dirges over the body and miserable heart of his cousin; and that if she appeared to me somewhat ill-favored, or not so beautiful as fame reported her, it was because of the bad nights and worse days that she passed in that enchantment, as I could see by the great dark circles round her eyes, and her sickly complexion; 'her sallowness, and the rings round her eyes,' said he, 'are not caused by the periodical ailment usual with women, for it is many months and even years since she has had any, but by the grief her own heart suffers because of that which she holds in her hand perpetually, and which recalls and brings back to her memory the sad fate of her lost lover; were it not for this, hardly would the great Dulcinea del Toboso, so celebrated in all these parts, and even in all the world, come up to her for beauty, grace, and gayety.'

"'Hold hard!' said I at this, 'tell your story as you ought, Señor Don Montesinos, for you know very well that all comparisons are odious, and there is no occasion to compare one person with another; the peerless Dulcinea del Toboso is what she is, and the lady Doña Belerma is what *she* is and has been, and that's enough.' To which he made answer, 'Forgive me, Señor Don Quixote; I own I was wrong and spoke unadvisedly in saying that the lady Dulcinea could scarcely come up to the lady Belerma; for it were enough for me to have learned, by what means I know not, that you are her knight, to make me bite my tongue out before I compared her to anything save heaven itself.' After this apology which the great Montesinos made me, my heart recovered itself from the shock I had received in hearing my lady compared with Belerma."

"Still I wonder," said Sancho, "that your worship did not get upon the old fellow and bruise every bone of him with kicks, and pluck his beard until you didn't leave a hair in it."

"Nay, Sancho, my friend," said Don Quixote, "it would not have been right in me to do that, for we are all bound to pay respect to the aged, even though they be not knights, but especially those who are, and who are enchanted; I only know I gave him as good as he brought in the many other questions and answers we exchanged."

"I can not understand, Señor Don Quixote," remarked the cousin here, "how it is that your worship, in such a short space of time as you have been below there, could have seen so many things, and said and answered so much."

"How long is it since I went down?" asked Don Quixote.

"Little better than an hour," replied Sancho.

"That can not be," returned Don Quixote, "because night overtook me while I was there, and day came, and it was night again and day again three times; so that, by my reckoning, I have been three days in those remote regions beyond our ken."

"My master must be right," replied Sancho; "for as everything that has happened to him is by enchantment, maybe what seems to us an hour would seem three days and nights there."

"That's it," said Don Quixote.

"And did your worship eat anything all that time, señor?" asked the cousin.

"I never touched a morsel," answered Don Quixote, "nor did I even feel hunger, or think of it."

"And do the enchanted eat?" said the cousin.

"They neither eat," said Don Quixote; "nor are they subject to the greater excrements, though it is thought that their nails, beards, and hair grow."

"And do the enchanted sleep, now, señor?" asked Sancho.

"Certainly not," replied Don Quixote; "at least, during those three days I was with them not one of them closed an eye, nor did I either."

"The proverb, 'Tell me what company thou keepest and I'll tell thee what thou art,' is to the point here," said Sancho; "your worship keeps company with enchanted people that are always fasting and watching; what wonder is it, then, that you neither eat nor sleep while you are with them? But forgive me, señor, if I say that of all this you have told us now, may God take me—I was just going to say the devil—if I believe a single particle."

"What!" said the cousin, "has Señor Don Quixote, then, been lying? Why, even if he wished it he has not had time to imagine and put together such a host of lies."

"I don't believe my master lies," said Sancho.

"If not, what dost thou believe?" asked Don Quixote.

"I believe," replied Sancho, "that this Merlin, or those enchanters who enchanted the whole crew your worship says you saw and discoursed with down there, stuffed your imagination or your mind with all this rigmarole you have been treating us to, and all that is still to come."

"All that might be, Sancho," replied Don Quixote; "but it is not so, for everything that I have told you I saw with my own eyes, and touched with my own hands. But what will you say when I tell you now how, among the countless other marvellous things Montesinos showed me (of which at leisure and at the proper time I will give thee an account in the course of our journey, for they would not be all in place here), he showed me three country girls who went skipping and capering like goats over the pleasant fields there, and the instant I beheld them I knew one to be the peerless Dulcinea del Toboso, and the other two those same country girls that were with her and that we spoke to on the road from El Toboso! I asked Montesinos if he knew them, and he told me he did not, but he thought they must be some enchanted ladies of distinction, for it was only a few days before that they had made their appearance in those meadows; but I was not to be surprised at that, because there were a great many other ladies there of times past and present, enchanted in various strange shapes, and among them he had recognized Queen Guinevere and her dame Quintañona, she who poured out the wine for Lancelot when he came from Britain."

When Sancho Panza heard his master say this he was ready to take leave of his senses, or die with laughter; for, as he knew the real truth about the pretended enchantment of Dulcinea, in which he himself had been the enchanter and concocter of all the evidence, he made up his mind at last that, beyond all doubt, his master was out of his wits and stark mad, so he said to him, "It was an evil hour, a worse season, and a sorrowful day, when your worship, dear master mine, went down to the other world, and an unlucky moment when you met with Señor Montesinos, who has sent you back to us like this. You were well enough here above in your full senses, such as God had given you, delivering maxims and giving advice at every turn, and not as you are now, talking the greatest nonsense that can be imagined."

"As I know thee, Sancho," said Don Quixote, "I heed not thy words."

"Nor I your worship's," said Sancho, "whether you beat me or kill me for those I have spoken, and will speak if you don't correct and mend your own. But tell me, while we are still at peace, how or by what did you recognize the lady our mistress; and if you spoke to her, what did you say, and what did she answer?"

"I recognized her," said Don Quixote, "by her wearing the same garments she wore when thou didst point her out to me. I spoke to her, but she did not utter a word in reply; on the contrary, she turned her back on me and took to flight, at such a pace that a crossbow bolt could not have overtaken her. I wished to follow her, and would have done so had not Montesinos recommended me not to take the trouble as it would be useless, particularly as the time was drawing near when it would be necessary for me to quit the cavern. He told me, moreover, that in course of time he would let me know how he and Belerma, and Durandarte, and all who were there, were to be disenchanted. But of all I saw and observed down there, what gave me most pain was, that while Montesinos was speaking to me, one of the two companions of the hapless Dulcinea approached me on one side, without my having seen her coming and with tears in her eyes said to me, in a low, agitated voice, 'My lady Dulcinea del To-

boso kisses your worship's hands, and entreats you to do her the favor of letting her know how you are; and, being in great need, she also entreats your worship as earnestly as she can to be so good as to lend her half a dozen reals, or as much as you may have about you, on this new dimity petticoat that I have here; and she promises to repay them very speedily.' I was amazed and taken aback by such a message, and turning to Señor Montesinos I asked him, 'Is it possible, Señor Montesinos, that persons of distinction under enchantment can be in need?' To which he replied, 'Believe me, Señor Don Quixote, that which is called need is to be met with everywhere, and penetrates all quarters and reaches every one, and does not spare even the enchanted; and as the lady Dulcinea del Toboso sends to beg those six reals, and the pledge is to all appearance a good one, there is nothing for it but to give them to her, for no doubt she must be in some great strait.' 'I will take no pledge of her,' I replied, 'nor yet can I give her what she asks, for all I have is four reals'; which I gave (they were those which thou, Sancho, gavest me the other day to bestow in alms upon the poor I met along the road), and I said, 'Tell your mistress, my dear, that I am grieved to the heart because of her distresses, and wish I was a Fucar[1] to remedy them, and that I would have her know that I can not be, and ought not to be, in health while deprived of the happiness of seeing her and enjoying her discreet conversation, and that I implore her as earnestly as I can, to allow herself to be seen and addressed by this her captive servant and forlorn knight. Tell her, too, that when she least expects it she will hear it announced that I have made an oath and vow after the fashion of that which the Marquis of Mantua made to avenge his nephew Baldwin, when he found him at the point of death in the heart of the mountains, which was, not to eat bread off a table-cloth, and the other trifling matters which he added, until he had avenged him; and I will make the same to take no rest, and to roam the seven regions of the earth more thoroughly than the Infante Don Pedro of Portugal ever roamed them, until I have disenchanted her.' 'All that, and more, you owe my lady,' was the damsel's answer to me, and taking the four reals, instead of making me a courtesy she cut a caper, springing two full yards into the air."

"O blessed God!" exclaimed Sancho aloud

[1] The Spanish form of Fugger, the name of the great Augsburg capitalists of the sixteenth century.

at this, "is it possible that such things can be in the world, and that enchanters and enchantments can have such power in it as to have changed my master's right senses into a craze so full of absurdity! O señor, señor, for God's sake, consider yourself, have a care for your honor, and give no credit to this silly stuff that has left you scant and short of wits."

"Thou talkest in this way because thou lovest me, Sancho," said Don Quixote; "and not being experienced in the things of the world, everything that has some difficulty about it, seems to thee impossible; but time will pass, as I said before, and I will tell thee some of the things I saw down there which will make thee believe what I have related now, the truth of which admits of neither reply nor question."

Chapter 24

Wherein are related a thousand trifling matters, as trivial as they are necessary to the right understanding of this great history

He who translated this great history from the original written by its first author, Cid Hamet Benengeli, says that on coming to the chapter giving the adventures of the cave of Montesinos he found written on the margin of it, in Hamet's own hand, these exact words:

"I can not convince or persuade myself that everything that is written in the preceding chapter could have precisely happened to the valiant Don Quixote; and for this reason, that all the adventures that have occurred up to the present have been possible and probable; but as for this one of the cave, I see no way of accepting it as true, as it passes all reasonable bounds. For me to believe that Don Quixote could lie, he being the most truthful gentleman and the noblest knight of his time, is impossible; he would not have told a lie though he were shot to death with arrows. On the other hand, I reflect that he related and told the story with all the circumstances detailed, and that he could not in so short a space have fabricated such a vast complication of absurdities; if, then, this adventure seems apocryphal, it is no fault of mine; and so, without affirming its falsehood or its truth, I write it down. Decide for thyself in thy wisdom, reader; for I am not bound, nor is it in my power, to do more; though certain it is they say that at the time of his death he retracted, and said he had invented it, thinking it matched and tallied with the adventures he had read of in his histories." And then he goes on to say:

The cousin was amazed as well at Sancho's boldness as at the patience of his master, and concluded that the good temper the latter displayed arose from the happiness he felt at having seen his lady Dulcinea, even enchanted as she was; because otherwise the words and language Sancho had addressed to him deserved a thrashing; for indeed he seemed to him to have been rather impudent to his master, to whom he now observed, "I, Señor Don Quixote of La Mancha, look upon the time I have spent in travelling with your worship as very well employed, for I have gained four things in the course of it; the first is that I have made your acquaintance, which I consider great good fortune; the second, that I have learned what the cave of Montesinos contains, together with the transformations of Guadiana and of the lake of Ruidera, which will be of use to me for the Spanish Ovid that I have in hand; the third, to have discovered the antiquity of cards, that they were in use at least in the time of Charlemagne, as may be inferred from the words you say Durandarte uttered when, at the end of that long spell while Montesinos was talking to him he woke up and said, 'Patience and shuffle.' This phrase and expression he could not have learned while he was enchanted, but only before he had become so, in France, and in the time of the aforesaid emperor Charlemagne. And this demonstration is just the thing for me for that other book I am writing, *The Supplement to Polydore Vergil on the Invention of Antiquities;* for I believe he never thought of inserting that of cards in his book, as I mean to do in mine, and it will be a matter of great importance, particularly when I can cite so grave and veracious an authority as Señor Durandarte. And the fourth thing is, that I have ascertained the source of the river Guadiana, heretofore unknown to mankind."

"You are right," said Don Quixote; "but I should like to know, if by God's favor they grant you a license to print those books of yours—which I doubt—to whom do you mean to dedicate them?"

"There are lords and grandees in Spain to whom they can be dedicated," said the cousin.

"Not many," said Don Quixote; "not that they are unworthy of it, but because they do not care to accept books and incur the obligation of making the return that seems due to the author's labor and courtesy. One prince I know who makes up for all the rest, and more—how much more, if I ventured to say, perhaps should stir up envy in many a noble breast; bu let this stand over for some more convenient time, and let us go and look for some place to shelter ourselves to-night."

"Not far from this," said the cousin, "there is a hermitage, where there lives a hermit, who they say was a soldier, and who has the reputation of being a good Christian and a very intelligent and charitable man. Close to the hermitage he has a small house which he built at his own cost, but though small it is large enough for the reception of guests."

"Has this hermit any hens, do you think?" asked Sancho.

"Few hermits are without them," said Don Quixote; "for those we see now-a-days are not like the hermits of the Egyptian deserts, who were clad in palm-leaves, and lived on the roots of the earth. But do not think that by praising these I am disparaging the others; all I mean to say is, that the penances of those of the present day do not come up to the asceticism and austerity of former times; but it does not follow from this that they are not all worthy; at least I think them so; and at the worst the hypocrite who pretends to be good does less harm than the open sinner."

At this point they saw approaching the spot where they stood a man on foot, proceeding at a rapid pace, and beating a mule loaded with lances and halberds. When he came up to them, he saluted them and passed on without stopping. Don Quixote called to him, "Stay, good fellow; you seem to be making more haste than suits that mule."

"I can not stop, señor," answered the man; "for the arms you see I carry here, are to be used to-morrow, so I must not delay; God be with you. But if you want to know what I am carrying them for, I mean to lodge to-night at the inn that is beyond the hermitage, and if you be going the same road you will find me there, and I will tell you some curious things; once more God be with you"; and he urged on his mule at such a pace that Don Quixote had no time to ask him what these curious things were that he meant to tell them; and as he was somewhat inquisitive, and always tortured by his anxiety to learn something new, he decided to set out at once, and go and pass the night at the inn instead of stopping at the hermitage, where the cousin would have had them halt. Accordingly they mounted and all three took the direct road for the inn, which they reached a little before nightfall. On the road the cousin proposed they should go up to the hermitage to drink a sup. The instant Sancho heard this he

steered his Dapple towards it, and Don Quixote and the cousin did the same; but it seems Sancho's bad luck so ordered it that the hermit was not at home, for so a sub-hermit they found in the hermitage told them. They called for some of the best. She replied that her master had none, but that if they liked cheap water she would give it with great pleasure.

"If I found any in water," said Sancho, "there are wells along the road where I could have had enough of it. Ah, Camacho's wedding, and plentiful house of Don Diego, how often do I miss you!"

Leaving the hermitage, they pushed on towards the inn, and a little farther they came upon a youth who was pacing along in front of them at no great speed, so that they overtook him. He carried a sword over his shoulder, and slung on it a budget or bundle of his clothes apparently, probably his breeches or pantaloons, and his cloak and a shirt or two; for he had on a short jacket of velvet with a gloss like satin on it in places, and had his shirt out; his stockings were of silk, and his shoes square-toed as they wear them at court. His age might have been eighteen or nineteen; he was of a merry countenance, and to all appearance of an active habit, and he went along singing *seguidillas* to beguile the wearisomeness of the road. As they came up with him he was just finishing one, which the cousin got by heart and they say ran thus—

> I'm off to the wars
> For the want of pence,
> Oh, had I but money
> I'd show more sense.

The first to address him was Don Quixote, who said, "You travel very airily, sir gallant; whither bound, may we ask, if it is your pleasure to tell us?"

To which the youth replied, "The heat and my poverty are the reason of my travelling so airily, and it is to the wars that I am bound."

"How poverty?" asked Don Quixote; "the heat one can understand."

"Señor," replied the youth, "in this bundle I carry velvet pantaloons to match this jacket; if I wear them out on the road, I shall not be able to make a decent appearance in them in the city, and I have not the wherewithal to buy others; and so for this reason, as well as to keep myself cool, I am making my way in this fashion to overtake some companies of infantry that are not twelve leagues off, in which I shall enlist, and there will be no want of baggage trains to travel with after that to the place of embarkation, which they say will be Carthagena; I would rather have the King for a master, and serve him in the wars, than serve a court pauper."

"And did you get any bounty, now?" asked the cousin.

"If I had been in the service of some grandee of Spain or personage of distinction," replied the youth, "I should have been safe to get it; for that is the advantage of serving good masters, that out of the servants' hall men come to be ancients or captains, or get a good pension. But I, to my misfortune, always served place hunters and adventurers, whose keep and wages were so miserable and scanty that half went in paying for the starching of one's collar; it would be a miracle indeed if a page volunteer ever got anything like a reasonable bounty."

"And tell me, for Heaven's sake," asked Don Quixote, "is it possible, my friend, that all the time you served you never got any livery?"

"They gave me two," replied the page; "but just as when one quits a religious community before making profession, they strip him of the dress of the order and give him back his own clothes, so did my masters return me mine; for as soon as the business on which they came to court was finished, they went home and took back the liveries they had given merely for show."

"What spilorceria!—as an Italian would say," said Don Quixote; "but for all that, consider yourself happy in having left court with as worthy an object as you have, for there is nothing on earth more honorable or profitable than serving, first of all God, and then one's king and natural lord, particularly in the profession of arms, by which, if not more wealth, at least more honor is to be won than by letters, as I have said many a time; for though letters may have founded more great houses than arms, still those founded by arms have I know not what superiority over those founded by letters, and a certain splendor belonging to them that distinguishes them above all. And bear in mind what I am now about to say to you, for it will be of great use and comfort to you in time of trouble; it is, not to let your mind dwell on the adverse chances that may befall you; for the worst of all is death, and if it be a good death, the best of all is to die. They asked Julius Cæsar, the valiant Roman emperor, what was the best death. He answered, that which is unexpected, which comes suddenly and unforeseen; and though he answered like a pagan, and one without the knowledge of the true God, yet, as far as

sparing our feelings is concerned, he was right: for suppose you are killed in the first engagement or skirmish, whether by a cannon ball or blown up by mine, what matters it? It is only dying, and all is over; and according to Terence, a soldier shows better dead in battle, than alive and safe in flight; and the good soldier wins fame in proportion as he is obedient to his captains and those in command over him. And remember, my son, that it is better for the soldier to smell of gunpowder than of civet, and that if old age should come upon you in this honorable calling, though you may be covered with wounds and crippled and lame, it will not come upon you without honor, and that such as poverty can not lessen; especially now that provisions are being made for supporting and relieving old and disabled soldiers; for it is not right to deal with them after the fashion of those who set free and get rid of their black slaves when they are old and useless, and, turning them out of their houses under the pretence of making them free, make them slaves to hunger, from which they can not expect to be released except by death. But for the present I won't say more than get ye up behind me on my horse as far as the inn, and sup with me there, and to-morrow you shall pursue your journey, and God give you as good speed as your intentions deserve."

The page did not accept the invitation to mount, though he did that to supper at the inn; and here they say Sancho said to himself, "God be with you for a master; is it possible that a man who can say things so many and so good as he has said just now, can say that he saw the impossible absurdities he reports about the cave of Montesinos? Well, well, we shall see."

And now, just as night was falling, they reached the inn, and it was not without satisfaction that Sancho perceived his master took it for a real inn, and not for a castle as usual. The instant they entered Don Quixote asked the landlord after the man with the lances and halberds, and was told that he was in the stable seeing to his mule; which was what Sancho and the cousin proceeded to do for their beasts, giving the best manger and the best place in the stable to Rocinante.

Chapter 25

Wherein is set down the braying adventure, and the droll one of the puppet-showman, together with the memorable divinations of the divining ape

DON QUIXOTE's bread would not bake, as the common saying is, until he had heard and learned the curious things promised by the man who carried the arms. He went to seek him where the innkeeper said he was, and having found him, bade him say now at any rate what he had to say in answer to the question he had asked him on the road. "The tale of my wonders must be taken more leisurely and not standing," said the man; "let me finish foddering my beast, good sir; and then I'll tell you things that will astonish you."

"Don't wait for that," said Don Quixote; "I'll help you in everything," and so he did, sifting the barley for him and cleaning out the manger; a degree of humility which made the other feel bound to tell him with a good grace what he had asked; so seating himself on a bench, with Don Quixote beside him, and the cousin, the page, Sancho Panza, and the landlord, for a senate and an audience, he began his story in this way:

"You must know that in a village four leagues and a half from this inn, it so happened that one of the *regidors*,[1] by the tricks and roguery of a servant girl of his (it's too long a tale to tell), lost an ass: and though he did all he possibly could to find it, it was all to no purpose. A fortnight might have gone by, so the story goes, since the ass had been missing, when, as the *regidor* who had lost it was standing in the plaza, another *regidor* of the same town said to him, 'Pay me for good news, gossip; your ass has turned up.' 'That I will, and well, gossip,' said the other; 'but tell us, where has he turned up?' 'In the forest,' said the finder; 'I saw him this morning without pack-saddle or harness of any sort, and so lean that it went to one's heart to see him. I tried to drive him before me and bring him to you, but he is already so wild and shy that when I went near him, he made off into the thickest part of the forest. If you have a mind that we two should go back and look for him, let me put up this she-ass at my house and I'll be back at once.' 'You will be doing me a great kindness,' said the owner of the ass, 'and I'll try to pay it back in the same coin.' It is with all these circumstances, and in the very same way I am telling it now, that those who know all about the matter tell the story. Well then, the two *regidors* set off on foot, arm in arm for the forest, and coming to the place where they hoped to find the ass they could not find him, nor was he to be seen anywhere about, search as they might. Seeing, then, that there was no sign of him, the *regidor* who had seen him said to the other, 'Look here, gossip; a plan has oc-

[1] Officers who have charge of the expenditure of the municipality.

curred to me, by which, beyond a doubt, we shall manage to discover the animal, even if he is stowed away in the bowels of the earth, not to say the forest. Here it is. I can bray to perfection, and if you can ever so little, the thing's as good as done.' 'Ever so little, did you say, gossip?' said the other; 'by God, I'll not give in to anybody, not even to the asses themselves.' 'We'll soon see,' said the second *regidor*, 'for my plan is, that you should go on one side of the forest, and I the other, so as to go all round about it; and every now and then you will bray and I will bray; and it can not be but that the ass will hear us, and answer us if he is in the forest.' To which the owner of the ass replied, 'It's an excellent plan, I declare, gossip, and worthy of your great genius'; and the two separating as agreed, it so fell out that they brayed almost at the same moment, and each, deceived by the braying of the other, ran to look, fancying the ass had turned up at last. When they came in sight of one another, said the loser, 'Is it possible, gossip, that it was not my ass that brayed?' 'No, it was I,' said the other. 'Well then, I can tell you, gossip,' said the ass's owner, 'that between you and an ass there's not an atom of difference as far as braying goes, for I never in all my life saw or heard anything more natural.' 'Those praises and compliments belong to you more justly than to me, gossip,' said the inventor of the plan; 'for, by the God that made me, you might give a couple of brays odds to the best and most finished brayer in the world; the tone you have got is deep, your voice is well kept up as to time and pitch, and your finishing notes come thick and fast; in fact, I own myself beaten, and yield the palm to you, and give in to you in this rare accomplishment.' 'Well then,' said the owner, 'I'll set a higher value on myself for the future, and consider that I know something, as I have an excellence of some sort; for though I always thought I brayed well, I never supposed I came up to the pitch of perfection you say.' 'And I say too,' said the second, 'that there are rare gifts going to loss in the world, and that they are ill bestowed upon those who don't know how to make use of them.' 'Ours,' said the owner of the ass, 'unless it is in cases like what we have in hand, can not be of any service to us, and even in this God grant they may be of some use.' So saying they separated, and took to their braying once more, but every instant they were deceiving one another, and coming to meet one another again, until they arranged by way of countersign, so as to know that it was they and not the ass, to give two brays, one after the other. In this way, doubling the brays at every step, they made the complete circuit of the forest, but the lost ass never gave them an answer or even the sign of one. How could the poor ill-starred brute have answered, when, in the thickest part of the forest, they found him devoured by wolves? As soon as he saw him his owner said, 'I was wondering he did not answer, for if he wasn't dead he'd have brayed when he heard us, or he'd have been no ass; but for the sake of having heard you bray to such perfection, gossip, I count the trouble I have taken to look for him well bestowed, even though I have found him dead.' 'It's in a good hand, gossip,' said the other; 'if the abbot sings well, the acolyte is not much behind him.' So they returned disconsolate and hoarse to their village, where they told their friends, neighbors, and acquaintances what had befallen them in their search for the ass, each crying up the other's perfection in braying. The whole story came to be known and spread abroad through the villages of the neighborhood; and the devil, who never sleeps, with his love for sowing dissensions and scattering discord everywhere, blowing mischief about and making quarrels out of nothing, contrived to make the people of the other towns fall to braying whenever they saw any one from our village, as if to throw the braying of our *regidors* in our teeth. Then the boys took to it, which was the same thing for it as getting into the hands and mouths of all the devils of hell; and braying spread from one town to another in such a way that the men of the braying town are as easy to be known as blacks are to be known from whites, and the unlucky joke has gone so far that several times the scoffed have come out in arms and in a body to do battle with the scoffers, and neither king nor rook, fear nor shame, can mend matters. Tomorrow or the day after, I believe, the men of my town, that is, of the braying town, are going to take the field against another village two leagues away from ours, one of those that persecute us most; and that we may turn out well prepared I have bought these lances and halberds you have seen. These are the curious things I told you I had to tell, and if you don't think them so, I have got no others"; and with this the worthy fellow brought his story to a close.

Just at this moment there came in at the gate of the inn a man entirely clad in chamois leather, hose, breeches, and doublet, who said in a loud voice, "Señor host, have you room? Here's the divining ape and the show of the *Release of Melisendra* just coming."

"Ods body!" said the landlord, "why, it's Master Pedro! We're in for a grand night!"

I forgot to mention that the said Master Pedro had his left eye and nearly half his cheek covered with a patch of green taffety, showing that something ailed all that side.

"Your worship is welcome, Master Pedro," continued the landlord; "but where are the ape and the show, for I don't see them?"

"They are close at hand," said he in the chamois leather, "but I came on first to know if there was any room."

"I'd make the duke of Alva himself clear out to make room for Master Pedro," said the landlord; "bring in the ape and the show; there's company in the inn to-night that will pay to see that and the cleverness of the ape."

"So be it by all means," said the man with the patch; "I'll lower the price, and be well satisfied if I only pay my expenses; and now I'll go back and hurry on the cart with the ape and the show"; and with this he went out of the inn.

Don Quixote at once asked the landlord what this Master Pedro was, and what was the show and what was the ape he had with him; to which the landlord replied, "This is a famous puppet-showman, who for some time past has been going about this Mancha de Aragon, exhibiting a show of the *Release of Melisendra* by the famous Don Gaiferos, one of the best and best represented stories that have been seen in this part of the kingdom for many a year; he has also with him an ape with the most extraordinary gift ever seen in an ape or imagined in a human being; for if you ask him anything, he listens attentively to the question, and then jumps on his master's shoulder, and pressing close to his ear tells him the answer, which Master Pedro then delivers. He says a great deal more about things past than about things to come; and though he does not always hit the truth in every case, most times he is not far wrong, so that he makes us fancy he has got the devil in him. He gets two reals for every question if the ape answers; I mean if his master answers for him after he has whispered into his ear; and so it is believed that this same Master Pedro is very rich. He is a 'gallant man' as they say in Italy, and good company, and leads the finest life in the world; talks more than six, drinks more than a dozen, and all by his tongue, and his ape, and his show."

Master Pedro now came back, and in a cart

followed the show and the ape—a big one, without a tail and with buttocks as bare as felt, but not vicious-looking. As soon as Don Quixote saw him, he asked him, "Can you tell me, sir fortune-teller, what fish do we catch, and how will it be with us? See, here are my two reals," and he bade Sancho give them to Master Pedro; but he answered for the ape and said, "Señor, this animal does not give any answer or information touching things that are to come; of things past he knows something, and more or less of things present."

"Gad," said Sancho, "I would not give a farthing to be told what's past with me, for who knows that better than I do myself? And to pay for being told what I know would be mighty foolish. But as you know things present, here are my two reals, and tell me, most excellent sir ape, what is my wife Teresa Panza doing now, and what is she diverting herself with?"

Master Pedro refused to take the money, saying, "I will not receive payment in advance or until the service has been first rendered"; and then with his right hand he gave a couple of slaps on his left shoulder, and with one spring the ape perched himself upon it, and putting his mouth to his master's ear began chattering his teeth rapidly; and having kept this up as long as one would be saying a credo, with another spring he brought himself to the ground, and the same instant Master Pedro ran in great haste and fell upon his knees before Don Quixote, and embracing his legs exclaimed, "These legs do I embrace as I would embrace the two pillars of Hercules, O illustrious reviver of knight-errantry, so long consigned to oblivion! O never yet duly extolled knight, Don Quixote of La Mancha, courage of the faint-hearted, prop of the tottering, arm of the fallen, staff and counsel of all who are unfortunate!"

Don Quixote was thunderstruck, Sancho astounded, the cousin staggered, the page astonished, the man from the braying town agape, the landlord in perplexity, and, in short, every one amazed at the words of the puppet-showman, who went on to say, "And thou, worthy Sancho Panza, the best squire and squire to the best knight in the world! Be of good cheer, for thy good wife Teresa is well, and she is at this moment hackling a pound of flax; and more by token she has at her left hand a jug with a broken spout that holds a good drop of wine, which she solaces herself at her work."

"That I can well believe," said Sancho. "She is a lucky one, and if it was not for her jealousy I would not change her for the giantess Andandona, who by my master's account was a very clever and worthy woman; my Teresa is one of those that won't let themselves want for anything, though their heirs may have to pay for it."

"Now I declare," said Don Quixote, "he who reads much and travels much sees and knows a great deal. I say so because what amount of persuasion could have persuaded me that there are apes in the world that can divine as I have seen now with my own eyes? For I am that very Don Quixote of La Mancha this worthy animal refers to, though he has gone rather too far in my praise; but whatever I may be, I thank Heaven that it has endowed me with a tender and compassionate heart, always disposed to do good to all and harm to none."

"If I had money," said the page, "I would ask señor ape what will happen me in the peregrination I am making."

To this Master Pedro, who had by this time risen from Don Quixote's feet, replied, "I have already said that this little beast gives no answer as to the future; but if he did, not having money would be of no consequence, for to oblige Señor Don Quixote, here present, I would give up all the profits in the world. And now, because I have promised it, and to afford him pleasure, I will set up my show and offer entertainment to all who are in the inn, without any charge whatever." As soon as he heard this, the landlord, delighted beyond measure, pointed out a place where the show might be fixed, which was done at once.

Don Quixote was not very well satisfied with the divinations of the ape, as he did not think it proper that an ape should divine anything, either past or future; so while Master Pedro was arranging the show, he retired with Sancho into a corner of the stable, where, without being overheard by any one, he said to him, "Look here, Sancho, I have been seriously thinking over this ape's extraordinary gift, and have come to the conclusion that beyond doubt this Master Pedro, his master, has a pact, tacit or express, with the devil."

"If the packet is express from the devil," said Sancho, "it must be a very dirty packet no doubt; but what good can it do Master Pedro to have such packets?"

"Thou dost not understand me, Sancho," said Don Quixote; "I only mean he must have made some compact with the devil to infuse this power into the ape, that he may get his living, and after he has grown rich he will give him his soul, which is what the enemy of mankind wants; this I am led to believe by observing that the ape only answers about things past or present, and the devil's knowledge extends no further; for the future he knows only by guesswork, and that not always; for it is reserved for God alone to know the times and the seasons, and for him there is neither past nor future; all is present. This being as it is, it is clear that this ape speaks by the spirit of the devil; and I am astonished they have not denounced him to the Holy Office, and put him to the question, and forced it out of him by whose virtue it is that he divines; because it is certain this ape is not an astrologer; neither his master nor he sets up, or knows how to set up, those figures they call judiciary, which are now so common in Spain that there is not a jade, or page, or old cobbler, that will not undertake to set up a figure as readily as pick up a knave of cards from the ground, bringing to naught the marvellous truth of the science by their lies and ignorance. I know of a lady who asked one of these figure schemers whether her little lap-dog would be in pup and would breed, and how many and of what color the little pups would be. To which señor astrologer, after having set up his figure, made answer that the bitch would be in pup, and would drop three pups, one green, another bright red, and the third parti-colored, provided she conceived between eleven and twelve either of the day or night, and on a Monday or Saturday; but as things turned out, two days after this the bitch died of a surfeit, and señor planet-ruler had the credit all over the place of being a most profound astrologer, as most of these planet-rulers have."

"Still," said Sancho, "I would be glad if your worship would make Master Pedro ask his ape whether what happened your worship in the cave of Montesinos is true; for, begging your worship's pardon, I, for my part, take it to have been all flam and lies, or at any rate something you dreamt."

"That may be," replied Don Quixote; "however, I will do what you suggest; though I have my own scruples about it."

At this point Master Pedro came up in quest of Don Quixote, to tell him the show was now ready and to come and see it, for it was worth seeing. Don Quixote explained his wish to him, and begged him to ask his ape at once to tell him whether certain things which had happened to him in the cave of Montesinos were

dreams or realities, for to him they appeared to partake of both. Upon this Master Pedro, without answering, went back to fetch the ape, and, having placed it in front of Don Quixote and Sancho, said: "See here, señor ape, this gentleman wishes to know whether certain things which happened to him in the cave called the cave of Montesinos were false or true." On his making the usual sign the ape mounted on his left shoulder and seemed to whisper in his ear, and Master Pedro said at once, "The ape says that the things you saw or that happened to you in that cave are, part of them false, part true; and that he only knows this and no more as regards this question; but if your worship wishes to know more, on Friday next he will answer all that may be asked him, for his virtue is at present exhausted, and will not return to him till Friday, as he has said."

"Did I not say, señor," said Sancho, "that I could not bring myself to believe that all your worship said about the adventures in the cave was true, or even the half of it?"

"The course of events will tell, Sancho," replied Don Quixote; "time, that discloses all things, leaves nothing that it does not drag into the light of day, though it be buried in the bosom of the earth. But enough of that for the present; let us go and see worthy Master Pedro's show, for I am sure there must be something novel in it."

"Something!" said Master Pedro; "this show of mine has sixty thousand novel things in it; let me tell you, Señor Don Quixote, it is one of the best-worth-seeing things in the world this day; but *operibus credite et non verbis*, and now let's get to work, for it is growing late, and we have a great deal to do and to say and show."

Don Quixote and Sancho obeyed him and went to where the show was already put up and uncovered, set all around with lighted wax tapers which made it look splendid and bright. When they came to it Master Pedro ensconced himself inside it, for it was he who had to work the puppets, and a boy, a servant of his, posted himself outside to act as showman and explain the mysteries of the exhibition, having a wand in his hand to point to the figures as they came out. And so, all who were in the inn being arranged in front of the show, some of them standing, and Don Quixote, Sancho, the page, and cousin, accommodated with the best places, the interpreter began to say what he will hear or see who reads or hears the next chapter.

Chapter 26

Wherein is continued the droll adventure of the puppet-showman, together with other things in truth right good

ALL were silent, Tyrians and Trojans; I mean all who were watching the show were hanging on the lips of the interpreter of its wonders, when drums and trumpets were heard to sound inside it and cannon to go off. The noise was soon over, and then the boy lifted up his voice and said, "This true story which is here represented to your worships is taken word for word from the French chronicles and from the Spanish ballads that are in everybody's mouth, and in the mouths of the boys about the streets. Its subject is the release by Señor Don Gaiferos of his wife Melisendra, when a captive in Spain at the hands of the Moors in the City of Sansueña, for so they called then what is now called Saragossa; and there you may see how Don Gaiferos is playing at the tables, just as they sing it—

> *At the tables playing Don Gaiferos sits,*
> *For Melisendra is forgotten now.*

And that personage who appears there with a crown on his head and a sceptre in his hand is the emperor Charlemagne, the supposed father of Melisendra, who, angered to see his son-in-law's inaction and unconcern, comes in to chide him; and observe with what vehemence and energy he chides him, so that you would fancy he was going to give him half a dozen raps with his sceptre; and indeed there are authors who say he did give them, and sound ones too; and after having said a great deal to him about imperilling his honor by not affecting the release of his wife, he said, so the tale runs,

> *Enough I've said, see to it now.*

Observe, too, how the emperor turns away, and leaves Don Gaiferos fuming; and you see now how, in a burst of anger, he flings the table and the board far from him and calls in haste for his armor, and asks his cousin Don Roland for the loan of his sword, Durindana, and how Don Roland refuses to lend it, offering him his company in the difficult enterprise he is undertaking; but he, in his valor and anger, will not accept it, and says that he alone will suffice to rescue his wife, even though she were imprisoned deep in the centre of the earth, and with this he retires to arm himself and set out on his journey at once. Now let your worships turn your eyes to that tower that appears there, which is supposed to be one of the towers of the *alcázar* of Saragossa, now called the Aljafería; that lady who appears on that balcony dressed in Moorish fashion is the peerless Melisendra, for many a time she used to gaze from thence upon the road to France, and seek consolation in her captivity by thinking of Paris and her husband. Observe, too, a new incident which now occurs, such as, perhaps, never was seen. Do you not see that Moor, who silently and stealthily, with his finger on his lip, approaches Melisendra from behind? Observe now how he prints a kiss upon her lips, and what a hurry she is in to spit, and wipe them with the white sleeve of her smock, and how she bewails herself, and tears her fair hair as though it were to blame for the wrong. Observe, too, that the stately Moor who is in that corridor is King Marsilio of Sansueña, who having seen the Moor's insolence, at once orders him (though his kinsman and a great favorite of his) to be seized and given two hundred lashes, while carried through the streets of the city according to custom, with criers going before him and officers of justice behind; and here you see them come out to execute the sentence, although the offence has been scarcely committed; for among the Moors there are no indictments nor remands as with us."

Here Don Quixote called out, "Child, child, go straight on with your story, and don't run into curves and slants, for to establish a fact clearly there is need of a great deal of proof and confirmation"; and said Master Pedro from within, "Boy, stick to your text and do as the gentleman bids you; it's the best plan; keep to your plain song, and don't attempt harmonies, for they are apt to break down from being over fine."

"I will," said the boy, and he went on to say, "This figure that you see here on horseback, covered with a Gascon cloak, is Don Gaiferos himself, whom his wife, now avenged of the insult of the amorous Moor, and taking her stand on the balcony of the tower with a calmer and more tranquil countenance, has perceived without recognizing him; and she addresses her husband, supposing him to be some traveller, and holds with him all that conversation and colloquy in the ballad that runs—

> *If you, sir knight, to France are bound,*
> *Oh! for Gaiferos ask—*

which I do not repeat here because prolixity begets disgust; suffice it to observe how Don Gaiferos discovers himself, and that by her joyful gestures Melisendra shows us she has recognized him; and what is more, we now see she lowers herself from the balcony to place herself on the haunches of her good husband's horse. But ah! unhappy lady, the edge of her petticoat has caught on one of the bars of the balcony, and she is left hanging in the air, unable to reach the ground. But you see how compassionate Heaven sends aid in our sorest need; Don Gaiferos advances, and without minding whether the rich petticoat is torn or not, he seizes her and by force brings her to the ground, and then with one jerk places her on the haunches of his horse, astraddle like a man, and bids her hold on tight and clasp her arms round his neck, crossing them on his breast so as not to fall, for the lady Melisendra was not used to that style of riding. You see, too, how the neighing of the horse shows his satisfaction with the gallant and beautiful burden he bears in his lord and lady.

You see how they wheel round and quit the city, and in joy and gladness take the road to Paris. Go in peace, O peerless pair of true lovers! May you reach your longed-for fatherland in safety, and may fortune interpose no impediment to your prosperous journey; may the eyes of your friends and kinsmen behold you enjoying in peace and tranquillity the remaining days of your life—and that they may be as many as those of Nestor!"

Here Master Pedro called out again and said, "Simplicity, boy! None of your high flights; all affectation is bad."

The interpreter made no answer, but went on to say, "There was no want of idle eyes, that see everything, to see Melisendra come down and mount, and word was brought to King Marsilio, who at once gave orders to sound the alarm; and see what a stir there is, and how the city is drowned with the sound of the bells pealing in all the towers of all the mosques."

"Nay, nay," said Don Quixote at this; "on that point of the bells Master Pedro is very inaccurate, for bells are not in use among the Moors; only kettledrums, and a kind of small trumpet somewhat like a clarion; to ring bells this way in Sansueña is unquestionably a great absurdity."

On hearing this, Master Pedro stopped ringing, and said, "Don't look into trifles, Señor Don Quixote, or want to have things up to a pitch of perfection that is out of reach. Are there not almost every day a thousand comedies represented all round us full of thousands of inaccuracies and absurdities, and, for all that, they have a successful run, and are listened to

not only with applause, but with admiration and all the rest of it? Go on, boy, and don't mind; for so long as I fill my pouch, no matter if I show as many inaccuracies as there are motes in a sunbeam."

"True enough," said Don Quixote; and the boy went on: "See what a numerous and glittering crowd of horsemen issues from the city in pursuit of the two faithful lovers, what a blowing of trumpets there is, what sounding of horns, what beating of drums and tabors; I fear me they will overtake them and bring them back tied to the tail of their own horse, which would be a dreadful sight."

Don Quixote, however, seeing such a swarm of Moors and hearing such a din, thought it would be right to aid the fugitives, and standing up he exclaimed in a loud voice, "Never, while I live, will I permit foul play to be practised in my presence on such a famous knight and fearless lover as Don Gaiferos. Halt! ill-born rabble, follow him not nor pursue him, or ye will have to reckon with me in battle!" and suiting the action to the word, he drew his sword, and with one bound placed himself close to the show, and with unexampled rapidity and fury began to shower down blows on the puppet troop of Moors, knocking over some, decapitating others, maiming this one and demolishing that; and among many more he delivered one down-stroke which, if Master Pedro had not ducked, made himself small, and got out of the way, would have sliced off his head as easily as if it had been made of almond-paste. Master Pedro kept shouting, "Hold hard! Señor Don Quixote! can't you see they're not real Moors you're knocking down and killing and destroying, but only little pasteboard figures! Look—sinner that I am!—how you're wrecking and ruining all that I'm worth!" But in spite of this, Don Quixote did not leave off discharging a continuous rain of cuts, slashes, downstrokes, and backstrokes, and at length, in less than the space of two credos, he brought the whole show to the ground, with all its fittings and figures shivered and knocked to pieces, King Marsilio badly wounded, and the Emperor Charlemagne with his crown and head split in two. The whole audience was thrown into confusion, the ape fled to the roof of the inn, the cousin was frightened, the page was terrified, and even Sancho Panza himself was in mighty fear, for, as he swore after the storm was over, he had never seen his master in such a furious passion.

The complete destruction of the show being thus accomplished, Don Quixote became a little calmer, and said, "I wish I had here before me now all those who do not or will not believe how useful knights-errant are in the world; just think, if I had not been here present, what would have become of the brave Don Gaiferos and the fair Melisendra! Depend upon it, by this time those dogs would have overtaken them and inflicted some outrage upon them. So, then, long live knight-errantry beyond everything living on earth this day!"

"Let it live, and welcome," said Master Pedro at this in a feeble voice, "and let me die, for I am so unfortunate that I can say with King Don Rodrigo—

Yesterday was I lord of Spain—
.   .   .   .
To-day I've not a turret left
That I may call mine own.

Not half an hour, nay, barely a minute ago, I saw myself lord of kings and emperors, with my stables filled with countless horses, and my trunks and bags with gay dresses unnumbered; and now I find myself ruined and laid low, destitute and a beggar, and above all without my ape, for, by my faith, my teeth will have to sweat for it before I have him caught; and all through the reckless fury of this sir knight here, who, they say, protects the fatherless, and rights wrongs, and does other charitable deeds; but whose generous intentions have been found wanting in my case only, blessed and praised be the highest heavens! Verily, knight of the rueful figure he must be to have disfigured mine."

Sancho Panza was touched by Master Pedro's words, and said to him, "Don't weep and lament, Master Pedro; you break my heart; let me tell you my master, Don Quixote, is so catholic and scrupulous a Christian that, if he can make out that he has done you any wrong, he will own it, and be willing to pay for it and make it good, and something over and above."

"Only let Señor Don Quixote pay me for some part of the work he has destroyed," said Master Pedro, "and I would be content, and his worship would ease his conscience, for he can not be saved who keeps what is another's against the owner's will, and makes no restitution."

"That is true," said Don Quixote; "but at present I am not aware that I have got anything of yours, Master Pedro."

"What!" returned Master Pedro; "and these relics lying here on the bare hard ground—what scattered and shattered them but the invincible strength of that mighty arm? And whose were the bodies they belonged to but mine? And what did I get my living by but them?"

"Now am I fully convinced," said Don Quixote, "of what I had many a time before believed; that the enchanters who persecute me do nothing more than put figures like these before my eyes, and then change and turn them into what they please. In truth and earnest, I assure you gentlemen who now hear me, that to me everything that has taken place here seemed to take place literally, that Melisendra was Melisendra, Don Gaiferos Don Gaiferos, Marsilio Marsilio, and Charlemagne Charlemagne. That was why my anger was roused; and to be faithful to my calling as a knight-errant I sought to give aid and protection to those who fled, and with this good intention I did what you have seen. If the result has been the opposite of what I intended, it is no fault of mine, but of those wicked beings that persecute me; but, for all that, I am willing to condemn myself in costs for this error of mine, though it did not proceed from malice; let Master Pedro see what he wants for the spoiled figures, for I agree to pay it at once in good and current money of Castile."

Master Pedro made him a bow, saying, "I expected no less of the rare Christianity of the valiant Don Quixote of La Mancha, true helper and protector of all destitute and needy vagabonds; master landlord here and the great Sancho Panza shall be the arbitrators and appraisers between your worship and me of what these dilapidated figures are worth or may be worth."

The landlord and Sancho consented, and then Master Pedro picked up from the ground King Marsilio of Saragossa with his head off, and said, "Here you see how impossible it is to restore this king to his former state, so I think, saving your better judgments, that for his death, decease, and demise, four reals and a half may be given me."

"Proceed," said Don Quixote.

"Well then, for this cleavage from top to bottom," continued Master Pedro, taking up the split Emperor Charlemagne, "it would not be much if I were to ask five reals and a quarter "

"It's not little," said Sancho.

"Nor is it much," said the landlord; "make it even, and say five reals."

"Let him have the whole five and a quarter," said Don Quixote; "for the sum total of this notable disaster does not stand on a quarter more or less; and make an end of it quickly, Master Pedro, for it's getting on to supper-time, and I have some hints of hunger."

"For this figure," said Master Pedro, "that is

without a nose, and wants an eye, and is the fair Melisendra, I ask, and I am reasonable in my charge, two reals and twelve maravedís."

"The very devil must be in it," said Don Quixote, "if Melisendra and her husband are not by this time at least on the French border, for the horse they rode on seemed to me to fly rather than gallop; so you need n't try to sell me the cat for the hare, showing me here a noseless Melisendra when she is now, may be, enjoying herself at her ease with her husband in France. God help every one to his own, Master Pedro, and let us all proceed fairly and honestly; and now go on."

Master Pedro, perceiving that Don Quixote was beginning to wander, and return to his original fancy, was not disposed to let him escape, so he said to him, "This cannot be Melisendra, but must be one of the damsels that waited on her; so if I'm given sixty maravedís for her, I'll be content and sufficiently paid."

And so he went on, putting values on ever so many more smashed figures, which, after the two arbitrators had adjusted them to the satisfaction of both parties, came to forty reals and three quarters; and over and above this sum, which Sancho at once disbursed, Master Pedro asked for two reals for his trouble in catching the ape.

"Let him have them, Sancho," said Don Quixote; "not to catch the ape, but to get drunk; and two hundred would I give this minute for the good news, to any one who could tell me positively, that the lady Doña Melisendra and Señor Don Gaiferos were now in France and with their own people."

"No one could tell us that better than my ape," said Master Pedro, "but there's no devil that could catch him now; I suspect, however, that affection and hunger will drive him to come looking for me to-night; but to-morrow will soon be here and we shall see."

In short, the puppet-show storm passed off, and all supped in peace and good fellowship at Don Quixote's expense, for he was the height of generosity. Before it was daylight the man with the lances and halberds took his departure, and soon after daybreak the cousin and the page came to bid Don Quixote farewell, the former returning home, the latter resuming his journey, towards which, to help him, Don Quixote gave him twelve reals. Master Pedro did not care to engage in any more palaver with Don Quixote, whom he knew right well; so he rose before the sun, and having got together the remains of his show and caught his ape, he too

went off to seek his adventures. The landlord, who did not know Don Quixote, was as much astonished at his mad freaks as at his generosity. To conclude, Sancho, by his master's orders, paid him very liberally, and taking leave of him they quitted the inn at about eight in the morning and took to the road, where we will leave them to pursue their journey, for this is necessary in order to allow certain other matters to be set forth, which are required to clear up this famous history.

Chapter 27

Wherein it is shown who Master Pedro and his ape were, together with the mishap Don Quixote had in the braying adventure, which he did not conclude as he would have liked or as he had expected

CID HAMET, the chronicler of this great history, begins this chapter with these words, "I swear as a catholic Christian"; with regard to which his translator says that Cid Hamet's swearing as a catholic Christian, he being—as no doubt he was—a Moor, only meant that, just as a catholic Christian taking an oath swears, or ought to swear, what is true, and tell the truth in what he avers, so he was telling the truth, as much as if he swore as a catholic Christian, in all he chose to write about Don Quixote, especially in declaring who Master Pedro was and what was the divining ape that astonished all the villages with his divinations. He says, then, that he who has read the First Part of this history will remember well enough the Gines de Pasamonte whom, with other galley slaves, Don Quixote set free in the Sierra Morena; a kindness for which he afterwards got poor thanks and worse payment from that evil-minded, ill-conditioned set. This Gines de Pasamonte—Don Ginesillo de Paropilla, Don Quixote called him—it was that stole Dapple from Sancho Panza; which, because by the fault of the printers neither the how nor the when was stated in the First Part, has been a puzzle to a good many people, who attribute to the bad memory of the author what was the error of the press. In fact, however, Gines stole him while Sancho Panza was asleep on his back, adopting the plan and device that Brunello had recourse to when he stole Sacripante's horse from between his legs at the siege of Albracca; and, as has been told, Sancho afterwards recovered him. This Gines, then, afraid of being caught by the officers of justice, who were looking for him to punish him for his numberless rascalities and offences (which were so many and so great that he himself wrote a big book giving an account of them), resolved to shift his quarters into the kingdom of Aragon, and cover up his left eye, and take up the trade of a puppet-showman; for this, as well as juggling, he knew how to practise to perfection. From some released Christians returning from Barbary, it so happened, he bought the ape, which he taught to mount upon his shoulder on his making a certain sign, and to whisper, or seem to do so, in his ear. Thus prepared, before entering any village whither he was bound with his show and his ape, he used to inform himself at the nearest village, or from the most likely person he could find, as to what particular things had happened there, and to whom; and bearing them well in mind, the first thing he did was to exhibit his show, sometimes one story, sometimes another, but all lively, amusing, and familiar. As soon as the exhibition was over he brought forward the accomplishments of his ape, assuring the public that he divined all the past and the present, but as to the future he had no skill. For each question answered he asked two reals, and for some he made a reduction, just as he happened to feel the pulse of the questioners; and when now and then he came to houses where things that he knew of had happened to the people living there, even if they did not ask him a question, not caring to pay for it, he would make the sign to the ape and then declare that it had said so and so, which fitted the case exactly. In this way he acquired a prodigious name and all ran after him; on other occasions, being very crafty, he would answer in such a way that the answers suited the questions; and as no one cross-questioned him or pressed him to tell how his ape divined, he made fools of them all and filled his pouch. The instant he entered the inn he knew Don Quixote and Sancho, and with that knowledge it was easy for him to astonish them and all who were there; but it would have cost him dear had Don Quixote brought down his hand a little lower when he cut off King Marsilio's head and destroyed all his horsemen, as related in the preceding chapter.

So much for Master Pedro and his ape; and now to return to Don Quixote of La Mancha,—after he had left the inn he determined to visit, first of all, the banks of the Ebro and that neighborhood, before entering the city of Saragossa, for the ample time there was still to spare before the jousts left him enough for all. With this object in view he followed the road and travelled along it for two days, without meeting any adventure worth committing to writing, until on the third day, as he was ascending a hill, he heard a great noise of drums, trumpets, and musket-shots. At first he imagined some regiment of soldiers was passing that way, and to see them he spurred Rocinante and mounted the hill. On reaching the top he saw at the foot of it over two hundred men, as it seemed to him, armed with weapons of various sorts, lances, cross-bows, partisans, halberds, and pikes, and a few muskets and a great many bucklers. He descended the slope and approached the band near enough to see distinctly the flags, make out the colors and distinguish the devices they bore, especially one on a standard or ensign of white satin, on which there was painted in a very life-like style an ass like a little Sard,[1] with its head up, its mouth open and its tongue out, as if it were in the act and attitude of braying; and round it were inscribed in large characters these two lines—

> They did not bray in vain,
> Our alcaldes twain.

From this device Don Quixote concluded that these people must be from the braying town, and he said so to Sancho, explaining to him what was written on the standard. At the same time he observed that the man who had told them about the matter was wrong in saying that the two who brayed were *regidors,* for according to the lines on the standard they were *alcaldes.* To which Sancho replied, "Señor, there's nothing to stick at in that, for maybe the *regidors* who brayed then came to be *alcaldes* of their town afterwards, and so they may go by both titles; moreover, it has nothing to do with the truth of the story whether the brayers were *alcaldes* or *regidors,* provided at any rate they did bray; for an *alcalde* is just as likely to bray as a *regidor.*" They perceived, in short, clearly that the town which had been twitted had turned out to do battle with some other that had jeered it more than was fair or neighborly.

Don Quixote proceeded to join them, not a little to Sancho's uneasiness, for he never relished mixing himself up in expeditions of that sort. The members of the troop received him into the midst of them, taking him to be some one who was on their side. Don Quixote, putting up his visor, advanced with an easy bearing and demeanor to the standard with the ass, and all the chief men of the army gathered round him to look at him, staring at him with the usual amazement that everybody felt on seeing him for the first time. Don Quixote, seeing them examining him so attentively, and that none of

[1] A Sardinian pony.

them spoke to him or put any question to him, determined to take advantage of their silence; so, breaking his own, he lifted up his voice and said, "Worthy sirs, I entreat you as earnestly as I can not to interrupt an argument I wish to address to you, until you find it displeases or wearies you; and if that come to pass, on the slightest hint you give me I will put a seal upon my lips and a gag upon my tongue."

They all bade him say what he liked, for they would listen to him willingly.

With this permission Don Quixote went on to say, "I, sirs, am a knight-errant whose calling is that of arms, and whose profession is to protect those who require protection, and give help to such as stand in need of it. Some days ago I became acquainted with your misfortune and the cause which impels you to take up arms again and again to revenge yourselves upon your enemies; and having many times thought over your business in my mind, I find that, according to the laws of combat, you are mistaken in holding yourselves insulted; for a private individual can not insult an entire community; unless it be by defying it collectively as a traitor, because he can not tell who in particular is guilty of the treason for which he defies it. Of this we have an example in Don Diego Ordoñez de Lara, who defied the whole town of Zamora, because he did not know that Vellido Dolfos alone had committed the treachery of slaying his King; and therefore he defied them all, and the vengeance and the reply concerned all; though, to be sure, Señor Don Diego went rather too far, indeed very much beyond the limits of a defiance; for he had no occasion to defy the dead, or the waters, or the fishes, or those yet unborn, and all the rest of it as set forth; but let that pass, for when anger breaks out there's no father, governor, or bridle to check the tongue. The case being, then, that no one person can insult a kingdom, province, city, state, or entire community, it is clear there is no reason for going out to avenge the defiance of such an insult, inasmuch as it is not one. A fine thing it would be if the people of the clock town were to be at loggerheads every moment with every one who called them by that name—or the Cazoleros, Berengeneros, Ballenatos, Jaboneros,[1] or the bearers of all the other names and titles that are always in the mouths of the boys and common people! It would be a nice business indeed if all these illustrious cities were to take huff and revenge themselves and go about perpetually making trombones of their swords in every petty quarrel! No, no; God forbid! There are four things for which sensible men and well-ordered States ought to take up arms, draw their swords, and risk their persons, lives and properties. The first is to defend the Catholic faith; the second, to defend one's life, which is in accordance with natural and divine law; the third, in defence of one's honor, family and property; the fourth, in the service of one's King in a just war; and if to these we choose to add a fifth (which may be included in the second), in defence of one's country. To these five, as it were capital causes, there may be added some others that may be just and reasonable, and make it a duty to take up arms; but to take them up for trifles and things to laugh at and be amused by rather than offended, looks as though he who did so was altogether wanting in common sense. Moreover, to take an unjust revenge (and there cannot be any just one) is directly opposed to the sacred law that we acknowledge, wherein we are commanded to do good to our enemies and to love them that hate us; a command which, though it seems somewhat difficult to obey, is only so to those who have in them less of God than of the world, and more of the flesh than of the spirit; for Jesus Christ, God and true man, who never lied, and could not and can not lie, said as our law-giver, that his yoke was easy and his burden light; he would not, therefore, have laid any command upon us that it was impossible to obey. Thus, sirs, you are bound to keep quiet by human and divine law."

"The devil take me," said Sancho to himself at this, "but this master of mine is a tologian; or, if not, faith he's as like one as one egg is like another."

Don Quixote stopped to take breath, and, observing that silence was still preserved, had a mind to continue his discourse, and would have done so had not Sancho interposed with his smartness; for he, seeing his master pause, took the lead, saying, "My lord Don Quixote of La Mancha, who once was called The Knight of the Rueful Countenance, but now is called the Knight of the Lions, is a gentleman of great discretion who knows Latin and his mother tongue

---

[1] The Cazoleros were the people of Valladolid, so called because of their townsman, Cazalla, burned as a Lutheran in 1559; the Berengeneros were the Toledans, *berengenas*, or egg-plants, being grown in large quantities in the neighborhood; the inhabitants of Madrid were nicknamed the Ballenatos— the whalemen—from a story that they took a mule's pack-saddle, floating down the Manzanares in a flood, for a whale. Who the people of the clock town and the Jaboneros—the soapmen—were is uncertain.

like a bachelor, and in everything that he deals with or advises proceeds like a good soldier, and has all the laws and ordinances of what they call combat at his fingers' ends; so you have nothing to do but to let yourselves be guided by what he says, and on my head be it if it is wrong. Besides which, you have been told that it is folly to take offence at merely hearing a bray. I remember when I was a boy I brayed as often as I had a fancy, without any one hindering me, and so elegantly and naturally that when I brayed all the asses in the town would bray; but I was none the less for that the son of my parents, who were greatly respected; and though I was envied because of the gift by more than one of the high and mighty ones of the town, I did not care two farthings for it; and that you may see I am telling the truth, wait a bit and listen, for this art, like swimming, once learnt is never forgotten"; and then, taking hold of his nose, he began to bray so vigorously that all the valleys around rang again.

One of those, however, that stood near him, fancying he was mocking them, lifted up a long staff he had in his hand, and smote him such a blow with it that Sancho dropped helpless to the ground. Don Quixote, seeing him so roughly handled, attacked the man who had struck him lance in hand, but so many thrust themselves between them that he could not avenge him. Far from it, finding a shower of stones rained upon him, and crossbows and muskets unnumbered levelled at him, he wheeled Rocinante round and, as fast as his best gallop could take him, fled from the midst of them, commending himself to God with all his heart to deliver him out of this peril, in dread every step of some ball coming in at his back and coming out at his breast, and every minute drawing his breath to see whether it had gone from him. The members of the band, however, were satisfied with seeing him take to flight, and did not fire on him. They put up Sancho, scarcely restored to his senses, on his ass, and let him go after his master; not that he was sufficiently in his wits to guide the beast, but Dapple followed the footsteps of Rocinante, from whom he could not remain a moment separated. Don Quixote having got some way off looked back, and seeing Sancho coming, waited for him, as he perceived that no one followed him. The men of the troop stood their ground till night, and as the enemy did not come out to battle, they returned to their town in high spirits and exulting; and had they been aware of the ancient custom of the Greeks, they would have erected a trophy on the spot.

Chapter 28

Of matters that Benengeli says he who reads them will know, if he reads them with attention

WHEN the brave man flees, treachery is manifest, and it is for wise men to reserve themselves for better occasions. This proved to be the case with Don Quixote, who, giving way before the fury of the townsfolk and the hostile intentions of the angry troop, took to flight and, without a thought of Sancho or the danger in which he was leaving him, retreated to such a distance as he thought made him safe. Sancho, lying across his ass, followed him, as has been said, and at length came up, having by this time recovered his senses, and on joining him let himself drop off Dapple at Rocinante's feet, sore, bruised, and belabored. Don Quixote dismounted to examine his wounds, but finding him whole from head to foot, he said to him, angrily enough, "In an evil hour didst thou take to braying, Sancho! Where hast thou learned that it is well done to mention the rope in the house of the man that has been hanged? To the music of brays what harmonies couldst thou expect to get but cudgels? Give thanks to God, Sancho, that they signed the cross on thee just now with a stick, and did not mark thee *per signum crucis* with a cutlass."

"I'm not equal to answering," said Sancho, "for I feel as if I was speaking through my shoulders; let us mount and get away from this; I'll keep from braying, but not from saying that knights-errant fly and leave their good squires to be pounded like privet, or made meal of at the hands of their enemies."

"He does not fly who retires," returned Don Quixote; "for I would have thee know, Sancho, that the valor which is not based upon a foundation of prudence is called rashness, and the exploits of the rash men are to be attributed rather to good fortune than to courage; and so I own that I retired, but not that I fled; and therein I have followed the example of many valiant men who have reserved themselves for better times; the histories are full of instances of this, but as it would not be any good to thee or pleasure to me, I will not recount them to thee now."

Sancho was by this time mounted with the help of Don Quixote, who then himself mounted Rocinante, and at a leisurely pace they proceeded to take shelter in a grove which was in sight about a quarter of a league off. Every now and then Sancho gave vent to deep sighs and dismal groans, and on Don Quixote asking him what caused such acute suffering, he replied that, from the end of his backbone up to the nape of his neck, he was so sore that it nearly drove him out of his senses.

"The cause of that soreness," said Don Quixote, "will be, no doubt, that the staff wherewith they smote thee being a very long one, it caught thee all down the back, where all the parts that are sore are situated, and had it reached any farther thou wouldst be sorer still."

"By God," said Sancho, "your worship has relieved me of a great doubt, and cleared up the point for me in elegant style! Body o' me! is the cause of my soreness such a mystery that there 's any need to tell me I am sore everywhere the staff hit me? If it was my ankles that pained me there might be something in going divining why they did, but it is not much to divine that I'm sore where they thrashed me. By my faith, master mine, the ills of others hang by a hair; every day I am discovering more and more how little I have to hope for from keeping company with your worship; for if this time you have allowed me to be drubbed, the next time, or a hundred times more, we'll have the blanketings of the other day over again, and all the other pranks which, if they have fallen on my shoulders now, will be thrown in my teeth by-and-by. I would do a great deal better (if I was not an ignorant brute that will never do any good all my life), I would do a great deal better, I say, to go home to my wife and children and support them and bring them up on what God may please to give me, instead of following your worship along roads that lead nowhere and paths that are none at all, with little to drink and less to eat. And then when it comes to sleeping! Measure out seven feet on the earth, brother squire, and if that's not enough for you, take as many more, for you may have it all your own way and stretch yourself to your heart's content. Oh that I could see burnt and turned to ashes the first man that meddled with knight-errantry, or at any rate the first who chose to be squire to such fools as all the knights-errant of past times must have been! Of those of the present day I say nothing, because, as your worship is one of them, I respect them, and because I know your worship knows a point more than the devil in all you say and think."

"I would lay a good wager with you, Sancho," said Don Quixote, "that now that you are talking on without any one to stop you, you don't feel a pain in your whole body. Talk away, my son, say whatever comes into your head or mouth, for so long as you feel no pain, the irritation your impertinences give me will be a pleasure to

me; and if you are so anxious to go home to your wife and children, God forbid that I should prevent you; you have money of mine; see how long it is since we left our village this third time, and how much you can and ought to earn every month, and pay yourself out of your own hand."

"When I worked for Tomé Carrasco, the father of the bachelor Samson Carrasco that your worship knows," replied Sancho, "I used to earn two ducats a month besides my food; I can't tell what I can earn with your worship, though I know a knight-errant's squire has harder times of it than he who works for a farmer; for after all, we who work for farmers, however much we toil all day, at the worst, at night, we have our olla supper and sleep in a bed, which I have not slept in since I have been in your worship's service, if it wasn't the short time we were in Don Diego de Miranda's house, and the feast I had with the skimmings I took off Camacho's pots, and what I ate, drank, and slept in Basilio's house; all the rest of the time I have been sleeping on the hard ground under the open sky, exposed to what they call the inclemencies of heaven, keeping life in me with scraps of cheese and crusts of bread, and drinking water either from the brooks or from the springs we come to on these by-paths we travel."

"I own, Sancho," said Don Quixote, "that all thou sayest is true; how much, thinkest thou, ought I to give thee over and above what Tomé Carrasco gave thee?"

"I think," said Sancho, "that if your worship was to add on two reals a month I'd consider myself well paid; that is, as far as the wages of my labor go; but to make up to me for your worship's pledge and promise to give me the government of an island, it would be fair to add six reals more, making thirty in all."

"Very good," said Don Quixote; "it is twenty-five days since we left our village, so reckon up, Sancho, according to the wages you have made out for yourself, and see how much I owe you in proportion, and pay yourself, as I said before, out of your own hand."

"O body o' me!" said Sancho, "but your worship is very much out in that reckoning; for when it comes to the promise of the island we must count from the day your worship promised it to me to this present hour we are at now."

"Well, how long is it, Sancho, since I promised it to you?" said Don Quixote.

"If I remember rightly," said Sancho, "it must be over twenty years, three days more or less."

Don Quixote gave himself a great slap on the forehead and began to laugh heartily, and said he, "Why, I have not been wandering, either in the Sierra Morena or in the whole course of our sallies, but barely two months, and thou sayest, Sancho, that it is twenty years since I promised thee the island. I believe now thou wouldst have all the money thou hast of mine go in thy wages. If so, and if that be thy pleasure, I give it to thee now, once and for all, and much good may it do thee, for so long as I see myself rid of such a good-for-nothing squire, I'll be glad to be left a pauper without a rap. But tell me, thou perverter of the squirely rules of knight-errantry, where hast thou ever seen or read that any knight-errant's squire made terms with his lord, 'you must give me so much a month for serving you'? Plunge, O scoundrel, rogue, monster—for such I take thee to be—plunge, I say, into the *mare magnum* of their histories; and if thou shalt find that any squire ever said or thought what thou hast said now, I will let thee nail it on my forehead, and give me, over and above, four sound slaps in the face. Turn the rein, or the halter, of thy Dapple, and begone home; for one single step farther thou shalt not make in my company. O bread thanklessly received! O promises ill-bestowed! O man more beast than human being! Now, when I was about to raise thee to such a position, that, in spite of thy wife, they would call thee 'my lord,' thou art leaving me? Thou art going now when I had a firm and fixed intention of making thee lord of the best island in the world? Well, as thou thyself hast said before now, honey is not for the mouth of the ass. Ass thou art, ass thou wilt be, and ass thou wilt end when the course of thy life is run; for I know it will come to its close before thou dost perceive or discern that thou art a beast."

Sancho regarded Don Quixote earnestly while he was giving him his rating, and was so touched by remorse that the tears came to his eyes, and in a piteous and broken voice he said to him, "Master mine, I confess that, to be a complete ass, all I want is a tail; if your worship will only fix one on to me, I'll look on it as rightly placed, and I'll serve you as an ass all the remaining days of my life. Forgive me and have pity on my folly, and remember I know but little, and, if I talk much, it's more from infirmity than malice; but he who sins and mends commends himself to God."

"I should have been surprised, Sancho," said Don Quixote, "if thou hadst not introduced some bit of a proverb into thy speech. Well, well, I forgive thee, provided thou dost mend and not show thyself in future so fond of thine own interest, but try to be of good cheer and take heart, and encourage thyself to look forward to the fulfilment of my promises, which, by being delayed, does not become impossible."

Sancho said he would do so, and keep up his heart as best he could. They then entered the grove, and Don Quixote settled himself at the foot of an elm, and Sancho at that of a beech, for trees of this kind and others like them always have feet but no hands. Sancho passed the night in pain, for with the evening dews the blow of the staff made itself felt all the more. Don Quixote passed it in his never-failing meditations; but, for all that, they had some winks of sleep, and with the appearance of daylight they pursued their journey in quest of the banks of the famous Ebro, where that befell them which will be told in the following chapter.

Chapter 29

Of the famous adventure of the enchanted bark

BY stages as already described or left undescribed, two days after quitting the grove Don Quixote and Sancho reached the river Ebro, and the sight of it was a great delight to Don Quixote as he contemplated and gazed upon the charms of its banks, the clearness of its stream, the gentleness of its current and the abundance of its crystal waters; and the pleasant view revived a thousand tender thoughts in his mind. Above all, he dwelt upon what he had seen in the cave of Montesinos; for though Master Pedro's ape had told him that of those things part was true, part false, he clung more to their truth than to their falsehood, the very reverse of Sancho, who held them all to be downright lies.

As they were thus proceeding, then, they discovered a small boat, without oars or any other gear, that lay at the water's edge tied to the stem of a tree growing on the bank. Don Quixote looked all round, and seeing nobody, at once, without more ado, dismounted from Rocinante and bade Sancho get down from Dapple and tie both beasts securely to the trunk of a poplar or willow that stood there. Sancho asked him the reason of this sudden dismounting and tying. Don Quixote made answer, "Thou must know, Sancho, that this bark here is plainly, and without the possibility of any alternative, calling and inviting me to enter it, and in it go to give aid to some knight or other person of distinction in need of it, who is no doubt in some sore strait; for this is the way of the books of chivalry and of the enchanters who figure and speak in them. When a knight is involved in some difficulty from which he can not be delivered save by the hand of another knight, though they may be at a distance of two or three thousand leagues or more one from the other, they either take him up on a cloud, or they provide a bark for him to get into, and in less than the twinkling of an eye they carry him where they will and where his help is required; and so, Sancho, this bark is placed here for the same purpose; this is as true as that it is now day, and ere this one passes tie Dapple and Rocinante together, and then in God's hand be it to guide us; for I would not hold back from embarking, though bare-footed friars were to beg me."

"As that's the case," said Sancho, "and your worship chooses to give in to these—I don't know if I may call them absurdities—at every turn, there's nothing for it but to obey and bow the head, bearing in mind the problem, 'Do as thy master bids thee, and sit down to table with him'; but for all that, for the sake of easing my conscience, I want to warn your worship that it is my opinion this bark is no enchanted one, but belongs to some of the fishermen of the river, for they catch the best shad in the world here."

As Sancho said this, he tied the beasts, leaving them to the care and protection of the enchanters with sorrow enough in his heart. Don Quixote bade him not be uneasy about deserting the animals, for he who would carry themselves over such longinquous roads and regions would take care to feed them.

"I don't understand that logiquous," said Sancho, "nor have I ever heard the word all the days of my life."

"Longinquous," replied Don Quixote, "means far off; but it is no wonder thou dost not understand it, for thou art not bound to know Latin, like some who pretend to know it and don't."

"Now they are tied," said Sancho; "what are we to do next?"

"What?" said Don Quixote, "cross ourselves and weigh anchor; I mean, embark and cut the moorings by which the bark is held"; and jumping into it, followed by Sancho, he cut the rope, and the bark began to drift away slowly from the bank. But when Sancho saw himself somewhere about two yards out in the river, he began to tremble and give himself up for lost; but nothing distressed him more than hearing Dapple bray and seeing Rocinante struggling to get loose, and said he to his master, "Dapple is braying in grief at our leaving him, and Rocinante is trying to escape and plunge in after us. O dear friends, peace be with you, and may this madness that is taking us away from you, turned

into sober sense, bring us back to you." And with this he fell weeping so bitterly, that Don Quixote said to him, sharply and angrily, "What art thou afraid of, cowardly creature? What art thou weeping at, heart of butter-paste? Who pursues or molests thee, thou soul of a tame mouse? What dost thou want, unsatisfied in the very heart of abundance? Art thou, perchance, tramping barefoot over the Riphæan mountains, instead of being seated on a bench like an archduke on the tranquil stream of this pleasant river, from which in a short space we shall come out upon the broad sea? But we must have already emerged and gone seven hundred or eight hundred leagues; and if I had here an astrolabe to take the altitude of the pole, I could tell thee how many we have travelled, though either I know little, or we have already crossed or shall shortly cross the equinoctial line which parts the two opposite poles midway."

"And when we come to that lane your worship speaks of," said Sancho, "how far shall we have gone?"

"Very far," said Don Quixote, "for of the three hundred and sixty degrees that this terraqueous globe contains, as computed by Ptolemy, the greatest cosmographer known, we shall have travelled one-half when we come to the line I spoke of."

"By God," said Sancho, "your worship gives me a nice authority for what you say, putrid Dolly something transmogrified, or whatever it is."

Don Quixote laughed at the interpretation Sancho put upon "computed," and the name of the cosmographer Ptolemy, and said he, "Thou must know, Sancho, that with the Spaniards and those who embark at Cadiz for the East Indies, one of the signs they have to show them when they have passed the equinoctial line I told thee of, is, that the lice die upon everybody on board the ship, and not a single one is left, or to be found in the whole vessel if they gave its weight in gold for it; so, Sancho, thou mayest as well pass thy hand down thy thigh, and if thou comest upon anything alive we shall be no longer in doubt; if not, then we have crossed."

"I don't believe a bit of it," said Sancho; "still, I'll do as your worship bids me; though I don't know what need there is for trying these experiments, for I can see with my own eyes that we have not moved five yards away from the bank, or shifted two yards from where the animals stand, for there are Rocinante and Dapple in the very same place where we left them; and watching a point, as I do now, I swear by all that's good, we are not stirring or moving at the pace of an ant."

"Try the test I told thee of, Sancho," said Don Quixote, "and don't mind any other, for thou knowest nothing about colures, lines, parallels, zodiacs, ecliptics, poles, solstices, equinoxes, planets, signs, bearings, the measures of which the celestial and terrestrial spheres are composed; if thou wert acquainted with all these things, or any portion of them, thou wouldst see clearly how many parallels we have cut, what signs we have seen, and what constellations we have left behind and are now leaving behind. But again I tell thee, feel and hunt, for I am certain thou art cleaner than a sheet of smooth white paper."

Sancho felt, and passing his hand gently and carefully down to the hollow of his left knee, he looked up at his master and said, "Either the test is a false one, or we have not come to where your worship says, nor within many leagues of it."

"Why, how so?" asked Don Quixote; "hast thou come upon aught?"

"Ay, and aughts," replied Sancho; and shaking his fingers he washed his whole hand in the river along which the boat was quietly gliding in midstream, not moved by any occult intelligence or invisible enchanter, but simply by the current, just there smooth and gentle.

They now came in sight of some large water mills that stood in the middle of the river, and the instant Don Quixote saw them he cried out to Sancho, "Seest thou there, my friend? there stands the city, castle, or fortress, where there is, no doubt, some knight in durance, or ill-used queen, or infanta, or princess, in aid of whom I am brought hither."

"What the devil city, fortress, or castle is your worship talking about, señor?" said Sancho; "don't you see that those are mills that stand in the river to grind corn?"

"Hold thy peace, Sancho," said Don Quixote; "though they look like mills they are not so; I have already told thee that enchantments transform things and change their proper shapes; I do not mean to say they really change them from one form into another, but that it seems as though they did, as experience proved in the transformation of Dulcinea, sole refuge of my hopes."

By this time, the boat, having reached the middle of the stream, began to move less slowly than hitherto. The millers belonging to the mills, when they saw the boat coming down the river, and on the point of being sucked in by the draught of the wheels, ran out in haste, several of them, with long poles to stop it, and being all mealy, with faces and garments covered with flour, they presented a sinister appearance. They raised loud shouts, crying, "Devils of men, where are you going to? Are you mad? Do you want to drown yourselves, or dash yourselves to pieces among these wheels?"

"Did I not tell thee, Sancho," said Don Quixote at this, "that we had reached the place where I am to show what the might of my arm can do? See what ruffians and villains come out against me; see what monsters oppose me; see what hideous countenances come to frighten us! You shall soon see, scoundrels!" And then standing up in the boat he began in a loud voice to hurl threats at the millers, exclaiming, "Ill-conditioned and worse-counselled rabble, restore to liberty and freedom the person ye hold in durance in this your fortress or prison, high or low or of whatever rank or quality he be, for I am Don Quixote of La Mancha, otherwise called the Knight of the Lions, for whom, by the disposition of Heaven above, it is reserved to give a happy issue to this adventure"; and so saying he drew his sword and began making passes in the air at the millers, who, hearing but not understanding all this nonsense, strove to stop the boat, which was now getting into the rushing channel of the wheels. Sancho fell upon his knees devoutly appealing to Heaven to deliver him from such imminent peril; which it did by the activity and quickness of the millers, who, pushing against the boat with their poles, stopped it, not, however, without upsetting it and throwing Don Quixote and Sancho into the water; and lucky it was for Don Quixote that he could swim like a goose, though the weight of his armor carried him twice to the bottom; and had it not been for the millers, who plunged in and hoisted them both out, it would have been Troy town with the pair of them. As soon as, more drenched than thirsty, they were landed, Sancho went down on his knees and with clasped hands and eyes raised to heaven, prayed a long and fervent prayer to God to deliver him evermore from the rash projects and attempts of his master. The fishermen, the owners of the boat, which the mill-wheels had knocked to pieces, now came up, and seeing it smashed they proceeded to strip Sancho and to demand payment for it from Don Quixote; but he with great calmness, just as if nothing had happened to him, told the millers and fishermen that he would pay for the bark most cheerfully, on condition that they delivered up to him, free and unhurt, the person or persons that were in durance in that castle of theirs.

"What persons or what castle art thou talking of, madman?" said one of the millers; "art thou for carrying off the people who come to grind corn in these mills?"

"That's enough," said Don Quixote to himself, "it would be preaching in the desert to attempt by entreaties to induce this rabble to do any virtuous action. In this adventure two mighty enchanters must have encountered one another, and one frustrates what the other attempts; one provided the bark for me, and the other upset me; God help us, this world is all machinations and schemes at cross purposes one with the other. I can do no more." And then turning towards the mills he said aloud, "Friends, whoe'er ye be that are immured in that prison, forgive me that, to my misfortune and yours, I cannot deliver you from your misery; this adventure is doubtless reserved and destined for some other knight."

So saying he settled with the fishermen, and paid fifty reals for the boat, which Sancho handed to them very much against the grain, saying, "With a couple more bark businesses like this we shall have sunk our whole capital."

The fishermen and the millers stood staring in amazement at the two figures, so very different to all appearance from ordinary men, and were wholly unable to make out the drift of the observations and questions Don Quixote addressed to them; and coming to the conclusion that they were madmen, they left them and betook themselves, the millers to their mills, and the fishermen to their huts. Don Quixote and Sancho returned to their beasts, and to their life of beasts, and this was the end of the adventure of the enchanted bark.

Chapter 30

Of Don Quixote's adventure with a fair huntress

THEY reached their beasts in low spirits and bad humor enough, knight and squire, Sancho particularly, for with him what touched the stock of money touched his heart, and when any was taken from him he felt as if he was robbed of the apples of his eyes. In fine, without exchanging a word, they mounted and quitted the famous river, Don Quixote absorbed in thoughts of his love, Sancho in thinking of his advancement, which just then, it seemed to him, he was very far from securing; for, fool as he was, he saw clearly enough that his master's acts were all or most of them utterly senseless; and he began to cast about for an opportunity of retiring from his service and going home some day, without entering into any explanations or taking any

farewell of him. Fortune, however, ordered matters after a fashion very much the opposite of what he contemplated.

It so happened that the next day towards sunset, on coming out of a wood, Don Quixote cast his eyes over a green meadow, and at the far end of it observed some people, and as he drew nearer saw that it was a hawking party. Coming closer, he distinguished among them a lady of graceful mien, on a pure white palfrey or hackney caparisoned with green trappings and a silver-mounted side-saddle. The lady was also in green, and so richly and splendidly dressed that splendor itself seemed personified in her. On her left hand she bore a hawk, a proof to Don Quixote's mind that she must be some great lady and the mistress of the whole hunting party, which was the fact; so he said to Sancho, "Run, Sancho, my son, and say to that lady on the palfrey with the hawk that I, the Knight of the Lions, kiss the hands of her exalted beauty, and if her excellence will grant me leave I will go and kiss them in person and place myself at her service for aught that may be in my power and her highness may command; and mind, Sancho, how thou speakest, and take care not to thrust in any of thy proverbs into thy message."

"You've got a likely one here to thrust any in!" said Sancho; "leave me alone for that! Why, this is not the first time in my life I have carried messages to high and exalted ladies."

"Except that thou didst carry to the lady Dulcinea," said Don Quixote, "I know not that thou hast carried any other, at least in my service."

"That is true," replied Sancho; "but pledges don't distress a good paymaster, and in a house where there's plenty supper is soon cooked; I mean there's no need of telling or warning me about anything; for I'm ready for everything and know a little of everything."

"That I believe, Sancho," said Don Quixote; "go and good luck to thee, and God speed thee."

Sancho went off at top speed, forcing Dapple out of his regular pace, and came to where the fair huntress was standing, and dismounting knelt before her and said, "Fair lady, that knight that you see there, the Knight of the Lions by name, is my master, and I am a squire of his, and at home they call me Sancho Panza. This same Knight of the Lions, who was called not long since the Knight of the Rueful Countenance, sends by me to say may it please your highness to give him leave that, with your permission, approbation, and consent, he may come and carry out his wishes, which are, as he says and I believe, to serve your exalted loftiness and beauty; and if you give it, your ladyship will do a thing which will redound to your honor, and he will receive a most distinguished favor and happiness."

"You have indeed, worthy squire," said the lady, "delivered your message with all the formalities such messages require; rise up, for it is not right that the squire of a knight so great as he of the Rueful Countenance, of whom we have already heard a great deal here, should remain on his knees; rise, my friend, and bid your master welcome to the services of myself and the duke my husband, in a country house we have here."

Sancho got up, charmed as much by the beauty of the good lady as by her high-bred air and her courtesy, but, above all, by what she had said about having heard of his master, the Knight of the Rueful Countenance; for if she did not call him Knight of the Lions it was no doubt because he had so lately taken the name. "Tell me, brother squire," asked the duchess (whose title, however, is not known), "this master of yours, is he not one of whom there is a history extant in print, called *The Ingenious Gentleman, Don Quixote of La Mancha,* who has for the lady of his heart a certain Dulcinea del Toboso?"

"He is the same, señora," replied Sancho; "and that squire of his who figures, or ought to figure, in the said history under the name of Sancho Panza, is myself, unless they have changed me in the cradle, I mean in the press."

"I am rejoiced at this," said the duchess; "go, brother Panza, and tell your master that he is welcome to my estate, and that nothing could happen to me that could give me greater pleasure."

Sancho returned to his master mightily pleased with this gratifying answer, and told him all the great lady had said to him, lauding to the skies, in his rustic phrase, her rare beauty, her graceful gayety, and her courtesy. Don Quixote drew himself up briskly in his saddle, fixed himself in his stirrups, settled his visor, gave Rocinante the spur, and with an easy bearing advanced to kiss the hands of the duchess, who, having sent to summon the duke her husband, told him while Don Quixote was approaching all about the message; and as both of them had read the First Part of this history, and from it were aware of Don Quixote's crazy turn, they awaited him with the greatest delight and anxiety to make his acquaintance, meaning to fall in with his humor and agree with everything he said, and, so long as he stayed with them, to treat him as a

knight-errant, with all the ceremonies usual in the books of chivalry they had read, for they themselves were very fond of them.

Don Quixote now came up with his visor raised, and as he seemed about to dismount Sancho made haste to go and hold his stirrup for him; but in getting down off Dapple he was so unlucky as to hitch his foot in one of the ropes of the pack-saddle in such a way that he was unable to free it, and was left hanging by it with his face and breast on the ground. Don Quixote, who was not used to dismount without having the stirrup held, fancying that Sancho had by this time come to hold it for him, threw himself off with a lurch and brought Rocinante's saddle after him, which was no doubt badly girthed, and saddle and he both came to the ground; nor without discomfiture to him and abundant curses muttered between his teeth against the unlucky Sancho, who had his foot still in the shackles. The duke ordered his huntsmen to go to the help of knight and squire, and they raised Don Quixote sorely shaken by his fall; and he, limping, advanced as best he could to kneel before the noble pair. This, however, the duke would by no means permit; on the contrary, dismounting from his horse, he went and embraced Don Quixote, saying, "I am grieved, Sir Knight of the Rueful Countenance, that your first experience on my ground should have been such an unfortunate one as we have seen; but the carelessness of squires is often the cause of worse accidents."

"That which has happened me in meeting you, mighty prince," replied Don Quixote, "can not be unfortunate, even if my fall had not stopped short of the depths of the bottomless pit, for the glory of having seen you would have lifted me up and delivered me from it. My squire, God's curse upon him, is better at unloosing his tongue in talking impertinence than in tightening the girths of a saddle to keep it steady; but however I may be, fallen or raised up, on foot or on horseback, I shall always be at your service and that of my lady the duchess, your worthy consort, worthy queen of beauty and paramount princess of courtesy."

"Gently, Señor Don Quixote of La Mancha," said the duke; "where my lady Doña Dulcinea del Toboso is, it is not right that other beauties should be praised."

Sancho, by this time released from his entanglement, was standing by, and before his master could answer he said, "There is no denying, and it must be maintained, that my lady Dulcinea del Toboso is very beautiful; but the hare jumps up where one least expects it; and I have heard say that what we call nature is like a potter that makes vessels of clay, and he who makes one fair vessel can as well make two, or three, or a hundred; I say so because, by my faith, my lady the duchess is in no way behind my mistress the lady Dulcinea del Toboso."

Don Quixote turned to the duchess and said, "Your highness may conceive that never had knight-errant in this world a more talkative or a droller squire than I have, and he will prove the truth of what I say, if your highness is pleased to accept of my services for a few days."

To which the duchess made answer, "That worthy Sancho is droll I consider a very good thing, because it is a sign that he is shrewd; for drollery and sprightliness, Señor Don Quixote, as you very well know, do not take up their abode with dull wits; and as good Sancho is droll and sprightly I here set him down as shrewd."

"And talkative," added Don Quixote.

"So much the better," said the duke, "for many droll things can not be said in few words; but not to lose time in talking, come, great Knight of the Rueful Countenance"—

"Of the Lions, your highness must say," said Sancho, "for there is no Rueful Countenance nor any such character now."

"He of the Lions be it," continued the duke; "I say, let Sir Knight of the Lions come to a castle of mine close by, where he shall be given that reception which is due to so exalted a personage, and which the duchess and I are wont to give to all knights-errant who come there."

By this time Sancho had fixed and girthed Rocinante's saddle, and Don Quixote having got on his back and the duke mounted a fine horse, they placed the duchess in the middle and set out for the castle. The duchess desired Sancho to come to her side, for she found infinite enjoyment in listening to his shrewd remarks. Sancho required no pressing, but pushed himself in between them and made a fourth in the conversation, to the great amusement of the duchess and the duke, who thought it rare good fortune to receive such a knight-errant and such a homely squire in their castle.

Chapter 31
Which treats of many and great matters

SUPREME was the satisfaction that Sancho felt at seeing himself, as it seemed, an established favorite with the duchess, for he looked forward to finding in her castle what he had found in Don Diego's house and in Basilio's; he was always fond of good living, and always seized

by the forelock any opportunity of feasting himself whenever it presented itself. The history informs us, then, that before they reached the country house or castle, the duke went on in advance and instructed all his servants how they were to treat Don Quixote; and so the instant he came up to the castle gates with the duchess, two lackeys or equerries, clad in what they call morning gowns of fine crimson satin reaching to their feet, hastened out, and catching Don Quixote in their arms before he saw or heard them, said to him, "Your highness should go and take my lady the duchess off her horse." Don Quixote obeyed, and great bandying of compliments followed between the two over the matter; but in the end the duchess's determination carried the day, and she refused to get down or dismount from her palfrey except in the arms of the duke, saying she did not consider herself worthy to impose so unnecessary a burden on so great a knight. At length the duke came out to take her down, and as they entered a spacious court two fair damsels came forward and threw over Don Quixote's shoulders a large mantle of the finest scarlet cloth, and at the same instant all the galleries of the court were lined with the men-servants and women-servants of the household, crying, "Welcome, flower and cream of knight-errantry!" while all or most of them flung pellets filled with scented water over Don Quixote and the duke and duchess; at all which Don Quixote was greatly astonished, and this was the first time that he thoroughly felt and believed himself to be a knight-errant in reality and not merely in fancy, now that he saw himself treated in the same way as he had read of such knights being treated in days of yore.

Sancho, deserting Dapple, hung on to the duchess and entered the castle, but feeling some twinges of conscience at having left the ass alone, he approached a respectable duenna who had come out with the rest to receive the duchess, and in a low voice he said to her, "Señora Gonzalez, or however your grace may be called"—

"I am called Doña Rodriguez de Grijalba," replied the duenna; "what is your will, brother?" To which Sancho made answer, "I should be glad if your worship would do me the favor to go out to the castle gate, where you will find a gray ass of mine; make them, if you please, put him in the stable, or put him there yourself, for the poor little beast is rather easily frightened and cannot bear being alone at all."

"If the master is as wise as the man," said the duenna, "we have got a fine bargain. Be off with you, brother, and bad luck to you and him who brought you here; go, look after your ass, for we, the duennas of this house, are not used to work of that sort."

"Well then, in troth," returned Sancho, "I have heard my master, who is the very treasure-finder of stories, telling the story of Lancelot when he came from Britain, say that ladies waited upon him and duennas upon his hack; and, if it comes to my ass, I wouldn't change him for Señor Lancelot's hack."

"If you are a jester, brother," said the duenna, 'keep your drolleries for some place where they'll pass muster and be paid for; for you'll get nothing from me but a fig."

"At any rate, it will be a very ripe one," said Sancho, "for you won't lose the trick in years by a point too little."

"Son of a bitch," said the duenna, all aglow with anger, "whether I'm old or not, it's with God I have to reckon, not with you, you garlic-stuffed scoundrel!" and she said it so loud, that the duchess heard it, and turning round and seeing the duenna in such a state of excitement, and her eyes flaming so, asked whom she was wrangling with.

"With this good fellow here," said the duenna, "who has particularly requested me to go and put an ass of his that is at the castle gate into the stable, holding it up to me as an example that they did the same I don't know where—that some ladies waited on one Lancelot, and duennas on his hack; and what is more, to wind up with, he called me old."

"That," said the duchess, "I should have considered the greatest affront that could be offered me"; and addressing Sancho, she said to him, "You must know, friend Sancho, that Doña Rodriguez is very youthful, and that she wears that hood more for authority and custom sake than because of her years."

"May all the rest of mine be unlucky," said Sancho, "if I meant it that way; I only spoke because the affection I have for my ass is so great, and I thought I could not commend him to a more kind-hearted person than the lady Doña Rodriguez."

Don Quixote, who was listening, said to him, "Is this proper conversation for the place, Sancho?"

"Señor," replied Sancho, "every one must mention what he wants wherever he may be; I thought of Dapple here, and I spoke of him here; if I had thought of him in the stable I would have spoken there."

On which the duke observed, "Sancho is quite right, and there is no reason at all to find fault with him; Dapple shall be fed to his heart's content, and Sancho may rest easy, for he shall be treated like himself."

While this conversation, amusing to all except Don Quixote, was proceeding, they ascended the staircase and ushered Don Quixote into a chamber hung with rich cloth of gold and brocade; six damsels relieved him of his armor and waited on him like pages, all of them prepared and instructed by the duke and duchess as to what they were to do, and how they were to treat Don Quixote, so that he might see and believe they were treating him like a knight-errant. When his armor was removed, there stood Don Quixote in his tight-fitting breeches and chamois doublet, lean, lanky, and long, with cheeks that seemed to be kissing each other inside; such a figure, that if the damsels waiting on him had not taken care to check their merriment (which was one of the particular directions their master and mistress had given them), they would have burst with laughter. They asked him to let himself be stripped that they might put a shirt on him, but he would not on any account, saying that modesty became knights-errant just as much as valor. However, he said they might give the shirt to Sancho; and shutting himself in with him in a room where there was a sumptuous bed, he undressed and put on the shirt; and then, finding himself alone with Sancho, he said to him, "Tell me, thou new-fledged buffoon and old booby, dost thou think it right to offend and insult a duenna so deserving of reverence and respect as that one just now? Was that a time to bethink thee of thy Dapple, or are these noble personages likely to let the beasts fare badly when they treat their owners in such elegant style? For God's sake, Sancho, restrain thyself, and don't show the thread so as to let them see what a coarse, boorish texture thou art of. Remember, sinner that thou art, the master is the more esteemed the more respectable and well-bred his servants are; and that one of the greatest advantages that princes have over other men is that they have servants as good as themselves to wait on them. Dost thou not see—short-sighted being that thou art, and unlucky mortal that I am!—that if they perceive thee to be a coarse clown or a dull blockhead, they will suspect me to be some impostor or swindler? Nay, nay, Sancho friend, keep clear, oh, keep clear of these stumbling-blocks; for he who falls into the way of being a chatterbox and droll, drops into a wretched buffoon the first time he trips; bridle thy tongue, consider and weigh thy words before they escape thy mouth, and bear in mind we are now in quarters whence, by God's help, and the strength of my arm, we shall come forth mightily advanced in fame and fortune."

Sancho promised him with much earnestness to keep his mouth shut, and to bite off his tongue before he uttered a word that was not altogether to the purpose and well considered, and told him he might make his mind easy on that point, for it should never be discovered through him what they were.

Don Quixote dressed himself, put on his baldric with his sword, threw the scarlet mantle over his shoulders, placed on his head a montera of green satin that the damsels had given him, and thus arrayed passed out into the large room, where he found the damsels drawn up in double file, the same number on each side, all with the appliances for washing the hands, which they presented to him with profuse obeisances and ceremonies. Then came twelve pages, together with the seneschal, to lead him to dinner, as his hosts were already waiting for him. They placed him in the midst of them, and with much pomp and stateliness they conducted him into another room, where there was a sumptuous table laid with but four covers. The duchess and the duke came out to the door of the room to receive him, and with them a grave ecclesiastic, one of those who rule noblemen's houses; one of those who, not being born magnates themselves, never know how to teach those who are how to behave as such; one of those who would have the greatness of great folk measured by their own narrowness of mind; one of those who, when they try to introduce economy into the household they rule, lead it into meanness. One of this sort, I say, must have been the grave churchman who came out with the duke and duchess to receive Don Quixote.

A vast number of polite speeches were exchanged, and at length, taking Don Quixote between them, they proceeded to sit down to table. The duke pressed Don Quixote to take the head of the table, and, though he refused, the entreaties of the duke were so urgent that he had to accept it.

The ecclesiastic took his seat opposite to him, and the duke and duchess those at the sides. All this time Sancho stood by, gaping with amazement at the honor he saw shown to his master by these illustrious persons; and observing all the ceremonious pressing that had passed between the duke and Don Quixote to induce him to take his seat at the head of the table, he said, "If your worship will give me leave I will tell you a story of what happened in my village about this matter of seats."

The moment Sancho said this Don Quixote trembled, making sure that he was about to say something foolish. Sancho glanced at him, and guessing his thoughts, said, "Don't be afraid of my going astray, señor, or saying anything that won't be pat to the purpose; I haven't forgotten the advice your worship gave me just now about talking much or little, well or ill."

"I have no recollection of anything, Sancho," said Don Quixote; "say what thou wilt, only say it quickly."

"Well then," said Sancho, "what I am going to say so true that my master Don Quixote, who is here present, will be me from lying."

"Lie as much as thou wilt for all I care, Sancho," said Don Quixote, "for I am not going to stop thee; but consider what thou art going to say."

"I have so considered and reconsidered it," said Sancho, "that the bell-ringer's in a safe berth; as will be seen by what follows."

"It would be well," said Don Quixote, "if your highnesses would order them to turn out this idiot, for he will talk a heap of nonsense."

"By the life of the duke, Sancho shall not be taken away from me for a moment," said the duchess; "I am very fond of him, for I know he is very discreet."

"Discreet be the days of your holiness," said Sancho, "for the good opinion you have of my wit, though there's none in me; but the story I want to tell is this. There was an invitation given by a gentleman of my town, a very rich one, and one of quality, for he was one of the Alamos of Medina del Campo, and married to Doña Mencía de Quiñones, the daughter of Don Alonso de Marañon, Knight of the Order of Santiago, that was drowned at the Herradura— him there was that quarrel about years ago in our village, that my master Don Quixote was mixed up in, to the best of my belief, that Tomasillo the scapegrace, the son of Balbastro the smith, was wounded in.—Isn't all this true, master mine? As you live, say so, that these gentlefolk may not take me for some lying chatterer."

"So far," said the ecclesiastic, "I take you to be more a chatterer than a liar; but I don't know what I shall take you for by-and-by."

"Thou citest so many witnesses and proofs, Sancho," said Don Quixote, "that I have no choice but to say thou must be telling the truth; go on, and cut the story short, for thou art taking the way not to make an end for two days to come."

"He is not to cut it short," said the duchess; "on the contrary, for my gratification, he is to tell it as he knows it, though he should not finish it these six days; and if he took so many they would be to me the pleasantest I ever spent."

"Well then, sirs, I say," continued Sancho, 'that this same gentleman, whom I know as well as I do my own hands, for it's not a bow-shot from my house to his, invited a poor but respectable laborer"—

"Get on, brother," said the churchman; "at the rate you are going you will not stop with your story short of the next world."

"I'll stop less than half-way, please God," said Sancho; "and so I say this laborer, coming to the house of the gentleman I spoke of that invited him—rest his soul, he is now dead; and more by token he died the death of an angel, so they say; for I was not there, for just at that time I had gone to reap at Tembleque"—

"As you live, my son," said the churchman, "make haste back from Tembleque, and finish your story without burying the gentleman, unless you want to make more funerals."

"Well then, it so happened," said Sancho, "that as the pair of them were going to sit down to table—and I think I can see them now plainer than ever"—

Great was the enjoyment of the duke and duchess derived from the irritation the worthy churchman showed at the long-winded, halting way Sancho had of telling his story, while Don Quixote was chafing with rage and vexation.

"So, as I was saying," continued Sancho, "as the pair of them were going to sit down to table, as I said, the laborer insisted upon the gentleman's taking the head of the table, and the gentleman insisted upon the laborer's taking it, as his orders should be obeyed in his own house; but the laborer, who plumed himself on his politeness and good-breeding, would not on any account, until the gentleman, out of patience, putting his hands on his shoulders, compelled him by force to sit down, saying, 'Sit down, you stupid lout, for wherever I sit will be the head to you'; and that's the story, and, troth, I think it hasn't been brought in amiss here."

Don Quixote turned all colors, which, on his sunburnt face, mottled it till it looked like jasper. The duke and duchess suppressed their laughter so as not altogether to mortify Don Quixote, for they saw through Sancho's impertinence; and to change the conversation, and keep Sancho from uttering more absurdities,

the duchess asked Don Quixote what news he had of the lady Dulcinea, and if he had sent her any presents of giants or miscreants lately, for he could not but have vanquished a good many.

To which Don Quixote replied, "Señora, my misfortunes, though they had a beginning, will never have an end. I have vanquished giants and I have sent her caitiffs and miscreants; but where are they to find her if she is enchanted and turned into the most ill-favored peasant wench that can be imagined?"

"I don't know," said Sancho Panza; "to me she seems the fairest creature in the world; at any rate, in nimbleness and jumping she won't give in to a tumbler; by my faith, señora duchess, she leaps from the ground on to the back of an ass like a cat."

"Have you seen her enchanted, Sancho?" asked the duke.

"What, seen her!" said Sancho; "why, who the devil was it but myself that first thought of the enchantment business? She is as much enchanted as my father."

The ecclesiastic, when he heard them talking of giants and caitiffs and enchantments, began to suspect that this must be Don Quixote of La Mancha, whose story the duke was always reading; and he had himself often reproved him for it, telling him it was foolish to read such fooleries; and becoming convinced that his suspicion was correct, addressing the duke, he said very angrily to him, "Señor, your excellence will have to give an account to God for what this good man does. This Don Quixote or Don Simpleton, or whatever his name is, can not, I imagine, be such a blockhead as your excellence would have him, holding out encouragement to him to go on with his vagaries and follies." Then turning to address Don Quixote he said, "And you, numskull, who put it into your head that you are a knight-errant, and vanquish giants and capture miscreants? Go your ways in a good hour, and in a good hour be it said to you: Go home and bring up your children if you have any, and attend to your business, and give over going wandering about the world, gaping and making a laughing-stock of yourself to all who know you and all who don't. Where, in Heaven's name, have you discovered that there are or ever were knights-errant? Where are there giants in Spain or miscreants in La Mancha, or enchanted Dulcineas, or all the rest of the silly things they tell about you?"

Don Quixote listened attentively to the reverend gentleman's words, and as soon as he perceived he had done speaking, regardless of the presence of the duke and duchess, he sprang to his feet with angry looks and an agitated countenance, and said—But the reply deserves a chapter to itself.

Chapter 32

Of the reply Don Quixote gave his censurer, with other incidents, grave and droll

DON QUIXOTE, then, having risen to his feet, trembling from head to foot like a man dosed with mercury, said in a hurried, agitated voice, "The place I am in, the presence in which I stand, and the respect I have and always have had for the profession to which your worship belongs, hold and bind the hands of my just indignation; and as well for these reasons as because I know, as every one knows, that a gownsman's weapon is the same as a woman's, the tongue, I will with mine engage in equal combat with your worship, from whom one might have expected good advice instead of foul abuse. Pious, well-meant reproof requires a different demeanor and arguments of another sort; at any rate, to have reproved me in public, and so roughly, exceeds the bounds of proper reproof, for that comes better with gentleness than with rudeness; and it is not seemly to call the sinner roundly blockhead and booby, without knowing anything of the sin that is reproved. Come, tell me, for which of the stupidities you have observed in me do you condemn and abuse me, and bid me go home and look after my house and wife and children without knowing whether I have any? Is nothing more needed than to get a footing, by hook or by crook, in other people's houses to rule over the masters (and that, perhaps, after having been brought up in all the straitness of some seminary, and without having ever seen more of the world than may lie within twenty or thirty leagues round), to fit one to lay down the law rashly for chivalry, and pass judgment on knights-errant? Is it, haply, an idle occupation, or is the time ill-spent that is spent in roaming the world in quest, not of its enjoyments, but of those arduous toils whereby the good mount upwards to the abodes of everlasting life? If gentlemen, great lords, nobles, men of high birth, were to rate me as a fool I should take it as an irreparable insult; but I care not a farthing if clerks who have never entered upon or trod the paths of chivalry should think me foolish. Knight I am, and knight I will die, if such be the pleasure of the Most High. Some take the broad road of overweening ambition; others that of mean and servile flattery; others that of deceitful hypocrisy, and some that of true religion; but I, led by my star, follow the narrow path of knight-errantry, and in pursuit of that calling I despise wealth, but not honor. I have redressed injuries, righted wrongs, punished insolences, vanquished giants, and crushed monsters; I am in love, for no other reason than that it is incumbent on knights-errant to be so; but though I am, I am no carnal-minded lover, but one of the chaste, platonic sort. My intentions are always directed to worthy ends, to do good to all and evil to none; and if he who means this, does this, and makes this his practice deserves to be called a fool, it is for your highnesses to say, O most excellent duke and duchess."

"Good, by God!" cried Sancho; "say no more in your own defence, master mine, for there's nothing more in the world to be said, thought, or insisted on; and besides, when this gentleman denies, as he has, that there are or ever have been any knights-errant in the world, is it any wonder if he knows nothing of what he has been talking about?"

"Perhaps, brother," said the ecclesiastic, "you are that Sancho Panza that is mentioned, to whom your master has promised an island?"

"Yes, I am," said Sancho, "and what's more, I am one who deserves it as much as any one; I am one of the sort—'Attach thyself to the good, and thou wilt be one of them,' and of those, 'Not with whom thou art bred, but with whom thou art fed,' and of those, 'Who leans against a good tree, a good shade covers him'; I have leant upon a good master, and I have been for months going about with him, and please God I shall be just such another; long life to him and long life to me, for neither will he be in any want of empires to rule, or I of islands to govern."

"No, Sancho my friend, certainly not," said the duke, "for in the name of Señor Don Quixote I confer upon you the government of one of no small importance that I have at my disposal."

"Go down on thy knees, Sancho," said Don Quixote, "and kiss the feet of his excellence for the favor he has bestowed upon thee."

Sancho obeyed, and on seeing this the ecclesiastic stood up from table completely out of temper, exclaiming, "By the gown I wear, I am almost inclined to say that your excellence is as great a fool as these sinners. No wonder they are mad, when people who are in their senses sanction their madness! I leave your excellence with them, for so long as they are in the house, I will remain in my own, and spare myself the trouble of reproving what I can not remedy"; and without uttering another word, or eating another morsel, he went off, the entreaties of the duke and duchess being entirely unavailing to stop him; not that the duke said much to him, for he could not, because of the laughter his uncalled-for anger provoked.

When he had done laughing, he said to Don Quixote, "You have replied on your own behalf so stoutly, Sir Knight of the Lions, that there is no occasion to seek further satisfaction for this, which, though it may look like an offence, is not so at all, for, as women can give no offence, no more can ecclesiastics, as you very well know."

"That is true," said Don Quixote, "and the reason is, that he who is not liable to offence can not give offence to any one. Women, children, and ecclesiastics, as they can not defend themselves, though they may receive offence can not be insulted, because between the offence and the insult there is, as your excellence very well knows, this difference: the insult comes from one who is capable of offering it, and does so, and maintains it; the offence may come from any quarter without carrying insult. To take an example: a man is standing unsuspectingly in the street and ten others come up armed and beat him; he draws his sword and quits himself like a man, but the number of his antagonists makes it impossible for him to effect his purpose and avenge himself; this man suffers an offence but not an insult. Another example will make the same thing plain: a man is standing with his back turned, another comes up and strikes him, and after striking him takes to flight, without waiting an instant, and the other pursues him but does not overtake him; he who received the blow received an offence, but not an insult, because an insult must be maintained. If he who struck him, though he did so sneakingly and treacherously, had drawn his sword and stood and faced him, then he who had been struck would have received offence and insult at the same time; offence because he was struck treacherously, insult because he who struck him maintained what he had done, standing his ground without taking to flight. And so, according to the laws of the accursed duel, I may have received offence, but not insult, for neither women nor children can maintain it, nor can they wound, nor have they any way of standing their ground, and it is just the same with those connected with religion; for these three sorts of persons are without arms offensive or defensive, and so, though naturally they are bound to defend themselves, they have no right to offend anybody; and though I said just now I might have received offence, I say now certainly not, for he who can not receive an insult can still less give one; for which

reasons I ought not to feel, nor do I feel, aggrieved at what that good man said to me; I only wish he had stayed a little longer, that I might have shown him the mistake he makes in supposing and maintaining that there are not and never have been any knights-errant in the world; had Amadis or any of his countless descendants heard him say as much, I am sure it would not have gone well with his worship."

"I will take my oath of that," said Sancho; "they would have give him a slash that would have slit him down from top to toe like a pomegranate or a ripe melon; they were likely fellows to put up with jokes of that sort! By my faith, I'm certain if Reinaldos of Montalvan had heard the little man's words he would have given him such a spank on the mouth that he wouldn't have spoken for the next three years; ay, let him tackle them, and he'll see how he'll get out of their hands!"

The duchess, as she listened to Sancho, was ready to die with laughter, and in her own mind she set him down as droller and madder than his master; and there were a good many just then who were of the same opinion.

Don Quixote finally grew calm, and dinner came to an end, and as the cloth was removed four damsels came in, one of them with a silver basin, another with a jug also of silver, a third with two fine white towels on her shoulder, and the fourth with her arms bared to the elbows, and in her white hands (for white they certainly were) a round ball of Naples soap. The one with the basin approached, and with arch composure and impudence, thrust it under Don Quixote's chin, who, wondering at such a ceremony, said never a word, supposing it to be the custom of that country to wash beards instead of hands; he therefore stretched his out as far as he could, and at the same instant the jug began to pour and the damsel with the soap rubbed his beard briskly, raising snowflakes, for the soap lather was no less white, not only over the beard, but all over the face, and over the eyes of the submissive knight, so that they were perforce obliged to keep shut. The duke and duchess, who had not known anything about this, waited to see what would come of this strange washing. The barber damsel, when she had him a hand's breadth deep in lather, pretended that there was no more water, and bade the one with the jug go and fetch some, while Señor Don Quixote waited. She did so, and Don Quixote was left the strangest and most ludicrous figure that could be imagined. All those present, and there were a good many, were watching him, and as they saw him there with half a yard of neck, and that uncommonly brown, his eyes shut, and his beard full of soap, it was a great wonder, and only by great discretion, that they were able to restrain their laughter. The damsels, the concocters of the joke, kept their eyes down, not daring to look at their master and mistress; and as for them, laughter and anger struggled within them, and they knew not what to do, whether to punish the audacity of the girls, or to reward them for the amusement they had received from seeing Don Quixote in such a plight.

At length the damsel with the jug returned and they made an end of washing Don Quixote, and the one who carried the towels very deliberately wiped him and dried him; and all four together making him a profound obeisance and courtesy, they were about to go, when the duke, lest Don Quixote should see through the joke, called out to the one with the basin saying, "Come and wash me, and take care that there is water enough." The girl, sharp-witted and prompt, came and placed the basin for the duke as she had done for Don Quixote, and they soon had him well soaped and washed, and having wiped him dry they made their obeisance and retired. It appeared afterwards that the duke had sworn that if they had not washed him as they had Don Quixote he would have punished them for their impudence, which they adroitly atoned for by soaping him as well.

Sancho observed the ceremony of the washing very attentively, and said to himself, "God bless me, if it were only the custom in this country to wash squires' beards too as well as knights'! For by God and upon my soul I want it badly; and if they gave me a scrape of the razor besides I'd take it as a still greater kindness."

"What are you saying to yourself, Sancho?" asked the duchess.

"I was saying, señora," he replied, "that in the courts of other princes, when the cloth is taken away, I have always heard say they give water for the hands, but not lye for the beard; and that shows it is good to live long that you may see much; to be sure, they say too that he who lives a long life must undergo much evil; though to undergo a washing of that sort is pleasure rather than pain."

"Don't be uneasy, friend Sancho," said the duchess; "I will take care that my damsels wash you, and even put you in the tub if necessary."

"I'll be content with the beard," said Sancho, "at any rate for the present; and as for the future, God has decreed what is to be."

"Attend to worthy Sancho's request, seneschal," said the duchess, "and do exactly what he wishes."

The seneschal replied that Señor Sancho should be obeyed in everything; and with that he went away to dinner and took Sancho along with him, while the duke and duchess and Don Quixote remained at table discussing a great variety of things, but all bearing on the calling of arms and knight-errantry.

The duchess begged Don Quixote, as he seemed to have a retentive memory, to describe and portray to her the beauty and features of the lady Dulcinea del Toboso, for, judging by what fame trumpeted abroad of her beauty, she felt sure she must be the fairest creature in the world, nay, in all La Mancha.

Don Quixote sighed on hearing the duchess's request, and said, "If I could pluck out my heart, and lay it on a plate on this table here before your highness's eyes, it would spare my tongue the pain of telling what can hardly be thought of, for in it your excellence would see her portrayed in full. But why should I attempt to depict and describe in detail, and feature by feature, the beauty of the peerless Dulcinea, the burden being one worthy of other shoulders than mine, an enterprise wherein the pencils of Parrhasius, Timantes, and Apelles, and the graver of Lysippus ought to be employed, to paint it in pictures and carve it in marble and bronze, and Ciceronian and Demosthenian eloquence to sound its praises?"

"What does Demosthenian mean, Señor Don Quixote?" said the duchess; "it is a word I never heard in all my life."

"Demosthenian eloquence," said Don Quixote, "means the eloquence of Demosthenes, as Ciceronian means that of Cicero, who were the two most eloquent orators in the world."

"True," said the duke; "you must have lost your wits to ask such a question. Nevertheless, Señor Don Quixote would greatly gratify us if he would depict her to us; for never fear, even in an outline or sketch she will be something to make the fairest envious."

"I would do so certainly," said Don Quixote, "had she not been blurred to my mind's eye by the misfortune that fell upon her a short time since, one of such a nature that I am more ready to weep over it than to describe it. For your highnesses must know that, going a few days back to kiss her hands and receive her benediction, approbation, and permission for this third sally, I found her altogether a different being from the one I sought; I found her enchanted

nd changed from a princess into a peasant, from
fair to foul, from an angel into a devil, from fragrant to pestiferous, from refined to clownish,
from a dignified lady into a jumping tomboy,
from light to darkness, and, in a word, from Dulcinea del Toboso into a coarse Sayago wench."

"God bless me!" said the duke aloud at this,
'who can have done the world such an injury?
Who can have robbed it of the beauty that glad-
dened it, of the grace and gayety that charmed
it, of the modesty that shed a lustre upon it?"

"Who?" replied Don Quixote; "who could it
be but some malignant enchanter of the many
that persecute me out of envy—that accursed
race born into the world to obscure and bring to
naught the achievements of the good, and glorify and exalt the deeds of the wicked? Enchanters have persecuted me, enchanters persecute
me still, and enchanters will continue to persecute me until they have sunk me and my lofty
chivalry in the deep abyss of oblivion; and they
injure and wound me where they know I feel it
most. For to deprive a knight-errant of his lady
is to deprive him of the eyes he sees with, of the
sun that gives him light, of the food whereby he
lives. Many a time before have I said it, and I
say it now once more, a knight-errant without a
lady is like a tree without leaves, a building
without a foundation, or a shadow without the
body that causes it."

"There is no denying it," said the duchess;
'but still, if we are to believe the history of Don
Quixote that has come out here lately with general applause, it is to be inferred from it, if I mistake not, that you never saw the lady Dulcinea,
and that the said lady is nothing in the world
but an imaginary lady, one that you yourself begot and gave birth to in your brain, and adorned
with whatever charms and perfections you
chose."

"There is a good deal to be said on that point,"
said Don Quixote; "God knows whether there
be any Dulcinea or not in the world, or whether
she is imaginary or not imaginary; these are
things the proof of which must not be pushed to
extreme lengths. I have not begotten nor given
birth to my lady, though I behold her as she
needs must be, a lady who contains in herself
all the qualities to make her famous throughout the world, beautiful without blemish, dignified without haughtiness, tender and yet modest, gracious from courtesy and courteous from
good breeding, and lastly of exalted lineage, because beauty shines forth and excels with a higher degree of perfection upon good blood than
in the fair of lowly birth."

"That is true," said the duke; "but Señor Don
Quixote will give me leave to say what I am constrained to say by the story of his exploits that I
have read, from which it is to be inferred that,
granting there is a Dulcinea in El Toboso, or
out of it, and that she is in the highest degree
beautiful as you have described her to us, as regards the loftiness of her lineage she is not on a
par with the Orianas, Alastrajareas, Madasimas,
or others of that sort, with whom, as you well
know, the histories abound."

"To that I may reply," said Don Quixote,
"that Dulcinea is the daughter of her own works,
and that virtues rectify blood, and that lowly
virtue is more to be regarded and esteemed than
exalted vice. Dulcinea, besides, has that within
her that may raise her to be a crowned and scep-
tred queen; for the merit of a fair and virtuous
woman is capable of performing greater miracles;
and virtually, though not formally, she has in
herself higher fortunes."

"I protest, Señor Don Quixote," said the duchess, "that in all you say, you go most cautiously
and lead in hand, as the saying is; henceforth I
will believe myself, and I will take care that every one in my house believes, even my lord the
duke if needs be, that there is a Dulcinea in El
Toboso, and that she is living to-day, and that
she is beautiful and nobly born and deserves to
have such a knight as Señor Don Quixote in her
service, and that is the highest praise that it is in
my power to give her or that I can think of. But
I can not help entertaining a doubt, and having
a certain grudge against Sancho Panza; the
doubt is this, that the aforesaid history declares
that the said Sancho Panza, when he carried a
letter on your worship's behalf to the said lady
Dulcinea, found her sifting a sack of wheat; and
more by token it says it was red wheat; a thing
which makes me doubt the loftiness of her lineage.

To this Don Quixote made answer, "Señora,
your highness must know that everything or almost everything that happens to me transcends
the ordinary limits of what happens to other
knights-errant; whether it be that it is directed
by the inscrutable will of destiny, or by the malice of some jealous enchanter. Now it is an established fact that all or most famous knights-
errant have some special gift, one that of being
proof against enchantment, another that of being made of such invulnerable flesh that he can
not be wounded, as was the famous Roland, one
of the twelve peers of France, of whom it is related that he could not be wounded except in
the sole of his left foot, and that it must be with

the point of a stout pin and not with any other
sort of weapon whatever; and so, when Bernardo
del Carpio slew him at Roncesvalles, finding
that he could not wound him with steel, he lifted him up from the ground in his arms and
strangled him, calling to mind seasonably the
death which Hercules inflicted on Antæus, the
fierce giant that they say was the son of Terra.
I would infer from what I have mentioned that
perhaps I may have some gift of this kind, not
that of being invulnerable, because experience
has many times proved to me that I am of tender
flesh and not at all impenetrable; nor that of being proof against enchantment, for I have already seen myself thrust into a cage, in which all
the world would not have been able to confine
me except by force of enchantments. But as I
delivered myself from that one, I am inclined
to believe that there is no other that can hurt
me; and so, these enchanters, seeing that they
can not exert their vile craft against my person,
revenge themselves on what I love most, and
seek to rob me of life by maltreating that of Dulcinea in whom I live; and therefore I am convinced that when my squire carried my message
to her, they changed her into a common peasant girl, engaged in such a mean occupation as
sifting wheat; I have already said, however, that
that wheat was not red wheat, nor wheat at all,
but grains of orient pearl. And as a proof of all
this, I must tell your highnesses that, coming to
El Toboso a short time back, I was altogether
unable to discover the palace of Dulcinea; and
that the next day, though Sancho, my squire,
saw her in her own proper shape, which is the
fairest in the world, to me she appeared to be a
coarse, ill-favored, farm-wench, and by no means
a well-spoken one, she who is propriety itself.
And so, as I am not and, so far as one can judge,
can not be enchanted, she it is that is enchanted,
that is smitten, that is altered, changed, and
transformed; in her have my enemies revenged
themselves upon me, and for her shall I live in
ceaseless tears, until I see her in her pristine
state. I have mentioned this lest anybody should
mind what Sancho said about Dulcinea's winnowing or sifting; for, as they changed her to
me, it is no wonder if they changed her to him.
Dulcinea is illustrious and well-born, and of
one of the gentle families of El Toboso, which
are many, ancient, and good. Therein, most assuredly, not small is the share of the peerless
Dulcinea, through whom her town will be famous and celebrated in ages to come, as Troy
was through Helen, and Spain through La Cava,

though with a better title and tradition. For another thing; I would have your graces understand
that Sancho Panza is one of the drollest squires
that ever served knight-errant; sometimes there
is a simplicity about him so acute that it is an
amusement to try and make out whether he is
simple or sharp; he has mischievous tricks that
stamp him rogue, and blundering ways that
prove him a booby; he doubts everything and believes everything; when I fancy he is on the
point of coming down headlong from sheer stupidity, he comes out with something shrewd
that sends him up to the skies. After all, I would
not exchange him for another squire, though I
were given a city to boot, and therefore I am in
doubt whether it will be well to send him to the
government your highness has bestowed upon
him; though I perceive in him a certain aptitude
for the work of governing, so that, with a little
trimming of his understanding, he would manage any government as easily as the king does
his taxes; and moreover, we know already by ample experience that it does not require much cleverness or much learning to be a governor, for
there are a hundred round about us that scarcely
know how to read, and govern like gerfalcons.
The main point is that they should have good
intentions and be desirous of doing right in all
things, for they will never be at a loss for persons to advise and direct them in what they have
to do, like those knight-governors who, being no
lawyers, pronounce sentences with the aid of
an assessor. My advice to him will be to take
no bribe and surrender no right, and I have
some other little matters in reserve, that shall
be produced in due season for Sancho's
benefit and the advantage of the island he is
to govern."

The duke, duchess, and Don Quixote had
reached this point in their conversation, when
they heard voices and a great hubbub in the
palace, and Sancho burst abruptly into the room
all glowing with anger, with a straining-cloth
by way of a bib, and followed by several servants, or, more properly speaking, kitchen-boys
and other underlings, one of whom carried a
small trough full of water, that from its color
and impurity was plainly dishwater. The one
with the trough pursued him and followed him
everywhere he went, endeavoring with the utmost persistence to thrust it under his chin, while
another kitchen-boy seemed anxious to wash his
beard.

"What is all this, brothers?" asked the duchess. "What is it? What do you want to do to this

good man? What! do you forget he is a governor-elect?"

To which the barber kitchen-boy replied, "The gentleman will not let himself be washed as is customary, and as my lord the duke and the señor his master have been."

"Yes, I will," said Sancho, in a great rage; "but I'd like it to be with cleaner towels, clearer lye, and not such dirty hands; for there's not so much difference between me and my master that he should be washed with angels' water and I with devil's lye. The customs of countries and princes' palaces are only good so long as they give no annoyance; but the way of washing they have here is worse than doing penance. I have a clean beard, and I don't require to be refreshed in that fashion, and whoever comes to wash me or touch a hair of my head, I mean to say my beard, with all due respect be it said, I'll give him a punch that will leave my fist sunk in his skull; for cirimonies and soapings of this sort are more like jokes than the polite attentions of one's host."

The duchess was ready to die with laughter when she saw Sancho's rage and heard his words; but it was no pleasure to Don Quixote to see him in such a sorry trim, with the dingy towel about him, and the hangers-on of the kitchen all round him; so making a low bow to the duke and duchess, as if to ask their permission to speak, he addressed the rout in a dignified tone: "Holloa, gentlemen! you let that youth alone, and go back to where you came from, or anywhere else if you like; my squire is as clean as any other person, and those troughs are as bad as narrow thin-necked jars to him; take my advice and leave him alone, for neither he nor I understand joking."

Sancho took the word out of his mouth and went on, "Nay, let them come and try their jokes on the country bumpkin, for it's about as likely I'll stand them as that it's now midnight! Let them bring me a comb here, or what they please, and curry this beard of mine, and if they get anything out of it that offends against cleanliness, let them clip me to the skin."

Upon this, the duchess, laughing all the while, said, "Sancho Panza is right, and always will be in all he says; he is clean, and, as he says himself, he does not require to be washed; and if our ways do not please him, he is free to choose. Besides, you promoters of cleanliness have been excessively careless and thoughtless, I don't know if I ought not to say audacious, to bring troughs and wooden utensils and kitchen dish-clouts, instead of basins and jugs of pure gold and towels

of holland, to such a person and such a beard; but, after all, you are ill-conditioned and ill-bred, and spiteful as you are, you can not help showing the grudge you have against the squires of knights-errant."

The impudent servitors, and even the seneschal who came with them, took the duchess to be speaking in earnest, so they removed the straining-cloth from Sancho's neck, and with something like shame and confusion of face went off all of them and left him; whereupon he, seeing himself safe out of that extreme danger, as it seemed to him, ran and fell on his knees before the duchess, saying, "From great ladies great favors may be looked for; this which your grace has done me to-day can not be requited with less than wishing I was dubbed a knight-errant, to devote myself all the days of my life to the service of so exalted a lady. I am a laboring man, my name is Sancho Panza, I am married, I have children, and I am serving as a squire; if in any one of these ways I can serve your highness, I will not be longer in obeying than your grace in commanding."

"It is easy to see, Sancho," replied the duchess, "that you have learned to be polite in the school of politeness itself; I mean to say it is easy to see that you have been nursed in the bosom of Señor Don Quixote, who is, of course, the cream of good breeding and flower of ceremony—or cirimony, as you would say yourself. Fair be the fortunes of such a master and such a servant, the one the cynosure of knight-errantry, the other the star of squirely fidelity! Rise, Sancho, my friend; I will repay your courtesy by taking care that my lord the duke makes good to you the promised gift of the government as soon as possible."

With this, the conversation came to an end, and Don Quixote retired to take his midday sleep; but the duchess begged Sancho, unless he had a very great desire to go to sleep, to come and spend the afternoon with her and her damsels in a very cool chamber. Sancho replied that, though he certainly had the habit of sleeping four or five hours in the heat of the day in summer, to serve her excellence he would try with all his might not to sleep even one that day, and that he would come in obedience to her command, and with that he went off. The duke gave fresh orders with respect to treating Don Quixote as a knight-errant, without departing in the smallest particular from the style in which, as the stories tell us, they used to treat the knights of old.

Chapter 33

Of the delectable discourse which the duchess and her damsels held with Sancho Panza, well worth reading and noting

THE history records that Sancho did not sleep that afternoon, but in order to keep his word came, before he had well done dinner, to visit the duchess, who, finding enjoyment in listening to him, made him sit down beside her on a low seat, though Sancho, out of pure good breeding, wanted not to sit down; the duchess, however, told him he was to sit down as governor and talk as squire, as in both respects he was worthy of even the chair of the Cid Ruy Diaz the Campeador. Sancho shrugged his shoulders, obeyed, and sat down, and all the duchess's damsels and duennas gathered round him, waiting in profound silence to hear what he would say. It was the duchess, however, who spoke first, saying, "Now that we are alone, and that there is nobody here to overhear us, I should be glad if the señor governor would relieve me of certain doubts I have, rising out of the history of the great Don Quixote that is now in print. One is: inasmuch as worthy Sancho never saw Dulcinea, I mean the lady Dulcinea del Toboso, nor took Don Quixote's letter to her, for it was left in the memorandum book in the Sierra Morena, how did he dare to invent the answer and all that about finding her sifting wheat, the whole story being a deception and falsehood, and so much to the prejudice of the peerless Dulcinea's good name, a thing that is not at all becoming the character and fidelity of a good squire?"

At these words, Sancho, without uttering one in reply, got up from his chair, and with noiseless steps, with his body bent and his finger on his lips, went all round the room lifting up the hangings; and this done, he came back to his seat and said, "Now, señora, that I have seen that there is no one except the bystanders listening to us on the sly, I will answer what you have asked me, and all you may ask me, without fear or dread. And the first thing I have got to say is, that for my own part I hold my master Don Quixote to be stark mad, though sometimes he says things that, to my mind, and indeed everybody's that listens to him, are so wise, and run in such a straight furrow, that Satan himself could not have said them better; but for all that, really, and beyond all question, it's my firm belief he is cracked. Well, then, as this is clear to my mind, I can venture to make him believe things that have neither head nor tail, like that affair of the answer to the letter, and that other

of six or eight days ago, which is not yet in history, that is to say, the affair of the enchantment of my lady Dulcinea; for I made him believe she is enchanted, though there's no more truth in it than over the hills of Úbeda."

The duchess begged him to tell her about the enchantment or deception, so Sancho told the whole story exactly as it had happened, and his hearers were not a little amused by it; and then resuming, the duchess said, "In consequence of what worthy Sancho has told me, a doubt starts up in my mind, and there comes a kind of whisper to my ear that says, 'If Don Quixote be mad, crazy, and cracked, and Sancho Panza his squire knows it, and, notwithstanding, serves and follows him, and goes trusting to his empty promises, there can be no doubt he must be still madder and sillier than his master; and that being so, it will be cast in your teeth, señora duchess, if you give the said Sancho an island to govern; for how will he who does not know how to govern himself know how to govern others?' "

"By God, señora," said Sancho, "but that doubt comes timely; but your grace may say it out, and speak plainly, or as you like; for I know what you say is true, and if I were wise I should have left my master long ago; but this was my fate, this was my bad luck; I can't help it, I must follow him; we're from the same village, I have eaten his bread, I'm fond of him, I'm grateful, he gave me his ass-colts, and above all I'm faithful; so it's quite impossible for anything to separate us, except the pickaxe and shovel. And if your highness does not like to give me the government you promised, God made me without it, and maybe your not giving it to me will be all the better for my conscience, for fool as I am I know the proverb 'to her hurt the ant got wings,' and it may be that Sancho the squire will get to heaven sooner than Sancho the governor. 'They make as good bread here as in France,' and 'by night all cats are gray,' and 'a hard case enough his, who hasn't broken his fast at two in the afternoon,' and 'there's no stomach a hand's breadth bigger than another,' and the same can be filled 'with straw or hay,' as the saying is, and 'the little birds of the field have God for their purveyor and caterer,' and 'four yards of Cuenca frieze keep one warmer than four of Segovia broadcloth,' and 'when we quit this world and are put underground the prince travels by as narrow a path as the journeyman,' and 'the Pope's body does not take up more feet of earth than the sacristan's,' for all that the one is higher than the other; for when we go to our graves we all pack ourselves up and make ourselves small, or rather they pack us up and make us small in spite of us, and then—good night to us. And I say once more, if your ladyship does not like to give me the island because I'm a fool, like a wise man I will take care to give myself no trouble about it; I have heard say that 'behind the cross there's the devil,' and that 'all that glitters is not gold,' and that from among the oxen, and the ploughs, and the yokes, Wamba the husbandman was taken to be made King of Spain, and from among brocades, and pleasures, and riches, Roderick was taken to be devoured by adders, if the verses of the old ballads don't lie."

"To be sure they don't lie!" exclaimed Doña Rodriguez, the duenna, who was one of the listeners. "Why, there's a ballad that says they put King Rodrigo alive into a tomb full of toads, and adders, and lizards, and that two days afterwards the King, in a plaintive, feeble voice, cried out from within the tomb—

> *They gnaw me now, they gnaw me now,*
> *There where I most did sin.*

And according to that the gentleman has good reason to say he would rather be a laboring man than a king, if vermin are to eat him."

The duchess could not help laughing at the simplicity of her duenna, or wondering at the language and proverbs of Sancho, to whom she said, "Worthy Sancho knows very well that when once a knight has made a promise he strives to keep it, though it should cost him his life. My lord and husband the duke, though not one of the errant sort, is none the less a knight for that reason, and will keep his word about the promised island, in spite of the envy and malice of the world. Let Sancho be of good cheer; for when he least expects it he will find himself seated on the throne of his island and seat of dignity, and will take possession of his government that he may discard it for another of three-bordered brocade. The charge I give him is to be careful how he governs his vassals, bearing in mind that they are all loyal and well-born."

"As to governing them well," said Sancho, "there's no need of charging me to do that, for I'm kind-hearted by nature, and full of compassion for the poor; 'there's no stealing the loaf from him who kneads and bakes'; and by my faith it won't do to throw false dice with me; I am an old dog, and I know all about '*tus, tus*'; I can be wide awake if need be, and I don't let clouds come before my eyes, for I know where the shoe pinches me; I say so, because with me the good will have support and protection, and the bad neither footing nor access. And it seems to me that, in governments, to make a beginning is everything; and maybe, after having been governor a fortnight, I'll take kindly to the work and know more about it than the field labor I have been brought up to."

"You are right, Sancho," said the duchess, "for no one is born ready taught, and the bishops are made out of men and not out of stones. But to return to the subject we were discussing just now, the enchantment of the lady Dulcinea, I look upon it as certain, and something more than evident, that Sancho's idea of practising a deception upon his master, making him believe that the peasant girl was Dulcinea and that if he did not recognize her it must be because she was enchanted, was all a device of one of the enchanters that persecute Don Quixote. For in truth and earnest, I know from good authority that the coarse country wench who jumped up on the ass was and is Dulcinea del Toboso, and that worthy Sancho, though he fancies himself the deceiver, is the one that is deceived; and that there is no more reason to doubt the truth of this, than of anything else we never saw. Señor Sancho Panza must know that we too have enchanters here that are well disposed to us, and tell us what goes on in the world, plainly and distinctly, without subterfuge or deception; and believe me, Sancho, that agile country lass was and is Dulcinea del Toboso, who is as much enchanted as the mother that bore her; and when we least expect it, we shall see her in her own proper form, and then Sancho will be disabused of the error he is under at present."

"All that's very possible," said Sancho Panza; "and now I'm willing to believe what my master says about what he saw in the cave of Montesinos, where he says he saw the lady Dulcinea del Toboso in the very same dress and apparel that I said I had seen her in when I enchanted her all to please myself. It must be all exactly the other way, as your ladyship says; because it is impossible to suppose that out of my poor wit such a cunning trick could be concocted in a moment, nor do I think my master is so mad that by my weak and feeble persuasion he could be made to believe a thing so out of all reason. But, señora, your excellence must not therefore think me ill-disposed, for a dolt like me is not bound to see into the thoughts and plots of those vile enchanters. I invented all that to escape my master's scolding, and not with any intention of hurting him; and if it has turned out differently, there is a God in heaven who judges our hearts."

"That is true," said the duchess; "but tell me,

Sancho, what is this you say about the cave of Montesinos, for I should like to know."

Sancho upon this related to her, word for word, what has been said already touching that adventure, and having heard it the duchess said, "From this occurrence it may be inferred that, as the great Don Quixote says he saw there the same country wench Sancho saw on the way from El Toboso, it is, no doubt, Dulcinea, and that there are some very active and exceedingly busy enchanters about.'

"So I say," said Sancho, "and if my lady Dulcinea is enchanted, so much the worse for her, and I'm not going to pick a quarrel with my master's enemies, who seem to be many and spiteful. The truth is that the one I saw was a country wench, and I set her down to be a country wench; and if that was Dulcinea it must not be laid at my door, nor should I be called to answer for it or take the consequences. But they must go nagging at me every step—'Sancho said it, Sancho did it, Sancho here, Sancho there,' as if Sancho was nobody at all, and not that same Sancho Panza that's now going all over the world in books, so Samson Carrasco told me, and he's at any rate one that's a bachelor of Salamanca; and people of that sort can't lie, except when the whim seizes them or they have some very good reason for it. So there's no occasion for anybody to quarrel with me; and then I have a good character, and, as I have heard my master say, 'a good name is better than great riches'; let them only stick me into this government and they'll see wonders, for one who has been a good squire will be a good governor."

"All worthy Sancho's observations," said the duchess, "are Catonian sentences, or at any rate out of the very heart of Michael Verino himself, who *florentibus occidit annis*. In fact, to speak in his own style, 'under a bad cloak there's often a good drinker.'"

"Indeed, señora," said Sancho, "I never yet drank out of wickedness; from thirst I have very likely, for I have nothing of the hypocrite in me; I drink when I'm inclined, or, if I'm not inclined, when they offer it to me, so as not to look either strait-laced or ill-bred; for when a friend drinks one's health what heart can be so hard as not to return it? But if I put on my shoes I don't dirty them; besides, squires to knights-errant mostly drink water, for they are always wandering among woods, forests and meadows, mountains and crags, without a drop of wine to be had if they gave their eyes for it."

"So I believe," said the duchess; "and now

let Sancho go and take his sleep, and we will talk by-and-by at greater length, and settle how he may soon go and stick himself into the government, as he says."

Sancho once more kissed the duchess's hand, and entreated her to be so kind as to let good care be taken of his Dapple, for he was the light of his eyes.

"What is Dapple?" said the duchess.

"My ass," said Sancho, "which, not to mention him by that name, I'm accustomed to call Dapple; I begged this lady duenna here to take care of him when I came into the castle, and she got as angry as if I had said she was ugly or old, though it ought to be more natural and proper for duennas to feed asses than to ornament chambers. God bless me! what a spite a gentleman of my village had against these ladies!"

"He must have been some clown," said Doña Rodriguez the duenna; "for if he had been a gentleman and well-born he would have exalted them higher than the horns of the moon."

"That will do," said the duchess; "no more of this; hush, Doña Rodriguez, and let Señor Panza rest easy and leave the treatment of Dapple in my charge, for as he is a treasure of Sancho's, I'll put him on the apple of my eye."

"It will be enough for him to be in the stable," said Sancho, "for neither he nor I are worthy to rest a moment in the apple of your highness's eye, and I'd as soon stab myself as consent to it; for though my master says that in civilities it is better to lose by a card too many than a card too few, when it comes to civilities to asses we must mind what we are about and keep within due bounds."

"Take him to your government, Sancho," said the duchess, "and there you will be able to make as much of him as you like, and even release him from work and pension him off."

"Don't think, señora duchess, that you have said anything absurd," said Sancho; "I have seen more than two asses go to governments, and for me to take mine with me would be nothing new."

Sancho's words made the duchess laugh again and gave her fresh amusement, and dismissing him to sleep she went away to tell the duke the conversation she had had with him, and between them they plotted and arranged to play a joke upon Don Quixote that was to be a rare one and entirely in knight-errantry style, and in that same style they practised several upon him, so much in keeping and so clever that they form the best adventures this great history contains.

Chapter 34

Which relates how they learned the way in which they were to disenchant the peerless Dulcinea del Toboso, which is one of the rarest adventures in this book

GREAT was the pleasure the duke and duchess took in the conversation of Don Quixote and Sancho Panza; and, more bent than ever upon the plan they had of practising some jokes upon them that should have the look and appearance of adventures, they took as their basis of action what Don Quixote had already told them about the cave of Montesinos, in order to play him a famous one. But what the duchess marvelled at above all was that Sancho's simplicity could be so great as to make him believe as absolute truth that Dulcinea had been enchanted, when it was he himself who had been the enchanter and trickster in the business. Having, therefore, instructed their servants in everything they were to do, six days afterwards they took him out to hunt, with as great a retinue of huntsmen and beaters as a crowned king could take.

They presented Don Quixote with a hunting suit, and Sancho with another of the finest green cloth; but Don Quixote declined to put his on, saying that he must soon return to the hard pursuit of arms, and could not carry wardrobes or stores with him. Sancho, however, took what they gave him, meaning to sell it the first opportunity he had.

The appointed day having arrived, Don Quixote armed himself, and Sancho arrayed himself, and mounted on his Dapple (for he would not give him up though they offered him a horse), he placed himself in the midst of the troop of huntsmen. The duchess came out splendidly attired, and Don Quixote, in pure courtesy and politeness, held the rein of her palfrey, though the duke wanted not to allow him; and at last they reached a wood that lay between two high mountains, where, after occupying various posts, ambushes, and paths, and distributing the party in different positions, the hunt began with great noise, shouting, and hallooing, so that, between the baying of the hounds and the blowing of the horns, they could not hear one another. The duchess dismounted, and with a sharp boar-spear in her hand posted herself where she knew the wild boars were in the habit of passing. The duke and Don Quixote likewise dismounted and placed themselves on either side of her. Sancho took up a position in the rear of all without dismounting from Dapple, whom he dared not desert lest some mischief

should befall him. Scarcely had they taken their stand in a line with several of their servants, when they saw a huge boar, closely pressed by the hounds and followed by the huntsmen, making towards them, grinding his teeth and tusks, and scattering foam from his mouth. As soon as he saw him Don Quixote, bracing his shield on his arm, and drawing his sword, advanced to meet him; the duke with his boar-spear did the same; but the duchess would have gone in front of them all had not the duke prevented her. Sancho alone, deserting Dapple at the sight of the mighty beast, took to his heels as hard as he could and strove in vain to mount a tall oak. As he was clinging to a branch, however, half-way up in his struggle to reach the top, the bough, such was his ill-luck and hard fate, gave way, and caught in his fall by a broken limb of the oak, he hung suspended in the air unable to reach the ground. Finding himself in this position, and that the green coat was beginning to tear, and reflecting that if the fierce animal came that way he might be able to get at him, he began to utter such cries, and call for help so earnestly, that all who heard him and did not see him felt sure he must be in the teeth of some wild beast. In the end the tusked boar fell pierced by the blades of the many spears they held in front of him; and Don Quixote, turning round at the cries of Sancho, for he knew by them that it was he, saw him hanging from the oak head downwards, with Dapple, who did not forsake him in his distress, close beside him; and Cid Hamet observes that he seldom saw Sancho Panza without seeing Dapple, or Dapple without seeing Sancho Panza; such was their attachment and loyalty one to the other. Don Quixote went over and unhooked Sancho, who, as soon as he found himself released and on the ground, looked at the rent in his hunting-coat and was grieved to the heart, for he thought he had got a patrimonial estate in that suit.

Meanwhile they had slung the mighty boar across the back of a mule, and having covered it with sprigs of rosemary and branches of myrtle, they bore it away as the spoils of victory to some large field-tents which had been pitched in the middle of the wood, where they found the tables laid and dinner served, in such grand and sumptuous style that it was easy to see the rank and magnificence of those who had provided it. Sancho, as he showed the rents in his torn suit to the duchess, observed, "If we had been hunting hares, or after small birds, my coat would have been safe from being in the plight it's in; I don't know what pleasure one can find in lying in wait for an animal that may take your life with his tusk if he gets at you. I recollect having heard an old ballad sung that says,

> By bears be thou devoured, as erst
> Was famous Favila."

"That," said Don Quixote, "was a Gothic king, who, going a hunting, was devoured by a bear."

"Just so," said Sancho; "and I would not have kings and princes expose themselves to such dangers for the sake of a pleasure which, to my mind, ought not to be one, as it consists in killing an animal that has done no harm whatever."

"Quite the contrary, Sancho; you are wrong there," said the duke; "for hunting is more suitable and requisite for kings and princes than for anybody else. The chase is the emblem of war; it has its stratagems, wiles, and crafty devices for overcoming the enemy in safety; in it extreme cold and intolerable heat have to be borne, indolence and sleep are despised, the bodily powers are invigorated, the limbs of him who engages in it are made supple, and, in a word, it is a pursuit which may be followed without injury to any one and with enjoyment to many; and the best of it is, it is not for everybody, as fieldsports of other sorts are, except hawking, which also is only for kings and great lords. Reconsider your opinion therefore, Sancho, and when you are governor take to hunting, and you will find the good of it."

"Nay," said Sancho, "the good governor should have a broken leg and keep at home; it would be a nice thing if, after people had been at the trouble of coming to look for him on business, the governor were to be away in the forest enjoying himself; the government would go on badly in that fashion. By my faith, señor, hunting and amusements are more fit for idlers than for governors; what I intend to amuse myself with, is playing all fours at Eastertime, and bowls on Sundays and holidays; for these huntings don't suit my condition or agree with my conscience."

"God grant it may turn out so," said the duke; "because it's a long step from saying to doing."

"Be that as it may," said Sancho, "'pledges don't distress a good paymaster,' and 'he whom God helps does better than he who gets up early,' and 'it's the tripes that carry the feet and not the feet the tripes;' I mean to say that if God gives me help and I do my duty honestly, no doubt I'll govern better than a gerfalcon. Nay, let them only put a finger in my mouth, and they'll see whether I can bite or not."

"The curse of God and all his saints upon thee, thou accursed Sancho!" exclaimed Don Quixote; "when will the day come—as I have often said to thee—when I shall hear thee make one single coherent, rational remark without proverbs? Pray, your highnesses, leave this fool alone, for he will grind your souls between, not to say two, but two thousand proverbs, dragged in as much in season, and as much to the purpose as—may God grant as much health to him, or to me if I want to listen to them!"

"Sancho Panza's proverbs," said the duchess, "though more in number than the Greek Commander's,[1] are not therefore less to be esteemed for the conciseness of the maxims. For my own part, I can say they give me more pleasure than others that may be better brought in and more seasonably introduced."

In pleasant conversation of this sort they passed out of the tent into the wood, and the day was spent in visiting some of the posts and hiding-places, and then night closed in, not, however, as brilliantly or tranquilly as might have been expected at the season, for it was then midsummer; but bringing with it a kind of haze that greatly aided the project of the duke and duchess; and thus, as night began to fall, and a little after twilight set in, suddenly the whole wood on all four sides seemed to be on fire, and shortly after, here, there, on all sides, a vast number of trumpets and other military instruments were heard, as if several troops of cavalry were passing through the wood. The blaze of the fire and the noise of the warlike instruments almost blinded the eyes and deafened the ears of those that stood by, and indeed of all who were in the wood. Then there were heard repeated lelilies after the fashion of the Moors when they rush to battle; trumpets and clarions brayed, drums beat, fifes played, so unceasingly and so fast that he could not have had any senses who did not lose them with the confused din of so many instruments. The duke was astounded, the duchess amazed, Don Quixote wondering, Sancho Panza trembling, and indeed, even they who were aware of the cause were frightened. In their fear, silence fell upon them, and a postilion, in the guise of a demon, passed in front of them, blowing, in lieu of a bugle, a huge hollow horn that gave out a horrible hoarse note.

"Ho there! brother courier," cried the duke, "who are you? Where are you going? What

[1] Hernan Nuñez, a professor of Greek, made a collection of proverbs. He was Commander of the Order of Santiago, and hence commonly called the Greek Commander.

troops are these that seem to be passing through the wood?"

To which the courier replied in a harsh, discordant voice, "I am the devil; I am in search of Don Quixote of La Mancha; those who are coming this way are six troops of enchanters, who are bringing on a triumphal car the peerless Dulcinea del Toboso; she comes under enchantment, together with the gallant Frenchman Montesinos, to give instructions to Don Quixote as to how she, the said lady, may be disenchanted."

"If you were the devil, as you say and as your appearance indicates," said the duke, "you would have known the said knight Don Quixote of La Mancha, for you have him here before you."

"By God and upon my conscience," said the devil, "I never observed it, for my mind is occupied with so many different things that I was forgetting the main thing I came about."

"This demon must be an honest fellow and a good Christian," said Sancho; "for if he wasn't he wouldn't swear by God and his conscience; I feel sure now there must be good souls even in hell itself."

Without dismounting, the demon then turned to Don Quixote and said, "The unfortunate but valiant knight Montesinos sends me to thee, the Knight of the Lions (would that I saw thee in their claws), bidding me tell thee to wait for him wherever I may find thee, as he brings with him her whom they call Dulcinea del Toboso, that he may show thee what is needful in order to disenchant her; and as I came for no more I need stay no longer; demons of my sort be with thee, and good angels with these gentles"; and so saying he blew his huge horn, turned about and went off without waiting for a reply from any one.

They all felt fresh wonder, but particularly Sancho and Don Quixote; Sancho to see how, in defiance of the truth, they would have it that Dulcinea was enchanted; Don Quixote because he could not feel sure whether what had happened to him in the cave of Montesinos was true or not; and as he was deep in these cogitations the duke said to him, "Do you mean to wait, Señor Don Quixote?"

"Why not?" replied he; "here will I wait, fearless and firm, though all hell should come to attack me."

"Well, then, if I see another devil or hear another horn like the last, I'll wait here as much as in Flanders," said Sancho.

Night now closed in more completely, and many lights began to flit through the wood, just as those fiery exhalations from the earth, that look like shooting stars to our eyes, flit through the heavens; a frightful noise, too, was heard, like that made by the solid wheels the ox-carts usually have, by the harsh, ceaseless creaking of which, they say, the bears and wolves are put to flight, if there happen to be any where they are passing. In addition to all this commotion, there came a further disturbance to increase the tumult, for now it seemed as if in truth, on all four sides of the wood, four encounters or battles were going on at the same time; in one quarter resounded the dull noise of a terrible cannonade, in another numberless muskets were being discharged, the shouts of the combatants sounded almost close at hand, and farther away the Morrish lelilies were raised again and again. In a word, the bugles, the horns, the clarions, the trumpets, the drums, the cannon, the musketry, and above all the tremendous noise of the carts, all made up together a din so confused and terrific that Don Quixote had need to summon up all his courage to brave it; but Sancho's gave way, and he fell fainting on the skirt of the duchess's robe, who let him lie there and promptly bade them throw water in his face. This was done, and he came to himself by the time that one of the carts with the creaking wheels reached the spot. It was drawn by four plodding oxen all covered with black housings; on each horn they had fixed a large lighted wax taper, and on the top of the cart was constructed a raised seat, on which sat a venerable old man with a beard whiter than the very snow, and so long that it fell below his waist; he was dressed in a long robe of black buckram; for as the cart was thickly set with a multitude of candles it was easy to make out everything that was on it. Leading it were two hideous demons, also clad in buckram, with countenances so frightful that Sancho, having once seen them, shut his eyes so as not to see them again. As soon as the cart came opposite the spot the old man rose from his lofty seat, and standing up said in a loud voice, "I am the sage Lirgandeo," and without another word the cart then passed on.

Behind it came another of the same form, with another aged man enthroned, who, stopping the cart, said in a voice no less solemn than that of the first, "I am the sage Alquife, the great friend of Urganda the Unknown," and passed on. Then another cart came by at the same pace, but the occupant of the throne was not old like the others, but a man stalwart and robust, and of a forbidding countenance, who as he came up said in a voice far hoarser and more devilish, "I am the enchanter Archelaus, the mortal enemy of

Amadis of Gaul and all his kindred," and then passed on. Having gone a short distance the three carts halted and the monotonous noise of their wheels ceased, and soon after they heard another, not noise, but sound of sweet, harmonious music, of which Sancho was glad, taking it to be a good sign; and said he to the duchess, from whom he did not stir a step, for an instant, "Señora, where there's music there can't be mischief."

"Nor where there are lights and it's bright," said the duchess; to which Sancho replied, "Fire gives light, and it's bright where there are bonfires, as we see by those that are all around us, and perhaps may burn us; but music is a sign of mirth and merry-making."

"That remains to be seen," said Don Quixote, who was listening to all that passed; and he was right, as is shown in the following chapter.

Chapter 35
*Wherein is continued the instruction given to
Don Quixote touching the disenchantment
of Dulcinea, together with other
marvellous incidents*

THEY saw advancing towards them, to the sound of this pleasing music, what they call a triumphal car, drawn by six gray mules with white linen housings, on each of which was mounted a penitent, robed also in white, with a large lighted wax taper in his hand. The car was twice or, perhaps, three times as large as the former ones, and in front and on the sides stood twelve more penitents, all as white as snow and all with lighted tapers, a spectacle to excite fear as well as wonder; and on a raised throne was seated a nymph draped in a multitude of silver-tissue veils with an embroidery of countless gold spangles glittering all over them, that made her appear, if not richly, at least brilliantly, apparelled. She had her face covered with thin transparent sendal, the texture of which did not prevent the fair features of a maiden from being distinguished, while the numerous lights made it possible to judge of her beauty and of her years, which seemed to be not less than seventeen but not to have yet reached twenty. Beside her was a figure in a robe of state, as they call it, reaching to the feet, while the head was covered with a black veil. But the instant the car was opposite the duke and duchess and Don Quixote the music of the clarions ceased, and then that of the lutes and harps on the car, and the figure in the robe rose up, and flinging it apart and removing the veil from its face, disclosed to their eyes the shape of Death itself, fleshless and hideous, at which sight Don Quixote felt uneasy, Sancho frightened, and the duke and duchess displayed a certain trepidation. Having risen to its feet, this living death, in a sleepy voice and with a tongue hardly awake, held forth as follows:

*I am that Merlin who the legends say
The devil had for father, and the lie
Hath gathered credence with the lapse of time.
Of magic prince, of Zoroastric lore
Monarch and treasurer, with jealous eye
I view the efforts of the age to hide
The gallant deeds of doughty errant knights,
Who are, and ever have been, dear to me.
    Enchanters and magicians and their kind
Are mostly hard of heart; not so am I;
For mine is tender, soft, compassionate,
And its delight is doing good to all.
In the dim caverns of the gloomy Dis,
Where, tracing mystic lines and characters,
My soul abideth now, there came to me
The sorrow-laden plaint of her, the fair,
The peerless Dulcinea del Toboso.
I knew of her enchantment and her fate,
From high-born dame to peasant wench transformed;
And touched with pity, first I turned the leaves
Of countless volumes of my devilish craft,
And then, in this grim grisly skeleton
Myself incasing, hither have I come
To show where lies the fitting remedy
To give relief in such a piteous case.
    O thou, the pride and pink of all that wear
The adamantine steel! O shining light,
O beacon, polestar, path and guide of all
Who, scorning slumber and the lazy down,
Adopt the toilsome life of bloodstained arms!
To thee, great hero who all praise transcends,
La Mancha's lustre and Iberia's star,
Don Quixote, wise as brave, to thee I say—
For peerless Dulcinea del Toboso
Her pristine form and beauty to regain,
'Tis needful that thy esquire Sancho shall,
On his own sturdy buttocks bared to heaven,
Three thousand and three hundred lashes lay,
And they that smart and sting and hurt him well.
Thus have the authors of her woe resolved.
And this is, gentles, wherefore I have come.*

"By all that's good," exclaimed Sancho at this, "I'll just as soon give myself three stabs with a dagger as three, not to say three thousand, lashes. The devil take such a way of disenchanting! I don't see what my backside has got to do with enchantments. By God, if Señor Merlin has not found out some other way of disenchanting the lady Dulcinea del Toboso, she may go to her grave enchanted."

"But I'll take you, Don Clown stuffed with garlic," said Don Quixote, "and tie you to a tree as naked as when your mother brought you forth, and give you, not to say three thousand three hundred, but six thousand six hundred lashes, and so well laid on that they won't be got rid of if you try three thousand three hundred times; don't answer me a word or I'll tear your soul out."

On hearing this Merlin said, "That will not do, for the lashes worthy Sancho has to receive must be given of his own free will and not by force, and at whatever time he pleases, for there is no fixed limit assigned to him; but it is permitted him, if he likes to commute by half the pain of this whipping, to let them be given by the hand of another, though it may be somewhat weighty."

"Not a hand, my own or anybody else's, weighty or weighable, shall touch me," said Sancho. "Was it I that gave birth to the lady Dulcinea del Toboso, that my backside is to pay for the sins of her eyes? My master, indeed, that's a part of her—for he's always calling her 'my life' and 'my soul,' and his stay and prop—may and ought to whip himself for her and take all the trouble required for her disenchantment. But for me to whip myself! *Abernuncio!*"

As soon as Sancho had done speaking the nymph in silver that was at the side of Merlin's ghost stood up, and removing the thin veil from her face disclosed one that seemed to all something more than exceedingly beautiful; and with a masculine freedom from embarrassment and in a voice not very like a lady's, addressing Sancho directly, said, "Thou wretched squire, soul of a pitcher, heart of a cork tree, with bowels of flint and pebbles; if, thou impudent thief, they bade thee throw thyself down from some lofty tower; if, enemy of mankind, they asked thee to swallow a dozen of toads, two of lizards, and three of adders; if they wanted thee to slay thy wife and children with a sharp murderous cimeter, it would be no wonder for thee to show thyself stubborn and squeamish. But to make a piece of work about three thousand three hundred lashes, what every poor little charity-boy gets every month—it is enough to amaze, astonish, astound the compassionate bowels of all who hear it, nay, all who come to hear it in the course of time. Turn, O miserable, hard-hearted animal, turn, I say, those timorous owl's eyes upon these of mine that are compared to radiant stars, and thou wilt see them weeping trickling streams and rills, and tracing furrows, tracks, and paths over the fair fields of my cheeks. Let it move thee, crafty, ill-conditioned monster, to see my blooming youth—still in its teens, for I am not yet twenty—wasting and withering away beneath the husk of a rude peasant wench; and if I do not appear in that shape now, it is a special favor Señor Merlin here has granted me, to the sole end that my beauty may soften thee; for the tears of beauty in distress turn rocks into cotton and tigers into ewes. Lay on to that hide of thine, thou great untamed brute, rouse up thy lusty vigor that only urges thee to eat and eat, and set free the softness of my flesh, the gentleness of my nature, and the fairness of my face. And if thou wilt not relent or come to reason for me, do so for the sake of that poor knight thou hast beside thee; thy master I mean, whose soul I can this moment see, how he has it stuck in his throat not ten fingers from his lips, and only waiting for thy inflexible or yielding reply to make its escape by his mouth or go back again into his stomach."

Don Quixote on hearing this felt his throat, and turning to the duke he said, "By God, señor, Dulcinea says true, I have my soul stuck here in my throat like the nut of a crossbow."

"What say you to this, Sancho?" said the duchess.

"I say, señora," returned Sancho, "what I said before; as for the lashes, *abernuncio!*"

"*Abrenuncio,* you should say, Sancho, and not as you do," said the duke.

"Let me alone, your highness," said Sancho. "I'm not in a humor now to look into niceties or a letter more or less, for these lashes that are to be given me, or I'm to give myself, have so upset me, that I don't know what I'm saying or doing. But I'd like to know of this lady, my lady Dulcinea del Toboso, where she learned this way she has of asking favors. She comes to ask me to score my flesh with lashes, and she calls me soul of a pitcher, and great untamed brute, and a string of foul names that the devil is welcome to. Is my flesh brass? or is it anything to me whether she is enchanted or not? Does she bring with her a basket of fair linen, shirts, kerchiefs, socks—not that I wear any—to coax me? No, nothing but one piece of abuse after another, though she knows the proverb they have here that 'an ass loaded with gold goes lightly up a mountain,' and that 'gifts break rocks,' and 'praying to God and plying the hammer,' and that 'one "take" is better than two "I'll give thee's."' Then there's my master, who ought to stroke me down and pet me to make me turn wool and carded cotton; he says if he gets hold of me he'll tie me naked to a tree and double the tale of lashes on me. These tender-hearted gentry should consider that it's not merely a squire, but a governor they are asking to whip himself; just as if it was 'drink with cherries.' Let them learn, plague take them, the right way to ask, and beg, and behave themselves; for all times are not alike, nor are people always in good humor. I'm just now ready to burst with grief at seeing my green coat torn, and they come to ask me to whip myself of my own free will, I having as little fancy for it as for turning cacique."

"Well then, the fact is, friend Sancho," said the duke, "that unless you become softer than a ripe fig, you shall not get hold of the government. It would be a nice thing for me to send my islanders a cruel governor with flinty bowels, who won't yield to the tears of afflicted damsels or to the prayers of wise, magisterial, ancient enchanters and sages. In short, Sancho, either you must be whipped by yourself, or they must whip you, or you shan't be governor."

"Señor," said Sancho, "won't two days' grace be given me to consider what is best for me?"

"No, certainly not," said Merlin; "here, this minute, and on the spot, the matter must be settled; either Dulcinea will return to the cave of Montesinos and to her former condition of peasant wench, or else in her present form shall be carried to the Elysian fields, where she will remain waiting until the number of stripes is completed."

"Now then, Sancho!" said the duchess, "show courage, and gratitude for your master Don Quixote's bread that you have eaten; we are all bound to oblige and please him for his benevolent disposition and lofty chivalry. Consent to this whipping, my son; to the devil with the devil, and leave fear to milksops, for 'a stout heart breaks bad luck,' as you very well know."

To this Sancho replied with an irrelevant remark, which, addressing Merlin, he made to him, "Will your worship tell me, Señor Merlin, —when that courier devil came up he gave my master a message from Señor Montesinos, charging him to wait for him here, as he was coming to arrange how the lady Doña Dulcinea del Toboso was to be disenchanted; but up to the present we have not seen Montesinos, nor anything like him."

To which Merlin made answer, "The devil, friend Sancho, is a blockhead and a great scoundrel; I sent him to look for your master, but not with a message from Montesinos but from myself; for Montesinos is in his cave expecting, or, more properly speaking, waiting for his disenchantment; for there's the tail to be skinned yet for him; if he owes you anything, or you have

any business to transact with him, I'll bring him to you and put him where you choose; but for the present make up your mind to consent to this penance, and believe me it will be very good for you, for soul as well as for body—for your soul because of the charity with which you perform it, for your body because I know that you are of a sanguine habit and it will do you no harm to draw a little blood."

"There are a great many doctors in the world; even the enchanters are doctors," said Sancho; "however, as everybody tells me the same thing —though I can't see it myself—I say I am willing to give myself the three thousand three hundred lashes, provided I am to lay them on whenever I like, without any fixing of days or times; and I'll try and get out of debt as quickly as I can, that the world may enjoy the beauty of the lady Dulcinea del Toboso; as it seems, contrary to what I thought, that she is beautiful after all. It must be a condition, too, that I am not to be bound to draw blood with the scourge, and that if any of the lashes happen to be flyflappers they are to count. Item, that, in case I should make any mistake in the reckoning, Señor Merlin, as he knows everything, is to keep count, and let me know how many are still wanting or over the number."

"There will be no need to let you know of any over," said Merlin, "because, when you reach the full number, the lady Dulcinea will at once, and that very instant, be disenchanted, and will come in her gratitude to seek out the worthy Sancho, and thank him, and even reward him for the good work. So you have no cause to be uneasy about stripes too many or too few; heaven forbid I should cheat any one of even a hair of his head."

"Well then, in God's hands be it," said Sancho; "in the hard case I'm in I give in; I say I accept the penance on the conditions laid down."

The instant Sancho uttered these last words the music of the clarions struck up once more, and again a host of muskets were discharged, and Don Quixote hung on Sancho's neck kissing him again and again on the forehead and cheeks. The duchess and the duke and all who stood by expressed the greatest satisfaction, the car began to move on, and as it passed the fair Dulcinea bowed to the duke and duchess and made a low courtesy to Sancho.

And now bright smiling dawn came on apace; the flowers of the field, revived, raised up their heads, and the crystal waters of the brooks, murmuring over the gray and white pebbles, hastened to pay their tribute to the expectant rivers; the glad earth, the unclouded sky, the fresh breeze, the clear light, each and all showed that the day that came treading on the skirts of morning would be calm and bright. The duke and duchess, pleased with their hunt and at having carried out their plans so cleverly and successfully, returned to their castle resolved to follow up their joke; for to them there was no reality that could afford them more amusement.

Chapter 36

Wherein is related the strange and undreamt-of adventure of the Distressed Duenna, alias the Countess Trifaldi, together with a letter which Sancho Panza wrote to his wife, Teresa Panza

THE duke had a majordomo of a very facetious and sportive turn, and he it was that played the part of Merlin, made all the arrangements for the late adventure, composed the verses, and got a page to represent Dulcinea; and now, with the assistance of his master and mistress, he got up another of the drollest and strangest contrivance that can be imagined.

The duchess asked Sancho the next day if he had made a beginning with his penance task which he had to perform for the disenchantment of Dulcinea. He said he had, and had given himself five lashes overnight.

The duchess asked him what he had given them with.

He said with his hand.

"That," said the duchess, "is more like giving one's self slaps than lashes; I am sure the sage Merlin will not be satisfied with such tenderness; worthy Sancho must make a scourge with claws, or a cat-o'-nine tails, that will make itself felt; for it's with blood that letters enter, and the release of so great a lady as Dulcinea will not be granted so cheaply, or at such a paltry price; and remember, Sancho, that works of charity done in a lukewarm and half-hearted way are without merit and of no avail."

To which Sancho replied, "If your ladyship will give me a proper scourge or cord, I'll lay on with it, provided it does not hurt too much; for you must know, boor as I am, my flesh is more cotton than hemp, and it won't do for me to destroy myself for the good of anybody else."

"So be it by all means," said the duchess; "to-morrow I'll give you a scourge that will be just the thing for you, and will accommodate itself to the tenderness of your flesh, as if it was its own sister."

Then said Sancho, "Your highness must know, dear lady of my soul, that I have a letter written to my wife, Teresa Panza, giving her an account of all that has happened me since I left her; I have it here in my bosom, and there's nothing wanting but to put the address to it; I'd be glad if your discretion would read it, for I think it runs in the governor style; I mean the way governors ought to write."

"And who dictated it?" asked the duchess.

"Who should have dictated but myself, sinner as I am?" said Sancho.

"And did you write it yourself?" said the duchess.

"That I didn't," said Sancho; "for I can neither read nor write, though I can sign my name."

"Let us see it," said the duchess, "for never fear but you display in it the quality and quantity of your wit."

Sancho drew out an open letter from his bosom, and the duchess taking it, found it ran in this fashion:

SANCHO PANZA'S LETTER TO HIS WIFE, TERESA PANZA.

If I was well whipped I went mounted like a gentleman; if I have got a good government it is at the cost of a good whipping. Thou wilt not understand this just now, my Teresa; by-and-by thou wilt know what it means. I may tell thee, Teresa, I mean thee to go in a coach, for that is a matter of importance, because every other way of going is going on all-fours. Thou art a governor's wife; take care that nobody speaks evil of thee behind thy back. I send thee here a green hunting suit that my lady the duchess gave me; alter it so as to make a petticoat and bodice for our daughter. Don Quixote, my master, if I am to believe what I hear in these parts, is a madman of some sense, and a droll blockhead, and I am no way behind him. We have been in the cave of Montesinos, and the sage Merlin has laid hold of me for the disenchantment of Dulcinea del Toboso, her that is called Aldonza Lorenzo over there. With three thousand three hundred lashes, less five, that I'm to give myself, she will be left as entirely disenchanted as the mother that bore her. Say nothing of this to any one; for, make thy affairs public, and some will say they are white and others will say they are black. I shall leave this in a few days for my government, to which I am going with a mighty great desire to make money, for they tell me all new governors set out with the same desire; I will feel the pulse of it and will let thee know if thou art to come and live with me or not. Dapple is well and sends many remembrances to thee; I am not going to leave him behind though they took me away to be Grand Turk. My lady the duchess kisses thy hands a thousand times; do thou make a return with two thousand, for, as my master says, nothing costs less or is cheaper than civility. God has not been pleased to provide another valise for me with another hundred crowns, like the one the other day; but never mind, my Teresa, the bell-ringer is in safe quarters, and all will come out in the scouring of the government; only it troubles me greatly what they tell me,—that once I have tried it I will eat my hands off after it; and if that is so it will not come very cheap to me; though to be sure the maimed have a benefice of their own in the alms they beg for; so that one way or another thou wilt be rich and in luck. God give it to thee as he can, and keep me to serve thee. From this castle, the 20th of July, 1614.

Thy husband, the governor,
SANCHO PANZA.

When she had done reading the letter the duchess said to Sancho, "On two points the worthy governor goes rather astray; one is in saying or hinting that this government has been bestowed upon him for the lashes that he is to give himself, when he knows (and he can not deny it) that when my lord the duke promised it to him nobody ever dreamt of such a thing as lashes; the other is that he shows himself here to be very covetous; and I would not have him a money-seeker, for 'covetousness bursts the bag,' and the covetous governor does ungoverned justice."

"I don't mean it that way, señora," said Sancho; "and if you think the letter doesn't run as it ought to do, it's only to tear it up and make another; and maybe it will be a worse one if it is left to my gumption."

"No, no," said the duchess, "this one will do, and I wish the duke to see it."

With this they betook themselves to a garden where they were to dine, and the duchess showed Sancho's letter to the duke, who was highly delighted with it. They dined, and after the cloth had been removed and they had amused themselves for a while with Sancho's rich conversation, the melancholy sound of a fife and harsh discordant drum made itself heard. All seemed somewhat put out by this dull, confused, martial harmony, especially Don Quixote, who could not keep his seat from pure disquietude; as to Sancho, it is needless to say that fear drove him to his usual refuge, the side or the skirts of the duchess; and indeed and in truth the sound they heard was a most doleful and melancholy one. While they were still in uncertainty they saw advancing towards them through the garden two men clad in mourning robes so long and flowing that they trailed upon the ground. As they marched they beat two great drums which were likewise draped in black, and beside them came the fife player, black and sombre like the others. Following these there came a personage of gigantic stature enveloped rather than clad in a gown of the deepest black, the skirt of which was of prodigious dimensions. Over the gown, girdling or crossing his figure, he had a broad baldric which was also black, and from which hung a huge cimeter with a black scabbard and furniture. He had his face covered with a transparent black veil, through which might be descried a very long beard as white as snow.

He came on keeping step to the sound of the drums with great gravity and dignity; and, in short, his stature, his gait, the sombreness of his appearance and his following might well have struck with astonishment, as they did, all who beheld him without knowing who he was. With this measured pace and in this guise he advanced to kneel before the duke, who, with the others, awaited him standing. The duke, however, would not on any account allow him to speak until he had risen. The terrific object obeyed, and standing up, removed the veil from his face and disclosed the most enormous, the longest, the whitest and the thickest beard that human eyes had ever beheld until that moment, and then fetching up a grave, sonorous voice from the depths of his broad, capacious chest, and fixing his eyes on the duke, he said, "Most high and mighty señor, my name is Trifaldin of the White Beard; I am squire to the Countess Trifaldi, otherwise called the Distressed Duenna, on whose behalf I bear a message to your highness, which is that your magnificence will be pleased to grant her leave and permission to come and tell you her trouble, which is one of the strangest and most wonderful that the mind most familiar with trouble in the world could have imagined; but first she desires to know if the valiant and never vanquished knight, Don Quixote of La Mancha, is in this your castle, for she has come in quest of him on foot and without breaking her fast from the kingdom of Kandy to your realms here; a thing which may and ought to be regarded as a miracle or set down to enchantment; she is even now at the gate of this fortress or plaisance, and only waits for your permission to enter. I have spoken." And with that he coughed and stroked down his beard with both his hands, and stood very tranquilly waiting for the response of the duke, which was to this effect: "Many days ago, worthy squire Trifaldin of the White Beard, we heard of the misfortune of my lady the

Countess of Trifaldi, whom the enchanters have caused to be called the Distressed Duenna. Bid her enter, O stupendous squire, and tell her that the valiant knight Don Quixote of La Mancha is here, and from his generous disposition she may safely promise herself every protection and assistance; and you may tell her, too, that if my aid be necessary it will not be withheld, for I am bound to give it to her by my quality of knight, which involves the protection of women of all sorts, especially widowed, wronged, and distressed dames, such as her ladyship seems to be."

On hearing this Trifaldin bent the knee to the ground, and making a sign to the fifer and drummers to strike up, he turned and marched out of the garden to the same notes and at the same pace as when he entered, leaving them all amazed at his bearing and solemnity. Turning to Don Quixote, the duke said, "After all, renowned knight, the mists of malice and ignorance are unable to hide or obscure the light of valor and virtue. I say so, because your excellence has been barely six days in this castle, and already the unhappy and the afflicted come in quest of you from lands far distant and remote, and not in coaches or on dromedaries, but on foot and fasting, confident that in that mighty arm they will find a cure for their sorrows and troubles; thanks to your great achievements, which are circulated all over the known earth."

"I wish, señor duke," replied Don Quixote, "that blessed ecclesiastic, who at table the other day showed such ill-will and bitter spite against knights-errant, were here now to see with his own eyes whether knights of the sort are needed in the world; he would at any rate learn by experience that those suffering any extraordinary affliction or sorrow, in extreme cases and unusual misfortunes do not go to look for a remedy to the houses of jurists or village sacristans, or to the knight who has never attempted to pass the bounds of his own town, or to the indolent courtier who only seeks for news to repeat and talk of, instead of striving to do deeds and exploits for others to relate and record. Relief in distress, help in need, protection for damsels, consolation for widows, are to be found in no sort of persons better than in knights-errant; and I give unceasing thanks to Heaven that I am one, and regard any misfortune or suffering that may befall me in the pursuit of so honorable a calling as endured to good purpose. Let this duenna come and ask what she will, for I will effect her relief by the might of my

arm and the dauntless resolution of my bold heart."

Chapter 37

Wherein is continued the notable adventure of the Distressed Duenna

THE duke and duchess were extremely glad to see how readily Don Quixote fell in with their scheme; but at this moment Sancho observed, "I hope this señora duenna won't be putting any difficulties in the way of the promise of my government; for I have heard a Toledo apothecary, who talked like a goldfinch, say that where duennas were mixed up nothing good could happen. God bless me, how he hated them, that same apothecary! And so what I'm thinking is, if all duennas, of whatever sort or condition they may be, are plagues and busybodies, what must they be that are distressed, like this Countess Three-skirts or Three-tails! —for in my country skirts or tails, tails or skirts, it's all one."

"Hush, friend Sancho," said Don Quixote; "since this lady duenna comes in quest of me from such a distant land she can not be one of those the apothecary meant; moreover this is a countess, and when countesses serve as duennas it is in the service of queens and empresses, for in their own houses they are mistresses paramount and have other duennas to wait on them."

To this Doña Rodriguez, who was present, made answer, "My lady the duchess has duennas in her service that might be countesses if it was the will of fortune; 'but laws go as kings like'; let nobody speak ill of duennas, above all of ancient maiden ones; for though I am not one myself, I know and am aware of the advantage a maiden duenna has over one that is a widow; but 'he who clipped us has kept the scissors.'"

"For all that," said Sancho, "there's so much to be clipped about duennas, so my barber said, that 'it will be better not to stir the rice even though it sticks.'"

"These squires," returned Doña Rodriguez, "are alway our enemies; and as they are the haunting spirits of the antechambers and watch us at every step, whenever they are not saying their prayers (and that's often enough) they spend their time in tattling about us, digging up our bones and burying our good name. But I can tell these walking blocks that we will live in spite of them, and in great houses too, though we die of hunger and cover our flesh, be it delicate or not, with widow's weeds, as one covers or hides a dunghill on a procession day. By my faith, if it were permitted me and time allowed, I could prove, not only to those here present, but to all the world, that there is no virtue that is not to be found in a duenna."

"I have no doubt," said the duchess, "that my good Doña Rodriguez is right, and very much so; but she had better bide her time for fighting her own battle and that of the rest of the duennas, so as to crush the calumny of that vile apothecary, and root out the prejudice in the great Sancho Panza's mind."

To which Sancho replied, "Ever since I have sniffed the governorship I have got rid of the humors of a squire, and I don't care a wild fig for all the duennas in the world."

They would have carried on this duenna dispute further had they not heard the notes of the fife and drums once more, from which they concluded that the Distressed Duenna was making her entrance. The duchess asked the duke if it would be proper to go out to receive her, as she was a countess and a person of rank.

"In respect of her being a countess," said Sancho, before the duke could reply, "I am for your highnesses going out to receive her; but in respect of her being a duenna, it is my opinion you should not stir a step."

"Who bade thee meddle in this, Sancho?" said Don Quixote.

"Who, señor?" said Sancho; "I meddle for I have a right to meddle, as a squire who has learned the rules of courtesy in the school of your worship, the most courteous and best bred knight in the whole world of courtliness; and in these things, as I have heard your worship say, as much is lost by a card too many as by a card too few, and to one who has his ears open, few words."

"Sancho is right," said the duke; "we'll see what the countess is like, and by that measure the courtesy that is due to her."

And now the drums and fife made their entrance as before; and here the author brought this short chapter to an end and began the next, following up the same adventure, which is one of the most notable in the history.

Chapter 38

Wherein is told the Distressed Duenna's tale of her misfortunes

FOLLOWING the melancholy musicians there filed into the garden as many as twelve duennas, in two lines, all dressed in ample mourning robes apparently of milled serge, with hoods of fine white gauze so long that they allowed only the border of the robe to be seen. Behind them came the Countess Trifaldi, the squire Trifaldin of the White Beard leading her by the hand, clad in the finest unnapped black baize, such that, had it a nap, every tuft would have shown as big as a Martos chick-pea; the tail, or skirt, or whatever it might be called, ended in three points which were borne up by the hands of three pages, likewise dressed in mourning, forming an elegant geometrical figure with the three acute angles made by the three points, from which all who saw the peaked skirt concluded that it must be because of it the countess was called Trifaldi, as though it were Countess of the Three Skirts; and Benengeli says it was so, and that by her right name she was called the Countess Lobuna, because wolves bred in great numbers in her country; and if, instead of wolves, they had been foxes, she would have been called the Countess Zorruna, as it was the custom in those parts for lords to take distinctive titles from the thing or things most abundant in their dominions; this countess, however, in honor of the new fashion of her skirt, dropped Lobuna and took up Trifaldi.

The twelve duennas and the lady came on at procession pace, their faces being covered with black veils, not transparent ones like Trifaldin's, but so close that they allowed nothing to be seen through them. As soon as the band of duennas was fully in sight, the duke, the duchess, and Don Quixote stood up, as well as all who were watching the slow-moving procession. The twelve duennas halted and formed a lane, along which the Distressed One advanced, Trifaldin still holding her hand. On seeing this the duke, the duchess, and Don Quixote went some twelve paces forward to meet her. She then, kneeling on the ground, said in a voice hoarse and rough, rather than fine and delicate, "May it please your highnesses not to offer such courtesies to this your servant, I should say to this your handmaid, for I am in such distress that I shall never be able to make a proper return, because my strange and unparalleled misfortune has carried off my wits, and I know not whither; but it must be a long way off, for the more I look for them the less I find them."

"He would be wanting in wits, señora countess," said the duke, "who did not perceive your worth by your person, for at a glance it may be seen it deserves all the cream of courtesy and flower of polite usage"; and raising her up by the hand he led her to a seat beside the duchess, who likewise received her with great urbanity. Don Quixote remained silent, while Sancho was dying to see the features of Trifaldi and one or two of her many duennas; but there was no possibility of it until they themselves displayed them of their own accord and free will.

All kept still, waiting to see who would break silence, which the Distressed Duenna did in these words: "I am confident, most mighty lord, most fair lady, and most discreet company, that my most miserable misery will be accorded a reception no less dispassionate than generous and condolent in your most valiant bosoms, for it is one that is enough to melt marble, soften diamonds, and mollify the steel of the most hardened hearts in the world; but ere it is proclaimed to your hearing, not to say your ears, I would fain be enlightened whether there be present in this society, circle, or company, that knight immaculatissimus, Don Quixote de la Manchissima, and his squirissimus Panza."

"The Panza is here," said Sancho, before any one could reply, "and Don Quixotissimus too; and so, most distressedest Duenissima, you may say what you willissimus, for we are all readissimus to do you any servissimus."

On this Don Quixote rose, and addressing the Distressed Duenna, said, "If your sorrows, afflicted lady, can indulge in any hope of relief from the valor or might of any knight-errant, here are mine, which, feeble and limited though they be, shall be entirely devoted to your service. I am Don Quixote of La Mancha, whose calling it is to give aid to the needy of all sorts; and that being so, it is not necessary for you, señora, to make any appeal to benevolence, or deal in preambles, only to tell your woes plainly and straightforwardly: for you have hearers that will know how, if not to remedy them, to sympathize with them."

On hearing this, the Distressed Duenna made as though she would throw herself at Don Quixote's feet, and actually did fall before them and said, as she strove to embrace them, "Before these feet and legs I cast myself, O unconquered knight, as before, what they are, the foundations and pillars of knight-errantry; these feet I desire to kiss, for upon their steps hangs and depends the sole remedy for my misfortune, O valorous errant, whose veritable achievements leave behind and eclipse the fabulous ones of the Amadises, Esplandians, and Belianises!" Then turning from Don Quixote to Sancho Panza, and grasping his hands, she said, "O thou, most loyal squire that ever served knight-errant in this present age or ages past, whose goodness is more extensive than the beard of Trifaldin my companion here present, well mayest thou boast thyself that, in serving the great Don Quixote, thou art serving, summed up in one, the whole host of knights that have ever borne arms in the world. I conjure thee, by what thou owest to thy most loyal goodness, that thou wilt become my kind intercessor with thy master, that he speedily give aid to this most humble and most unfortunate countess."

To this Sancho made answer, "As to my goodness, señora, being as long and as great as your squire's beard, it matters very little to me; may I have my soul well bearded and mustached when it comes to quit this life, that's the point; about beards here below I care little or nothing; but without all these blandishments and prayers, I will beg my master (for I know he loves me, and, besides, he has need of me just now for a certain business) to help and aid your worship as far as he can; unpack your woes and lay them before us, and leave us to deal with them, for we'll be all of one mind."

The duke and duchess, as it was they who had made the experiment of this adventure, were ready to burst with laughter at all this, and between themselves they commended the clever acting of the Trifaldi, who, returning to her seat, said, "Queen Doña Maguncia reigned over the famous kingdom of Kandy, which lies between the great Trapobana and the Southern Sea, two leagues beyond Cape Comorin. She was the widow of King Archipiela, her lord and husband, and of their marriage they had issue the Princess Antonomasia, heiress of the kingdom; which Princess Antonomasia was reared and brought up under my care and direction, I being the oldest and highest in rank of her mother's duennas. Time passed, and the young Antonomasia reached the age of fourteen, and such a perfection of beauty, that nature could not raise it higher. Then, it must not be supposed her intelligence was childish; she was as intelligent as she was fair, and she was fairer than all the world; and is so still, unless the envious fates and hard-hearted sisters three have cut for her the thread of life. But that they have not, for Heaven will not suffer so great a wrong to Earth, as it would be to pluck unripe the grapes of the fairest vineyard on its surface. Of this beauty, to which my poor feeble tongue has failed to do justice, countless princes, not only of that country, but of others, were enamoured, and among them a private gentleman, who was at the court, dared to raise his thoughts to the heaven of so great beauty, trusting to his youth, his gallant bearing, his numerous accomplishments and graces, and his quickness and readiness of wit; for I may tell your highness, if I am not wearying you, that he played the guitar so as to make it speak, and he was, besides, a poet and a great dancer, and he could make bird-cages so well, that by making them alone he might have gained a livelihood, had he found himself reduced to utter poverty; and gifts and graces of this kind are enough to bring down a mountain, not to say a tender young girl. But all his gallantry, wit, and gayety, all his graces and accomplishments, would have been of little or no avail towards gaining the fortress of my pupil, had not the impudent thief taken the precaution of gaining me over first. First, the villain and heartless vagabond sought to win my good-will and purchase my compliance, so as to get me, like a treacherous warder, to deliver up to him the keys of the fortress I had in charge. In a word, he gained an influence over my mind, and overcame my resolutions with I know not what trinkets and jewels he gave me; but it was some verses I heard him singing one night from a grating that opened on the street where he lived, that, more than anything else, made me give way and led to my fall; and if I remember rightly they ran thus:

> From that sweet enemy of mine
> My bleeding heart hath had its wound:
> And to increase the pain I'm bound
> To suffer and to make no sign.

The lines seemed pearls to me and his voice sweet as sirup; and afterwards, I may say ever since then, looking at the misfortune into which I have fallen, I have thought that poets, as Plato advised, ought to be banished from all well-ordered States; at least the amatory ones, for they write verses, not like those of *The Marquis of Mantua*, that delight and draw tears from the women and children, but sharp-pointed conceits that pierce the heart like soft thorns, and like the lightning strike it, leaving the raiment uninjured. Another time he sang:

> Come Death, so subtly veiled that I
> Thy coming know not, how or when,
> Lest it should give me life again
> To find how sweet it is to die.

—and other verses and burdens of the same sort, such as enchant when sung and fascinate when written. And then, when they condescend to compose a sort of verse that was at that time in vogue in Kandy, which they call *seguidillas!* Then it is that hearts leap and laughter breaks forth, and the body grows restless and all the senses turn quicksilver. And so I say, sirs, that these troubadours richly deserve to be banished to the isles of the lizards. Though it is not they that are in fault, but the simpletons that extol them, and the fools that believe in them; and had I been the faithful duenna I should have been, his stale conceits would have never moved me, nor should I have been taken in by such phrases as 'in death I live,' 'in ice I burn,' 'in flames I shiver,' 'hopeless I hope,' 'I go and stay,' and paradoxes of that sort which their writings are full of. And then when they promise the Phœnix of Arabia, the crown of Ariadne, the horses of the Sun, the pearls of the South, the gold of Tibar, and the balsam of Panchaia! Then it is they give a loose to their pens, for it costs them little to make promises they have no intention or power of fulfilling. But where am I wandering to? Woe is me, unfortunate being! What madness or folly leads me to speak of the faults of others, when there is so much to be said about my own? Again, woe is me, hapless that I am! it was not verses that conquered me, but my own simplicity; it was not music made me yield, but my own imprudence; my own great ignorance and little caution opened the way and cleared the path for Don Clavijo's advances, for that was the name of the gentleman I have referred to; and so, with my help as go-between, he found his way many a time into the chamber of the deceived Antonomasia (deceived not by him but by me) under the title of a lawful husband; for, sinner though I was, I would not have allowed him to approach the edge of her shoe-sole without being her husband. No, no, not that; marriage must come first in any business of this sort that I take in hand. But there was one hitch in this case, which was that of inequality of rank, Don Clavijo being a private gentleman, and the Princess Antonomasia, as I said, heiress to the kingdom. The entanglement remained for some time a secret, kept hidden by my cunning precautions, until I perceived that a certain expansion of waist in Antonomasia must before long disclose it, the dread of which made us all three take counsel together, and it was agreed that before the mischief came to light, Don Clavijo should demand Antonomasia as his wife before the Vicar, in virtue of an agreement to marry him made by the princess, and draughted by my wit in such binding terms that the might of Samson could not have broken it. The necessary steps were taken; the Vicar saw the agreement, and took the lady's confession; she confessed every thing in full, and he ordered her into the custody of a very worthy *alguacil* of the Court."

"Are there *alguacils* of the Court in Kandy, too," said Sancho at this, "and poets, and *seguidillas?* I swear I think the world is the same all over! But make haste, Señora Trifaldi; for it is late, and I am dying to know the end of this long story."

"I will," replied the countess.

Chapter 39

In which the Trifaldi continues her marvellous and memorable story

By every word that Sancho uttered, the duchess was as much delighted as Don Quixote was driven to desperation. He bade him hold his tongue, and the Distressed One went on to say: "At length, after much questioning and answering, as the princess held to her story, without changing or varying her previous declaration, the Vicar gave his decision in favor of Don Clavijo, and she was delivered over to him as his lawful wife; which the queen Doña Maguncia, the princess Antonomasia's mother, so took to heart, that within the space of three days we buried her."

"She died, no doubt," said Sancho.

"Of course," said Trifaldin; "they don't bury living people in Kandy, only the dead."

"Señor Squire," said Sancho, "a man in a swoon has been known to be buried before now, in the belief that he was dead; and it struck me that queen Maguncia ought to have swooned rather than died; because with life a great many things come right, and the princess's folly was not so great that she need feel it so keenly. If the lady had married some page of hers, or some other servant of the house, as many another has done, so I have heard say, then the mischief would have been past curing. But to marry such an elegant accomplished gentleman as has been just now described to us—indeed, indeed, though it was a folly, it was not such a great one as you think; for according to the rules of my master here—and he won't allow me to lie—as of men of letters bishops are made, so of gentlemen knights, specially if they be errant, kings and emperors may be made."

"Thou art right, Sancho," said Don Quixote, "for with a knight-errant, if he has but two fingers' breadth of good fortune, it is on the cards to become the mightiest lord on earth. But let the distressed señora proceed; for I suspect she has got yet to tell us the bitter part of this so far sweet story."

"The bitter is indeed to come," said the countess; "and such bitter that colocynth is sweet and oleander toothsome in comparison. The queen, then, being dead, and not in a swoon, we buried her; and hardly had we covered her with earth, hardly had we said our last farewells, when, *quis talia fando temperet a lachrymis?* over the queen's grave there appeared, mounted upon a wooden horse, the giant Malambruno, Maguncia's first cousin, who besides being cruel is an enchanter; and he, to revenge the death of his cousin, punish the audacity of Don Clavijo, and in wrath at the contumacy of Antonomasia, left them both enchanted by his art on the grave itself; she being changed into an ape of brass, and he into a horrible crocodile of some unknown metal; while between the two there stands a pillar, also of metal, with certain characters in the Syriac language inscribed upon it, which, being translated into Kandian, and now into Castilian, contain the following sentence: *These two rash lovers shall not recover their former shape until the valiant Manchegan comes to do battle with me in single combat; for the Fates reserve this unexampled adventure for his mighty valor alone.* This done, he drew from its sheath a huge broad cimeter, and seizing me by the hair he made as though he meant to cut my throat and shear my head clean off. I was terror-stricken, my voice stuck in my throat, and I was in the deepest distress; nevertheless I summoned up my strength as well as I could, and in a trembling and piteous voice I addressed such words to him as induced him to stay the infliction of a punishment so severe. He then caused all the duennas of the palace, those that are here present, to be brought before him; and after having dwelt upon the enormity of our offence, and denounced duennas, their characters, their evil ways and worse intrigues, laying to the charge of all what I alone was guilty of, he said he would not visit us with capital punishment, but with others of a slow nature which would be in effect civil death forever; and the very instant he ceased speaking we all felt the pores of our faces opening, and pricking us, as if with the points of needles. We at once put our hands up to our faces and found ourselves in the state you now see."

Here the Distressed One and the other duennas raised the veils with which they were covered, and disclosed countenances all bristling with beards, some red, some black, some white, and some grizzled, at which spectacle the duke and duchess made a show of being filled with wonder. Don Quixote and Sancho were overwhelmed with amazement, and the bystanders lost in astonishment, while the Trifaldi went on to say: "Thus did that malevolent villain Malambruno punish us, covering the tenderness and softness of our faces with these rough bristles! Would to Heaven that he had swept off our heads with his enormous cimeter instead of obscuring the light of our countenances with these wool-combings that cover us! For if we look into the matter, sirs (and what I am now going to say I would say with eyes flowing like fountains, only that the thought of our misfortune and the oceans they have already wept, keep them as dry as barley spears, and so I say it without tears), where, I ask, can a duenna with a beard go to? What father or mother will feel pity for her? Who will help her? For, if even when she has a smooth skin, and a face tortured by a thousand kinds of washes and cosmetics, she can hardly get anybody to love her, what will she do when she shows a countenance turned into a thicket? Oh duennas, companions mine! it was an unlucky moment when we were born, and an ill-starred hour when our fathers begot us!" And as she said this she showed signs of being about to faint.

Chapter 40

Of matters relating and belonging to this adventure and to this memorable history

VERILY and truly all those who find pleasure in histories like this ought to show their gratitude to Cid Hamet, its original author, for the scrupulous care he has taken to set before us all its minute particulars, not leaving anything, however trifling it may be, that he does not make clear and plain. He portrays the thoughts, he reveals the fancies, he answers implied questions, clears up doubts, sets objections at rest, and, in a word, makes plain the smallest points the most inquisitive can desire to know. O renowned author! O happy Don Quixote! O famous Dulcinea! O droll Sancho Panza! All and each, may ye live countless ages for the delight and amusement of the dwellers on earth!

The history goes on to say that when Sancho saw the Distressed One faint he exclaimed: "I swear by the faith of an honest man and the shades of all my ancestors the Panzas, that never I did see or hear of, nor has my master related or conceived in his mind, such an adventure as this. A thousand devils—not to curse thee—take thee, Malambruno, for an enchanter and a giant! Couldst thou find no other sort of punishment for these sinners but bearding them? Would it not have been better—it would have been better for them—to have taken off half their noses from the middle downwards, even though they'd have snuffled when they spoke, than to have put beards on them? I'll bet they have not the means of paying anybody to shave them."

"That is the truth, señor," said one of the twelve; "we have not the money to get ourselves shaved, and so we have, some of us, taken to using sticking-plasters by way of an economical remedy, for by applying them to our faces and plucking them off with a jerk we are left as bare and smooth as the bottom of a stone mortar. There are, to be sure, women in Kandy that go about from house to house to remove down, and trim eyebrows, and make cosmetics for the use of the women, but we, the duennas of my lady, would never let them in, for most of them have a flavor of agents that have ceased to be principals; and if we are not relieved by Señor Don Quixote we shall be carried to our graves with beards."

"I will pluck out my own in the land of the Moors," said Don Quixote, "if I don't cure yours."

At this instant the Trifaldi recovered from her swoon and said, "The chink of that promise, valiant knight, reached my ears in the midst of my swoon, and has been the means of reviving me and bringing back my senses; and so once more I implore you, illustrious errant, indomitable sir, to let your gracious promises be turned into deeds.

"There shall be no delay on my part," said Don Quixote. "Bethink you, señora, of what I must do, for my heart is most eager to serve you."

"The fact is," replied the Distressed One, "it is five thousand leagues, a couple more or less, from this to the kingdom of Kandy, if you go by land; but if you go through the air and in a straight line, it is three thousand two hundred and twenty-seven. You must know, too, that Malambruno told me that, whenever fate provided the knight our deliverer, he himself would send him a steed far better and with less tricks than a post-horse; for he will be that same wooden horse on which the valiant Pierres carried off the fair Magalona; which said horse is guided by a peg he has in his forehead that serves for a bridle, and flies through the air with such rapidity that you would fancy the very devils were carrying him. This horse, according to ancient tradition, was made by Merlin. He lent him to Pierres, who was a friend of his, and who made long journeys with him, and, as has been said, carried off the fair Magalona, bearing her through the air on its haunches and making all who beheld them from the earth gape with astonishment; and he never lent him save to those whom he loved or those who paid him well; and since the great Pierres we know of no one having mounted him until now. From him Malambruno stole him by his magic art, and he has him now in his possession, and makes use of him in his journeys which he constantly makes through different parts of the world; he is here to-day, to-morrow in France, and the next day in Potosi; and the best of it is the said horse neither eats nor sleeps nor wears out shoes, and goes at an ambling pace through the air without wings, so that he whom he has mounted upon him can carry a cup full of water in his hand without spilling a drop, so smoothly and easily does he go, and for this reason the fair Magalona enjoyed riding him greatly."

"For going smoothly and easily," said Sancho at this, "give me my Dapple, though he can't go through the air; but on the ground I'll back him against all the amblers in the world."

They all laughed, and the Distressed One continued: "And this same horse, if so be that Malambruno is disposed to put an end to our sufferings, will be here before us ere the night shall have advanced half an hour; for he announced to me that the sign he would give me whereby I might know that I had found the knight I was in quest of, would be to send me the horse wherever he might be, speedily and promptly."

"And how many is there room for on this horse?" asked Sancho.

"Two," said the Distressed One, "one in the saddle, and the other on the croup; and generally these two are knight and squire, when there is no damsel that's being carried off."

"I'd like to know, Señora Distressed One," said Sancho, "what is the name of this horse?"

"His name," said the Distressed One, "is not the same as Bellerophon's horse that was called Pegasus, or Alexander the Great's, called Bucephalus, or Orlando Furioso's, the name of which was Brigliador, nor yet Bayard, the horse of Reinaldos of Montalvan, nor Frontino like Ruggiero's, nor Bootes or Peritoa, as they say the horses of the sun were called, nor is he called Orelia, like the horse on which the unfortunate Rodrigo, the last king of the Goths, rode to the battle where he lost his life and his kingdom."

"I'll bet," said Sancho, "that as they have given him none of these famous names of well-known horses, no more have they given him the name of my master's Rocinante, which for being apt surpasses all that have been mentioned."

"That is true," said the bearded countess, "still it fits him very well, for he is called Clavileño the Swift, which name is in accordance with its being made of wood, with the peg he has in his forehead, and with the swift pace at which he travels; and so, as far as name goes, he may compare with the famous Rocinante."

"I have nothing to say against his name," said Sancho; "but with what sort of a bridle or halter is he managed?"

"I have said already," said the Trifaldi, "that it is with a peg, by turning which to one side or the other the knight who rides him makes him go as he pleases, either through the upper air, or skimming and almost sweeping the earth, or else in that middle course that is sought and followed in all well-regulated proceedings."

"I'd like to see him," said Sancho; "but to fancy I'm going to mount him, either in the saddle or on the croup, is to ask pears of the elm-tree. A good joke indeed! I can hardly keep my seat upon Dapple, and on a pack-saddle softer than silk itself, and here they'd have me hold on upon haunches of plank without pad or cushion of any sort! Gad, I have no notion of bruising myself to get rid of any one's beard; let each one shave himself as best he can; I'm not going to accompany my master on any such long journey; besides, I can't give any help to the shaving of these beards as I can to the disenchantment of my lady Dulcinea."

"Yes, you can, my friend," replied the Trifaldi; "and so much, that without you, so I understand, we shall be able to do nothing."

"In the king's name!" exclaimed Sancho, "what have squires got to do with the adventures of their masters? Are they to have the fame of such as they go through, and we the labor? Body o' me! if the historians would only say, 'such and such a knight finished such and such an adventure, but with the help of so and so, his squire, without which it would have been impossible for him to accomplish it'; but they write curtly, 'Don Paralipomenon of the Three Stars accomplished the adventure of the six monsters'; without mentioning such a person as his squire, who was there all the time, just as if there was no such being. Once more, sirs, I say my master may go alone, and much good may it do him; and I'll stay here in the company of my lady the duchess; and may be when he comes back, he will find the lady Dulcinea's affair ever so much advanced; for I mean in leisure hours, and at idle moments, to give myself a spell of whipping without so much as a hair to cover me."

"For all that you must go if it be necessary, my good Sancho," said the duchess, "for they are worthy folk who ask you; and the faces of these ladies must not remain overgrown in this way because of your idle fears; that would be a hard case indeed."

"In the king's name, once more!" said Sancho; "if this charitable work were to be done for the sake of damsels in confinement or charity-girls, a man might expose himself to some hardships; but to bear it for the sake of stripping beards off duennas! Devil take it! I'd sooner see them all bearded, from the highest to the lowest, and from the most prudish to the most affected."

"You are very hard on duennas, Sancho my friend," said the duchess; "you incline very much to the opinion of the Toledo apothecary. But indeed you are wrong; there are duennas in my house that may serve as patterns of duennas; and here is my Doña Rodriguez, who will not allow me to say otherwise."

"Your excellence may say it if you like," said the Rodriguez; "for God knows the truth of everything; and whether we duennas are good or bad, bearded or smooth, we are our mothers' daughters like other women; and as God sent us into the world, he knows why he did, and on his mercy I rely, and not on anybody's beard."

"Well, Señora Rodriguez, Señora Trifaldi, and present company," said Don Quixote, "I trust in Heaven that it will look with kindly eyes upon your troubles, for Sancho will do as I bid him. Only let Clavileño come and let me find myself face to face with Malambruno, and I am certain no razor will shave you more easily than my sword shall shave Malambruno's head off his shoulders; for 'God bears with the wicked, but not forever.'"

"Ah!" exclaimed the Distressed One at this, "may all the stars of the celestial regions look down upon your greatness with benign eyes, valiant knight, and shed every prosperity and valor upon your heart, that it may be the shield and safeguard of the abused and downtrodden race of duennas, detested by apothecaries, sneered at by squires, and made game of by pages. Ill betide the jade that in the flower of her youth would not sooner become a nun than a duenna! unfortunate beings that we are, we duennas! Though we may be descended in the direct male line from Hector of Troy himself, our mistresses never fail to address us as 'you' if they think it makes queens of them. O giant Malambruno, though thou art an enchanter, thou art true to thy promises. Send us now the peerless Clavileño, that our misfortune may be brought to an end; for if the hot weather sets in and these beards of ours are still there, alas for our lot!"

The Trifaldi said this in such a pathetic way that she drew tears from the eyes of all the bystanders, and made even Sancho's fill up; and he resolved in his heart to accompany his master to the uttermost ends of the earth, if so be the removal of the wool from those veritable countenances depended upon it.

Chapter 41

Of the arrival of Clavileño and the end of this protracted adventure

AND now night came, and with it the appointed time for the arrival of the famous horse Clavileño, the non-appearance of which was already beginning to make Don Quixote uneasy, for it struck him that, as Malambruno was so long about sending it, either he himself was not the knight for whom the adventure was reserved, or else Malambruno did not dare to meet him in single combat. But lo! suddenly there came into the garden four wild men all clad in green ivy bearing on their shoulders a great wooden horse. They placed it on its feet on the ground, and one of the wild men said, "Let the knight who has heart for it mount this machine."

Here Sancho exclaimed, "I don't mount, for neither have I the heart nor am I a knight."

"And let the squire, if he has one," continued the wild-man, "take his seat on the croup, and let him trust the valiant Malambruno; for by no sword save his, nor by the malice of any other, shall he be assailed. It is but to turn this peg the horse has in his neck, and he will bear them through the air to where Malambruno awaits them; but lest the vast elevation of their course should make them giddy, their eyes must be covered until the horse neighs, which will be the sign of their having completed their journey."

With these words, leaving Clavileño behind them, they retired with easy dignity the way they came. As soon as the Distressed One saw the horse, almost in tears she exclaimed to Don Quixote, "Valiant knight, the promise of Malambruno has proved trustworthy; the horse has come, our beards are growing, and by every hair in them we all of us implore thee to shave and shear us, as it is only mounting him with thy squire and making a happy beginning with your new journey."

"That I will, Señora Countess Trifaldi," said Don Quixote, "most gladly and with right good-will, without stopping to take a cushion or put on my spurs, so as not to lose time, such is my desire to see you, señora, and all these duennas shaved clean."

"That I won't," said Sancho, "with good will or bad will, or any way at all; and if this shaving can't be done without my mounting on the croup, my master had better look out for another squire to go with him, and these ladies for some other way of making their faces smooth; I'm no witch to have a taste for travelling through the air. What would my islanders say when they heard their governor was going strolling about on the winds? And another thing, as it is three thousand and odd leagues from this to Kandy, if the horse tires, or the giant take huff, we'll be half a dozen years getting back, and there won't be isle or island in the world that will know me: and so, as it is a common saying 'in delay there's danger,' and 'when they offer thee a heifer run with a halter,' these ladies' beards must excuse me; 'Saint Peter is very well in Rome'; I mean I am very well in this house where so much is made of me, and I hope for such a good thing from the master as to see myself a governor."

"Friend Sancho," said the duke at this, "the island that I have promised you is not a moving one, or one that will run away; it has roots so deeply buried in the bowels of the earth that it will be no easy matter to pluck it up or shift it from where it is; you know as well as I do that there is no sort of office of any importance that is not obtained by a bribe of some kind, great or small; well then, that which I look to receive for this government is that you go with your master Don Quixote, and bring this memorable adventure to a conclusion; and whether you return on Clavileño as quickly as his speed seems to promise, or adverse fortune brings you back on foot travelling as a pilgrim from hostel to hostel and from inn to inn, you will always find your island on your return where you left it, and your islanders with the same eagerness they have always had to receive you as their governor, and my good-will will remain the same; doubt not the truth of this, Señor Sancho, for that would be grievously wronging my disposition to serve you."

"Say no more, señor," said Sancho; "I am a poor squire and not equal to carrying so much courtesy; let my master mount; bandage my eyes and commit me to God's care, and tell me if I may commend myself to our Lord or call upon the angels to protect me when we go towering up there."

To this the Trifaldi made answer, "Sancho, you may freely commend yourself to God or whom you will; for Malambruno though an enchanter is a Christian, and works his enchantments with great circumspection, taking very good care not to fall out with any one."

"Well then," said Sancho, "God and the most holy Trinity of Gaeta give me help!"

"Since the memorable adventure of the fulling mills," said Don Quixote, "I have never seen Sancho in such a fright as now; were I as superstitious as others his abject fear would cause me some little trepidation of spirit. But come here, Sancho, for with the leave of these gentles I would say a word or two to thee in private"; and drawing Sancho aside among the trees of the garden and seizing both his hands he said, "Thou seest, brother Sancho, the long journey we have before us, and God knows when we shall return, or what leisure or opportunities this business will allow us; I wish thee therefore to retire now to thy chamber, as though thou wert going to fetch something required for the road, and in a trice give thyself if it be only five hundred lashes on account of the three thousand three hundred to which thou art bound; it will be all to the good, and to make a beginning with a thing is to have it half finished."

"By God," said Sancho, "but your worship must be out of your senses! This is like the common saying, 'You see me with child, and you want me a virgin.' Just as I'm about to go sitting on a bare board, your worship would have me score my backside! Indeed, indeed, your worship is not reasonable. Let us be off to shave these duennas; and on our return I promise on my word to make such haste to wipe off all that's due as will satisfy your worship; I can't say more."

"Well, I will comfort myself with that promise, my good Sancho," replied Don Quixote, "and I believe thou wilt keep it; for indeed though stupid thou art veracious."

"I'm not voracious," said Sancho, "only peckish; but even if I was a little, still I'd keep my word."

With this they went back to mount Clavileño, and as they were about to do so Don Quixote said, "Cover thine eyes, Sancho, and mount; for one who sends for us from lands so far distant can not mean to deceive us for the sake of the paltry glory to be derived from deceiving persons who trust in him; though all should turn out the contrary of what I hope, no malice will be able to dim the glory of having undertaken this exploit."

Let us be off, señor," said Sancho, "for I have taken the beards and tears of these ladies deeply to heart, and I shan't eat a bite to relish it until I have seen them restored to their former smoothness. Mount, your worship, and blindfold yourself, for if I am to go on the croup, it is plain the rider in the saddle must mount first."

"That is true," said Don Quixote, and, taking a handkerchief out of his pocket, he begged the Distressed One to bandage his eyes very carefully; but after having them bandaged he uncovered them again, saying, "If my memory does not deceive me, I have read in Virgil of the Palladium of Troy, a wooden horse the Greeks offered to the goddess Pallas, which was big with armed knights, who were afterwards the destruction of Troy; so it would be as well to see, first of all, what Clavileño has in his stomach."

"There is no occasion," said the Distressed One; "I will be bail for him, and I know that Malambruno has nothing tricky or treacherous about him; you may mount without any fear, Señor Don Quixote; on my head be it if any harm befalls you."

Don Quixote thought that to say anything further with regard to his safety would be putting his courage in an unfavorable light; and so, without more words, he mounted Clavileño, and tried the peg, which turned easily; and as he had no stirrups and his legs hung down, he looked like nothing so much as a figure in some Roman triumph painted or embroidered on a Flemish tapestry.

Much against the grain, and very slowly, Sancho proceeded to mount, and, after settling himself as well as he could on the croup, found it rather hard and not at all soft, and asked the duke if it would be possible to oblige him with a pad of some kind, or a cushion; even if it were off the couch of his lady the duchess, or the bed of one of the pages; as the haunches of that horse were more like marble than wood. On this the Trifaldi observed that Clavileño would not bear any kind of harness or trappings, and that his best plan would be to sit sideways like a woman, as in that way he would not feel the hardness so much.

Sancho did so, and, bidding them farewell, allowed his eyes to be bandaged, but immediately afterwards uncovered them again, and looking tenderly and tearfully on those in the garden, bade them help him in his present strait with plenty of Paternosters and Ave Marias, that God might provide some one to say as many for them, whenever they found themselves in a similar emergency.

At this Don Quixote exclaimed, "Art thou on the gallows, thief, or at thy last moment, to use pitiful entreaties of that sort? Cowardly, spiritless creature, art thou not in the very place the fair Magalona occupied, and from which she descended, not into the grave, but to become Queen of France; unless the histories lie? And I who am here beside thee, may I not put myself on a par with the valiant Pierres, who pressed this very spot that I now press? Cover thine eyes, cover thine eyes, abject animal, and let not thy fear escape thy lips, at least, in my presence."

"Let them blindfold me," said Sancho; "as you won't let me commend myself or be commended to God, is it any wonder if I am afraid there is a region of devils about here that will carry us off to Peralvillo?" [1]

They were then blindfolded, and Don Quixote, finding himself settled to his satisfaction, felt for the peg, and the instant he placed his fingers on it, all the duennas and all who stood by lifted up their voices exclaiming, "God guide thee, valiant knight! God be with thee, intrepid squire! Now, now ye go cleaving the air more swiftly than an arrow! Now ye begin to amaze and astonish all who are gazing at you from the earth! Take care not to wobble about, valiant Sancho! Mind thou fall not, for thy fall will be worse than that rash youth's who tried to steer the chariot of his father the Sun!"

As Sancho heard the voices, clinging tightly to his master and winding his arms round him, he said, "Señor, how do they make out we are going up so high, if their voices reach us here and they seem to be speaking quite close to us?"

"Don't mind that, Sancho," said Don Quixote; "for as affairs of this sort and flights like this are out of the common course of things, you can see and hear as much as you like a thousand leagues off; but don't squeeze me so tight or thou wilt upset me; and really I know not what thou hast to be uneasy or frightened at, for I can safely swear I never mounted a smoother-going steed all the days of my life; one would fancy we never stirred from one place. Banish fear,

[1] Peralvillo, a small town where the Holy Brotherhood used to execute their prisoners.

my friend, for indeed everything is going as it ought, and we have the wind astern."

"That's true," said Sancho, "for such a strong wind comes against me on this side, that it seems as if people were blowing on me with a thousand pair of bellows"; which was the case; they were puffing at him with a great pair of bellows; for the whole adventure was so well planned by the duke, the duchess, and their majordomo, that nothing was omitted to make it perfectly successful.

Don Quixote now, feeling the blast, said, "Beyond a doubt, Sancho, we must have already reached the second region of the air, where the hail and snow are generated; the thunder, the lightning, and the thunderbolts are engendered in the third region, and if we go on ascending at this rate, we shall shortly plunge into the region of fire, and I know not how to regulate this peg, so as not to mount up where we shall be burned."

And now they began to warm their faces, from a distance, with tow that could be easily set on fire and extinguished again, fixed on the end of a cane. On feeling the heat Sancho said, "May I die if we are not already in that fire place, or very near it, for a good part of my beard has been singed, and I have a mind, señor, to uncover and see whereabouts we are."

"Do nothing of the kind," said Don Quixote; "remember the true story of the licentiate Torralva that the devils carried flying through the air riding on a stick with his eyes shut; who in twelve hours reached Rome and dismounted at Torre di Nona, which is a street of the city, and saw the whole sack and storming and the death of Bourbon, and was back in Madrid the next morning, where he gave an account of all he had seen; and he said moreover that as he was going through the air, the devil bade him open his eyes, and he did so, and saw himself so near the body of the moon, so it seemed to him, that he could have laid hold of it with his hand, and that he did not dare to look at the earth lest he should be seized with giddiness. So that, Sancho, it will not do for us to uncover ourselves, for he who has us in charge will be responsible for us; and perhaps we are gaining an altitude and mounting up to enable us to descend at one swoop on the Kingdom of Kandy, as the saker or falcon does on the heron, so as to seize it however high it may soar; and though it seems to us not half an hour since we left the garden, believe me we must have travelled a great distance."

"I don't know how that may be," said Sancho;

"all I know is that if the Señora Magallanes or Magalona was satisfied with this croup, she could not have been very tender of flesh."

The duke, the duchess, and all in the garden were listening to the conversation of the two heroes, and were beyond measure amused by it; and now, desirous of putting a finishing touch to this rare and well-contrived adventure, they applied a light to Clavileño's tail with some tow, and the horse, being full of squibs and crackers, immediately blew up with a prodigious noise, and brought Don Quixote and Sancho Panza to the ground half singed. By this time the bearded band of duennas, the Trifaldi and all, had vanished from the garden, and those that remained lay stretched on the ground as if in a swoon. Don Quixote and Sancho got up rather shaken, and, looking about them, were filled with amazement at finding themselves in the same garden from which they had started, and seeing such a number of people stretched on the ground; and their astonishment was increased when at one side of the garden they perceived a tall lance planted in the ground, and hanging from it by two cords of green silk a smooth, white parchment on which there was the following inscription in large gold letters: *The illustrious knight Don Quixote of La Mancha has, by merely attempting it, finished and concluded the adventure of the Countess Trifaldi, otherwise called the Distressed Duenna; Malambruno is now satisfied on every point, the chins of the duennas are now smooth and clean, and King Don Clavigo and Queen Antonomasia in their original form; and when the squirely flagellation shall have been completed, the white dove shall find herself delivered from the pestiferous gerfalcons that persecute her, and in the arms of her beloved mate; for such is the decree of the sage Merlin, arch-enchanter of enchanters.*

As soon as Don Quixote had read the inscription on the parchment he perceived clearly that it referred to the disenchantment of Dulcinea, and returning hearty thanks to Heaven that he had with so little danger achieved so grand an exploit as to restore to their former complexion the countenances of those venerable duennas, now no longer visible, he advanced towards the duke and duchess, who had not yet come to themselves, and taking the duke by the hand he said, "Be of good cheer, worthy sir, be of good cheer; it's nothing at all; the adventure is now over and without any harm done, as the inscription fixed on this post shows plainly."

The duke came to himself slowly and like one

recovering consciousness after a heavy sleep, and the duchess and all who had fallen prostrate about the garden did the same, with such demonstrations of wonder and amazement that they would have almost persuaded one that what they pretended so adroitly in jest had happened to them in reality. The duke read the placard with half-shut eyes, and then ran to embrace Don Quixote with open arms, declaring him to be the best knight that had ever been seen in any age. Sancho kept looking about for the Distressed One, to see what her face was like without the beard, and if she was as fair as her elegant person promised; but they told him that, the instant Clavileño descended flaming through the air and came to the ground, the whole band of duennas with the Trifaldi vanished, and that they were already shaved and without a stump left.

The duchess asked Sancho how he had fared on that long journey, to which Sancho replied, "I felt, señora, that we were flying through the region of fire, as my master told me, and I wanted to uncover my eyes for a bit; but my master, when I asked leave to uncover myself, would not let me; but as I have a little bit of curiosity about me, and a desire to know what is forbidden and kept from me, quietly and without any one seeing me I drew aside the handkerchief covering my eyes ever so little, close to my nose, and from underneath looked towards the earth, and it seemed to me that it was altogether no bigger than a grain of mustard seed, and that the men walking on it were little bigger than hazel nuts; so you may see how high we must have got to them."

To this the duchess said, "Sancho, my friend, mind what you are saying; it seems you could not have seen the earth, but only the men walking on it; it is plain that if the earth looked to you like a grain of mustard seed, and each man like a hazel nut, one man alone would have covered the whole earth."

"That is true," said Sancho, "but for all that I got a glimpse of a bit of one side of it, and saw it all."

"Take care, Sancho," said the duchess, "with a bit of one side one does not see the whole of what one looks at."

"I don't understand that way of looking at things," said Sancho; "I only know that your ladyship will do well to bear in mind that as we were flying by enchantment so I might have seen the whole earth and all the men by enchantment, whatever way I looked; and if you won't believe this, no more will you believe that, uncovering myself nearly to the eyebrows, I saw myself so close to the sky that there was not a palm and a half between me and it; and by everything that I can swear by, señora, it is mighty great! And it so happened we came by where the seven she-goats are,[1] and by God and upon my soul, as in my youth I was a goatherd in my own country, as soon as I saw them I felt a longing to be among them for a little, and if I had not given way to it I think I'd have burst. So I come and take, and what do I do? without saying anything to anybody, not even to my master, softly and quietly I got down from Clavileño and amused myself with the goats—which are like violets, like flowers—for nigh three-quarters of an hour; and Clavileño never stirred or moved from one spot."

"And while the good Sancho was amusing himself with the goats," said the duke, "how did Señor Don Quixote amuse himself?"

To which Don Quixote replied, "As all these things and such like occurrences are out of the ordinary course of nature, it is no wonder that Sancho says what he does; for my own part I can only say that I did not uncover my eyes either above or below, nor did I see sky or earth or sea or shore. It is true I felt that I was passing through the region of the air, and even that I touched that of fire; but that we passed farther I cannot believe; for the region of fire being between the heaven of the moon and the last region of the air, we could not have reached that heaven where the seven she-goats Sancho speaks of are without being burned; and as we were not burned, either Sancho is lying or Sancho is dreaming."

"I am neither lying nor dreaming," said Sancho; "only ask me the tokens of those same goats, and you'll see by that whether I'm telling the truth or not."

"Tell us them then, Sancho," said the duchess.

"Two of them," said Sancho, "are green, two blood-red, two blue, and one a mixture of all colors."

"An odd sort of goat, that," said the duke; "in this earthly region of ours we have no such colors; I mean goats of such colors."

"That's very plain," said Sancho; "of course there must be a difference between the goats of heaven and the goats of the earth."

"Tell me, Sancho," said the duke, "did you see any he-goat among those she-goats?"

"No, señor," said Sancho; "but I have heard

[1] The Pleiades.

say that none ever passed the horns of the moon."

They did not care to ask him anything more about his journey, for they saw he was in the vein to go rambling all over the heavens giving an account of everything that went on there, without having ever stirred from the garden. Such, in short, was the end of the adventure of the Distressed Duenna, which gave the duke and duchess laughing matter not only for the time being, but for all their lives, and Sancho something to talk about for ages, if he lived so long; but Don Quixote, coming close to his ear, said to him, "Sancho, as you would have us believe what you saw in heaven, I require you to believe me as to what I saw in the cave of Montesinos; I say no more."

Chapter 42

Of the counsels which Don Quixote gave Sancho Panza before he set out to govern the island, together with other well-considered matters

THE duke and duchess were so well pleased with the successful and droll result of the adventure of the Distressed One, that they resolved to carry on the joke, seeing what a fit subject they had to deal with for making it all pass for reality. So having laid their plans and given instructions to their servants and vassals how to behave to Sancho in his government of the promised island, the next day, that following Clavileño's flight, the duke told Sancho to prepare and get ready to go and be governor, for his islanders were already looking out for him as for the showers of May.

Sancho made him an obeisance, and said, "Ever since I came down from heaven, and from the top of it beheld the earth, and saw how little it is, the great desire I had to be a governor has been partly cooled in me; for what is there grand in being ruler on a grain of mustard seed, or what dignity or authority in governing half a dozen men about as big as hazel nuts; for, so far as I could see, there were no more on the whole earth? If your lordship would be so good as to give me ever so small a bit of heaven, were it no more than half a league, I'd rather have it than the best island in the world."

"Take notice, friend Sancho," said the duke, "I can not give a bit of heaven, no not so much as the breadth of my nail, to any one; rewards and favors of that sort are reserved for God alone. What I can give I give you, and that is a real, genuine island, compact, well-proportioned, and uncommonly fertile and fruitful, where, if you know how to use your opportunities, you may, with the help of the world's riches, gain those of heaven."

"Well then," said Sancho, "let the island come; and I'll try and be such a governor, that in spite of scoundrels I'll go to heaven; and it's not from any craving to quit my own humble condition or better myself, but from the desire I have to try what it tastes like to be a governor."

"If you once make trial of it, Sancho," said the duke, "you'll eat your fingers off after the government, so sweet a thing is it to command and be obeyed. Depend upon it when your master comes to be emperor (as he will beyond a doubt from the course his affairs are taking), it will be no easy matter to wrest the dignity from him, and he will be sore and sorry at heart to have been so long without becoming one."

"Señor," said Sancho, "it is my belief it's a good thing to be in command, if it's only over a drove of cattle."

"May I be buried with you, Sancho," said the duke, "but you know everything; I hope you will make as good a governor as your sagacity promises, and that is all I have to say; and now remember to-morrow is the day you must set out for the government of the island, and this evening they will provide you with the proper attire for you to wear, and all things requisite for your departure."

"Let them dress me as they like," said Sancho; "however I'm dressed I'll be Sancho Panza."

"That's true," said the duke; "but one's dress must be suited to the office or rank one holds; for it would not do for a jurist to dress like a soldier, or a soldier like a priest. You, Sancho, shall go partly as a lawyer, partly as a captain, for, in the island I am giving you, arms are needed as much as letters, and letters as much as arms."

"Of letters I know but little," said Sancho, "for I don't even know the A B C; but it is enough for me to have the Christus[1] in my memory to be a good governor. As for arms, I'll handle those they give me till I drop, and then, God be my help!"

"With so good a memory," said the duke, "Sancho can not go wrong in anything."

Here Don Quixote joined them; and learning what passed, and how soon Sancho was to go to his government, he with the duke's per-

[1] The cross prefixed to the alphabet in schoolbooks.

mission took him by the hand, and retired to his room with him for the purpose of giving him advice as to how he was to demean himself in his office. As soon as they had entered the chamber he closed the door after him, and almost by force made Sancho sit down beside him, and in a quiet tone thus addressed him: "I give infinite thanks to Heaven, friend Sancho, that before I have met with any good luck, fortune has come forward to meet thee. I who counted upon my good fortune to discharge the recompense of thy services, find myself still waiting for advancement, while thou, before the time, and contrary to all reasonable expectation, seest thyself blessed in the fulfilment of thy desires. Some will bribe, beg, solicit, rise early, entreat, persist, without attaining the object of their suit; while another comes, and without knowing why or wherefore, finds himself invested with the place or office so many have sued for; and here it is that the common saying, 'There is good luck as well as bad luck in suits,' applies. Thou, who, to my thinking, art beyond all doubt a dullard, without early rising or night watching or taking any trouble, with the mere breath of knight errantry that has breathed upon thee, seest thyself without more ado governor of an island, as though it were a mere matter of course. This I say, Sancho, that thou attribute not the favor thou hast received to thine own merits, but give thanks to Heaven that disposes matters beneficently, and secondly thanks to the great power the profession of knight-errantry contains in itself. With a heart, then, inclined to believe what I have said to thee, attend, my son, to thy Cato here who would counsel thee and be thy pole-star and guide to direct and pilot thee to a safe haven out of this stormy sea wherein thou art about to ingulf thyself; for offices and great trusts are nothing else but a mighty gulf of troubles.

"First of all, my son, thou must fear God, for in the fear of him is wisdom, and being wise thou canst not err in aught.

"Secondly, thou must keep in view what thou art, striving to know thyself, the most difficult thing to know that the mind can imagine. If thou knowest thyself, it will follow thou wilt not puff thyself up like the frog that strove to make himself as large as the ox; if thou dost, the recollection of having kept pigs in thine own country will serve as the ugly feet for the wheel of thy folly."

"That's the truth," said Sancho; "but that was when I was a boy; afterwards when I was something more of a man it was geese I kept, not pigs. But to my thinking that has nothing to do with it; for not all who are governors come of a kingly stock."

"True," said Don Quixote, "and for that reason those who are not of noble origin should take care that the dignity of the office they hold be accompanied by a gentle suavity, which wisely managed will save them from the sneers of malice that no station escapes.

"Glory in thy humble birth, Sancho, and be not ashamed of saying thou art peasant-born; for when it is seen thou art not ashamed no one will set himself to put thee to the blush; and pride thyself rather upon being one of lowly virtue than a lofty sinner. Countless are they who, born of mean parentage, have risen to the highest dignities, pontifical and imperial, and of the truth of this I could give thee instances enough to weary thee.

"Remember, Sancho, if thou make virtue thy aim, and take a pride in doing virtuous actions, thou wilt have no cause to envy those who are born princes and lords, for blood is an inheritance, but virtue an acquisition, and virtue has in itself a worth that blood does not possess.

"This being so, if perchance any one of thy kinsfolk should come to see thee when thou art in thine island, thou art not to repel or slight him, but on the contrary to welcome him, entertain him, and make much of him; for in so doing thou wilt be approved of Heaven (which is not pleased that any should despise what it hath made), and wilt comply with the laws of well-ordered nature.

"If thou carriest thy wife with thee (and it is not well for those that administer governments to be long without their wives), teach and instruct her, and strive to smooth down her natural roughness; for all that may be gained by a wise governor may be lost and wasted by a boorish stupid wife.

"If perchance thou art left a widower—a thing which may happen—and in virtue of thy office seekest a consort of higher degree, choose not one to serve thee for a hook, or for a fishing-rod, or for the hood of thy 'won't have it';[1] for verily, I tell thee, for all the judge's wife receives, the husband will be held accountable at the general calling to account; where he will have to repay in death fourfold, items that in life he regarded as naught.

"Never go by arbitrary law, which is so much

[1] An allusion to the popular joke against the begging friars, who were said to make a pretence of refusing gifts; hinting, however, that they might be thrown into their hood.

favored by ignorant men who plume themselves on cleverness.

"Let the tears of the poor man find with thee more compassion, but not more justice, than the pleadings of the rich.

"Strive to lay bare the truth, as well amid the promises and presents of the rich man, as amid the sobs and entreaties of the poor.

"When equity may and should be brought into play, press not the utmost rigor of the law against the guilty; for the reputation of the stern judge stands not higher than that of the compassionate.

"If perchance thou permittest the staff of justice to swerve, let it be not by the weight of a gift, but by that of mercy.

"If it should happen to thee to give judgment in the cause of one who is thine enemy, turn thy thoughts away from thy injury and fix them on the justice of the case.

"Let not thine own passion blind thee in another man's cause; for the errors thou wilt thus commit will be most frequently irremediable; or if not, only to be remedied at the expense of thy good name and fortune.

"If any handsome woman come to seek justice of thee, turn away thine eyes from her tears and thine ears from her lamentations, and consider deliberately the merits of her demand, if thou wouldst not have thy reason swept away by her weeping, and thy rectitude by her sighs.

"Abuse not by word him whom thou hast to punish in deed, for the pain of punishment is enough for the unfortunate without the addition of thine objurgations.

"Bear in mind that the culprit who comes under thy jurisdiction is but a miserable man subject to all the propensities of our depraved nature, and so far as may be in thy power show thyself lenient and forbearing; for though the attributes of God are all equal, to our eyes that of mercy is brighter and loftier than that of justice.

"If thou followest these precepts and rules, Sancho, thy days will be long, thy fame eternal, thy reward abundant, thy felicity unutterable; thou wilt marry thy children as thou wouldst; they and thy grandchildren will bear titles; thou wilt live in peace and concord with all men; and, when life draws to a close, death will come to thee in calm and ripe old age, and the light and loving hands of thy great-grandchildren will close thine eyes.

"What I have thus far addressed to thee are instructions for the adornment of thy mind; listen now to those which tend to that of the body."

Chapter 43

Of the second set of counsels Don Quixote gave Sancho Panza

WHO, hearing the foregoing discourse of Don Quixote, would not have set him down for a person of great good sense and greater rectitude of purpose? But, as has been frequently observed in the course of this great history, he only talked nonsense when he touched on chivalry, and in discussing all other subjects showed that he had a clear and unbiassed understanding; so that at every turn his acts gave the lie to his intellect, and his intellect to his acts; but in the case of these second counsels that he gave Sancho he showed himself to have a lively turn of humor, and displayed conspicuously his wisdom, and also his folly.

Sancho listened to him with the deepest attention, and endeavored to fix his counsels in his memory, like one who meant to follow them and by their means bring the full promise of his government to a happy issue. Don Quixote, then, went on to say:

"With regard to the mode in which thou shouldst govern thy person and thy house, Sancho, the first charge I have to give thee is to be clean, and to cut thy nails, not letting them grow as some do, whose ignorance makes them fancy that long nails are an ornament to their hands, as if those excrescences they neglect to cut were nails, and not the talons of a lizard-catching kestrel—a filthy and unnatural abuse.

"Go not ungirt and loose, Sancho; for disordered attire is a sign of an unstable mind, unless indeed the slovenliness and slackness is to be set down to craft, as was the common opinion in the case of Julius Cæsar.

"Ascertain cautiously what thy office may be worth; and if it will allow thee to give liveries to thy servants, give them respectable and serviceable, rather than showy and gay ones, and divide them between thy servants and the poor; that is to say, if thou canst clothe six pages, clothe three and three poor men, and thus thou wilt have pages for heaven and pages for earth; the vainglorious never think of this new mode of giving liveries.

"Eat not garlic nor onions, lest they find out thy boorish origin by the smell; walk slowly and speak deliberately, but not in such a way as to make it seem thou art listening to thyself; for all affectation is bad.

"Dine sparingly and sup more sparingly still; for the health of the whole body is forged in the workshop of the stomach.

"Be temperate in drinking, bearing in mind that wine in excess keeps neither secrets nor promises.

"Take care, Sancho, not to chew on both sides, and not to eruct in anybody's presence."

"Eruct!" said Sancho; "I don't know what that means."

"To eruct, Sancho," said Don Quixote, "means to belch, and that is one of the filthiest words in the Spanish language, though a very expressive one; and therefore nice folk have had recourse to the Latin, and instead of belch say eruct, and instead of belches say eructations; and if some do not understand these terms it matters little, for custom will bring them into use in the course of time, so that they will be readily understood; that is the way a language is enriched; custom and the public are all-powerful there."

"In truth, señor," said Sancho, "one of the counsels and cautions I mean to bear in mind shall be this, not to belch, for I'm constantly doing it."

"Eruct, Sancho, not belch," said Don Quixote.

"Eruct, I shall say henceforth, and I swear not to forget it," said Sancho.

"Likewise, Sancho," said Don Quixote, "thou must not mingle such a quantity of proverbs in thy discourse as thou dost; for though proverbs are short maxims, thou dost drag them in so often by the head and shoulders that they savor more of nonsense than of maxims."

"God alone can cure that," said Sancho; "for I have more proverbs in me than a book, and when I speak they come so thick together into my mouth that they fall to fighting among themselves to get out; that's why my tongue lets fly the first that come, though they may not be pat to the purpose. But I'll take care henceforward to use such as befit the dignity of my office; for 'in a house where there's plenty, supper is soon cooked,' and 'he who binds does not wrangle,' and 'the bell-ringer's in a safe berth,' and 'giving and keeping require brains.'"

"That's it, Sancho!" said Don Quixote; "pack, tack, string proverbs together; nobody is hindering thee! 'My mother beats me, and I go on with my tricks.' I am bidding thee avoid proverbs, and here in a second thou hast shot out a whole litany of them, which have as much to do with what we are talking about as 'over the hills of Úbeda.' Mind, Sancho, I do not say that a proverb aptly brought in is objectionable; but to pile up and string together proverbs at random makes conversation dull and vulgar.

"When thou ridest on horseback, do not go lolling with thy body on the back of the saddle, nor carry thy legs stiff or sticking out from the horse's belly, nor yet sit so loosely that one would suppose thou wert on Dapple; for the seat on a horse makes gentlemen of some and grooms of others.

"Be moderate in thy sleep; for he who does not rise early does not get the benefit of the day; and remember, Sancho, diligence is the mother of good fortune, and indolence, its opposite, never yet attained the object of an honest ambition.

"The last counsel I will give thee now, though it does not tend to bodily improvement, I would have thee carry carefully in thy memory, for I believe it will be no less useful to thee than those I have given thee already, and it is this—never engage in a dispute about families, at least in the way of comparing them one with another; for necessarily one of those compared will be better than the other, and thou wilt be hated by the one thou hast disparaged, and get nothing in any shape from the one thou hast exalted.

"Thy attire shall be hose of full length, a long jerkin, and a cloak a trifle longer; loose breeches by no means, for they are becoming neither for gentlemen nor for governors.

"For the present, Sancho, this is all that has occurred to me to advise thee; as time goes by and occasions arise my instructions shall follow, if thou take care to let me know how thou art circumstanced."

"Señor," said Sancho, "I see well enough that all these things your worship has said to me are good, holy, and profitable; but what use will they be to me if I don't remember one of them? To be sure that about not letting my nails grow, and marrying again if I have the chance, will not slip out of my head; but all that other hash, muddle, and jumble—I don't and can't recollect any more of it than of last year's clouds; so it must be given me in writing; for though I can't either read or write, I'll give it to my confessor to drive it into me and remind me of it whenever it is necessary."

"Ah, sinner that I am!" said Don Quixote, "how bad it looks in governors not to know how to read or write; for let me tell thee, Sancho, when a man knows not how to read, or is left-handed, it argues one of two things: either that he was the son of exceedingly mean and lowly parents, or that he himself was so incorrigible and ill-conditioned that neither good company nor good teaching could make any impression on him. It is a great defect that thou laborest under, and therefore I would have thee learn at any rate to sign thy name."

"I can sign my name well enough," said Sancho, "for when I was steward of the brotherhood in my village I learned to make certain letters, like the marks on bales of goods, which they told me made out my name. Besides I can pretend my right hand is disabled and make some one else sign for me, for 'there's a remedy for everything except death'; and as I shall be in command and hold the staff, I can do as I like; moreover, 'he who has the alcalde for his father—,' and I'll be governor, and that's higher than alcalde. Only come and see! Let them make light of me and abuse me; 'they'll come for wool and go back shorn'; 'whom God loves, his house is sweet to him'; 'the silly sayings of the rich pass for saws in the world'; and as I'll be rich, being a governor, and at the same time generous, as I mean to be, no fault will be seen in me. 'Only make yourself honey and the flies will suck you'; 'as much as thou hast so much art thou worth,' as my grandmother used to say; and 'thou canst have no revenge of a man of substance.'"

"Oh, God's curse upon thee, Sancho!" here exclaimed Don Quixote; "sixty thousand devils fly away with thee and thy proverbs! For the last hour thou hast been stringing them together and inflicting the pangs of torture on me with every one of them. Those proverbs will bring thee to the gallows one day, I promise thee; thy subjects will take the government from thee, or there will be revolts among them, all because of them. Tell me, where dost thou pick them up, thou booby? How dost thou apply them, thou blockhead? For with me, to utter one and make it apply properly, I have to sweat and labor as if I were digging."

"By God, master mine," said Sancho, "your worship is making a fuss about very little. Why the devil should you be vexed if I make use of what is my own? And I have got nothing else, nor any other stock in trade except proverbs and more proverbs; and here are four just this instant come into my head, pat to the purpose and like pears in a basket; but I won't repeat them, for 'Sage silence is called Sancho.'"

"That, Sancho, thou art not," said Don Quixote; "for not only art thou not sage silence, but thou art pestilent prate and perversity; still I would like to know what four proverbs have just now come into thy memory, for I have been turning over mine own—and it is a good one—and not one occurs to me."

"What can be better," said Sancho, "than 'never put thy thumbs between two back teeth'; and 'to *"get out of my house"* and *"what do you want with my wife?"* there is no answer'; and 'whether the pitcher hits the stone, or the stone the pitcher, it's a bad business for the pitcher'; all which fit to a hair? For no one should quarrel with his governor, or him in authority over him, because he will come off the worst, as he does who puts his finger between two back teeth, and if they are not back teeth it makes no difference, so long as they are teeth; and to whatever the governor may say there's no answer, any more than to 'get out of my house' and 'what do you want with my wife?' and then, as for that about the stone and the pitcher, a blind man could see that. So that he who sees the mote in another's eye had need to see the beam in his own, that it be not said of himself, 'the dead woman was frightened at the one with her throat cut'; and your worship knows well that the fool knows more in his own house than the wise man in another's."

"Nay, Sancho," said Don Quixote, "the fool knows nothing, either in his own house or in anybody else's, for no wise structure of any sort can stand on a foundation of folly; but let us say no more about it, Sancho, for if thou governest badly, thine will be the fault and mine the shame; but I comfort myself with having done my duty in advising thee as earnestly and as wisely as I could; and thus I am released from my obligations and my promise. God guide thee, Sancho, and govern thee in thy government, and deliver me from the misgiving I have that thou wilt turn the whole island upside down, a thing I might prevent by explaining to the duke what thou art and telling him that all that fat little person of thine is nothing else but a sack full of proverbs and sauciness."

"Señor," said Sancho, "if your worship thinks I'm not fit for this government, I give it up on the spot; for the mere black of the nail of my soul is dearer to me than my whole body; and I can live just as well, simple Sancho, on bread and onions, as governor, on partridges and capons; and what's more, while we're asleep we're all equal, great and small, rich and poor. But if your worship looks into it, you will see it was your worship alone that put me on to this business of governing; for I know no more about the government of islands than a buzzard; and if there's any reason to think that because of my being a governor the devil will get hold of me, I'd rather go Sancho to heaven than governor to hell."

"By God, Sancho," said Don Quixote, "for those last words thou hast uttered alone, I consider thou deservest to be governor of a thousand islands. Thou hast good natural instincts, without which no knowledge is worth anything; commend thyself to God, and try not to swerve in the pursuit of thy main object; I mean, always make it thy aim and fixed purpose to do right in all matters that come before thee, for Heaven always helps good intentions; and now let us go to dinner, for I think my lord and lady are waiting for us."

Chapter 44

How Sancho Panza was conducted to his government, and of the strange adventure that befell Don Quixote in the castle

IT is stated, they say, in the true original of this history, that when Cid Hamet came to write this chapter, his interpreter did not translate it as he wrote it—that is, as a kind of complaint the Moor made against himself for having taken in hand a story so dry and of so little variety as this of Don Quixote, for he found himself forced to speak perpetually of him and Sancho, without venturing to indulge in digressions and episodes more serious and more interesting. He said, too, that to go on, mind, hand, and pen always restricted to writing upon one single subject, and speaking through the mouths of a few characters, was intolerable drudgery, the result of which was never equal to the author's labor, and that to avoid this he had in the First Part availed himself of the device of novels, like *The Ill-advised Curiosity* and *The Captive Captain*, which stand, as it were, apart from the story; the others that are given there being incidents which occurred to Don Quixote himself and could not be omitted. He also thought, he says, that many, engrossed by the interest attaching to the exploits of Don Quixote, would take none in the novels, and pass them over hastily or impatiently without noticing the elegance and art of their composition, which would be very manifest were they published by themselves and not as mere adjuncts to the crazes of Don Quixote or the simplicities of Sancho. Therefore in this Second Part he thought it best not to insert novels, either separate or interwoven, but only episodes, something like them, arising out of the circumstances the facts present; and even these sparingly, and with no more words than suffice to make them plain; and as he confines and restricts himself to the narrow limits of the narrative, though he has ability, capacity, and brains enough to deal with the whole universe, he requests that his labors may not be despised, and that credit be given him, not for what he writes, but for what he has refrained from writing; and so he goes on with his story, saying that the day Don Quixote gave the counsels to Sancho, the same afternoon after dinner he handed them to him in writing so that he might get some one to read them to him. They had scarcely, however, been given to him when he let them drop, and they fell into the hands of the duke, who showed them to the duchess, and they were both amazed afresh at the madness and wit of Don Quixote. To carry on the joke, then, the same evening they despatched Sancho with a large following to the village that was to serve him for an island. It happened that the person who had him in charge was a majordomo of the duke's, a man of great discretion and humor—and there can be no humor without discretion—and the same who played the part of the Countess Trifaldi in the comical way that has been already described; and thus qualified, and instructed by his master and mistress as to how to deal with Sancho, he carried out their scheme admirably. Now it came to pass that as soon as Sancho saw this majordomo he seemed in his features to recognize those of the Trifaldi, and turning to his master, he said to him, "Señor, either the devil will carry me off, here on this spot, righteous and believing, or your worship will own to me that the face of this majordomo of the duke's here is the very face of the Distressed One."

Don Quixote regarded the majordomo attentively, and having done so, said to Sancho, "There is no reason why the devil should carry thee off, Sancho, either righteous or believing—and what thou meanest by that I know not; the face of the Distressed One is that of the majordomo, but for all that the majordomo is not the Distressed One; for his being so would involve a mighty contradiction; but this is not the time for going into questions of the sort, which would be involving ourselves in an inextricable labyrinth. Believe me, my friend, we must pray earnestly to our Lord that he deliver us both from wicked wizards and enchanters."

"It is no joke, señor," said Sancho, "for before this I heard him speak, and it seemed exactly as if the voice of the Trifaldi was sounding in my ears. Well, I'll hold my peace; but I'll take care to be on the look-out henceforth for any sign that may be seen to confirm or do away with this suspicion."

"Thou wilt do well, Sancho," said Don Quixote, "and thou wilt let me know all thou discoverest on the subject, and all that befalls thee in thy government."

Sancho at last set out attended by a great number of people. He was dressed in the garb of a lawyer, with a gaban of tawny watered camlet over all and a montera cap of the same material, and mounted à la jineta upon a mule. Behind him, in accordance with the duke's orders, followed Dapple with brand new ass-trappings and ornaments of silk, and from time to time Sancho turned round to look at his ass, so well pleased to have him with him that he would not have changed places with the Emperor of Germany. On taking leave he kissed the hands of the duke and duchess and got his master's blessing, which Don Quixote gave him with tears, and he received blubbering. Let worthy Sancho go in peace, and good luck to him, Gentle Reader; and look out for two bushels of laughter, which the account of how he behaved himself in office will give thee. In the meantime turn thy attention to what happened to his master the same night, and if thou dost not laugh thereat, at any rate thou wilt stretch thy mouth with a grin; for Don Quixote's adventures must be honored either with wonder or with laughter.

It is recorded, then, that as soon as Sancho had gone, Don Quixote felt his loneliness, and had it been possible for him to revoke the mandate and take away the government from him, he would have done so. The duchess observed his dejection and asked him why he was melancholy; because, she said, if it was for the loss of Sancho, there were squires, duennas, and damsels in her house who would wait upon him to his full satisfaction.

"The truth is, señora," replied Don Quixote, "that I do feel the loss of Sancho; but that is not the main cause of my looking sad; and of all the offers your excellence makes me, I accept only the good-will with which they are made, and as to the remainder I entreat of your excellence to permit and allow me alone to wait upon myself in my chamber."

"Indeed, Señor Don Quixote," said the duchess, "that must not be; four of my damsels, as beautiful as flowers, shall wait upon you."

"To me," said Don Quixote, "they will not be flowers, but thorns to pierce my heart. They, or anything like them, shall as soon enter my chamber as fly. If your highness wishes to gratify me still further, though I deserve it not, permit me to please myself, and wait upon myself in my own room; for I place a barrier between my inclinations and my virtue, and I do not wish to break this rule through the generosity your highness is disposed to display towards me; and, in short, I will sleep in my clothes, sooner than allow any one to undress me."

"Say no more, Señor Don Quixote, say no more," said the duchess; "I assure you I will give orders that not even a fly, not to say a damsel, shall enter your home. I am not the one to undermine the propriety of Señor Don Quixote, for it strikes me that among his many virtues the one that is pre-eminent is that of modesty. Your worship may undress and dress in private and in your own way, as you please and when you please, for there will be no one to hinder you; and in your chamber you will find all the utensils requisite to supply the wants of one who sleeps with his door locked, to the end that no natural needs compel you to open it. May the great Dulcinea del Toboso live a thousand years, and may her fame extend all over the surface of the globe, for she deserves to be loved by a knight so valiant and so virtuous; and may kind Heaven infuse zeal into the heart of our governor Sancho Panza to finish off his discipline speedily, so that the world may once more enjoy the beauty of so grand a lady."

To which Don Quixote replied, "Your highness has spoken like what you are; from the mouth of a noble lady nothing bad can come; and Dulcinea will be more fortunate, and better known to the world by the praise of your highness than by all the eulogies the greatest orators on earth could bestow upon her."

"Well, well, Señor Don Quixote," said the duchess, "it is nearly supper-time, and the duke is probably waiting; come, let us go to supper, and retire to rest early, for the journey you made yesterday from Kandy was not such a short one but that it must have caused you some fatigue."

"I feel none, señora," said Don Quixote, "for I would go so far as to swear to your excellence that in all my life I never mounted a quieter beast, or a pleasanter paced one, than Clavileño; and I don't know what could have induced Malambruno to discard a steed so swift and so gentle, and burn it so recklessly as he did."

"Probably," said the duchess, "repenting of the evil he had done to the Trifaldi and company, and others, and the crimes he must have committed as a wizard and enchanter, he resolved to make away with all the instruments of his craft; and so burned Clavileño as the chief one, and that which mainly kept him restless, wandering from land to land; and by its ashes and the trophy of the placard the valor of the great Don Quixote of La Mancha is established forever."

Don Quixote renewed his thanks to the duchess; and having supped, retired to his chamber alone, refusing to allow any one to enter with him to wait on him, such was his fear of encountering temptations that might lead or drive him to forget his chaste fidelity to his lady Dulcinea; for he had always present to his mind the virtue of Amadis, that flower and mirror of knights-errant. He locked the door behind him, and by the light of two wax candles undressed himself, but as he was taking off his stockings— O disaster unworthy of such a personage!— there came a burst, not of sighs, or anything belying his delicacy or good breeding, but of some two dozen stitches in one of his stockings, that made it look like a window-lattice. The worthy gentleman was beyond measure distressed, and just then he would have given an ounce of silver to have had half a drachm of green silk there; I say green silk, because the stockings were green.

Here Cid Hamet exclaimed as he was writing, "O poverty, poverty! I know not what could have possessed the great Cordovan poet to call thee 'holy gift ungratefully received.' Although a Moor, I know well enough from the intercourse I have had with Christians that holiness consists in charity, humility, faith, obedience, and poverty; but for all that, I say he must have a great deal of godliness who can find any satisfaction in being poor; unless, indeed, it be the kind of poverty one of the greatest saints refers to, saying, 'possess all things as though ye possessed them not'; which is what they call poverty in spirit. But thou, that other poverty— for it is of thee I am speaking now—why dost thou love to fall out with gentlemen and men of good birth more than with other people? Why dost thou compel them to smear the cracks in their shoes, and to have the buttons of their coats, one silk, another hair, and another glass? Why must their ruffs be always crinkled like endive leaves, and not crimped with a crimping iron?" (From this we may perceive the antiquity of starch and crimped ruffs.) Then he goes on: "Poor gentleman of good family! always cockering up his honor, dining miserably and in secret, and making a hypocrite of the toothpick with which he sallies out into the street after eating nothing to oblige him to use it! Poor fellow, I say, with his nervous honor, fancying they perceive a league off the patch on his shoe, the sweat-stains on his hat, the shabbiness of his cloak, and the hunger of his stomach!"

All this was brought home to Don Quixote by the bursting of his stitches; however, he comforted himself on perceiving that Sancho had left behind a pair of travelling boots, which he resolved to wear the next day. At last he went to bed, out of spirits and heavy at heart, as much because he missed Sancho as because of the irreparable disaster to his stockings, the stitches of which he would have even taken up with silk of another color, which is one of the greatest signs of poverty a gentleman can show in the course of his never-failing embarrassments. He put out the candles; but the night was warm and he could not sleep; he rose from his bed and opened slightly a grated window that looked out on a beautiful garden, and as he did so he perceived and heard people walking and talking in the garden. He set himself to listen attentively, and those below raised their voices so that he could hear these words:

"Urge me not to sing, Emerencia, for thou knowest that ever since this stranger entered the castle and my eyes beheld him, I cannot sing but only weep; besides my lady is a light rather than a heavy sleeper, and I would not for all the wealth of the world that she found us here; and even if she were asleep and did not waken, my singing would be in vain, if this strange Æneas, who has come into my neighborhood to flout me, sleeps on and wakens not to hear it."

"Heed not that, dear Altisidora," replied a voice; "the duchess is no doubt asleep, and everybody in the house save the lord of thy heart and disturber of thy soul; for just now I perceived him open the grated window of his chamber, so he must be awake; sing, my poor sufferer, in a low sweet tone to the accompaniment of thy harp; and even if the duchess hears us we can lay the blame on the heat of the night."

"That is not the point, Emerencia," replied Altisidora, "it is that I would not that my singing should lay bare my heart, and that I should be thought a light and wanton maiden by those who know not the mighty power of love; but come what may; better a blush on the cheek than a sore in the heart"; and here a harp softly touched made itself heard. As he listened to all this Don Quixote was in a state of breathless amazement, for immediately the countless adventures like this, with windows, gratings, gardens, serenades, love-makings, and languishings, that he had read of in his trashy books of chivalry, came to his mind. He at once concluded that some damsel of the duchess's was in love with him, and that her modesty forced her to keep her passion secret. He trembled lest he should fall, and made an inward resolution not to yield; and commending himself with all his might and soul to his lady Dulcinea he made up his mind to listen to the music; and to let them know he was there he gave a pretended sneeze, at which the damsels were not a little delighted, for all they wanted was that Don Quixote should hear them. So having tuned the harp, Altisidora, running her hand across the strings, began this ballad:

> O thou that art above in bed,
>   Between the holland sheets,
> A-lying there from night till morn,
>   With outstretched legs asleep;
>
> O thou, most valiant knight of all
>   The famed Manchegan breed,
> Of purity and virtue more
>   Than gold of Araby;
>
> Give ear unto a suffering maid,
>   Well-grown but evil-starr'd,
> For those two suns of thine have lit
>   A fire within her heart.
>
> Adventures seeking thou dost rove,
>   To others bringing woe;
> Thou scatterest wounds, but, ah, the balm
>   To heal them dost withhold!
>
> Say, valiant youth, and so may God
>   Thy enterprises speed,
> Didst thou the light mid Libya's sands
>   Or Jaca's rocks first see?
>
> Did scaly serpents give thee suck?
>   Who nursed thee when a babe?
> Wert cradled in the forest rude,
>   Or gloomy mountain cave?
>
> O Dulcinea may be proud,
>   That plump and lusty maid;
> For she alone hath had the power
>   A tiger fierce to tame.
>
> And she for this shall famous be
>   From Tagus to Jarama,
> From Manzanares to Genil,
>   From Duero to Arlanza.
>
> Fain would I change with her, and give
>   A petticoat to boot,
> The best and bravest that I have,
>   All trimmed with gold galloon.
>
> O for to be the happy fair
>   Thy mighty arms enfold,

> Or even sit beside thy bed
>   And scratch thy dusty poll!
>
> I rave,—to favors such as these
>   Unworthy to aspire;
> Thy feet to tickle were enough
>   For one so mean as I.
>
> What caps, what slippers silver-laced,
>   Would I on thee bestow!
> What damask breeches make for thee;
>   What fine long holland cloaks!
>
> And I would give thee pearls that should
>   As big as oak-galls show;
> So matchless big that each might well
>   Be called the great "Alone." [1]
>
> Manchegan Nero, look not down
>   From thy Tarpeian Rock
> Upon this burning heart, nor add
>   The fuel of thy wrath.
>
> A virgin soft and young am I,
>   Not yet fifteen years old;
> (I'm only three months past fourteen,
>   I swear upon my soul).
>
> I hobble not nor do I limp,
>   All blemish I'm without,
> And as I walk my lily locks
>   Are trailing on the ground.
>
> And though my nose be rather flat,
>   And though my mouth be wide,
> My teeth like topazes exalt
>   My beauty to the sky.
>
> Thou knowest that my voice is sweet,
>   That is if thou dost hear;
> And I am moulded in a form
>   Somewhat below the mean.
>
> These charms, and many more, are thine,
>   Spoils to thy spear and bow all;
> A damsel of this house am I,
>   By name Altisidora.

Here the lay of the heart-stricken Altisidora came to an end, while the warmly wooed Don Quixote began to feel alarm; and with a deep sigh he said to himself, "O that I should be such an unlucky knight that no damsel can set eyes on me but falls in love with me! O that the peerless Dulcinea should be so unfortunate that they cannot let her enjoy my incomparable constancy in peace! What would ye with her, ye queens? Why do ye persecute her, ye empresses? Why do ye pursue her, ye virgins of from fourteen to fifteen? Leave the unhappy being to triumph,

[1] One of the pearls of the Spanish crown was called *La Sola*, being unmatched for size.

rejoice and glory in the lot love has been pleased to bestow upon her in surrendering my heart and yielding up my soul to her. Ye love-smitten host, know that to Dulcinea only I am dough and sugar-paste, flint to all others; for her I am honey, for you aloes. For me Dulcinea alone is beautiful, wise, virtuous, graceful, and high-bred, and all others are ill-favored, foolish, light, and low-born. Nature sent me into the world to be hers and no other's; Altisidora may weep or sing, the lady for whose sake they belabored me in the castle of the enchanted Moor may give way to despair, but I must be Dulcinea's, boiled or roast, pure, courteous, and chaste, in spite of all the magic-working powers on earth." And with that he shut the window with a bang, and, as much out of temper and out of sorts as if some great misfortune had befallen him, stretched himself on his bed, where we will leave him for the present, as the great Sancho Panza, who is about to set up his famous government, now demands our attention.

Chapter 45

Of how the great Sancho Panza took possession of his island, and of how he made a beginning in governing

O PERPETUAL discoverer of the antipodes, torch of the world, eye of heaven, sweet stimulator of the water-coolers! Thymbræus here, Phœbus there, now archer, now physician, father of poetry, inventor of music; thou that always risest and, notwithstanding appearances, never settest! To thee, O Sun, by whose aid man begetteth man, to thee I appeal to help me and lighten the darkness of my wit that I may be able to proceed with scrupulous exactitude in giving an account of the great Sancho Panza's government; for without thee I feel myself weak, feeble, and uncertain.

To come to the point, then—Sancho with all his attendants arrived at a village of some thousand inhabitants, and one of the largest the duke possessed. They informed him that it was called the island of Barataria, either because the name of the village was Baratario, or because of the joke by way of which the government had been conferred upon him.[1] On reaching the gates of the town, which was a walled one, the municipality came forth to meet him, the bells rang out a peal, and the inhabitants showed every sign of general satisfaction; and with great pomp they conducted him to the

[1] *Barato*, in old Spanish, meant a trick or a practical joke.

principal church to give thanks to God, and then with burlesque ceremonies they presented him with the keys of the town, and acknowledged him as perpetual governor of the island of Barataria. The costume, the beard, and the fat squat figure of the new governor astonished all those who were not in the secret, and even all who were, and they were not a few. Finally, leading him out of the church they carried him to the judgment seat and seated him on it, and the duke's majordomo said to him, "It is an ancient custom in this island, señor governor, that he who comes to take possession of this famous island is bound to answer a question which shall be put to him, and which must be a somewhat knotty and difficult one; and by his answer the people take the measure of their new governor's wit, and hail with joy or deplore his arrival accordingly."

While the majordomo was making this speech Sancho was gazing at several large letters inscribed on the wall opposite his seat, and as he could not read he asked what that was painted on the wall. The answer was, "Señor, there is written and recorded the day on which your lordship took possession of this island, and the inscription says, *This day, the so-and-so of such-and-such a month and year, Señor Don Sancho Panza took possession of this island; many years may he enjoy it.*"

"And whom do they call Don Sancho Panza?" asked Sancho.

"Your lordship," replied the majordomo; "for no other Panza but the one who is now seated in that chair has ever entered this island."

"Well then, let me tell you, brother," said Sancho, "I haven't got the 'Don,' nor has any one of my family ever had it; my name is plain Sancho Panza, and Sancho was my father's name, and Sancho was my grandfather's, and they were all Panzas, without any Dons or Doñas tacked on; I suspect that in this island there are more Dons than stones; but never mind; God knows what I mean, and maybe if my government lasts four days I'll weed out these Dons that no doubt are as great a nuisance as the midges, they're so plenty. Let the majordomo go on with his question, and I'll give the best answer I can, whether the people deplore or not."

At this instant there came into court two old men, one carrying a cane by way of a walking-stick, and the one who had no stick said, "Señor, some time ago I lent this good man ten gold-crowns in gold to gratify him and do him a service, on the condition that he was to return them to me whenever I should ask for them. A long time passed before I asked for them, for I would not put him to any greater straits to return them than he was in when I lent them to him; but thinking he was growing careless about payment I asked for them once and several times; and not only will he not give them back, but he denies that he owes them, and says I never lent him any such crowns; or if I did, that he repaid them; and I have no witnesses either of the loan, or of the payment, for he never paid me; I want your worship to put him to his oath, and if he swears he returned them to me I forgive him the debt here and before God."

"What say you to this, good old man, you with the stick?" said Sancho.

To which the old man replied, "I admit, señor, that he lent them to me; but let your worship lower your staff, and as he leaves it to my oath, I'll swear that I gave them back, and paid him really and truly."

The governor lowered the staff, and as he did so the old man who had the stick handed it to the other old man to hold for him while he swore, as if he found it in his way; and then laid his hand on the cross of the staff, saying that it was true the ten crowns that were demanded of him had been lent him; but that he had with his own hand given them back into the hand of the other, and that he, not recollecting it, was every minute asking for them.

Seeing this the great governor asked the creditor what answer he had to make to what his opponent said. He said that no doubt his debtor had told the truth, for he believed him to be an honest man and a good Christian, and he himself must have forgotten when and how he had given him back the crowns; and that from that time forth he would make no further demand upon him.

The debtor took his stick again, and bowing his head left the court. Observing this, and how, without another word, he made off, and observing too the resignation of the plaintiff, Sancho buried his head in his bosom and remained for a short space in deep thought, with the forefinger of his right hand on his brow and nose; then he raised his head and bade them call back the old man with the stick, for he had already taken his departure. They brought him back, and as soon as Sancho saw him he said, "Honest man, give me that stick, for I want it."

"Willingly," said the old man; "here it is, señor," and he put it into his hand.

Sancho took it and handing it to the other old man, said to him, "Go, and God be with you; for now you are paid."

"I, señor!" returned the old man; "why, is this cane worth ten gold-crowns?"

"Yes," said the governor, "or if not I am the greatest dolt in the world; now you will see whether I have got the head-piece to govern a whole kingdom"; and he ordered the cane to be broken in two, there, in the presence of all. It was done, and in the middle of it they found ten gold-crowns. All were filled with amazement, and looked upon their governor as another Solomon. They asked him how he had come to the conclusion that the ten crowns were in the cane; he replied that, observing how the old man who swore gave the stick to his opponent while he was taking the oath, and swore that he had really and truly given him the crowns, and how as soon as he had done swearing he asked for the stick again, it came into his head that the sum demanded must be inside it; and from this he said it might be seen that God sometimes guides those who govern in their judgments, even though they may be fools; besides he had heard the curate himself mention just such another case, and he had so good a memory, that if it was not that he forgot everything he wished to remember, there would not be such a memory in all the island. To conclude, the old men went off, one crestfallen, and the other in high contentment, all who were present were astonished, and he who was recording the words, deeds, and movements of Sancho could not make up his mind whether he was to look upon him and set him down as a fool or as a man of sense.

As soon as this case was disposed of, there came into court a woman holding on with a tight grip to a man dressed like a well-to-do cattle dealer, and she came forward making a great outcry and exclaiming, "Justice, señor governor, justice! and if I don't get it on earth I'll go look for it in heaven. Señor governor of my soul, this wicked man caught me in the middle of the fields here and used my body as if it was an ill-washed rag, and, woe is me! got from me what I had kept these three-and-twenty years and more, defending it against Moors and Christians, natives and strangers; and I always as hard as an oak, and keeping myself as pure as a salamander in the fire, or wool among the brambles, for this good fellow to come now with clean hands to handle me!"

"It remains to be proved whether this gallant has clean hands or not," said Sancho; and turning to the man he asked him what he had to say in answer to the woman's charge.

He all in confusion made answer, "Sirs, I am a poor pig dealer, and this morning I left the village to sell (saving your presence) four pigs, and between dues and cribbings they got out of me little less than the worth of them. As I was returning to my village I fell in on the road with this good dame, and the devil who makes a coil and a mess out of everything, yoked us together. I paid her fairly, but she not contented laid hold of me and never let go until she brought me here; she says I forced her, but she lies by the oath I swear or am ready to swear; and this is the whole truth and every particle of it."

The governor on this asked him if he had any money in silver about him; he said he had about twenty ducats in a leather purse in his bosom. The governor bade him take it out and hand it to the complainant; he obeyed trembling; the woman took it, and making a thousand salaams to all and praying to God for the long life and health of the señor governor who had such regard for distressed orphans and virgins, she hurried out of court with the purse grasped in both her hands, first looking, however, to see if the money it contained was silver.

As soon as she was gone Sancho said to the cattle dealer, whose tears were already starting and whose eyes and heart were following his purse, "Good fellow, go after that woman and take the purse from her, by force even, and come back with it here"; and he did not say it to one who was a fool or deaf, for the man was off at once like a flash of lightning, and ran to do as he was bid.

All the bystanders waited anxiously to see the end of the case, and presently both man and woman came back at even closer grips than before, she with her petticoat up and the purse in the lap of it, and he struggling hard to take it from her, but all to no purpose, so stout was the woman's defence, she all the while crying out, "Justice from God and the world! see here, señor governor, the shamelessness and boldness of this villain, who in the middle of the town, in the middle of the street, wanted to take from me the purse your worship bade him give me."

"And did he take it?" asked the governor.

"Take it!" said the woman; "I'd let my life be taken from me sooner than the purse. A pretty child I'd be! It's another sort of cat they must throw in my face, and not that poor scurvy knave. Pincers and hammers, mallets and chisels would not get it out of my grip; no, nor lions' claws; the soul from out of my body first!"

"She is right," said the man; "I own myself beaten and powerless; I confess I haven't the strength to take it from her"; and he let go his hold of her.

Upon this the governor said to the woman, "Let me see that purse, my worthy and sturdy friend." She handed it to him at once, and the governor returned it to the man, and said to the unforced mistress of force, "Sister, if you had shown as much, or only half as much, spirit and vigor in defending your body as you have shown in defending that purse, the strength of Hercules could not have forced you. Be off, and God speed you, and bad luck to you, and don't show your face in all this island, or within six leagues of it on any side, under pain of two hundred lashes; be off at once, I say, you shameless, cheating shrew."

The woman was cowed and went off disconsolately, hanging her head; and the governor said to the man, "Honest man, go home with your money, and God speed you; and for the future, if you don't want to lose it, see that you don't take it into your head to yoke with anybody." The man thanked him as clumsily as he could and went his way, and the bystanders were again filled with admiration at their new governor's judgments and sentences.

Next, two men, one apparently a farm-laborer, and the other a tailor, for he had a pair of shears in his hand, presented themselves before him, and the tailor said, "Señor governor, this laborer and I come before your worship by reason of this honest man coming to my shop yesterday (for saving everybody's presence I'm a passed tailor, God be thanked), and putting a piece of cloth into my hands and asking me, 'Señor, will there be enough in this cloth to make me a cap?' Measuring the cloth I said there would. He probably suspected—as I supposed, and I supposed right—that I wanted to steal some of the cloth, led to think so by his own roguery and the bad opinion people have of tailors; and he told me to see if there would be enough for two. I guessed what he would be at, and I said 'yes.' He, still following up his original unworthy notion, went on adding cap after cap, and I 'yes' after 'yes,' until we got as far as five. He has just this moment come for them; and I gave them to him, but he won't pay me for the making; on the contrary, he calls upon me to pay *him,* or else return his cloth."

"Is all this true, brother?" said Sancho.

"Yes, señor," replied the man; "but will your worship make him show the five caps he has made me?"

"With all my heart," said the tailor; and drawing his hand from under his cloak he showed five caps stuck upon the five fingers of it, and said, "there are the five caps this good man asks for; and by God and upon my conscience I haven't a scrap of cloth left, and I'll let the work be examined by the inspectors of the trade."

All present laughed at the number of caps and the novelty of the suit; Sancho set himself to think for a moment, and then said, "It seems to me that in this case it is not necessary to deliver long-winded arguments, but only to give off-hand the judgment of an honest man; and so my decision is that the tailor lose the making and the laborer the cloth, and that the caps go to the prisoners in the jail, and let there be no more about it."

If the previous decision about the cattle dealer's purse excited the admiration of the bystanders, this provoked their laughter; however, the governor's orders were after all executed. All this, having been taken down by his chronicler, was at once despatched to the duke, who was looking out for it with great eagerness; and here let us leave the good Sancho; for his master, sorely troubled in mind by Altisidora's music, has pressing claims upon us now.

Chapter 46

Of the terrible bell and cat fright that Don Quixote got in the course of the enamoured Altisidora's wooing

WE left Don Quixote wrapped up in the reflections which the music of the enamoured maid Altisidora had given rise to. He went to bed with them, and just like fleas they would not let him sleep or get a moment's rest, and the broken stitches of his stockings helped them. But as Time is fleet and no obstacle can stay his course, he came riding on the hours, and morning very soon arrived. Seeing which Don Quixote quitted the soft down, and, nowise slothful, dressed himself in his chamois suit and put on his travelling boots to hide the disaster to his stockings. He threw over him his scarlet mantle, put on his head a montera of green velvet trimmed with silver edging, flung across his shoulder the baldric with his good trenchant sword, took up a large rosary that he always carried with him, and with great solemnity and precision of gait proceeded to the ante-chamber where the duke and duchess were already dressed and waiting for him. But as he passed through a gallery, Altisidora and the other damsel, her friend, were lying in wait for him, and the instant Altisidora saw him she pretended to faint, while her friend caught her in her lap, and began hastily unlacing the bosom of her dress.

Don Quixote observed it, and approaching them said, "I know very well what this seizure arises from."

"I know not from what," replied the friend, "for Altisidora is the healthiest damsel in all this house, and I have never heard her complain all the time I have known her. A plague of all the knights-errant in the world, if they be all ungrateful! Go away, Señor Don Quixote; for this poor child will not come to herself again so long as you are here."

To which Don Quixote returned, "Do me the favor, señora, to let a lute be placed in my chamber to-night; and I will comfort this poor maiden to the best of my power; for in the early stages of love a prompt disillusion is an approved remedy"; and with this he retired, so as not to be remarked by any who might see him there.

He had scarcely withdrawn when Altisidora, recovering from her swoon, said to her companion, "The lute must be left, for no doubt Don Quixote intends to give us some music; and being his it will not be bad."

They went at once to inform the duchess of what was going on, and of the lute Don Quixote asked for, and she, delighted beyond measure, plotted with the duke and her two damsels to play him a trick that should be amusing but harmless; and in high glee they waited for night, which came quickly as the day had come; and as for the day, the duke and duchess spent it in charming conversation with Don Quixote.

When eleven o'clock came, Don Quixote found a guitar in his chamber; he tried it, opened the window, and perceived that some persons were walking in the garden; and having passed his fingers over the frets of the guitar and tuned it as well as he could, he spat and cleared his chest, and then with a voice a little hoarse but full-toned, he sang the following ballad, which he had himself that day composed:

> *Mighty Love the hearts of maidens*
> *Doth unsettle and perplex,*
> *And the instrument he uses*
> *Most of all is idleness.*
>
> *Sewing, stitching, any labor,*
> *Having always work to do,*

To the poison Love instilleth
   Is the antidote most sure.

And to proper-minded maidens
   Who desire the matron's name
Modesty's a marriage portion,
   Modesty their highest praise.

Men of prudence and discretion,
   Courtiers gay and gallant knights,
With the wanton damsels dally,
   But the modest take to wife.

There are passions, transient, fleeting,
   Loves in hostelries declared,
Sunrise loves, with sunset ended,
   When the guest hath gone his way.

Love that springs up swift and sudden,
   Here to-day, to-morrow flown,
Passes, leaves no trace behind it,
   Leaves no image on the soul.

Painting that is laid on painting
   Maketh no display or show;
Where one beauty's in possession
   There no other can take hold.

Dulcinea del Toboso
   Painted on my heart I wear;
Never from its tablets, never,
   Can her image be eras'd.

The quality of all in lovers
   Most esteemed is constancy;
'T is by this that love works wonders,
   This exalts them to the skies.

Don Quixote had got so far with his song, to which the duke, the duchess, Altisidora, and nearly the whole household of the castle were listening, when all of a sudden from a gallery above that was exactly over his window they let down a cord with more than a hundred bells attached to it, and immediately after that discharged a great sack full of cats, which also had bells of smaller size tied to their tails. Such was the din of the bells and the squalling of the cats, that though the duke and duchess were the contrivers of the joke they were startled by it, while Don Quixote stood paralyzed with fear; and as luck would have it, two or three of the cats made their way through the grating of his chamber, and flying from one side to the other, made it seem as if there was a legion of devils at large in it. They extinguished the candles that were burning in the room, and rushed about seeking some way of escape; the cord with the large bells never ceased rising and falling; and most of the people of the cas-

tle, not knowing what was really the matter, were at their wits' end with astonishment. Don Quixote sprang to his feet, and drawing his sword, began making passes at the grating, shouting out, "Avaunt, malignant enchanters! avaunt, ye witchcraft-working rabble! I am Don Quixote of La Mancha, against whom your evil machinations avail not nor have any power." And turning upon the cats that were running about the room, he made several cuts at them. They dashed at the grating and escaped by it, save one that, finding itself hard pressed by the slashes of Don Quixote's sword, flew at his face and held on to his nose tooth and nail, with the pain of which he began to shout his loudest. The duke and duchess hearing this, and guessing what it was, ran with all haste to his room, and as the poor gentleman was striving with all his might to detach the cat from his face, they opened the door with a master-key and went in with lights and witnessed the unequal combat. The duke ran forward to part the combatants, but Don Quixote cried out aloud, "Let no one take him from me; leave me hand to hand with this demon, this wizard, this enchanter; I will teach him, I myself, who Don Quixote of La Mancha is." The cat, however, never minding these threats, snarled and held on; but at last the duke pulled it off and flung it out of the window. Don Quixote was left with a face as full of holes as a sieve, and a nose not in very good condition, and greatly vexed that they did not let him finish the battle he had been so stoutly fighting with that villain of an enchanter. They sent for some oil of John's wort, and Altisidora herself with her own fair hands bandaged all the wounded parts; and as she did so she said to him in a low voice, "All these mishaps have befallen thee, hard-hearted knight, for the sin of thy insensibility and obstinacy; and God grant thy squire Sancho may forget to whip himself, so that that dearly beloved Dulcinea of thine may never be released from her enchantment, and that thou mayest never enjoy her or come to her bed, at least while I who adore thee am alive."

To all this Don Quixote made no answer except to heave deep sighs, and then stretched himself on his bed, thanking the duke and duchess for their kindness, not because he stood in any fear of that bell-ringing rabble of enchanters in cat shape, but because he recognized their good intentions in coming to his rescue. The duke and duchess left him to repose and withdrew greatly relieved at the unfortunate result of the joke; as they never thought the adventure would have fallen so heavy on Don Quixote or cost him so dear, for it cost him five days of confinement to his bed, during which he had another adventure, pleasanter than the late one, which his chronicler will not relate just now, in order that he may turn his attention to Sancho Panza, who was proceeding with great diligence and drollery in his government.

Chapter 47

Wherein is continued the account of how Sancho Panza conducted himself in his government

THE history says that from the justice court they carried Sancho to a sumptuous palace, where in a spacious chamber there was a table laid out with royal magnificence. The clarions sounded as Sancho entered the room, and four pages came forward to present him with water for his hands, which Sancho received with great dignity. The music ceased, and Sancho seated himself at the head of the table, for there was only that seat placed, and no more than the one cover laid. A personage, who it appeared afterwards was a physician, placed himself standing by his side with a whalebone wand in his hand. They then lifted up a fine white cloth covering fruit and a great variety of dishes of different sorts; one who looked like a student said grace, and a page put a laced bib on Sancho, while another who played the part of head carver placed a dish of fruit before him. But hardly had he tasted a morsel when the man with the wand touched the plate with it, and they took it away from before him with the utmost celerity. The carver, however, brought him another dish, and Sancho proceeded to try it; but before he could get at it, not to say taste it, already the wand had touched it and a page had carried it off with the same promptitude as the fruit. Sancho seeing this was puzzled, and looking from one to another asked if this dinner was to be eaten after the fashion of a jugglery trick.

To this he with the wand replied, "It is not to be eaten, señor governor, except as is usual and customary in other islands where there are governors. I, señor, am a physician, and I am paid a salary in this island to serve its governors as such, and I have a much greater regard for their health than for my own, studying day and night making myself acquainted with the governor's constitution, in order to be able to cure him when he falls sick. The chief thing I have

to do is to attend at his dinners and suppers and allow him to eat what appears to me to be fit for him and keep from him what I think will do him harm and be injurious to his stomach; and therefore I ordered that plate of fruit to be removed as being too moist, and that other dish I ordered to be removed as being too hot and containing many spices that stimulate thirst; for he who drinks much kills and consumes the radical moisture wherein life consists."

"Well then," said Sancho, "that dish of roast partridges there that seems so savory will not do me any harm."

To this the physician replied, "Of those my lord the governor shall not eat so long as I live."

"Why so?" said Sancho.

"Because," replied the doctor, "our master Hippocrates, the polestar and beacon of medicine, says in one of his aphorisms *omnis saturatio mala, perdicis autem pessima,* which means 'all repletion is bad, but that of partridge is the worst of all.'"

"In that case," said Sancho, "let señor doctor see among the dishes that are on the table what will do me most good and least harm, and let me eat it, without tapping it with his stick; for by the life of the governor, and so may God suffer me to enjoy it, but I'm dying of hunger; and in spite of the doctor and all he may say, to deny me food is the way to take my life instead of prolonging it."

"Your worship is right, señor governor," said the physician; "and therefore your worship, I consider, should not eat of those stewed rabbits there, because it is a furry kind of food; if that veal were not roasted and served with pickles, you might try it; but it is out of the question."

"That big dish that is smoking farther off," said Sancho, "seems to me to be an *olla podrida,* and out of the diversity of things in such *ollas,* I can't fail to light upon something tasty and good for me."

"*Absit,*" said the doctor; "far from us be any such base thought! There is nothing in the world less nourishing than an *olla podrida;* to canons, or rectors of colleges, or peasants' weddings with your *ollas podridas,* but let us have none of them on the tables of governors, where everything that is present should be delicate and refined; and the reason is, that always, everywhere and by everybody, simple medicines are more esteemed than compound ones, for we cannot go wrong in those that are simple, while in the compound we may, by merely altering the quantity of the things composing them. But what I am of opinion the governor should eat now in order to preserve and fortify his health is a hundred or so of wafer cakes and a few thin slices of conserve of quinces, which will settle his stomach and help his digestion."

Sancho on hearing this threw himself back in his chair and surveyed the doctor steadily, and in a solemn tone asked him what his name was and where he had studied.

He replied, "My name, Señor Governor, is Doctor Pedro Recio de Aguero, I am a native of a place called Tirteafuera which lies between Caracuel and Almodóvar del Campo, on the right-hand side, and I have the degree of doctor from the university of Osuna."

To which Sancho, glowing all over with rage, returned, "Then let Doctor Pedro Recio de Mal-aguero, native of Tirteafuera,[1] a place that's on the right-hand side as we go from Caracuel to Almodóvar del Campo, graduate of Osuna, get out of my presence at once; or I swear by the sun I'll take a cudgel, and by dint of blows, beginning with him, I'll not leave a doctor in the whole island; at least of those I know to be ignorant; for as to learned, wise, sensible physicians, them I will reverence and honor as divine persons. Once more I say let Pedro Recio get out of this or I'll take this chair I am sitting on and break it over his head. And if they call me to account for it, I'll clear myself by saying I served God in killing a bad doctor— a general executioner. And now give me something to eat, or else take your government; for a trade that does not feed its master is not worth two beans."

The doctor was dismayed when he saw the governor in such a passion, and he would have made a *Tirteafuera* out of the room but that the same instant a posthorn sounded in the street; and the carver putting his head out of the window turned round and said, "It's a courier from my lord the duke, no doubt with some despatch of importance."

The courier came in all sweating and flurried, and taking a paper from his bosom, placed it in the governor's hands. Sancho handed it to the majordomo and bade him read the superscription, which ran thus:

To DON SANCHO PANZA, GOVERNOR OF THE IS-LAND OF BARATARIA, INTO HIS OWN HANDS OR THOSE OF HIS SECRETARY.

Sancho when he heard this said, "Which of you is my secretary?" "I am, señor," said one of those present, "for I can read and write, and am

[1] *Recio* means obstinate, *mal-agüero*, evil omen. *Tirteafuera* means literally "take thyself off.

a Biscayan." "With that addition," said Sancho, "you might be secretary to the emperor himself; open this paper and see what it says." The new-born secretary obeyed, and having read the contents said the matter was one to be discussed in private. Sancho ordered the chamber to be cleared, the majordomo and the carver only remaining; so the doctor and the others withdrew, and then the secretary read the letter, which was as follows:

It has come to my knowledge, Señor Don Sancho Panza, that certain enemies of mine and of the island are about to make a furious attack upon it some night, I know not when. It behooves you to be on the alert and keep watch, that they surprise you not. I also know by trustworthy spies that four persons have entered the town in disguise in order to take your life, because they stand in dread of your great capacity; keep your eyes open and take heed who approaches you to address you, and eat nothing that is presented to you. I will take care to send you aid if you find yourself in difficulty, but in all things you will act as may be expected of your judgment. From this place, the Sixteenth of August, at four in the morning.

Your friend,
THE DUKE.

Sancho was astonished, and those who stood by made believe to be so too, and turning to the majordomo he said to him, "What we have got to do first, and it must be done at once, is to put Doctor Recio in the lock-up; for if any one wants to kill me it is he, and by a slow death and the worst of all, which is hunger."

"Likewise," said the carver, "it is my opinion your worship should not eat anything that is on this table, for the whole was a present from some nuns; and as they say, 'behind the cross there's the devil.'"

"I don't deny it," said Sancho; "so for the present give me a piece of bread and four pound or so of grapes; no poison can come in them; for the fact is I can't go on without eating; and if we are to be prepared for these battles that are threatening us we must be well provisioned; for it is the tripes that carry the heart and not the heart the tripes. And you, secretary, answer my lord the duke and tell him that all his commands shall be obeyed to the letter, as he directs; and say from me to my lady the duchess that I kiss her hands, and that I beg of her not to forget to send my letter and bundle to my wife Teresa Panza by a messenger; and I will take it as a great favor and will not fail to serve her in all that may lie within my power; and as you are about it you may enclose a kiss of the hand to my master Don Quixote that he may see I am grateful bread; and as a good secretary and a good Biscayan you may add whatever you like, and whatever will come in best; and now take away this cloth and give me something to eat, and I'll be ready to meet all the spies and assassins and enchanters that may come against me or my island."

At this instant a page entered saying, "Here is a farmer on business, who wants to speak to your lordship on a matter of great importance, he says."

"It's very odd," said Sancho, "the ways of these men on business; is it possible they can be such fools as not to see that an hour like this is no hour for coming on business? We who govern and we who are judges—are we not men of flesh and blood, are we not to be allowed the time required for taking rest, unless they'd have us made of marble? By God and on my conscience, if the government remains in my hands (which I have a notion it won't), I'll bring more than one man on business to order. However, tell this good man to come in; but take care first of all that he is not some spy or one of my assassins."

"No, my lord," said the page, "for he looks like a simple fellow, and either I know very little or he is as good as good bread."

"There is nothing to be afraid of," said the majordomo, "for we are all here."

"Would it be possible, carver," said Sancho, "now that Doctor Pedro Recio is not here, to let me eat something solid and substantial, if it were even a piece of bread and an onion?"

"To-night at supper," said the carver, "the shortcomings of the dinner shall be made good, and your lordship shall be fully satisfied and contented."

"God grant it," said Sancho.

The farmer now came in, a well-favored man that one might see a thousand leagues off was an honest fellow and a good soul. The first thing he said was, "Which is the señor governor here?"

"Which should it be," said the secretary, "but he who is seated in the chair?"

"Then I humble myself before him," said the farmer; and going on his knees he asked for his hand, to kiss it. Sancho refused it, and bade him stand up and say what he wanted. The farmer obeyed, and then said, "I am a farmer, señor, a native of Miguelturra, a village two leagues from Ciudad Real."

"Another Tirteafuera!" said Sancho; "say on, brother; I know Miguelturra very well I can tell you, for it's not very far from my own town."

"The case is this, señor," continued the farmer, "that by God's mercy I am married with the leave and license of the holy Roman Catholic Church; I have two sons, students, and the younger is studying to become bachelor, and the elder to be licentiate; I am a widower, for my wife died, or more properly speaking, a bad doctor killed her on my hands, giving her a purge when she was with child; and if it had pleased God that the child had been born, and was a boy, I would have put him to study for doctor, that he might not envy his brothers the bachelor and the licentiate."

"So that if your wife had not died, or had not been killed, you would not now be a widower," said Sancho.

"No, señor, certainly not," said the farmer.

"We've got that much settled," said Sancho; "get on, brother, for it's more bedtime than business-time."

"Well then," said the farmer, "this son of mine who is going to be a bachelor fell in love in the said town with a damsel called Clara Perlerina, daughter of Andres Perlerino, a very rich farmer, and this name of Perlerines does not come to them by ancestry or descent, but because all the family are paralytics, and for a better name they call them Perlerines though to tell the truth the damsel is as fair as an Oriental pearl, and like a flower of the field, if you look at her on the right side; on the left not so much, for on that side she wants an eye that she lost by smallpox; and though her face is thickly and deeply pitted, those who love her say they are not pits that are there, but the graves where the hearts of her lovers are buried. She is so cleanly that not to soil her face she carries her nose turned up, as they say, so that one would fancy it was running away from her mouth; and with all this she looks extremely well, for she has a wide mouth; and but for wanting ten or a dozen teeth and grinders she might compare and compete with the comeliest. Of her lips I say nothing, for they are so fine and thin that, if lips might be reeled, one might make a skein of them; but being of a different color from ordinary lips they are wonderful, for they are mottled, blue, green, and purple—let my lord the governor pardon me for painting so minutely the charms of her who some time or other will be my daughter; for I love her, and I don't find her amiss."

"Paint what you will," said Sancho; "I enjoy your painting, and if I had dined there could be no dessert more to my taste than your portrait."

"That I have still to furnish," said the farmer; "but a time may come when we may be able if we are not now; and I can tell you, señor, if I could paint her gracefulness and her tall figure, it would astonish you; but that is impossible because she is bent double with her knees up to her mouth; but for all that it is easy to see that if she could stand up she'd knock her head against the ceiling; and she would have given her hand to my bachelor ere this, only that she can't stretch it out, for it's contracted; but still one can see its elegance and fine make by its long furrowed nails."

"That will do, brother," said Sancho; "consider you have painted her from head to foot; what is it you want now? Come to the point without all this beating about the bush, and all these scraps and additions."

"I want your worship, señor," said the farmer, "to do me the favor of giving me a letter of recommendation to the girl's father, begging him to be so good as to let this marriage take place, as we are not ill-matched either in the gifts of fortune or of nature; for to tell the truth, señor governor, my son is possessed of a devil, and there is not a day but the evil spirits torment him three or four times; and from having once fallen into the fire, he has his face puckered up like a piece of parchment, and his eyes watery and always running; but he has the disposition of an angel, and if it was not for belaboring and pummelling himself he'd be a saint."

"Is there anything else you want, good man?" said Sancho.

"There's another thing I'd like," said the farmer, "but I'm afraid to mention it; however, out it must; for after all I can't let it be rotting in my breast, come what may. I mean, señor, that I'd like your worship to give me three hundred or six hundred ducats as a help to my bachelor's portion, to help him in setting up house, I mean; for they must, in short, live by themselves, without being subject to the interferences of their fathers-in-law."

"Just see if there's anything else you'd like? said Sancho, "and don't hold back from mentioning it out of bashfulness or modesty."

"No, indeed there is not," said the farmer.

The moment he said this the governor started to his feet, and seizing the chair he had been sitting on exclaimed, "By all that's good you ill-bred, boorish Don Bumpkin, if you don't get out of this at once and hide yourself from my sight, I'll lay your head open with this chair. You whoreson rascal, you devil's own painter, and is it at this hour you come to ask me for six hundred ducats! How should I have them, you stinking brute? And why should I give them to you if I had them, you knave and blockhead? What have I to do with Miguelturra or the whole family of the Perlerines? Get out I say, or by the life of my lord the duke I'll do as I said. You're not from Miguelturra, but some knave sent here from hell to tempt me. Why, you villain, I have not yet had the government half a day, and you want me to have six hundred ducats already!"

The carver made signs to the farmer to leave the room, which he did with his head down, and to all appearance in terror lest the governor should carry his threats into effect, for the rogue knew very well how to play his part. But let us leave Sancho in his wrath, and peace be with them all; and let us return to Don Quixote, whom we left with his face bandaged and doctored after the cat wounds, of which he was not cured for eight days; and on one of these there befell him what Cid Hamet promises to relate with that exactitude and truth with which he is wont to set forth everything connected with this great history, however minute it may be.

Chapter 48

Of what befell Don Quixote with Doña Rodriguez, the duchess's Duenna, together with other occurrences worthy of record and eternal remembrance

EXCEEDINGLY moody and dejected was the sorely wounded Don Quixote, with his face bandaged and marked, not by the hand of God, but by the claws of a cat, mishaps incidental to knight-errantry. Six days he remained without appearing in public, and one night as he lay awake thinking of his misfortunes and of Altisidora's pursuit of him, he perceived that some one was opening the door of his room with a key, and he at once made up his mind that the enamoured damsel was coming to make an assault upon his chastity and put him in danger of failing in the fidelity he owed to his lady Dulcinea del Toboso. "No," said he, firmly persuaded of the truth of his idea (and he said it loud enough to be heard), "the greatest beauty upon earth shall not avail to make me renounce my adoration of her whom I bear stamped and graved in the core of my heart and the secret depths of my bowels; be thou, lady mine, transformed into a clumsy country wench, or into a nymph of golden Tagus weaving a web of silk and gold, let Merlin or Montesinos hold thee captive where they will; where'er thou art, thou art mine, and where'er I am, I must be thine." The very instant he had uttered these words, the door opened. He stood up on the bed wrapped from head to foot in a yellow satin coverlet, with a cap on his head, and his face and his mustaches tied up, his face because of the scratches, and his mustaches to keep them from drooping and falling down, and in this trim he looked the most extraordinary scarecrow that could be conceived. He kept his eyes fixed on the door, and just as he was expecting to see the love-smitten and unhappy Altisidora make her appearance, he saw coming in a most venerable duenna, in a long white-bordered veil that covered and enveloped her from head to foot. Between the fingers of her left hand she held a short lighted candle, while with her right she shaded it to keep the light from her eyes, which were covered by spectacles of great size, and she advanced with noiseless steps, treading very softly.

Don Quixote kept an eye upon her from his watch-tower, and observing her costume and noting her silence, he concluded that it must be some witch or sorceress that was coming in such a guise to work him some mischief, and he began crossing himself at a great rate. The spectre still advanced, and on reaching the middle of the room, looked up and saw the energy with which Don Quixote was crossing himself; and if he was scared by seeing such a figure as hers, she was terrified at the sight of his; for the moment she saw his tall yellow form with the coverlet and the bandages that disfigured him, she gave a loud scream, and exclaiming, "Jesus! what's this I see?" let fall the candle in her fright, and then finding herself in the dark, turned about to make off, but stumbling on her skirts in her consternation, she measured her length with a mighty fall.

Don Quixote in his trepidation began saying, "I conjure thee, phantom, or whatever thou art, tell me what thou art and what thou wouldst with me. If thou art a soul in torment, say so, and all that my powers can do I will do for thee; for I am a Catholic Christian and love to do good to all the world, and to this end I have embraced the order of knight-errantry to which I belong, the province of which extends to doing good even to souls in purgatory."

The unfortunate duenna hearing herself thus conjured, by her own fear guessed Don Quixote's, and in a low plaintive voice answered, "Senor Don Quixote—if so be you are indeed Don Quixote—I am no phantom or spectre or soul in purgatory, as you seem to think, but Doña Rodriguez, duenna of honor to my lady the duchess, and I come to you with one of those grievances your worship is wont to redress."

"Tell me, Señora Doña Rodriguez," said Don Quixote, "do you perchance come to transact any go-between business? Because I must tell you I am not available for anybody's purpose, thanks to the peerless beauty of my lady Dulcinea del Toboso. In short, Señora Doña Rodriguez, if you will leave out and put aside all love messages, you may go and light your candle and come back, and we will discuss all the commands you have for me and whatever you wish, saving only, as I said, all seductive communications."

"I carry nobody's messages, señor," said the duenna; "little you know me. Nay, I'm not far enough advanced in years to take to any such childish tricks. God be praised I have a soul in my body still, and all my teeth and grinders in my mouth, except one or two that the colds, so common in this Aragon country, have robbed me of. But wait a little, while I go and light my candle, and I will return immediately and lay my sorrows before you as before one who relieves those of all the world"; and without staying for an answer she quitted the room and left Don Quixote tranquilly meditating while he waited for her. A thousand thoughts at once suggested themselves to him on the subject of this new adventure, and it struck him as being ill done and worse advised in him to expose himself to the danger of breaking his plighted faith to his lady; and said he to himself, "Who knows but that the devil, being wily and cunning, may be trying now to entrap me with a duenna, having failed with empresses, queens, duchesses, marchionesses, and countesses? Many a time have I heard it said by many a man of sense that he will sooner offer you a flat-nosed wench than a Roman-nosed one; and who knows but this privacy, this opportunity, this silence, may awaken my sleeping desires, and lead me in these my latter years to fall where I have never tripped? In cases of this sort it is better to flee than to await the battle. But I must be out of my senses to think and utter such nonsense; for it is impossible that a long, white-hooded, spectacled duenna could stir up or excite a wanton thought in the most graceless bosom in the world. Is there a duenna on earth that has fair flesh? Is there a duenna in the world that escapes being ill-tempered, wrinkled, and prudish? Avaunt, then, ye duenna crew, undelightful to all mankind. Oh, but that lady did well who, they say, had at the end of her reception room a couple of figures of duennas with spectacles and lace-cushions, as if at work, and those statues served quite as well to give an air of propriety to the room as if they had been real duennas."

So saying he leaped off the bed, intending to close the door and not allow Señora Rodriguez to enter; but as he went to shut it Señora Rodriguez returned with a wax candle lighted, and having a closer view of Don Quixote, with the coverlet round him, and his bandages and nightcap, she was alarmed afresh, and retreating a couple of paces, exclaimed, "Am I safe, sir knight? for I don't look upon it as a sign of very great virtue that your worship should have got up out of bed."

"I may well ask the same, señora," said Don Quixote; "and I do ask whether I shall be safe from being assailed and forced?"

"Of whom and against whom do you demand that security, sir knight?" said the duenna.

"Of you and against you I ask it," said Don Quixote; "for I am not marble, nor are you brass, nor is it now ten o'clock in the morning, but midnight, or a trifle past it I fancy, and we are in a room more secluded and retired than the cave could have been where the treacherous and daring Æneas enjoyed the fair soft-hearted Dido. But give me your hand, señora; I require no better protection than my own continence, and my own sense of propriety; as well as that which is inspired by that venerable head-dress"; and so saying he kissed her right hand and took it in his own, she yielding it to him with equal ceremoniousness. And here Cid Hamet inserts a parenthesis in which he says that to have seen the pair marching from the door to the bed, linked hand in hand in this way, he would have given the best of the two tunics he had.

Don Quixote finally got into bed, and Doña Rodriguez took her seat on a chair at some little distance from his couch, without taking off her spectacles or putting aside the candle. Don Quixote wrapped the bedclothes round him and covered himself up completely, leaving nothing but his face visible, and as soon as they had both regained their composure he broke silence, saying, "Now, Señora Doña Rodriguez, you may unbosom yourself and out with everything you have in your sorrowful heart and afflicted bowels; and by me you shall be listened to with chaste ears, and aided by compassionate exertions."

"I believe it," replied the duenna; "from your worship's gentle and winning presence only such a Christian answer could be expected. The fact is, then, Señor Don Quixote, that though you see me seated in this chair, here in the middle of the kingdom of Aragon, and in the attire of a despised outcast duenna, I am from the Asturias of Oviedo, and of a family with which many of the best of the province are connected by blood; but my untoward fate and the improvidence of my parents, who, I know not how, were unseasonably reduced to poverty, brought me to the court of Madrid, where as a provision and to avoid greater misfortunes, my parents placed me as seamstress in the service of a lady of quality, and I would have you know that for hemming and sewing I have never been surpassed by any all my life. My parents left me in service and returned to their own country, and a few years later went, no doubt, to heaven, for they were excellent good Catholic Christians. I was left an orphan with nothing but the miserable wages and trifling presents that are given to servants of my sort in palaces; but about this time, without any encouragement on my part, one of the esquires of the household fell in love with me, a man somewhat advanced in years, full-bearded and personable, and above all as good a gentleman as the king himself, for he came of a mountain stock. We did not carry on our loves with such secrecy but that they came to the knowledge of my lady, and she, not to have any fuss about it, had us married with the full sanction of the holy mother Roman Catholic Church, of which marriage a daughter was born to put an end to my good fortune, if I had any; not that I died in childbirth, for I passed through it safely and in due season, but because shortly afterward my husband died of a certain shock he received, and had I time to tell you of it I know your worship would be surprised"; and here she began to weep bitterly and said, "Pardon me, Señor Don Quixote, if I am unable to control myself, for every time I think of my unfortunate husband my eyes fill up with tears. God bless me, with what an air of dignity he used to carry my lady behind him on a stout mule as black as jet! for in those days they did not use coaches or chairs, as they say they do now, and ladies rode behind their squires. This much at least I cannot help telling you, that you may observe the good breeding and punctiliousness of my worthy husband. As he was turning into the Calle de Santiago in

Madrid, which is rather narrow, one of the *alcaldes* of the Court, with two *alguacils* before him, was coming out of it, and as soon as my good squire saw him he wheeled his mule about and made as if he would turn and accompany him. My lady, who was riding behind him, said to him in a low voice, 'What are you about, you sneak, don't you see that I am here?' The *alcalde* like a polite man pulled up his horse and said to him, 'Proceed, señor, for it is I, rather, who ought to accompany my lady Doña Casilda'—for that was my mistress's name. Still my husband, cap in hand, persisted in trying to accompany the *alcalde*, and seeing this my lady, filled with rage and vexation, pulled out a big pin, or, I rather think, a bodkin, out of her needle-case and drove it into his back with such force that my husband gave a loud yell, and writhing fell to the ground with his lady. Her two lackeys ran to raise her up, and the *alcalde* and the *alguacils* did the same; the Guadalajara gate was all in commotion—I mean the idlers congregated there; my mistress came back on foot, and my husband hurried away to a barber's shop protesting that he was run right through the guts. The courtesy of my husband was noised abroad to such an extent, that the boys gave him no peace in the street; and on this account, and because he was somewhat shortsighted, my lady dismissed him; and it was chagrin at this I am convinced beyond a doubt that brought on his death. I was left a helpless widow, with a daughter on my hands growing up in beauty like the sea-foam; at length, however, as I had the character of being an excellent needlewoman, my lady the duchess, then lately married to my lord the duke, offered to take me with her to this kingdom of Aragon, and my daughter also, and here as time went by my daughter grew up and with her all the graces in the world; she sings like a lark, dances quick as thought, foots it like a gypsy, reads and writes like a schoolmaster, and does sums like a miser; of her neatness I say nothing, for the running water is not purer, and her age is now, if my memory serves me, sixteen years five months and three days, one more or less. To come to the point, the son of a very rich farmer living in a village of my lord the duke's, not very far from here, fell in love with this girl of mine; and in short, how I know not, they came together, and under the promise of marrying her he made a fool of my daughter, and will not keep his word. And though my lord the duke is aware of it (for I have complained to him, not once but many and many a time, and entreated him to order the farmer to

marry my daughter), he turns a deaf ear and will scarcely listen to me; the reason being that as the deceiver's father is so rich, and lends him money, and is constantly going security for his debts, he does not like to offend or annoy him in any way. Now, señor, I want your worship to take it upon yourself to redress this wrong either by entreaty or by arms; for by what all the world says you came into it to redress grievances and right wrongs and help the unfortunate. Let your worship put before you the unprotected condition of my daughter, her grace, her youth, and all the perfections I have said she possesses; and before God and on my conscience, out of all the damsels my lady has, there is not one that comes up to the sole of her shoe, and the one they call Altisidora, and looked upon as the boldest and gayest of them, put in comparison with my daughter, does not come within two leagues of her. For I would have you know, señor, all is not gold that glitters, and that same little Altisidora has more forwardness than good looks, and more impudence than modesty; besides being not very sound, for she has such a disagreeable breath that one cannot bear to be near her for a moment; and even my lady the duchess—but I'll hold my tongue, for they say that walls have ears."

"For Heaven's sake, Doña Rodriguez, what ails my lady the duchess?" asked Don Quixote.

"Adjured in that way," replied the duenna, "I cannot help answering the question and telling the whole truth. Señor Don Quixote, have you observed the comeliness of my lady the duchess, that smooth complexion of hers like a burnished polished sword, those two cheeks of milk and carmine, that gay lively step with which she treads or rather seems to spurn the earth, so that one would fancy she went radiating health wherever she passed? Well then, let me tell you she may thank, first of all God, for this, and next, two issues that she has, one in each leg, by which all the evil humors, of which the doctors say she is full, are discharged."

"Blessed Virgin!" exclaimed Don Quixote; "and is it possible that my lady the duchess has drains of that sort? I would not have believed it if the bare-foot friars had told it me; but as the lady Doña Rodriguez says so, it must be so. But surely such issues, and in such places, do not discharge humors, but liquid amber. Verily, I do believe now that this practice of opening issues is a very important matter for the health."

Don Quixote had hardly said this, when the chamber door flew open with a loud bang, and with the start the noise gave her Doña Rodriguez let the candle fall from her hand, and the room was left as dark as a wolf's mouth, as the saying is. Suddenly the poor duenna felt two hands seize her by the throat, so tightly that she could not croak, while some one else, without uttering a word, very briskly hoisted up her petticoats, and with what seemed to be a slipper began to lay on so heartily that any one would have felt pity for her; but although Don Quixote felt it he never stirred from his bed, but lay quiet and silent, nay apprehensive that his turn for a drubbing might be coming. Nor was the apprehension an idle one; for leaving the duenna (who did not dare to cry out) well-basted, the silent executioners fell upon Don Quixote, and stripping him of the sheet and the coverlet, they pinched him so fast and so hard that he was driven to defend himself with his fists, and all this in marvellous silence. The battle lasted nearly half an hour, and then the phantoms fled; Doña Rodriguez gathered up her skirts, and bemoaning her fate went out without saying a word to Don Quixote, and he, sorely pinched, puzzled, and dejected, remained alone, and there we will leave him, wondering who could have been the perverse enchanter who had reduced him to such a state; but that shall be told in due season, for Sancho claims our attention, and the methodical arrangement of the story demands it.

Chapter 49

Of what happened Sancho in making the round of his island

WE left the great governor angered and irritated by that portrait-painting rogue of a farmer who, instructed by the majordomo, as the majordomo was by the duke, tried to practise upon him; he however, fool, boor, and clown as he was, held his own against them all, saying to those round him and to Doctor Pedro Recio, who as soon as the private business of the duke's letter was disposed of had returned to the room, "Now I see plainly enough that judges and governors ought to be and must be made of brass not to feel the importunities of the applicants that at all times and all seasons insist on being heard, and having their business despatched, and their own affairs and no others attended to, come what may; and if the poor judge does not hear them and settle the matter—either because he cannot or because that is not the time set apart for hearing them—forthwith they abuse him, and run him down, and gnaw at his bones, and even pick holes in his pedigree. You silly, stupid applicant, don't be in a hurry; wait for

the proper time and season for doing business; don't come at dinner-hour, or at bedtime; for judges are only flesh and blood, and must give to Nature what she naturally demands of them; all except myself, for in my case I give her nothing to eat, thanks to Señor Doctor Pedro Recio Tirteafuera here, who would have me die of hunger, and declares that death to be life; and the same sort of life may God give him and all his kind—I mean the bad doctors; for the good ones deserve palms and laurels."

All who knew Sancho Panza were astonished to hear him speak so elegantly, and did not know what to attribute it to unless it were that office and grave responsibility either smarten or stupefy men's wits. At last Doctor Pedro Recio Aguero of Tirteafuera promised to let him have supper that night, though it might be in contravention of all the aphorisms of Hippocrates. With this the governor was satisfied and looked forward to the approach of night and supper-time with great anxiety; and though time, to his mind, stood still and made no progress, nevertheless the hour he so longed for came, and they gave him a beef salad with onions and some boiled calves' feet rather far gone. At this he fell to with greater relish than if they had given him francolins from Milan, pheasants from Rome, veal from Sorrento, partridges from Moron, or geese from Lavajos, and turning to the doctor at supper he said to him, "Look here, señor doctor, for the future don't trouble yourself about giving me dainty things or choice dishes to eat, for it will be only taking my stomach off its hinges; it is accustomed to goat, cow, bacon, hung beef, turnips and onions; and if by any chance it is given these palace dishes, it receives them squeamishly, and sometimes with loathing. What the head-carver had best do is to serve me with what they call *ollas podridas* (and the rottener they are the better they smell); and he can put whatever he likes into them, so long as it is good to eat, and I'll be obliged to him, and will requite him some day. But let nobody play pranks on me, for either we are or we are not; let us live and eat in peace and good-fellowship, for when God sends the dawn, he sends it for all. I mean to govern this island without giving up a right or taking a bribe; let every one keep his eye open, and look out for the arrow; for I can tell them 'the devil's in Cantillana,' and if they drive me to it they'll see something that will astonish them. Nay! make yourself honey and the flies will eat you."

"Of a truth, señor governor," said the carver, "your worship is in the right of it in everything you have said; and I promise you in the name of all the inhabitants of this island that they will serve your worship with all zeal, affection, and goodwill, for the mild kind of government you have given a sample of to begin with, leaves them no ground for doing or thinking anything to your worship's disadvantage."

"That I believe," said Sancho; "and they would be great fools if they did or thought otherwise; once more I say, see to my feeding and my Dapple's, for that is the great point and what is most to the purpose; and when the hour comes let us go the rounds, for it is my intention to purge this island of all manner of uncleanness and of all idle good-for-nothing vagabonds; for I would have you know, my friends, that lazy idlers are the same thing in a State as the drones in a hive, that eat up the honey the industrious bees make. I mean to protect the husbandman, to preserve to the gentleman his privileges, to reward the virtuous, and above all to respect religion and honor its ministers. What say you to that, my friends? Is there anything in what I say, or am I talking to no purpose?"

"There is so much in what your worship says, señor governor," said the majordomo, "that I am filled with wonder when I see a man like your worship, entirely without learning (for I believe you have none at all), say such things, and so full of sound maxims and sage remarks, very different from what was expected of your worship's intelligence by those who sent us or by us who came here. Every day we see something new in this world; jokes become realities, and the jokers find the tables turned upon them."

Night came, and with the permission of Doctor Pedro Recio, the governor had supper. They then got ready to go the rounds, and he started with the majordomo, the secretary, the head-carver, the chronicler charged with recording his deeds, and *alguacils* and notaries enough to form a fair-sized squadron. In the midst marched Sancho with his staff, as fine a sight as one could wish to see, and but a few streets of the town had been traversed when they heard a noise as of a clashing of swords. They hastened to the spot, and found that the combatants were but two, who seeing the authorities approaching stood still, and one of them exclaimed, "Help, in the name of God and the king! Are men to be allowed to rob in the middle of this town, and rush out and attack people in the very streets?"

"Be calm, my good man," said Sancho, "and tell me what the cause of this quarrel is; for I am the governor."

Said the other combatant, "Señor governor, I will tell you in a very few words. Your worship must know that this gentleman has just now won more than a thousand reals in that gambling house opposite, and God knows how. I was there, and gave more than one doubtful point in his favor, very much against what my conscience told me. He made off with his winnings, and when I made sure he was going to give me a crown or so at least by way of a present, as it is usual and customary to give men of quality of my sort who stand by to see fair or foul play, and back up swindles, and prevent quarrels, he pocketed his money and left the house. Indignant at this I followed him, and speaking him fairly and civilly asked him to give me if it were only eight reals, for he knows I am an honest man and that I have neither profession nor property, for my parents never brought me up to any or left me any; but the rogue, who is a greater thief than Cacus and a greater sharper than Andradilla, would not give me more than four reals; so your worship may see how little shame and conscience he has. But by my faith if you had not come up I'd have made him disgorge his winnings, and he'd have learned what the range of the steelyard was."

"What say you to this?" asked Sancho. The other replied that all his antagonist said was true, and that he did not choose to give him more than four reals because he very often gave him money; and that those who expected presents ought to be civil and take what is given them with a cheerful countenance, and not make any claim against winners unless they know them for certain to be sharpers and their winnings to be unfairly won; and that there could be no better proof that he himself was an honest man than his having refused to give anything; for sharpers always pay tribute to lookers-on who know them."

"This is true," said the majordomo; "let your worship consider what is to be done with these men."

"What is to be done," said Sancho, "is this; you, the winner, be you good, bad, or indifferent, give this assailant of yours a hundred reals at once, and you must disburse thirty more for the poor prisoners; and you who have neither profession nor property, and hang about the island in idleness, take these hundred reals now, and some time of the day tomorrow quit the island under sentence of banishment for ten years, and under pain of completing it in another life if you violate the sentence, for I'll hang you on a gibbet, or at least the hangman will by my orders; not a word from either of you, or I'll make him feel my hand."

The one paid down the money and the other took it, and the latter quitted the island, while the other went home; and then the governor said, "Either I am not good for much, or I'll get rid of these gambling houses, for it strikes me they are very mischievous."

"This one at least," said one of the notaries, "your worship will not be able to get rid of, for a great man owns it, and what he loses every year is beyond all comparison more than what he makes by the cards. On the minor gambling houses your worship may exercise your power, and it is they that do most harm and shelter the most barefaced practices; for in the houses of lords and gentlemen of quality the notorious sharpers dare not attempt to play their tricks; and as the vice of gambling has become common, it is better that men should play in houses of repute than in some tradesman's, where they catch an unlucky fellow in the small hours of the morning and skin him alive."

"I know already, notary, that there is a good deal to be said on that point," said Sancho.

And now a tipstaff came up with a young man in his grasp, and said, "Señor governor, this youth was coming towards us, and as soon as he saw the officers of justice he turned about and ran like a deer, a sure proof that he must be some evil-doer; I ran after him, and had it not been that he stumbled and fell, I should never have caught him."

"What did you run for, fellow?" said Sancho.

To which the young man replied, "Señor, it was to avoid answering all the questions officers of justice put."

"What are you by trade?"

"A weaver."

"And what do you weave?"

"Lance heads, with your worship's good leave."

"You're facetious with me! You plume yourself on being a wag? Very good; and where were you going just now?"

"To take the air, señor."

"And where does one take the air in this island?"

"Where it blows."

"Good! your answers are very much to the point; you are a smart youth; but take notice that I am the air, and that I blow upon you astern, and send you to jail. Ho there! lay hold of him and take him off; I'll make him sleep there tonight without air."

"By God," said the young man, "your worship will make me sleep in jail just as soon as make me king."

"Why shan't I make thee sleep in jail?" said Sancho. "Have I not the power to arrest thee and release thee whenever I like?"

"All the power your worship has," said the young man, "won't be able to make me sleep in jail."

"How? not able!" said Sancho; "take him away at once where he'll see his mistake with his own eyes, even if the jailer is willing to exert his interested generosity on his behalf; for I'll lay a penalty of two thousand ducats on him if he allows him to stir a step from the prison."

"That's ridiculous," said the young man; "the fact is, all the men on earth will not make me sleep in prison."

"Tell me, you devil," said Sancho, "have you got any angel that will deliver you, and take off the irons I am going to order them to put upon you?"

"Now, señor governor," said the young man in a sprightly manner, "let us be reasonable and come to the point. Granted your worship may order me to be taken to prison, and have irons and chains put on me, and to be shut up in a cell, and may lay heavy penalties on the jailer if he lets me out, and that he obeys your orders; still, if I don't choose to sleep, and choose to remain awake all night without closing an eye, will your worship with all your power be able to make me sleep if I don't choose?"

"No, truly," said the secretary, "and the fellow has made his point."

"So then," said Sancho, "it would be entirely of your own choice you would keep from sleeping; not in opposition to my will?"

"No, señor," said the youth, "certainly not."

"Well then, go, and God be with you," said Sancho; "be off home to sleep, and God give you sound sleep, for I don't want to rob you of it; but for the future, let me advise you don't joke with the authorities, because you may come across some one who will bring down the joke on your own skull."

The young man went his way, and the governor continued his round, and shortly afterwards two tipstaffs came up with a man in custody, and said, "Señor governor, this person, who seems to be a man, is not so, but a woman, and not an ill-favored one, in man's clothes." They raised two or three lanterns to her face, and by their light they distinguished the features of a woman to all appearance of the age of sixteen or a little more, with her hair gathered into a gold and green silk net, and fair as a thousand pearls. They scanned her from head to foot, and observed that she had on red silk stockings with garters of white taffety bordered with gold and pearl; her breeches were of green and gold stuff, and under an open jacket or jerkin of the same she wore a doublet of the finest white and gold cloth; her shoes were white and such as men wear; she carried no sword at her belt, but only a richly ornamented dagger, and on her fingers she had several handsome rings. In short, the girl seemed fair to look at in the eyes of all, and none of those who beheld her knew her, the people of the town said they could not imagine who she was, and those who were in the secret of the jokes that were to be practised upon Sancho were the ones who were most surprised, for this incident or discovery had not been arranged by them; and they watched anxiously to see how the affair would end.

Sancho was fascinated by the girl's beauty, and he asked her who she was, where she was going, and what had induced her to dress herself in that garb. She with her eyes fixed on the ground answered in modest confusion, "I cannot tell you, señor, before so many people what it is of such consequence to me to have kept secret; one thing I wish to be known, that I am no thief or evil-doer, but only an unhappy maiden whom the power of jealousy has led to break through the respect that is due to modesty."

Hearing this the majordomo said to Sancho, "Make the people stand back, señor governor, that this lady may say what she wishes with less embarrassment."

Sancho gave the order, and all except the majordomo, the head-carver, and the secretary fell back. Finding herself then in the presence of no more, the damsel went on to say, "I am the daughter, sirs, of Pedro Perez Mazorca, the wool-farmer of this town, who is in the habit of coming very often to my father's house."

"That won't do, señora," said the majordomo; "for I know Pedro Perez very well, and I know he has no child at all, either son or daughter; and besides, though you say he is your father, you add then that he comes very often to your father's house."

"I have already noticed that," said Sancho.

"I am confused just now, sirs," said the damsel, "and I don't know what I am saying; but the truth is that I am the daughter of Diego de la Llana, whom you must all know."

"Ay, that will do," said the majordomo; "for I know Diego de la Llana, and know that he is a gentleman of position and a rich man, and that he has a son and a daughter, and that since he was left a widower nobody in all this town can speak to having seen his daughter's face; for he

keeps her so closely shut up that he does not give even the sun a chance of seeing her; and for all that report says she is extremely beautiful."

"It is true," said the damsel, "and I am that daughter; whether report lies or not as to my beauty, you, sirs, will have decided by this time, as you have seen me"; and with this she began to weep bitterly.

On seeing this the secretary leant over to the head-carver's ear, and said to him in a low voice, "Something serious has no doubt happened this poor maiden, that she goes wandering from home in such a dress and at such an hour, and one of her rank too." "There can be no doubt about it," returned the carver, "and moreover her tears confirm your suspicion." Sancho gave her the best comfort he could, and entreated her to tell them without any fear what had happened her, as they would all earnestly and by every means in their power endeavor to relieve her.

"The fact is, sirs," said she, "that my father has kept me shut up these ten years, for so long is it since the earth received my mother. Mass is said at home in a sumptuous chapel, and all this time I have seen but the sun in the heaven by day, and the moon and the stars by night; nor do I know what streets are like, or plazas, or churches, or even men, except my father and a brother I have, and Pedro Perez the wool-farmer; whom, because he came frequently to our house, I took it into my head to call my father, to avoid naming my own. This seclusion and the restrictions laid upon my going out, were it only to church, have been keeping me unhappy for many a day and month past; I longed to see the world, or at least the town where I was born, and it did not seem to me that this wish was inconsistent with the respect maidens of good quality should have for themselves. When I heard them talking of bull-fights taking place, and of javelin games, and of acting plays, I asked my brother, who is a year younger than myself, to tell me what sort of things these were, and many more that I had never seen; he explained them to me as well as he could, but the only effect was to kindle in me a still stronger desire to see them. At last, to cut short the story of my ruin, I begged and entreated my brother—O that I had never made such an entreaty"—And once more she gave way to a burst of weeping.

"Proceed, señora," said the majordomo, "and finish your story of what has happened to you, for your words and tears are keeping us all in suspense."

"I have but little more to say, though many a

tear to shed," said the damsel; "for ill-placed desires can only be paid for in some such way."

The maiden's beauty had made a deep impression on the head-carver's heart, and he again raised his lantern for another look at her, and thought they were not tears she was shedding, but seed-pearl or dew of the meadow, nay, he exalted them still higher, and made Oriental pearls of them, and fervently hoped her misfortune might not be so great a one as her tears and sobs seemed to indicate. The governor was losing patience at the length of time the girl was taking to tell her story, and told her not to keep them waiting any longer; for it was late, and there still remained a good deal of the town to be gone over.

She, with broken sobs and half-suppressed sighs, went on to say, "My misfortune, my misadventure, is simply this, that I entreated my brother to dress me up as a man in a suit of his clothes, and take me some night, when our father was asleep, to see the whole town; he, overcome by my entreaties, consented, and dressing me in this suit and himself in clothes of mine that fitted him as if made for him (for he has not a hair on his chin, and might pass for a very beautiful young girl), to-night, about an hour ago, more or less, we left the house, and guided by our youthful and foolish impulse we made the circuit of the whole town, and then, as we were about to return home, we saw a great troop of people coming, and my brother said to me, 'Sister, this must be the round, stir your feet and put wings to them, and follow me as fast as you can, lest they recognize us, for that would be a bad business for us'; and so saying he turned about and began, I cannot say to run but to fly; in less than six paces I fell from fright, and then the officer of justice came up and carried me before your worships, where I find myself put to shame before all these people as whimsical and vicious."

"So then, señora," said Sancho, "no other mishap has befallen you, nor was it jealousy that made you leave home, as you said at the beginning of your story?"

"Nothing has happened me," said she, "nor was it jealousy that brought me out, but merely a longing to see the world, which did not go beyond seeing the streets of this town."

The appearance of the tipstaffs with her brother in custody, whom one of them had overtaken as he ran away from his sister, now fully confirmed the truth of what the damsel said. He had nothing on but a rich petticoat and a short blue damask cloak with fine gold lace, and his head was uncovered and adorned only with its own hair, which looked like rings of gold, so bright and curly was it. The governor, the majordomo, and the carver went aside with him, and, unheard by his sister, asked him how he came to be in that dress, and he with no less shame and embarrassment told exactly the same story as his sister, to the great delight of the enamoured carver; the governor, however, said to them, "In truth, young lady and gentleman, this has been a very childish affair, and to explain your folly and rashness there was no necessity for all this delay and all these tears and sighs; for if you had said we are so-and-so, and we escaped from our father's house in this way in order to ramble about, out of mere curiosity and with no other object, there would have been an end of the matter, and none of these little sobs and tears and all the rest of it."

"That is true," said the damsel, "but you see the confusion I was in was so great it did not let me behave as I ought."

"No harm has been done," said Sancho; "come, we will leave you at your father's house; perhaps they will not have missed you; and another time don't be so childish or eager to see the world; for a respectable damsel and a broken leg should keep at home; and the woman and the hen by gadding about are soon lost; and she who is eager to see is also eager to be seen; I say no more."

The youth thanked the governor for his kind offer to take them home, and they directed their steps towards the house, which was not far off. On reaching it the youth threw a pebble up at a grating, and immediately a woman-servant who was waiting for them came down and opened the door to them, and they went in, leaving the party marvelling as much at their grace and beauty as at the fancy they had for seeing the world by night and without quitting the village; which, however, they set down to their youth.

The head-carver was left with a heart pierced through and through, and he made up his mind on the spot to demand the damsel in marriage of her father on the morrow, making sure she would not be refused him as he was a servant of the duke's; and even to Sancho ideas and schemes of marrying the youth to his daughter Sanchica suggested themselves, and he resolved to open the negotiation at the proper season, persuading himself that no husband could be refused to a governor's daughter. And so the night's round came to an end, and a couple of days later the government, whereby all his plans were overthrown and swept away, as will be seen farther on.

Chapter 50

Wherein is set forth who the enchanters and executioners were who flogged the duenna and pinched Don Quixote, and also what befell the page who carried the letter to Teresa Panza, Sancho Panza's wife

CID HAMET, the painstaking investigator of the minute points of this veracious history, says that when Doña Rodriguez left her own room to go to Don Quixote's, another duenna who slept with her observed her, and as all duennas are fond of prying, listening, and sniffing, she followed her so silently that the good Rodriguez never perceived it; and as soon as the duenna saw her enter Don Quixote's room, not to fail in a duenna's invariable practice of tattling, she hurried off that instant to report to the duchess how Doña Rodriguez was closeted with Don Quixote. The duchess told the duke, and asked him to let her and Altisidora go and see what the said duenna wanted with Don Quixote. The duke gave them leave, and the pair cautiously and quietly crept to the door of the room and posted themselves so close to it that they could hear all that was said inside. But when the duchess heard how the Rodriguez had made public the Aranjuez of her issues [1] she could not restrain herself, nor Altisidora either; and so, filled with rage and thirsting for vengeance, they burst into the room and tormented Don Quixote and flogged the duenna in the manner already described; for indignities offered to their charms and self-esteem mightily provoke the anger of women and make them eager for revenge. The duchess told the duke what had happened, and he was much amused by it; and she, in pursuance of her design of making merry and diverting herself with Don Quixote, despatched the page who had played the part of Dulcinea in the negotiations for her disenchantment (which Sancho Panza in the cares of government had forgotten all about) to Teresa Panza his wife with her husband's letter and another from herself, and also a great string of fine coral beads as a present.

Now the history says this page was very sharp and quick-witted; and eager to serve his lord and lady he set off very willingly for Sancho's village. Before he entered it he observed a number of women washing in a brook, and asked them if they could tell him whether there lived there a woman of the name of Teresa Panza, wife of one Sancho Panza, squire to a knight called Don

Quixote of La Mancha. At the question a young girl who was washing stood up and said, "Teresa Panza is my mother, and that Sancho is my father, and that knight is our master."

"Well then, miss," said the page, "come and show me where your mother is, for I bring her a letter and a present from your father."

"That I will with all my heart, señor," said the girl, who seemed to be about fourteen, more or less; and leaving the clothes she was washing to one of her companions, and without putting anything on her head or feet, for she was bare-legged and had her hair hanging about her, away she skipped in front of the page's horse, saying, "Come, your worship, our house is at the entrance of the town, and my mother is there, sorrowful enough at not having had any news of my father this ever so long."

"Well," said the page, "I am bringing her such good news that she will have reason to thank God for it."

And then, skipping, running, and capering, the girl reached the town, but before going into the house she called out at the door, "Come out, mother Teresa, come out, come out; here's a gentleman with letters and other things from my good father." At these words her mother Teresa Panza came out spinning a bundle of flax, in a gray petticoat (so short was it one would have fancied "they to her shame had cut it short" [2]), a gray bodice of the same stuff, and a smock. She was not very old, though plainly past forty, strong, healthy, vigorous, and sun-dried; and seeing her daughter and the page on horseback, she exclaimed, "What's this, child? What gentleman is this?"

"A servant of my lady, Doña Teresa Panza," replied the page; and suiting the action to the word he flung himself off his horse, and with great humility advanced to kneel before the lady Teresa, saying, "Let me kiss your hand, Señora Doña Teresa, as the lawful and only wife of Señor Don Sancho Panza, rightful governor of the island of Barataria."

"Ah, señor, get up, don't do that," said Teresa; "for I'm not a bit of a court lady, but only a poor countrywoman, the daughter of a clod-crusher, and the wife of a squire-errant and not of any governor at all."

"You are," said the page, "the most worthy wife of a most arch-worthy governor; and as a proof of what I say accept this letter and this present"; and at the same time he took out of his pocket a string of coral beads with gold clasps,

---

[1] Issues are called *fuentes,* "fountains," and the fountains of Aranjuez are famous in Spain.

[2] Docking the skirts was a punishment for misconduct in old times.

and placed it on her neck, and said, "This letter is from his lordship the governor, and the other as well as these coral beads from my lady the duchess, who sends me to your worship."

Teresa stood lost in astonishment, and her daughter just as much, and the girl said, "May I die but our master Don Quixote's at the bottom of this; he must have given father the government or country he so often promised him."

"That is the truth," said the page; "for it is through Señor Don Quixote that Señor Sancho is now governor of the island of Barataria, as will be seen by this letter."

"Will your worship read it to me, noble sir?" said Teresa; "for though I can spin I can't read, not a scrap."

"Nor I either," said Sanchica; "but wait a bit, and I'll go and fetch some one who can read it, either the curate himself or the bachelor Samson Carrasco, and they'll come gladly to hear any news of my father."

"There is no need to fetch anybody," said the page; "for though I can't spin I can read, and I'll read it"; and so he read it through, but as it has already been given it is not inserted here; and then he took out the other one from the duchess, which ran as follows:

FRIEND TERESA, Your husband Sancho's good qualities, of heart as well as of head, induced and compelled me to request my husband the duke to give him the government of one of his many islands. I am told he governs like a gerfalcon, of which I am very glad, and my lord the duke, of course, also; and I am very thankful to Heaven that I have not made a mistake in choosing him for that same government; for I would have Señora Teresa know that a good governor is hard to find in this world, and may God make me as good as Sancho's way of governing. Herewith I send you, my dear, a string of coral beads with gold clasps; I wish they were Oriental pearls; but "he who gives thee a bone does not wish to see thee dead"; a time will come when we shall become acquainted and meet one another, but God knows the future. Commend me to your daughter Sanchica, and tell her from me to hold herself in readiness, for I mean to make a high match for her when she least expects it. They tell me there are big acorns in your village; send me a couple of dozen or so, and I shall value them greatly as coming from your hand; and write to me at length to assure me of your health and well-being; and if there be anything you stand in need of, it is but to open your mouth, and that shall be the measure; and so God keep you.

From this place.

Your loving friend,
THE DUCHESS

"Ah, what a good, plain, lowly lady!" said

Teresa when she heard the letter; "that I may be buried with ladies of that sort, and not the gentlewomen we have in this town, that fancy because they are gentlewomen the wind must not touch them, and go to church with as much airs as if they were queens, no less, and seem to think they are disgraced if they look at a farmer's wife! And see here how this good lady, for all she's a duchess, calls me 'friend,' and treats me as if I was her equal—and equal may I see her with the tallest church-tower in La Mancha! And as for the acorns, señor, I'll send her ladyship a peck and such big ones that one might come to see them as a show and a wonder. And now, Sanchica, see that the gentleman is comfortable; put up his horse, and get some eggs out of the stable, and cut plenty of bacon, and let's give him his dinner like a prince; for the good news he has brought, and his own bonny face deserve it all; and meanwhile I'll run out and give the neighbors the news of our good luck, and father curate, and Master Nicholas the barber, who are and always have been such friends of thy father's."

"That I will, mother," said Sanchica; "but mind, you must give me half of that string; for I don't think my lady the duchess could have been so stupid as to send it all to you."

"It is all for thee, my child," said Teresa; "but let me wear it round my neck for a few days; for verily it seems to make my heart glad."

"You will be glad, too," said the page, "when you see the bundle there is in this portmanteau, for it is a suit of the finest cloth, that the governor only wore one day out hunting and now sends, all for Señora Sanchica."

"May he live a thousand years," said Sanchica, "and the bearer as many, nay two thousand, if needful."

With this Teresa hurried out of the house with the letters, and with the string of beads round her neck, and went along thrumming the letters as if they were a tambourine, and by chance coming across the curate and Samson Carrasco she began capering and saying, "None of us poor now, faith! We've got a little government! Ay, let the finest fine lady tackle me, and I'll give her a setting down!"

"What's all this, Teresa Panza," said they; "what madness is this, and what papers are those?"

"The madness is only this," said she, "that these are the letters of duchesses and governors, and these I have on my neck are fine coral beads, with ave marias and paternosters of beaten gold, and I am a governess."

"God help us," said the curate, "we don't understand you, Teresa, or know what you are talking about."

"There, you may see it yourselves," said Teresa, and she handed them the letters.

The curate read them out for Samson Carrasco to hear, and Samson and he regarded one another with looks of astonishment at what they had read, and the bachelor asked who had brought the letters. Teresa in reply bade them come with her to her house and they would see the messenger, a most elegant youth, who had brought another present which was worth as much more. The curate took the coral beads from her neck and examined them again and again, and having satisfied himself as to their fineness he fell to wondering afresh, and said, "By the gown I wear I don't know what to say or think of these letters and presents; on the one hand I can see and feel the fineness of these coral beads, and on the other I read how a duchess sends to beg for a couple of dozen of acorns."

"Square that if you can," said Carrasco; "well, let's go and see the messenger, and from him we'll learn something about this mystery that has turned up."

They did so, and Teresa returned with them. They found the page sifting a little barley for his horse, and Sanchica cutting a rasher of bacon to be paved with eggs for his dinner. His looks and his handsome apparel pleased them both greatly; and after they had saluted him courteously, and he them, Samson begged him to give them his news, as well of Don Quixote as of Sancho Panza, for, he said, though they had read the letters from Sancho and her ladyship the duchess, they were still puzzled and could not make out what was meant by Sancho's government, and above all of an island, when all or most of those in the Mediterranean belonged to his majesty.

To this the page replied, "As to Señor Sancho Panza's being a governor there is no doubt whatever; but whether it is an island or not that he governs, with that I have nothing to do; suffice it that it is a town of more than a thousand inhabitants; with regard to the acorns I may tell you my lady the duchess is so unpretending and unassuming that, not to speak of sending to beg for acorns from a peasant woman, she has been known to send to ask for the loan of a comb from one of her neighbors; for I would have your worships know that the ladies of Aragon, though they are just as illustrious, are not so punctilious and haughty as the Castilian ladies; they treat people with greater familiarity."

In the middle of this conversation Sanchica came in with her skirt full of eggs, and said she to the page, "Tell me, señor, does my father wear trunk-hose since he has been governor?"

"I have not noticed," said the page; "but no doubt he wears them."

"Ah! my God!" said Sanchica, "what a sight it must be to see my father in tights! Is n't it odd that ever since I was born I have had a longing to see my father in trunk-hose?"

"As things go you will see that if you live," said the page; "by God, he is in the way to take the road with a sunshade if the government only lasts him two months more."

The curate and the bachelor could see plainly enough that the page spoke in a waggish vein; but the fineness of the coral beads, and the hunting suit that Sancho sent (for Teresa had already shown it to them) did away with the impression; and they could not help laughing at Sanchica's wish, and still more when Teresa said, "Señor curate, look about if there's anybody here going to Madrid or Toledo, to buy me a hooped petticoat, a proper fashionable one of the best quality; for indeed and indeed I must do honor to my husband's government as well as I can; nay, if I am put to it, I'll go to court and set up a coach like all the world; for she who has a governor for her husband may very well have one and keep one."

"And why not, mother!" said Sanchica; "would to God it were to-day instead of to-morrow, even though they were to say when they saw me seated in the coach with my mother, 'See that rubbish, that garlic-stuffed fellow's daughter, how she goes stretched at her ease in a coach as if she was a she-pope!' But let them tramp through the mud, and let me go in my coach with my feet off the ground. Bad luck to backbiters all over the world; 'let me go warm and the people may laugh.' Do I say right, mother?"

"To be sure you do, my child," said Teresa; "and all this good luck, and even more, my good Sancho foretold me; and thou wilt see, my daughter, he won't stop till he has made me a countess; for to make a beginning is everything in luck; and as I have heard thy good father say many a time (for besides being thy father he's the father of proverbs too), 'When they offer thee a heifer, run with a halter; when they offer thee a government, take it; when they would give thee a county, seize it; when they say "Here, here!" to thee with something good, swallow it.' Oh no! go to sleep, and don't answer the strokes of good fortune and the lucky chances that are knocking at the door of your house!"

"And what do I care," added Sanchica, "whether anybody says when he sees me holding my head up, 'The dog saw himself in hempen breeches,' and the rest of it?"

Hearing this the curate said, "I do believe that all this family of the Panzas are born with a sackful of proverbs in their insides, every one of them; I never saw one of them that does not pour them out at all times and on all occasions."

"That is true," said the page, "for Señor Governor Sancho utters them at every turn; and though a great many of them are not to the purpose, still they amuse one, and my lady the duchess and the duke praise them highly."

"Then you still maintain that all this about Sancho's government is true, señor," said the bachelor, "and that there actually is a duchess who sends him presents and writes to him? Because we, although we have handled the presents and read the letters, don't believe it, and suspect it to be something in the line of our fellow-townsman Don Quixote, who fancies that everything is done by enchantment; and for this reason I am almost ready to say that I'd like to touch and feel your worship to see whether you are a mere ambassador of the imagination or a man of flesh and blood."

"All I know, sirs," replied the page, "is that I am a real ambassador, and that Señor Sancho Panza is governor as a matter of fact, and that my lord and lady the duke and duchess can give, and have given him this same government, and that I have heard the said Sancho Panza bears himself very stoutly therein; whether there be any enchantment in all this or not, it is for your worships to settle between you; for that's all I know by the oath I swear, and that is by the life of my parents whom I have still alive, and love dearly."

"It may be so," said the bachelor; "but *dubitat Augustinus.*"

"Doubt who will," said the page; "what I have told you is the truth, and that will always rise above falsehood as oil above water; if not *operibus credite, et non verbis.* Let one of you come with me, and he will see with his eyes what he does not believe with his ears."

"It's for me to make that trip," said Sanchica; "take me with you, señor, behind you on your horse; for I'll go with all my heart to see my father."

"Governors' daughters," said the page, "must not travel along the roads alone, but accompanied by coaches and litters and a great number of attendants."

"By God," said Sanchica, "I can go just as well mounted on a she-ass as in a coach; what a dainty lass you must take me for!"

"Hush, girl," said Teresa; "you don't know what you're talking about; the gentleman is quite right, for 'as the time so the behavior'; when it was Sancho it was 'Sancha'; when it is governor it's 'señora'; I don't know if I'm right."

"Señora Teresa says more than she is aware of," said the page; "and now give me something to eat and let me go at once, for I mean to return this evening."

"Come and do penance with me," said the curate at this; "for Señora Teresa has more will than means to serve so worthy a guest."

The page refused, but had to consent at last for his own sake; and the curate took him home with him very gladly, in order to have an opportunity of questioning him at leisure about Don Quixote and his doings. The bachelor offered to write the letters in reply for Teresa; but she did not care to let him mix himself up in her affairs, for she thought him somewhat given to joking; and so she gave a cake and a couple of eggs to a young acolyte who was a penman, and he wrote for her two letters, one for her husband and the other for the duchess, dictated out of her own head, and these are not the worst inserted in this great history, as will be seen farther on.

Chapter 51

Of the progress of Sancho's government, and other such entertaining matters

DAY came after the night of the governor's round; a night which the head-carver passed without sleeping, so full were his thoughts of the face and air and beauty of the disguised damsel, while the majordomo spent what was left of it in writing an account to his lord and lady of all Sancho said and did, being as much amazed at his sayings as at his doings, for there was a mixture of shrewdness and simplicity in all his words and deeds. The señor governor got up, and by Doctor Pedro Recio's directions they made him break his fast on a little conserve and four sups of cold water, which Sancho would have readily exchanged for a piece of bread and a bunch of grapes; but seeing there was no help for it, he submitted with no little sorrow of heart and discomfort of stomach; Pedro Recio having persuaded him that light and delicate diet enlivened the wits, and that was what was most essential for persons placed in command and in responsible situations, where they have to employ not only the bodily powers but those of the mind also.

By means of this sophistry Sancho was made to endure hunger, and hunger so keen that in his heart he cursed the government, and even him who had given it to him; however, with his hunger and his conserve he undertook to deliver judgments that day, and the first thing that came before him was a question that was submitted to him by a stranger, in the presence of the majordomo and the other attendants, and it was in these words: "Senor, a large river separated two districts of one and the same lordship—will your worship please to pay attention, for the case is an important and a rather knotty one? Well then, on this river there was a bridge, and at one end of it a gallows, and a sort of tribunal, where four judges commonly sat to administer the law which the lord of the river, the bridge and the lordship had enacted, and which was to this effect, 'If any one crosses by this bridge from one side to the other he shall declare on oath where he is going and with what object; and if he swears truly, he shall be allowed to pass, but if falsely, he shall, without any remission, be put to death for it by hanging on the gallows erected there.' Though the law and its severe penalty were known, many persons crossed, but in their declarations it was easy to see at once they were telling the truth, and the judges let them pass free. It happened, however, that one man, when they came to take his declaration, swore and said that by the oath he took he was going to die upon that gallows that stood there, and nothing else. The judges held a consultation over the oath, and they said, 'If we let this man pass free he has sworn falsely, and by the law he ought to die; but if we hang him, as he swore he was going to die on that gallows, and therefore swore the truth, by the same law he ought to go free.' It is asked of your worship, señor governor, what are the judges to do with this man? For they are still in doubt and perplexity; and having heard of your worship's acute and exalted intellect, they have sent me to entreat your worship on their behalf to give your opinion on this very intricate and puzzling case."

To this Sancho made answer, "Indeed those gentlemen the judges that send you to me might have spared themselves the trouble, for I have more of the obtuse than the acute in me; however, repeat the case over again, so that I may understand it, and then perhaps I may be able to hit the point."

The querist repeated again and again what he had said before, and then Sancho said, "It seems to me I can set the matter right in a moment, and in this way; the man swears that he is going to die upon the gallows; but if he dies upon it, he has sworn the truth, and by the law enacted deserves to go free and pass over the bridge; but if they don't hang him, then he has sworn falsely, and by the same law deserves to be hanged."

"It is as the señor governor says," said the messenger; "and as regards a complete comprehension of the case, there is nothing left to desire or hesitate about."

"Well then I say," said Sancho, "that of this man they should let pass the part that has sworn truly, and hang the part that has lied; and in this way the conditions of the passage will be fully complied with."

"But then, señor governor," replied the querist, "the man will have to be divided into two parts; and if he is divided of course he will die; and so none of the requirements of the law will be carried out, and it is absolutely necessary to comply with it."

"Look here, my good sir," said Sancho; "either I'm a numskull or else there is the same reason for this passenger dying as for his living and passing over the bridge; for if the truth saves him the falsehood equally condemns him; and that being the case it is my opinion you should say to the gentlemen who sent you to me that as the arguments for condemning him and for absolving him are exactly balanced, they should let him pass freely, as it is always more praiseworthy to do good than to do evil; this I would give signed with my name if I knew how to sign; and what I have said in this case is not out of my own head, but one of the many precepts my master Don Quixote gave me the night before I left to become governor of this island, that came into my mind, and it was this, that when there was any doubt about the justice of a case I should lean to mercy; and it is God's will that I should recollect it now, for it fits this case as if it was made for it."

"That is true," said the majordomo; "and I maintain that Lycurgus himself, who gave laws to the Lacædemonians, could not have pronounced a better decision than the great Panza has given; let the morning's audience close with this, and I will see that the señor governor has dinner entirely to his liking."

"That's all I ask for—fair play," said Sancho; "give me my dinner, and then let it rain cases and questions on me, and I'll despatch them in a twinkling."

The majordomo kept his word, for he felt it against his conscience to kill so wise a governor by hunger; particularly as he intended to have done with him that same night, playing off the last joke he was commissioned to practise upon him.

It came to pass, then, that after he had dined that day, in opposition to the rules and aphorisms of Doctor Tirteafuera, as they were taking away the cloth there came a courier with a letter from Don Quixote for the governor. Sancho ordered the secretary to read it to himself, and if there was nothing in it that demanded secrecy to read it aloud. The secretary did so, and after he had skimmed the contents he said, "It may well be read aloud, for what Señor Don Quixote writes to your worship deserves to be printed or written in letters of gold, and it is as follows."

Don Quixote of La Mancha's Letter to Sancho Panza, Governor of the Island of Barataria.

When I was expecting to hear of thy stupidities and blunders, friend Sancho, I have received intelligence of thy displays of good sense, for which I give special thanks to Heaven that can raise the poor from the dunghill and of fools to make wise men. They tell me thou dost govern as if thou wert a man, and art a man as if thou wert a beast, so great is the humility wherewith thou dost comport thyself. But I would have thee bear in mind, Sancho, that very often it is fitting and necessary for the authority of office to resist the humility of the heart; for the seemly array of one who is invested with grave duties should be such as they require and not measured by what his own humble tastes may lead him to prefer. Dress well; a stick dressed up does not look like a stick; I do not say thou shouldst wear trinkets or fine raiment, or that being a judge thou shouldst dress like a soldier, but that thou shouldst array thyself in the apparel thy office requires, and that at the same time it be neat and handsome. To win the good-will of the people thou governest there are two things, among others, that thou must do; one is to be civil to all (this, however, I told thee before) and the other to take care that food be abundant, for there is nothing that vexes the heart of the poor more than hunger and high prices. Make not many proclamations; but those thou makest take care that they be good ones, and above all that they be observed and carried out; for proclamations that are not observed are the same as if they did not exist; nay, they encourage the idea that the prince who had the wisdom and authority to make them had not the power to enforce them; and laws that threaten and are not enforced come to be like the log, the king of the frogs, that frightened them at first, but that in time they despised and mounted upon. Be a father to virtue and a step-father to vice. Be not always strict, nor yet always lenient, but observe a mean between these two extremes, for in that is the aim of wisdom. Visit the jails, the slaughter-houses, and the market-places; for the presence of the governor is of great importance in such places; it comforts the prisoners who are in hopes of a speedy release, it is the bugbear of the butchers who have then to give just weight, and it is the terror of the market-women for the same reason. Let it not be seen that thou art (even if perchance thou art, which I do not believe) covetous, a follower of women, or a glutton; for when the people and those that have dealings with thee become aware of thy special weakness they will bring their batteries to bear upon thee in that quarter, till they have brought thee down to the depths of perdition. Consider and reconsider, con and con over again the advice and the instructions I gave thee before thy departure hence to thy government, and thou wilt see that in them, if thou dost follow them, thou hast a help at hand that will lighten for thee the troubles and difficulties that beset governors at every step. Write to thy lord and lady and show thyself grateful to them, for ingratitude is the daughter of pride, and one of the greatest sins we know of; and he who is grateful to those who have been good to him shows that he will be so to God also who has bestowed and still bestows so many blessings upon him.

My lady the duchess sent off a messenger with thy suit and another present to thy wife Teresa Panza; we expect the answer every moment. I have been a little indisposed through a certain cat-scratching I came in for, not very much to the benefit of my nose; but it was nothing; for if there are enchanters who maltreat me, there are also some who defend me. Let me know if the majordomo who is with thee had any share in the Trifaldi performance, as thou didst suspect; and keep me informed of everything that happens to thee, as the distance is so short; all the more as I am thinking of giving over very shortly this idle life I am now leading, for I was not born for it. A thing has occurred to me which I am inclined to think will put me out of favor with the duke and duchess; but though I am sorry for it I do not care, for after all I must obey my calling rather than their pleasure, in accordance with the common saying *amicus Plato, sed magis amica veritas*. I quote this Latin to thee because I conclude that since thou hast been a governor thou wilt have learned it. Adieu; God keep thee from being an object of pity to any one.

Thy friend
Don Quixote of La Mancha

Sancho listened to the letter with great attention, and it was praised and considered wise by all who heard it; he then rose up from table, and calling his secretary shut himself in with him in his own room, and without putting it off any longer set about answering his master Don Quixote at once; and he bade the secretary write down what he told him without adding or suppressing anything, which he did, and the answer was to the following effect.

SANCHO PANZA'S LETTER TO DON QUIXOTE OF LA MANCHA.

The pressure of business is so great upon me that I have no time to scratch my head or even to cut my nails; and I wear them so long—God send a remedy for it. I say this, master of my soul, that you may not be surprised if I have not until now sent you word of how I fare, well or ill, in this government, in which I am suffering more hunger than when we two were wandering through the woods and wastes.

My lord the duke wrote to me the other day to warn me that certain spies had got into this island to kill me; but up to the present I have not found out any except a certain doctor who receives a salary in this town for killing all the governors that come here; he is called Doctor Pedro Recio, and is from Tirteafuera; so you see what a name he has to make me dread dying under his hands. This doctor says of himself that he does not cure diseases when there are any, but prevents them coming, and the medicines he uses are diet and more diet, until he brings one down to bare bones; as if leanness was not worse than fever.

In short he is killing me with hunger, and I am dying myself of vexation; for when I thought I was coming to this government to get my meat hot and my drink cool, and take my ease between holland sheets on feather beds, I find I have come to do penance as if I was a hermit; and as I don't do it willingly I suspect that in the end the devil will carry me off.

So far I have not handled any dues or taken any bribes, and I don't know what to think of it; for here they tell me that the governors that come to this island, before entering it have plenty of money either given to them or lent to them by the people of the town, and that this is the usual custom not only here but with all who enter upon governments.

Last night going the rounds I came upon a fair damsel in man's clothes, and a brother of hers dressed as a woman; my head-carver has fallen in love with the girl, and has in his own mind chosen her for a wife, so he says, and I have chosen the youth for a son-in-law; to-day we are going to explain our intentions to the father of the pair, who is one Diego de la Llana, a gentleman and an old Christian as much as you please.

I have visited the market-places, as your worship advises me, and yesterday I found a stall-keeper selling new hazelnuts and proved her to have mixed a bushel of old empty rotten nuts with a bushel of new; I confiscated the whole for the children of the charity school, who will know how to distinguish them well enough, and I sentenced her not to come into the market-place for a fortnight; they told me I did bravely. I can tell your worship it is commonly said in this town that there are no people worse than the marketwomen, for they are all barefaced, unconscionable, and impudent, and I can well believe it from what I have seen of them in other towns.

I am very glad my lady the duchess has written to my wife Teresa Panza and sent her the present your worship speaks of; and I will strive to show myself grateful when the time comes; kiss her hands for me, and tell her I say she has not thrown it into a sack with a hole in it, as she will see in the end. I should not like your worship to have any difference with my lord and lady; for if you fall out with them it is plain it must do me harm; and as you give me advice to be grateful it will not do for your worship not to be so yourself to those who have shown you such kindness, and by whom you have been treated so hospitably in their castle.

That about the cat-scratching I don't understand; but I suppose it must be one of the ill-turns the wicked enchanters are always doing your worship; when we meet I shall know all about it. I wish I could send your worship something; but I don't know what to send, unless it be some very curious clyster pipes, to work with bladders, that they make in this island; but if the office remains with me I'll find out something to send, one way or another. If my wife Teresa Panza writes to me, pay the postage and send me the letter, for I have a very great desire to hear how my house and wife and children are going on. And so, may God deliver your worship from evil-minded enchanters, and bring me well and peacefully out of this government, which I doubt, for I expect to take leave of it and my life together, from the way Doctor Pedro Recio treats me.

Your worship's servant
SANCHO PANZA THE GOVERNOR

The secretary sealed the letter, and immediately dismissed the courier; and those who were carrying on the joke against Sancho putting their heads together arranged how he was to be dismissed from the government. Sancho spent the afternoon in drawing up certain ordinances relating to the good government of what he fancied the island; and he ordained that there were to be no provision hucksters in the State, and that men might import wine into it from any place they pleased, provided they declared the quarter it came from, so that a price might be put upon it according to its quality, reputation, and the estimation it was held in; and he that watered his wine, or changed the name, was to forfeit his life for it. He reduced the prices of all manner of shoes, boots, and stockings, but of shoes in particular, as they seemed to him to run extravagantly high. He established a fixed rate for servants' wages, which were becoming recklessly exorbitant. He laid extremely heavy penalties upon those who sang lewd or loose songs either by day or night. He decreed that no blind man should sing of any miracle in verse, unless he could produce authentic evidence that it was true, for it was his opinion that most of those the blind men sing are trumped up, to the detriment of the true ones. He established and created an *alguacil* of the poor, not to harass them, but to examine them and see whether they really were so; for many a sturdy thief or drunkard goes about under cover of a make-believe crippled limb or a sham sore. In a word, he made so many good rules that to this day they are preserved there, and are called *The constitutions of the great governor Sancho Panza.*

Chapter 52

Wherein is related the adventure of the second distressed or afflicted duenna, otherwise called Doña Rodriguez

CID HAMET relates that Don Quixote being now cured of his scratches felt that the life he was leading in the castle was entirely inconsistent with the order of chivalry he professed, so he determined to ask the duke and duchess to permit him to take his departure for Saragossa, as the time of the festival was now drawing near, and he hoped to win there the suit of armor which is the prize at festivals of the sort. But one day at table with the duke and duchess, just as he was about to carry his resolution into effect and ask for their permission, lo and behold suddenly there came in through the door of the great hall two women, as they afterwards proved to be, draped in mourning from head to foot, one of whom approaching Don Quixote flung herself at full length at his feet, pressing her lips to them, and uttering moans so sad, so deep, and so doleful that she put all who heard and saw her into a state of perplexity; and though the duke and duchess supposed it must be some joke their servants were playing off upon Don Quixote, still the earnest way the woman sighed and moaned and wept puzzled them and made them feel uncertain, until Don Quixote, touched with compassion, raised her up and made her unveil herself and remove the mantle from her tearful face. She complied and disclosed what no one could have ever anticipated, for she disclosed the countenance of Doña Rodriguez, the duenna of the house; the other female in mourning being her daughter, who had been made a fool of by the rich farmer's son. All who knew her were filled with astonishment, and the duke and duchess more than any; for though they thought her a simpleton and a weak creature, they did not think her capable of crazy pranks. Doña Rodriguez, at length, turning to her master and mistress said to them, "Will your excellencies be pleased to

permit me to speak to this gentleman for a moment, for it is requisite I should do so in order to get successfully out of the business in which the boldness of an evil-minded clown has involved me?"

The duke said that for his part he gave her leave, and that she might speak with Señor Don Quixote as much as she liked.

She then, turning to Don Quixote and addressing herself to him said, "Some days since, valiant knight, I gave you an account of the injustice and treachery of a wicked farmer to my dearly beloved daughter, the unhappy damsel here before you, and you promised me to take her part and right the wrong that has been done her; but now it has come to my hearing that you are about to depart from this castle in quest of such fair adventures as God may vouchsafe to you; therefore, before you take the road, I would that you challenge this froward rustic, and compel him to marry my daughter in fulfilment of the promise he gave her to become her husband before he seduced her; for to expect that my lord the duke will do me justice is to ask pears from the elm tree, for the reason I stated privately to your worship; and so may our Lord grant you good health and forsake us not."

To these words Don Quixote replied very gravely and solemnly, "Worthy duenna, check your tears, or rather dry them, and spare your sighs; for I take it upon myself to obtain redress for your daughter, for whom it would have been better not to have been so ready to believe lovers' promises, which are for the most part quickly made and very slowly performed; and so, with my lord the duke's leave, I will at once go in quest of this inhuman youth, and will find him out and challenge him and slay him, if so be he refuses to keep his promised word; for the chief object of my profession is to spare the humble and chastise the proud; I mean, to help the distressed and destroy the oppressors."

"There is no necessity," said the duke, "for your worship to take the trouble of seeking out the rustic of whom this worthy duenna complains, nor is there any necessity, either, for asking my leave to challenge him; for I admit him duly challenged, and will take care that he is informed of the challenge, and accepts it, and comes to answer it in person to this castle of mine, where I shall afford to both a fair field, observing all the conditions which are usually and properly observed in such trials, and observing too justice to both sides, as all princes who offer a free field to combatants within the limits of their lordships are bound to do."

"Then with that assurance and your highness's good leave," said Don Quixote, "I hereby for this once waive my privilege of gentle blood, and come down and put myself on a level with the lowly birth of the wrong-doer, making myself equal with him and enabling him to enter into combat with me; and so, I challenge and defy him, though absent, on the plea of his malfeasance in breaking faith with this poor damsel, who was a maiden and now by his misdeed is none; and say that he shall fulfil the promise he gave her to become her lawful husband, or else stake his life upon the question."

And then plucking off a glove he threw it down in the middle of the hall, and the duke picked it up, saying, as he had said before, that he accepted the challenge in the name of his vassal, and fixed six days thence as the time, the courtyard of the castle as the place, and for arms the customary ones of knights, lance and shield and full armor, with all the other accessories, without trickery, guile, or charms of any sort, and examined and passed by the judges of the field. "But first of all," he said, "it is requisite that this worthy duenna and unworthy damsel should place their claim for justice in the hands of Don Quixote; for otherwise nothing can be done, nor can the said challenge be brought to a lawful issue."

"I do so place it," replied the duenna.

"And I too," added her daughter, all in tears and covered with shame and confusion.

This declaration having been made, and the duke having settled in his own mind what he would do in the matter, the ladies in black withdrew, and the duchess gave orders that for the future they were not to be treated as servants of hers, but as lady adventurers who came to her house to demand justice; so they gave them a room to themselves and waited on them as they would on strangers, to the consternation of the other women-servants, who did not know where the folly and impudence of Doña Rodriguez and her unlucky daughter would stop.

And now, to complete the enjoyment of the feast and bring the dinner to a satisfactory end, lo and behold the page who had carried the letters and presents to Teresa Panza, the wife of the governor Sancho, entered the hall; and the duke and duchess were very well pleased to see him, being anxious to know the result of his journey; but when they asked him the page said in reply that he could not give it before so many people or in a few words, and begged their excellences to be pleased to let it wait for a private opportunity, and in the meantime amuse themselves with these letters; and taking out the letters he placed them in the duchess's hand. One bore by way of address, *Letter for my lady the Duchess So-and-so, of I don't know where*; and the other, *To my husband Sancho Panza, governor of the island of Barataria, whom God prosper longer than me*. The duchess's bread would not bake, as the saying is, until she had read her letter; and having looked over it herself and seen that it might be read aloud for the duke and all present to hear, she read out as follows.

Teresa Panza's Letter to the Duchess.

The letter your highness wrote me, my lady, gave me great pleasure, for indeed I found it very welcome. The string of coral beads is very fine, and my husband's hunting suit does not fall short of it. All this village is very much pleased that your ladyship has made a governor of my good man Sancho; though nobody will believe it, particularly the curate, and Master Nicholas the barber, and the bachelor Samson Carrasco; but I don't care for that, for so long as it is true, as it is, they may all say what they like; though, to tell the truth, if the coral beads and the suit had not come I would not have believed it either; for in this village everybody thinks my husband a numskull, and except for governing a flock of goats, they cannot fancy what sort of government he can be fit for. God grant it, and direct him according as he sees his children stand in need of it. I am resolved with your worship's leave, lady of my soul, to make the most of this fair day, and go to Court to stretch myself at ease in a coach, and make all those I have envying me already burst their eyes out; so I beg your excellence to order my husband to send me a small trifle of money, and to let it be something to speak of, because one's expenses are heavy at the Court; for a loaf costs a real, and meat thirty maravedís a pound, which is beyond everything; and if he does not want me to go let him tell me in time, for my feet are on the fidgets to be off; and my friends and neighbors tell me that if my daughter and I make a figure and a brave show at Court, my husband will come to be known far more by me than I by him, for of course plenty of people will ask, "Who are those ladies in that coach?" and some servant of mine will answer, "The wife and daughter of Sancho Panza, governor of the island of Barataria"; and in this way Sancho will become known, and I'll be thought well of, and 'to Rome for everything.' I am as vexed as vexed can be that they have gathered no acorns this year in our village; for all that I send your highness about half a peck that I went to the wood to gather and pick out one by one myself, and I could find no bigger ones; I wish they were as big as ostrich eggs.

Let not your high mightiness forget to write to me; and I will take care to answer, and let you know how I am, and whatever news there may be in this place, where I remain, praying our Lord to have your highness in his keeping and not to forget me.

Sancha, my daughter, and my son, kiss your worship's hands.

She who would rather see your ladyship than write to you,

Your servant,
TERESA PANZA

All were greatly amused by Teresa Panza's letter, but particularly the duke and duchess; and the duchess asked Don Quixote's opinion whether they might open the letter that had come for the governor, which she suspected must be very good. Don Quixote said that to gratify them he would open it, and did so, and found that it ran as follows.

TERESA PANZA'S LETTER TO HER HUSBAND SANCHO PANZA.

I got thy letter, Sancho of my soul, and I promise thee and swear as a Catholic Christian that I was within two fingers' breadth of going mad, I was so happy. I can tell thee, brother, when I came to hear that thou wert a governor I thought I should have dropped dead with pure joy; and thou knowest they say sudden joy kills as well as great sorrow; and as for Sanchica thy daughter, she leaked from sheer happiness. I had before me the suit thou didst send me, and the coral beads my lady the duchess sent me round my neck, and the letters in my hands, and there was the bearer of them standing by, and in spite of all this I verily believed and thought that what I saw and handled was all a dream; for who could have thought that a goat-herd would come to be a governor of islands? Thou knowest, my friend, what my mother used to say, that one must live long to see much; I say it because I expect to see more if I live longer; for I don't expect to stop until I see thee a farmer of taxes or a collector of revenue, which are offices where, though the devil carries off those who make a bad use of them, still they make and handle money. My lady the duchess will tell thee the desire I have to go to the Court; consider the matter and let me know thy pleasure; I will try to do honor to thee by going in a coach.

Neither the curate, nor the barber, nor the bachelor, nor even the sacristan, can believe that thou art a governor, and they say the whole thing is a delusion or an enchantment affair, like everything belonging to thy master Don Quixote; and Samson says he must go in search of thee and drive the government out of thy head and the madness out of Don Quixote's skull; I only laugh, and look at my string of beads, and plan out the dress I am going to make for our daughter out of thy suit. I sent some acorns to my lady the duchess; I wish they had been gold. Send me some strings of pearls if they are in fashion in that island. Here is the news of the village; La Berrueca has married her daughter to a good-for-nothing painter, who came here to paint anything that might turn up. The council gave him

an order to paint his Majesty's arms over the door of the town hall; he asked two ducats, which they paid him in advance; he worked for eight days, and at the end of them had nothing painted, and then said he had no turn for painting such trifling things; he returned the money, and for all that has married on the pretence of being a good workman; to be sure he has now laid aside his paintbrush and taken a spade in hand, and goes to the field like a gentleman. Pedro Lobo's son has received the first orders and tonsure, with the intention of becoming a priest. Minguilla, Mingo Silvato's granddaughter, found it out, and has gone to law with him on the score of having given her promise of marriage. Evil tongues say she is with child by him, but he denies it stoutly. There are no olives this year, and there is not a drop of vinegar to be had in the whole village. A company of soldiers passed through here; when they left they took away with them three of the girls of the village; I will not tell thee who they are; perhaps they will come back, and they will be sure to find those who will take them for wives with all their blemishes, good or bad. Sanchica is making bonelace; she earns eight maravedís a day clear, which she puts into a money-box as a help towards house furnishing; but now that she is a governer's daughter thou wilt give her a portion without her working for it. The fountain in the plaza has run dry. A flash of lightning struck the gibbet, and I wish they all lit there. I look for an answer to this, and to know thy mind about my going to the Court; and so, God keep thee longer than me, or as long, for I would not leave thee in this world without me.

Thy wife,
TERESA PANZA

The letters were applauded, laughed over, relished, and admired; and then, as if to put the seal to the business, the courier arrived, bringing the one Sancho sent to Don Quixote, and this, too, was read out, and it raised some doubts as to the governor's simplicity. The duchess withdrew to hear from the page about his adventures in Sancho's village, which he narrated at full length without leaving a single circumstance unmentioned. He gave her the acorns, and also a cheese which Teresa had given him as being particularly good and superior to those of Tronchon. The duchess received it with greatest delight, in which we will leave her, to describe the end of the government of the great Sancho Panza, flower and mirror of all governors of islands.

Chapter 53

Of the troublous end and termination Sancho Panza's government came to

To fancy that in this life anything belonging to it will remain forever in the same state, is an idle fancy; on the contrary, in it everything seems to go in a circle, I mean round and round. The spring succeeds the summer, the summer the fall, the fall the autumn, the autumn the winter, and the winter the spring, and so time rolls with never-ceasing wheel. Man's life alone, swifter than time, speeds onward to its end without any hope of renewal, save it be in that other life which is endless and boundless. Thus saith Cid Hamet the Mahometan philosopher; for there are many that by the light of nature alone, without the light of faith, have a comprehension of the fleeting nature and instability of this present life and the endless duration of that eternal life we hope for; but our author is here speaking of the rapidity with which Sancho's government came to an end, melted away, disappeared, vanished as it were in smoke and shadow. For as he lay in bed on the night of the seventh day of his government, sated, not with bread and wine, but with delivering judgments and giving opinions and making laws and proclamations, just as sleep, in spite of hunger, was beginning to close his eyelids, he heard such a noise of bell-ringing and shouting that one would have fancied the whole island was going to the bottom. He sat up in bed and remained listening intently to try if he could make out what could be the cause of so great an uproar; not only, however, was he unable to discover what it was, but as countless drums and trumpets now helped to swell the din of the bells and shouts, he was more puzzled than ever, and filled with fear and terror; and getting up he put on a pair of slippers because of the dampness of the floor, and without throwing a dressing-gown or anything of the kind over him he rushed out of the door of his room, just in time to see approaching along a corridor a band of more than twenty persons with lighted torches and naked swords in their hands, all shouting out, "To arms, to arms, Señor Governor, to arms! The enemy is in the island in countless numbers, and we are lost unless your skill and valor come to our support."

Keeping up this noise, tumult, and uproar, they came to where Sancho stood dazed and bewildered by what he saw and heard, and as they approached one of them called out to him, "Arm at once, your lordship, if you would not have yourself destroyed and the whole island lost."

"What have I to do with arming?" said Sancho. "What do I know about arms or supports? Better leave all that to my master Don Quixote, who will settle it and make all safe in a trice; for I, sinner that I am, God help me, don't understand these scuffles."

"Ah, Señor Governor," said another, "what slackness of mettle this is! Arm yourself; here are arms for you, offensive and defensive; come out to the plaza and be our leader and captain; it falls upon you by right to be so, for you are our governor."

"Arm me then, in God's name," said Sancho, and they at once produced two large shields they had come provided with, and placed them upon him over his shirt, without letting him put on anything else, one shield in front and the other behind, and passing his arms through openings they had made, they bound him tight with ropes, so that there he was walled and boarded up as straight as a spindle and unable to bend his knees or stir a single step. In his hand they placed a lance, on which he leant to keep himself from falling, and as soon as they had him thus fixed, they bade him march forward and lead them on and give them all courage; for with him for their guide and lamp and morning star, they were sure to bring their business to a successful issue.

"How am I to march, unlucky being that I am?" said Sancho, "when I can't stir my kneecaps, for these boards I have bound so tight to my body won't let me. What you must do is to carry me in your arms, and lay me across or set me upright in some postern, and I'll hold it either with this lance or with my body."

"On, Señor Governor!" cried another, "it is fear more than the boards that keeps you from moving; make haste, stir yourself, for there is no time to lose; the enemy is increasing in numbers, the shouts grow louder, and the danger is pressing."

Urged by these exhortations and reproaches the poor governor made an attempt to advance, but fell to the ground with such a crash that he fancied he had broken himself all to pieces. There he lay like a tortoise enclosed in its shell, or a side of bacon between two kneading-troughs, or a boat bottom up on the beach; nor did the gang of jokers feel any compassion for him when they saw him down; so far from that, extinguishing their torches they began to shout afresh and to renew the calls to arms with such energy, trampling on poor Sancho, and slashing at him over the shield with their swords in such a way that, if he had not gathered himself together and made himself small and drawn in his head between the shields, it would have fared badly with the poor governor, as, squeezed into that narrow compass, he lay, sweating and sweating again, and commending himself with all his heart to God to deliver him from his present peril. Some stumbled over him, others fell upon him, and one there was who took up a position on top of him for some time, and from thence as if from a watch-tower issued orders to the troops, shouting out, "Here, our side! Here the enemy is thickest! Hold the breach there! Shut that gate! Barricade those ladders! Here with your stink-pots of pitch and resin, and kettles of boiling oil! Block the streets with feather beds!" In short, in his ardor he mentioned every little thing, and every implement and engine of war by means of which an assault upon a city is warded off, while the bruised and battered Sancho, who heard and suffered all, was saying to himself, "O if it would only please the Lord to let the island be lost at once, and I could see myself either dead or out of this torture!" Heaven heard his prayer, and when he least expected it he heard voices exclaiming, "Victory, victory! The enemy retreats beaten! Come, Señor Governor, get up, and come and enjoy the victory, and divide the spoils that have been won from the foe by the might of that invincible arm."

"Lift me up," said the wretched Sancho in a woe-begone voice. They helped him to rise, and as soon as he was on his feet he said, "The enemy I have beaten you may nail to my forehead; I don't want to divide the spoils of the foe, I only beg and entreat some friend, if I have one, to give me a sup of wine, for I'm parched with thirst, and wipe me dry, for I'm turning to water."

They rubbed him down, fetched him wine and unbound the shields, and he seated himself upon his bed, and with fear, agitation, and fatigue he fainted away. Those who had been concerned in the joke were now sorry they had pushed it so far; however, the anxiety his fainting away had caused them was relieved by his returning to himself. He asked what o'clock it was; they told him it was just daybreak. He said no more, and in silence began to dress himself, while all watched him, waiting to see what the haste with which he was putting on his clothes meant.

He got himself dressed at last, and then, slowly, for he was sorely bruised and could not go fast, he proceeded to the stable, followed by all who were present, and going up to Dapple embraced him and gave him a loving kiss on the forehead, and said to him, not without tears in his eyes, "Come along, comrade and friend and partner of my toils and sorrows; when I was with you and had no cares to trouble me except mending your harness and feeding your litte carcass, happy were my hours, my days, and my years; but since I left you, and mounted the towers of ambition and pride, a thousand miseries, a thousand troubles, and four thousand anxieties have entered into my soul"; and all the while he was speaking in this strain he was fixing the pack-saddle on the ass, without a word from any one. Then having Dapple saddled, he, with great pain and difficulty, got up on him, and addressing himself to the major-domo, the secretary, the head-carver, and Pedro Recio the doctor and several others who stood by, he said, "Make way, gentlemen, and let me go back to my old freedom; let me go look for my past life, and raise myself up from this present death. I was not born to be a governor or protect islands or cities from the enemies that choose to attack them. Ploughing and digging, vine-dressing and pruning, are more in my way than defending provinces or kingdoms. Saint Peter is very well at Rome; I mean each of us is best following the trade he was born to. A reaping-hook fits my hand better than a governor's sceptre; I'd rather have my fill of *gazpacho* than be subject to the misery of a meddling doctor who kills me with hunger, and I'd rather lie in summer under the shade of an oak, and in winter wrap myself in a double sheepskin jacket in freedom, than go to bed between holland sheets and dress in sables under the restraint of a government. God be with your worships, and tell my lord the duke that 'naked I was born, naked I find myself, I neither lose nor gain'; I mean that without a farthing I came into this government, and without a farthing I go out of it, very different from the way governors commonly leave other islands. Stand aside and let me go; I have to plaster myself, for I believe every one of my ribs is crushed, thanks to the enemies that have been trampling over me to-night."

"That is unnecessary, Señor Governor," said Doctor Recio, "for I will give your worship a draught against falls and bruises that will soon make you as sound and strong as ever; and as for your diet I promise your worship to behave better, and let you eat plentifully of whatever you like."

"You spoke late," said Sancho. "I'd as soon turn Turk as stay any longer. Those jokes won't pass a second time. By God I'd as soon remain in this government, or take another, even if it was offered me between two plates, as fly to heaven without wings. I am of the breed of the Panzas, and they are every one of them obstinate, and if they once say 'odds,' odds it must be, no matter if it is evens, in spite of all the world. Here in this stable I leave the ant's wings that lifted me up into the air for the swifts and other birds to eat me, and let's take to level ground and our feet once more; and if they're not shod in pinked shoes of cordovan, they won't want for rough sandals of hemp; 'every ewe to her like,' 'and let no one stretch his leg beyond the length of the sheet'; and now let me pass, for it's growing late with me."

To this the majordomo said, "Señor Governor, we would let your worship go with all our hearts, though it sorely grieves us to lose you, for your wit and Christian conduct naturally make us regret you; but it is well known that every governor, before he leaves the place where he has been governing, is bound first of all to render an account. Let your worship do so for the ten days you have held the government, and then you may go and the peace of God go with you."

"No one can demand it of me," said Sancho, "but he whom my lord the duke shall appoint; I am going to meet him, and to him I will render an exact one; besides, when I go forth naked as I do, there is no other proof needed to show that I have governed like an angel."

"By God the great Sancho is right," said Doctor Recio, "and it is my opinion we should let him go, for the duke will be beyond measure glad to see him."

They all agreed to this, and allowed him to go, first offering to bear him company and furnish him with all he wanted for his own comfort or for the journey. Sancho said he did not want anything more than a little barley for Dapple, and half a cheese and half a loaf for himself; for the distance being so short there was no occasion for any better or bulkier provant. They all embraced him, and he with tears embraced all of them, and left them filled with admiration not only at his remarks but at his firm and sensible resolution.

Chapter 54

Which deals with matters relating to this history and no other

The duke and duchess resolved that the challenge Don Quixote had, for the reason already mentioned, given their vassal, should be proceeded with; and as the young man was in Flanders, whither he had fled to escape having Doña Rodriguez for a mother-in-law, they arranged to substitute for him a Gascon lackey, named Tosilos, first of all carefully instructing him in all he had to do. Two days later the duke told Don Quixote that in four days from that time his opponent would present himself on the field of battle armed as a knight, and would maintain that the damsel lied by half a beard, nay a whole beard, if she affirmed that he had given her a promise of marriage. Don Quixote was greatly pleased at the news, and promised himself to do wonders in the lists, and reckoned it rare good fortune that an opportunity should have offered for letting his noble hosts see what the might of his strong arm was capable of; and so in high spirits and satisfaction he awaited the expiration of the four days, which measured by his impatience seemed spinning themselves out into four hundred ages. Let us leave them to pass as we do other things, and go and bear Sancho company, as mounted on Dapple, half glad, half sad, he paced along on his road to join his master, in whose society he was happier than in being governor of all the islands in the world. Well then, it so happened that before he had gone a great way from the island of his government (and whether it was island, city, town, or village that he governed he never troubled himself to inquire) he saw coming along the road he was travelling six pilgrims with staves, foreigners of that sort that beg for alms singing; who as they drew near arranged themselves in a line and lifting up their voices all together began to sing in their own language something that Sancho could not understand, with the exception of one word which sounded plainly "alms," from which he gathered that it was alms they asked for in their song; and being, as Cid Hamet says, remarkably charitable, he took out of his *alforjas* the half loaf and half cheese he had been provided with, and gave them to them, explaining to them by signs that he had nothing else to give them. They received them very gladly, but exclaimed, "*Geld! Geld!*"

"I don't understand what you want of me, good people," said Sancho.

On this one of them took a purse out of his bosom and showed it to Sancho, by which he comprehended they were asking for money, and putting his thumb to his throat and spreading his hand upwards he gave them to understand that he had not the sign of a coin about him, and urging Dapple forward he broke through them. But as he was passing, one of them who had been examining him very closely rushed towards him, and flinging his arms round him exclaimed in a loud voice and good Spanish, "God bless me! What's this I see? Is it possible that I hold in my arms my dear friend, my good neighbor Sancho Panza? But there's no doubt about it, for I'm not asleep, nor am I drunk just now."

Sancho was surprised to hear himself called by his name and to find himself embraced by a foreign pilgrim, and after regarding him steadily without speaking he was still unable to recognize him; but the pilgrim perceiving his perplexity cried, "What! and is it possible, Sancho Panza, that thou dost not know thy neighbor Ricote, the Morisco shopkeeper of thy village?"

Sancho upon this looking at him more carefully began to recall his features, and at last recognized him perfectly, and without getting off the ass threw his arms round his neck saying, "Who the devil could have known thee, Ricote, in this mummer's dress thou art in? Tell me, who has frenchified thee, and how dost thou dare to return to Spain, where if they catch thee and recognize thee it will go hard enough with thee?"

"If thou dost not betray me, Sancho," said the pilgrim, "I am safe; for in this dress no one will recognize me; but let us turn aside out of the road into that grove there where my comrades are going to eat and rest, and thou shalt eat with them there, for they are very good fellows; I shall have time enough to tell thee then all that has happened to me since I left our village in obedience to his Majesty's edict that threatened such severities against the unfortunate people of my nation, as thou hast heard."

Sancho complied, and Ricote having spoken to the other pilgrims they withdrew to the grove they saw, turning a considerable distance out of the road. They threw down their staves, took off their pilgrim's cloaks and remained in their under-clothing; they were all good-looking young fellows, except Ricote, who was a man somewhat advanced in years. They carried *alforjas* all of them, and all apparently well filled, at least with things provocative of thirst, such as would summon it from two leagues off. They stretched themselves on the ground, and making a tablecloth of the grass they spread upon it bread, salt, knives, walnuts, scraps of cheese, and well-picked ham-bones which if they were past gnawing were not past sucking. They also put down a black dainty called, they say, caviar, and made of the eggs of fish, a great thirst-wakener. Nor was there any lack of olives, dry, it is true, and without any seasoning, but for all that toothsome and pleasant. But what made the best show in the field of the banquet was half a dozen *botas* of wine, for each of them produced his own from his *alforjas;* even the good Ricote, who from a Morisco had transformed himself into a German or Dutchman, took out his, which in size might have vied with the five others. They then began to eat with very great relish and very leisurely, making the most of each morsel—very small ones of everything—they took up on the point of the knife; and then all at the same moment raised their arms and *botas* aloft, the mouths pressed to their mouths, and all eyes fixed on heaven just as if they were taking aim at it; and in this attitude they remained ever so long, wagging their heads from side to side as if in acknowledgment of the pleasure they were enjoying while they decanted the bowels of the bottles into their own stomachs.

Sancho beheld all, "and nothing gave him pain"; so far from that, acting on the proverb he knew so well, "when thou art at Rome do as thou seest," he asked Ricote for his *bota* and took aim like the rest of them, and with not less enjoyment. Four times did the *botas* bear being uplifted, but the fifth it was all in vain, for they were dryer and more sapless than a rush by that time, which made the jollity that had been kept up so far begin to flag.

Every now and then some one of them would grasp Sancho's right hand in his own saying, *"Español y Tudesqui tuto uno bon compaño";* and Sancho would answer, *"Bon compaño, jura Di,"* and then go off into a fit of laughter that lasted an hour, without a thought for the moment of anything that had befallen him in his government; for cares have very little sway over us while we are eating and drinking. At length, the wine having come to an end with them, drowsiness began to come over them, and they dropped asleep on their very table and tablecloth. Ricote and Sancho alone remained awake, for they had eaten more and drunk less, and Ricote drawing Sancho aside, they seated themselves at the foot of a beech, leaving the pilgrims buried in sweet sleep; and without once falling into his own Morisco tongue Ricote spoke as follows in pure Castilian:

"Thou knowest well, neighbor and friend Sancho Panza, how the proclamation or edict his Majesty commanded to be issued against those of my nation filled us all with terror and dismay; me at least it did, insomuch that I think before the time granted us for quitting Spain was out, the full force of the penalty had already fallen upon me and upon my children.

I decided, then, and I think wisely (just like one who knows that at a certain date the house he lives in will be taken from him, and looks out beforehand for another to change into), I decided, I say, to leave the town myself, alone and without my family, and go to seek out some place to remove them to comfortably and not in the hurried way in which the others took their departure; for I saw very plainly, and so did all the older men among us, that the proclamations were not mere threats, as some said, but positive enactments which would be enforced at the appointed time; and what made me believe this was what I knew of the base and extravagant designs which our people harbored, designs of such a nature that I think it was a divine inspiration that moved his Majesty to carry out a resolution so spirited; not that we were all guilty, for some there were true and steadfast Christians; but they were so few that they could make no head against those who were not; and it was not prudent to cherish a viper in the bosom by having enemies in the house. In short it was with just cause that we were visited with the penalty of banishment, a mild and lenient one in the eyes of some, but to us the most terrible that could be inflicted upon us. Wherever we are we weep for Spain; for after all we were born there and it is our natural fatherland. Nowhere do we find the reception our unhappy condition needs; and in Barbary and all the parts of Africa where we counted upon being received, succored, and welcomed, it is there they insult and ill-treat us. We knew not our good fortune until we lost it; and such is the longing we almost all of us have to return to Spain, that most of those who like myself know the language, and there are many who do, come back to it and leave their wives and children forsaken yonder, so great is their love for it; and now I know by experience the meaning of the saying, sweet is the love of one's country.

"I left our village, as I said, and went to France, but though they gave us a kind reception there I was anxious to see all I could. I crossed into Italy, and reached Germany, and there it seemed to me we might live with more freedom, as the inhabitants do not pay any attention to trifling points; every one lives as he likes, for in most parts they enjoy liberty of conscience. I took a house in a town near Augsburg, and then joined these pilgrims, who are in the habit of coming to Spain in great numbers every year to visit the shrines, which they look upon as their Indies and a sure and certain source of gain. They travel nearly all over

it, and there is no town out of which they do not go full up of meat and drink, as the saying is, and with a real, at least, in money, and they come off at the end of their travels with more than a hundred crowns saved, which, changed into gold, they smuggle out of the kingdom either in the hollow of their staves or in the patches of their pilgrim's cloaks or by some device of their own, and carry to their own country in spite of the guards at the posts and passes where they are searched. Now my purpose is, Sancho, to carry away the treasure that I left buried, which, as it is outside the town, I shall be able to do without risk, and to write, or cross over from Valencia, to my daughter and wife, who I know are at Algiers, and find some means of bringing them to some French port and thence to Germany, there to await what it may be God's will to do with us; for, after all, Sancho, I know well that Ricota my daughter and Francisca Ricota my wife are Catholic Christians, and though I am not so much so, still I am more of a Christian than a Moor, and it is always my prayer to God that he will open the eyes of my understanding and show me how I am to serve him; but what amazes me and I cannot understand is why my wife and daughter should have gone to Barbary rather than to France, where they could live as Christians."

To this Sancho replied, "Remember, Ricote, that may not have been open to them, for Juan Tiopieyo thy wife's brother took them, and being a true Moor he went where he could go most easily; and another thing I can tell thee, it is my belief thou art going in vain to look for what thou hast left buried, for we heard they took from thy brother-in-law and thy wife a great quantity of pearls and money in gold which they brought to be passed."

"That may be," said Ricote; "but I know they did not touch my hoard, for I did not tell them where it was, for fear of accidents; and so, if thou wilt come with me, Sancho, and help me to take it away and conceal it, I will give thee two hundred crowns wherewith thou mayest relieve thy necessities, and, as thou knowest, I know they are many."

"I would do it," said Sancho; "but I am not at all covetous, for I gave up an office this morning in which, if I was, I might have made the walls of my house of gold and dined off silver plates before six months were over; and so for this reason, and because I feel I would be guilty of treason to my king if I helped his enemies, I would not go with thee if instead of promising me two hundred crowns thou wert to give me four hundred here in hand."

"And what office is this thou hast given up, Sancho?" asked Ricote.

"I have given up being governor of an island," said Sancho, "and such a one, faith, as you won't find the like of easily."

"And where is this island?" said Ricote.

"Where?" said Sancho; "two leagues from here, and it is called the island of Barataria."

"Nonsense! Sancho," said Ricote; "islands are away out in the sea; there are no islands on the mainland."

"What? No islands!" said Sancho; "I tell thee, friend Ricote, I left it this morning, and yesterday I was governing there as I pleased like a sagittarius; but for all that I gave it up, for it seemed to me a dangerous office, a governor's."

"And what hast thou gained by the government?" asked Ricote.

"I have gained," said Sancho, "the knowledge that I am no good for governing, unless it is a drove of cattle, and that the riches that are to be got by these governments are got at the cost of one's rest and sleep, ay and even one's food; for in islands the governors must eat little, especially if they have doctors to look after their health."

"I don't understand thee, Sancho," said Ricote; "but it seems to me all nonsense thou art talking. Who would give thee islands to govern? Is there any scarcity in the world of cleverer men than thou art for governors? Hold thy peace, Sancho, and come back to thy senses, and consider whether thou wilt come with me as I said to help me to take away the treasure I left buried (for indeed it may be called a treasure, it is so large), and I will give thee wherewithal to keep thee, as I told thee."

"And I have told thee already, Ricote, that I will not," said Sancho; "let it content thee that by me thou shalt not be betrayed, and go thy way in God's name and let me go mine; for I know that well-gotten gain may be lost, but ill-gotten gain is lost, itself and its owner likewise."

"I will not press thee, Sancho," said Ricote; "but tell me, wert thou in our village when my wife and daughter and brother-in-law left it?"

"I was so," said Sancho; "and I can tell thee thy daughter left it looking so lovely that all the village turned out to see her, and everybody said she was the fairest creature in the world. She wept as she went, and embraced all her friends and acquaintances and those who came out to see her, and she begged them all to commend her to God and Our Lady his mother, and this in such a touching way that it made me

weep myself, though I'm not much given to tears commonly; and, faith, many a one would have liked to hide her, or go out and carry her off on the road; but the fear of going against the king's command kept them back. The one who showed himself most moved was Don Pedro Gregorio, the rich young heir thou knowest of, and they say he was deep in love with her; and since she left he has not been seen in our village, and we all suspect he has gone after her to steal her away, but so far nothing has been heard of it."

"I always had a suspicion that gentleman had a passion for my daughter," said Ricote; "but as I felt sure of my Ricota's virtue it gave me no uneasiness to know that he loved her, for thou must have heard it said, Sancho, that the Morisco women seldom or never engage in amours with the old Christians; and my daughter, who I fancy thought more of being a Christian than of love-making, would not trouble herself about the attentions of this heir."

"God grant it," said Sancho, "for it would be a bad business for both of them; but now let me be off, friend Ricote, for I want to reach where my master Don Quixote is to-night."

"God be with thee, brother Sancho," said Ricote; "my comrades are beginning to stir, and it is time, too, for us to continue our journey"; and then they both embraced, and Sancho mounted Dapple, and Ricote leant upon his staff, and so they parted.

Chapter 55

Of what befell Sancho on the road, and other things that cannot be surpassed

THE length of time he delayed with Ricote prevented Sancho from reaching the duke's castle that day, though he was within half a league of it when night, somewhat dark and cloudy, overtook him. This, however, as it was summer time, did not give him much uneasiness, and he turned aside out of the road intending to wait for morning; but his ill luck and hard fate so willed it that as he was searching about for a place to make himself as comfortable as possible, he and Dapple fell into a deep dark hole that lay among some very old buildings. As he fell he commended himself with all his heart to God, fancying he was not going to stop until he reached the depths of the bottomless pit; but it did not turn out so, for at little more than thrice a man's height Dapple touched bottom, and he found himself sitting on him without having received any hurt or damage whatever. He felt himself all over and held his breath to try whether he was quite sound or had a hole made in him anywhere, and finding himself all right and whole and in perfect health he was profuse in his thanks to God our Lord for the mercy that had been shown him, for he thought surely he had been broken into a thousand pieces. He also felt along the sides of the pit with his hands to see if it were possible to get out of it without help, but he found they were quite smooth and afforded no hold anywhere, at which he was greatly distressed, especially when he heard how pathetically and dolefully Dapple was bemoaning himself, and no wonder he complained, nor was it from ill-temper, for in truth he was not in a very good case.

"Alas," said Sancho, "what unexpected accidents happen at every step to those who live in this miserable world! Who would have said that one who saw himself yesterday sitting on a throne, governor of an island, giving orders to his servants and his vassals, would see himself to-day buried in a pit without a soul to help him, or servant or vassal to come to his relief! Here must we perish with hunger, my ass and myself, if indeed we don't die first, he of his bruises and injuries, and I of grief and sorrow. At any rate I shall not be as lucky as my master Don Quixote of La Mancha, when he went down into the cave of that enchanted Montesinos, where he found people to make more of him than if he had been in his own house; for it seems he came in for a table laid out and a bed ready made. There he saw fair and pleasant visions, but here I shall see, I imagine, toads and adders. Unlucky wretch that I am, what an end my follies and fancies have come to! They'll take up my bones out of this, when it is Heaven's will that I'm found, picked clean, white and polished, and my good Dapple's with them, and by that, perhaps, it will be found out who we are, at least by such as have heard that Sancho Panza never separated from his ass, nor his ass from Sancho Panza. Unlucky wretches, I say again, that our hard fate should not let us die in our own country and among our own people, where if there was no help for our misfortune, at any rate there would be some one to grieve for it and to close our eyes as we passed away! O comrade and friend, how ill have I repaid thy faithful services! Forgive me, and entreat Fortune, as well as thou canst, to deliver us out of this miserable strait we are both in; and I promise to put a crown of laurel on thy head, and make thee look like a poet laureate, and give thee double feeds."

In this strain did Sancho bewail himself, and his ass listened to him, but answered him never a word, such was the distress and anguish the poor beast found himself in. At length, after a night spent in bitter moanings and lamentations, day came, and by its light Sancho perceived that it was wholly impossible to escape out of that pit without help, and he fell to bemoaning his fate and uttering loud shouts to find out if there was any one within hearing; but all his shouting was only crying in the wilderness, for there was not a soul anywhere in the neighborhood to hear him, and then at last he gave himself up for dead. Dapple was lying on his back, and Sancho helped him to his feet, which he was scarcely able to keep; and then taking a piece of bread out of his *alforjas* which had shared their fortunes in the fall, he gave it to the ass, to whom it was not unwelcome, saying to him as if he understood him, "With bread all sorrows are less."

And now he perceived on one side of the pit a hole large enough to admit a person if he stooped and squeezed himself into a small compass. Sancho made for it, and entered it by creeping, and found it wide and spacious on the inside, which he was able to see as a ray of sunlight that penetrated what might be called the roof showed it all plainly. He observed, too, that it opened and widened out into another spacious cavity; seeing which he made his way back to where the ass was, and with a stone began to pick away the clay from the hole until in a short time he had made room for the beast to pass easily, and this accomplished, taking him by the halter, he proceeded to traverse the cavern to see if there was any outlet at the other end. He advanced, sometimes in the dark, sometimes with light, but never without fear; "God Almighty help me!" said he to himself; "this that is a misadventure to me would make a good adventure for my master Don Quixote. He would have been sure to take these depths and dungeons for flowery gardens or the palaces of Galiana, and would have counted upon issuing out of this darkness and imprisonment into some blooming meadow; but I, unlucky that I am, hopeless and spiritless, expect at every step another pit deeper than the first to open under my feet and swallow me up for good; 'welcome evil, if thou comest alone.'"

In this way and with these reflections he seemed to himself to have travelled rather more than half a league, when at last he perceived a dim light that looked like daylight and found its way in on one side, showing that this road, which appeared to him the road to the other world, led to some opening.

Here Cid Hamet leaves him, and returns to Don Quixote, who in high spirits and satisfaction was looking forward to the day fixed for the battle he was to fight with him who had robbed Doña Rodriguez's daughter of her honor, for whom he hoped to obtain satisfaction for the wrong and injury shamefully done to her. It came to pass, then, that having sallied forth one morning to practise and exercise himself in what he would have to do in the encounter he expected to find himself engaged in the next day, as he was putting Rocinante through his paces or pressing him to the charge, he brought his feet so close to a pit that but for reining him in tightly it would have been impossible for him to avoid falling into it. He pulled him up, however, without a fall, and coming a little closer examined the hole without dismounting; but as he was looking at it he heard loud cries proceeding from it, and by listening attentively was able to make out that he who uttered them was saying, "Ho, above there! is there any Christian that hears me, or any charitable gentleman that will take pity on a sinner buried alive, or an unfortunate disgoverned governor?"

It struck Don Quixote that it was the voice of Sancho Panza he heard, whereat he was taken aback and amazed, and raising his own voice as much as he could, he cried out, "Who is below there? Who is that complaining?"

"Who should be here, or who should complain," was the answer, "but the forlorn Sancho Panza, for his sins and for his ill-luck governor of the island of Barataria, squire that was to the famous knight Don Quixote of La Mancha?"

When Don Quixote heard this his amazement was redoubled and his perturbation grew greater than ever, for it suggested itself to his mind that Sancho must be dead, and that his soul was in torment down there; and carried away by this idea he exclaimed, "I conjure thee by everything that as a Catholic Christian I can conjure thee by, tell me who thou art; and if thou art a soul in torment, tell me what thou wouldst have me do for thee; for as my profession is to give aid and succor to those that need it in this world, it will also extend to aiding and succoring the distressed of the other, who cannot help themselves."

"In that case," answered the voice, "your worship who speaks to me must be my master Don Quixote of La Mancha; nay, from the tone of the voice it is plain it can be nobody else."

"Don Quixote I am," replied Don Quixote, "he whose profession it is to aid and succor the living and the dead in their necessities; wherefore tell me who thou art, for thou art keeping me in suspense; because, if thou art my squire Sancho Panza, and art dead, since the devils have not carried thee off, and thou art by God's mercy in purgatory, our holy mother the Roman Catholic Church has intercessory means sufficient to release thee from the pains thou art in; and I for my part will plead with her to that end, so far as my substance will go; without further delay, therefore, declare thyself, and tell me who thou art."

"By all that's good," was the answer, "and by the birth of whomsoever your worship chooses, I swear, Señor Don Quixote of La Mancha, that I am your squire Sancho Panza, and that I have never died all my life; but that, having given up my government for reasons that would require more time to explain, I fell last night into this pit where I am now, and Dapple is witness and won't let me lie, for more by token he is here with me."

Nor was this all; one would have fancied the ass understood what Sancho said, because that moment he began to bray so loudly that the whole cave rang again.

"Famous testimony!" exclaimed Don Quixote; "I know that bray as well as if I was its mother, and thy voice, too, my Sancho. Wait while I go to the duke's castle, which is close by, and I will bring some one to take thee out of this pit into which thy sins no doubt have brought thee."

"Go, your worship," said Sancho, "and come back quick for God's sake; for I cannot bear being buried alive here any longer, and I'm dying of fear."

Don Quixote left him, and hastened to the castle to tell the duke and duchess what had happened to Sancho, and they were not a little astonished at it, although they could easily understand his having fallen, from the confirmatory circumstance of the cave which had been in existence there from time immemorial; but they could not imagine how he had quitted the government without their receiving any intimation of his coming. To be brief, they fetched ropes and tackle, as the saying is, and by dint of many hands and much labor they drew up Dapple and Sancho Panza out of the darkness into the light of day. A student who saw him remarked, "That's the way all bad governors should come out of their governments, as this sinner comes out of the depths of the pit, dead with hunger, pale, and I suppose without a farthing."

Sancho overheard him and said, "It is eight or ten days, brother growler, since I entered upon the government of the island they gave me, and all that time I never had a bellyfull of victuals, no not for an hour; doctors persecuted me and enemies crushed my bones; nor had I any opportunity of taking bribes or levying taxes; and if that be the case, as it is, I don't deserve, I think, to come out in this fashion, but 'man proposes and God disposes'; and God knows what is best, and what suits each one best; and 'as the occasion, so the behaviour'; and 'let nobody say "I won't drink of this water" '; and 'where one thinks there are flitches, there are no pegs'; God knows my meaning and that's enough; I say no more, though I could."

"Be not angry or annoyed at what thou hearest, Sancho," said Don Quixote, "or there will never be an end of it; keep a safe conscience and let them say what they like; for trying to stop slanderers' tongues is like trying to put gates to the open plain. If a governor comes out of his government rich, they say he has been a thief; and if he comes out poor, that he has been a noodle and a blockhead."

"They'll be pretty sure this time," said Sancho, "to set me down for a fool rather than a thief."

Thus talking, and surrounded by boys and a crowd of people, they reached the castle, where in one of the corridors the duke and duchess stood waiting for them; but Sancho would not go up to see the duke until he had first put up Dapple in the stable, for he said he had passed a very bad night in his last quarters; then he went upstairs to see his lord and lady, and kneeling before them he said, "Because it was your highnesses' pleasure, not because of any desert of my own, I went to govern your island of Barataria, which I entered naked, 'and naked I find myself; I neither lose nor gain.' Whether I have governed well or ill, I have had witnesses who will say what they think fit. I have answered questions, I have decided causes, and always dying of hunger, for Dr. Pedro Recio of Tirteafuera, the islandish and governorish doctor, would have it so. Enemies attacked us by night and put us in a great quandary, but the people of the island say they came off safe and victorious by the might of my arm; and may God give them as much health as there's truth in what they say. In short, during that time I have weighed the cares and responsibilities governing brings with it, and by my reckoning I

find my shoulders can't bear them, nor are they a load for my loins or arrows for my quiver; and so, before the government threw me over, I preferred to throw the government over; and yesterday morning I left the island as I found it, with the same streets, houses, and roofs it had when I entered it. I asked no loan of anybody, nor did I try to fill my pocket; and though I meant to make some useful laws, I made hardly any, as I was afraid they would not be kept; for in that case it comes to the same thing to make them or not to make them. I quitted the island, as I said, without any escort except my ass; I fell into a pit, I pushed on through it, until this morning by the light of the sun I saw an outlet, but not so easy a one but that, had not Heaven sent me my master Don Quixote, I'd have stayed there till the end of the world. So now, my lord and lady duke and duchess, here is your governor Sancho Panza, who in the bare ten days he has held the government has come by the knowledge that he would not give anything to be governor, not to say of an island, but of the whole world; and that point being settled, kissing your worships' feet, and imitating the game of the boys when they say 'leap thou, and give me one,' I take a leap out of the government and pass into the service of my master Don Quixote; for after all, though in it I eat my bread in fear and trembling, at any rate I take my fill; and for my part, so long as I'm full, it's all alike to me whether it's with carrots or with partridges."

Here Sancho brought his long speech to an end, Don Quixote having been the whole time in dread of his uttering a host of absurdities; and when he found him leave off with so few, he thanked Heaven in his heart. The duke embraced Sancho and told him he was heartily sorry he had given up the government so soon, but that he would see that he was provided with some other post on his estate less onerous and more profitable. The duchess also embraced him, and gave orders that he should be taken good care of, as it was plain to see he had been badly treated and worse bruised.

Chapter 56

Of the prodigious and unparalleled battle that took place between Don Quixote of La Mancha and the lackey Tosilos in defence of the daughter of the duenna Doña Rodriguez

THE duke and duchess had no reason to regret the joke that had been played upon Sancho

Panza in giving him the government; especially as their majordomo returned the same day, and gave them a minute account of almost every word and deed that Sancho uttered or did during the time; and to wind up with eloquently described to them the attack upon the island and Sancho's fright and departure, with which they were not a little amused. After this the history goes on to say that the day fixed for the battle arrived, and that the duke, after having repeatedly instructed his lackey Tosilos how to deal with Don Quixote so as to vanquish him without killing or wounding him, gave orders to have the heads removed from the lances, telling Don Quixote that Christian charity, on which he plumed himself, could not suffer the battle to be fought with so much risk and danger to life; and that he must be content with the offer of a battle-field on his territory (though that was against the decree of the holy council, which prohibits all challenges of the sort) and not push such an arduous venture to its extreme limits. Don Quixote bade his excellence arrange all matters connected with the affair as he pleased, as on his part he would obey him in everything. The dread day, then, having arrived, and the duke having ordered a spacious stand to be erected facing the court of the castle for the judges of the field and the appellant duennas, mother and daughter, vast crowds flocked from all the villages and hamlets of the neighborhood to see the novel spectacle of the battle; nobody, dead or alive, in those parts having ever seen or heard of such a one.

The first person to enter the field and the lists was the master of the ceremonies, who surveyed and paced the whole ground to see that there was nothing unfair and nothing concealed to make the combatants stumble or fall; then the duennas entered and seated themselves, enveloped in mantles covering their eyes, nay even their bosoms, and displaying no slight emotion as Don Quixote appeared in the lists. Shortly afterwards, accompanied by several trumpets and mounted on a powerful steed that threatened to crush the whole place, the great lackey Tosilos made his appearance on one side of the courtyard with his visor down and stiffly cased in a suit of stout shining armor. The horse was a manifest Frieslander, broad-backed and flea-bitten, and with half a hundred of wool hanging to each of its fetlocks. The gallant combatant came well primed by his master the duke as to how he was to bear himself against the valiant Don Quixote of La Mancha; being warned that he must on no account slay him, but strive

to shirk the first encounter so as to avoid the risk of killing him, as he was sure to do if he met him full tilt. He crossed the courtyard at a walk, and coming to where the duennas were placed stopped to look at her who demanded him for a husband; the marshal of the field summoned Don Quixote, who had already presented himself in the courtyard, and standing by the side of Tosilos he addressed the duennas, and asked them if they consented that Don Quixote of La Mancha should do battle for their right. They said they did, and that whatever he should do in that behalf they declared rightly done, final and valid. By this time the duke and duchess had taken their places in a gallery commanding the enclosure, which was filled to overflowing with a multitude of people eager to see this perilous and unparalleled encounter. The conditions of the combat were that if Don Quixote proved the victor his antagonist was to marry the daughter of Doña Rodriguez; but if he should be vanquished his opponent was released from the promise that was claimed against him and from all obligations to give satisfaction. The master of the ceremonies apportioned the sun to them, and stationed them, each on the spot where he was to stand. The drums beat, the sound of the trumpets filled the air, the earth trembled under foot, the hearts of the gazing crowd were full of anxiety, some hoping for a happy issue, some apprehensive of an untoward ending to the affair, and lastly, Don Quixote, commending himself with all his heart to God our Lord and to the lady Dulcinea del Toboso, stood waiting for them to give the necessary signal for the onset. Our lackey, however, was thinking of something very different; he only thought of what I am now going to mention.

It seems that as he stood contemplating his enemy she struck him as the most beautiful woman he had ever seen all his life; and the little blind boy whom in our streets they commonly call Love had no mind to let slip the chance of triumphing over a lackey heart, and adding it to the list of his trophies; and so, stealing gently upon him unseen, he drove a dart two yards long into the poor lackey's left side and pierced his heart through and through; which he was able to do quite at his ease, for Love is invisible, and comes in and goes out as he likes, without anyone calling him to account for what he does. Well then, when they gave the signal for the onset our lackey was in an ecstasy, musing upon the beauty of her whom he had already made mistress of his liberty, and so he paid no attention to the sound of the trumpet, unlike Don Quixote, who was off the instant he heard it, and, at the highest speed Rocinante was capable of, set out to meet his enemy, his good squire Sancho shouting lustily as he saw him start, "God guide thee, cream and flower of knights-errant! God give thee the victory, for thou hast the right on thy side!"

But though Tosilos saw Don Quixote coming at him he never stirred a step from the spot where he was posted; and instead of doing so called loudly to the marshal of the field, to whom when he came up to see what he wanted he said, "Señor, is not this battle to decide whether I marry or do not marry that lady?" "Just so," was the answer. "Well then," said the lackey, "I feel qualms of conscience, and I should lay a heavy burden upon it if I were to proceed any further with the combat; I therefore declare that I yield myself vanquished, and that I am willing to marry the lady at once."

The marshal of the field was lost in astonishment at the words of Tosilos; and as he was one of those who were privy to the arrangement of the affair he knew not what to say in reply. Don Quixote pulled up in mid career when he saw that his enemy was not coming on to the attack. The duke could not make out the reason why the battle did not go on; but the marshal of the field hastened to him to let him know what Tosilos said, and he was amazed and extremely angry at it. In the meantime Tosilos advanced to where Doña Rodriguez sat and said in a loud voice, "Señora, I am willing to marry your daughter, and I have no wish to obtain by strife and fighting what I can obtain in peace and without any risk to my life."

The valiant Don Quixote heard him, and said, "As that is the case I am released and absolved from my promise; let them marry by all means, and as God our Lord has given her, may Saint Peter add his blessing."

The duke had now descended to the courtyard of the castle, and going up to Tosilos he said to him, "Is it true, sir knight, that you yield yourself vanquished, and that moved by scruples of conscience you wish to marry this damsel?"

"It is, señor," replied Tosilos.

"And he does well," said Sancho, "for what thou hast to give to the mouse, give to the cat, and it will save thee all trouble."

Tosilos meanwhile was trying to unlace his helmet, and he begged them to come to his help at once, as his power of breathing was failing him, and he could not remain so long shut up in that confined space. They removed it in all haste, and his lackey features were revealed to public gaze. At this sight Doña Rodriguez and her daughter raised a mighty outcry, exclaiming, "This is a trick! This is a trick! They have put Tosilos, my lord the duke's lackey, upon us in place of the real husband. The justice of God and the king against such trickery, not to say roguery!"

"Do not distress yourselves, ladies," said Don Quixote, "for this is no trickery or roguery; or if it is, it is not the duke who is at the bottom of it, but those wicked enchanters who persecute me, and who, jealous of my reaping the glory of this victory, have turned your husband's features into those of this person, who you say is a lackey of the duke's; take my advice, and notwithstanding the malice of my enemies marry him, for beyond a doubt he is the very one you wish to get for a husband."

When the duke heard this all his anger was near vanishing in a fit of laughter, and he said, "The things that happen to Señor Don Quixote are so extraordinary that I am ready to believe this lackey of mine is not one; but let us adopt this plan and device; let us put off the marriage for, say, a fortnight, and let us keep this person about whom we are uncertain in close confinement, and perhaps in the course of that time he may return to his original shape; for the spite which the enchanters entertain against Señor Don Quixote cannot last so long, especially as it is of so little advantage to them to practise these deceptions and transformations."

"Oh, señor," said Sancho, "those scoundrels are well used to changing whatever concerns my master from one thing into another. A knight that he overcame some time back, called the Knight of the Mirrors, they turned into the shape of the bachelor Samson Carrasco of our town and a great friend of ours; and my lady Dulcinea del Toboso they have turned into a common country wench; so I suspect this lackey will have to live and die a lackey all the days of his life."

Here the Rodriguez's daughter exclaimed, "Let him be who he may, this man that claims me for a wife; I am thankful to him for the same, for I had rather be the lawful wife of a lackey than the cheated mistress of a gentleman; though he who played me false is nothing of the kind."

To be brief, all the talk and all that had happened ended in Tosilos being shut up until it was seen how his transformation turned out. All hailed Don Quixote as victor, but the greater number were vexed and disappointed at finding that the combatants they had been so anxiously waiting for had not battered one another to pieces, just as the boys are disappointed when the man they are waiting to see hanged does not come out, because the prosecution or the court has pardoned him. The people dispersed, the duke and Don Quixote returned to the castle, they locked up Tosilos, Doña Rodriguez and her daughter remained perfectly contented when they saw that any way the affair must end in marriage, and Tosilos wanted nothing else.

Chapter 57

Which treats of how Don Quixote took leave of the duke, and of what followed with the witty and impudent Altisidora, one of the duchess's damsels

DON QUIXOTE now felt it right to quit a life of such idleness as he was leading in the castle; for he fancied that he was making himself sorely missed by suffering himself to remain shut up and inactive amid the countless luxuries and enjoyments his hosts lavished upon him as a knight-errant; and he felt too that he would have to render a strict account to Heaven of that indolence and seclusion; and so one day he asked the duke and duchess to grant him permission to take his departure. They gave it, showing at the same time that they were very sorry he was leaving them. The duchess gave his wife's letters to Sancho Panza, who shed tears over them, saying, "Who would have thought that such grand hopes as the news of my government bred in my wife Teresa Panza's breast would end in my going back now to the vagabond adventures of my master Don Quixote of La Mancha? Still I'm glad to see my Teresa behaved as she ought in sending the acorns, for if she had not sent them I should have been sorry, and she'd have shown herself ungrateful. It is a comfort to me that they can't call that present a bribe; for I had got the government already when she sent them, and it's but reasonable that those who have had a good turn done them should show their gratitude, if it's only with a trifle. After all I went into the government naked, and I come out of it naked; so I can say with a safe conscience—and that's no small matter—'naked I was born, naked I find myself, I neither lose nor gain.'"

Thus did Sancho soliloquize on the day of their departure, as Don Quixote, who had the night before taken leave of the duke and duchess, coming out made his appearance at an early hour in full armor in the courtyard of the castle. The whole household of the castle were watching him from the corridors, and the duke and duchess, too, came out to see him. Sancho was mounted on his Dapple, with his *alforjas,* valise, and provender, supremely happy because the duke's majordomo, the same that had acted the part of the Trifaldi, had given him a little purse with two hundred gold crowns to meet the necessary expenses of the road, but of this Don Quixote knew nothing as yet. While all were, as has been said, observing him, suddenly from among the duennas and handmaidens of the duchess the impudent and witty Altisidora lifted up her voice and said in pathetic tones:

> *Give ear, cruel knight;*
> *Draw rein; where's the need*
> *Of spurring the flanks*
> *Of that ill-broken steed?*
> *From what art thou flying?*
> *No dragon I am,*
> *Not even a sheep,*
> *But a tender young lamb.*
> *Thou hast jilted a maiden*
> *As fair to behold*
> *As nymph of Diana*
> *Or Venus of old.*
> *Bireno,*[1] *Æneas, what worse shall I call thee?*
> *Barabbas go with thee! All evil befall thee!*
>
> *In thy claws, ruthless robber,*
> *Thou bearest away*
> *The heart of a meek*
> *Loving maid for thy prey,*
> *Three kerchiefs thou stealest,*
> *And garters a pair,*
> *From legs than the whitest*
> *Of marble more fair;*
> *And the sighs that pursue thee*
> *Would burn to the ground*
> *Two thousand Troy Towns,*
> *If so many were found.*
> *Bireno, Æneas, what worse shall I call thee?*
> *Barabbas go with thee! All evil befall thee!*
>
> *May no bowels of mercy*
> *To Sancho be granted,*
> *And thy Dulcinea*
> *Be left still enchanted,*
> *May thy falsehood to me*
> *Find its punishment in her,*
> *For in my land the just*
> *Often pays for the sinner.*
> *May thy grandest adventures*
> *Discomfitures prove,*
> *May thy joys be all dreams,*
> *And forgotten thy love.*

[1] Bireno, Duke of Zealand, who deserted Olympia, daughter of the Count of Holland.

Bireno, Æneas, what worse shall I call thee?
Barabbas go with thee! All evil befall thee!

> *May thy name be abhorred*
>   *For thy conduct to ladies,*
> *From London to England,*
>   *From Seville to Cadiz;*
> *May thy cards be unlucky,*
>   *Thy hands contain ne'er a*
> *King, seven, or ace*
>   *When thou playest primera;*
> *When thy corns are cut*
>   *May it be to the quick;*
> *When thy grinders are drawn*
>   *May the roots of them stick.*
> *Bireno, Æneas, what worse shall I call thee?*
> *Barabbas go with thee! All evil befall thee!*

All the while the unhappy Altisidora was bewailing herself in the above strain Don Quixote stood staring at her; and without uttering a word in reply to her he turned round to Sancho and said, "Sancho my friend, I conjure thee by the life of thy forefathers tell me the truth; say, hast thou by any chance taken the three kerchiefs and the garters this love-sick maid speaks of?"

To this Sancho made answer, "The three kerchiefs I have; but the garters, as much as 'over the hills of Úbeda.'"

The duchess was amazed at Altisidora's assurance; she knew that she was bold, lively, and impudent, but not so much so as to venture to make free in this fashion; and not being prepared for the joke, her astonishment was all the greater. The duke had a mind to keep up the sport, so he said, "It does not seem to me well done in you, sir knight, that after having received the hospitality that has been offered you in this very castle, you should have ventured to carry off even three kerchiefs, not to say my handmaid's garters. It shows a bad heart and does not tally with your reputation. Restore her garters, or else I defy you to mortal combat, for I am not afraid of rascally enchanters changing or altering my features as they changed his who encountered you into those of my lackey, Tosilos."

"God forbid," said Don Quixote, "that I should draw my sword against your illustrious person from which I have received such great favors. The kerchiefs I will restore, as Sancho says he has them; as to the garters that is impossible, for I have not got them, neither has he; and if your handmaiden here will look in her hiding-places, depend upon it she will find them. I have never been a thief, my lord duke, nor do I mean to be so long as I live if God cease not to have me in his keeping. This damsel by her own confession

speaks as one in love, for which I am not to blame, and therefore need not ask pardon, either of her or of your excellence, whom I entreat to have a better opinion of me, and once more to give me leave to pursue my journey."

"And may God so prosper it, Señor Don Quixote," said the duchess, "that we may always hear good news of your exploits; God speed you; for the longer you stay, the more you inflame the hearts of the damsels who behold you; and as for this one of mine, I will so chastise her that she will not transgress again, either with her eyes or with her words."

"One word and no more, O valiant Don Quixote, I ask you to hear," said Altisidora, "and that is that I beg your pardon about the theft of the garters; and by God and upon my soul I have got them on, and I have fallen into the same blunder as he did who went looking for his ass being all the while mounted on it."

"Didn't I say so?" said Sancho. "I'm a likely one to hide thefts! Why, if I wanted to deal in them, opportunities came ready enough to me in my government."

Don Quixote bowed his head, and saluted the duke and duchess and all the bystanders, and wheeling Rocinante round, Sancho following him on Dapple, he rode out of the castle, shaping his course for Saragossa.

Chapter 58

Which tells how adventures came crowding on Don Quixote in such numbers that they gave one another no breathing-time

WHEN Don Quixote saw himself in the open country, free, and relieved from the attentions of Altisidora, he felt at his ease, and in fresh spirits to take up the pursuit of chivalry once more; and turning to Sancho he said, "Freedom, Sancho, is one of the most precious gifts that Heaven has bestowed upon men; no treasures that the earth holds buried or the sea conceals can compare with it; for freedom, as for honor, life may and should be ventured; and on the other hand, captivity is the greatest evil that can fall to the lot of man. I say this, Sancho, because thou hast seen the good cheer, the abundance we have enjoyed in this castle we are leaving; well then, amid those dainty banquets and snow-cooled beverages I felt as though I was undergoing the straits of hunger, because I did not enjoy them with the same freedom as if they had been mine own; for the sense of being under an obligation to return benefits and favors received is a restraint that checks the independence of the spirit. Happy he, to whom Heaven has given a piece of bread for which he is not bound to give thanks to any but Heaven itself!"

"For all your worship says," said Sancho, "it is not becoming that there should be no thanks on our part for two hundred gold crowns that the duke's majordomo has given me in a little purse which I carry next my heart, like a warming plaster or comforter, to meet any chance calls; for we shan't always find castles where they'll entertain us; now and then we may light upon roadside inns where they'll cudgel us."

In conversation of this sort the knight and squire errant were pursuing the journey, when, after they had gone a little more than half a league, they perceived some dozen men dressed like laborers stretched upon their cloaks on the grass of a green meadow eating their dinner. They had beside them what seemed to be white sheets concealing some objects under them, standing upright or lying flat, and arranged at intervals. Don Quixote approached the diners, and, saluting them courteously first, he asked them what it was those cloths covered.

"Señor," answered one of the party, "under these cloths are some images carved in relief intended for a *retablo* we are putting up in our village; we carry them covered up that they may not be soiled, and on our shoulders that they may not be broken."

"With your good leave," said Don Quixote, "I should like to see them; for images that are carried so carefully no doubt must be fine ones."

"I should think they were!" said the other; "let the money they cost speak for that; for as a matter of fact there is not one of them that does not stand us in more than fifty ducats; and that your worship may judge; wait a moment, and you shall see with your own eyes"; and getting up from his dinner he went and uncovered the first image, which proved to be one of Saint George on horseback with a dragon writhing at his feet and the lance thrust down its throat with all that fierceness that is usually depicted. The whole group was one blaze of gold, as the saying is. On seeing it Don Quixote said, "That knight was one of the best knights-errant the army of Heaven ever owned; he was called Don Saint George, and he was moreover a defender of maidens. Let us see this next one."

The man uncovered it, and it was seen to be that of Saint Martin on his horse, dividing his cloak with the beggar. The instant Don Quixote saw it he said, "This knight too was one of the Christian adventurers; but I believe he was generous rather than valiant, as thou mayest per-

ceive, Sancho, by his dividing his cloak with the beggar and giving him half of it; no doubt it was winter at the time, for otherwise he would have given him the whole of it, so charitable was he."

"It was not that, most likely," said Sancho, "but that he held with the proverb that says, 'For giving and keeping there's need of brains.'"

Don Quixote laughed, and asked them to take off the next cloth, underneath which was seen the image of the patron saint of the Spains seated on horseback, his sword stained with blood, trampling on Moors and treading heads under foot; and on seeing it Don Quixote exclaimed, "Ay, this is a knight, and of the squadrons of Christ! This one is called Don Saint James the Moorslayer, one of the bravest saints and knights the world ever had or heaven has now."

They then raised another cloth which it appeared covered Saint Paul falling from his horse, with all the details that are usually given in representations of his conversion. When Don Quixote saw it, rendered in such lifelike style that one would have said Christ was speaking and Paul answering, "This," he said, "was in his time the greatest enemy that the Church of God our Lord had, and the greatest champion it will ever have; a knight-errant in life, a steadfast saint in death, an untiring laborer in the Lord's vineyard, a teacher of the Gentiles, whose school was heaven, and whose instructor and master was Jesus Christ himself."

There were no more images, so Don Quixote bade them cover them up again, and said to those who had brought them. "I take it as a happy omen, brothers, to have seen what I have; for these saints and knights were of the same profession as myself, which is the calling of arms; only there is this difference between them and me, that they were saints, and fought with divine weapons, and I am a sinner and fight with human ones. They won heaven by force of arms, for Heaven suffereth violence; and I, so far, know not what I have won by dint of my sufferings; but if my Dulcinea del Toboso were to be released from hers, perhaps with mended fortunes and a mind restored to itself I might direct my steps in a better path than I am following at present."

"May God hear and sin be deaf," said Sancho to this.

The men were filled with wonder, as well at the figure as at the words of Don Quixote, though they did not understand one half of what he meant by them. They finished their dinner, took their images on their backs, and bidding farewell to Don Quixote resumed their journey.

Sancho was amazed afresh at the extent of his master's knowledge, as much as if he had never known him, for it seemed to him that there was no story or event in the world that he had not at his fingers' ends and fixed in his memory, and he said to him, "In truth, master mine, if this that has happened to us to-day is to be called an adventure, it has been one of the sweetest and pleasantest that have befallen us in the whole course of our travels; we have come out of it unbelabored and undismayed, neither have we drawn sword nor have we smitten the earth with our bodies, nor have we been left famishing; blessed be God that he has let me see such a thing with my own eyes!"

"Thou sayest well, Sancho," said Don Quixote, "but remember all times are not alike nor do they always run the same way; and these things the vulgar commonly call omens, which are not based upon any natural reason, will by him who is wise be esteemed and reckoned happy accidents merely. One of these believers in omens will get up of a morning, leave his house, and meet a friar of the blessed Saint Francis, and, as if he had met a griffin, he will turn about and go home. With another Mendoza the salt is spilt on his table, and gloom is spilt over his heart, as if nature was obliged to give warning of coming misfortunes by means of such trivial things as these. The wise man and the Christian should not trifle with what it may please Heaven to do. Scipio on coming to Africa stumbled as he leaped on shore; his soldiers took it as a bad omen; but he, clasping the soil with his arms, exclaimed, 'Thou canst not escape me, Africa, for I hold thee tight between my arms.' Thus, Sancho, meeting those images has been to me a most happy occurrence."

"I can well believe it," said Sancho; "but I wish your worship would tell me what is the reason that the Spaniards, when they are about to give battle, in calling on that Saint James the Moorslayer, say 'Santiago and close Spain!' Is Spain, then, open, so that it is needful to close it; or what is the meaning of this form?"

"Thou art very simple, Sancho," said Don Quixote; "God, look you, gave that great knight of the Red Cross to Spain as her patron saint and protector, especially in those hard struggles the Spaniards had with the Moors; and therefore they invoke and call upon him as their defender in all their battles; and in these he has been many a time seen beating down, trampling under foot, destroying and slaughtering the Hagarene squadrons in the sight of all; of which fact I could give thee many examples recorded in truthful Spanish histories."

Sancho changed the subject, and said to his master, "I marvel, señor, at the boldness of Altisidora, the duchess's handmaid; he whom they call Love must have cruelly pierced and wounded her; they say he is a little blind urchin who, though blear-eyed, or more properly speaking sightless, if he aims at a heart, be it ever so small, hits it and pierces it through and through with its arrows. I have heard it said too that the arrows of Love are blunted and robbed of their points by maidenly modesty and reserve; but with this Altisidora it seems they are sharpened rather than blunted."

"Bear in mind, Sancho," said Don Quixote, "that love is influenced by no consideration, recognizes no restraints of reason, and is of the same nature as death, that assails alike the lofty palaces of kings and the humble cabins of shepherds; and when it takes entire possession of a heart, the first thing it does is to banish fear and shame from it; and so without shame Altisidora declared her passion, which excited in my mind embarrassment rather than commiseration."

"Notable cruelty!" exclaimed Sancho; "unheard-of ingratitude! I can only say for myself that the very smallest loving word of hers would have subdued me and made a slave of me. The devil! What a heart of marble, what bowels of brass, what a soul of mortar! But I can't imagine what it is that this damsel saw in your worship that could have conquered and captivated her so. What gallant figure was it, what bold bearing, what sprightly grace, what comeliness of feature, which of these things by itself, or what altogether, could have made her fall in love with you? For indeed and in truth many a time I stopped to look at your worship from the sole of your foot to the topmost hair of your head, and I see more to frighten one than to make one fall in love; moreover I have heard say that beauty is the first and main thing that excites love, and as your worship has none at all, I don't know what the poor creature fell in love with."

"Recollect, Sancho," replied Don Quixote, "there are two sorts of beauty, one of the mind, the other of the body; that of the mind displays and exhibits itself in intelligence, in modesty, in honorable conduct, in generosity, in good breeding; and all these qualities are possible and may exist in an ugly man; and when it is this sort of beauty and not that of the body that is the attraction, love is apt to spring up suddenly and violently. I, Sancho, perceive clearly enough that I am not beautiful, but at the same time I know I am not hideous; and it is enough for an honest man not to be a monster to be an object of love, if only he possesses the endowments of mind I have mentioned."

While engaged in this discourse they were making their way through a wood that lay beyond the road, when suddenly, without expecting anything of the kind, Don Quixote found himself caught in some nets of green cord stretched from one tree to another; and unable to conceive what it could be, he said to Sancho, "Sancho, it strikes me this affair of these nets will prove one of the strangest adventures imaginable. May I die if the enchanters that persecute me are not trying to entangle me in them and delay my journey, by way of revenge for my obduracy towards Altisidora. Well then let me tell them that if these nets, instead of being green cord, were made of the hardest diamonds, or stronger than that wherewith the jealous god of blacksmiths enmeshed Venus and Mars, I would break them as easily as if they were made of rushes or cotton threads." But just as he was about to press forward and break through all, suddenly from among some trees two shepherdesses of surpassing beauty presented themselves to his sight—or at least damsels dressed like shepherdesses, save that their jerkins and sayas were of fine brocade; that is to say, the sayas were rich farthingales of gold-embroidered tabby. Their hair, that in its golden brightness vied with the beams of the sun itself, fell loose upon their shoulders and was crowned with garlands twined with green laurel and red everlasting; and their years to all appearance were not under fifteen nor above eighteen. Such was the spectacle that filled Sancho with amazement, fascinated Don Quixote, made the sun halt in his course to behold them, and held all four in a strange silence. One of the shepherdesses, at length, was the first to speak and said to Don Quixote, "Hold, sir knight, and do not break these nets; for they are not spread here to do you any harm, but only for our amusement; and as I know you will ask why they have been put up, and who we are, I will tell you in a few words. In a village some two leagues from this, where there are many people of quality and rich gentlefolk, it was agreed upon by a number of friends and relations to come with their wives, sons and daughters, neighbors, friends and kinsmen, and make holiday in this spot which is one of the pleasantest in the whole neighborhood, setting up a new pastoral Arcadia among ourselves, we maidens dressing ourselves as shepherdesses and the youths as shepherds. We have prepared two eclogues, one by the famous poet Garcilaso, the other by the most ex-cellent Camoens, in its own Portuguese tongue, but we have not as yet acted them. Yesterday was the first day of our coming here; we have a few of what they say are called field-tents pitched among the trees on the bank of an ample brook that fertilizes all these meadows; last night we spread these nets in the trees here to snare the silly little birds that startled by the noise we make may fly into them. If you please to be our guest, señor, you will be welcomed heartily and courteously, for here just now neither care nor sorrow shall enter."

She held her peace and said no more, and Don Quixote made answer, "Of a truth, fairest lady, Actæon when he unexpectedly beheld Diana bathing in the stream could not have been more fascinated and wonderstruck than I at the sight of your beauty. I commend your mode of entertainment, and thank you for the kindness of your invitation; and if I can serve you, you may command me with full confidence of being obeyed, for my profession is none other than to show myself grateful, and ready to serve persons of all conditions, but especially persons of quality such as your appearance indicates; and if, instead of taking up, as they probably do, but a small space, these nets took up the whole surface of the globe, I would seek out new worlds through which to pass, so as not to break them; and that ye may give some degree of credence to this exaggerated language of mine, know that it is no less than Don Quixote of La Mancha that makes this declaration to you, if indeed it be that such a name has reached your ears."

"Ah! friend of my soul," instantly exclaimed the other shepherdess, "what great good fortune has befallen us! Seest thou this gentleman we have before us? Well then let me tell thee he is the most valiant and the most devoted and the most courteous gentleman in all the world, unless a history of his achievements that has been printed and I have read is telling lies and deceiving us. I will lay a wager that this good fellow who is with him is one Sancho Panza his squire, whose drolleries none can equal."

"That's true," said Sancho; "I am that same droll and squire you speak of, and this gentleman is my master Don Quixote of La Mancha, the same that's in the history and that they talk about."

"Oh, my friend," said the other, "let us entreat him to stay; for it will give our fathers and brothers infinite pleasure; I too have heard just what thou hast told me of the valor of the one and the drolleries of the other; and what is more, of him they say that he is the most constant and loyal lover that was ever heard of, and that his lady is one Dulcinea del Toboso, to whom all over Spain the palm of beauty is awarded."

"And justly awarded," said Don Quixote, "unless, indeed, your unequalled beauty makes it a matter of doubt. But spare yourselves the trouble, ladies, of pressing me to stay, for the urgent calls of my profession do not allow me to take rest under any circumstances."

At this instant there came up to the spot where the four stood a brother of one of the two shepherdesses, like them in shepherd costume, and as richly and gayly dressed as they were. They told him that their companion was the valiant Don Quixote of La Mancha, and the other Sancho his squire, of whom he knew already from having read their history. The gay shepherd offered him his services and begged that he would accompany him to their tents, and Don Quixote had to give way and comply. And now the game was started, and the nets were filled with a variety of birds that deceived by the color fell into the danger they were flying from. Upwards of thirty persons, all gayly attired as shepherds and shepherdesses, assembled on the spot, and were at once informed who Don Quixote and his squire were, whereat they were not a little delighted, as they knew of him already through his history. They repaired to the tents, where they found tables laid out, and choicely, plentifully, and neatly furnished. They treated Don Quixote as a person of distinction, giving him the place of honor, and all observed him, and were full of astonishment at the spectacle. At last the cloth being removed, Don Quixote with great composure lifted up his voice and said:

"One of the greatest sins that men are guilty of is—some will say pride—but I say ingratitude, going by the common saying that hell is full of ingrates. This sin, so far as it has lain in my power, I have endeavored to avoid ever since I have enjoyed the faculty of reason; and if I am unable to requite good deeds that have been done me by other deeds, I substitute the desire to do so; and if that be not enough I make them known publicly; for he who declares and makes known the good deeds done to him would repay them by others if it were in his power, and for the most part those who receive are the inferiors of those who give. Thus, God is superior to all because he is the supreme giver, and the offerings of man fall short by an infinite distance of being a full return for the gifts of God; but gratitude in some degree makes up for this deficiency and shortcoming. I therefore, grateful for the favor that has been extended to me here, and unable to

make a return in the same measure, restricted as I am by the narrow limits of my power, offer what I can and what I have to offer in my own way; and so I declare that for two full days I will maintain in the middle of this highway leading to Saragossa, that these ladies disguised as shepherdesses, who are here present, are the fairest and most courteous maidens in the world, excepting only the peerless Dulcinea del Toboso, sole mistress of my thoughts, be it said without offence to those who hear me, ladies and gentlemen."

On hearing this Sancho, who had been listening with great attention, cried out in a loud voice, "Is it possible there is any one in the world who will dare to say and swear that this master of mine is a madman? Say, gentlemen shepherds, is there a village priest, be he ever so wise or learned, who could say what my master has said; or is there knight-errant, whatever renown he may have as a man of valor, that could offer what my master has offered now?"

Don Quixote turned upon Sancho, and with a countenance glowing with anger said to him, "Is it possible, Sancho, there is any one in the whole world who will say thou art not a fool, with a lining to match, and I know not what trimmings of impertinence and roguery? Who asked thee to meddle in my affairs, or to inquire whether I am a wise man or a blockhead? Hold thy peace; answer me not a word; saddle Rocinante if he be unsaddled; and let us go to put my offer into execution; for with the right that I have on my side thou mayest reckon as vanquished all who shall venture to question it"; and in a great rage, and showing his anger plainly, he rose from his seat, leaving the company lost in wonder, and making them feel doubtful whether they ought to regard him as a madman or a rational being. In the end, though they sought to dissuade him from involving himself in such a challenge, assuring him they admitted his gratitude as fully established, and needed no fresh proofs to be convinced of his valiant spirit, as those related in the history of his exploits were sufficient, still Don Quixote persisted in his resolve; and mounted on Rocinante, bracing his buckler on his arm and grasping his lance, he posted himself in the middle of a high road that was not far from the green meadow. Sancho followed on Dapple, together with all the members of the pastoral gathering, eager to see what would be the upshot of his vainglorious and extraordinary proposal.

Don Quixote, then, having, as has been said, planted himself in the middle of the road, made the welkin ring with words to this effect: "Ho ye travellers and wayfarers, knights, squires, folk on foot or on horseback, who pass this way or shall pass in the course of the next two days! Know that Don Quixote of La Mancha, knight-errant, is posted here to maintain by arms that the beauty and courtesy enshrined in the nymphs that dwell in these meadows and groves surpass all upon earth, putting aside the lady of my heart, Dulcinea del Toboso. Wherefore, let him who is of the opposite opinion come on, for here I await him."

Twice he repeated the same words, and twice they fell unheard by any adventurer; but fate, that was guiding affairs for him from better to better, so ordered it that shortly afterwards there appeared on the road a crowd of men on horseback, many of them with lances in their hands, all riding in a compact body and in great haste. No sooner had those who were with Don Quixote seen them than they turned about and withdrew to some distance from the road, for they knew that if they staid some harm might come to them; but Don Quixote with intrepid heart stood his ground, and Sancho Panza shielded himself with Rocinante's hind-quarters. The troop of lances came up, and one of them who was in advance began shouting to Don Quixote, "Get out of the way, you son of the devil, or these bulls will knock you to pieces!"

"Rabble!" returned Don Quixote, "I care nothing for bulls, be they the fiercest Jarama breeds on its banks. Confess at once, scoundrels, that what I have declared is true; else ye have to deal with me in combat."

The herdsman had no time to reply, nor Don Quixote to get out of the way if he wished; and so the drove of fierce bulls and tame bullocks, together with the crowd of herdsmen and others who were taking them to be penned up at a village where they were to be run the next day, passed over Don Quixote and over Sancho, Rocinante and Dapple, hurling them all to the earth and rolling them over on the ground. Sancho was left crushed, Don Quixote half stunned, Dapple belabored, and Rocinante in no very sound condition. They all got up, however, at length, and Don Quixote in great haste, stumbling here and falling there, started off running after the drove, shouting out, "Hold! stay! ye rascally rabble, a single knight awaits you, and he is not of the temper or opinion of those who say, 'For a flying enemy make a bridge of silver.'" The retreating party in their haste, however, did not stop for that, or heed his menaces any more than last year's clouds. Weariness

brought Don Quixote to a halt, and more enraged than avenged he sat down on the road to wait until Sancho, Rocinante and Dapple came up. When they reached him master and man mounted once more, and without going back to bid farewell to the mock or imitation Arcadia, and more in humiliation than contentment, they continued their journey.

Chapter 59

Wherein is related the strange thing, which may be regarded as an adventure, that happened to Don Quixote

A CLEAR limpid spring which they discovered in a cool grove relieved Don Quixote and Sancho of the dust and fatigue due to the unpolite behavior of the bulls, and by the side of this, having turned Dapple and Rocinante loose without headstall or bridle, the forlorn pair, master and man, seated themselves. Sancho had recourse to the larder of his *alforjas* and took out of them what he called the *prog;* Don Quixote rinsed his mouth and bathed his face, by which cooling process his flagging energies were revived. Out of pure vexation he remained without eating, and out of pure politeness Sancho did not venture to touch a morsel of what was before him, but waited for his master to act as taster. Seeing, however, that, absorbed in thought, he was forgetting to carry the bread to his mouth, he said never a word, and trampling every sort of good breeding under foot, began to stow away in his paunch the bread and cheese that came to his hand.

"Eat, Sancho my friend," said Don Quixote; "support life, which is of more consequence to thee than to me, and leave me to die under the pain of my thoughts and pressure of my misfortunes. I was born, Sancho, to live dying, and thou to die eating; and to prove the truth of what I say, look at me, printed in histories, famed in arms, courteous in behavior, honored by princes, courted by maidens; and after all, when I looked forward to palms, triumphs, and crowns, won and earned by my valiant deeds, I have this morning seen myself trampled on, kicked, and crushed by the feet of unclean and filthy animals. This thought blunts my teeth, paralyzes my jaws, cramps my hands, and robs me of all appetite for food; so much so that I have a mind to let myself die of hunger, the cruelest death of all deaths."

"So then," said Sancho, munching hard all the time, "your worship does not agree with the proverb that says, 'Let Martha die, but let her die with a full belly.' I, at any rate, have no mind to kill myself; so far from that, I mean to do as the cobbler does, who stretches the leather with his teeth until he makes it reach as far as he wants. I'll stretch out my life by eating until it reaches the end Heaven has fixed for it; and let me tell you, señor, there's no greater folly than to think of dying of despair as your worship does; take my advice, and after eating lie down and sleep a bit on this green grass-mattress, and you will see that when you awake you'll feel something better."

Don Quixote did as he recommended, for it struck him that Sancho's reasoning was more like a philosopher's than a blockhead's, and said he, "Sancho, if thou wilt do for me what I am going to tell thee my ease of mind would be more assured and my heaviness of heart not so great; and it is this; to go aside a little while I am sleeping in accordance with thy advice, and, making bare thy carcass to the air, to give thyself three or four hundred lashes with Rocinante's reins, on account of the three thousand and odd thou art to give thyself for the disenchantment of Dulcinea; for it is a great pity that the poor lady should be left enchanted through thy carelessness and negligence."

"There is a good deal to be said on that point," said Sancho; "let us both go to sleep now, and after that, God has decreed what will happen. Let me tell your worship that for a man to whip himself in cold blood is a hard thing, especially if the stripes fall upon an ill-nourished and worse-fed body. Let my lady Dulcinea have patience, and when she is least expecting it, she will see me made a riddle of with whipping, and 'until death it's all life'; I mean that I have still life in me, and the desire to make good what I have promised."

Don Quixote thanked him, and ate a little, and Sancho a good deal, and then they both lay down to sleep, leaving those two inseparable friends and comrades, Rocinante and Dapple, to their own devices and to feed unrestrained upon the abundant grass with which the meadow was furnished. They woke up rather late, mounted once more and resumed their journey, pushing on to reach an inn which was in sight, apparently a league off. I say an inn, because Don Quixote called it so, contrary to his usual practice of calling all inns castles. They reached it, and asked the landlord if they could put up there. He said yes, with as much comfort and as good fare as they could find in Saragossa. They dismounted, and Sancho stowed away his larder in a room of which the landlord gave him the key. He took the beasts to the stable, fed them, and came back

to see what orders Don Quixote, who was seated on a bench at the door, had for him, giving special thanks to Heaven that this inn had not been taken for a castle by his master. Supper-time came, and they repaired to their room, and Sancho asked the landlord what he had to give them for supper. To this the landlord replied that his mouth should be the measure; he had only to ask what he would; for that inn was provided with the birds of the air and the fowls of the earth and the fish of the sea.

"There's no need of all that," said Sancho; "if they'll roast us a couple of chickens we'll be satisfied, for my master is delicate and eats little, and I'm not over and above gluttonous."

The landlord replied he had no chickens, for the kites had stolen them.

"Well then," said Sancho, "let Señor Landlord tell them to roast a pullet, so that it is a tender one."

"Pullet! My father!" said the landlord; "indeed and in truth it's only yesterday I sent over fifty to the city to sell; but saving pullets ask what you will."

"In that case," said Sancho, "you will not be without veal or kid."

"Just now," said the landlord, "there's none in the house, for it's all finished; but next week there will be enough and to spare."

"Much good that does us," said Sancho; "I'll lay a bet that all these short-comings are going to wind up in plenty of bacon and eggs."

"By God," said the landlord, "my guest's wits must be precious dull; I tell him I have neither pullets nor hens, and he wants me to have eggs! Talk of other dainties, if you please, and don't ask for hens again."

"Body o' me!" said Sancho, "let's settle the matter; say at once what you have got, and let us have no more words about it."

"In truth and earnest, Señor Guest," said the landlord, "all I have is a couple of cow-heels like calves' feet, or a couple of calves' feet like cow-heels; they are boiled with chick-pease, onions, and bacon, and at this moment they are crying 'Come eat me, come eat me.'"

"I mark them for mine on the spot," said Sancho; "let nobody touch them; I'll pay better for them than any one else, for I could not wish for anything more to my taste; and I don't care a pin whether they are feet or heels."

"Nobody shall touch them," said the landlord; "for the other guests I have, being persons of high quality, bring their own cook and caterer and larder with them."

"If you come to people of quality," said Sancho, "there's nobody more so than my master; but the calling he follows does not allow of larders or store-rooms; we lay ourselves down in the middle of a meadow, and fill ourselves with acorns or medlars."

Here ended Sancho's conversation with the landlord, Sancho not caring to carry it any farther by answering him; for he had already asked him what calling or what profession it was his master was of.

Supper-time having come, then, Don Quixote betook himself to his room, the landlord brought in the stew-pan just as it was, and he sat himself down to sup very resolutely. It seems that in another room, which was next to Don Quixote's, with nothing but a thin partition to separate it, he overheard these words, "As you live, Señor Don Jeronimo, while they are bringing supper, let us read another chapter of the Second Part of *Don Quixote of La Mancha*."

The instant Don Quixote heard his own name he started to his feet and listened with open ears to catch what they said about him, and heard the Don Jeronimo who had been addressed say in reply, "Why would you have us read that absurd stuff, Don Juan, when it is impossible for any one who has read the First Part of the history of *Don Quixote of La Mancha* to take any pleasure in reading this Second Part?"

"For all that," said he who was addressed as Don Juan, "we shall do well to read it, for there is no book so bad but it has something good in it. What displeases me most in it is that it represents Don Quixote as now cured of his love for Dulcinea del Toboso."[1]

On hearing this Don Quixote, full of wrath and indignation, lifted up his voice and said, "Whoever he may be who says that Don Quixote of La Mancha has forgotten or can forget Dulcinea del Toboso, I will teach him with equal arms that what he says is very far from the truth; for neither can the peerless Dulcinea del Toboso be forgotten, nor can forgetfulness have a place in Don Quixote; his motto is constancy, and his profession to maintain the same with his life and never wrong it."

"Who is this that answers us?" said they in the next room.

"Who should it be," said Sancho, "but Don Quixote of La Mancha himself, who will make good all he has said and all he will say; for

[1] Avellaneda makes Aldonza Lorenzo write to Quixote threatening him with a beating for calling her Princess and Dulcinea, and Don Quixote, stung by her ingratitude, resolves to look out for another mistress.

pledges don't trouble a good paymaster?"

Sancho had hardly uttered these words when two gentlemen, for such they seemed to be, entered the room, and one of them, throwing his arms round Don Quixote's neck, said to him, "Your appearance cannot leave any question as to your name, nor can your name fail to identify your appearance; unquestionably, señor, you are the real Don Quixote of La Mancha, cynosure and morning star of knight-errantry, despite and in defiance of him who has sought to usurp your name and bring to naught your achievements, as the author of this book which I here present to you has done"; and with this he put a book which his companion carried into the hands of Don Quixote, who took it, and without replying began to run his eye over it; but he presently returned it saying, "In the little I have seen I have discovered three things in this author that deserve to be censured. The first is some words that I have read in the preface; the next that the language is Aragonese, for sometimes he writes without article; and the third, which above all stamps him as ignorant, is that he goes wrong and departs from the truth in the most important part of the history, for here he says that my squire Sancho Panza's wife is called Mari Gutierrez, when she is called nothing of the sort, but Teresa Panza; and when a man errs on such an important point as this there is good reason to fear that he is in error on every other point in the history."

"A nice sort of historian, indeed!" exclaimed Sancho at this; "he must know a deal about our affairs when he calls my wife Teresa Panza, Mari Gutierrez; take the book again, señor, and see if I am in it and if he has changed my name."

"From your talk, friend," said Don Jeronimo, "no doubt you are Sancho Panza, Señor Don Quixote's squire."

"Yes, I am," said Sancho; "and I'm proud of it."

"Faith, then," said the gentleman, "this new author does not handle you with the decency that displays itself in your person; he makes you out a heavy feeder and a fool, and not in the least droll, and a very different being from the Sancho described in the First Part of your master's history."

"God forgive him," said Sancho; "he might have left me in my corner without troubling his head about me; 'let him who knows how ring the bells'; 'Saint Peter is very well in Rome.'"

The two gentlemen pressed Don Quixote to come into their room and have supper with them, as they knew very well there was nothing in that inn fit for one of his sort. Don Quixote, who was always polite, yielded to their request and supped with them. Sancho stayed behind with the stew-pan, and invested with plenary delegated authority seated himself at the head of the table, and the landlord sat down with him, for he was no less fond of cow-heel and calves' feet than Sancho was.

While at supper Don Juan asked Don Quixote what news he had of the lady Dulcinea del Toboso, was she married, had she been brought to bed, or was she with child, or did she in maidenhood, still preserving her modesty and delicacy, cherish the remembrance of the tender passion of Señor Don Quixote?

To this he replied, "Dulcinea is a maiden still, and my passion more firmly rooted than ever, our intercourse unsatisfactory as before, and her beauty transformed into that of a foul country wench"; and then he proceeded to give them a full and particular account of the enchantment of Dulcinea, and of what had happened him in the cave of Montesinos, together with what the sage Merlin had prescribed for her disenchantment, namely the scourging of Sancho.

Exceeding great was the amusement the two gentlemen derived from hearing Don Quixote recount the strange incidents of his history; and if they were amazed by his absurdities they were equally amazed by the elegant style in which he delivered them. On the one hand they regarded him as a man of wit and sense, and on the other he seemed to them a maundering blockhead, and they could not make up their minds whereabouts between wisdom and folly they ought to place him.

Sancho having finished his supper, and left the landlord in the X condition, repaired to the room where his master was, and as he came in said, "May I die, sirs, if the author of this book your worships have got has any mind that we should agree; as he calls me glutton (according to what your worships say) I trust he does not call me drunkard too."

"But he does," said Don Jeronimo; "I cannot remember, however, in what way, though I know his words are offensive, and what is more, lying, as I can see plainly by the physiognomy of the worthy Sancho before me."

"Believe me," said Sancho, "the Sancho and the Don Quixote of this history must be different persons from those that appear in the one Cid Hamet Benengeli wrote, who are ourselves; my master valiant, wise, and true in love, and I simple, droll, and neither glutton nor drunkard."

"I believe it," said Don Juan; "and were it possible, an order should be issued that no one should have the presumption to deal with anything relating to Don Quixote, save his original author Cid Hamet; just as Alexander commanded that no one should presume to paint his portrait save Apelles."

"Let him who will paint me," said Don Quixote; "but let him not abuse me; for patience will often break down when they heap insults upon it."

"None can be offered to Señor Don Quixote," said Don Juan, "that he himself will not be able to avenge, if he does not ward it off with the shield of his patience, which, I take it, is great and strong."

A considerable portion of the night passed in conversation of this sort, and though Don Juan wished Don Quixote to read more of the book to see what it was all about, he was not to be prevailed upon, saying that he treated it as read and pronounced it utterly silly; and, if by any chance it should come to the author's ears that he had had it in his hand, he did not want him to flatter himself with the idea that he had read it; for our thoughts, and still more our eyes, should keep themselves aloof from what is obscene and filthy.

They asked him whither he meant to direct his steps. He replied, to Saragossa, to take part in the harness jousts which were held in that city every year. Don Juan told him that the new history described how Don Quixote, let him be who he might, took part there in a tilting at the ring, utterly devoid of invention, poor in mottoes, very poor in costume, though rich in sillinesses.

"For that very reason," said Don Quixote, "I will not set foot in Saragossa; and by that means I shall expose to the world the lie of this new history writer, and people will see that I am not the Don Quixote he speaks of."

"You will do quite right," said Don Jeronimo; "and there are other jousts at Barcelona in which Señor Don Quixote may display his prowess."

"That is what I mean to do," said Don Quixote; "and as it is now time, I pray your worships to give me leave to retire to bed, and to place and retain me among the number of your greatest friends and servants."

"And me too," said Sancho; "maybe I'll be good for something."

With this they exchanged farewells, and Don Quixote and Sancho retired to their room, leaving Don Juan and Don Jeronimo amazed to see the medley he made of his good sense and his craziness; and they felt thoroughly convinced that these, and not those their Aragonese author described, were the genuine Don Quixote and Sancho. Don Quixote rose betimes, and bade adieu to his hosts by knocking at the partition of the other room. Sancho paid the landlord magnificently, and recommended him either to say less about the providing of his inn or to keep it better provided.

Chapter 60

Of what happened to Don Quixote on his way to Barcelona

IT was a fresh morning giving promise of a cool day as Don Quixote quitted the inn, first of all taking care to ascertain the most direct road to Barcelona without touching upon Saragossa; so anxious was he to make out this new historian, who they said abused him so, to be a liar. Well, as it fell out, nothing worthy of being recorded happened him for six days, at the end of which, having turned aside out of the road, he was overtaken by night in a thicket of oak or cork trees; for on this point Cid Hamet is not as precise as he usually is on other matters.

Master and man dismounted from their beasts, and as soon as they had settled themselves at the foot of the trees, Sancho, who had had a good noontide meal that day, let himself, without more ado, pass the gates of sleep. But Don Quixote, whom his thoughts, far more than hunger, kept awake, could not close an eye, and roamed in fancy to and fro through all sorts of places. At one moment it seemed to him that he was in the cave of Montesinos and saw Dulcinea, transformed into a country wench, skipping and mounting upon her she-ass; again that the words of the sage Merlin were sounding in his ears, setting forth the conditions to be observed and the exertions to be made for the disenchantment of Dulcinea. He lost all patience when he considered the laziness and want of charity of his squire Sancho; for to the best of his belief he had only given himself five lashes, a number paltry and disproportioned to the vast number required. At this thought he felt such vexation and anger that he reasoned the matter thus: "If Alexander the Great cut the Gordian knot, saying, 'To cut comes to the same thing as to untie,' and yet did not fail to become lord paramount of all Asia, neither more nor less could happen now in Dulcinea's disenchantment if I scourge Sancho against his will; for, if it is the condition of the remedy that Sancho shall receive three thousand and odd lashes, what does it matter to me whether he inflicts them himself, or some one else inflicts them, when the essential point is that he receives them, let them come from whatever quarter they may?"

With this idea he went over to Sancho, having first taken Rocinante's reins and arranged them so as to be able to flog him with them, and began to untie the points (the common belief is he had but one in front) by which his breeches were held up; but the instant he approached him Sancho woke up in his full senses and cried out, "What is this? Who is touching me and untrussing me?"

"It is I," said Don Quixote, "and I come to make good thy shortcomings and relieve my own distresses; I come to whip thee, Sancho, and wipe off some portion of the debt thou hast undertaken. Dulcinea is perishing, thou art living on regardless, I am dying of hope deferred; therefore untruss thyself with a good will, for mine it is, here, in this retired spot, to give thee at least two thousand lashes."

"Not a bit of it," said Sancho; "let your worship keep quiet, or else by the living God the deaf shall hear us; the lashes I pledged myself to must be voluntary and not forced upon me, and just now I have no fancy to whip myself; it is enough if I give you my word to flog and flap myself when I have a mind."

"It will not do to leave it to thy courtesy, Sancho," said Don Quixote, "for thou art hard of heart and, though a clown, tender of flesh"; and at the same time he strove and struggled to untie him.

Seeing this Sancho got up, and grappling with his master he gripped him with all his might in his arms, and giving him a trip with the heel stretched him on the ground on his back, and pressing his right knee on his chest held his hands in his own so that he could neither move nor breathe.

"How now, traitor!" exclaimed Don Quixote. "Dost thou revolt against thy master and natural lord? Dost thou rise against him who gives thee his bread?"

"I neither put down king, nor set up king," said Sancho; "I only stand up for myself who am my own lord; if your worship promises me to be quiet, and not offer to whip me now, I'll let you go free and unhindered; if not—

> *Traitor and Doña Sancha's foe,*
> *Thou diest on the spot.*"

Don Quixote gave his promise, and swore by the life of his thoughts not to touch so much as a hair of his garments, and to leave him entirely free and to his own discretion to whip himself whenever he pleased.

Sancho rose and removed some distance from the spot, but as he was about to place himself leaning against another tree he felt something touch his head, and putting up his hands encountered somebody's two feet with shoes and stockings on them. He trembled with fear and made for another tree, where the very same thing happened to him, and he fell a-shouting, calling upon Don Quixote to come and protect him. Don Quixote did so, and asked him what had happened to him, and what he was afraid of. Sancho replied that all the trees were full of men's feet and legs. Don Quixote felt them, and guessed at once what it was, and said to Sancho, "Thou hast nothing to be afraid of, for these feet and legs that thou feelest but canst not see belong no doubt to some outlaws and freebooters that have been hanged on these trees; for the authorities in these parts are wont to hang them up by twenties and thirties when they catch them; whereby I conjecture that I must be near Barcelona"; and it was, in fact, as he supposed; with the first light they looked up and saw that the fruit hanging on those trees were freebooters' bodies.

And now day dawned; and if the dead freebooters had scared them, their hearts were no less troubled by upwards of forty living ones, who all of a sudden surrounded them, and in the Catalan tongue bade them stand and wait until their captain came up. Don Quixote was on foot with his horse unbridled and his lance leaning against a tree, and in short completely defenceless; he thought it best therefore to fold his arms and bow his head and reserve himself for a more favorable occasion and opportunity. The robbers made haste to search Dapple, and did not leave him a single thing of all he carried in the *alforjas* and in the valise; and lucky it was for Sancho that the duke's crowns and those he brought from home were in a girdle that he wore round him; but for all that these good folk would have stripped him, and even looked to see what he had hidden between the skin and flesh, but for the arrival at that moment of their captain, who was about thirty-four years of age apparently, strongly built, above the middle height, of stern aspect and swarthy complexion. He was mounted upon a powerful horse, and had on a coat of mail, with four of the pistols they call *petronels* in that country at his waist. He saw that his squires (for so they call those who follow that trade) were about to rifle Sancho Panza, but he ordered them to desist and

was at once obeyed, so the girdle escaped. He wondered to see the lance leaning against the tree, the shield on the ground, and Don Quixote in armor and dejected, with the saddest and most melancholy face that sadness itself could produce; and going up to him he said, "Be not so cast down, good man, for you have not fallen into the hands of any inhuman Busiris, but into Roque Guinart's, which are more merciful than cruel."

"The cause of my dejection," returned Don Quixote, "is not that I have fallen into thy hands, O valiant Roque, whose fame is bounded by no limits on earth, but that my carelessness should have been so great that thy soldiers should have caught me unbridled, when it is my duty, according to the rule of knight-errantry which I profess, to be always on the alert and at all times my own sentinel; for let me tell thee, great Roque, had they found me on my horse, with my lance and shield, it would not have been very easy for them to reduce me to submission, for I am Don Quixote of La Mancha, he who hath filled the whole world with his achievements."

Roque Guinart at once perceived that Don Quixote's weakness was more akin to madness than to swagger; and though he had sometimes heard him spoken of, he never regarded the things attributed to him as true, nor could he persuade himself that such a humor could become dominant in the heart of man; he was extremely glad, therefore, to meet him and test at close quarters what he had heard of him at a distance; so he said to him, "Despair not, valiant knight, nor regard as an untoward fate the position in which thou findest thyself; it may be that by these slips thy crooked fortune will make itself straight; for Heaven by strange circuitous ways, mysterious and incomprehensible to man, raises up the fallen and makes rich the poor."

Don Quixote was about to thank him, when they heard behind them a noise as of a troop of horses; there was, however, but one, riding on which at a furious pace came a youth, apparently about twenty years of age, clad in green damask edged with gold and breeches and a loose frock, with a hat looped up in the Walloon fashion, tight-fitting polished boots, gilt spurs, dagger and sword, and in his hand a musketoon, and a pair of pistols at his waist.

Roque turned round at the noise and perceived this comely figure, which drawing near thus addressed him, "I came in quest of thee, valiant Roque, to find in thee if not a remedy at least relief in my misfortune; and not to keep thee in suspense, for I see thou dost not recognize me, I will tell thee who I am; I am Claudia Jeronima, the daughter of Simon Forte, thy good friend, and special enemy of Clauquel Torrellas, who is thine also as being of the faction opposed to thee. Thou knowest that this Torrellas has a son who is called, or at least was not two hours since, Don Vicente Torrellas. Well, to cut short the tale of my misfortune, I will tell thee in a few words what this youth has brought upon me. He saw me, he paid court to me, I listened to him, and unknown to my father, I loved him; for there is no woman, however secluded she may live or close she may be kept, who will not have opportunities and to spare for following her headlong impulses. In a word, he pledged himself to be mine, and I promised to be his, without carrying matters any further. Yesterday I learned that, forgetful of his pledge to me, he was about to marry another, and that he was to go this morning to plight his troth, intelligence which overwhelmed and exasperated me; my father not being at home I was able to adopt this costume you see, and urging my horse to speed I overtook Don Vicente about a league from this, and without waiting to utter reproaches or hear excuses I fired this musket at him, and these two pistols besides, and to the best of my belief I must have lodged more than two bullets in his body, opening doors to let my honor go free, enveloped in his blood. I left him there in the hands of his servants, who did not dare and were not able to interfere in his defence, and I come to seek from thee a safe-conduct into France, where I have relatives with whom I can live; and also to implore thee to protect my father, so that Don Vicente's numerous kinsmen may not venture to wreak their lawless vengeance upon him."

Roque, filled with admiration at the gallant bearing, high spirit, comely figure, and adventure of the fair Claudia, said to her, "Come, señora, let us go and see if thy enemy is dead; and then we will consider what will be best for thee." Don Quixote, who had been listening to what Claudia said and Roque Guinart said in reply to her, exclaimed, "Nobody need trouble himself with the defence of this lady, for I take it upon myself. Give me my horse and arms, and wait for me here; I will go in quest of this knight, and dead or alive I will make him keep his word plighted to so great beauty."

"Nobody need have any doubt about that," said Sancho, "for my master has a very happy knack of matchmaking; it's not many days since he forced another man to marry, who in the same way backed out of his promise to another maiden; and if it had not been for his persecutors the enchanters changing the man's proper shape into a lackey's the said maiden would not be one this minute."

Roque, who was paying more attention to the fair Claudia's adventure than to the words of master or man, did not hear them; and ordering his squires to restore to Sancho everything they had stripped Dapple of, he directed them to return to the place where they had been quartered during the night, and then set off with Claudia at full speed in search of the wounded or slain Don Vicente. They reached the spot where Claudia met him, but found nothing there save freshly spilt blood; looking all around, however, they descried some people on the slope of a hill above them, and concluded, as indeed it proved to be, that it was Don Vicente, whom either dead or alive his servants were removing to attend to his wounds or to bury him. They made haste to overtake them, which as the party moved slowly, they were able to do with ease. They found Don Vicente in the arms of his servants, whom he was entreating in a broken feeble voice to leave him there to die, as the pain of his wounds would not suffer him to go any farther. Claudia and Roque threw themselves off their horses and advanced toward him; the servants were overawed by the appearance of Roque, and Claudia was moved by the sight of Don Vicente, and going up to him half tenderly half sternly, she seized his hand and said to him, "Hadst thou given me this according to our compact thou hadst never come to this pass."

The wounded gentleman opened his all but closed eyes, and recognizing Claudia said, "I see clearly, fair and mistaken lady, that it is thou that hast slain me, a punishment not merited or deserved by my feelings towards thee, for never did I mean to, nor could I, wrong thee in thought or deed."

"It is not true, then," said Claudia, "that thou wert going this morning to marry Leonora the daughter of the rich Balvastro?"

"Assuredly not," replied Don Vicente; "my cruel fortune must have carried those tidings to thee to drive thee in thy jealousy to take my life; and to assure thyself of this, press my hand and take me for thy husband if thou wilt; I have no better satisfaction to offer thee for the wrong thou fanciest thou hast received from me."

Claudia wrung his hand, and her own heart was so wrung that she lay fainting on the bleeding breast of Don Vicente, whom a death spasm seized the same instant. Roque was in perplexity and knew not what to do; the servants ran to fetch water to sprinkle their faces, and brought some and bathed them with it. Claudia recovered from her fainting fit, but not so Don Vicente from the paroxysm that had overtaken him, for his life had come to an end. On perceiving this, Claudia, when she had convinced herself that her beloved husband was no more, rent the air with her sighs and made the heavens ring with her lamentations; she tore her hair and scattered it to the winds, she beat her face with her hands and showed all the signs of grief and sorrow that could be conceived to come from an afflicted heart. "Cruel, reckless woman!" she cried, "how easily wert thou moved to carry out a thought so wicked! O furious force of jealousy, to what desperate lengths dost thou lead those that give thee lodging in their bosoms! O husband, whose unhappy fate in being mine hath borne thee from the marriage bed to the grave!"

So vehement and so piteous were the lamentations of Claudia that they drew tears from Roque's eyes, unused as they were to shed them on any occasion. The servants wept, Claudia swooned away again and again, and the whole place seemed a field of sorrow and an abode of misfortune. In the end Roque Guinart directed Don Vicente's servants to carry his body to his father's village, which was close by, for burial. Claudia told him she meant to go to a monastery of which an aunt of hers was abbess, where she intended to pass her life with a better and everlasting spouse. He applauded her pious resolution, and offered to accompany her whithersoever she wished, and to protect her father against the kinsmen of Don Vicente and all the world, should they seek to injure him. Claudia would not on any account allow him to accompany her; and thanking him for his offers as well as she could, took leave of him in tears. The servants of Don Vicente carried away his body, and Roque returned to his comrades, and so ended the love of Claudia Jeronima; but what wonder, when it was the insuperable and cruel might of jealousy that wove the web of her sad story?

Roque Guinart found his squires at the place to which he had ordered them, and Don Quixote on Rocinante in the midst of them delivering a harangue to them in which he urged them to give up a mode of life so full of peril, as well to the soul as to the body; but as most of them were Gascons, rough lawless fellows, his speech did not make much impression on them. Roque on coming up asked Sancho if his men had re-

turned and restored to him the treasures and jewels they had stripped off Dapple. Sancho said they had, but that three kerchiefs that were worth three cities were missing.

"What are you talking about, man?" said one of the bystanders; "I have got them, and they are not worth three reals."

"That is true," said Don Quixote; "but my squire values them at the rate he says, as having been given me by the person who gave them."

Roque Guinart ordered them to be restored at once; and making his men fall in in line he directed all the clothing, jewellery, and money that they had taken since the last distribution to be produced; and making a hasty valuation, and reducing what could not be divided into money, he made shares for the whole band so equitably and carefully, that in no case did he exceed or fall short of strict distributive justice.

When this had been done, and all left satisfied, contented, and pleased, Roque observed to Don Quixote, "If this scrupulous exactness were not observed with these fellows there would be no living with them."

Upon this Sancho remarked, "From what I have seen here, justice is such a good thing that there is no doing without it, even among the thieves themselves."

One of the squires heard this, and raising the butt-end of his arquebuse would no doubt have broken Sancho's head with it had not Roque Guinart called out to him to hold his hand. Sancho was frightened out of his wits, and vowed not to open his lips so long as he was in the company of these people.

At this instant one or two of those squires who were posted as sentinels on the roads to watch who came along them and report what passed to their chief, came up and said, "Señor, there is a great troop of people not far off coming along the road to Barcelona."

To which Roque replied, "Hast thou made out whether they are of the sort that are after us, or of the sort we are after?"

"The sort we are after," said the squire.

"Well then, away with you all," said Roque, "and bring them here to me at once without letting one of them escape."

They obeyed, and Don Quixote, Sancho, and Roque, left by themselves, waited to see what the squires brought, and while they were waiting Roque said to Don Quixote, "It must seem a strange sort of life to Señor Don Quixote, this of ours, strange adventures, strange incidents, and all full of danger; and I do not wonder that it should seem so, for in truth I must own there is no mode of life more restless or anxious than ours. What led me into it was a certain thirst for vengeance, which is strong enough to disturb the quietest hearts. I am by nature tender-hearted and kindly, but, as I said, the desire to revenge myself for a wrong that was done me so overturns all my better impulses that I keep on in this way of life in spite of what conscience tells me; and as one depth calls to another, and one sin to another sin, revenges have linked themselves together, and I have taken upon myself not only my own but those of others: it pleases God, however, that, though I see myself in this maze of entanglements, I do not lose all hope of escaping from it and reaching a safe port."

Don Quixote was amazed to hear Roque utter such excellent and just sentiments, for he did not think that among those who followed such trades as robbing, murdering, and waylaying, there could be any one capable of a virtuous thought, and he said in reply, "Señor Roque, the beginning of health lies in knowing the disease and in the sick man's willingness to take the medicines which the physician prescribes; you are sick, you know what ails you, and Heaven, or more properly speaking God, who is our physician, will administer medicines that will cure you, and cure gradually, and not of a sudden or by a miracle; besides, sinners of discernment are nearer amendment than those who are fools; and as your worship has shown good sense in your remarks, all you have to do is to keep up a good heart and trust that the weakness of your conscience will be strengthened. And if you have any desire to shorten the journey and put yourself easily in the way of salvation, come with me, and I will show you how to become a knight-errant, a calling wherein so many hardships and mishaps are encountered that if they be taken as penances they will lodge you in heaven in a trice."

Roque laughed at Don Quixote's exhortation, and changing the conversation he related the tragic affair of Claudia Jeronima, at which Sancho was extremely grieved; for he had not found the young woman's beauty, boldness, and spirit at all amiss.

And now the squires despatched to make the prize came up, bringing with them two gentlemen on horseback, two pilgrims on foot, and a coach full of women with some six servants on foot and on horseback in attendance on them, and a couple of muleteers whom the gentlemen had with them. The squires made a ring round them, both victors and vanquished maintaining profound silence, waiting for the great Roque Guinart to speak. He asked the gentlemen who they were, whither they were going, and what money they carried with them; "Señor," replied one of them, "we are two captains of Spanish infantry; our companies are at Naples, and we are on our way to embark in four galleys which they say are at Barcelona under orders for Sicily; and we have about two or three hundred crowns, with which we are, according to our notions, rich and contented, for a soldier's poverty does not allow a more extensive hoard."

Roque asked the pilgrims the same questions he had put to the captains, and was answered that they were going to take ship for Rome, and that between them they might have about sixty reals. He asked also who was in the coach, whither they were bound and what money they had, and one of the men on horseback replied, "The persons in the coach are my lady Doña Guiomar de Quiñones, wife of the president of the ecclesiastical court at Naples, her little daughter, a handmaid and a duenna; we six servants are in attendance upon her, and the money amounts to six hundred crowns."

"So then," said Roque Guinart, "we have got here nine hundred crowns and sixty reals; my soldiers must number some sixty; see how much there falls to each, for I am a bad arithmetician."

As soon as the robbers heard this they raised a shout of "Long life to Roque Guinart, in spite of the *lladres*[1] that seek his ruin!"

The captains showed plainly the concern they felt, the president's lady was downcast, and and the pilgrims did not at all enjoy seeing their property confiscated. Roque kept them in suspense in this way for a while; but he had no desire to prolong their distress, which might be seen a bowshot off, and turning to the captains he said, "Sirs, will your worships be pleased of your courtesy to lend me sixty crowns, and her ladyship the president's wife eighty, to satisfy this band that follows me, for 'it is by his singing the abbot gets his dinner'; and then you may at once proceed on your journey, free and unhindered, with a safe conduct which I shall give you, so that if you come across any other bands of mine that I have scattered in these parts, they may do you no harm; for I have no intention of doing injury to soldiers, or to any woman, especially one of quality."

Profuse and hearty were the expressions of gratitude with which the captains thanked Roque for his courtesy and generosity; for such they regarded his leaving them their own money.

[1] Thieves.

Señora Doña Guiomar de Quiñones wanted to throw herself out of the coach to kiss the feet and hands of the great Roque, but he would not suffer it on any account; so far from that, he begged her pardon for the wrong he had done her under pressure of the inexorable necessities of his unfortunate calling. The president's lady ordered one of her servants to give the eighty crowns that had been assessed as her share at once, for the captains had already paid down their sixty. The pilgrims were about to give up the whole of their little hoard, but Roque bade them keep quiet, and turning to his men he said, "Of these crowns two fall to each man and twenty remain over; let ten be given to these pilgrims, and the other ten to this worthy squire that he may be able to speak favorably of this adventure"; and then having writing materials, with which he always went provided, brought to him, he gave them in writing a safe-conduct to the leaders of his bands; and bidding them farewell let them go free and filled with admiration at his magnanimity, his generous disposition, and his unusual conduct, and inclined to regard him as an Alexander the Great rather than a notorious robber.

One of the squires observed in his mixture of Gascon and Catalan, "This captain of ours would make a better friar than highwayman; if he wants to be so generous another time, let it be with his own property and not ours."

The unlucky wight did not speak so low but that Roque overheard him, and drawing his sword almost split his head in two, saying, "That is the way I punish impudent saucy fellows." They were all taken aback, and not one of them dared to utter a word, such deference did they pay him. Roque then withdrew to one side and wrote a letter to a friend of his at Barcelona, telling him that the famous Don Quixote of La Mancha, the knight-errant of whom there was so much talk, was with him, and was, he assured him, the drollest and wisest man in the world; and that in four days from that date, that is to say, on Saint John the Baptist's Day, he was going to deposit him in full armor mounted on his horse Rocinante, together with his squire Sancho on an ass, in the middle of the strand of the city; and bidding him give notice of this to his friends the Niarros, that they might divert themselves with them. He wished, he said, his enemies the Cadells could be deprived of this pleasure; but that was impossible, because the crazes and shrewd sayings of Don Quixote and the humors of his squire Sancho Panza could not help giving general pleasure to all the world. He despatched the letter by one of his squires, who, exchanging the costume of a highwayman for that of a peasant, made his way into Barcelona and gave it to the person to whom it was directed.

Chapter 61

Of what happened to Don Quixote on entering Barcelona, together with other matters that partake of the true rather than of the ingenious

DON QUIXOTE passed three days and three nights with Roque, and had he passed three hundred years he would have found enough to observe and wonder at in his mode of life. At daybreak they were in one spot, at dinner-time in another; sometimes they fled without knowing from whom, at other times they lay in wait, not knowing for what. They slept standing, breaking their slumbers to shift from place to place. There was nothing but sending out spies and scouts, posting sentinels and blowing the matches of arquebuses, though they carried but few, for almost all used flint-locks. Roque passed his nights in some place or other apart from his men, that they might not know where he was, for the many proclamations the viceroy of Barcelona had issued against his life kept him in fear and uneasiness, and he did not venture to trust any one, afraid that even his own men would kill him or deliver him up to the authorities; of a truth, a weary miserable life! At length, by unfrequented roads, short cuts, and secret paths, Roque, Don Quixote, and Sancho, together with six squires, set out for Barcelona. They reached the strand on Saint John's Eve during the night; and Roque, after embracing Don Quixote and Sancho (to whom he presented the ten crowns he had promised but had not until then given), left them with many expressions of good-will on both sides.

Roque went back, while Don Quixote remained on horseback, just as he was, waiting for day, and it was not long before the countenance of the fair Aurora began to show itself at the balconies of the east, gladdening the grass and flowers, if not the ear; though to gladden that too there came at the same moment a sound of clarions and drums, and a din of bells, and a tramp, tramp, and cries of "Clear the way there!" of the passengers, that seemed to issue from the city. The dawn made way for the sun that with a face broader than a buckler began to rise slowly above the low line of the horizon; Don Quixote and Sancho gazed all around them; they beheld the sea, a sight until then unseen by them; it struck them as exceedingly spacious and broad, much more so than the lakes of Ruidera which they had seen in La Mancha. They saw the galleys along the beach, which, lowering their awnings, displayed themselves decked with streamers and pennons that trembled in the breeze and kissed and swept the water, while on board the bugles, trumpets, and clarions were sounding and filling the air far and near with melodious warlike notes. Then they began to move and execute a kind of skirmish upon the calm water, while a vast number of horsemen on fine horses and in showy liveries, issuing from the city, engaged on their side in a somewhat similar movement. The soldiers on board the galleys kept up a ceaseless fire, which they on the walls and forts of the city returned, and the heavy cannon rent the air with the tremendous noise they made, to which the gangway guns of the galleys replied. The bright sea, the smiling earth, the clear air—though at times darkened by the smoke of the guns—all seemed to fill the whole multitude with unexpected delight. Sancho could not make out how it was that those great masses that moved over the sea had so many feet.

And now the horsemen in livery came galloping up with shouts and outlandish cries and cheers to where Don Quixote stood amazed and wondering; and one of them, he to whom Roque had sent word, addressing him exclaimed, "Welcome to our city, mirror, beacon, star and cynosure of all knight-errantry in its widest extent! Welcome, I say, valiant Don Quixote of La Mancha; not the false, the fictitious, the apocryphal, that these latter days have offered us in lying histories, but the true, the legitimate, the real one that Cid Hamet Benengeli, flower of historians, has described to us!"

Don Quixote made no answer, nor did the horsemen wait for one, but wheeling and wheeling again with all their followers, they began curvetting round Don Quixote, who, turning to Sancho, said, "These gentlemen have plainly recognized us; I will wager they have read our history, and even that newly printed one by the Aragonese."

The cavalier who addressed Don Quixote again approached him and said, "Come with us, Señor Don Quixote, for we are all of us your servants and great friends of Roque Guinart's"; to which Don Quixote returned, "If courtesy breeds courtesy, yours, sir knight, is daughter or very nearly akin to the great Roque's; carry me where you please; I will have no will but yours,

especially if you deign to employ it in your service."

The cavalier replied with words no less polite, and then, all closing in around him, they set out with him for the city to the music of the clarions and the drums. As they were entering it, the wicked one, who is the author of all mischief, and the boys who are wickeder than the wicked one, contrived that a couple of these audacious irrepressible urchins should force their way through the crowd, and lifting up, one of them Dapple's tail and the other Rocinante's, insert a bunch of furze under each. The poor beasts felt the strange spurs and added to their anguish by pressing their tails tight, so much so that, cutting a multitude of capers, they flung their masters to the ground. Don Quixote, covered with shame and out of countenance, ran to pluck the plume from his poor jade's tail, while Sancho did the same for Dapple. His conductors tried to punish the audacity of the boys, but there was no possibility of doing so, for they hid themselves among the hundreds of others that were following them. Don Quixote and Sancho mounted once more, and with the same music and acclamations reached their conductor's house, which was large and stately, that of a rich gentleman, in short; and there for the present we will leave them, for such is Cid Hamet's pleasure.

Chapter 62

Which deals with the adventure of the enchanted head, together with other trivial matters which cannot be left untold

DON QUIXOTE's host was one Don Antonio Moreno by name, a gentleman of wealth and intelligence, and very fond of diverting himself in any fair and good-natured way; and having Don Quixote in his house he set about devising modes of making him exhibit his mad points in some harmless fashion; for jests that give pain are no jests, and no sport is worth anything if it hurts another. The first thing he did was to make Don Quixote take off his armor, and lead him, in that tight chamois suit we have already described and depicted more than once, out on a balcony overhanging one of the chief streets of the city, in full view of the crowd and of the boys, who gazed at him as they would at a monkey. The cavaliers in livery careered before him again as though it were for him alone, and not to enliven the festival of the day, that they wore it, and Sancho was in high delight, for it seemed to him that, how he knew not, he had fallen upon another Camacho's wedding, another house like Don Diego de Morena's, another castle like the duke's. Some of Don Antonio's friends dined with him that day, and all showed honor to Don Quixote and treated him as a knight-errant, and he, becoming puffed up and exalted in consequence, could not contain himself for satisfaction. Such were the drolleries of Sancho that all the servants of the house, and all who heard him, were kept hanging upon his lips. While at table Don Antonio said to him, "We hear, worthy Sancho, that you are so fond of *manjar blanco* and force-meats balls, that if you have any left, you keep them in your bosom for the next day."

"No, señor, that's not true," said Sancho, "for I am more cleanly than greedy, and my master Don Quixote here knows well that we two are used to live for a week on a handful of acorns or nuts. To be sure, if it so happens that they offer me a heifer I run with a halter; I mean, I eat what I'm given, and make use of opportunities as I find them; but whoever says that I'm an out-of-the-way eater or not cleanly, let me tell him that he is wrong; and I'd put it in a different way if I did not respect the honorable beards that are at the table."

"Indeed," said Don Quixote, "Sancho's moderation and cleanliness in eating might be inscribed and graved on plates of brass, to be kept in eternal remembrance in ages to come. It is true that when he is hungry there is a certain appearance of voracity about him, for he eats at a great pace and chews with both jaws; but cleanliness he is always mindful of; and when he was governor he learned how to eat daintily, so much so that he eats grapes, and even pomegranate pips, with a fork."

"What!" said Don Antonio, "has Sancho been a governor?"

"Ay," said Sancho, "and of an island called Barataria. I governed it to perfection for ten days; and lost my rest all the time; and learned to look down upon all the governments in the world; I got out of it by taking to flight, and fell into a pit where I gave myself up for dead, and out of which I escaped alive by a miracle."

Don Quixote then gave them a minute account of the whole affair of Sancho's government, with which he greatly amused his hearers.

On the cloth being removed Don Antonio, taking Don Quixote by the hand, passed with him into a distant room in which there was nothing in the way of furniture except a table, apparently of jasper, resting on a pedestal of the same, upon which was set up, after the fashion of the busts of the Roman emperors, ahead which seemed to be of bronze. Don Antonio traversed the whole apartment with Don Quixote and walked round the table many times, and then said, "Now, Señor Don Quixote, that I am satisfied that no one is listening to us, and that the door is shut, I will tell you of one of the rarest adventures, or more properly speaking strange things, that can be imagined, on condition that you will keep what I say to you in the remotest recesses of secrecy."

"I swear it," said Don Quixote, "and for greater security I will put a flag-stone over it; for I would have you know, Señor Don Antonio" (he had by this time learned his name), "that you are addressing one who, though he has ears to hear, has no tongue to speak; so that you may safely transfer whatever you have in your bosom into mine, and rely upon it that you have consigned it to the depths of silence."

"In reliance upon that promise," said Don Antonio, "I will astonish you with what you shall see and hear, and relieve myself of some of the vexation it gives me to have no one to whom I can confide my secrets, for they are not of a sort to be intrusted to everybody."

Don Quixote was puzzled, wondering what could be the object of such precautions; whereupon Don Antonio taking his hand passed it over the bronze head and the whole table and the pedestal of jasper on which it stood, and then said, "This head, Señor Don Quixote, has been made and fabricated by one of the greatest magicians and wizards the world ever saw, a Pole, I believe, by birth, and a pupil of the famous Escotillo of whom such marvellous stories are told. He was here in my house, and for a consideration of a thousand crowns that I gave him he constructed this head, which has the property and virtue of answering whatever questions are put to its ear. He observed the points of the compass, he traced figures, he studied the stars, he watched favorable moments, and at length brought it to the perfection we shall see to-morrow, for on Fridays it is mute, and this being Friday we must wait till the next day. In the interval your worship may consider what you would like to ask it; and I know by experience that in all its answers it tells the truth."

Don Quixote was amazed at the virtue and property of the head, and was inclined to disbelieve Don Antonio; but seeing what a short time he had to wait to test the matter, he did not choose to say anything except that he thanked him for having revealed to him so mighty a secret. They then quitted the room, Don Antonio locked the door, and they repaired to the chamber where the rest of the gentlemen were assembled. In the meantime Sancho had recounted to them several of the adventures and accidents that had happened to his master.

That afternoon they took Don Quixote out for a stroll, not in his armor but in street costume, with a surcoat of tawny cloth upon him, that at that season would have made ice itself sweat. Orders were left with the servants to entertain Sancho so as not to let him leave the house. Don Quixote was mounted, not on Rocinante, but upon a tall mule of easy pace and handsomely caparisoned. They put the surcoat on him, and on the back, without his perceiving it, they stitched a parchment on which they wrote in large letters, "This is Don Quixote of La Mancha." As they set out upon their excursion the placard attracted the eyes of all who chanced to see him, and as they read out, "This is Don Quixote of La Mancha," Don Quixote was amazed to see how many people gazed at him, called him by his name, and recognized him, and turning to Don Antonio, who rode at his side, he observed to him, "Great are the privileges knight-errantry involves, for it makes him who professes it known and famous in every region of the earth; see, Don Antonio, even the very boys of this city know me without ever having seen me."

"True, Señor Don Quixote," returned Don Antonio; "for as fire cannot be hidden or kept secret, virtue cannot escape being recognized; and that which is attained by the profession of arms shines distinguished above all others."

It came to pass, however, that as Don Quixote was proceeding amid the acclamations that have been described, a Castilian, reading the inscription on his back, cried out in a loud voice, "The devil take thee for a Don Quixote of La Mancha! What! art thou here, and not dead of the countless drubbings that have fallen on thy ribs? Thou art mad; and if thou wert so by thyself, and kept thyself within thy madness, it would not be so bad; but thou hast the gift of making fools and blockheads of all who have anything to do with thee or say to thee. Why, look at these gentlemen bearing thee company! Get thee home, blockhead, and see after thy affairs, and thy wife and children, and give over these fooleries that are sapping thy brains and skimming away thy wits."

"Go your own way, brother," said Don Antonio, "and don't offer advice to those who don't ask you for it. Señor Don Quixote is in his full senses, and we who bear him company are not fools; virtue is to be honored wherever it may be found; go, and bad luck to you, and don't meddle where you are not wanted."

"By God, your worship is right," replied the Castilian; "for to advise this good man is to kick against the pricks; still for all that it fills me with pity that the sound wit they say the blockhead has in everything should dribble away by the channel of his knight-errantry; but may the bad luck your worship talks of follow me and all my descendants, if, from this day forth, though I should live longer than Methuselah, I ever give advice to anybody even if he asks me for it."

The advice-giver took himself off, and they continued their stroll; but so great was the press of the boys and people to read the placard, that Don Antonio was forced to remove it as if he were taking off something else.

Night came and they went home, and there was a ladies dancing party, for Don Antonio's wife, a lady of rank and gayety, beauty and wit, had invited some friends of hers to come and do honor to her guest and amuse themselves with his strange delusions. Several of them came, they supped sumptuously, and the dance began about ten o'clock. Among the ladies were two of a mischievous and frolicsome turn, and, though perfectly modest, somewhat free in playing tricks for harmless diversion sake. These two were so indefatigable in taking Don Quixote out to dance that they tired him down, not only in body but in spirit. It was a sight to see the figure Don Quixote made, long, lank, lean, and yellow, his garments clinging tight to him, ungainly, and above all anything but agile. The gay ladies made secret love to him, and he on his part secretly repelled them, but finding himself hard pressed by their blandishments he lifted up his voice and exclaimed, "Fugite, partes adversæ! Leave me in peace, unwelcome overtures; avaunt, with your desires, ladies, for she who is queen of mine, the peerless Dulcinea del Toboso, suffers none but hers to lead me captive and subdue me"; and so saying he sat down on the floor in the middle of the room, tired out and broken down by all this exertion in the dance.

Don Antonio directed him to be taken up bodily and carried to bed, and the first that laid hold of him was Sancho, saying as he did so, "In an evil hour you took to dancing, master mine; do you fancy all mighty men of valor are dancers, and all knights-errant given to capering? If you do, I can tell you you are mistaken; there's many a man would rather undertake to kill a giant than cut a caper. If it had been the shoe-fling you were at I could take your place, for I can do the shoe-fling like a gerfalcon; but I'm no good at dancing."

With these and other observations Sancho set the whole ball-room laughing, and then put his master to bed, covering him up well so that he might sweat out any chill caught after his dancing.

The next day Don Antonio thought he might as well make trial of the enchanted head, and with Don Quixote, Sancho, and two others, friends of his, besides the two ladies that had tired out Don Quixote at the ball, who had remained for the night with Don Antonio's wife, he locked himself up in the chamber where the head was. He explained to them the property it possessed and intrusted the secrets to them, telling them that now for the first time he was going to try the virtue of the enchanted head; but except Don Antonio's two friends no one else was privy to the mystery of the enchantment, and if Don Antonio had not first revealed it to them they would have been inevitably reduced to the same state of amazement as the rest, so artfully and skilfully was it contrived.

The first to approach the ear of the head, was Don Antonio himself, and in a low voice but not so low as not to be audible to all, he said to it, "Head, tell me by the virtue that lies in thee what am I at this moment thinking of?"

The head, without any movement of the lips, answered in a clear and distinct voice, so as to be heard by all, "I cannot judge of thoughts."

All were thunderstruck at this, and all the more so as they saw that there was nobody anywhere near the table or in the whole room that could have answered.

"How many of us are here?" asked Don Antonio once more; and it was answered him in the same way softly, "Thou and thy wife, with two friends of thine and two of hers, and a famous knight called Don Quixote of La Mancha, and a squire of his, Sancho Panza by name."

Now there was fresh astonishment; now everyone's hair was standing on end with awe; and Don Antonio retiring from the head exclaimed, "This suffices to show me that I have not been deceived by him who sold thee to me, O sage head, talking head, answering head, wonderful head! Let some one else go and put what question he likes to it."

And as women are commonly impulsive and inquisitive, the first to come forward was one of the two friends of Don Antonio's wife, and her question was, "Tell me, Head, what shall I do to be very beautiful?" and the answer she got was, "Be very modest."

"I question thee no further," said the fair querist.

Her companion then came up and said, "I should like to know, Head, whether my husband loves me or not"; the answer given to her was, "Think how he uses thee, and thou mayest guess"; and the married lady went off saying, "That answer did not need a question; for of course the treatment one receives shows the disposition of him from whom it is received."

Then one of Don Antonio's two friends advanced and asked it, "Who am I?" "Thou knowest," was the answer. "That is not what I ask thee," said the gentleman, "but to tell me if thou knowest me." "Yes, I know thee, thou art Don Pedro Noriz," was the reply.

"I do not seek to know more," said the gentleman, "for this is enough to convince me, O Head, that thou knowest everything"; and as he retired the other friend came forward and asked it, "Tell me, Head, what are the wishes of my eldest son?"

"I have said already," was the answer, "that I cannot judge of wishes; however, I can tell thee the wish of thy son is to bury thee."

"That's 'what I see with my eyes I point out with my finger,' " said the gentleman, "so I ask no more."

Don Antonio's wife came up and said, "I know not what to ask thee, Head; I would only seek to know of thee if I shall have many years of enjoyment of my good husband"; and the answer she received was, "Thou shalt, for his vigor and his temperate habits promise many years of life, which by their intemperance others so often cut short."

Then Don Quixote came forward and said, "Tell me, thou that answerest, was that which I describe as having happened to me in the cave of Montesinos the truth or a dream? Will my squire Sancho's whipping be accomplished without fail? Will the disenchantment of Dulcinea be brought about?"

"As to the question of the cave," was the reply, "there is much to be said; there is something of both in it. Sancho's whipping will proceed leisurely. The disenchantment of Dulcinea will attain its due consummation."

"I seek to know no more," said Don Quixote; "let me but see Dulcinea disenchanted, and I will consider that all the good fortune I could wish for has come upon me all at once."

The last questioner was Sancho, and his questions were, "Head, shall I by any chance have another government? Shall I ever escape from the hard life of a squire? Shall I get back to see my wife and children?" To which the answer came, "Thou shalt govern in thy house; and if thou returnest to it thou shalt see thy wife and children; and on ceasing to serve thou shalt cease to be a squire."

"Good, by God!" said Sancho Panza; "I could have told myself that; the prophet Perogrullo could have said no more."

"What answer wouldst thou have, beast?" said Don Quixote; "is it not enough that the replies this head has given suit the questions put to it?"

"Yes, it is enough," said Sancho; "but I should like it to have made itself plainer and told me more."

The questions and answers came to an end here, but not the wonder with which all were filled, except Don Antonio's two friends who were in the secret. This Cid Hamet Benengeli thought fit to reveal at once, not to keep the world in suspense, fancying that the head had some strange magical mystery in it. He says, therefore, that on the model of another head, the work of an image-maker, which he had seen at Madrid, Don Antonio made this one at home for his own amusement and to astonish ignorant people; and its mechanism was as follows. The table was of wood painted and varnished to imitate jasper, and the pedestal on which it stood was of the same material, with four eagles' claws projecting from it to support the weight more steadily. The head, which resembled a bust or figure of a Roman emperor, and was colored like bronze, was hollow throughout, as was the table, into which it was fitted so exactly that no trace of the joining was visible. The pedestal of the table was also hollow and communicated with the throat and neck of the head, and the whole was in communication with another room underneath the chamber in which the head stood. Through the entire cavity in the pedestal, table, throat and neck of the bust or figure, there passed a tube of tin carefully adjusted and concealed from sight. In the room below corresponding to the one above was placed the person who was to answer, with his mouth to the tube, and the voice, as in an ear-trumpet, passed from above downwards, and from below upwards, the words coming clearly and distinctly; it was impossible, thus, to detect the trick. A nephew of Don Antonio's, a smart, sharp-witted student, was the answerer, and as he had been told beforehand by his uncle who the persons were that would come with him that day into the chamber where the head was, it was an easy matter

for him to answer the first question at once and correctly; the others he answered by guess-work, and being clever, cleverly. Cid Hamet adds that this marvellous contrivance stood for some ten or twelve days; but that, as it became noised abroad through the city that he had in his house an enchanted head that answered all who asked questions of it, Don Antonio, fearing it might come to the ears of the watchful sentinels of our faith, explained the matter to the inquisitors, who commanded him to break it up and have done with it, lest the ignorant vulgar should be scandalized. By Don Quixote, however, and by Sancho the head was still held to be an enchanted one, and capable of answering questions, though more to Don Quixote's satisfaction than Sancho's.

The gentlemen of the city, to gratify Don Antonio and also to do the honors to Don Quixote, and give him an opportunity of displaying his folly, made arrangements for a tilting at the ring in six days from that time, which, however, for the reason that will be mentioned hereafter, did not take place.

Don Quixote took a fancy to stroll about the city quietly and on foot, for he feared that if he went on horseback the boys would follow him; so he and Sancho and two servants that Don Antonio gave him set out for a walk. Thus it came to pass that going along one of the streets Don Quixote lifted up his eyes and saw written in very large letters over a door, "Books printed here," at which he was vastly pleased, for until then he had never seen a printing office, and he was curious to know what it was like. He entered with all his following, and saw them drawing sheets in one place, correcting in another, setting up type here, revising there; in short all the work that is to be seen in great printing offices. He went up to one case and asked what they were about there; the workmen told him, he watched them with wonder, and passed on. He approached one man, among others, and asked him what he was doing. The workman replied, "Señor, this gentleman here" (pointing to a man of prepossessing mien and appearance and a certain gravity of look) "has translated an Italian book into our Spanish tongue, and I am setting it up in type for the press."

"What is the title of the book?" asked Don Quixote; to which the author replied, "Señor, in Italian the book is called Le Bagatelle."

"And what does Le Bagatelle import in our Spanish?" asked Don Quixote.

"Le Bagatelle," said the author, "is as though

we should say in Spanish *Los Juguetes;* but though the book is humble in name it has good solid matter in it."

"I," said Don Quixote, "have some little smattering of Italian, and I plume myself on singing some of Ariosto's stanzas; but tell me, señor—I do not say this to test your ability, but merely out of curiosity—have you ever met with the word *pignatta* in your book?"

"Yes, often," said the author.

"And how do you render that in Spanish?" asked Don Quixote.

"How should I render it," returned the author, "but by *olla*"?

"Body o' me," exclaimed Don Quixote, "what a proficient you are in the Italian language! I would lay a good wager that where they say in Italian *piace* you say in Spanish *place,* and where they say *più* you say *mas,* and you translate *sù* by *arriba* and *giù* by *abajo.*"

"I translate them so of course," said the author, "for those are their proper equivalents."

"I would venture to swear," said Don Quixote, "that your worship is not known in the world, which always begrudges their reward to rare wits and praiseworthy labors. What talents lie wasted there! What genius thrust away into corners! What worth left neglected! Still it seems to me that translation from one language into another, if it be not from the queens of languages, the Greek and the Latin, is like looking at Flemish tapestries on the wrong side; for though the figures are visible, they are full of threads, that make them indistinct, and they do not show with the smoothness and brightness of the right side; and translation from easy languages argues neither ingenuity nor command of words, any more than transcribing or copying out one document from another. But I do not mean by this to draw the inference that no credit is to be allowed for the work of translating, for a man may employ himself in ways worse and less profitable to himself. This estimate does not include two famous translators, Doctor Cristóbal de Figueroa, in his *Pastor Fido,* and Don Juan de Jáuregui, in his *Aminta,* wherein by their felicity they leave it in doubt which is the translation and which the original. But tell me, are you printing this book at your own risk, or have you sold the copyright to some bookseller?"

"I print at my own risk," said the author, "and I expect to make a thousand ducats at least by this first edition, which is to be of two thousand copies that will go off in a twinkling at six reals apiece."

"A fine calculation you are making!" said Don Quixote; "it is plain you don't know the ins and outs of the printers, and how they play into one another's hands. I promise you when you find yourself saddled with two thousand copies you will feel so sore that it will astonish you, particularly if the book is a little out of the common and not in any way highly spiced."

"What!" said the author, "would your worship, then, have me give it to a bookseller who will give three maravedís for the copyright and think he is doing me a favor in giving me that? I do not print my books to win fame in the world, for I am known in it already by my works; I want to make money, without which reputation is not worth a rap."

"God send your worship good luck," said Don Quixote; and he moved on to another case, where he saw them correcting a sheet of a book with the title of *Light of the Soul;* noticing it he observed, "Books like this, though there are many of the kind, are the ones that deserve to be printed, for many are the sinners in these days, and lights unnumbered are needed for all that are in darkness."

He passed on, and saw they were also correcting another book, and when he asked its title they told him it was called, *The Second Part of the Ingenious Gentleman Don Quixote of La Mancha,* by a certain person of Tordesillas.

"I have heard of this book already," said Don Quixote, "and verily and on my conscience I thought it had been by this time burned to ashes as a meddlesome intruder; but its *Martinmas* will come to it as it does to every pig; [1] for fictions have the more merit and charm about them the more nearly they approach the truth or what looks like it; and true stories, the truer they are the better they are"; and so saying he walked out of the printing office with a certain amount of displeasure in his looks. That same day Don Antonio arranged to take him to see the galleys that lay at the beach, whereat Sancho was in high delight, as he had never seen any all his life. Don Antonio sent word to the commandant of the galleys that he intended to bring his guest, the famous Don Quixote of La Mancha, of whom the commandant and all the citizens had already heard, that afternoon to see them; and what happened on board of them will be told in the next chapter.

[1] Martinmas was the great day for pig-killing in Spain.

Chapter 63

Of the mishap that befell Sancho Panza through the visit to the galleys, and the strange adventure of the fair Morisco

PROFOUND were Don Quixote's reflections on the reply of the enchanted head, not one of them, however, hitting on the secret of the trick, but all concentrated on the promise, which he regarded as a certainty, of Dulcinea's disenchantment. This he turned over in his mind again and again with great satisfaction to himself, fully persuaded that he would shortly see its fulfilment; and as for Sancho, though, as has been said, he hated being a governor, still he had a longing to be giving orders and finding himself obeyed once more; this is the misfortune that being in authority, even in jest, brings with it.

To resume; that afternoon their host Don Antonio Moreno and his two friends, with Don Quixote and Sancho, went to the galleys. The commandant had been already made aware of his good fortune in seeing two such famous persons as Don Quixote and Sancho, and the instant they came to the shore all the galleys struck their awnings and the clarions rang out. A skiff covered with rich carpets and cushions of crimson velvet was immediately lowered into the water, and as Don Quixote stepped on board of it, the leading galley fired her gangway gun, and the other galleys did the same; and as he mounted the starboard ladder the whole crew saluted him (as is the custom when a personage of distinction comes on board a galley) by exclaiming "Hu, hu, hu," three times. The general, for so we shall call him, a Valencian gentleman of rank, gave him his hand and embraced him, saying, "I shall mark this day with a white stone as one of the happiest I can expect to enjoy in my lifetime, since I have seen Señor Don Quixote of La Mancha, pattern and image wherein we see contained and condensed all that is worthy in knight-errantry."

Don Quixote, delighted beyond measure with such a lordly reception, replied to him in words no less courteous. All then proceeded to the poop, which was very handsomely decorated, and seated themselves on the bulwark benches; the boatswain passed along the gangway and piped all hands to strip, which they did in an instant. Sancho, seeing such a number of men stripped to the skin, was taken aback, and still more when he saw them spread the awning so briskly that it seemed to him as if all the devils were at work at it; but all this was cakes and fancy bread to what I am going to tell now. Sancho was seated on the captain's stage, close to the aftermost rower on the right-hand side. He, previously instructed in what he was to do, laid hold of Sancho, hoisting him up in his arms, and the whole crew, who were standing ready, beginning on the right, proceeded to pass him on, whirling him along from hand to hand and from bench to bench with such rapidity that it took the sight out of poor Sancho's eyes, and he made quite sure that the devils themselves were flying away with him; nor did they leave off with him until they had sent him back along the left side and deposited him on the poop; and the poor fellow was left bruised and breathless and all in a sweat, and unable to comprehend what it was that had happened to him.

Don Quixote when he saw Sancho's flight without wings asked the general if this was the usual ceremony with those who came on board the galleys for the first time; for, if so, as he had no intention of adopting them as a profession, he had no mind to perform such feats of agility, and if any one offered to lay hold of him to whirl him about, he vowed to God he would kick his soul out; and as he said this he stood up and clapped his hand upon his sword. At this instant they struck the awning and lowered the yard with a prodigious rattle. Sancho thought heaven was coming off its hinges and going to fall on his head, and full of terror he ducked it and buried it between his knees; nor were Don Quixote's knees altogether under control, for he too shook a little, squeezed his shoulders together and lost color. The crew then hoisted the yard with the same rapidity and clatter as when they lowered it, all the while keeping silence as though they had neither voice nor breath. The boatswain gave the signal to weigh anchor, and leaping upon the middle of the gangway began to lay on to the shoulders of the crew with his *courbash* or whip, and to haul out gradually to sea.

When Sancho saw so many red feet (for such he took the oars to be) moving altogether, he said to himself, "It's these that are the real enchanted things, and not the ones my master talks of. What can those wretches have done to be whipped in that way; and how does that one man who goes along there whistling dare to whip so many? I declare this is hell, or at least purgatory!"

Don Quixote, observing how attentively Sancho regarded what was going on, said to him, "Ah, Sancho my friend, how quickly and cheaply might you finish off the disenchantment of Dulcinea, if you would strip to the waist and take your place among those gentlemen! Amid the pain and sufferings of so many you would not feel your own much; and moreover perhaps the sage Merlin would allow each of these lashes, being laid on with a good hand, to count for ten of those which you must give yourself at last."

The general was about to ask what these lashes were, and what was Dulcinea's disenchantment, when a sailor exclaimed, "Monjuich signals that there is an oared vessel off the coast to the west."

On hearing this the general sprang upon the gangway crying, "Now then, my sons, don't let her give us the slip! It must be some Algerine corsair brigantine that the watch-tower signals to us." The three others immediately came alongside the chief galley to receive their orders. The general ordered two to put out to sea while he with the other kept in shore, so that in this way the vessels could not escape them. The crews plied the oars driving the galleys so furiously that they seemed to fly. The two that had put out to sea, after a couple of miles sighted a vessel which, so far as they could make out, they judged to be one of fourteen or fifteen banks, and so she proved. As soon as the vessel discovered the galleys she went about with the object and in the hope of making her escape by her speed; but the attempt failed, for the chief galley was one of the fastest vessels afloat, and overhauled her so rapidly that they on board the brigantine saw clearly there was no possibility of escaping, and the rais [captain] therefore would have had them drop their oars and give themselves up so as not to provoke the captain in command of our galleys to anger. But chance directing things otherwise, so ordered it that just as the chief galley came close enough for those on board her to hear the shouts from her calling on them to surrender, two Toraquis, that is to say drunken Turks, that with a dozen more were on board the brigantine, discharged their muskets, killing two of the soldiers that lined the sides of our vessel. Seeing this the general swore he would not leave one of those he found on board the vessel alive, but as he bore down furiously upon her she slipped away from him beneath the oars. The galley shot a good way ahead; those on board the vessel saw their case was desperate, and while the galley was coming about they made sail, and by sailing and rowing once more tried to sheer off: but their activity did not do them as much good as their rashness did them harm, for the galley coming up with them in a little more than half a mile threw her oars over them and took the whole of them alive.

The other two galleys now joined company, and all four returned with the prize to the beach, where a vast multitude stood waiting for them, eager to see what they brought back. The general anchored close in, and perceived that the viceroy of the city was on the shore. He ordered the skiff to push off to fetch him, and the yard to be lowered for the purpose of hanging forthwith the rais and the rest of the men taken on board the vessel, about six-and-thirty in number, all smart fellows and most of them Turkish musketeers. He asked which was the rais of the brigantine, and was answered in Spanish by one of the prisoners (who afterwards proved to be a Spanish renegade), "This young man, señor, that you see here is our rais," and he pointed to one of the handsomest and most gallant-looking youths that could be imagined. He did not seem to be twenty years of age.

"Tell me, reckless dog," said the general, "what led thee to kill my soldiers, when thou sawest it was impossible for thee to escape? Is that the way to behave to chief galleys? Knowest thou not that rashness is not valor? Faint prospects of success should make men bold, but not rash."

The rais was about to reply, but the general could not at that moment listen to him, as he had to hasten to receive the viceroy, who was now coming on board the galley, and with him certain of his attendants and some of the people.

"You have had a good chase, Señor General," said the viceroy.

"Your excellency shall soon see how good, by the game strung up to this yard," replied the general.

"How so?" returned the viceroy.

"Because," said the general, "against all law, reason, and usages of war they have killed on my hands two of the best soldiers on board these galleys, and I have sworn to hang every man that I have taken, but above all this youth who is the rais of the brigantine," and he pointed to him as he stood with his hands already bound and the rope round his neck, ready for death.

The viceroy looked at him, and seeing him so well-favored, so graceful, and so submissive, he felt a desire to spare his life, the comeliness of the youth furnishing him at once with a letter of recommendation. He therefore questioned him, saying, "Tell me, rais, art thou Turk, Moor, or renegade?"

To which the youth replied, also in Spanish, "I am neither Turk, nor Moor, nor renegade."

"What art thou, then?" said the viceroy.

"A Christian woman," replied the youth.

"A woman and a Christian, in such a dress and in such circumstances! It is more marvellous than credible," said the viceroy.

"Suspend the execution of the sentence, gentlemen," said the youth; "your vengeance will not lose much by waiting while I tell you the story of my life."

What heart could be so hard as not to be softened by these words, at any rate so far as to listen to what the unhappy youth had to say? The general bade him say what he pleased, but not to expect pardon for his flagrant offence. With this permission the youth began in these words.

"Born of Morisco parents, I am of that nation, more unhappy than wise, upon which of late a sea of woes has poured down. In the course of our misfortune I was carried to Barbary by two uncles of mine, for it was in vain that I declared I was a Christian, as in fact I am, and not a mere pretended one, or outwardly, but a true Catholic Christian. It availed me nothing with those charged with our sad expatriation to protest this, nor would my uncles believe it; on the contrary, they treated it as an untruth and a subterfuge set up to enable me to remain behind in the land of my birth; and so, more by force than of my own will, they took me with them. I had a Christian mother, and a father who was a man of sound sense and a Christian too; I imbibed the Catholic faith with my mother's milk, I was well brought up, and neither in word nor in deed did I, I think, show any sign of being a Morisco. To accompany these virtues, for such I hold them, my beauty, if I possess any, grew with my growth; and great as was the seclusion in which I lived it was not so great but that a young gentleman, Don Gaspar Gregorio by name, eldest son of a gentleman who is lord of a village near ours, contrived to find opportunities of seeing me. How he saw me, how we met, how his heart was lost to me, and mine not kept from him, would take too long to tell, especially at a moment when I am in dread of the cruel cord that threatens me interposing between tongue and throat; I will only say, therefore, that Don Gregorio chose to accompany me in our banishment. He joined company with the Moriscoes who were going forth from other villages, for he knew their language very well, and on the voyage he struck up a friendship with my two uncles who were carrying me with them; for my father, like a wise and far-sighted man, as soon as he heard the first edict for our expulsion, quitted the village and departed in quest of some refuge for us abroad. He left hidden and buried, at a spot of which I alone have knowledge, a large quantity of pearls and precious stones of great value, together with a sum of money in gold cruzadoes and doubloons. He charged me on no account to touch the treasure, if by any chance they expelled us before his return. I obeyed him, and with my uncles, as I have said, and others of our kindred and neighbors, passed over to Barbary, and the place where we took up our abode was Algiers, much the same as if we had taken it up in hell itself. The king heard of my beauty, and report told him of my wealth, which was in some degree fortunate for me. He summoned me before him, and asked me what part of Spain I came from, and what money and jewels I had. I mentioned the place, and told him the jewels and the money were buried there; but that they might easily be recovered if I myself went back for them. All this I told him, in dread lest my beauty and not his own covetousness should influence him. While he was engaged in conversation with me, they brought him word that in company with me was one of the handsomest and most graceful youths that could be imagined. I knew at once that they were speaking of Don Gaspar Gregorio, whose comeliness surpasses the most highly vaunted beauty. I was troubled when I thought of the danger he was in, for among those barbarous Turks a fair youth is more esteemed than a woman, be she ever so beautiful. The king immediately ordered him to be brought before him that he might see him, and asked me if what they said about the youth was true. I then, almost as if inspired by Heaven, told him it was, but that I would have him to know it was not a man, but a woman like myself, and I entreated him to allow me to go and dress her in the attire proper to her, so that her beauty might be seen to perfection, and that she might present herself before him with less embarrassment. He bade me go by all means, and said that the next day we should discuss the plan to be adopted for my return to Spain to carry away the hidden treasure. I saw Don Gaspar, I told him the danger he was in if he let it be seen he was a man, I dressed him as a Moorish woman, and that same afternoon I brought him before the king, who was charmed when he saw him, and resolved to keep the damsel and make a present of her to the Grand Signor; and to avoid the risk she might run among the women of his seraglio, and distrustful of himself, he commanded her to be placed in the house of some Moorish ladies of rank who would protect and attend to her; and thither he was taken at once. What we both suffered (for I cannot deny but I love him), may be left to the imagination of those who are separated if they love one another dearly. The king then arranged that I should return to Spain in this brigantine, and that two Turks, those who killed your soldiers, should accompany me. There also came with me this Spanish renegade"—and here she pointed to him who had first spoken—"whom I know to be secretly a Christian, and to be more desirous of being left in Spain than of returning to Barbary. The rest of the crew of the brigantine are Moors and Turks, who merely serve as rowers. The two Turks, greedy and insolent, instead of obeying the orders we had to land me and this renegade in Christian dress (with which we came provided) on the first Spanish ground we came to, chose to run along the coast and make some prize if they could, fearing that if they put us ashore first, we might, in case of some accident befalling us, make it known that the brigantine was at sea, and thus, if there happened to be any galleys on the coast, they might be taken. We sighted this shore last night, and knowing nothing of these galleys we were discovered, and the result was what you have seen. To sum up, there is Don Gregorio in woman's dress, among women, in imminent danger of his life; and here am I, with hands bound, in expectation, or rather in dread, of losing my life, of which I am already weary. Here, sirs, ends my sad story, as true as it is unhappy; all I ask of you is to allow me to die like a Christian, for, as I have already said, I am not to be charged with the offence of which those of my nation are guilty"; and she stood silent, her eyes filled with moving tears, accompanied by plenty from the bystanders. The viceroy, touched with compassion, went up to her without speaking, and with his own hands untied the cord that bound the fair hands of the Moorish girl.

But all the while the Morisco Christian was telling her strange story, an elderly pilgrim, who had come on board of the galley at the same time as the viceroy, kept his eyes fixed upon her; and the instant she ceased speaking he threw himself at her feet, and embracing them said in a voice broken by sobs and sighs, "O Ana Felix, my unhappy daughter, I am thy father Ricote, come back to look for thee, unable to live without thee, my soul that thou art!"

At these words of his Sancho opened his eyes and raised his head, which he had been holding down, brooding over his unlucky excursion; and looking at the pilgrim he recognized in him that same Ricote he met the day he quitted his government, and felt satisfied that this was his daughter. She being now unbound embraced her father, mingling her tears with his, while he addressing the general and the viceroy said, "This, sirs, is my daughter, more unhappy in her adventures than in her name. She is Ana Felix, surnamed Ricote, celebrated as much for her own beauty as for my wealth. I quitted my native land in search of some shelter or refuge for us abroad, and having found one in Germany I returned in this pilgrim's dress, in the company of some other German pilgrims, to seek my daughter and take up a large quantity of treasure I had left buried. My daughter I did not find, the treasure I found and have with me; and now, in this strange roundabout way you have seen, I find the treasure that more than all makes me rich, my beloved daughter. If our innocence and her tears and mine can with strict justice open the door to clemency, extend it to us, for we never had any intention of injuring you, nor do we in any way sympathize with the aims of our people, who have been justly banished."

"I know Ricote well," said Sancho at this, "and I know too that what he says about Ana Felix being his daughter is true; but as to those other particulars about going and coming, and having good or bad intentions, I say nothing."

While all present stood amazed at this strange occurrence the general said, "At any rate your tears will not allow me to keep my oath; live, fair Ana Felix, all the years that Heaven has allotted you; but these rash insolent fellows must pay the penalty of the crime they have committed"; and with that he gave orders to have the two Turks who had killed his two soldiers hanged at once in the yard-arm. The viceroy, however, begged him earnestly not to hang them, as their behavior savored rather of madness than of bravado. The general yielded to the viceroy's request, for revenge is not easily taken in cold blood. They then tried to devise some scheme for rescuing Don Gaspar Gregorio from the danger in which he had been left. Ricote offered for that object more than two thousand ducats that he had in pearls and gems; they proposed several plans, but none so good as that suggested by the renegade already mentioned, who offered to return to Algiers in a small vessel of about six banks, manned by Christian rowers, as he knew where, how, and when he could and should land, nor was he ignorant of the house in which Don Gaspar was staying. The general and the viceroy had some hesitation about placing confidence in the renegade and intrusting him with the Christians who were to row, but Ana Felix said she could answer for him, and her father offered to go and pay the ransom of the Christians if by any chance they should not be forthcoming. This, then, being agreed upon, the viceroy landed, and Don Antonio Moreno took the fair Morisco and her father home with him, the viceroy charging him to give them the best reception and welcome in his power, while on his own part he offered all that his house contained for their entertainment; so great was the goodwill and kindliness the beauty of Ana Felix had infused into his heart.

Chapter 64

Treating of the adventure which gave Don Quixote more unhappiness than all that had hitherto befallen him

THE wife of Don Antonio Moreno, so the history says, was extremely happy to see Ana Felix in her house. She welcomed her with great kindness, charmed as well by her beauty as by her intelligence; for in both respects the fair Morisco was richly endowed, and all the people of the city flocked to see her as though they had been summoned by the ringing of the bells.

Don Quixote told Don Antonio that the plan adopted for releasing Don Gregorio was not a good one, for its risks were greater than its advantages, and that it would be better to land himself with his arms and horse in Barbary; for he would carry him off in spite of the whole Moorish host, as Don Gaiferos carried off his wife Melisendra.

"Remember, your worship," observed Sancho on hearing him say so, "Senor Don Gaiferos carried off his wife from the mainland, and took her to France by land; but in this case, if by chance we carry off Don Gregorio, we have no way of bringing him to Spain, for there's the sea between."

"There's a remedy for everything except death," said Don Quixote; "if they bring the vessel close to the shore we shall be able to get on board though all the world strive to prevent us."

"Your worship hits it off mighty well and mighty easy," said Sancho; "but 'it's a long step from saying to doing'; and I hold to the renegade, for he seems to me an honest good-hearted fellow."

Don Antonio then said that if the renegade did not prove successful, the expedient of the great Don Quixote's expedition to Barbary should be adopted. Two days afterwards the renegade put to sea in a light vessel of six oars

a-side manned by a stout crew, and two days later the galleys made sail eastward, the general having begged the viceroy to let him know all about the release of Don Gregorio and about Ana Felix, and the viceroy promised to do as he requested.

One morning as Don Quixote went out for a stroll along the beach, arrayed in full armor (for, as he often said, that was "his only gear, his only rest the fray," and he never was without it for a moment), he saw coming towards him a knight, also in full armor, with a shining moon painted on his shield, who, on approaching sufficiently near to be heard, said in a loud voice, addressing himself to Don Quixote, "Illustrious knight, and never sufficiently extolled Don Quixote of La Mancha, I am the Knight of the White Moon, whose unheard-of achievements will perhaps have recalled him to thy memory. I come to do battle with thee and prove the might of thy arm, to the end that I make thee acknowledge and confess that my lady, let her be who she may, is incomparably fairer than thy Dulcinea del Toboso. If thou dost acknowledge this fairly and openly, thou shalt escape death and save me the trouble of inflicting it upon thee; if thou fightest and I vanquish thee, I demand no other satisfaction than that, laying aside arms and abstaining from going in quest of adventures, thou withdraw and betake thy self to thine own village for the space of a year, and live there without putting hand to sword, in peace and quiet and beneficial repose, the same being needed for the increase of thy substance and the salvation of thy soul; and if thou dost vanquish me, my head shall be at thy disposal, my arms and horse thy spoils, and the renown of my deeds transferred and added to thine. Consider which will be thy best course, and give me thy answer speedily, for this day is all the time I have for the despatch of this business."

Don Quixote was amazed and astonished, as well at the Knight of the White Moon's arrogance, as at his reason for delivering the defiance, and with calm dignity he answered him, "Knight of the White Moon, of whose achievements I have never heard until now, I will venture to swear you have never seen the illustrious Dulcinea; for had you seen her I know you would have taken care not to venture yourself upon this issue, because the sight would have removed all doubt from your mind that there ever has been or can be a beauty to be compared with hers; and so, not saying you lie, but merely that you are not correct in what you state, I accept your challenge, with the conditions you have proposed, and at once, that the day you have fixed may not expire; and from your conditions I except only that of the renown of your achievements being transferred to me, for I know not of what sort they are nor what they may amount to; I am satisfied with my own, such as they be. Take, therefore, the side of the field you choose, and I will do the same; and to whom God shall give it may Saint Peter add his blessing."

The Knight of the White Moon had been seen from the city, and it was told the viceroy how he was in conversation with Don Quixote. The viceroy, fancying it must be some fresh adventure got up by Don Antonio Moreno or some other gentleman of the city, hurried out at once to the beach accompanied by Don Antonio and several other gentlemen, just as Don Quixote was wheeling Rocinante round in order to take up the necessary distance. The viceroy upon this, seeing that the pair of them were evidently preparing to come to the charge, put himself between them, asking them what it was that led them to engage in combat all of a sudden in this way. The Knight of the White Moon replied that it was a question of precedence of beauty; and briefly told him what he had said to Don Quixote, and how the conditions of the defiance agreed upon on both sides had been accepted. The viceroy went over to Don Antonio, and asked in a low voice did he know who the Knight of the White Moon was, or was it some joke they were playing on Don Quixote. Don Antonio replied that he neither knew who he was nor whether the defiance was in joke or earnest. This answer left the viceroy in a state of perplexity, not knowing whether he ought to let the combat go on or not; but unable to persuade himself that it was anything but a joke he fell back, saying, "If there be no other way out of it, gallant knights, except to confess or die, and Don Quixote is inflexible, and your worship of the White Moon still more so, in God's hand it be, and fall on."

He of the White Moon thanked the viceroy in courteous and well-chosen words for the permission he gave them, and so did Don Quixote, who then, commending himself with all his heart to Heaven and to his Dulcinea, as was his custom on the eve of any combat that awaited him, proceeded to take a little more distance, as he saw his antagonist was doing the same; then, without blast of trumpet or other warlike instrument to give them the signal to charge, both at the same instant wheeled their horses;

and he of the White Moon, being the swifter, met Don Quixote after having traversed two-thirds of the course, and there encountered him with such violence that, without touching him with his lance (for he held it high, to all appearance purposely), he hurled Don Quixote and Rocinante to the earth, a perilous fall. He sprang upon him at once, and placing the lance over his visor said to him, "You are vanquished, sir knight, nay dead unless you admit the conditions of our defiance."

Don Quixote, bruised and stupefied, without raising his visor said in a weak feeble voice as if he were speaking out of a tomb, "Dulcinea del Toboso is the fairest woman in the world, and I the most unfortunate knight on earth; it is not fitting that this truth should suffer by my feebleness; drive your lance home, sir knight, and take my life, since you have taken away my honor."

"That will I not, in sooth," said he of the White Moon; "live the fame of the lady Dulcinea's beauty undimmed as ever; all I require is that the great Don Quixote retire to his own home for a year, or for so long a time as shall by me be enjoined upon him, as we agreed before engaging in this combat."

The viceroy, Don Antonio, and several others who were present, heard all this, and heard too how Don Quixote replied that so long as nothing in prejudice of Dulcinea was demanded of him, he would observe all the rest like a true and loyal knight. The engagement given, he of the White Moon wheeled about, and making obeisance to the viceroy with a movement of the head, rode away into the city at a half gallop. The viceroy bade Don Antonio hasten after him, and by some means or other find out who he was. They raised Don Quixote up and uncovered his face, and found him pale and bathed with sweat. Rocinante from the mere hard measure he had received lay unable to stir for the present. Sancho, wholly dejected and woebegone, knew not what to say or do. He fancied that all was a dream, that the whole business was a piece of enchantment. Here was his master defeated, and bound not to take up arms for a year. He saw the light of the glory of his achievements obscured; the hopes of the promises lately made him swept away like smoke before the wind; Rocinante, he feared, was crippled for life, and his master's bones out of joint; for if he were only shaken out of his madness it would be no small luck. In the end they carried him into the city in a hand-chair which the viceroy sent for, and thither the viceroy himself returned, eager to ascertain who this Knight of the White Moon was who had left Don Quixote in such a sad plight.

Chapter 65

Wherein is made known who the Knight of the White Moon was; likewise Don Gregorio's release, and other events

DON ANTONIO MORENO followed the Knight of the White Moon, and a number of boys followed him too, nay pursued him, until they had him fairly housed in a hostel in the heart of the city. Don Antonio, eager to make his acquaintance, entered also; a squire came out to meet him and remove his armor, and he shut himself into a lower room, still attended by Don Antonio, whose bread would not bake until he had found out who he was. He of the White Moon, seeing then that the gentleman would not leave him, said, "I know very well, señor, what you have come for; it is to find out who I am; and as there is no reason why I should conceal it from you, while my servant here is taking off my armor I will tell you the true state of the case, without leaving out anything. You must know, señor, that I am called the bachelor Samson Carrasco. I am of the same village as Don Quixote of La Mancha, whose craze and folly make all of us who know him feel pity for him, and I am one of those who have felt it most; and persuaded that his chance of recovery lay in quiet and keeping at home and in his own house, I hit upon a device for keeping him there. Three months ago, therefore, I went out to meet him as a knight-errant, under the assumed name of the Knight of the Mirrors, intending to engage him in combat and overcome him without hurting him, making it the condition of our combat that the vanquished should be at the disposal of the victor. What I meant to demand of him (for I regarded him as vanquished already) was that he should return to his own village, and not leave it for a whole year, by which time he might be cured. But fate ordered it otherwise, for he vanquished me and unhorsed me, and so my plan failed. He went his way, and I came back conquered, covered with shame, and sorely bruised by my fall, which was a particularly dangerous one. But this did not quench my desire to meet him again and overcome him, as you have seen to-day. And as he is so scrupulous in his observance of the laws of knight-errantry, he will, no doubt, in order to keep his word, obey the injunction I have laid upon him. This, señor, is how the matter stands, and I have nothing more to tell you. I implore of you not to betray me, or tell Don Quixote who I am; so that my honest endeavors may be successful, and that a man of excellent wits—were he only rid of the fooleries of chivalry—may get them back again."

"O señor," said Don Antonio, "may God forgive you the wrong you have done the whole world in trying to bring the most amusing madman in it back to his senses. Do you not see, señor, that the gain by Don Quixote's sanity can never equal the enjoyment his crazes give? But my belief is that all the señor bachelor's pains will be of no avail to bring a man so hopelessly cracked to his senses again; and if it were not uncharitable, I would say may Don Quixote never be cured, for by his recovery we lose not only his own drolleries, but his squire Sancho Panza's too, any one of which is enough to turn melancholy itself into merriment. However, I'll hold my peace and say nothing to him, and we'll see whether I am right in my suspicion that Señor Carrasco's efforts will be fruitless."

The bachelor replied that at all events the affair promised well, and he hoped for a happy result from it; and putting his services at Don Antonio's commands he took his leave of him; and having had his armor packed at once upon a mule, he rode away from the city the same day on the horse he rode to battle, and returned to his own country without meeting any adventure calling for record in this veracious history.

Don Antonio reported to the viceroy what Carrasco told him, and the viceroy was not very well pleased to hear it, for with Don Quixote's retirement there was an end to the amusement of all who knew any thing of his mad doings.

Six days did Don Quixote keep his bed, dejected, melancholy, moody and out of sorts, brooding over the unhappy event of his defeat. Sancho strove to comfort him, and among other things he said to him, "Hold up your head, señor, and be of good cheer if you can, and give thanks to Heaven that if you have had a tumble to the ground you have not come off with a broken rib; and, as you know that where they give they take, and that there are not always flitches where there are pegs, a fig for the doctor, for there's no need of him to cure this ailment. Let us go home, and give over going about in search of adventures in strange lands and places; rightly looked at, it is I that am the greater loser, though it is your worship that has had the worst usage. With the government I gave up all wish to be a governor again, but I did not give up all longing to be a count; and that will never come to pass if your worship gives up becoming a king by renouncing the calling of chivalry; and so my hopes are going to turn into smoke."

"Peace, Sancho," said Don Quixote; "thou seest my suspension and retirement is not to exceed a year; I shall soon return to my honored calling, and I shall not be at a loss for a kingdom to win and a county to bestow on thee."

"May God hear it and sin be deaf," said Sancho; "I have always heard say that a good hope is better than a bad holding."

As they were talking Don Antonio came in looking extremely pleased and exclaiming, "Pay me for my good news, Señor Don Quixote! Don Gregorio and the renegade who went for him have come ashore—ashore do I say? They are by this time in the viceroy's house, and will be here immediately."

Don Quixote cheered up a little and said, "Of a truth I am almost ready to say I should have been glad had it turned out just the other way, for it would have obliged me to cross over to Barbary, where by the might of my arm I should have restored to liberty, not only Don Gregorio, but all the Christian captives there are in Barbary. But what am I saying, miserable being that I am? Am I not he that has been conquered? Am I not he that has been overthrown? Am I not he who must not take up arms for a year? Then what am I making professions for; what am I bragging about; when it is fitter for me to handle the distaff than the sword?"

"No more of that, señor," said Sancho; "'let the hen live, even though it be with her pip'; 'to-day for thee and to-morrow for me'; in these affairs of encounters and whacks one must not mind them, 'for he that falls to-day may get up to-morrow'; unless indeed he chooses to lie in bed, I mean gives way to weakness and does not pluck up fresh spirit for fresh battles; let your worship get up now to receive Don Gregorio; for the household seems to be in a bustle, and no doubt he has come by this time"; and so it proved, for as soon as Don Gregorio and the renegade had given the viceroy an account of the voyage out and home, Don Gregorio, eager to see Ana Felix, came with the renegade to Don Antonio's house. When they carried him away from Algiers he was in woman's dress; on board the vessel, however, he exchanged it for that of a captive who escaped with him; but in what-

ever dress he might be he looked like one to be loved and served and esteemed, for he was surpassingly well-favored, and to judge by appearances some seventeen or eighteen years of age. Ricote and his daughter came out to welcome him, the father with tears, the daughter with bashfulness. They did not embrace each other, for where there is deep love there will never be overmuch boldness. Seen side by side, the comeliness of Don Gregorio and the beauty of Ana Felix were the admiration of all who were present. It was silence that spoke for the lovers at that moment, and their eyes were the tongues that declared their pure and happy feelings. The renegade explained the measures and means he had adopted to rescue Don Gregorio, and Don Gregorio at no great length, but in a few words, in which he showed that his intelligence was in advance of his years, described the peril and embarrassment he found himself in among the women with whom he had sojourned. To conclude, Ricote liberally recompensed and rewarded as well the renegade as the men who had rowed; and the renegade effected his readmission into the body of the Church and was reconciled with it, and from a rotten limb became by penance and repentance a clean and sound one.

Two days later the viceroy discussed with Don Antonio the steps they should take to enable Ana Felix and her father to stay in Spain, for it seemed to them there could be no objection to a daughter who was so good a Christian and a father to all appearance so well disposed remaining there. Don Antonio offered to arrange the matter at the capital, whither he was compelled to go on some other business, hinting that many a difficult affair was settled there with the help of favor and bribes.

"Nay," said Ricote, who was present during the conversation, "it will not do to rely upon favor or bribes, because with the great Don Bernardino de Velasco, Conde de Salazar, to whom his Majesty has intrusted our expulsion, neither entreaties nor promises, bribes nor appeals to compassion, are of any use; for though it is true he mingles mercy with justice, still, seeing that the whole body of our nation is tainted and corrupt, he applies to it the cautery that burns rather than the salve that soothes; and thus, by prudence, sagacity, care, and the fear he inspires, he has borne on his mighty shoulders the weight of this great policy and carried it into effect, all our schemes and plots, importunities and wiles, being ineffectual to blind his Argus eyes, ever on the watch lest one of us should remain behind in concealment, and like a hidden root come in course of time to sprout and bear poisonous fruit in Spain, now cleansed, and relieved of the fear in which our vast numbers kept it. Heroic resolve of the great Philip the Third, and unparalleled wisdom to have intrusted it to the said Don Bernardino de Velasco!"

"At any rate," said Don Antonio, "when I am there I will make all possible efforts, and let Heaven do as pleases it best; Don Gregorio will come with me to relieve the anxiety which his parents must be suffering on account of his absence; Ana Felix will remain in my house with my wife, or in a monastery; and I know the viceroy will be glad that the worthy Ricote should stay with him until we see what terms I can make."

The viceroy agreed to all that was proposed; but Don Gregorio on learning what had passed declared he could not and would not on any account leave Ana Felix; however, as it was his purpose to go and see his parents and devise some way of returning for her, he fell in with the proposed arrangement. Ana Felix remained with Don Antonio's wife, and Ricote in the viceroy's house.

The day for Don Antonio's departure came; and two days later that for Don Quixote's and Sancho's, for Don Quixote's fall did not suffer him to take the road sooner. There were tears and sighs, swoonings and sobs, at the parting between Don Gregorio and Ana Felix. Ricote offered Don Gregorio a thousand crowns if he would have them, but he would not take any save five which Don Antonio lent him and he promised to repay at the capital. So the two of them took their departure, and Don Quixote and Sancho afterwards, as has been already said, Don Quixote without his armor and in travelling gear, and Sancho on foot, Dapple being loaded with the armor.

Chapter 66

Which treats of what he who reads
will see, or what he who has it
read to him will hear

As he left Barcelona, Don Quixote turned to gaze upon the spot where he had fallen. "Here Troy was," said he; "here my ill-luck, not my cowardice, robbed me of all the glory I had won; here Fortune made me the victim of her caprices; here the lustre of my achievements was dimmed; here, in a word, fell my happiness never to rise again."

"Señor," said Sancho on hearing this, "it is the part of brave hearts to be patient in adversity just as much as to be glad in prosperity; I judge by myself, for, if when I was a governor I was glad, now that I am a squire and on foot I am not sad; and I have heard say that she whom commonly they call Fortune is a drunken whimsical jade, and what is more, blind, and therefore neither sees what she does, nor knows whom she casts down or whom she sets up."

"Thou art a great philosopher, Sancho," said Don Quixote; "thou speakest very sensibly; I know not who taught thee. But I can tell thee there is no such thing as Fortune in the world, nor does anything which takes place there, be it good or bad, come about by chance, but by the special pre-ordination of Heaven; and hence the common saying that each of us is the maker of his own fortune. I have been that of mine; but not with the proper amount of prudence, and my self-confidence has therefore made me pay dearly; for I ought to have reflected that Rocinante's feeble strength could not resist the mighty bulk of the Knight of the White Moon's horse. In a word, I ventured it, I did my best, I was overthrown, but though I lost my honor I did not lose nor can I lose the virtue of keeping my word. When I was a knight-errant, daring and valiant, I supported my achievements by hand and deed, and now that I am a humble squire I will support my words by keeping the promise I have given. Forward then, Sancho my friend, let us go to keep the year of the novitiate in our own country, and in that seclusion we shall pick up fresh strength to return to the by me never-forgotten calling of arms."

"Señor," returned Sancho, "travelling on foot is not such a pleasant thing that it makes me feel disposed or tempted to make long marches. Let us leave this armor hung up on some tree, instead of some one that has been hanged; and then with me on Dapple's back and my feet off the ground we will arrange the stages as your worship pleases to measure them out; but to suppose that I am going to travel on foot, and make long ones, is to suppose nonsense."

"Thou sayest well, Sancho," said Don Quixote; "let my armor be hung up for a trophy, and under it or round it we will carve on the trees what was inscribed on the trophy of Roland's armor—

These let none move
Who dareth not his might with Roland prove."

"That's the very thing," said Sancho; "and if it was not that we should feel the want of

Rocinante on the road, it would be as well to leave him hung up too."

"And yet, I had rather not have either him or the armor hung up," said Don Quixote, "that it may not be said, 'for good service a bad return.'"

"Your worship is right," said Sancho; "for, as sensible people hold, 'the fault of the ass must not be laid on the packsaddle'; and, as in this affair the fault is your worship's, punish yourself and don't let your anger break out against the already battered and bloody armor, or the meekness of Rocinante, or the tenderness of my feet, trying to make them travel more than is reasonable."

In converse of this sort the whole of that day went by, as did the four succeeding ones, without anything occurring to interrupt their journey, but on the fifth as they entered a village they found a great number of people at the door of an inn enjoying themselves, as it was a holiday. Upon Don Quixote's approach a peasant called out, "One of these two gentlemen who come here, and who don't know the parties, will tell us what we ought to do about our wager."

"That I will, certainly," said Don Quixote, "and according to the rights of the case, if I can manage to understand it."

"Well, here it is, worthy sir," said the peasant; "a man of this village who is so fat that he weighs twenty stone challenged another, a neighbor of his, who does not weigh more than nine, to run a race. The agreement was that they were to run a distance of a hundred paces with equal weights; and when the challenger was asked how the weights were to be equalized he said that the other, as he weighed nine stone, should put eleven in iron on his back, and that in this way the twenty stone of the thin man would equal the twenty stone of the fat one."

"Not at all," exclaimed Sancho at once, before Don Quixote could answer; "it's for me, that only a few days ago left off being a governor and a judge, as all the world knows, to settle these doubtful questions and give an opinion in disputes of all sorts."

"Answer in God's name, Sancho my friend," said Don Quixote, "for I am not fit to give crumbs to a cat, my wits are so confused and upset."

With this permission Sancho said to the peasants who stood clustered round him, waiting with open mouths for the decision to come from his, "Brothers, what the fat man requires is not in reason, nor has it a shadow of justice in it; because, if it be true, as they say, that the challenged may choose the weapons, the other has no right to choose such as will prevent and keep him from winning. My decision, therefore, is that the fat challenger prune, peel, thin, trim and correct himself, and take eleven stone of his flesh off his body, here or there, as he pleases, and as suits him best; and being in this way reduced to nine stone weight, he will make himself equal and even with nine stone of his opponent, and they will be able to run on equal terms."

"By all that's good," said one of the peasants as he heard Sancho's decision, "but the gentleman has spoken like a saint, and given judgment like a canon! But I'll be bound the fat man won't part with an ounce of his flesh, not to say eleven stone."

"The best plan will be for them not to run," said another, "so that neither the thin man break down under the weight, nor the fat one strip himself of his flesh; let half the wager be spent in wine, and let's take these gentlemen to the tavern where there's the best, and 'over me be the cloak when it rains.'"

"I thank you, sirs," said Don Quixote; "but I cannot stop for an instant, for sad thoughts and unhappy circumstances force me to seem discourteous and to travel apace"; and spurring Rocinante he pushed on, leaving them wondering at what they had seen and heard, at his own strange figure and at the shrewdness of his servant, for such they took Sancho to be; and another of them observed, "If the servant is so clever, what must the master be? I'll bet, if they are going to Salamanca to study, they'll come to be *alcaldes* of the court in a trice; for it's a mere joke—only to read and read, and have interest and good luck; and before a man knows where he is he finds himself with a staff in his hand or a mitre on his head."

That night master and man passed out into the fields in the open air, and the next day as they were pursuing their journey they saw coming towards them a man on foot with *alforjas* slung over his shoulder and a javelin or spiked staff in his hand, the very cut of a foot courier; who, as soon as he came close to Don Quixote, increased his pace and half running came up to him, and embracing his right thigh, for he could reach no higher, exclaimed with evident pleasure, "O Señor Don Quixote of La Mancha, what happiness it will be to the heart of my lord the duke when he knows your worship is coming back to his castle, for he is still there with my lady the duchess!"

"I do not recognize you, friend," said Don Quixote, "nor do I know who you are, unless you tell me."

"I am Tosilos, my lord the duke's lackey, Señor Don Quixote," replied the courier; "he who refused to fight your worship about marrying the daughter of Doña Rodriguez."

"God bless me!" exclaimed Don Quixote; "is it possible that you are he whom mine enemies the enchanters changed into the lackey you speak of in order to rob me of the honor of that battle?"

"Nonsense, good sir!" said the messenger; "there was no enchantment or transformation at all; I entered the lists just as much lackey Tosilos as I came out of them lackey Tosilos. I thought to marry without fighting, for the girl had taken my fancy; but my scheme had a very different result, for as soon as your worship had left the castle my lord the duke had a hundred strokes of the stick given me for having acted contrary to the orders he gave me before engaging in the combat; and the end of the whole affair is that the girl has become a nun, and Doña Rodriguez has gone back to Castile, and I am now on my way to Barcelona with a packet of letters for the viceroy which my master is sending him. If your worship would like a drop, sound though warm, I have a gourd here full of the best, and some scraps of Tronchon cheese that will serve as a provocative and wakener of your thirst if so be it is asleep."

"I take the offer," said Sancho; "no more compliments about it; pour out, good Tosilos, in spite of all the enchanters in the Indies."

"Thou art indeed the greatest glutton in the world, Sancho," said Don Quixote; "and the greatest booby on earth, not to be able to see that this courier is enchanted and this Tosilos a sham one; stop with him and take thy fill; I will go on slowly and wait for thee to come up with me."

The lackey laughed, unsheathed his gourd, unwalletted his scraps, and taking out a small loaf of bread he and Sancho seated themselves on the green grass, and in peace and good fellowship finished off the contents of the *alforjas* down to the bottom, so resolutely that they licked the wrapper of the letters, merely because it smelt of cheese.

Said Tosilos to Sancho, "Beyond a doubt, Sancho my friend, this master of thine ought to be a madman."

"Ought!" said Sancho; "he owes no man anything; he pays for everything, particularly when the coin is madness. I see it plain enough, and I tell him so plain enough; but what's the use? especially now that it is all over with him, for here he is beaten by the Knight of the White Moon."

Tosilos begged him to explain what had happened to him, but Sancho replied that it would not be good manners to leave his master waiting for him; and that some other day if they met there would be time enough for that; and then getting up, after shaking his doublet and brushing the crumbs out of his beard, he drove Dapple on before him, and bidding adieu to Tosilos left him and rejoined his master, who was waiting for him under the shade of a tree.

Chapter 67

Of the resolution which Don Quixote formed to turn shepherd and to take to a life in the fields while the year for which he had given his word was running its course; with other events truly delectable and happy

IF a multitude of reflections used to harass Don Quixote before he had been overthrown, a great many more harassed him since his fall. He was under the shade of a tree, as has been said, and there, like flies on honey, thoughts came crowding upon him and stinging him. Some of them turned upon the disenchantment of Dulcinea, others upon the life he was about to lead in his enforced retirement. Sancho came up and spoke in high praise of the generous disposition of the lackey Tosilos.

"Is it possible, Sancho," said Don Quixote, "that thou dost still think that he yonder is a real lackey? Apparently it has escaped thy memory that thou hast seen Dulcinea turned and transformed into a peasant wench, and the Knight of the Mirrors into the bachelor Carrasco; all the work of the enchanters that persecute me. But tell me now, didst thou ask this Tosilos, as thou callest him, what has become of Altisidora, did she weep over my absence, or has she already consigned to oblivion the love thoughts that used to afflict her when I was present?"

"The thoughts that I had," said Sancho, "were not such as to leave time for asking fool's questions. Body o' me, señor! is your worship in a condition now to inquire into other people's thoughts, above all love thoughts?"

"Look ye, Sancho," said Don Quixote, "there is a great difference between what is done out of love and what is done out of gratitude. A knight may very possibly be proof against love;

but it is impossible, strictly speaking, for him to be ungrateful. Altisidora, to all appearance, loved me truly; she gave me the three kerchiefs thou knowest of; she wept at my departure, she cursed me, she abused me, casting shame to the winds she bewailed herself in public; all signs that she adored me; for the wrath of lovers always ends in curses. I had no hopes to give her, nor treasures to offer her, for mine are given to Dulcinea, and the treasures of knights-errant are like those of the fairies, illusory and deceptive; all I can give her is the place in my memory I keep for her, without prejudice, however, to that which I hold devoted to Dulcinea, whom thou art wronging by thy remissness in whipping thyself and scourging that flesh—would that I saw it eaten by wolves—which would rather keep itself for the worms than for the relief of that poor lady."

"Señor," replied Sancho, "if the truth is to be told, I cannot persuade myself that the whipping of my backside has anything to do with the disenchantment of the enchanted; it is like saying, 'If your head aches rub ointment on your knees'; at any rate I'll make bold to swear that in all the histories dealing with knight-errantry that your worship has read you have never come across anybody disenchanted by whipping; but whether or no I'll whip myself when I have a fancy for it, and the opportunity serves for scourging myself comfortably."

"God grant it," said Don Quixote; "and Heaven give thee grace to take it to heart and own the obligation thou art under to help my lady, who is thine also, inasmuch as thou art mine."

As they pursued their journey talking in this way they came to the very same spot where they had been trampled on by the bulls. Don Quixote recognized it, and said he to Sancho, "This is the meadow where we came upon those gay shepherdesses and gallant shepherds who were trying to revive and imitate the pastoral Arcadia there, an idea as novel as it was happy, in emulation whereof, if so be thou dost approve of it, Sancho, I would have ourselves turn shepherds, at any rate for the time I have to live in retirement. I will buy some ewes and everything else requisite for the pastoral calling; and, I under the name of the shepherd Quixotiz, and thou as the shepherd Panzino, we will roam the woods and groves and meadows singing songs here, lamenting in elegies there, drinking of the crystal waters of the springs or limpid brooks or flowing rivers. The oaks will yield us their sweet fruit with bountiful hand, the trunks of the hard cork-trees a

seat, the willows shade, the roses perfume, the wide-spread meadows carpets tinted with a thousand dyes; the clear pure air will give us breath, the moon and stars lighten the darkness of the night for us, song shall be our delight, lamenting our joy, Apollo will supply us with verses, and love with conceits whereby we shall make ourselves famed forever. not only in this but in ages to come."

"Egad," said Sancho, "but that sort of life squares, nay corners, with my notions; and what is more the bachelor Samson Carrasco and Master Nicholas the barber won't have well seen it before they'll want to follow it and turn shepherds along with us; and God grant it may not come into the curate's head to join the sheepfold too, he's so jovial and fond of enjoying himself."

"Thou art in the right of it, Sancho," said Don Quixote; "and the bachelor Samson Carrasco, if he enters the pastoral fraternity, as no doubt he will, may call himself the shepherd Samsonino, or perhaps the shepherd Carrascon; Nicholas the barber may call himself Niculoso, as old Boscan formerly was called Nemoroso; as for the curate I don't know what name we can fit to him unless it be something derived from his title, and we call him the shepherd Curiambro. For the shepherdesses whose lovers we shall be, we can pick names as we would pears; and as my lady's name does just as well for a shepherdess's as for a princess's, I need not trouble myself to look for one that would suit her better; to thine, Sancho, thou canst give what name thou wilt."

"I don't mean to give her any but Teresona," said Sancho, "which will go well with her stoutness and with her own right name, as she is called Teresa; and then when I sing her praises in my verses I'll show how chaste my passion is, for I'm not going to look for better bread than ever came from wheat in other men's houses. It won't do for the curate to have a shepherdess, for the sake of good example; and if the bachelor chooses to have one, that is his lookout."

"God bless me, Sancho my friend!" said Don Quixote, "what a life we shall lead! What hautboys and Zamora bagpipes we shall hear, what tabors, timbrels, and rebecs! And then if among all these different sorts of music that of the *albogues* is heard, almost all the pastoral instruments will be there."

"What are *albogues*?" asked Sancho, "for I never in my life heard tell of them or saw them."

"*Albogues*," said Don Quixote, "are brass

plates like candlesticks that struck against one another on the hollow side make a noise which, if not very pleasing or harmonious, is not disagreeable and accords very well with the rude notes of the bagpipe and tabor. The word *albogue* is Morisco, as are all those in our Spanish tongue that begin with *al*; for example, *almohaza, almorzar, alhombra, alguacil, alhucema, almacen, alcancia*, and others of the same sort, of which there are not many more; our language has only three that are Morisco and end in *i*, which are *borcegui, zaquizami*, and *maravedi*; *alheli* and *alfaqui* are seen to be Arabic, as well by the *al* at the beginning as by the *i* they end with. I mention this incidentally, the chance allusion to *albogues* having reminded me of it; and it will be of great assistance to us in the perfect practice of this calling that I am something of a poet, as thou knowest, and that besides the bachelor Samson Carrasco is an accomplished one. Of the curate I say nothing; but I will wager he has some spice of the poet in him, and no doubt Master Nicholas too, for all barbers, or most of them, are guitar players and stringers of verses. I will bewail my separation; thou shalt glorify thyself as a constant lover; the shepherd Carrascon will figure as a rejected one, and the curate Curiambro as whatever may please him best; and so all will go as gayly as heart could wish."

To this Sancho made answer, "I am so unlucky, señor, that I'm afraid the day will never come when I shall see myself at such a calling. O what neat spoons I'll make when I'm a shepherd! What messes, creams, garlands, pastoral odds and ends! And if they don't get me a name for wisdom, they'll not fail to get me one for ingenuity. My daughter Sanchica will bring us our dinner to the pasture. But stay—she's good-looking, and shepherds there are with more mischief than simplicity in them; I would not have her 'come for wool and go back shorn'; love-making and lawless desires are just as common in the fields as in the cities, and in shepherds' shanties as in royal palaces; 'do away with the cause, you do away with the sin,' and 'if eyes don't see heart don't break,' and 'better a clear escape than good men's prayers.'"

"A truce to thy proverbs, Sancho," exclaimed Don Quixote; "any one of those thou hast uttered would suffice to explain thy meaning; many a time have I recommended thee not to be so lavish with proverbs and to exercise some moderation in delivering them; but it seems to me it is only preaching in the desert; 'my mother beats me and I go on with my tricks.'"

"It seems to me," said Sancho, "that your worship is like the common saying, 'Said the frying-pan to the kettle, Get away, blackbreech.' You chide me for uttering proverbs, and you string them in couples yourself."

"Observe, Sancho," replied Don Quixote, "I bring in proverbs to the purpose, and when I quote them they fit like a ring to the finger; thou bringest them in by the head and shoulders, in such a way that thou dost drag them in, rather than introduce them; if I am not mistaken, I have told thee already that proverbs are short maxims drawn from the experience and observation of our wise men of old; but the proverb that is not to the purpose is a piece of nonsense and not a maxim. But enough of this; as nightfall is drawing on let us retire some little distance from the high road to pass the night; what is in store for us to-morrow God knoweth."

They turned aside, and supped late and poorly, very much against Sancho's will, who turned over in his mind the hardships attendant upon knight-errantry in woods and forests, even though at times plenty presented itself in castles and houses, as at Don Diego de Miranda's, at the wedding of Camacho the Rich, and at Don Antonio Moreno's; he reflected, however, that it could not be always day, nor always night; and so that night he passed in sleeping, and his master in waking.

Chapter 68

Of the bristly adventure that befell Don Quixote

THE night was somewhat dark, for though there was a moon in the sky it was not in a quarter where she could be seen; for sometimes the lady Diana goes on a stroll to the antipodes, and leaves the mountains all black and the valleys in darkness. Don Quixote obeyed nature so far as to sleep his first sleep, but did not give way to the second, very different from Sancho, who never had any second, because with him sleep lasted from night till morning, wherein he showed what a sound constitution and how few cares he had. Don Quixote's cares kept him restless, so much so that he awoke Sancho and said to him, "I am amazed, Sancho, at the unconcern of thy temperament. I believe thou art made of marble or hard brass, incapable of any emotion or feeling whatever. I lie awake while thou sleepest, I weep while thou singest. I am faint with fasting while thou art sluggish and torpid from pure repletion. It is the duty of good servants to share the sufferings and feel the sorrows of their masters, if it be only for the sake of appearances. See the calmness of the night, the solitude of the spot, inviting us to break our slumbers by a vigil of some sort. Rise as thou livest, and retire a little distance, and with a good heart and cheerful courage give thyself three or four hundred lashes on account of Dulcinea's disenchantment score; and this I entreat of thee, making it a request, for I have no desire to come to grips with thee a second time, as I know thou hast a heavy hand. As soon as thou hast laid them on we will pass the rest of the night, I singing my separation, thou thy constancy, making a beginning at once with the pastoral life we are to follow at our village."

"Señor," replied Sancho, "I'm no monk to get up out of the middle of my sleep and scourge myself, nor does it seem to me that one can pass from one extreme of the pain of whipping to the other of music. Will your worship let me sleep, and not worry me about whipping myself? or you'll make me swear never to touch a hair of my doublet, not to say my flesh."

"O hard heart!" said Don Quixote, "O pitiless squire! O bread ill-bestowed and favors ill-acknowledged, both those I have done thee and those I mean to do thee! Through me hast thou seen thyself a governor, and through me thou seest thyself in immediate expectation of being a count, or obtaining some other equivalent title, for I—*post tenebras spero lucem.*"

"I don't know what that is," said Sancho; "all I know is that so long as I am asleep I have neither fear nor hope, trouble nor glory; and good luck betide him that invented sleep, the cloak that covers over all a man's thoughts, the food that removes hunger, the drink that drives away thirst, the fire that warms the cold, the cold that tempers the heat, and, to wind up with, the universal coin wherewith everything is bought, the weight and balance that makes the shepherd equal with the king and the fool with the wise man. Sleep, I have heard say, has only one fault, that it is like death; for between a sleeping man and a dead man there is very little difference."

"Never have I heard thee speak so elegantly as now, Sancho," said Don Quixote; "and here I begin to see the truth of the proverb thou dost sometimes quote, 'Not with whom thou art bred, but with whom thou art fed.'"

"Ha, by my life, master mine," said Sancho, "it's not I that am stringing proverbs now, for they drop in pairs from your worship's mouth faster than from mine; only there is this difference between mine and yours, that yours are well-timed and mine are untimely; but anyhow, they are all proverbs."

At this point they became aware of a harsh indistinct noise that seemed to spread through all the valleys around. Don Quixote stood up and laid his hand upon his sword, and Sancho ensconced himself under Dapple and put the bundle of armor on one side of him and the ass's pack-saddle on the other, in fear and trembling as great as Don Quixote's perturbation. Each instant the noise increased and came nearer to the two terrified men, or at least to one, for as to the other, his courage is known to all. The fact of the matter was that some men were taking above six hundred pigs to sell at a fair, and were on their way with them at that hour, and so great was the noise they made and their grunting and blowing, that they deafened the ears of Don Quixote and Sancho Panza, and they could not make out what it was. The widespread grunting drove came on in a surging mass, and without showing any respect for Don Quixote's dignity or Sancho's, passed right over the pair of them, demolishing Sancho's intrenchments, and not only upsetting Don Quixote but sweeping Rocinante off his feet into the bargain; and what with the trampling and the grunting, and the pace to which the unclean beasts went, pack-saddle, armor, Dapple and Rocinante were left scattered on the ground and Sancho and Don Quixote at their wits' end.

Sancho got up as best he could and begged his master to give him his sword, saying he wanted to kill half a dozen of those dirty unmannerly pigs, for he had by this time found out that that was what they were.

"Let them be, my friend," said Don Quixote; "this insult is the penalty of my sin; and it is the righteous chastisement of Heaven that jackals should devour a vanquished knight, and wasps sting him and pigs trample him under foot."

"I suppose it is the chastisement of Heaven, too," said Sancho, "that flies should prick the squires of vanquished knights, and lice eat them, and hunger assail them. If we squires were the sons of the knights we serve, or their very near relations, it would be no wonder if the penalty of their misdeeds overtook us, even to the fourth generation. But what have the Panzas to do with the Quixotes? Well, well, let's lie down again and sleep out what little of the night there's left, and God will send us dawn and we shall be all right."

"Sleep thou, Sancho," returned Don Quixote, "for thou wast born to sleep as I was born to watch; and during the time it now wants of dawn I will give a loose rein to my thoughts, and seek a vent for them in a little madrigal which, unknown to thee, I composed in my head last night."

"I should think," said Sancho, "that the thoughts that allow one to make verses cannot be of great consequence; let your worship string verses as much as you like and I'll sleep as much as I can"; and forthwith, taking the space of ground he required, he muffled himself up and fell into a sound sleep, undisturbed by bond, debt, or trouble of any sort. Don Quixote, propped up against the trunk of a beech or a cork tree—for Cid Hamet does not specify what kind of a tree it was—sang in this strain to the accompaniment of his own sighs:

"When in my mind
I muse, O Love, upon thy cruelty,
*   To death I flee,*
In hope therein the end of all to find.

"But drawing near
That welcome haven in my sea of woe,
*   Such joy I know,*
That life revives, and still I linger here.

"Thus life doth slay,
And death again to life restoreth me;
*   Strange destiny,*
That deals with life and death as with a play!"

He accompanied each verse with many sighs and not a few tears, just like one whose heart was pierced with grief at his defeat and his separation from Dulcinea.

And now daylight came, and the sun smote Sancho on the eyes with his beams. He awoke, roused himself up, shook himself and stretched his lazy limbs, and seeing the havoc the pigs had made with his stores he cursed the drove, and more besides. Then the pair resumed their journey, and as evening closed in they saw coming towards them some ten men on horseback and four or five on foot. Don Quixote's heart beat quick and Sancho's quailed with fear, for the persons approaching them carried lances and bucklers, and were in very warlike guise. Don Quixote turned to Sancho and said, "If I could make use of my weapons, and my promise had not tied my hands, I would count this host that comes against us but cakes and fancy bread; but perhaps it may prove something different from what we apprehend." The men on horseback now came up, and raising their lances surrounded Don Quixote in silence, and pointed them at his back and breast, menacing him with death. One of those on foot, putting his finger to his lips as a sign to him to be silent, seized Rocinante's bridle and drew him out of the road, and the others driving Sancho and Dapple before them, and all maintaining a strange silence, followed in the steps of the one who led Don Quixote. The latter two or three times attempted to ask where they were taking him to and what they wanted, but the instant he began to open his lips they threatened to close them with the points of their lances; and Sancho fared the same way, for the moment he seemed about to speak one of those on foot punched him with a goad, and Dapple likewise, as if he too wanted to talk. Night set in, they quickened their pace, and the fears of the two prisoners grew greater, especially as they heard themselves assailed with—"Get on, ye Troglodytes"; "Silence, ye barbarians"; "March, ye cannibals"; "No murmuring, ye Scythians"; "Don't open your eyes, ye murderous Polyphemes, ye bloodthirsty lions," and such-like names with which their captors harassed the ears of the wretched master and man. Sancho went along saying to himself, "We, tortolites, barbers, animals! I don't like those names at all; 'it's in a bad wind our corn is being winnowed'; 'misfortune comes upon us all at once like sticks on a dog,' and God grant it may be no worse than them that this unlucky adventure has in store for us."

Don Quixote rode completely dazed, unable with the aid of all his wits to make out what could be the meaning of these abusive names they called them, and the only conclusion he could arrive at was that there was no good to be hoped for and much evil to be feared. And now, about an hour after midnight, they reached a castle which Don Quixote saw at once was the duke's, where they had been but a short time before. "God bless me!" said he, as he recognized the mansion, "what does this mean? It is all courtesy and politeness in this house; but with the vanquished good turns into evil, and evil into worse."

They entered the chief court of the castle and found it prepared and fitted up in a style that added to their amazement and doubled their fears, as will be seen in the following chapter.

Chapter 69

Of the strangest and most extraordinary adventure that befell Don Quixote in the whole course of this great history

THE horsemen dismounted, and, together with the men on foot, without a moment's delay taking up Sancho and Don Quixote bodily, they carried them into the court, all round which near a hundred torches fixed in sockets were burning, besides above five hundred lamps in the corridors, so that in spite of the night, which was somewhat dark, the want of daylight could not be perceived. In the middle of the court was a catafalque, raised about two yards above the ground and covered completely by an immense canopy of black velvet, and on the steps all round it white wax tapers burned in more than a hundred silver candlesticks. Upon the catafalque was seen the dead body of a damsel so lovely that by her beauty she made death itself look beautiful. She lay with her head resting upon a cushion of brocade and crowned with a garland of sweet-smelling flowers of divers sorts, her hands crossed upon her bosom, and between them a branch of yellow palm of victory. On one side of the court was erected a stage, where upon two chairs were seated two persons who from having crowns on their heads and sceptres in their hands appeared to be kings of some sort, whether real or mock ones. By the side of this stage, which was reached by steps, were two other chairs on which the men carrying the prisoners seated Don Quixote and Sancho, all in silence, and by signs giving them to understand that they too were to be silent; which, however, they would have been without any signs, for their amazement at all they saw held them tongue-tied. And now two persons of distinction, who were at once recognized by Don Quixote as his hosts the duke and duchess, ascended the stage attended by a numerous suite, and seated themselves on two gorgeous chairs close to the two kings, as they seemed to be. Who would not be amazed at this? Nor was this all, for Don Quixote had perceived that the dead body on the catafalque was that of the fair Altisidora. As the duke and duchess mounted the stage Don Quixote and Sancho rose and made them a profound obeisance, which they returned by bowing their heads slightly. At this moment an official crossed over, and approaching Sancho threw over him a robe of black buckram painted all over with flames of fire, and taking off his cap put upon his head a mitre such as those undergoing the sentence of the Holy Office wear; and whispered in his ear that he must not open his lips, or they would put a gag upon him, or take his life. Sancho surveyed himself from head to foot and saw himself all ablaze with flames; but as they did not burn him he did not care two farthings for them. He took off the mitre and seeing it painted with devils he put it on again, saying to himself, "Well, so far those don't burn me nor do these carry me off." Don Quixote surveyed him too, and though fear had got the better of his faculties, he could not help smiling to see the figure Sancho presented. And now from underneath the catafalque, so it seemed, there rose a low sweet sound of flutes, which, coming unbroken by human voice (for there silence itself kept silence), had a soft and languishing effect. Then, beside the pillow of what seemed to be the dead body, suddenly appeared a fair youth in a Roman habit, who, to the accompaniment of a harp which he himself played, sang in a sweet and clear voice these two stanzas:

While fair Altisidora, who the sport
Of cold Don Quixote's cruelty hath been,
Returns to life, and in this magic court
The dames in sables come to grace the scene,
And while her matrons all in seemly sort
My lady robes in baize and bombazine,
Her beauty and her sorrows will I sing
With defter quill than touched the Thracian string.

But not in life alone, methinks, to me
Belongs the office; Lady, when my tongue
Is cold in death, believe me unto thee
My voice shall raise its tributary song.
My soul, from this strait prison-house set free,
As o'er the Stygian lake it floats along,
Thy praises singing still shall hold its way,
And make the waters of oblivion stay.

At this point one of the two that looked like kings exclaimed, "Enough, enough, divine singer! It would be an endless task to put before us now the death and the charms of the peerless Altisidora, not dead as the ignorant world imagines, but living in the voice of fame and in the penance which Sancho Panza, here present, has to undergo to restore her to the long-lost light. Do thou, therefore, O Rhadamanthus, who sittest in judgment with me in the murky caverns of Dis, as thou knowest all that the inscrutable fates have decreed touching the resuscitation of this damsel, announce and declare it at once, that the happiness we look forward to from her restoration be no longer deferred."

No sooner had Minos the fellow judge of Rhadamanthus said this, than Rhadamanthus rising up said, "Ho, officials of this house, high and low, great and small, make haste hither one and all, and print on Sancho's face four-and-twenty smacks, and give him twelve pinches and six pin-thrusts in the back and arms; for upon this ceremony depends this restoration of Altisidora."

On hearing this Sancho broke silence and cried out, "By all that's good, I'll as soon let my face be smacked or handled as turn Moor. Body o' me! What has handling my face got to do with the resurrection of this damsel? The old woman took kindly to the blits'; they enchant Dulcinea, and whip me in order to disenchant her; Altisidora dies of ailments God was pleased to send her, and to bring her to life again they must give me four-and-twenty smacks, and prick holes in my body with pins, and raise weals on my arms with pinches! Try those jokes on a brother-in-law; I'm an old dog, and *"tus, tus"* is no use with me.' "

"Thou shalt die," said Rhadamanthus in a loud voice; "relent, thou tiger; humble thyself, proud Nimrod; suffer and be silent, for no impossibilities are asked of thee; it is not for thee to inquire into the difficulties in this matter; smacked thou must be, pricked thou shalt see thyself, and with pinches thou must be made to howl. Ho, I say, officials, obey my orders; or by the word of an honest man, ye shall see what ye were born for."

At this some duennas, advancing across the court, made their appearance in procession, one after the other, four of them with spectacles, and all with their right hands uplifted, showing four fingers of wrist to make their hands look longer, as is the fashion now-a-days. No sooner had Sancho caught sight of them than, bellowing like a bull, he exclaimed, "I might let myself be handled by all the world; but allow duennas to touch me—not a bit of it! Scratch my face, as my master was served in this very castle; run me through the body with burnished daggers; pinch my arms with red-hot pinchers; I'll bear all in patience to serve these gentlefolk; but I won't let duennas touch me, though the devil should carry me off!"

Here Don Quixote, too, broke silence, saying to Sancho, "Have patience, my son, and gratify these noble persons, and give all thanks to Heaven that it has infused such virtue into thy person, that by its sufferings thou canst disenchant the enchanted and restore to life the dead."

The duennas were now close to Sancho, and he, having become more tractable and reasonable, settling himself well in his chair presented his face and beard to the first, who delivered him a smack very stoutly laid on, and then made him a low courtesy.

"Less politeness and less paint, señor duenna," said Sancho; "by God your hands smell of vinegar-wash."

In fine, all the duennas smacked him and several others of the household pinched him; but what he could not stand was being pricked by the pins; and so, apparently out of patience, he started up out of his chair, and seizing a lighted torch that stood near him fell upon the duennas and the whole set of his tormentors, exclaiming, "Begone, ye ministers of hell; I'm not made of brass not to feel such out-of-the-way tortures."

At this instant Altisidora, who probably was tired of having been so long lying on her back, turned on her side; seeing which the bystanders cried out almost with one voice, "Altisidora is alive! Altisidora lives!"

Rhadamanthus bade Sancho put away his wrath, as the object they had in view was now attained. When Don Quixote saw Altisidora move, he went on his knees to Sancho saying to him, "Now is the time, son of my bowels, not to call thee my squire, for thee to give thyself some of those lashes thou art bound to lay on for the disenchantment of Dulcinea. Now, I say, is the time when the virtue that is in thee is ripe, and endowed with efficacy to work the good that is looked for from thee."

To which Sancho made answer, "That's trick upon trick, I think, and not honey upon pancakes; a nice thing it would be for a whipping to come now, on the top of pinches, smacks, and pin-proddings! You had better take a big stone and tie it round my neck, and pitch me into a well; I should not mind it much, if I'm to be always made the cow of the wedding for the cure of other people's ailments. Leave me alone; or else by God I'll fling the whole thing to the dogs, come what may."

Altisidora had by this time sat up on the catafalque, and as she did so the clarions sounded, accompanied by the flutes, and the voices of all present exclaiming, "Long life to Altisidora! long life to Altisidora!" the duke and duchess and the kings Minos and Rhadamanthus stood up, and all, together with Don Quixote and Sancho, advanced to receive her and take her down from the catafalque; and she, making as though she were recovering from a swoon, bowed her head to the duke and duchess and to the kings, and looking sideways at Don Quixote, said to him, "God forgive thee, insensible knight, for through thy cruelty I have been, to me it seems, more than a thousand years in the other world; and to thee, the most compassionate squire upon earth, I render thanks for the life I am now in possession of. From this day forth, friend Sancho, count as thine six smocks of mine which I bestow upon thee, to make as many shirts for thyself, and if they are not all quite whole, at any rate they are all clean."

Sancho kissed her hands in gratitude kneeling, and with the mitre in his hand. The duke bade them take it from him, and give him back his cap and doublet and remove the flaming robe. Sancho begged the duke to let them leave him the robe and mitre; as he wanted to take them home for a token and memento of that unexampled adventure. The duchess said they must leave them with him; for he knew already what a great friend of his she was. The duke then gave orders that the court should be cleared, and that all should retire to their chambers, and that Don Quixote and Sancho should be conducted to their old quarters.

Chapter 70

Which follows sixty-nine and deals with matters indispensable for the clear comprehension of this history

SANCHO slept that night in a cot in the same chamber with Don Quixote, a thing he would have gladly excused if he could, for he knew very well that with questions and answers his master would not let him sleep, and he was in no humor for talking much, as he still felt the pain of his late martyrdom, which interfered with his freedom of speech; and it would have been more to his taste to sleep in a hovel alone, than in that luxurious chamber in company. And so well founded did his apprehension prove, and so correct was his anticipation, that scarcely had his master got into bed when he said, "What dost thou think of to-night's adventure, Sancho? Great and mighty is the power of cold-hearted scorn, for thou with thine own eyes hast seen Altisidora slain, not by arrows, nor by the sword, nor by any warlike weapon, nor by deadly poisons, but by the thought of the sternness and scorn with which I have always treated her."

"She might have died and welcome," said Sancho, "when she pleased and how she pleased; and she might have left me alone, for I never made her fall in love or scorned her. I don't know nor can I imagine how the recovery of Altisidora, a damsel more fanciful than wise, can have, as I have said before, anything to do with the sufferings of Sancho Panza. Now I begin to see plainly and clearly that there are enchanters and enchanted people in the world; and may God deliver me from them, since I can't deliver myself; and so I beg of your wor-

ship to let me sleep and not ask me any more questions, unless you want me to throw myself out of the window."

"Sleep, Sancho my friend," said Don Quixote, "if the pinprodding and pinches thou hast received and the smacks administered to thee will let thee."

"No pain came up to the insult of the smacks," said Sancho, "for the simple reason that it was duennas, confound them, that gave them to me; but once more I entreat your worship to let me sleep, for sleep is relief from misery to those who are miserable when awake."

"Be it so, and God be with thee," said Don Quixote.

They fell asleep, both of them, and Cid Hamet, the author of this great history, took this opportunity to record and relate what it was that induced the duke and duchess to get up the elaborate plot that has been described. The bachelor Samson Carrasco, he says, not forgetting how he as the Knight of the Mirrors had been vanquished and overthrown by Don Quixote, which defeat and overthrow upset all his plans, resolved to try his hand again, hoping for better luck than he had before; and so, having learned where Don Quixote was from the page who brought the letter and present to Sancho's wife, Teresa Panza, he got himself new armor and another horse, and put a white moon upon his shield, and to carry his arms he had a mule led by a peasant, not by Tom Cecial his former squire for fear he should be recognized by Sancho or Don Quixote. He came to the duke's castle, and the duke informed him of the road and route Don Quixote had taken with the intention of being present at the jousts at Saragossa. He told him, too, of the jokes he had practised upon him, and of the device for the disenchantment of Dulcinea at the expense of Sancho's backside; and finally he gave him an account of the trick Sancho had played upon his master, making him believe that Dulcinea was enchanted and turned into a country wench; and of how the duchess, his wife, had persuaded Sancho that it was he himself who was deceived, inasmuch as Dulcinea was really enchanted; at which the bachelor laughed not a little, and marvelled as well at the sharpness and simplicity of Sancho as at the length to which Don Quixote's madness went. The duke begged of him if he found him (whether he overcame him or not) to return that way and let him know the result. This the bachelor did; he set out in quest of Don Quixote, and not finding him at Saragossa, he went on, and how he fared has been already told. He returned to the duke's castle and told him all, what the conditions of the combat were, and how Don Quixote was now, like a loyal knight-errant, returning to keep his promise of retiring to his village for a year, by which time, said the bachelor, he might perhaps be cured of his madness; for that was the object that had led him to adopt these disguises, as it was a sad thing for a gentleman of such good parts as Don Quixote to be a madman. And so he took his leave of the duke, and went home to his village to wait there for Don Quixote, who was coming after him. Thereupon the duke seized the opportunity of practising this mystification upon him; so much did he enjoy everything connected with Sancho and Don Quixote. He had the roads about the castle far and near, everywhere he thought Don Quixote was likely to pass on his return, occupied by large numbers of his servants on foot and on horseback, who were to bring him to the castle by fair means or foul, if they met him. They did meet him, and sent word to the duke, who, having already settled what was to be done, as soon as he heard of his arrival, ordered the torches and lamps in the court to be lit and Altisidora to be placed on the catafalque with all the pomp and ceremony that has been described, the whole affair being so well arranged and acted that it differed but little from reality. And Cid Hamet says, moreover, for his part he considers the concocters of the joke as crazy as the victims of it, and that the duke and duchess were not two fingers' breadth removed from being something like fools themselves when they took such pains to make game of a pair of fools.

As for the latter, one was sleeping soundly and the other lying awake occupied with his desultory thoughts, when daylight came to them bringing with it the desire to rise; for the lazy down was never a delight to Don Quixote, victor or vanquished. Altisidora, come back from death to life as Don Quixote fancied, following up the freak of her lord and lady, entered the chamber, crowned with the garland she had worn on the catafalque and in a robe of white taffeta embroidered with gold flowers, her hair flowing loose over her shoulders, and leaning upon a staff of fine black ebony. Don Quixote, disconcerted and in confusion at her appearance, huddled himself up and well-nigh covered himself altogether with the sheets and counterpane of the bed, tongue-tied, and unable to offer her any civility. Altisidora seated herself on a chair at the head of the bed, and, after a deep sigh, said to him in a feeble, soft voice, "When women of rank and modest maidens trample honor under foot, and give a loose to the tongue that breaks through every impediment, publishing abroad the inmost secrets of their hearts, they are reduced to sore extremities. Such a one am I, Señor Don Quixote of La Mancha, crushed, conquered, love-smitten, but yet patient under suffering and virtuous, and so much so that my heart broke with grief and I lost my life. For the last two days I have been dead, slain by the thought of the cruelty with which thou hast treated me, obdurate knight,

O harder thou than marble to my plaint;

or at least believed to be dead by all who saw me; and had it not been that Love, taking pity on me, let my recovery rest upon the sufferings of this good squire, there I should have remained in the other world."

"Love might very well have let it rest upon the sufferings of my ass, and I should have been obliged to him," said Sancho. "But tell me, señora—and may Heaven send you a tenderer lover than my master—what did you see in the other world? What goes on in hell? For of course that's where one who dies in despair is bound for."

"To tell you the truth," said Altisidora, "I cannot have died outright, for I did not go into hell; had I gone in, it is very certain I should never have come out again, do what I might. The truth is, I came to the gate, where some dozen or so of devils were playing tennis, all in breeches and doublets, with falling collars trimmed with Flemish bone-lace, and ruffles of the same that served them for wristbands, with four fingers' breadth of the arm exposed to make their hands look longer; in their hands they held rackets of fire; but what amazed me still more was that books, apparently full of wind and rubbish, served them for tennis balls, a strange and marvellous thing; this, however, did not astonish me so much as to observe that, although with players it is usual for the winners to be glad and the losers sorry, there in that game all were growling, all were snarling, and all were cursing one another."

"That's no wonder," said Sancho; "for devils, whether playing or not, can never be content, win or lose."

"Very likely," said Altisidora; "but there is another thing that surprises me too, I mean surprised me then, and that was that no ball outlasted the first throw or was of any use a second time; and it was wonderful the constant succession there was of books, new and old. To one of them, a brand-new, well-bound one, they gave such a stroke that they knocked the guts out of it and scattered the leaves about. 'Look what book that is,' said one devil to another, and the other replied, 'It is the *Second Part of the History of Don Quixote of La Mancha*, not by Cid Hamet, the original author, but by an Aragonese who by his own account is of Tordesillas.' 'Out of this with it,' said the first, 'and into the depths of hell with it out of my sight.' 'Is it so bad?' asked the other. 'So bad is it,' said the first, 'that if I had set myself deliberately to make a worse, I could not have done it.' They then went on with their game, knocking other books about; and I, having heard them mention the name of Don Quixote whom I love and adore so, took care to retain this vision in my memory."

"A vision it must have been, no doubt," said Don Quixote, "for there is no other I in the world; this history has been going about here for some time from hand to hand, but it does not stay long in any, for everybody gives it a taste of his foot. I am not disturbed by hearing that I am wandering in a fantastic shape in the darkness of the pit or in the daylight above, for I am not the one that history treats of. If it should be good, faithful, and true, it will have ages of life; but if it should be bad, from its birth to its burial will not be a very long journey."

Altisidora was about to proceed with her complaint against Don Quixote, when he said to her, "I have several times told you, señora, that it grieves me you should have set your affections on me, as from mine they can only receive gratitude, but no return. I was born to belong to Dulcinea del Toboso, and the fates, if there are any, dedicated me to her; and to suppose that any other beauty can take the place she occupies in my heart is to suppose an impossibility. This frank declaration should suffice to make you retire within the bounds of your modesty, for no one can bind himself to do impossibilities."

Hearing this, Altisidora, with a show of anger and agitation, exclaimed, "God's life! Don Stockfish, soul of a mortar, stone of a date, more obstinate and obdurate than a clown asked a favor when he has his mind made up, if I fall upon you I'll tear your eyes out! Do you fancy, then, Don Vanquished, Don Cudgelled, that I died for your sake? All that you have seen to-night has been make-believe; I'm not the woman to let the black of my nail suffer for such a camel, much less die!"

"That I can well believe," said Sancho; "for all that about lovers pining to death is absurd;

they may talk of it, but as for doing it—Judas may believe that."

While they were talking, the musician, singer, and poet, who had sung the two stanzas given above came in, and making a profound obeisance to Don Quixote said, "Will your worship, sir knight, reckon and retain me in the number of your most faithful servants, for I have long been a great admirer of yours, as well because of your fame as because of your achievements?"

"Will your worship tell me who you are," replied Don Quixote, "so that my courtesy may be answerable to your deserts?"

The young man replied that he was the musician and songster of the night before.

"Of a truth," said Don Quixote, "your worship has a most excellent voice; but what you sang did not seem to me very much to the purpose; for what have Garcilaso's stanzas to do with the death of this lady?"

"Don't be surprised at that," returned the musician; "for with the callow poets of our day the way is for every one to write as he pleases and pilfer where he chooses, whether it be germane to the matter or not, and now-a-days there is no piece of silliness they can sing or write that is not set down to poetic license."

Don Quixote was about to reply, but was prevented by the duke and duchess, who came in to see him, and with them there followed a long and delightful conversation, in the course of which Sancho said so many droll and saucy things that he left the duke and duchess wondering not only at his simplicity but at his sharpness. Don Quixote begged their permission to take his departure that same day, inasmuch as for a vanquished knight like himself it was fitter he should live in a pig-sty than in a royal palace. They gave it very readily, and the duchess asked him if Altisidora was in his good graces.

He replied, "Señora, let me tell your ladyship that this damsel's ailment comes entirely of idleness, and the cure for it is honest and constant employment. She herself has told me that lace is worn in hell; and as she must know how to make it, let it never be out of her hands; for when she is occupied in shifting the bobbins to and fro, the image or images of what she loves will not shift to and fro in her thoughts; this is the truth, this is my opinion, and this is my advice."

"And mine," added Sancho; "for I never in all my life saw a lace-maker that died for love; when damsels are at work their minds are more set on finishing their tasks than on thinking of their loves. I speak from my own experience; for when I'm digging I never think of my old woman; I mean my Teresa Panza, whom I love better than my own eyelids."

"You say well, Sancho," said the duchess, "and I will take care that my Altisidora employs herself henceforward in needlework of some sort; for she is extremely expert at it."

"There is no occasion to have recourse to that remedy, señora," said Altisidora; "for the mere thought of the cruelty with which this vagabond villain has treated me will suffice to blot him out of my memory without any other device; with your highness's leave I will retire, not to have before my eyes, I won't say his rueful countenance, but his abominable, ugly looks."

"That reminds me of the common saying, that 'he that rails is ready to forgive,'" said the duke.

Altisidora then, pretending to wipe away her tears with a handkerchief, made an obeisance to master and mistress and quitted the room.

"Ill luck betide thee, poor damsel," said Sancho, "ill luck betide thee! Thou hast fallen in with a soul as dry as a rush and a heart as hard as oak; had it been me, i' faith 'another cock would have crowed to thee.'"

So the conversation came to an end, and Don Quixote dressed himself and dined with the duke and duchess, and set out the same evening.

Chapter 71

Of what passed between Don Quixote and his squire Sancho on the way to their village

THE vanquished and afflicted Don Quixote went along very downcast in one respect and very happy in another. His sadness arose from his defeat, and his satisfaction from the thought of the virtue that lay in Sancho, as had been proved by the resurrection of Altisidora; though it was with difficulty he could persuade himself that the love-smitten damsel had been really dead. Sancho went along anything but cheerful, for it grieved him that Altisidora had not kept her promise of giving him the smocks; and turning this over in his mind he said to his master, "Surely, señor, I'm the most unlucky doctor in the world; there's many a physician that, after killing the sick man he had to cure, requires to be paid for his work, though it is only signing a bit of a list of medicines, that the apothecary and not he makes up, and, there, his labor is over; but with me, though to cure somebody else costs me drops of blood, smacks, pinches, pin-proddings, and whippings, nobody gives me a farthing. Well, I swear by all that's good if they put another patient into my hands, they'll have to grease them for me before I cure him; for 'it's by his singing the abbot gets his dinner,' and I'm not going to believe that Heaven has bestowed upon me the virtue I have, that I should deal it out to others all for nothing."

"Thou art right, Sancho my friend," said Don Quixote, "and Altisidora has behaved very badly in not giving thee the smocks she promised; and although that virtue of thine is *gratis data*—as it has cost thee no study whatever, any more than such study as thy personal sufferings may be—I can say for myself that if thou wouldst have payment for the lashes on account of the disenchantment of Dulcinea, I would have given it to thee freely ere this. I am not sure, however, whether payment will comport with the cure, and I would not have the reward interfere with the medicine. Still, I think there will be nothing lost by trying it; consider how much thou wouldst have, Sancho, and whip thyself at once, and pay thyself down with thine own hand, as thou hast money of mine."

At this proposal Sancho opened his eyes and his ears a palm's breadth wide, and in his heart very readily acquiesced in whipping himself, and said he to his master, "Very well then, señor, I'll hold myself in readiness to gratify your worship's wishes if I'm to profit by it; for the love of my wife and children forces me to seem grasping. Let your worship say how much you will pay me for each lash I give myself."

"If, Sancho," replied Don Quixote, "I were to requite thee as the importance and nature of the cure deserves, the treasures of Venice, the mines of Potosi, would be insufficient to pay thee. See what thou hast of mine, and put a price on each lash."

"Of them," said Sancho, "there are three thousand three hundred and odd; of these I have given myself five, the rest remain; let the five go for the odd ones, and let us take the three thousand three hundred, which at a quarter real apiece (for I will not take less though the whole world should bid me) make three thousand three hundred quarter reals; the three thousand are one thousand five hundred half reals, which make seven hundred and fifty reals; and the three hundred make a hundred and fifty half reals, which come to seventy-five reals, which added to the seven hundred and fifty make eight hundred and twenty-five reals in all. These I will stop out of what I have belonging to your worship, and I'll return home rich and content, though well whipped, for 'there's no taking trout'[1]—but I say no more."

"O blessed Sancho! O dear Sancho!" said Don Quixote; "how we shall be bound to serve thee, Dulcinea and I, all the days of our lives that Heaven may grant us! If she returns to her lost shape (and it cannot be but that she will) her misfortune will have been good fortune, and my defeat a most happy triumph. But look here, Sancho; when wilt thou begin the scourging? For if thou wilt make short work of it, I will give thee a hundred reals over and above."

"When?" said Sancho; "this night without fail. Let your worship order it so that we pass it out of doors and in the open air, and I'll scarify myself."

Night, longed for by Don Quixote with the greatest anxiety in the world, came at last, though it seemed to him that the wheels of Apollo's car had broken down, and that the day was drawing itself out longer than usual, just as is the case with lovers, who never make the reckoning of their desires agree with time. They made their way at length in among some pleasant trees that stood a little distance from the road, and there vacating Rocinante's saddle and Dapple's pack-saddle, they stretched themselves on the green grass and made their supper off Sancho's stores, and he making a powerful and flexible whip out of Dapple's halter and head-stall retreated about twenty paces from his master among some beech trees. Don Quixote seeing him march off with such resolution and spirit, said to him, "Take care, my friend, not to cut thyself to pieces; allow the lashes to wait for one another, and do not be in so great a hurry as to run thyself out of breath midway; I mean, do not lay on so strenuously as to make thy life fail thee before thou hast reached the desired number; and that thou mayest not lose by a card too much or too little, I will station myself apart and count on my rosary here the lashes thou givest thyself. May Heaven help thee as thy good intention deserves."

" 'Pledges don't distress a good paymaster,' " said Sancho; "I mean to lay on in such a way as without killing myself to hurt myself, for in that, no doubt, lies the essence of this miracle."

He then stripped himself from the waist upwards, and snatching up the rope he began to lay on and Don Quixote to count the lashes. He might have given himself six or eight when he began to think the joke no trifle, and its price very low; and holding his hand for a moment, he told his master that he cried off on the score

[1] "—with dry breeches" completes the proverb.

of a blind bargain, for each of those lashes ought to be paid for at the rate of half a real instead of a quarter.

"Go, on, Sancho my friend, and be not disheartened," said Don Quixote; "for I double the stakes as to price."

"In that case," said Sancho, "in God's hand be it, and let it rain lashes." But the rogue no longer laid them on his shoulders, but laid on to the trees, with such groans every now and then, that one would have thought at each of them his soul was being plucked up by the roots. Don Quixote, touched to the heart, and fearing he might make an end of himself, and that through Sancho's imprudence he might miss his own object, said to him, "As thou livest, my friend, let the matter rest where it is, for the remedy seems to me a very rough one, and it will be well to have patience; 'Zamora was not won in an hour.' If I have not reckoned wrong thou hast given thyself over a thousand lashes; that is enough for the present; for the ass, to put it in homely phrase, bears the load, but not the overload."

"No, no, señor," replied Sancho; "it shall never be said of me, 'The money paid, the arms broken'; go back a little further, your worship, and let me give myself at any rate a thousand lashes more; for in a couple of bouts like this we shall have finished off the lot, and there will be even cloth to spare."

"As thou art in such a willing mood," said Don Quixote, "may Heaven aid thee; lay on and I'll retire."

Sancho returned to his task with so much resolution that he soon had the bark stripped off several trees, such was the severity with which he whipped himself; and one time, raising his voice, and giving a beech a tremendous lash, he cried out, "Here dies Samson, and all with him!"

At the sound of his piteous cry and of the stroke of the cruel lash, Don Quixote ran to him at once, and seizing the twisted halter that served him for a *courbash,* said to him, "Heaven forbid, Sancho my friend, that to please me thou shouldst lose thy life, which is needed for the support of thy wife and children; let Dulcinea wait for a better opportunity, and I will content myself with a hope soon to be realized, and have patience until thou hast gained fresh strength so as to finish off this business to the satisfaction of everybody."

"As your worship will have it so, señor," said Sancho, "so be it; but throw your cloak over my shoulders, for I'm sweating and I don't want to take cold; it's a risk that novice disciplinants run."

Don Quixote obeyed, and stripping himself covered Sancho, who slept until the sun woke him; they then resumed their journey, which for the time being they brought to an end at a village that lay three leagues farther on. They dismounted at a hostelry which Don Quixote recognized as such and did not take to be a castle with moat, turrets, portcullis, and drawbridge; for ever since he had been vanquished he talked more rationally about everything, as will be shown presently. They quartered him in a room on the ground floor, where in place of leather hangings there were pieces of painted serge such as they commonly use in villages. On one of them was painted by some very poor hand the Rape of Helen, when the bold guest carried her off from Menelaus, and on the other was the story of Dido and Æneas, she on a high tower, as though she were making signals with a half sheet to her fugitive guest who was out at sea flying in a frigate or brigantine. He noticed in the two stories that Helen did not go very reluctantly, for she was laughing slyly and roguishly; but the fair Dido was shown dropping tears the size of walnuts from her eyes. Don Quixote as he looked at them observed, "Those two ladies were very unfortunate not to have been born in this age, and I unfortunate above all men not to have been born in theirs. Had I fallen in with those gentlemen, Troy would not have been burned or Carthage destroyed, for it would have been only for me to slay Paris, and all these misfortunes would have been avoided."

"I'll lay a bet," said Sancho, "that before long there won't be a tavern, roadside inn, hostelry, or barber's shop where the story of our doings won't be painted up; but I'd like it painted by the hand of a better painter than painted these."

"Thou art right, Sancho," said Don Quixote, "for this painter is like Orbaneja, a painter there was at Úbeda, who when they asked him what he was painting, used to say, 'Whatever it may turn out'; and if he chanced to paint a cock he would write under it, 'This is a cock,' for fear they might think it was a fox. The painter or writer, for it's all the same, who published the history of this new Don Quixote that has come out, must have been one of this sort I think, Sancho, for he painted or wrote 'whatever it might turn out'; or perhaps he is like a poet called Mauleon that was about the Court some years ago, who used to answer at haphazard whatever he was asked, and on one asking him what *Deum de Deo* meant, he replied *Dé donde diere*. But, putting this aside, tell me, Sancho, hast thou a mind to have another turn at thyself to-night, and wouldst thou rather have it indoors or in the open air?"

"Egad, señor," said Sancho, "for what I'm going to give myself, it comes all the same to me whether it is in a house or in the fields; still I'd like it to be among trees; for I think they are company for me and help me to bear my pain wonderfully."

"And yet it must not be, Sancho my friend," said Don Quixote; "but, to enable thee to recover strength, we must keep it for our own village; for at the latest we shall get there the day after to-morrow."

Sancho said he might do as he pleased; but that for his own part he would like to finish off the business quickly before his blood cooled and while he had an appetite, because "in delay there is apt to be danger" very often, and "praying to God and plying the hammer," and "one take was better than two I'll give thee's," and "a sparrow in the hand than a vulture on the wing."

"For God's sake, Sancho, no more proverbs!" exclaimed Don Quixote; "it seems to me thou art becoming *sicut erat* again; speak in a plain, simple, straightforward way, as I have often told thee, and thou wilt find the good of it."

"I don't know what bad luck it is of mine," said Sancho, "but I can't utter a word without a proverb, or a proverb that is not as good as an argument to my mind; however, I mean to mend if I can"; and so for the present the conversation ended.

Chapter 72

*Of how Don Quixote and Sancho
reached their village*

ALL that day Don Quixote and Sancho remained in the village and inn waiting for night, the one to finish off his task of scourging in the open country, the other to see it accomplished, for therein lay the accomplishment of his wishes. Meanwhile there arrived at the hostelry a traveller on horseback with three or four servants, one of whom said to him who appeared to be the master, "Here, Señor Don Álvaro Tarfe, your worship may take your siesta to-day; the quarters seem clean and cool."

When he heard this Don Quixote said to Sancho, "Look here, Sancho; on turning over the leaves of that book of the Second Part of my history I think I came casually upon this name of Don Álvaro Tarfe."

"Very likely," said Sancho; "we had better

let him dismount, and by-and-by we can ask about it."

The gentleman dismounted, and the landlady gave him a room on the ground floor opposite Don Quixote's and adorned with painted serge hangings of the same sort. The newly arrived gentleman put on a summer coat, and coming out to the gateway of the hostelry, which was wide and cool, addressing Don Quixote, who was pacing up and down there, he asked, "In what direction is your worship bound, gentle sir?"

"To a village near this which is my own village," replied Don Quixote; "and your worship, where are you bound for?"

"I am going to Granada, señor," said the gentleman, "to my own country."

"And a goodly country," said Don Quixote; "but will your worship do me the favor of telling me your name, for it strikes me it is of more importance to me to know it than I can well tell you."

"My name is Don Álvaro Tarfe," replied the traveller.

To which Don Quixote returned, "I have no doubt whatever that your worship is that Don Álvaro Tarfe who appears in print in the Second Part of the history of Don Quixote of La Mancha, lately printed and published by a new author."

"I am the same," replied the gentleman; "and that said Don Quixote, the principal personage in the said history, was a very great friend of mine, and it was I who took him away from home, or at least induced him to come to some jousts that were to be held at Saragossa, whither I was going myself; indeed, I showed him many kindnesses, and saved him from having his shoulders touched up by the executioner because of his extreme rashness."

"Tell me, Señor Don Álvaro," said Don Quixote, "am I at all like that Don Quixote you talk of?"

"No indeed," replied the traveller, "not a bit."

"And that Don Quixote"—said our one, "had he with him a squire called Sancho Panza?"

"He had," said Don Álvaro; "but though he had the name of being very droll, I never heard him say anything that had any drollery in it."

"That I can well believe," said Sancho at this, "for to come out with drolleries is not in everybody's line; and that Sancho your worship speaks of, gentle sir, must be some great scoundrel, dunderhead, and thief, all in one; for I am the real Sancho Panza, and I have more drolleries than if it rained them; let your worship only try; come along with me for a year or so, and

you will find they fall from me at every turn, and so rich and so plentiful that though mostly I don't know what I am saying I make everybody that hears me laugh. And the real Don Quixote of La Mancha, the famous, the valiant, the wise, the lover, the righter of wrongs, the guardian of minors and orphans, the protector of widows, the killer of damsels, he who has for his sole mistress the peerless Dulcinea del Toboso, is this gentleman before you, my master; all other Don Quixotes and all other Sancho Panzas are dreams and mockeries."

"By God I believe it," said Don Álvaro; "for you have uttered more drolleries, my friend, in the few words you have spoken than the other Sancho Panza in all I ever heard from him, and they were not a few. He was more greedy than well-spoken, and more dull than droll; and I am convinced that the enchanters who persecute Don Quixote the Good have been trying to persecute me with Don Quixote the Bad. But I don't know what to say, for I am ready to swear I left him shut up in the Casa del Nuncio at Toledo,[1] and here another Don Quixote turns up, though a very different one from mine."

"I don't know whether I am good," said Don Quixote, "but I can safely say I am not 'the Bad'; and to prove it, let me tell you, Señor Don Álvaro Tarfe, I have never in my life been in Saragossa; so far from that, when it was told me that this imaginary Don Quixote had been present at the jousts in that city, I declined to enter it, in order to drag his falsehood before the face of the world; and so I went on straight to Barcelona, the treasure-house of courtesy, haven of strangers, asylum of the poor, home of the valiant, champion of the wronged, pleasant exchange of firm friendships, and city unrivalled in site and beauty. And though the adventures that befell me there are not by any means matters of enjoyment, but rather of regret, I do not regret them, simply because I have seen it. In a word, Señor Don Álvaro Tarfe, I am Don Quixote of La Mancha, the one that fame speaks of, and not the unlucky one that has attempted to usurp my name and deck himself out in my ideas. I entreat your worship by your devoir as a gentleman to be so good as to make a declaration before the *alcalde* of this village that you never in all your life saw me until now, and that neither am I the Don Quixote in print in the Second Part, nor this Sancho Panza, my squire, the one your worship knew."

"That I will do most willingly," replied Don Álvaro; "though it amazes me to find two Don

[1]A madhouse; Avellaneda concludes by depositing Don Quixote in it.

Quixotes and two Sancho Panzas at once, as much alike in name as they differ in demeanor; and again I say and declare that what I saw I cannot have seen, and that what happened to me cannot have happened."

"No doubt your worship is enchanted, like my lady Dulcinea del Toboso," said Sancho; "and would to Heaven your disenchantment rested on my giving myself another three thousand and odd lashes like what I'm giving myself for her, for I'd lay them on without looking for anything."

"I don't understand that about the lashes," said Don Álvaro.

Sancho replied that it was a long story to tell, but he would tell him if they happened to be going the same road.

By this dinner-time arrived, and Don Quixote and Don Álvaro dined together. The *alcalde* of the village came by chance into the inn together with a notary, and Don Quixote laid a petition before him, showing that it was requisite for his rights that Don Álvaro Tarfe, the gentleman there present, should make a declaration before him that he did not know Don Quixote of La Mancha, also there present, and that he was not the one that was in print in a history entitled *Second Part of Don Quixote of La Mancha, by one Avellaneda of Tordesillas*. The *alcalde* finally put it in legal form, and the declaration was made with all the formalities required in such cases, at which Don Quixote and Sancho were in high delight, as if a declaration of the sort was of any great importance to them, and as if their words and deeds did not plainly show the difference between the two Don Quixotes and the two Sanchos. Many civilities and offers of service were exchanged by Don Álvaro and Don Quixote, in the course of which the great Manchegan displayed such good taste that he disabused Don Álvaro of the error he was under; and he, on his part, felt convinced he must have been enchanted, now that he had been brought in contact with two such opposite Don Quixotes.

Evening came, they set out for the village, and after about half a league two roads branched off, one leading to Don Quixote's village, the other the road Don Álvaro was to follow. In this short interval Don Quixote told him of his unfortunate defeat, and of Dulcinea's enchantment and the remedy, all which threw Don Álvaro into fresh amazement, and embracing Don Quixote and Sancho he went his way, and Don Quixote went his. That night he passed among trees again in order to give Sancho an opportunity of working out his penance, which he did in the same fashion as the night before, at the expense of the bark of the beech trees much more than of his back, of which he took such good care that the lashes would not have knocked off a fly had there been one there. The duped Don Quixote did not miss a single stroke of the count, and he found that together with those of the night before they made up three thousand and twenty-nine. The sun apparently had got up early to witness the sacrifice, and with his light they resumed their journey, discussing the deception practised on Don Álvaro, and saying how well done it was to have taken his declaration before a magistrate in such an unimpeachable form. That day and night they travelled on, nor did anything worth mention happen to them, unless it was that in the course of the night Sancho finished off his task, whereat Don Quixote was beyond measure joyful. He watched for daylight, to see if along the road he should fall in with his already disenchanted lady Dulcinea; and as he pursued his journey there was no woman he met that he did not go up to, to see if she was Dulcinea del Toboso, as he held it absolutely certain that Merlin's promises could not lie. Full of these thoughts and anxieties, they ascended a rising ground wherefrom they descried their own village, at the sight of which Sancho fell on his knees exclaiming, "Open thine eyes, longed-for home, and see how thy son Sancho Panza comes back to thee, if not very rich, very well whipped! Open thine arms and receive, too, thy son Don Quixote, who, if he comes vanquished by the arm of another, comes victor over himself, which, as he himself has told me, is the greatest victory any one can desire. I'm bringing back money, for if I was well whipped, I went mounted like a gentleman."

"Have done with these fooleries," said Don Quixote; "let us push on straight and get to our own place, where we will give free range to our fancies, and settle our plans for our future pastoral life."

With this they descended the slope and directed their steps to their village.

Chapter 73

Of the omens Don Quixote had as he entered his own village, and other incidents that embellish and give a color to this great history

AT the entrance of the village, so says Cid Hamet, Don Quixote saw two boys quarrelling on the village threshing-floor, one of whom said to the other, "Take it easy, Periquillo; thou shalt never see it again as long as thou livest."

Don Quixote heard this, and said he to Sancho, "Dost thou not mark, friend, what that boy said, 'Thou shalt never see it again as long as thou livest'?"

"Well," said Sancho, "what does it matter if the boy said so?"

"What!" said Don Quixote, "dost thou not see that, applied to the object of my desires, the words mean that I am never to see Dulcinea more?"

Sancho was about to answer, when his attention was diverted by seeing a hare come flying across the plain pursued by several greyhounds and sportsmen. In its terror it ran to take shelter and hide itself under Dapple. Sancho caught it alive and presented it to Don Quixote, who was saying, *"Malum signum, malum signum!* a hare flies, greyhounds chase it, Dulcinea appears not."

"Your worship's a strange man," said Sancho; "let's take it for granted that this hare is Dulcinea, and these greyhounds chasing it the malignant enchanters who turned her into a country wench; she flies, and I catch her and put her into your worship's hands, and you hold her in your arms and cherish her; what bad sign is that, or what ill omen is there to be found here?"

The two boys who had been quarrelling came over to look at the hare, and Sancho asked one of them what their quarrel was about. He was answered by the one who had said, "Thou shalt never see it again as long as thou livest," that he had taken a cage full of crickets from the other boy, and did not mean to give it back to him as long as he lived. Sancho took out four cuartos from his pocket and gave them to the boy for the cage, which he placed in Don Quixote's hands, saying, "There, señor! there are the omens broken and destroyed, and they have no more to do with our affairs, to my thinking, fool as I am, than with last year's clouds; and if I remember rightly I have heard the curate of our village say that it does not become Christians or sensible people to give any heed to these silly things; and even you yourself said the same to me some time ago, telling me that all Christians who minded omens were fools; but there's no need of making words about it; let us push on and go into our village."

The sportsmen came up and asked for their hare, which Don Quixote gave them. They then went on, and upon the green at the entrance of the town they came upon the curate and the bachelor Samson Carrasco busy with their bre-

viaries. It should be mentioned that Sancho had thrown, by way of a sumpter-cloth, over Dapple and over the bundle of armor, the buckram robe painted with flames which they had put upon him at the duke's castle the night Altisidora came back to life. He had also fixed the mitre on Dapple's head, the oddest transformation and decoration that ever ass in the world underwent. They were at once recognized by both the curate and the bachelor, who came towards them with open arms. Don Quixote dismounted and received them with a close embrace; and the boys, who are lynxes that nothing escapes, spied out the ass's mitre and came running to see it, calling out to one another, "Come here, boys, and see Sancho Panza's ass rigged out finer than Mingo, and Don Quixote's beast leaner than ever."

So at length, with the boys capering round them, and accompanied by the curate and the bachelor, they made their entrance into the town, and proceeded to Don Quixote's house, at the door of which they found his housekeeper and niece, whom the news of his arrival had already reached. It had been brought to Teresa Panza, Sancho's wife, as well, and she with her hair all loose and half naked, dragging Sanchica her daughter by the hand, ran out to meet her husband; but seeing him coming in by no means as good case as she thought a governor ought to be, she said to him, "How is it you come this way, husband? It seems to me you come tramping and footsore, and looking more like a disorderly vagabond than a governor."

"Hold your tongue, Teresa," said Sancho; "often where there are pegs there are no flitches; let's go into the house and there you'll hear strange things. I bring money, and that's the main thing, got by my own industry without wronging anybody."

"You bring the money, my good husband," said Teresa, "and no matter whether it was got this way or that; for, however you may have got it, you'll not have brought any new practice into the world."

Sanchica embraced her father and asked him if he brought her anything, for she had been looking out for him as for the showers of May; and she taking hold of him by the girdle on one side, and his wife by the hand, while the daughter led Dapple, they made for their house, leaving Don Quixote in his, in the hands of his niece and housekeeper, and in the company of the curate and the bachelor.

Don Quixote at once, without any regard to time or season, withdrew in private with the bachelor and the curate, and in a few words told them of his defeat, and of the engagement he was under not to quit his village for a year, which he meant to keep to the letter without departing a hair's breadth from it, as became a knight-errant bound by scrupulous good faith and the laws of knight-errantry; and of how he thought of turning shepherd for that year, and taking his diversion in the solitude of the fields, where he could with perfect freedom give range to his thoughts of love while he followed the virtuous pastoral calling; and he besought them, if they had not a great deal to do and were not prevented by more important business, to consent to be his companions, for he would buy sheep enough to qualify them for shepherds; and the most important point of the whole affair, he could tell them, was settled, for he had given them names that would fit them to a T. The curate asked what they were. Don Quixote replied that he himself was to be called the shepherd Quixotiz, and the bachelor the shepherd Carrascon, and the curate the shepherd Curiambro, and Sancho Panza the shepherd Pancino.

Both were astounded at Don Quixote's new craze; however, lest he should once more make off out of the village from them in pursuit of chivalry, they, trusting that in the course of the year he might be cured, fell in with his new project, applauded his crazy idea as a bright one, and offered to share the life with him. "And what's more," said Samson Carrasco, "I am, as all the world knows, a very famous poet, and I'll be always making verses, pastoral, or courtly, or as it may come into my head, to pass away our time in those secluded regions where we shall be roaming. But what is most needful, sirs, is that each of us should choose the name of the shepherdess he means to glorify in his verses, and that we should not leave a tree, be it ever so hard, without writing up and carving her name on it, as is the habit and custom of love-smitten shepherds."

"That's the very thing," said Don Quixote; "though I am relieved from looking for the name of an imaginary shepherdess, for there's the peerless Dulcinea del Toboso, the glory of these brook-sides, the ornament of these meadows, the mainstay of beauty, the cream of all the graces, and, in a word, the being to whom all praise is appropriate, be it ever so hyperbolical."

"Very true," said the curate; "but we the others must look about for accommodating shepherdesses that will answer our purpose one way or another."

"And," added Samson Carrasco, "if they fail us, we can call them by the names of the ones in print that the world is filled with, Filidas, Amarilises, Dianas, Fleridas, Galateas, Belisardas; for as they sell them in the market-places we may fairly buy them and make them our own. If my lady, or I should say my shepherdess, happens to be called Ana, I'll sing her praises under the name of Anarda, and if Francisca, I'll call her Francenia, and if Lucia, Lucinda, for it all comes to the same thing; and Sancho Panza, if he joins this fraternity, may glorify his wife Teresa Panza as Teresaina."

Don Quixote laughed at the adaptation of the name, and the curate bestowed vast praise upon the worthy and honorable resolution he had made, and again offered to bear him company all that he could spare from his imperative duties. And so they took their leave of him, recommending and beseeching him to take care of his health and treat himself to a generous diet.

It so happened his niece and the housekeeper overheard all the three of them said; and as soon as they were gone they both of them came in to Don Quixote, and said the niece, "What's this, uncle? Now that we are thinking you had come back to stay at home and lead a quiet respectable life there, are you going to get into fresh entanglements, and turn 'young shepherd, thou that comest here, young shepherd going there'? Nay! indeed 'the straw is too hard now to make pipes of.'"

"And," added the housekeeper, "will your worship be able to bear, out in the fields, the heats of summer, and the chills of winter, and the howling of the wolves? Not you; for that's a life and a business for hardy men, bred and seasoned to such work almost from the time they were in swaddling-clothes. Why, to make choice of evils, it's better to be a knight-errant than a shepherd! Look here, señor; take my advice—and I'm not giving it to you full of bread and wine, but fasting, and with fifty years upon my head—stay at home, look after your affairs, go often to confession, be good to the poor, and upon my soul be it if any evil comes to you."

"Hold your peace, my daughters," said Don Quixote; "I know very well what my duty is; help me to bed, for I don't feel very well; and rest assured that, knight-errant now or wandering shepherd to be, I shall never fail to have a care for your interests, as you will see in the end." And the good wenches (for that they undoubtedly were), the housekeeper and niece, helped him to bed, where they gave him something to eat and made him as comfortable as possible.

Chapter 74

Of how Don Quixote fell sick, and of the will he made, and how he died

As nothing that is man's can last forever, but all tends ever downwards from its beginning to its end, and above all man's life, and as Don Quixote's enjoyed no special dispensation from Heaven to stay its course, its end and close came when he least looked for it. For—whether it was of the dejection the thought of his defeat produced, or of Heaven's will that so ordered it—a fever settled upon him and kept him in his bed for six days, during which he was often visited by his friends the curate, the bachelor, and the barber, while his good squire Sancho Panza never quitted his bedside. They, persuaded that it was grief at finding himself vanquished, and the object of his heart, the liberation and disenchantment of Dulcinea, unattained, that kept him in this state, strove by all the means in their power to cheer him up; the bachelor bidding him take heart and get up to begin his pastoral life, for which he himself, he said, had already composed an eclogue that would take the shine out of all Sannazaro had ever written, and had bought with his own money two famous dogs to guard the flock, one called Barcino and the other Butron, which a herdsman of Quintanar had sold him.

But for all this Don Quixote could not shake off his sadness. His friends called in the doctor, who felt his pulse and was not very well satisfied with it, and said that in any case it would be well for him to attend to the health of his soul, as that of his body was in a bad way. Don Quixote heard this calmly; but not so his housekeeper, his niece, and his squire, who fell weeping bitterly, as if they had him lying dead before them. The doctor's opinion was that melancholy and depression were bringing him to his end. Don Quixote begged them to leave him to himself, as he had a wish to sleep a little. They obeyed, and he slept at one stretch, as the saying is, more than six hours, so that the housekeeper and niece thought he was going to sleep forever. But at the end of that time he woke up, and in a loud voice exclaimed, "Blessed be Almighty God, who has shown me such goodness. In truth his mercies are boundless, and the sins of men can neither limit them nor keep them back!"

The niece listened with attention to her uncle's words, and they struck her as more coherent than what usually fell from him, at least during his illness, so she asked, "What are you saying, señor? Has anything strange occurred? What mercies or what sins of men are you talking of?"

"The mercies, niece," said Don Quixote, "are those that God has this moment shown me, and with him, as I said, my sins are no impediment to them. My reason is now free and clear, rid of the dark shadows of ignorance that my unhappy constant study of those detestable books of chivalry cast over it. Now I see through their absurdities and deceptions, and it only grieves me that this destruction of my illusions has come so late that it leaves me no time to make some amends by reading other books that might be a light to my soul. Niece, I feel myself at the point of death, and I would fain meet it in such a way as to show that my life has not been so ill that I should leave behind me the name of a madman; for though I have been one, I would not that the fact should be made plainer at my death. Call in to me, my dear, my good friends the Curate, the Bachelor Samson Carrasco, and Master Nicholas the barber, for I wish to confess and make my will." But his niece was saved the trouble by the entrance of the three. The instant Don Quixote saw them he exclaimed, "Good news for you, good sirs, that I am no longer Don Quixote of La Mancha, but Alonso Quixano, whose way of life won for him the name of Good. Now am I the enemy of Amadis of Gaul and of the whole countless troop of his descendants; odious to me now are all the profane stories of knight-errantry; now I perceive my folly, and the peril into which reading them brought me; now, by God's mercy schooled into my right senses, I loathe them."

When the three heard him speak in this way, they had no doubt whatever that some new craze had taken possession of him; and said Samson, "What? Señor Don Quixote! Now that we have intelligence of the lady Dulcinea being disenchanted, are you taking this line; now, just as we are on the point of becoming shepherds, to pass our lives singing, like princes, are you thinking of turning hermit? Hush for Heaven's sake, be rational, and let's have no more nonsense."

"All that nonsense," said Don Quixote, "that until now has been a reality to my hurt, my death will, with Heaven's help, turn to my good. I feel, sirs, that I am rapidly drawing near death; a truce to jesting; let me have a confessor to confess me, and a notary to make my will; for in extremities like this, man must not trifle with his soul; and while the curate is confessing me let some one, I beg, go for the notary."

They looked at one another, wondering at Don Quixote's words; but, though uncertain, they were inclined to believe him, and one of the signs by which they came to the conclusion he was dying was this so sudden and complete return to his senses after having been mad; for to the words already quoted he added much more, so well expressed, so devout, and so rational, as to banish all doubt and convince them that he was sound of mind. The curate turned them all out, and left alone with him confessed him. The bachelor went for the notary and returned shortly afterwards with him and with Sancho, who, having already learned from the bachelor the condition his master was in, and finding the housekeeper and niece weeping, began to blubber and shed tears.

The confession over, the curate came out saying, "Alonso Quixano the Good is indeed dying, and is indeed in his right mind; we may now go in to him while he makes his will."

This news gave a tremendous impulse to the brimming eyes of the housekeeper, the niece, and Sancho Panza his good squire, making the tears burst from their eyes and a host of sighs from their hearts; for of a truth, as has been said more than once, whether as plain Alonso Quixano the Good, or as Don Quixote of La Mancha, Don Quixote was always of a gentle disposition and kindly in all his ways, and hence he was beloved, not only by those of his own house, but by all who knew him.

The notary came in with the rest, and as soon as the preamble of the will had been set out and Don Quixote had commended his soul to God with all the devout formalities that are usual, coming to the bequests, he said, "Item, it is my will that, touching certain moneys in the hands of Sancho Panza (whom in my madness I made my squire), inasmuch as between him and me there have been certain accounts and debits and credits, no claim be made against him, nor any account demanded of him in respect of them; but that if anything remain over and above, after he has paid himself what I owe him, the balance, which will be but little, shall be his, and much good may it do him; and if, as when I was mad I had a share in giving him the government of an island, so, now that I am in my senses, I could give him that of a kingdom, it should be his, for the simplicity of his character and the fidelity of his conduct deserve it." And then, turning to Sancho, he said, "Forgive me, my friend, that I led thee to seem as mad as myself, making thee fall into the same error I myself fell into, that there were and still are knights-errant in the world."

"Ah!" said Sancho weeping, "don't die, mas-ter, but take my advice and live many years; for the foolishest thing a man can do in this life is to let himself die without rhyme or reason, without anybody killing him, or any hands but melancholy's making an end of him. Come, don't be lazy, but get up from your bed and let us take to the fields in shepherd's trim as we agreed. Perhaps behind some bush we shall find the lady Dulcinea disenchanted, as fine as fine can be. If it be that you are dying of vexation at having been vanquished, lay the blame on me, and say you were overthrown because I had girthed Rocinante badly; besides you must have seen in your books of chivalry that it is a common thing for knights to upset one another, and for him who is conquered to-day to be conqueror to-morrow."

"Very true," said Samson, "and good Sancho Panza's view of these cases is quite right."

"Sirs, not so fast," said Don Quixote, " 'in last year's nests there are no birds this year.' I was mad, now I am in my senses; I was Don Quixote of La Mancha, I am now, as I said, Alonso Quixano the Good; and may my repentance and sincerity restore me to the esteem you used to have for me; and now let Master Notary proceed.

"Item, I leave all my property absolutely to Antonia Quixana my niece, here present, after all has been deducted from the most available portion of it that may be required to satisfy the bequests I have made. And the first disbursement I desire to be made is the payment of the wages I owe for the time my housekeeper has served me, with twenty ducats, over and above for a gown. The curate and the bachelor Samson Carrasco, now present, I appoint my executors.

"Item, it is my wish that if Antonia Quixana, my niece, desires to marry, she shall marry a man of whom it shall be first of all ascertained by information taken that he does not know what books of chivalry are; and if it should be proved that he does, and if, in spite of this, my niece insists upon marrying him, and does marry him, then that she shall forfeit the whole of what I have left her, which my executors shall devote to works of charity as they please.

"Item, I entreat the aforesaid gentlemen my executors, that if any happy chance should lead them to discover the author who is said to have written a history now going about under the title of Second Part of the Achievements of Don Quixote of La Mancha, they beg of him on my behalf as earnestly as they can to forgive me for having been, without intending it, the cause of his writing so many and such monstrous absurdities as he has written in it; for I am leaving the world with a feeling of compunction at having provoked him to write them."

With this he closed his will, and a faintness coming over him he stretched himself out at full length on the bed. All were in a flutter and made haste to relieve him, and during the three days he lived after that on which he made his will he fainted away very often. The house was all in confusion; but still the niece ate and the housekeeper drank and Sancho Panza enjoyed himself; for inheriting property wipes out or softens down in the heir the feeling of grief the dead man might be expected to leave behind him.

At last Don Quixote's end came, after he had received all the sacraments, and had in full and forcible terms expressed his detestation of books of chivalry. The notary was there at the time, and he said that in no book of chivalry had he ever read of any knight-errant dying in his bed so calmly and so like a Christian as Don Quixote, who amid the tears and lamentations of all present yielded up his spirit, that is to say died. On perceiving it the curate begged the notary to bear witness that Alonso Quixano the Good, commonly called Don Quixote of La Mancha, had passed away from his present life, and died naturally; and said he desired this testimony in order to remove the possibility of any other author save Cid Hamet Benengeli bringing him to life again falsely and making interminable stories out of his achievements.

Such was the end of the Ingenious Gentleman of La Mancha, whose village Cid Hamet would not indicate precisely, in order to leave all the towns and villages of La Mancha to contend among themselves for the right to adopt him and claim him as a son, as the seven cities of Greece contended for Homer. The lamentations of Sancho and the niece and housekeeper are omitted here, as well as the new epitaphs upon his tomb; Samson Carrasco, however, put the following:

A doughty gentleman lies here;
A stranger all his life to fear;
Nor in his death could Death prevail,
In that lost hour, to make him quail.

He for the world but little cared;
And at his feats the world was scared;

A crazy man his life he passed,
But in his senses died at last.

And said most sage Cid Hamet to his pen, "Rest here, hung up by this brass wire, upon this shelf, O my pen, whether of skilful make or clumsy cut I know not; here shalt thou remain long ages hence, unless presumptuous or malignant story-tellers take thee down to profane thee. But ere they touch thee warn them, and, as best thou canst, say to them:

Hold off! ye weaklings; hold your hands!
Adventure it let none,
For this emprise, my lord the king,
Was meant for me alone.

For me alone was Don Quixote born, and I for him; it was his to act; mine to write; we two together make but one, notwithstanding and in spite of that pretended Tordesillesque writer who has ventured or would venture with his great, coarse, ill-trimmed ostrich quill to write the achievements of my valiant knight;—no burden for his shoulders, nor subject for his frozen wit: whom, if perchance thou shouldst come to know him, thou shalt warn to leave at rest where they lie the weary mouldering bones of Don Quixote, and not to attempt to carry him off, in opposition to all the privileges of death, to Old Castile, making him rise from the grave where in reality and truth he lies stretched at full length, powerless to make any third expedition or new sally; for the two that he has already made, so much to the enjoyment and approval of everybody to whom they have become known, in this as well as in foreign countries, are quite sufficient for the purpose of turning into ridicule the whole of those made by the whole set of the knights-errant; and so doing shalt thou discharge thy Christian calling, giving good counsel to one that bears ill-will to thee. And I shall remain satisfied, and proud to have been the first who has ever enjoined the fruit of his writings as fully as he could desire; for my desire has been no other than to deliver over to the detestation of mankind the false and foolish tales of the books of chivalry, which, thanks to that of my true Don Quixote, are even now tottering, and doubtless doomed to fall forever. Farewell."

THE GREAT IDEAS, *Volumes 2 and 3*